C000175029

the best campsites
in France

alan rogers  publishing

experts in camping for over 40 years

Compiled by: Alan Rogers Guides Ltd

Designed by: Vine Design Ltd

Additional photography: T Lambelin, www.lambelin.com
Maps created by Customised Mapping (01769 540044)
contain background data provided by GisDATA Ltd

Maps are © Alan Rogers Guides and GisDATA Ltd 2011

© Alan Rogers Guides Ltd 2011

Published by: Alan Rogers Guides Ltd,
Spelmonden Old Oast, Goudhurst, Kent TN17 1HE
www.alanrogers.com Tel: 01580 214000

British Library Cataloguing-in-Publication Data:
A catalogue record for this book is available
from the British Library.

ISBN 978-1-906215-47-7

Printed in Great Britain by Stephens & George Print Group

Contents

Contents

Alan Rogers - in search of 'the best'

Alan Rogers Guides were first published over 40 years ago. Since Alan Rogers published the first campsite guide that bore his name, the range has expanded and now covers 27 countries in five separate guides. No fewer than 20 of the campsites selected by Alan for the first guide are still featured in our 2011 editions.

There are over 11,000 campsites in France of varying quality: this guide contains impartially written reports on almost 1,000, including many of the very finest, each being individually inspected and selected. We aim to provide you with a selection of the best, rather than information on all – in short, a more selective, qualitative approach. New, improved maps and indexes are also included, designed to help you find the choice of campsite that's right for you.

We hope you enjoy some happy and safe travels – and some pleasurable 'armchair touring' in the meantime!

" ...the campsites included in this book have been chosen entirely on merit, and no payment of any sort is made by them for their inclusion."

Alan Rogers, 1968

How do we find the best?

The criteria we use when inspecting and selecting campsites are numerous, but the most important by far is the question of good quality. People want different things from their choice of site so we try to include a range of campsite 'styles' to cater for a wide variety of preferences: from those seeking a small peaceful campsite in the heart of the countryside, to visitors looking for an 'all singing, all dancing' site in a popular seaside resort. Those with more specific interests, such as sporting facilities, cultural events or historical attractions, are also catered for.

The size of the site, whether it's part of a chain or privately owned, makes no difference in terms of it being required to meet our exacting standards in respect of its quality and it being 'fit for purpose'. In other words, irrespective of the size of the site, or the number of facilities it offers, we consider and evaluate the welcome, the pitches, the sanitary facilities, the cleanliness, the general maintenance and even the location.

Expert opinions

We rely on our dedicated team of Site Assessors, all of whom are experienced campers, caravanners or motorcaravanners, to visit and recommend campsites. Each year they travel some 100,000 miles around Europe inspecting new campsites for the guide and re-inspecting the existing ones. Our thanks are due to them for their enthusiastic efforts, their diligence and integrity.

We also appreciate the feedback we receive from many of our readers and we always make a point of following up complaints, suggestions or recommendations for possible new campsites. Of course we get a few grumbles too – but it really is a few, and those we do receive usually relate to overcrowding or to poor maintenance during the peak school holiday period. Please bear in mind that, although we are interested to hear about any complaints, we have no contractual relationship with the campsites featured in our guides and are therefore not in a position to intervene in any dispute between a reader and a campsite.

Independent and honest

Whilst the content and scope of the Alan Rogers guides have expanded considerably since the early editions, our selection of campsites still employs exactly the same philosophy and criteria as defined by Alan Rogers in 1968.

'telling it how it is'

Firstly, and most importantly, our selection is based entirely on our own rigorous and independent inspection and selection process. Campsites cannot buy their way into our guides – indeed the extensive Site Report which is written by us, not by the site owner, is provided free of charge so we are free to say what we think and to provide an honest, 'warts and all' description. This is written in plain English and without the use of confusing icons or symbols.

Looking for the best

Highly respected by site owners and readers alike, there is no better guide when it comes to forming an independent view of a campsite's quality. When you need to be confident in your choice of campsite, you need the Alan Rogers Guide.

- Sites only included on merit

- Sites cannot pay to be included

- Independently inspected, rigorously assessed

- Impartial reviews

- Over 40 years of expertise

Written in plain English, our guides are exceptionally easy to use, but a few words of explanation regarding the layout and content may be helpful. Regular readers will see that our site reports are grouped into 23 official regions (plus the Vendée) and then by the various départements in each of these regions in numerical order.

Index town

Site name
Postal address (including département) T: telephone number. E: email address
alanrogers.com web address (including Alan Rogers reference number)

A description of the site in which we try to give an idea of its general features – its size, its situation, its strengths and its weaknesses. This section should provide a picture of the site itself with reference to the facilities that are provided and if they impact on its appearance or character. We include details on pitch numbers, electricity (with amperage), hardstandings etc. in this section as pitch design, planning and terracing affects the site's overall appearance. Similarly we include reference to pitches used for caravan holiday homes, chalets, and the like. Importantly at the end of this column we indicate if there are any restrictions, e.g. no tents, no children, naturist sites.

Facilities
Lists more specific information on the site's facilities and amenities and, where available, the dates when these facilities are open (if not for the whole season). Off site: here we give distances to various local amenities, for example, local shops, the nearest beach, plus our featured activities (bicycle hire, fishing, horse riding, boat launching). Where we have space we list suggestions for activities and local tourist attractions.

Open: Site opening dates.

Directions
Separated from the main text in order that they may be read and assimilated more easily by a navigator en-route. Bear in mind that road improvement schemes can result in road numbers being altered.

GPS: references are provided in decimal format. All latitudes are North. Longitudes are East unless preceeded by a minus sign e.g. 48.71695 is North, 0.31254 is East and -0.31254 is West.

Charges 2011 (or a general guide)

Maps, campsite listings and indexes

For this 2011 guide we have changed the way in which we list our featured campsites and also the way in which we help you locate the sites within each region.

We now include a map immediately after our Introduction to that region. These maps show the towns near which one or more of our featured campsites are located.

Within each regional section of the guide, we list these towns and the site(s) in that vicinity in alphabetical order.

You will certainly need more detailed maps for navigation, for example the Michelin atlas. We provide G.P.S. coordinates for each site to assist you. Our three indexes will also help you to find a site by its reference number and name, by region and site name, or by the town where the site is situated.

Understanding the entries

Regions and départements

For administrative purposes France is divided into 23 official regions covering the 95 départements (similar to our counties). The départements included in each region are stated in our introductions, together with their official number (eg. the département of Manche is number 50). We use these département numbers as the first two digits of our campsite reference numbers, so any campsite in the Manche département will start with the number 50, prefixed with FR.

Facilities

Toilet blocks

We assume that toilet blocks will be equipped with WCs, washbasins with hot and cold water and hot showers with dividers or curtains, and will have all necessary shelves, hooks, plugs and mirrors. We also assume that there will be an identified chemical toilet disposal point, and that the campsite will provide water and waste water drainage points and bin areas. If not the case, we comment. We do mention certain features that some readers find important: washbasins in cubicles, facilities for babies, facilities for those with disabilities and motorcaravan service points. Readers with disabilities are advised to contact the site of their choice to ensure that facilities are appropriate to their needs.

Shop

Basic or fully supplied, and opening dates.

Bars, restaurants, takeaway facilities and entertainment

We try hard to supply opening and closing dates (if other than the campsite opening dates) and to identify if there are discos or other entertainment.

Children's play areas

Fenced and with safety surface (e.g. sand, bark or pea-gravel).

Swimming pools

If particularly special, we cover in detail in our main campsite description but reference is always included under our Facilities listings. We will also indicate the existence of water slides, sunbathing areas and other features. Opening dates, charges and levels of supervision are provided where we have been notified. There is a regulation whereby Bermuda shorts may not be worn in swimming pools (for health and hygiene reasons). It is worth ensuring that you do take 'proper' swimming trunks with you.

Leisure facilities

For example, playing fields, bicycle hire, organised activities and entertainment.

Dogs

If dogs are not accepted or restrictions apply, we state it here. Check the quick reference list at the back of the guide.

Off site

This briefly covers leisure facilities, tourist attractions, restaurants etc. nearby.

Charges

These are the latest provided to us by the sites. In those cases where 2011 prices have not been provided to us by the sites, we try to give a general guide.

Reservations

Necessary for high season (roughly mid-July to mid-August) in popular holiday areas (i.e. beach resorts). You can reserve many sites via our own Alan Rogers Travel Service or through other tour operators. Or be wholly independent and contact the campsite(s) of your choice direct, using the phone or e-mail numbers shown in the site reports, but please bear in mind that many sites are closed all winter.

Telephone Numbers

All numbers assume that you are phoning from within France.

To phone France from outside that country, prefix the number shown with the relevant International Code (00 33) and drop the first 0, shown as (0) in the numbers indicated.

Opening dates

These are advised to us during the early autumn of the previous year – sites can, and sometimes do, alter these dates before the start of the following season, often for good reasons. If you intend to visit shortly after a published opening date, or shortly before the closing date, it is wise to check that it will actually be open at the time required. Similarly some sites operate a restricted service during the low season, only opening some of their facilities (e.g. swimming pools) during the main season; where we know about this, and have the relevant dates, we indicate it – again if you are at all doubtful it is wise to check.

Sometimes, campsite amenities may be dependent on there being enough customers on site to justify their opening and, for this reason, actual opening dates may vary from those indicated.

Some French site owners are very relaxed when it comes to opening and closing dates. They may not be fully ready by their stated opening dates – grass and hedges may not all be cut or perhaps only limited sanitary facilities open. At the end of the season they also tend to close down some facilities and generally wind down prior to the closing date. Bear this in mind if you are travelling early or late in the season – it is worth phoning ahead.

The Camping Cheque low season touring system goes some way to addressing this in that many participating campsites will have all key facilities open and running by the opening date and these will remain fully operational until the closing date.

You're on your way!

Whether you're an 'old hand' in terms of camping and caravanning or are contemplating your first trip, a regular reader of our Guides or a new 'convert', we wish you well in your travels and hope we have been able to help in some way.

We are, of course, also out and about ourselves, visiting sites, talking to owners and readers, and generally checking on standards and new developments.

Our Accommodation section

Over recent years, more and more campsites have added high quality mobile home and chalet accommodation. In response to feedback from many of our readers, and to reflect this evolution in campsites, we have now decided to include a separate section on mobile homes and chalets. If a site offers this accommodation, it is indicated above the site report with a page reference where full details are given. We have chosen a number of sites offering some of the best accommodation available and have included full details of one or two accommodation types at these sites.

Please note however that many other campsites listed in this guide may also have a selection of accommodation for rent.

We wish all our readers thoroughly enjoyable Camping and Caravanning in 2011 – favoured by good weather of course!

The Alan Rogers Team

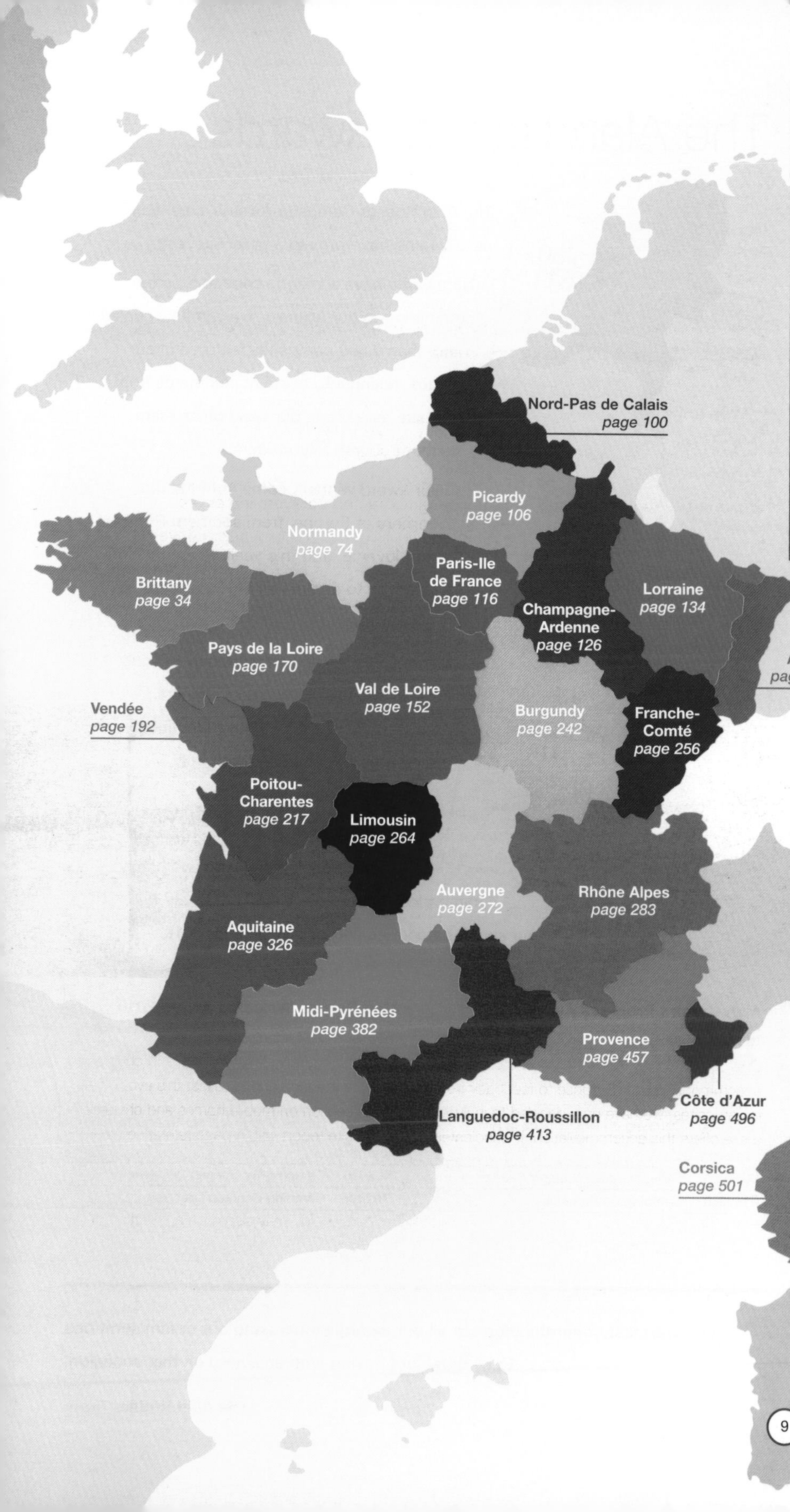

Nord-Pas de Calais
page 100

Picardy
page 106

Normandy
page 74

Paris-Ile
de France
page 116

Lorraine
page 134

Brittany
page 34

Champagne-
Ardenne
page 126

Alsace
page 144

Pays de la Loire
page 170

Val de Loire
page 152

Franche-
Comté
page 256

Vendée
page 192

Burgundy
page 242

Poitou-
Charentes
page 217

Limousin
page 264

Auvergne
page 272

Rhône Alpes
page 283

Aquitaine
page 326

Midi-Pyrénées
page 382

Provence
page 457

Côte d'Azur
page 496

Languedoc-Roussillon
page 413

Corsica
page 501

The Alan Rogers Awards

The Alan Rogers Campsite Awards were launched in 2004 and have proved a great success.

Our awards have a broad scope and before committing to our winners, we carefully consider more than 2,000 campsites featured in our guides, taking into account comments from our site assessors, our head office team and, of course, our readers.

Our award winners come from the four corners of Europe, from southern Portugal to Slovenia, and this year we are making awards to campsites in 13 different countries.

Needless to say, it's an extremely difficult task to choose our eventual winners, but we believe that we have identified a number of campsites with truly outstanding characteristics.

In each case, we have selected an outright winner, along with two highly commended runners-up. Listed below are full details of each of our award categories and our winners for 2010.

Alan Rogers Progress Award 2010

This award reflects the hard work and commitment undertaken by particular site owners to improve and upgrade their site.

Winner

FR40100	Camping du Domaine de la Rive *France*

Runners-up

AU0060	Ferienparadies Natterer See *Austria*
IT60360	Camping Ca'Pasquali *Italy*

Alan Rogers Welcome Award 2010

This award takes account of sites offering a particularly friendly welcome and maintaining a friendly ambience throughout reader's holidays.

Winner

FR38010	Kawan Village le Coin Tranquille *France*

Runners-up

NL6630	Camping Ter Spegelt *Netherlands*
IT62485	Camping Conca d'Oro *Italy*

Our warmest congratulations to all our award winners and our commiserations to all those not having won an award on this occasion.

The Alan Rogers Team

Alan Rogers Active Holiday Award 2010

This award reflects sites in outstanding locations which are ideally suited for active holidays, notably walking or cycling, but which could extend to include such activities as winter sports or water sports.

Winner

DE3820	Camping Havelberge *Germany*

Runners-up

SV4415	Camping Terme Catez *Slovenia*
FR65090	Camping du Soleil de Pibeste *France*

Alan Rogers Motorhome Award 2010

Motorhome sales are increasing and this award acknowledges sites which, in our opinion, have made outstanding efforts to welcome motorhome clients.

Winner

NL6200	Camping Erkemederstrand *Netherlands*

Runners-up

UK1340	Cornish Farm Touring Park *England*
FR30120	Campéole Ile des Papes *France*

Alan Rogers 4 Seasons Award 2010

This award is made to outstanding sites with extended opening dates and which welcome clients to a uniformly high standard throughout the year.

Winner

ES81300	Camping Int. de Calonge *Spain*

Runners-up

UK0970	Cofton Country Holidays *England*
DE3455	Gugel's Dreiländer Camping *Germany*

Alan Rogers Seaside Award 2010

This award is made for sites which we feel are outstandingly suitable for a really excellent seaside holiday.

Winner

FR83120	Camp du Domaine *France*

Runners-up

CR6716	Camping Lanterna *Croatia*
ES82000	Camping Cala Llevadó *Spain*

Alan Rogers Country Award 2010

This award contrasts with our former award and acknowledges sites which are attractively located in delightful, rural locations.

Winner

NL6425	Camping De Twee Bruggen *Netherlands*

Runners-up

FR24010	Kawan Château le Verdoyer *France*
UK7830	Glen Nevis Caravan Park *Scotland*

Alan Rogers Rented Accommodation Award 2010

Given the increasing importance of rented accommodation on many campsites, we feel that it is important to acknowledge sites which have made a particular effort in creating a high quality 'rented accommodation' park.

Winner

SV4270	Kamp Koren Kobarid *Slovenia*

Runners-up

FR66070	Yelloh! Village le Brasilia *France*
ES84830	Camping Tamarit Park Resort *Spain*

Alan Rogers Unique Site Award 2010

This award acknowledges sites with unique, outstanding features – something which simply cannot be found elsewhere and which is an important attraction of the site.

Winner

PO8175	Zmar-Eco Camping Resort *Portugal*

Runners-up

DK2170	Klim Strand Camping *Denmark*
ES80330	Camping Las Palmeras *Spain*

Alan Rogers Family Site Award 2010

Many sites claim to be child friendly but this award acknowledges the sites we feel to be the very best in this respect.

Winner

ES80400	Camping Las Dunas *Spain*

Runners-up

IT60030	Centro Vacanze Pra' Delle Torri *Italy*
LU7620	Europacamping Nommerlayen *Luxembourg*

Alan Rogers Readers' Award 2010

We believe our Readers' Award to be the most important. We simply invite our readers (by means of an on-line poll at www.alanrogers.com) to nominate the site they enjoyed most.

The outright winner for 2010 is:

Winner

IT60200	Camping Union Lido Vacanze *Italy*

Alan Rogers Special Award 2010

A special award is made to acknowledge sites which we feel have overcome a very significant setback, and have, not only returned to their former condition, but can fairly be considered to be even better than before. In 2010 we acknowledge one campsite which suffered storm damage and we feel qualifies for this award, but also wish to acknowledge the campsites of the Argens valley, Var, France, which suffered serious flood damage in June 2010 and have made highly impressive recoveries.

FR17340	Camping Au Port-Punay *France*
The campsites of the Argens valley	*Var, France*

The aims of the Travel Service are simple

- To provide convenience - a one-stop shop to make life easier.

- To provide peace of mind - when you need it most.

- To provide a friendly, knowledgeable, efficient service
  – when this can be hard to find.

- To provide a low cost means of organising your holiday
  – when prices can be so complicated.

When you book with us, you will be allocated an experienced Personal Travel Consultant to provide you with personal advice and manage every stage of your booking. Our Personal Travel Consultants have first-hand experience of many of our campsites and access to a wealth of information. They can check availability, provide a competitive price and tailor your holiday arrangements to your specific needs.

- Discuss your holiday plans with a friendly person with first-hand experience

- Let us reassure you that your holiday arrangements really are taken care of

- Tell us about your special requests and allow us to pass these on

- Benefit from advice which will save you money – the latest ferry deals and more

- Remember, our offices are in Kent not overseas and we do NOT operate a queuing system!

Call us for advice or an instant quote
01580 214000
or visit **www.alanrogers.com/travel**

Look for a campsite entry like this to indicate which campsites we can book for you.

The list is growing so please call for up to the minute information.

Value, Value, Value

Great Savings AND Complete Service

We work hard to offer quality and choice at remarkably low prices. And we pride ourselves on providing a friendly, personal service coupled with the in-depth knowledge of a specialist tour operator. We are not a large company and your holiday is important to us.

Our prices are based on the campsite's 'at-the-gate' prices. The campsite's own booking fees are not charged but are replaced by a standard Travel Service fee of just £45 per booking (not per site). Please bear in mind campsites typically charge a booking fee of around 30€ (perhaps £25) to customers booking direct - you will avoid this by booking with our Travel Service.

What's more, a campsite's own booking fee is charged at each campsite you visit. Our booking fee applies only once.

Our in-house travel team handles all aspects of your booking, for your peace of mind.

- FREE child places on many campsites – exclusive to the Travel Service
- Payment in sterling with no risk of exchange rate fluctuations
- Secure bookings – all campsite fees and deposits are paid in advance*
  with all ferry-inclusive holidays fully protected by our ABTA bond
- We have long-standing relationships with all campsites and Special Requests
  are passed on – details that can make a real difference
- Low cost ferries – special fares only available when booking a ferry-inclusive holiday
- A one-stop-shop for all your travel plans – campsite booking, overnight stops,
  low cost ferries and travel insurance – all in one place

  * excluding any nominal local tourist taxes, payable locally

Pitch only bookings

We're confident that our ferry inclusive booking service offers unbeatable value. However, if you have already booked your ferry then we can still make a pitch-only reservation for you (minimum 5 nights). Since our prices are based on our ferry inclusive service, you need to be aware that a non-ferry booking may result in slightly higher prices than if you were to book direct with the site.

It's all on-line

www.alanrogers.com/travel is a website designed to give you everything you need to know when planning your Alan Rogers inspected and selected campsite holiday. You'll find it useful for images and background information – allowing you to make a fully-informed decision. Then 'click' to book or just call us to discuss.

Our friendly, expert team of travel consultants is always happy to help on

01580 214000 – but they do go home sometimes!

www.alanrogers.com/travel

- Find latest special offers on campsites - **instantly**
- Check campsite availability - **instantly**
- Check ferry availability - **instantly**
- Find latest ferry deals - **instantly**
- Book your ferry online - **instantly**

Want our latest deals and offers?

Sign up for our regular email bulletin

www.alanrogers.com/subscribe

Crossing the Channel

One of the great advantages of booking your ferry-inclusive holiday with the Alan Rogers Travel Service is the tremendous value we offer. Our money-saving Ferry Deals have become legendary. As agents for all major cross-Channel operators we can book all your travel arrangements with the minimum of fuss and at the best possible rates.

(Please note we can only book ferry crossings in conjunction with a campsite holiday reservation)

Just call us for an instant quote
01580 214000

What's In A Name?
Differentiating between the groups

At Alan Rogers we have been inspecting and reviewing campsites since 1968. There's no question things are very different today: facilities, standards, professionalism, technology have all evolved beyond all recognition. But we find there is still room for individuality, style and personality.

Campsites may still be small and uncommercial with modest facilities and the charm of a family-run establishment. Others may be larger and offer the impressive amenities of a modern resort. Some may favour highlighting their historic pedigree and ambience, others prefer to stress their rural location.

To achieve these various aims, many have joined forces with other like-minded campsites to raise their profile via glossy brochures and the like. Of course it's not black and white but over the following pages we try to clarify the distinctions between some of these groups of campsites, each of which claim to be unique in their own way.

CAMPSITES AND RENTED ACCOMMODATION

Most Campéole campsites enjoy a great location close to water, first-class infrastructures and are designed where possible to sit harmoniously within their environments. They are popular with families with children of all ages, as well as couples and small groups.

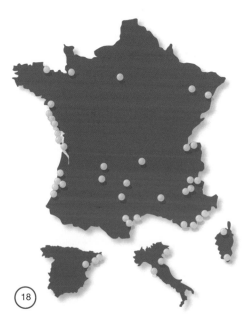

Campsites

Saint-Grégoire
Les Monts Colleux
Les Paludiers
La Grande Côte
Les Sirènes
Dornier
Le Platin
Les Amis de la Plage
Clairefontaine
Le Lac de Sanguinet
Le Vivier
Plage Sud
Navarrosse
Les Tourterelles
Le Val de Coise
Le Coiroux
Les Reflets du Quercy
La Boissière
Le Domaine de Combelles
La Cité
La Côte des Roses
Les Mûriers
Île des Papes
Eurosurf
Les Arbousiers
La Croix du Sud
Le Dramont
Le Belgodère
L'Avena
Le Clos du Lac
Camping du Lac
Le Courounba
Les Vaudois
La Nublière
La Pinède
Le Giessen
Le Brabois
Parc Etang
Castell Mar
Castell Montgri
Torre del Sol
Ca' Savio
Club del Sole Spina
L'Albatros

Campéole

In Their Own Words...

We will listen to you and advise you

Our helpful booking office is there to listen to you and to advise you accordingly. We can recommend a campsite suited to your needs and making a reservation is only a simple phone call away.

We will offer you a variety of holiday options

With over 40 destinations in France and elsewhere, around ten different types of accommodation, several possible lengths of stay and two arrival days per week, Campéole aims to provide maximum choice and flexibility.

We will ensure that our holidays are affordable for everyone

A range of services is available to make life easier for you during your holiday. We also guarantee the quality and comfort of our accommodation and therefore offer several solutions at different price levels.

We will all be committed to making a success of your holiday

The Campéole teams are professionals set on providing a holiday to remember. Each team member has your holiday at heart and will take it on themselves to make your stay as pleasant as possible.

We will cater for young children and teenagers

Campéole welcomes children and has created special amenities for them in its campsite villages: like Campéolito, popular with the little ones, or activity clubs for each age bracket and a dedicated Teen Space for teenagers.

We will create a friendly and festive atmosphere

On Campéole campsites you can take your pick from a range of sporting activities and join in the evening entertainments. Each site has a specific entertainment programme for all ages.

We will respect nature

Do your bit for the environment by opting for the unique Campéole holiday experience in unspoilt natural surroundings. Come and join us – we look forward to welcoming you!

www.campeole.co.uk

LES ★★★★
CASTELS
Hôtellerie de Plein Air

Les Castels is a well-established and highly regarded group of campsites set in the grounds of stunning châteaux, beautiful manors and charming country houses. This ensures unique natural settings for some of France's finest touring sites. You will be assured of a warm and courteous welcome, tranquil surroundings, great service and a taste of authentic French 'art de vivre'.

Campsites

Le Château de Galinée
Domaine de Keravel
Le Domaine des Ormes
La Grande Métairie
L'Orangerie de Lanniron
Le Ty Nadan
Château de la Grenouillère
Le Parc de Fierbois
L'Anse du Brick
Le Brévedent
Le Château de Iez Eaux
Le Château de Martragny
Le Château de Chanteloup
Le Domaine des Forges
L'Étang de la Brèche
La Garangeoire
La Forge de Sainte Marie
Le Val de Bonnal
La Bien-Assise
Le Domaine de Drancourt
Le Moulin du Roch
Le Ruisseau des Pyrénées
Saint-Avit Loisirs
Le Château de Leychoisier
Le Château de Poinsouze
Le Caussanel
Le Domaine de la Paille Basse
Les Gorges du Chambon
Le Petit Trianon de Saint Ustre
Séquoia Parc
Le Château de Boisson
Les Criques de Porteils
Le Domaine de Massereau
Domaine du Verdon
Douce Quiétude
Le Château de Rochetaillée
Camping l'Ardéchois
Le Domaine de Sévenier

Les Castels

In Their Own Words...

Quality Assured

All campsites subscribe to the Les Castels Quality Charter and it was the first group to join the respected Camping Qualité label - a guarantee of excellence in facilities and services.

Whether you're on the move or just lazing...

Many Les Castels campsites offer supervised activities for children: organised games, fun workshops, outings and picnics, singing, dancing and real shows. You can go off and leave your children behind with your mind at rest because you know they'll have fun and make new friends. There is a wide range of activities for the whole family: football, tennis, mountain biking, aqua aerobics, tree climbing, pedal boats, canoeing, archery, boules and more.

Preserving our environmental heritage

Choosing to holiday on a Les Castels campsite means you already share our values. Each property contributes largely to the historical, environmental and architectural heritage of its region.

Benefit with our loyalty programme, the Castellissime Card

Enjoy Castellissime Card advantages, all year round. Earn points during your stay in any of Les Castels campsites, then redeem them for up to 15%* price reductions on your next stay.
*season-based, from 2% to 15% (see website for details)

Premium offer: the freedom of the outdoor life plus the very best in contemporary comfort

All our sites can now offer the Les Castels essential art-of-living package:

- Prestigious, secluded, large pitches in magnificent settings.
- Stylishly furnished and decorated spacious accommodation (bungalows, mobile homes or chalets) offering their own private terraces.
- All you need to enjoy a heavenly holiday: barbecue, garden furniture, lounge chairs and a sunshade.
- VIP services: bed linen and towels included, cleaning supply kit, television or hi-fi sound system, free internet access, etc.

www.les-castels.com

Chalets en France

Chalets en France offer a chance to
holiday in beautiful French landscapes,
enjoying natural surroundings and
staying in comfortable chalets.
The friendly, knowledgeable staff have
a good understanding of local areas,
the history and culture and offer various
activities to help visitors explore.

Limousin

■ Les Hameaux de Miel,
   Beynat

■ Les Hameaux du Perrier,
   Lissac sur Couze

■ Les Cottages du Puy d'Agnoux,
   Meyrignac l'Eglise

Midi-Pyrénées

■ Les Hameaux des Lacs,
   Monclar de Quercy

■ Les Hameaux de Pomette,
   Cazals

Poitou-Charentes

■ Les Hameaux des Marines,
   St Denis d'Oléron

■ Chalets en France

■ **NEW** 2011

Chalets en France

In Their Own Words...

The environment and heritage

We aim to give you a great holiday, while allowing you to experience and support the natural surroundings and local culture and commerce. We help you to discover the local region and each campsite offers a number of excursions, visits and activities that we hope you will find interesting.

A great welcome makes for a great holiday

We aim to provide a first-rate welcome and personal service from our bilingual staff. Throughout the season our staff are well presented and courteous and we hope you will get to know them and value their expert input to your holiday. Our high quality chalets ensure a good night's sleep, pleasant surroundings and comfort in which to enjoy your holiday.

A little bit extra....

We aim to ensure that the little touches make a big difference.

- Fresh bread and pastries can be delivered daily to your door.
- Free WiFi in reception and bar is welcome for many these days.
- Sensible and considerate rules to ensure the enjoyment of all holidaymakers.
- Free children's club, all season, for children aged 5 – 12 years.

www.chalets-en-france.com

Campsites on a human scale

The Flower philosophy is to avoid the style of so-called 'factory campsites'; to ignore anonymous standardisation but celebrate individuality and personality. Campsites in this group are all modestly sized: high quality facilities, for sure, but all on a very personable level and with a distinct personal touch.

Campsites

| Les Vertes Feuilles |
| Domaine du Rompval |
| La Chênaie |
| Le Haut Dick |
| Les Chevaliers |
| Le Pil Koad |
| Les Deux Chênes |
| Le Cabellou-Plage |
| L'Océan |
| Le Kernest |
| Le Domaine de Pont Mahé |
| Les Brillas |
| L'Hermitage |
| La Bretonnière |
| La Canadienne |
| La Garenne |
| Le Mas de Mourgues |
| Le Marius |
| Les Bouleaux |
| La Presqu'ile de Champaubert |
| La Ferté Gaucher |
| Le Bois Fleuri |
| Les Etangs |
| Les Portes de Sancerre |
| Le Val de Loire |
| Le Lac de St-Cyr |
| Le Temps de Vivre |
| Les Nauves |
| Le Pontet |
| La Rivière Fleurie |
| Le Pressoir |
| Le Moulin de Périé |
| Les Pins |
| Les Ondines |
| Les Iles |
| Le Lac de Lislebonne |
| L'Aramis |
| Le Port de Lacombe |

Flower Campings

In Their Own Words...

Campsites on a human scale

On a Flower campsite you are not a number; you are not lost in the crowd. It's a sociable place, and camping is all about enjoying the company of others so the staff like to say hello and chat. We often remark on the warm and friendly 'micro climate' among residents on our campsites.

Quality campsites

On all our campsites, neither too big nor too small, quality is uppermost. We like small scale but we insist on high quality. We run campsites, we often live on campsites and we enjoy campsite life – we want you to enjoy it too. We have developed our ideal: camping on a human scale where you get to become part of the 'family', great facilities, wonderful locations. We hope this is your ideal too.

Discover the locality

The best advice we can give you is to get out of the campsite to explore our various regions. Each adds a real flavour to life: meet the local people, attend the local festivals and markets, and enjoy the local produce and the local traditions.

www.flowercampings.com

With around 100 campsites across Europe, Homair certainly offers a wide choice.
The group has been providing campsite holidays for over 20 years and is one of
France's leading mobile home holiday specialists, with 65,000 families staying
on their campsites each year.

Discover all our outdoor destinations

Homair

In Their Own Words...

Spending time with family

With Homair Vacances, each family member can have the time of their life: Kids will love the wide range of sports and activities on offer, grandparents will enjoy the gentle pleasures of life, and parents can enjoy the peace and quiet!

Home sweet mobile home

The Homair Vacances mobile homes are designed as small independent homes in which you will feel at ease very quickly. The mobile homes are independent and comfortable and are located in over 100 high-quality camping villages. You can choose your mobile home from a range of 12 types sleeping 2 to 6 people.

Vary the fun and pleasure creating new experiences

Homair Vacances welcome you to over 100 destinations in France, Italy, Croatia, Spain and Portugal, in some of the most prestigious touristic sites in the mountains, in the countryside or by the beach, which are all selected for their natural beauty and their vast cultural appeal.

Take a break

Homair Vacances offers everyone a wide choice of activities ranging from sports to shows, to parties and all kinds of evening entertainment… and also offers you great deals all year round, so that you can have longer holidays for less money.

www.homair.co.uk

Your holiday **"in nature's colours**
SUNELIA, WITH THE SUN

CAMPSITES - LEISURE RESORTS

Emerging in 2006, this is a group of 30 professionally run campsites sharing a common view towards quality and investment. With campsites located on the coast, countryside and mountains, there is 'something for everyone'. What's more, campsites are rated as either Sunêlia Club (livelier, plenty going on) or Sunêlia Zen (calmer, relaxed).

Campsites

Campsites
Campagne
La Ribeyre
Au Soleil d'Oc
Aluna Vacances
Le Ranc Davaine
L'Hippocampe
Lac de Panthier
Château Varennes
Côte Atlantique
Port'Land
La Pointe Saint-Gilles
L'Atlantique
Le Fief
Interlude
La Pointe du Médoc
Le Col Vert
Framissima Nature
Berrua
Le Col d'Ibardin
Côte Méditerranée
Internacional Amberes
Les Pins
Les Tropiques
Le California
Domaine de la Dragonnière
Le Clos du Rhône
Holiday Green
Perla di Mare
Résidence Lisa Maria
Villaggio dei Fiori
Montagne
Les Chalets du Logis d'Orres
Les Trois Vallées
Le Malazéou

Sunêlia

In Their Own Words...

All Sunêlia campsites are 3- or 4-star rated and guarantee facilities of the highest standards.

On each campsite you will receive a warm, personal welcome from Sunêlia-trained staff keen to ensure your stay is pleasant and comfortable.

Rather like a village, each Sunêlia campsite offers a range of services: restaurant, grocery store, barbecue, etc.

On Sunêlia sites, everything is laid on for children so that you can make the most of your free time with full peace of mind.

What is your Sunêlia style?

At the seaside, in the countryside, in the mountains, by the ocean: Sunêlia offers holidays tailored to your every whim...

Mountains: at the heart of the Alps or the Pyrenees, you can make the most of the pure air and exceptional environment to let off steam or recharge your batteries, as a family or with friends!

Countryside: An Auvergne campsite, or perhaps an Ardèche or Provence one... whatever your favourite destination, beautiful surroundings are guaranteed.

Seaside: From the glorious beaches of the Med (choose from many between the Côte d'Azur and the Pyrenees) to the charming little bays and rockpools of Brittany, via the sweeping Atlantic beaches. The choice is yours.

Sunêlia quality

Sunêlia is committed to sustainable tourism standards and the Clef Verte accreditation and Camping Qualité standards testify to this (Camping Qualité alone conforms to over 500 quality criteria).

www.sunelia.com

Villagecenter
L O I S I R S

Village Center is a group that has expanded from three sites in 2008 to its current network of over 30 sites, located in some of the most beautiful regions of France. There's quite a range of styles from simple (with limited amenities) to those which are rather more sophisticated. All sites in this group are owner-managed and most meet the standards of La Clef Verte.

Les Isles de Sola

Les Fontaines

Baie du Kernic

Bois de Pleuven

Parc de la Fecht

Ker Goh Lenn

Les Lupins

Parc des Allais

Les Almadies

Les Iles

Les Catalpas

Domaine du Bosquet

Aqua Viva

La Forêt

Le Moulin de David

Les Tours

Demeures du Ventoux

Coteau de la Marine

Eurolac

Rieumontagné

Mas des Cigales

Près du Verdon

Aurilandes

Les Vignes

Domaine des Iscles

Domaine du Golf

L'Europe

Les 7 Fonts

Le Castellas

Domaine de Manon

Le Fonsérane

Le Saint-Clair

Domaine d'Ensérune

Le Neptune

Domaine d'Anghione

■ Accommodation

■ Camping

30

Village Center

In Their Own Words...

With 30 years of experience and over 25 campsites, whatever kind of camping you fancy, Village Center can offer a great base for your holiday. Large pitches and modern accommodation in beautiful surroundings.

Mobile homes & chalets

There's always a friendly atmosphere and a great choice of accommodation for families or groups of friends. Choose between mobile homes, wooden chalets, bungalows and fully equipped tents: all the advantages of camping plus the comfort of custom-built accommodation.

Green credentials

We want you to enjoy your holiday and leave behind the routines and chores of daily life at home. That's why Village Center works together with La Clef Verte to guarantee the development of our sites (80% of our sites carry La Clef Verte accreditation). Moreover we renovate all mobile homes every three years.

Activities for the active

In high season you'll find a range of activities and entertainment designed to appeal to children and adults of all ages and preferences. Our campsites open their children's mini-clubs during all French school holidays.

Stunning locations

Village Center offers diverse destinations amid stunning scenery in beautiful French regions: the legends of Brittany, the endless horizons of the Atlantic coast, the soft sunsets of the south of France and the fantastic landscapes of the Midi-Pyrénées.

www.village-center.com

Created in 2000, Yelloh! Village is a network of camping villages which have become recognised for top-of-the-range camping and caravanning in France and Spain. The 46 Yelloh! Village campsites are professionally managed and offer high quality services and activities, well suited to active families and couples.

Campsites

1	La Côte de Nacre
2	Les Vikings
3	Les Pins
4	Le Ranolien
5	Les Mouettes
6	La Plage
7	L'Océan Breton
8	Port de Plaisance
9	Le Domaine d'Inly
10	Le Littoral
11	Yelloh! Soulac-sur-Mer
12	Les Grands Pins
13	Panorama du Pyla
14	Lous Seurrots
15	Punta Lago
16	Sylvamar
17	Ilbarritz
18	Mas Sant Josep
19	Le Brasilia
20	Le Pré Catalan
21	Le Sérignan Plage
22	Aloha
23	Le Club Farret
24	Mer et Soleil
25	Les Méditerranées – Nouvelle Floride/Charlemagne
26	La Petite Camargue
27	Les Petits Camarguais
28	Secrets de Camargue
29	Les Tournels
30	Domaine du Colombier
31	Yelloh! en Champagne
32	Yelloh! Paris/Ile-de-France
33	Parc du Val de Loire
34	Parc de Montsabert
35	Yelloh! Saint-Emilion
36	Lascaux Vacances
37	Le Lac des 3 Vallées
38	Le Bout du Monde
39	Domaine d'Arnauteille
40	Soleil Vivarais
41	La Plaine
42	Verdon Parc
43	Le Fayolan
44	Le Domaine des Bans
45	L'Etoile des Neiges
46	Le Pré Lombard

Yelloh! Village

In Their Own Words...

Commitment to your holidays from the first to the last day

From your reservation to your arrival at the campsite, we pride ourselves on our high level of service. We help you plan your stay in the best possible way with a comprehensive website and a welcoming, multi-lingual call-centre which also offers advice. At each campsite you will be welcomed by our smiling, dynamic team who will make you feel right at home. You will find top-of-the-range accommodation, wonderful beaches, lakes and rivers, play areas, quality equipment and swimming pools, either covered or heated. Our first-class infrastructure guarantees you a carefree holiday and our competent, trained organisers will inspire your confidence.

Our commitment to the environment

Yelloh! Village is committed to the protection of the beautiful natural surroundings. As a group we have chosen sustainable living on holidays by protecting natural resources, saving energy and water, recycling, thinking local and respecting local natural environments. Yelloh! Village campsites support indiginous architecture, car-free living, favour public transport when possible and encourage guests to embrace our eco-friendly attitude.

Our commitment to your entertainment and wellbeing on holiday

We aim to provide something for everyone, so feel free to come and join in our various organised activities. With a range of children's clubs, outdoor activities and evening entertainment there's plenty going on. Alternatively, if you prefer to simply relax and unwind during your holidays, you can plunge into a relaxing spa; the majority of our villages now offer a wide range of wellness centres and spas. Choose between saunas, jacuzzis, whirlpool baths, or expert massages, the choice is yours!

www.yellohvillage.co.uk

Miles of sandy beaches, hidden coves, charming towns and fishing villages, as well as unspoilt rolling countryside, all combine to make Brittany a unique holiday destination. The vibrant Breton spirit of the locals and excellent gastronomic heritage make it one of the most distinctive regions of France.

DÉPARTEMENTS: 22 CÔTES D'ARMOR, 29 FINISTÈRE, 35 ILLE-ET-VILAINE, 56 MORBIHAN

MAJOR CITIES: RENNES AND BREST

Brittany invites you to Be Breizh! and as 'Breizh' is the Breton word for Brittany, it's an invitation to get to know the real Brittany. It boasts some 1,700 miles of coastline so your own secluded cove is never far away along with endless stretches of golden sand. Archipelagos (of islands) dot the coast and allow you to escape to your own piece of paradise. Inland, the landscape alternates between enchanting forests of Arthurian legend, clusters of blue-shuttered stone cottages and mile upon mile of farmland all criss-crossed by tiny country roads. The region is world famous for its prehistoric standing stones and there are many perfectly preserved towns and villages steeped in local history and Celtic tradition to discover too.

Architectural gems await at every corner and can be found in the most unexpected of places, from wonderfully ornate churches to stately manor houses, castles and cathedrals. Farmers sell their produce at bustling weekly markets and local cuisine is a source of great pride. Expect Brittany's delicious seafood, fresh vegetables, indulgent butter and locally-reared meats to appear on every menu – as well as the famous crêpes.

Activities

The Canal de Nantes à Brest

The old railway line follows the canal as it snakes its way through the heart of Brittany. The tranquil 'green way' passes through unspoilt countryside and is great for walking, horse riding and cycling alike.

www.cotesdarmor.com

Cycling

Cycle the 100 km. of 'green way' from St Malo to Rennes and take in three historic towns rich in architecture and culture: St Malo, Dinan and Rennes. The route is that of the old railway line and passes through beautiful Breton countryside.

www.bretagne35.com

Nature

The Pink Granite Coast

From Perros-Guirec to Trébeurden, the granite with its rosy glow has been shaped by the wind and the waves into fantastic forms. Out to sea lie the Sept Îles, the biggest bird reserve in Europe.

www.cotesdarmor.com

Places of interest

The Rance estuary

The River Rance flows into the Channel at St Malo and its estuary is home to pretty fishing villages and peaceful harbours that are a delight to explore.

www.bretagne35.com

Golfe du Morbihan

This inland sea is dotted with islands and sailing boats bob in the sparkling water; the Golfe du Morbihan is a unique spot arguably best explored by boat. Nearby are the medieval town of Vannes, the world famous standing stones at Carnac and the wonderfully preserved medieval town of Josselin.

www.morbihan.com

Images © (left to right, top to bottom): unknown; Studio Diaphane; Jean-Patrick Gratien; Jean-Patrick Gratien; Jean-Patrick Gratien; Pascal Raso

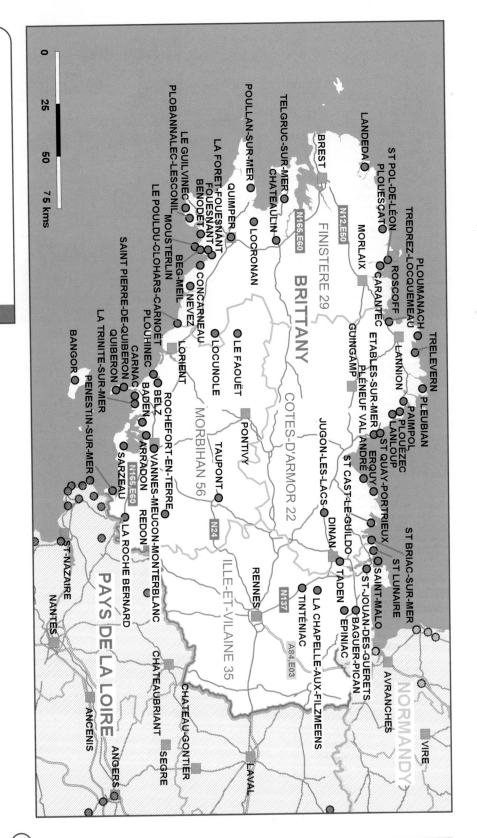

For latest campsite news, availability and prices visit
alanrogers.com

Arradon

Camping de Penboch

9 chemin de Penboch, F-56610 Arradon (Morbihan) T: 02 97 44 71 29. E: camping.penboch@wanadoo.fr
alanrogers.com/FR56040

Penboch is 200 metres by footpath from the shores of the Golfe du Morbihan with its many islands, and there is plenty to do, including watersports, fishing and boat trips. The site, in a peaceful, rural area, is divided into two – the main part, on open ground, with hedges and young trees, the other across a minor road in woodland with lots of shade. Penboch offers 175 pitches on flat grass, 105 are for touring and they are mostly divided into groups. Electricity (6/10A) is available on all pitches and most also have water and drainage. A Sites et Paysages member.

Facilities

Three toilet blocks, two on the main part (one heated) and one in the annex, include washbasins in cabins. There are new washing facilities including private family cabins (extra charge). Laundry facilities. Motorcaravan service point. Bar with snacks and takeaway. Shop (all 13/5-10/9). Heated pool with slide and paddling pool (1/5-19/9). Indoor pool (all season) with relaxation area, jacuzzi and massage tables. Good playground. WiFi in bar. Off site: Beach, fishing 200 m. Sailing, windsurfing 2 km. Bicycle hire 2 km. Golf and riding 6 km.

Open: 3 April - 25 September.

Directions

From N165 at Auray or Vannes, take D101 along northern shores of the Golfe du Morbihan; or leave N165 at D127 signed Ploeren and Arradon. Take turn to Arradon and site is signed. GPS: 47.62206, -2.8007

Charges guide

Per unit incl. 2 persons and electricity (10A)	€ 20,40 - € 38,50
extra person	€ 4,00 - € 6,20
child (2-7 yrs)	€ 3,00 - € 4,50
dog	€ 1,50 - € 3,50

Baden

Camping Mané Guernehué

52 rue Mané er Groez, F-56870 Baden (Morbihan) T: 02 97 57 02 06. E: info@camping-baden.com
alanrogers.com/FR56130

Located close to the Morbihan Gulf, Mané Guernehué is a smart, modern site with excellent amenities and a variety of pitches. Some are terraced beneath pine trees, others are in a former orchard with delightful views of the surrounding countryside. The 377 pitches are generally large, 200 being occupied by mobile homes and chalets. Most pitches have 10A electricity and a few also have water and drainage. Many are level but a few, particularly in the centre of the site, slope to varying degrees. An impressive new indoor pool complex has been added to the existing complex of outdoor pools and there is an equally impressive new spa and wellbeing facility.

Facilities

Three modern toilet blocks include washbasins in cabins. Facilities for disabled visitors. Washing machines and dryers. Small shop, bar and takeaway (9/4-1/9). Heated outdoor swimming pool (1/5-1/9). Heated indoor pool (all season), water slide, jacuzzi, gym and spa. Fishing. Minigolf. Pony trekking. Fitness room. Teenagers' room with games and TV. Play area. Tree top adventure area. Varied entertainment programme in high season. Mobile homes for rent. Off site: Beach, golf 3 km.

Open: 9 April - 1 November.

Directions

From Auray or Vannes use the D101 to Baden and watch for signs to site. GPS: 47.61419, -2.92596

Charges 2011

| Per unit incl. 2 persons and electricity | € 19,80 - € 42,80 |

Camping Cheques accepted.

Bangor

Flower Camping le Kernest

Bangor, F-56360 Belle Ile-en-Mer (Morbihan) T: 02 97 31 56 26. E: info@camping-kernest.com
alanrogers.com/FR56460

Belle Ile is a large island lying around 14 km. off the Quiberon peninsula. Access to the island can be made by ferry from either Quiberon, Vannes or Lorient (reservation is recommended in high season). Le Kernest is a family site and a member of the Flower group. It is located around 800 m. from a sandy beach with direct access by footpath. There are 100 pitches here, some of which are occupied by wooden chalets. Touring pitches are grassy and well shaded, and all have electrical connections. Leisure facilities on site include a tennis court and multisports terrain, as well as a snack bar. Numerous cycle tracks cross the island, including one around the perimeter.

Facilities

Shop. Snack bar. Takeaway. Tennis. Multisports terrain. Play area. TV room. Activity and entertainment programme. Chalets for rent. Off site: Nearest beach 800 m. (direct path). Riding. Fishing. Cycle tracks.

Open: 1 June - 30 September.

Directions

Upon arrival at Le Palais, follow signs to Bangor on D90 and then to Kernest. Site is well signed from here. GPS: 47.31479, -3.18912

Charges guide

Per unit incl. 2 persons and electricity	€ 13,90 - € 21,90
extra person	€ 3,50 - € 5,00
child (2-7 yrs)	€ 2,20 - € 3,50

For latest campsite news, availability and prices visit
alanrogers.com

Baguer-Pican
Camping le Vieux Chêne

Baguer-Pican, F-35120 Dol-de-Bretagne (Ille-et-Vilaine) T: 02 99 48 09 55. E: vieux.chene@wanadoo.fr
alanrogers.com/FR35000

This attractive, family owned site is situated between Saint Malo and Mont Saint Michel. Developed in the grounds of a country farmhouse dating from 1638, its young and enthusiastic owner has created a really pleasant, traditional atmosphere. In spacious, rural surroundings it offers 199 good sized pitches on gently sloping grass, most with 10A electricity, water tap and light. They are separated by bushes and flowers, with mature trees for shade. A very attractive tenting area (without electricity) is in the orchard. There are three lakes in the grounds and centrally located leisure facilities include a restaurant with a terrace overlooking an attractive pool complex. Some entertainment is provided in high season, which is free for children. The site is used by a Dutch tour operator (20 pitches). A Sites et Paysages member.

Facilities

Three very good, unisex toilet blocks, which can be heated, include washbasins in cabins, a baby room and facilities for disabled visitors. Small laundry. Motorcaravan services. Shop, bar, takeaway and restaurant (1/6-4/9). Heated swimming pool, paddling pool, slides (17/5-11/9; lifeguard July/Aug). TV room (satellite). Games room. Tennis. Minigolf. Giant chess. Play area. Riding in July/Aug. Fishing. Off site: Supermarket in Dol 3 km. Golf 12 km. Beach 20 km.

Open: 17 May - 25 September.

Directions

Site is by the D576 Dol-de-Bretagne - Pontorson road, just east of Baguer-Pican. It can be reached from the new N176 taking exit for Dol-Est and Baguer-Pican. GPS: 48.54924, -1.684

Charges 2011

Per unit incl. 2 persons and electricity	€ 19,50 - € 33,50

BRITTANY

★★★★
Camping - Caravaning
le Vieux Chêne

BAGUER PICAN
35120 DOL DE BRETAGNE
TÉL. 0033 2 99 48 09 55
FAX 0033 2 99 48 13 37
Website: www.camping-vieuxchene.fr

- *200 pitches,*
- *Tennis,*
- *Aquatic Park,*
- *Fishing ponds,*
- *Mini-golf,*
- *Mini-club,*
- *Snack-bar, Shop,*
- *Ponies...*

Beg-Meil
Camping de la Piscine

B.P. 12 Kerleya, Beg-Meil, F-29170 Fouesnant (Finistère) T: 02 98 56 56 06
E: contact@campingdelapiscine.com alanrogers.com/FR29170

There are many campsites in this area but La Piscine is notable for the care and attention to detail that contribute to the well-being of its visitors. Created by the Caradec family from an apple orchard, the 185 level, grass pitches are of a generous size and are separated by an interesting variety of hedges and trees. Water, drainage and electricity points are provided, normally one stand between two pitches. The small bar and takeaway (July and August) with terrace overlooking the pool complex provides a relaxing focal point. A quiet site, set back from the sea, La Piscine will appeal to families looking for good quality without too many on-site activities. A new covered, heated pool with sauna and massage facilities is planned for 2011. The nearby towns of Beg-Meil and Fouesnant, and, a little further, Quimper, are well worth a visit if only to taste the local cider and crêpes which are specialities of the area.

Facilities

Two refurbished toilet units include washbasins in cabins and showers. Facilities for disabled visitors. Laundry facilities. Motorcaravan service point. Shop. Takeaway (high season). Pool complex with three slides, waterfall and jacuzzi. Covered, heated pool planned. Sauna and solarium. Play area. BMX track. Bicycle hire. Half-court tennis. TV room. Entertainment organised in high season. Off site: Restaurants, bars, shops and supermarkets in Fouesnant 1 km. Beach 1 km. Fishing and riding within 4 km. Golf 7 km.

Open: 13 May - 12 September.

Directions

Site is 5 km. south of Fouesnant. Turn off N165 expressway at Coat Conq signed Concarneau and Fouesnant. At Fouesnant join D45 signed Beg-Meil and shortly turn right on D145 signed Mousterlin. In 1 km. turn left and follow signs to site. GPS: 47.86568, -4.01553

Charges guide

Per unit incl. 2 persons and electricity	€ 20,00 - € 30,60
extra person	€ 4,00 - € 6,30
child (2-10 yrs)	€ 2,00 - € 3,15

For latest campsite news, availability and prices visit

alanrogers.com

Bénodet

Camping du Letty

F-29950 Bénodet (Finistère) T: 02 98 57 04 69. E: reception@campingduletty.com

alanrogers.com/FR29030

The Guyader family have ensured that this excellent and attractive site has plenty to offer for all the family. With a charming ambience, the site on the outskirts of the popular resort of Bénodet spreads over 22 acres with 493 pitches, all for touring units. Groups of four to eight pitches are set in cul-de-sacs with mature hedging and trees to divide each group. Most pitches have electricity, water and drainage. Although there is no swimming pool here, the site has direct access to a small sandy beach, and has provided a floating pontoon (safe bathing depends on the tides). At the attractive floral entrance, former farm buildings provide a host of facilities including an extensively equipped fitness room and new 'wellness' rooms for massage and jacuzzis. There is also a modern, purpose built nightclub and bar providing high quality live entertainment most evenings (it is situated well away from most pitches to avoid disturbance).

Facilities

Six well placed toilet blocks are of good quality and include mixed style WCs, washbasins in large cabins and controllable hot showers (charged). One block includes a separate laundry and dog washing enclosures. Baby rooms. Separate facility for disabled visitors. Launderette. Hairdressing room. Motorcaravan service points. Well stocked shop. Extensive snack bar and takeaway. Bar with games room and night club. Library/reading room with four computer stations. Entertainment room with satellite TV. Fitness centre (no charge). Saunas, jacuzzi and solarium (all charged). Tennis and squash (charged). Boules. Archery. Well equipped play area. Entertainment and activities (July/Aug). WiFi in reception. Off site: Sailing, fishing, riding and golf all nearby. Bénodet and Quimper.

Open: 15 June - 6 September.

Directions

From N165 take D70 Concarneau exit. At first roundabout take D44 to Fouesnant. Turn right at T-junction. After 2 km. turn left to Fouesnant (still D44). Continue through La Forêt Fouesnant and Fouesnant, picking up signs for Bénodet. Shortly before Bénodet at roundabout turn left (signed Le Letty). Turn right at next mini-roundabout and site is 500 m. on left. GPS: 47.86700, -4.08783

Charges guide

Per person	€ 4,00 - € 6,50
child (1-6 yrs)	€ 2,00 - € 3,25
pitch incl. vehicle and electricity	€ 12,50 - € 15,00
dog	€ 2,30

For latest campsite news, availability and prices visit

alanrogers.com

Belz

Camping le Moulin des Oies

21 rue de la Côte, F-56550 Belz (Morbihan) T: 02 97 55 53 26. E: moulindesoies@wanadoo.fr

alanrogers.com/FR56500

This delightful rural site is lovingly cared for by the owners M. and Mme. Tregret. The 68 generously sized pitches (6A electricity) are grassy, level and marked by trees and shrubs. Separated from the sea by the width of a small road, the campsite has its own salt water inlet controlled by a sluice. Not being affected by the tide and with a small sandy beach, there is safe bathing at all times. To the side there is a shady grassed picnic area. The nearby town of Belz is within walking distance, with buses to the town of Lorient, Carnac and the Quiberon peninsular. A bus takes you to the railway station 6 km. away.

Facilities	Directions
Sanitary block with showers. Facilities for the disabled. Washing machine, games room, TV. Multisports court. Bar, restaurant and take away (Jul/Aug). Saltwater swimming pool with beach. Kitchen with dining area for campers. Bicycle hire. Only certain breeds of dog accepted. WiFi. Off site: Belz town 1km for shops, restaurants and transport services. Golf 6 km. Boat launching 50 m.	Leave the N165 at Auray. Take the D22 signed Lorient. At Belz the campsite is signed on the right after entering Belz. The campsite is 1km further. GPS: 47.680403, -3.175821

Open: 2 April - 26 September.

Charges guide

Per unit incl. 2 persons	€ 12,00 - € 14,00
electricity (6A)	€ 3,10
child (under 7 years)	€ 2,15

No credit cards.

Bénodet

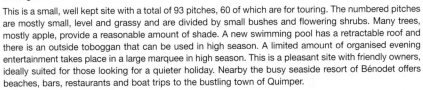

Flower Camping Aux 2 Chênes

Route de Kerangles, F-29950 Bénodet (Finistère) T: 02 98 56 62 01. E: querperot@wanadoo.fr

alanrogers.com/FR29460

This is a small, well kept site with a total of 93 pitches, 60 of which are for touring. The numbered pitches are mostly small, level and grassy and are divided by small bushes and flowering shrubs. Many trees, mostly apple, provide a reasonable amount of shade. A new swimming pool has a retractable roof and there is an outside toboggan that can be used in high season. A limited amount of organised evening entertainment takes place in a large marquee in high season. This is a pleasant site with friendly owners, ideally suited for those looking for a quieter holiday. Nearby the busy seaside resort of Bénodet offers beaches, bars, restaurants and boat trips to the bustling town of Quimper.

Facilities	Directions
One central toilet block provides washbasins mostly in cabins and pre-set showers (small). Washing machine. Shop and bar (July/Aug). Covered swimming pool. Toboggan (July/Aug). Adventure play area. Off site: Beach, fishing 300 m. Bicycle hire. riding 4 km. Golf 5 km.	Take the D44 from Fouesnant in the direction of Bénodet. Site on right in about 6.5 km. and is well signed. GPS: 47.886107, -4.038337

Open: 15 April - 31 October.

Charges guide

Per unit incl. 2 persons	€ 15,00 - € 19,00

Bénodet

Yelloh! Village Port de Plaisance

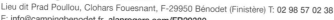

Lieu dit Prad Poullou, Clohars Fouesnant, F-29950 Bénodet (Finistère) T: 02 98 57 02 38
E: info@campingbenodet.fr alanrogers.com/FR29380

Sometimes larger campsites can lack ambiance, but it is not so with Port de Plaisance. This is a delightful, family run site with 340 pitches of which 77 are for touring campers, all with 6A electricity. The pitches are mostly in two areas, where they are hedged and positioned in small groups amongst the many mature trees and flowering shrubs. Although there are five holiday tour operators on site, their presence is unobtrusive because of careful positioning amongst the trees. This is truly a campsite with something for everybody, with a wide range of entertainment and activities provided over a long season. The restaurant that overlooks the pool complex boasts a very good menu. There is entertainment suitable for all ages, from up-to-date films to taster aquadiving lessons in the covered, heated pool. The marina at the mouth of the Odet river is 500 m. away, and from here you can enjoy a boat trip up to Quimper. The large seaside town of Bénodet, with all the shops, bars and restaurants that you could wish for is just 1 km. away.

Facilities

Three toilet blocks, older and simple in style, include British style toilets, showers and washing cubicles. Baby room. Facilities for disabled visitors. Laundry room. Shop, bar and restaurant (all season) and takeaway (15/5-15/9). Swimming pool complex with flumes and toboggan. Games room. Programme of entertainment. Multisport court. Aerial zipwire course. Bicycle hire. Massage room. WiFi in bar (charged). Dogs are not accepted 2/7-28/8. Off site: Bénodet 1 km. Fishing 1 km. Riding 2 km. Golf 3 km. Beach 1 km.

Open: 8 April - 18 September.

Directions

Take the D34 south from Quimper. Site is on the left just as you enter Bénodet.
GPS: 47.882065, -4.103282

Charges guide

Per unit incl. 2 persons and electricity (6A)	€ 15,00 - € 39,00
extra person	€ 4,00 - € 7,00
child (0-7 yrs)	free - € 4,00
dog	€ 4,00

Carantec

Yelloh! Village les Mouettes

50 route de La Grande Grève, F-29660 Carantec (Finistère) T: 02 98 67 02 46. E: camping@les-mouettes.com

alanrogers.com/FR29000

Les Mouettes is a sheltered site on the edge of an attractive bay with access to the sea at the front of the site. In a wooded setting with many attractive trees and shrubs, the 434 pitches include just 112 for touring units, all with electricity, water and drainage. The remainder are taken by tour operators and by around 172 mobile homes and chalets for rent. At the centre of the 'village' are shops, a restaurant, a bar, an entertainment stage, sports facilities and an impressive heated pool complex with swimming, paddling and water slide pools, plus a 'tropical river', jacuzzi and sauna.

Facilities	Directions
Three clean sanitary blocks include controllable showers, washbasins in cabins and mainly British toilets. Facilities for disabled visitors. Laundry. Motorcaravan services. Shop. Takeaway. Bar with TV. Crêperie/pizzeria/grill. Pool complex. Beauty Salon. Games rooms. Play area. Half-court tennis. Minigolf. Entertainment in main season. Large units should phone first. Dogs not accepted after 26/6. WiFi in central area (free). Off site: Fishing 1 km. Beach, sailing and golf all 2 km. Riding 6 km.	Carantec is 15 km. northwest of Morlaix and 15 km. by road from Roscoff. From D58 Roscoff - Morlaix road, turn east to Carantec on D173. In 4 km. site is signed to the left at roundabout immediately after passing supermarket on right. GPS: 48.65807, -3.92833

Open: 16 May - 6 September.

Charges guide

Per unit incl. 2 persons, electricity and water	€ 14,00 - € 44,00
extra person	€ 5,00 - € 7,00

Carnac

Camping les Menhirs

Allée Saint-Michel, F-56340 Carnac (Morbihan) T: 02 97 52 94 67. E: contad@lesmenhirs.com

alanrogers.com/FR56270

Although located within the built-up area of the popular resort of Carnac, and only 300 m. from the beach, this campsite feels much more rural. Catering for all ages, this is a friendly site and lively in high season with plenty of activities including evening entertainment and a club for children. There are 350 pitches; 154 touring pitches and the remainder used for mobile homes and chalets, of which the majority are used by tour operators. The touring pitches are in groups and are large, level and hedged. All have electricity (10A), water and drainage, and 14 have hardstanding. The central complex containing the pools and games areas, all overlooked by the bar and its terrace, makes a convivial focal point. The town and seafront can be explored on foot and the Brittany coast and the Gulf of Morbihan are within easy reach by car or bicycle. American motor homes should book ahead.

Facilities	Directions
Three spotless, modern, light toilet blocks with washbasins in cabins, facilities for children, babies and disabled visitors. A further en-suite unit for disabled visitors is by the pool complex. Laundry. Shop. Bar with satellite TV and takeaway (13/5-16/9). Heated indoor and outdoor swimming pools, the latter with slides (all season). Fitness complex with massage, multi-gym, jacuzzi, sauna and solarium. Multisport pitch. Tennis. Boules. Riding (1/7-31/8). Play areas. Children's club and evening entertainment (July/Aug). Internet access (charged). Off site: Beach 300 m. Bicycle hire 500 m. Golf 800 m. Sailing 1 km. Town centre 1 km. Bars and restaurants within easy walking distance.	From Auray take D786 to Carnac and Quiberon. After 5 km. turn south on D119 towards Carnac at roundabout. 600 m. beyond next roundabout fork left, signed La Trinité-sur-Mer and Plages. Keep straight on at lights. Fork left at first roundabout. Turn left at next roundabout (T-junction) and site is signed at 250 m. on left. GPS: 47.57653, -3.06890

Open: 23 April - 29 September.

Charges guide

Per unit incl. 2 persons	€ 22,65 - € 45,30
child (2-7 yrs)	€ 2,95 - € 5,90

CAMPING LES MENHIRS

Situated 300 m from the sandy beach and close to the centre of Carnac Plage, the Camping des menhirs offers a variety of high standard facilities: heated outdoor swimming pool, heated indoor swimming pool, sauna, jacuzzi, etc...

Bp 167 - Allée St Michel - 56343 Carnac - France
Tel: 0033 (0)2 97 52 94 67 - Fax: 0033 (0)2 97 52 25 38

contact@lesmenhirs.com
www.lesmenhirs.com

For latest campsite news, availability and prices visit

alanrogers.com

Carnac

Castel Camping la Grande Métairie

Route des Alignements de Kermario, B.P. 85, F-56342 Carnac (Morbihan) T: 02 97 52 24 01
E: info@lagrandemetairie.com alanrogers.com/FR56010

La Grande Métairie is a good quality site situated a little back from the sea, close to the impressive rows of the famous Carnac 'menhirs' (giant prehistoric standing stones). The site has 575 individual pitches (108 for touring units), surrounded by hedges and trees. All have electricity (some need long leads). The site is well known and popular and has many British visitors with 314 pitches taken by tour operators. It is ideal for families with children of all ages, but probably not suitable for those with walking difficulties. The site has a great deal to offer and is lively and busy over a long season. Musical evenings, barbecues and other organised events including occasional dances are held in an outdoor amphitheatre (pitches near these facilities may be noisy late at night – the bar closes at midnight). Paddocks with ponds are home for ducks, goats and ponies to watch and feed. There are also pony rides around the site. A super pool complex comprises heated indoor and outdoor pools, water slides and toboggans and a jacuzzi. A local market takes place at Carnac on Wednesdays and Sundays.

Facilities

Three large well maintained toilet blocks, with washbasins in cabins. Facilities for babies and disabled visitors. Laundry facilities. Motorcaravan service points. Shops (from 22/5). Bar lounge and terrace, restaurant and takeaway (all from 22/5). TV and games rooms. Swimming pool complex with bar. Playgrounds and playing field. Tennis. Minigolf. BMX track. Bicycle hire. Fishing. Zip-wire. Paintball. Helicopter rides (July/Aug). Amphitheatre. Organised events and entertainment. American motorhomes accepted up to 27 ft.
Off site: Riding 1 km. Nearest beach 3 km. Golf 12 km.

Open: 3 April - 11 September (all services from 22/5).

Directions

From N165 take Quiberon/Carnac exit onto the D768. After 5 km. turn south onto D119 towards Carnac. At roundabout and after 4 km. turn left (northeast) onto D196 to the site.
GPS: 47.5973, -3.0607

Charges guide

Per unit incl. 2 persons	
and electricity	€ 18,00 - € 43,40
extra person	€ 4,00 - € 7,70
child (4-7 yrs)	€ 3,50 - € 5,40

Route des Alignements de Kermario Tél. 33(0)2 97 52 24 01
B.P. 85 - 56342 Carnac Cedex Fax 33(0)2 97 52 83 58
www.lagrandemetairie.com

Carnac

Kawan Village le Moustoir

Route du Moustoir, F-56340 Carnac (Morbihan) T: 02 97 52 16 18. E: info@lemoustoir.com

alanrogers.com/FR56110

Camping le Moustoir is a friendly, family run site situated about three kilometres inland from the many beaches of the area and close to the famous 'alignments' of standing stones. Pitches are grassy and separated by shrubs and hedges, with several shaded by tall pine trees. There is a popular pool area with slides, swimming pool and a paddling pool with 'mushroom' fountain and a second covered pool complex. The bar and terrace become the social centre of the site in the evenings. A high season entertainment programme includes a daily Kids' Club attracting children of several nationalities. Whilst younger children can enjoy pony rides around the campsite, the older ones can swoop through the treetops on the new aerial adventure complex. For those who like to experience local cuisine, nearby Carnac, La Trinité-sur-Mer and Auray have restaurants and crêperies to suit all tastes. Carnac's Wednesday and Sunday markets are not to be missed.

Facilities

The substantial, traditional style toilet block is well maintained (outside peak season some sections may be closed). Motorcaravan service facilities. Shop, bar, restaurant and takeaway (all season). Heated swimming pool (21x8 m), water slides, and paddling pool (from 1/5). Heated indoor swimming pool (all season). Adventure playground. Tennis. Boules. Volleyball, football and basketball. Pool. 'Kids' Club'. Barrier deposit € 20. Off site: Watersports at Carnac Plage. Fishing, bicycle hire, riding 2 km. Beach 3 km. Golf 10 km.

Open: 1 April - 30 September.

Directions

From N165, take exit to D768 (Carnac and Quiberon). At second crossroads after 5 km. turn left (D119) towards Carnac. After 3 km. turn left (oblique turning) after a hotel. Site is 500 m. on left. GPS: 47.60825, -3.06587

Charges guide

Per unit incl. 2 persons	€ 19,60 - € 31,60
extra person	€ 4,90
child (2-7 yrs)	free - € 4,90

Camping Cheques accepted.

Kawan Village Le Moustoir | 71 Route du Moustoir | F-56340 Carnac
Tel: 0033 297 52 16 18 | info@lemoustoir.com | www.lemoustoir.com

Châteaulin

Camping la Pointe

Route de Saint-Coulitz, F-29150 Châteaulin (Finistère) T: 02 98 86 51 53. E: lapointecamping@aol.com

alanrogers.com/FR29280

This small, rural campsite situated by the river Aulne on the outskirts of Châteaulin, was taken over by new English owners Julie and Marcus Gregory in 2008. They have deleoped the site to provide a friendly and relaxed atmosphere. The 60 pitches vary in size and quality, all have 10A electricity and a few provide hardstanding for heavier units. There is a small kitchen garden complete with chickens where campers can purchase free range eggs and other produce and are also welcome to just sit and relax. A family/games room can be found above the well maintained toilet block. A short walk away (200 m) you will find the river Aulne where fishing is popular (permit required) and the towpath into the town for shops, bars, restaurants and a weekly market can either be walked or cycled.

Facilities

The toilet and shower block also provides facilities for disabled visitors. Baby changing area. Laundry facilities. Motorcaravan service facilities. Family/games room. Small shop for basics and bread. Fresh eggs and produce available from the kitchen garden. WiFi around reception area (free). Off site: Fishing in the Aulne 200 m (permit needed). Bicycle hire 2 km. Châteaulin 1.5 km. with shops, bars and restaurants. Nearest beach 20 km.

Open: 11 March - 15 October.

Directions

From Quimper or Brest on N165, exit at 'Châteaulin Centre'. From Châteaulin follow signs for St Coulitz. After 1.5 km. turn left and continue 100 m. Site well signed. GPS: 48.18746, -4.0848

Charges guide

Per unit incl. 2 persons and electricity	€ 19,50
extra person	€ 4,00
child (under 10 yrs)	€ 2,50

No credit cards.

For latest campsite news, availability and prices visit

alanrogers.com

Châteaulin

Camping de Rodaven

Rocade de Prat Bihan, F-29150 Châteaulin (Finistère) T: 02 98 86 32 93
E: campingderodaven@orange.fr alanrogers.com/FR29640

This former municipal campsite has been transformed by its enthusiastic owner M. Gerente into a most delightful place to stay. There are 100 generously sized, level, grassy pitches (40 with 10A electricity). They are divided by various flowering shrubs, small trees and, in a more open area of the site, by white lines on the grass. There is a small bar with a covered terrace. The site is alongside the Nantes Brest canal, which offers good fishing (permit required). Canoes are also available for hire on the site. The riverside town of Châteaulin is only 10 minutes walk away. Châteaulin is a picturesque Breton market town located on the river Aulne, where you will find shops, bars and restaurants. The cathedral city of Quimper, the medieval town of Locronan and the Crozon peninsula are all within easy reach. The nearest sandy beach is at Pentrez (15 km).

Facilities

Toilet and shower block with facilities for disabled campers. Washing machine and dryer. Bar. Play area. Bicycle and canoe hire. Archery, table tennis and boules. Fishing on canal (permit required). Off site: Swimming pool and tennis courts 200 m. Town centre 350 m. Nearest beach 15 km. Locronan and Quimper.

Open: 1 May - 30 September.

Directions

From the direction of Brest on N165 leave at first sign for Châteaulin and follow D770 to the town. Within the town follow signs for 'Piscine'. Opposite swimming pool you will see sign for the campsite. GPS: 48.189855, -4.090122

Charges guide

Per unit incl. 2 persons and electricity	€ 12,20 - € 13,70
extra person	€ 3,00
child (0-12 yrs)	€ 2,00
dog	€ 1,00

Concarneau

Camping les Sables Blancs

Avenue Le Dorlett, F-29900 Concarneau (Finistère) T: 02 98 97 16 44
E: contact@camping-lessablesblancs.com alanrogers.com/FR29150

This is an attractive, terraced site overlooking the sea on the outskirts of Concarneau. Most of the 108 touring pitches are shaded by large mature trees and shrubs and all have 10A electricity. Access to some could prove a little difficult for large units. A traditionally styled bar, restaurant and conservatory opens out onto a terrace with a swimming pool overlooking the Baie de la Forêt. Although the site is terraced with steep steps in places, the main touring pitches are on the top part of the site close to the main facilities. The site is run by young owners who work very hard and make you feel welcome. An advantage of the site's position is its close proximity to Concarneau, which is said to be the second largest fishing port in France.

Facilities

One new modern toilet block provides very good facilities including washbasins (both open and in cubicles) and showers. Facilities for babies and disabled visitors. New laundry facilities. Bar and restaurant (3/4-30/9). Heated outdoor swimming pool (23/4-15/9). Play area. Evening entertainment (July/Aug). Billiards room. WiFi in bar. Off site: Concarneau with shops, bars and restaurants. Beach 150 m. Riding 1 km. Bicycle hire, boat launching 1.5 km. Golf 6 km.

Open: 2 April - 31 October.

Directions

Leave the N165 for Concarneau on D70. Site is situated on the northern edge of town on the coast road. Well signed. GPS: 47.88195, -3.92915

Charges guide

Per unit incl. 2 persons	€ 13,00 - € 19,50

For latest campsite news, availability and prices visit

alanrogers.com

Concarneau
Flower Camping le Cabellou Plage

Avenue du Cabellou, F-29185 Concarneau (Finistère) T: 02 98 97 37 41
E: info@le-cabellou-plage.com alanrogers.com/FR29520

Le Cabellou Plage is a very pleasant, well maintained site located close to Concarneau. The large, grassy pitches are divided by young hedges, all have 10A electricity and some also have water and drainage. Many have fine views to the nearby beach and the old walled town beyond. The enthusiastic owner has tastefully landscaped many areas of the site with a profusion of shrubs and flowers. A large swimming pool on site is overlooked by a terrace and bar and the beach is just 25 m. away. La Cabellou is ideally situated for those wishing to visit Concarneau with its twice weekly market, Pont Aven and the cathedral city of Quimper.

Facilities

One modern toilet block is bright and cheerful and provides mainly open style washbasins and preset showers. Baby room. Facilities for disabled visitors. Laundry room. Shop. Bar with television and internet access. Swimming pool. Scuba lessons and water gymnastics. Bicycle hire. Off site: Bus stop outside site. Supermarkets, shops and restaurants in Concarneau 4 km. Tennis 3 km. Riding 7 km. Golf 10 km.

Open: 3 April - 18 September.

Directions

Site is just south of Concarneau. Take the D783 towards Tregunc. Turn right onto Avenue Cabellou. Site is well signed from here.
GPS: 47.85516, -3.90521

Charges guide

Per unit incl. 2 persons	
and electricity	€ 13,00 - € 22,00
with water and drainage	€ 15,00 - € 28,00
extra person	€ 3,00 - € 6,00
child (under 10 yrs)	free - € 5,00
pet	€ 3,00

Camping
le Cabellou Plage
✽ ✽ Bretagne Sud

A peninsula facing
Concarneau

Camping Qualité

Tél : 00 (33) 2 98 97 37 41 QUALITÉ TOURISME
www.le-cabellou-plage.com

Concarneau
Camping les Prés Verts

B.P. 612, Kernous-Plage, F-29186 Concarneau (Finistère) T: 02 98 97 09 74. E: info@presverts.com
alanrogers.com/FR29190

What sets this family site apart from the many others in this region are its more unusual features – its stylish pool complex with Romanesque style columns and statue, and its plants and flower tubs. The 150 pitches are mostly arranged on long, open, grassy areas either side of the main access roads. Specimen trees, shrubs or hedges divide the site into smaller areas. There is an area towards the rear of the site where the pitches have sea views. There is direct access to the sandy beach with no roads to cross (300 m). Concarneau is just 2.5 km. There are many marked coastal walks to enjoy in the area, plus watersports or boat and fishing trips available nearby. A Sites et Paysages member.

Facilities

Two toilet blocks provide unisex WCs, but separate washing facilities for ladies and men. Preset hot showers and washbasins in cabins for ladies, both closed 21.00-08.00 hrs. Some child-size toilets. Laundry facilities. Shop (1/7-25/8). Pizza service twice weekly. Heated swimming pool (1/6-31/8) and paddling pool. Playground (0-5 yrs). Minigolf (charged). Off site: Path to sandy/rocky beach 300 m. Coastal path. Riding 1 km. Bicycle hire 1.5 km. Supermarket 2 km. Golf 5 km.

Open: 1 May - 22 September.

Directions

Turn off C7 road, 2.5 km. north of Concarneau, where site is signed. Take third left after Hotel de l'Océan. GPS: 47.89616, -3.95433

Charges guide

Per unit incl. 2 persons	€ 16,00 - € 20,00
extra person	€ 4,80 - € 6,00
child (2-7 yrs)	€ 3,20 - € 4,00
electricity (2-10A)	€ 3,20 - € 7,00

For latest campsite news, availability and prices visit
alanrogers.com

Epiniac

Castel Camping le Domaine des Ormes

Epiniac, F-35120 Dol-de-Bretagne (Ille-et-Vilaine) T: 02 99 73 53 00. E: info@lesormes.com
alanrogers.com/FR35020

This impressive site, in the grounds of the Château des Ormes is in the north east part of Brittany, about 30 km. from the old town and ferry port of Saint-Malo. In an estate of wooded parkland and lakes, it has a pleasant atmosphere, busy in high season but peaceful at other times, with an impressive range of facilities. Of the 800 pitches only 160 are for tourers (120 with 6A electricity). They are of varying sizes and there is a choice of terrain – flat or gently sloping, wooded or open. The rest are occupied by tour operators (550) and by mobile homes (50 to rent).

Facilities

The toilet blocks are of fair standard, one recently refurbished, including washbasins in cabins and ample facilities for disabled visitors. A new, spacious block has family cubicles (shower and washbasin). Motorcaravan services. Supermarket, bar, restaurant, pizzeria and takeaway. Games room, bar and disco. Indoor and outdoor pools, aqua park with new 'wave' pool. Adventure play area. Golf. Bicycle hire. Fishing. Equestrian centre. Minigolf. Tennis. Sports ground. Paintball. Archery. Cricket club. WiFi in bar area (free). Off site: Beaches, sailing and boat launching 25 km.

Open: 16 May - 5 September (with all services).

Directions

Site is off D795 8 km. south of Dol-de-Bretagne, 11 km. north of Combourg.
GPS: 48.49030, -1.72787

Charges guide

Per person	€ 4,20 - € 7,50
child (under 13 yrs)	free - € 4,60
pitch incl. electricity (6A)	€ 18,60 - € 29,60
drainage	€ 1,70 - € 2,00
dog	€ 1,70 - € 2,00

Erquy

Camping le Vieux Moulin

14 rue des Moulins, F-22430 Erquy (Côtes d'Armor) T: 02 96 72 34 23. E: camp.vieux.moulin@wanadoo.fr
alanrogers.com/FR22050

Le Vieux Moulin is a family run site, just 2 km. from the little fishing port of Erquy on Brittany's Emerald Coast on the edge of a pine forest and nature reserve. It is about 900 m. from a beach of sand and shingle. Taking its name from the old mill opposite, the site has 173 pitches, all with electricity (6/9A) and some with water and drainage. One section of 39 pitches is arranged around a pond. Most pitches are of a fair size, arranged in squares, with trees giving shade. Evening entertainment is organised and there is a friendly pizzeria.

Facilities

Two good quality toilet blocks have mostly British style toilets and facilities for disabled visitors and babies. A further small block provides toilets and dishwashing only. Washing machines and dryer. Motorcaravan service point. Shop. Pizzeria and takeaway. Bar and terrace. Heated, covered pool complex with jacuzzi and paddling pool. Play areas. Tennis. Fitness gym. TV/games room. Bicycle hire. No electric barbecues. WiFi. Off site: Beach 900 m. Fishing 1.2 km. Golf and riding 7 km.

Open: 9 April - 17 September.

Directions

Site is 2 km. east of Erquy. Take minor road towards Les Hôpitaux and site is signed from junction of D786 and D34 roads. GPS: 48.63858, -2.44189

Charges guide

Per unit incl. 2 persons and electricity	€ 10,00 - € 19,90
extra person	€ 4,90 - € 6,10
child (under 7 yrs)	€ 3,80 - € 4,80
dog	€ 3,00 - € 4,00

Erquy

Camping Bellevue

Route de la libération, F-22430 Erquy (Côtes d'Armor) T: 02 96 72 33 04. E: campingbellevue@yahoo.fr
alanrogers.com/FR22210

Situated a mile from the beaches between Erquy and Pléneuf Val-André, Camping Bellevue offers a quiet country retreat with easy access to the cliffs of Cap Fréhel, Sables d'Or and St Cast. There are 140 pitches of which 120 are available for touring units, most with electricity (6/10A) and 20 with water and drainage. The site also has 20 mobile homes and tents to rent. Children are well catered for at this campsite – there are heated swimming and paddling pools, three play areas with minigolf, pétanque and volleyball. A Sites et Paysages member.

Facilities

Two modern, unisex toilet blocks are of a high standard. Some washbasins in cubicles. Facilities for disabled visitors. Laundry facilities. Shop and bar (15/6-10/9). Restaurant and takeaway (12/6-30/9). Swimming and paddling pools (Apr-Sept). Play areas. Games room. Minigolf. Pétanque. Entertainment and activities in high season. Multisport area. Max. 1 dog. Off site: Beach and fishing 2 km. Golf 4 km. Bicycle hire 5 km. Riding 6 km.

Open: 4 April - 30 September.

Directions

From St Brieuc road take D786 towards Erquy. Site is adjacent to the D786 at St Pabu and is well signed. GPS: 48.59426, -2.48475

Charges guide

Per unit incl. 2 persons and electricity (10A)	€ 20,30 - € 25,80
child (0-12 yrs)	free - € 4,40
extra person	€ 4,00 - € 5,00

For latest campsite news, availability and prices visit

alanrogers.com

Erquy

Yelloh! Village les Pins

Route du Guen, le Guen, F-22430 Erquy (Côtes d'Armor) T: 04 66 73 97 39. E: info@yellohvillage-les-pins.com
alanrogers.com/FR22360

Erquy is a pretty holiday resort nestling between two promontories. There are plenty of great sandy beaches around here, and one of the best is just 900 m. from this wooded site. Les Pins is a long-established site with many of the original facilities still in use. There are 235 touring pitches here and a further 148 pitches are occupied by mobile homes and chalets. The site boasts some impressive amenities including a top class swimming pool complex extending over 600 sq.m. with water slides, lazy river and various other water features.

Facilities

Four very old toilet blocks, all with mostly Turkish style toilets and other poor facilities. New facilities at the pools. Shop. Bar. Restaurant. Snack bar and takeaway (from 15/6). Large swimming pool complex with water slides and other features. Children's pool. Fitness centre. Sauna. Tennis. Play area. Activity and entertainment programme. Off site: Nearest beach 900 m. Fishing 900 m. Golf, riding and bicycle hire 2.5 km. Casino. Diving school.

Open: 26 April - 13 September.

Directions

From St Brieuc, take the northbound D786 to Erquy. Continue through the town following signs to Cap d'Erquy and the site is well indicated. GPS: 48.63841, -2.45565

Charges guide

Per unit incl. 2 persons and electricity	€ 17,00 - € 34,00
extra person (over 1 yr)	€ 4,00 - € 5,00

Etables-sur-Mer

Camping l'Abri Côtier

Ville Es Rouxel, F-22680 Etables-sur-Mer (Côtes d'Armor) T: 02 96 70 61 57
E: camping.abricotier@wanadoo.fr alanrogers.com/FR22100

L'Abri Côtier is a well cared for, family run site 500 m. from a sandy beach. Small and tranquil, it is arranged in two sections separated by a lane. The pitches are marked out on part level, part sloping grass, divided by mature trees and shrubs with some in a charming walled area. The second section has an orchard type setting. There are 120 touring pitches, all with electrical connections (long leads useful) and 60 are fully serviced. Tim and Pierrette Lee are busy with ideas for this very popular, friendly site.

Facilities

Good clean sanitary facilities include some washbasins in cabins and pushbutton showers. Facilities for disabled visitors. Baby bath/shower. Laundry room. Well stocked shop. Bar providing a simple takeaway service (plus set menu in high season). Covered terrace and games area. Sheltered, heated swimming pool with paddling pool and outdoor jacuzzi. Small play area. Some entertainment in peak season. WiFi in bar (charged). Off site: Beach and sailing 500 m. Restaurants and indoor pool in the village. Riding 1 km. Fishing and boat launching 2 km. Bicycle hire 4 km. Golf 10 km.

Open: 7 May - 14 September.

Directions

From N12 (Saint Brieuc bypass) take D786 towards St Quay Portrieux. After 12 km. ignore signs to Etables, pass Aire de la Chapelle on the right and take second left back towards Etables-sur-Mer (site signed). Take second right at top of hill to site at crossroads in 100 m. GPS: 48.63559, -2.83546

Charges guide

Per unit incl. 2 persons and electricity	€ 18,60 - € 22,60
extra person	€ 4,40 - € 4,90
child (under 7 yrs)	€ 3,00 - € 3,50

Fouesnant

Camping de PenHoat

Pointe de Mousterlin, 5 chemin de Kost ar Moor, F-29170 Fouesnant (Finistère) T: 02 98 56 51 89
E: caradec2@wanadoo.fr alanrogers.com/FR29630

This small rural campsite is set in two acres of trees, shrubs and well-tended flowerbeds. The 87 touring pitches are level, grassy, generous in size and separated by hedges and/or small trees. The 58 pitches with electricity (5/10A) may need long leads. The 32 mobile homes are mostly separated from the touring pitches. There are also six traditional gîtes for hire. The pleasant wooden chalet-style bar and takeaway has a covered terrace. Kayaks can be hired at the campsite. The long sandy beach is 300 m. away, and for lovers of wildlife, the protected Mousterlin nature reserve is next to the campsite. This site is ideally situated for walking and cycling on the excellent and safe paths of the 'Mousterllin marise' where a large variety of birds, plants and wildlife can be seen. Within a short drive you can visit the cathedral city of Quimper or the fishing port of Concarneau with its old walled town and busy market every Friday.

Facilities

Two toilet and shower blocks with facilities for campers with disabilities. Laundry. Nursery. Bar, takeaway and restaurant. Games room. Playground. Trampoline. Bicycle and kayak hire. Gîtes for hire. Off site: Beach 300 m. Riding 1 km. Shops in Fouesnant 6 km. Golf 6 km.

Open: 3 April - 30 September.

Directions

Site is 5 km. south of Fouesnant. Turn off N165 at Coat Cong signed Concarneau and Fouesnant. Join D45 signed Beg Meil and shortly turn right on D145 signed Mousterlin. Site signed in approx. 5 km. GPS: 47.851024, -4.035341

Charges guide

Per unit incl. 2 persons and electricity	€ 16,40 - € 20,10

For latest campsite news, availability and prices visit

alanrogers.com

Jugon-les-Lacs

Camping Au Bocage du Lac

Rue du Bocage, F-22270 Jugon-les-Lacs (Côtes d'Armor) T: 02 96 31 60 16. E: contact@campingjugon.com
alanrogers.com/FR22200

This well kept former municipal site has been updated over the past few years by the current owners M. and Mme. Riviere. It is on the edge of the village beside a lake, 25 km. from the sea. It offers 181 good sized pitches, all with electrical connections, set on gently sloping grass and divided by shrubs and bushes, with mature trees providing shade. Some 40 wooden chalets and mobile homes are interspersed with the touring pitches. On-site facilities include a good pool with children's section and sunbathing patio. There is also a small animal park.

Facilities

Two main sanitary blocks include facilities for disabled visitors. British and Turkish style WCs and some washbasins in cabins. Washing machine. Small shop. Bar. Swimming pool (15/6-10/9). Tennis. Football. Play area. Activity programmes July/Aug. Fishing. Bicycle hire. Off site: Supermarket in village 1 km. River 1 km.

Open: 1 April - 31 October.

Directions

From N176 (E401) Lamballe-Dinan road, 15 km. from Lamballe take turning for Jugon-les-Lacs. Site is signed shortly after. GPS: 48.40120, -2.31736

Charges guide

Per person	€ 3,70 - € 4,70
child (under 7 yrs)	€ 2,70 - € 3,20
pitch	€ 13,10 - € 17,40
electricity (5A)	€ 3,00

Camping ✳ ✳ ✳
Au Bocage du Lac

On the lakeside, in the pretty and historical town of Jugon Les Lacs, for both relaxation and leisure, you will find a wide range of activities : heated pool, water slide, paddling pool, childrens' mini camp, tennis, minigolf, sailing, fishing, walking. New sanitary block includes private cabins, facilities for babies. Rental of Chalets, Mobile Homes with view over the lake.
WELCOME TO BRITTANY!!
22270 Jugon les Lacs / Tél : 02.96.31.60.16
contact@campinglacbretagne.com / www.campinglacbretagne.com

Camping Qualité

La Roche Bernard

Camping Municipal le Pâtis

3 chemin du Pâtis, F-56130 La Roche Bernard (Morbihan) T: 02 99 90 60 13. E: camping.lrb@gmail.com
alanrogers.com/FR56080

This is another of those excellent municipal sites one comes across in France. Situated beside the River Vilaine, a 5 minute walk from the centre of the very attractive old town of La Roche Bernard and beside the port and marina, it provides 69 level grass, part-hedged pitches in bays of four, with 7A electricity and water; 18 special pitches for motorcaravans have been created at the entrance. Next door are a sailing school, boats to hire, fishing, tennis, archery, etc. A restaurant and bar are on the quayside, with others uphill in the town.

Facilities

There are two fully equipped sanitary blocks, one new and very modern, the other fully refurbished. Laundry room behind reception with washing machine and dryer. Small play area. Bicycle hire. Off site: Fishing 500 m. Riding 5 km. Golf 15 km.

Open: April - 30 September.

Directions

Go into town centre and follow signs for the Port around a one-way system and then a sharp turn down hill. GPS: 47.51817, -2.30317

Charges guide

Per unit incl. 2 persons and electricity	€ 13,50 - € 19,00
extra person	€ 3,50 - € 4,00
child (under 12 yrs)	€ 1,50 - € 2,00
dog	€ 1,50 - € 2,00

For latest campsite news, availability and prices visit
alanrogers.com

La Chapelle-aux-Filtzmeens

Domaine du Logis

Le Logis, F-35190 La Chapelle-aux-Filtzmeens (Ille-et-Vilaine) T: 02 99 45 25 45
E: domainedulogis@wanadoo.fr alanrogers.com/FR35080

This is an attractive rural site, set in the grounds of an old château. The site's facilities are housed in converted barns and farm buildings, which although old, are well maintained and equipped. There are a total of 180 pitches, 83 of which are for touring. The grass pitches are level, of a generous size and divided by mature hedges and trees. All have 10A electricity connections. This site would appeal to most age groups with plenty to offer the active including a new fitness room with a good range of modern equipment or for those who prefer to relax, perhaps a quiet days fishing beside the lake. The site is well placed for excursions to Mont Saint-Michel, Dinard and Dinan.

Facilities

One comfortable toilet block with washbasins and showers. Toilet and shower for disabled visitors. Laundry facilities. Bar with Sky TV (1/4-7/11). Restaurant and takeaway (1/7-29/8). Outdoor swimming pool (from 1/5). Fitness and games rooms. BMX circuit. Bicycle hire (€ 5 1/2 day, € 9 day). Unfenced play areas. Children's club (high season). Free WiFi-Internet access. Lake fishing. Off site: Boating on the canal. Riding 10 km.

Open: 1 April - 7 November.

Directions

Turn south off N176 onto D795 signed Dol-de-Bretagne. Continue to Combourg and then take D13 to La Chapelle-aux-Filtzmeens. Continue for 2 km. to site on right. GPS: 48.37716, -1.83705

Charges guide

Per unit incl. 2 persons and electricity	€ 20,40 - € 27,40
extra person	€ 4,00 - € 4,50
child (2-12 yrs)	€ 2,50
dog	€ 2,00

Camping Cheques accepted.

Camping Le Domaine du Logis****

35190 LA CHAPELLE AUX FILTZMEENS (Ille et Vilaine)
Tél.: 02 99 45 25 45 - Fax: 02 99 45 30 40 - E-mail: domainedulogis@wanadoo.fr - www.domainedulogis.com

La Forêt-Fouesnant

Camping de Kéranterec

Route de Port la Forêt, F-29940 La Forêt-Fouesnant (Finistère) T: 02 98 56 98 11
E: info@camping-keranterec.com alanrogers.com/FR29240

A well established family run site with a very French ambience, Kéranterec has 265 grassy pitches in two areas. The upper part of the site is more open and has little shade, and is also largely taken up by private mobile homes. The lower and more mature area is predominantly for tourers, with terraced pitches set in a former orchard. Spacious and divided by mature hedging, all pitches have electrical connections (25 m. cable advised) and most also offer water and drainage. Some pitches have shade from the many trees on the lower part of the site, and some also overlook the little cove at the rear of the site.

Facilities

Two modern, fully equipped toilet blocks kept very clean include washbasins in cubicles, baby baths and facilities for disabled visitors. Laundry facilities. Small shop and bar (15/6-10/9) and takeaway (1/7-31/8). TV room with satellite. Heated outdoor swimming pool (1/6-10/9) with paddling pool, jacuzzi and three slides and a covered, heated pool. Tennis. Boules. Play area. In July/Aug organised events and activities for all the family, and a free children's club. Free WiFi. Off site: Attractive sandy beach of Kerleven 10 minutes walk. Golf 0.8 km. Riding 2 km.

Open: 5 April - 21 September.

Directions

From N165 take D70 Concarneau exit. At first roundabout take D44 signed Fouesnant. After 2.5 km. turn right at T-junction, follow for 2.5 km. and turn left (Port La Forêt). Continue to roundabout, take second exit (straight ahead), signed Port La Forêt. After 1 km. turn left (site signed), in 400 m. turn left to site. GPS: 47.8991, -3.95198

Charges guide

Per person	€ 7,00 - € 8,50
child (1-7 yrs)	€ 3,00 - € 4,00
pitch incl. electricity	€ 13,00 - € 17,00

For latest campsite news, availability and prices visit
alanrogers.com

La Forêt-Fouesnant

Domaine du Saint Laurent

Kerleven, F-29940 La Forêt-Fouesnant (Finistère) T: 02 98 56 97 65. E: info@camping-du-saint-laurent.fr
alanrogers.com/FR29020

Saint-Laurent is a well established site, situated on a sheltered wooded slope bordering one of the many attractive little inlets that typify the Brittany coastline. The site is on the coastal footpath that leads from Kerleven to Concarneau. The 260 pitches are on level terraces, under tall trees. All are of average size (100 sq.m), divided by hedges and partly shaded, all have electricity connections. Around 60% of the pitches are occupied by site owned mobile homes. Touring pitches with the best sea views tend to be adjacent to the cliff edge and may not be suitable for families with young children. Access to some touring pitches can be a little difficult. The outdoor swimming pool (complete with paddling pool and two water slides) is overlooked by the bar terrace and adjacent to this is a covered pool. With organised activities and entertainment in high season, this site is an great choice for a lively family holiday, particularly for older children. There is direct access from the site to two small sandy bays, which empty at low tide to reveal numerous rock pools - ideal for children to explore.

Facilities

Two sanitary blocks provide combined shower and washbasin cubicles, separate washbasin cubicles, baby changing and facilities for disabled visitors. Washing machines, dryers and ironing. Small shop at reception (all season). Bar, snack bar and takeaway (1/7-31/8). Swimming pools. Gym and sauna. Canoe and boat hire. Two tennis courts (free). Play area. Entertainment in July/Aug. for adults and children (in English and French) with discos in the bar each evening. Bicycle hire. Internet access.

Open: 5 April - 29 September.

Directions

From N165 take D70 Concarneau exit. At first roundabout first exit D44 (Fouesnant). After 2.5 km. turn right at T-junction, follow for 2.5 km, then left (Port La Forêt). Continue to roundabout, straight ahead (Port La Forêt) and after 1 km. turn left (site signed here). In 400 m. left turn to site.
GPS: 47.8961, -3.9551

Charges guide

Per unit incl. 2 persons and electricity	€ 15,00 - € 33,00
extra person	€ 4,70 - € 7,00
child (2-7 yrs)	€ 2,60 - € 4,50

La Trinité-sur-Mer

Camping de la Plage

Plage de Kervilaine, F-56470 La Trinité-sur-Mer (Morbihan) T: 02 97 55 73 28. E: camping@camping-plage.com
alanrogers.com/FR56020

The Carnac/La Trinité area of Brittany is popular with British holidaymakers. Camping de la Plage is one of two sites close to each other and owned by members of the same family, with direct access to the safe sandy beach of Kervilaine Plage. There are 198 grass pitches of which 112 are for touring (34 are used by tour operators). All are hedged and have electricity (6/10A), water and drainage. The site has a slight slope and a few pitches reflect this; the narrow roads make it unsuitable for large units.

Facilities

Toilet blocks have washbasins in cubicles and facilities for disabled visitors and small children. Laundry facilities. Small swimming pool with water slides. Play areas including ball pool. Tennis. TV. Entertainment programme in high season for all ages. Bicycle hire. Beach. Internet access and WiFi (charged). Communal barbecue areas (gas or electric only on pitches). Off site: Fishing 50 m. Shop with bakery. Bar, restaurant, crêperie, takeaway (all 200 m). Sailing 1.5 km. Riding 3.5 km. Golf 13 km.

Open: 7 May - 19 September.

Directions

From N165 at Auray take D28 (La Trinité-sur-Mer). On through town following signs to Carnac-Plage on D186. Site signed off this road to the south. Take care to take road signed to Kervillen Plage where it forks. At seafront turn right. Site is 300 m. on right. Site is well signed. GPS: 47.57563, -3.02890

Charges guide

Per unit incl. 2 persons and electricity (10A)	€ 20,80 - € 40,80
extra person	€ 2,00 - € 5,20

La Trinité-sur-Mer

Camping de Kervilor

F-56470 La Trinité-sur-Mer (Morbihan) T: 02 97 55 76 75. E: ebideau@camping-kervilor.com

alanrogers.com/FR56050

Kervilor may be a good alternative for those who find the beach-side sites in La Trinité too busy and lively. In a village on the outskirts of the town, it has 230 pitches on flat grass and is attractively landscaped with trees (silver birch) and flowers giving a sense of spaciousness. The pitches are in groups divided by hedges, separated by shrubs and trees and all have electricity (6/10A). Around 116 are used for touring units. Used by tour operators (ten pitches). The site has a central pool complex with covered swimming and paddling pools, slides and fountains. Activities and entertainment are organised in high season. The pleasant port is only 1.5 km. with sandy beaches within 2 km.

Facilities

Two modern toilet blocks of a good standard with further facilities in an older block. They include many washbasins in cabins, facilities for disabled visitors and babies. Small laundry. Small shop and takeaway. Bar with terrace. Pool complex with covered pool. Play area. Minigolf, pétanque, tennis and volleyball. Bicycle hire. Only charcoal barbecues are permitted. WiFi in bar area. Off site: Town facilities 1.5 km. Sandy beach, fishing or riding 2 km. Golf 12 km.

Open: 1 April - 19 September.

Directions

Site is north of La Trinité-sur-Mer and is signed in the town centre. From Auray take D186 Quiberon road; turn left at site sign at Kergroix on D186 to La Trinité-sur-Mer, and left again at outskirts of town. GPS: 47.60213, -3.03672

Charges guide

Per unit incl. 2 persons	
and electricity	€ 22,00 - € 31,80
extra person	€ 3,95 - € 5,25
child (under 7 yrs)	€ 2,60 - € 3,45
dog	free - € 2,90

Camping Caravaning Kervilor
56470 La Trinité sur Mer, France
NEW! Covered Swimming Pool
Tel: +33 297 55 76 75
Fax: +33 297 55 87 26
ebideau@camping-kervilor.com
www.camping-kervilor.com

La Trinité-sur-Mer

Camping de la Baie

Plage de Kervillen, F-56470 La Trinité-sur-Mer (Morbihan) T: 02 97 55 73 42. E: contact@campingdelabaie.com

alanrogers.com/FR56030

This site is one of two owned by members of the same family. It is situated on the coast overlooking the safe, sandy beach of Kervilaine Plage, with its little rocky outcrops providing a naturally enclosed swimming area. This is a very friendly site, which is ideal for quiet or family holidays in an area with lots of local interest. There are 170 pitches, of which 48 are used by tour operators. The 92 touring pitches are all of good size, hedged and all have electricity (6/10A) water and drainage. Some shade is provided by mature and maturing trees. In the bar and restaurant complex, just outside the gate, one can sit and watch the sun set over the bay. The restaurant has an extensive menu, from excellent seafood to snacks, and much is also available from the takeaway. American motorhomes should book ahead.

Facilities

Two modern, very clean toilet blocks include well equipped baby rooms and full en-suite facilities for disabled visitors. Laundry facilities. Bar, restaurant and takeaway (open to the public all season). Well stocked shop (all season). Small (12 m.) swimming pool with slide. Play areas. Multi-sport pitches. TV room. Indoor games room. Bicycle hire. Internet access (charged). Off site: Beach, fishing and boat ramp 50 m. Tennis and minigolf 200 m. (shared with Camping de la Plage). Riding 5 km. Sailing school 1.5 km. Golf 5 km.

Open: 16 May - 13 September.

Directions

From the N165 at Auray take D28 signed La Trinité-sur-Mer. Keep on through the town following signs to Carnac Plage on D186. Site is well signed off this road to the south. Be careful to take the road signed to Kervilaine Plage where it forks. GPS: 47.57364, -3.02758

Charges guide

Per unit incl. 2 persons	
and electricity (10A)	€ 17,25 - € 35,00
child (under 2 years)	free
dog	free - € 1,30

Landéda
Camping des Abers
Dunes de Sainte Marguerite, F-29870 Landéda (Finistère) T: 02 98 04 93 35
E: camping-des-abers@wanadoo.fr alanrogers.com/FR29130

This delightful 12-acre site is in a beautiful location almost at the tip of the Presqu'île Sainte Marguerite on the northwestern shores of Brittany. The peninsula lies between the mouths (abers) of two rivers, Aber Wrac'h and Aber Benoît. Camping des Abers is set just back from a wonderful sandy beach with rocky outcrops and islands you can walk to at low tide. There are 180 pitches, landscaped and terraced, some with amazing views, others sheltered by mature hedges, trees and flowering shrubs. Hubert le Cuff and his team make you very welcome and speak excellent English.

Facilities	Directions
Three toilet blocks, all recently refurbished are kept very clean and provide washbasins in cubicles and showers (token). Good facilities for disabled visitors and babies. Laundry. Motorcaravan service point. Shop stocks essentials (25/5-22/9, limited hours low season). Simple takeaway dishes (1/7-31/8). Sandy play area. Games room. Hairdresser. Breton music and dancing. Cooking classes and guided walks arranged. Splendid beach with good bathing (best at high tide), fishing, windsurfing and other watersports. Long leads needed in places. Torch useful. Free internet and WiFi. Off site: Pizzeria next door. Tennis nearby. Sailing club 3 km. Riding 7 km. Golf 30 km.	Landéda is 55 km. west of Roscoff via D10 to Plouguerneau then D13 crossing river bridge (Aber Wrac'h) and turning west to Lannilis. From N12 Morlaix-Brest road turn north on D59 to Lannilis. Continue through town taking road to Landéda and from there follow signs for Dunes de Ste Marguerite, 'camping' and des Abers. GPS: 48.59306, -4.60305

Open: 28 April - 30 September.

Charges 2011

Per unit incl. 2 persons	
and electricity	€ 14,70 - € 16,30
extra person	€ 3,35 - € 3,70
child (under 7 yrs)	€ 1,90 - € 2,10
dog	€ 1,80 - € 2,00

Lanloup
Camping le Neptune
Ker Guistin, F-22580 Lanloup (Côtes d'Armor) T: 02 96 22 33 35. E: contact@leneptune.com
alanrogers.com/FR22160

Situated on the Côte de Goëlo at Lanloup, Le Neptune offers a peaceful, rural retreat for families. The friendly owners, François and Marie Jo Camard, keep the site neat and tidy and there is a regular programme of renovation. There are 84 level, grass pitches (65 for touring units) separated by trimmed hedges providing privacy and all with electricity (10A). There are also 21 mobile homes to rent. Within walking distance is the local village, with a restaurant and shop, and sandy beaches are only a short drive away. The area is good for cycling and walking.

Facilities	Directions
The modern, heated, toilet block is of a good standard, clean and well maintained and provides washbasins in cubicles and pushbutton showers. Facilities for disabled visitors. Laundry room. Motorcaravan services. No restaurant but good takeaway (all season). Small shop well stocked for basic needs. Bar with indoor and outdoor seating. Heated swimming pool with retractable roof (Easter-end Oct). Pétanque. Play area. Entertainment and children's activities in high season. Off site: Tennis 300 m. Fishing and beach 2 km. Golf 4 km. Riding 8 km. Restaurant and shop within walking distance.	Lanloup is 30 km. northwest of Saint Brieuc and 100 km. from both Roscoff and Saint-Malo. From N12 Saint Brieuc by-pass take D786 Paimpol (par la Côte). After 28 km. on approaching Lanloup, site is well signed, turning right at crossroads by café. GPS: 48.71372, -2.96704

Open: 1 April - 17 October.

Charges guide

Per unit incl. 2 persons	
and electricity	€ 18,00 - € 23,70
extra person	€ 4,00 - € 5,50
child (under 7 yrs)	€ 2,00 - € 3,50
Camping Cheques accepted.	

Le Faouët
Camping Municipal Beg Er Roch
Route de Lorient, F-56320 Le Faouët (Morbihan) T: 02 97 23 15 11. E: camping.lefaouet@wanadoo.fr
alanrogers.com/FR56310

Like many of today's municipal campsites this one is immaculate and offers excellent value. There are 52 well kept grassy pitches with electricity (10A) available. There are also a few furnished tents and mobile homes for rent. For those campers that are anglers, a river at the bottom of the site (fenced) provides salmon and trout fishing at a supplement. For the more energetic, the manager can provide details and maps of local walks. For shops and other amenities the town of Le Faouët is only 2 km. away.

Facilities	Directions
A single toilet block provides toilets, washbasins and showers. Facilities for campers with disabilities. Washing machine and dryer. Play area. Minigolf. Boules. Fishing. Large games room with TV and bar billiards.	Take the D769 north from Lorient to Le Faouët. Site is signed from this road. GPS: 48.01823, -3.47009

Open: 15 March - 30 September.

Charges guide

Per unit incl. 2 persons	
	€ 10,90 - € 13,85
extra person	€ 2,80 - € 3,90

For latest campsite news, availability and prices visit
alanrogers.com

Le Guilvinec

Yelloh! Village la Plage

F-29730 Le Guilvinec (Finistère) T: 02 98 58 61 90. E: info@yellohvillage-la-plage.com
alanrogers.com/FR29110

La Plage is a spacious site located beside a long sandy beach between the fishing town of Le Guilvinec and the watersports beaches of Penmarc'h on the southwest tip of Brittany. It is surrounded by tall trees which provide shelter and is made up of several flat, sandy meadows. The 410 pitches (200 for touring units) are arranged on either side of sandy access roads, mostly not separated but all numbered. There is less shade in the newer areas. Electricity is available on most pitches. Like all beach-side sites, the facilities receive heavy use.

Facilities

Four sanitary blocks provide modern, bright facilities including washbasins in cabins, good facilities for children and disabled campers. Laundry facilities. Motorcaravan service point. Shop with gas supplies. Bar, crêperie and takeaway (all open all season). Covered heated swimming pool with paddling pool and slide. Sauna and fitness complex. Play area. TV room. Tennis. Minigolf. Pétanque. Giant chess/draughts. Bicycle hire. Beach. Multisport and football fields. Entertainment all season. Off site: Fishing and watersports near. Riding 5 km. Golf 20 km.

Open: 9 April - 11 September.

Directions

Site is west of Guilvinec. From Pont l'Abbé, take the D785 road towards Penmarc'h, turn left on D57 signed Guilvinec. On entering Guilvinec fork right signed Port and camping. Follow road along coast to site on left. GPS: 47.8025, -4.3072

Charges guide

Per unit incl. 2 persons	
and electricity	€ 15,00 - € 41,00
extra person	€ 5,00 - € 7,00
child (3-10 yrs)	free - € 5,00

Le Pouldu-Clohars-Carnoët

Camping les Embruns

Rue du Philosophe Alain, le Pouldu, F-29360 Clohars-Carnoët (Finistère) T: 02 98 39 91 07
E: camping-les-embruns@wanadoo.fr alanrogers.com/FR29180

This site is unusual in that it is located in the heart of a village, yet is only 250 metres from a sandy cove. The entrance with its code operated barrier and wonderful floral displays, is the first indication that this is a well tended and well organised site, and the owners have won numerous regional and national awards for its superb presentation. The 180 pitches (100 occupied by mobile homes) are separated by trees, shrubs and bushes, and most have electricity (10A), water and drainage. There is a covered, heated swimming pool, a circular paddling pool and a water play pool. It is only a short walk to the village centre with all its attractions and services. It is also close to beautiful countryside and the Carnoët Forest which are good for walking and cycling.

Facilities

Two modern sanitary blocks, recently completely renewed and heated in winter, include mainly British style toilets, some washbasins in cubicles, baby baths and good facilities for disabled visitors. Family bathrooms. Laundry facilities. Motorcaravan service point. Shop and restaurant by entrance. Bar and terrace (1/7-31/8). Takeaway (20/6-5/9). Covered, heated swimming and paddling pools. Large games hall. Play area. Football field. Minigolf. Communal barbecue area. Daily activities for children and adults organised in July/Aug. Bicycle hire. Internet access and WiFi in reception area (charged). Off site: Sea and river fishing. Watersports. Beach 250 m. Riding 2 km.

Open: 8 April - 18 September.

Directions

From N165 take either 'Kervidanou, Quimperlé Ouest' exit or 'Kergostiou, Quimperlé Centre, Clohars Carnoët' exit and follow D16 to Clohars Carnoët. Then take D24 for Le Pouldu and follow site signs in village. GPS: 47.76867, -3.54508

Charges 2011

Per unit incl. 2 persons	
and electricity	€ 15,50 - € 30,80
extra person	€ 3,95 - € 5,80
child (under 7 yrs)	€ 2,60 - € 3,50
dog	€ 2,00 - € 2,50
Use of motorcaravan services € 4.	

521

Locunolé

Castel Camping le Ty-Nadan

Route d'Arzano, F-29310 Locunolé (Finistère) T: 02 98 71 75 47. E: infos@camping-ty-nadan.fr
alanrogers.com/FR29010

521

Ty-Nadan is a well organised site set amongst wooded countryside along the bank of the River Elle. There are 183 grassy pitches for touring units, many with shade and 99 fully serviced. The pool complex with slides and paddling pool is very popular as are the large indoor pool complex and indoor games area with a climbing wall. There is also an adventure play park and a 'Minikids' park for 5-8 year olds, not to mention tennis courts, table tennis, pool tables, archery and trampolines. This is a wonderful site for families with children. Several tour operators use the site. An exciting and varied programme of activities is offered throughout the season – canoe and sea kayaking expeditions, rock climbing, mountain biking, aqua-gym, paintball, horse riding or walking – all supervised by qualified staff. A full programme of entertainment for all ages is provided in high season including concerts, Breton evenings with pig roasts, dancing, etc. (be warned, you will be actively encouraged to join in!).

Facilities

Two older, split-level toilet blocks are of fair quality and include washbasins in cabins and baby rooms. A newer block provides easier access for disabled visitors. Washing machines and dryers. Restaurant, takeaway, bar and well stocked shop. Heated outdoor pool (17x8 m). Indoor pool. Small river beach (unfenced). Indoor badminton and rock climbing facility. Activity and entertainment programmes (all season). Horse riding centre. Bicycle hire. Boat hire. Canoe trips. Fishing. Internet access and WiFi (charged). Off site: Beaches 20 minutes by car. Golf 12 km.

Open: 27 March - 2 September.

Directions

Make for Arzano which is northeast of Quimperlé on the Pontivy road and turn off D22 just west of village at site sign. Site is about 3 km.
GPS: 47.90468, -3.47477

Charges guide

Per unit incl. 2 persons	
and electricity	€ 20,80 - € 47,80
extra person	€ 4,50 - € 9,10
child (2-6 yrs)	€ 1,90 - € 5,60
dog	€ 1,90 - € 6,00

Camping Cheques accepted.

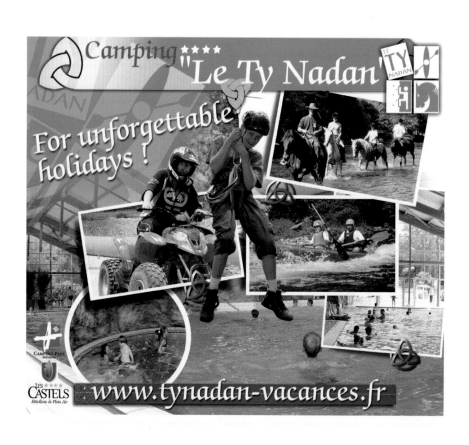

For latest campsite news, availability and prices visit
alanrogers.com

Locronan

Camping Locronan

Rue de la Troménie, F-29180 Locronan (Finistère) T: 02 98 91 87 76. E: contact@camping-locronan.fr

alanrogers.com/FR29650

Camping Locronan is a well cared for, friendly site on the edge of the village of Locronan (400 m). The site has a heated covered pool and a children's play area. The 100 pitches are level, grassy and divided by low hedges. They are arranged on four different levels as the site is on the side of a steep hill. Vehicle access between the levels is steep and pedestrian access is by wooden steps which would not be suitable for the disabled visitor. Many of the pitches offer panoramic views across the countryside to the distant bay of Douarnenez.

Facilities

Two modern toilet blocks have facilities for campers with disabilities. Laundry facilities. Covered swimming pool. Children's play area, shop. WiFi. Mobile homes and equipped tents for hire. Off site: Shops and restaurants in Locronan 300 m. Riding, tennis 300 m. Nearest beach 5 km. Walking and cycling tracks. Quimper 13 km.

Open: 9 April - 3 November.

Directions

Locronan lies to the northwest of Quimper. From there, head north on D39 and D63 (towards Douarnenez) until you reach the village. The site is clearly signed in the village.
GPS: 48.095824, -4.199181

Charges guide

Per unit incl. 2 persons and electricity (10A)	€ 22,80 - € 25,30
extra person	€ 4,00 - € 4,60
child (0-7 yrs)	€ 2,60 - € 2,90

Mousterlin

Camping le Grand Large

48 route du Grand Large, Mousterlin, F-29170 Fouesnant (Finistère) T: 02 98 56 04 06
E: grandlarge@franceloc.fr alanrogers.com/FR29290

Le Grand Large is a beach-side site situated on the Pointe de Mousterlin in natural surroundings. The site is separated from the beach by the road that follows the coast around the point. It is protected from the wind by an earth bank with trees and a fence. There are 260 pitches with just 51 places used for tourers. Electricity is available everywhere (long leads useful) and some pitches have drainage. A small river runs through the site but it is fenced. The ground is rather sandy in places with some shrubs and mature trees. Benodet (7 km) and Fouesnant (5 km) are nearby in different directions and the sandy beach is just up the steps and across the road. A family site, Le Grand Large would also suit nature lovers in low season as it is next to a large tract of protected land, Marais de Mousterlin, ideal for walking, cycling and birdwatching. The beach itself looks over the bay towards the Isles de Glénan.

Facilities

Two neat toilet blocks, the largest only opened in high season, include plenty of washbasins in cabins. Facilities for children in the larger block, with disabled visitors in both. Laundry facilities. Shop. Bar overlooking the sea with attractive terrace. Grill restaurant including takeaway. Swimming pool with paddling pool, water slides in separate pool. Tennis. Multisport court. Small play area. TV and games rooms. Bicycle hire. Off site: Beach, fishing 100 m. Golf and riding 5 km.

Open: 3 April - 12 September.

Directions

Site is 7 km. south of Fouesnant. Turn off N165 expressway at Coat Conq, signed Concarneau and Fouesnant. At Fouesnant take A45 signed Beg Meil, then follow signs to Mousterlin. In Mousterlin turn left and follow camping signs. GPS: 47.84200, -4.03533

Charges guide

Per unit incl. 2 persons and electricity	€ 15,00 - € 34,70
extra person	€ 4,70 - € 7,00
child (under 10 yrs)	€ 2,60 - € 4,50

For latest campsite news, availability and prices visit

alanrogers.com

Mousterlin

Sunêlia l'Atlantique

Kerbader, B.P. 11, F-29170 Fouesnant (Finistère) T: 02 98 56 14 44. E: sunelia@latlantique.fr

alanrogers.com/FR29350

L'Atlantique is quietly situated just outside Beg-Meil. The 432 pitches are predominantly used by tour operators with about 90 for independent visitors. Pitches are level and grassy, all with electricity, they are separated by low shrubs. Apple orchards used for cider production are also on the site. All the facilities are grouped together in the centre including an innovative play area and pool complex with both indoor and outdoor pools, water slides and a paddling pool. The sandy beach faces the Glénan Islands and is a pleasant 400 m. walk away through a nature reserve. Coastal paths await exploration and Concarneau, Pont-Aven and La Pointe du Raz are all nearby. An innovation for 2010 is ready erected and furnished tents and yurts. Pamper breaks are also available. These include massage, body treatments and accomodation. L'Atlantique is attempting to keep 'ahead of the game' and is succeeding. A lively family would find it difficult to become bored here, as there is something for all ages.

Facilities

Fully equipped toilet blocks (cleaned three times a day) include facilities for disabled visitors. Shop, bar, snack bar with takeaway meals and pizza (all 1/5-12/9). Heated outdoor and indoor pools, water complex with slides (all 1/5-12/9). Tennis. TV room. Billiards. Minigolf. Sports ground. Play area. Children's club (4-12 yrs) and evening entertainment in July/Aug. Bicycle hire. WiFi in bar (charged). Off site: Fishing 300 m. Windsurf hire 1 km. Boat hire 3 or 5 km. Riding 3 km. Golf 8 km.

Open: 23 April - 11 September.

Directions

From Fouesnant follow directions for Mousterlin for 2 km., then follow Chapelle de Kerbader. Site is signed. GPS: 47.856564, -4.020658

Charges guide

Per unit incl. 2 persons	
and electricity	€ 22,00 - € 39,00
extra person	€ 3,00 - € 7,00
child (0-10 yrs)	€ 2,00 - € 4,00
Low season reductions.	

Névez

Camping les Deux Fontaines

Feunteun Vilian, Raguenèz, F-29920 Névez (Finistère) T: 02 98 06 81 91. E: info@les2fontaines.fr

alanrogers.com/FR29470

Les Deux Fontaines is a large site with 288 pitches. Of these 115 are for touring, 118 are used by tour operators, and the remainder for mobile homes. The well cared for pitches are on grass, level and attractively laid out amongst mature trees and shrubs. All have 6/10A electricity connections. Trees have been carefully planted creating one area with silver birch, one with apple trees and another with palms and tropical plants. The pool complex is an excellent feature with chutes, flumes and waterfalls, and, new in 2010, a covered pool with adjacent gym and massage room. There are numerous daytime activities for all the family to enjoy and a variety of entertainment in the evening. A short drive away you can enjoy some of Britanny's most scenic coastline. Further afield you can visit the old walled town of Concarneau with its fishing port, the town of Nevez or Pont Aven, home to the painter Gauguin.

Facilities

Two good quality, modern toilet blocks have washbasins in cabins and preset showers. Separate facilities for disabled visitors. Laundry facilities. Well stocked shop. Bar. Takeaway (all season). Basic motorcaravan services. Large indoor and outdoor pool complex. Fitness and pamper room. Play area. Skateboard park. 6-hole golf course. Driving range. Rollerblade hire. Archery. WiFi in bar. Off site: Fishing 1 km. Bicycle hire, riding 5 km.

Open: 8 May - 12 September.

Directions

Travel south from Nevez on the D1. The site is on the left after 3 km. and is well signed. GPS: 47.79937, -3.79017

Charges guide

Per unit incl. 2 persons	
	€ 18,00 - € 31,00
extra person	€ 3,70 - € 6,00
child (2-7 yrs)	free - € 3,90
electricity (6A)	€ 3,80
No credit cards.	

For latest campsite news, availability and prices visit

alanrogers.com

Névez
Camping le Raguenès-Plage

19 rue des Iles, F-29920 Névez (Finistère) T: 02 98 06 80 69. E: info@camping-le-raguenes-plage.com
alanrogers.com/FR29090

Mme. Guyader and her family will ensure you receive a warm welcome on arrival at this well kept and pleasant site. Le Raguenès-Plage is an attractive and well laid out campsite with many shrubs and trees. The 287 pitches are a good size, flat and grassy, separated by trees and hedges. All have electricity, water and drainage. The site is used by two tour operators (15 pitches), and has 61 mobile homes of its own. A pool complex complete with new heated indoor pool and water toboggan is a key feature and is close to the friendly bar, restaurant, shop and takeaway. From the far end of the campsite a delightful five minute walk along a path and through a cornfield takes you down to a pleasant, sandy beach looking out towards the Ile Verte and the Presqu'île de Raguenès.

Facilities

Two clean, well maintained sanitary blocks include some British style toilets, washbasins in cabins, baby baths and facilities for disabled visitors. Laundry room. Motorcaravan service point. Small shop (from 15/5). Bar and restaurant (from 1/6) with outside terrace and takeaway. Reading and TV room, internet access point. Heated indoor and outdoor pools with sun terrace and paddling pool. Sauna (charged). Play areas. Games room. Various activities are organised in July/Aug. WiFi (charged). Off site: Beach, fishing and watersports 300 m. Supermarket 3 km. Riding 4 km.

Open: 1 April - 30 September.

Directions

From N165 take D24 Kerampaou exit. After 3 km. turn right towards Nizon and bear right at church in village following signs to Névez (D77). Continue through Névez, following signs to Raguenès. Continue for 3 km. to site entrance on left (entrance is quite small and easy to miss). GPS: 47.79337, -3.80049

Charges 2011

Per unit incl. 2 persons	
and electricity	€ 20,00 - € 35,90
extra person	€ 4,40 - € 6,00
child (under 7 yrs)	€ 2,20 - € 3,90
dog	€ 1,50 - € 3,20

Paimpol
Camping Municipal de Cruckin

Rue de Cruckin, Kérity, F-22500 Paimpol (Côtes d'Armor) T: 02 96 20 78 47
E: contact@camping-paimpol.com alanrogers.com/FR22250

A neat and well managed municipal site situated close to the historical fishing port of Cité des Islandais and within easy reach of the Ile de Bréhat. This is an ideal location for many interesting walks. The site has 130 well maintained, mostly level pitches set in both wooded and open areas and all have electricity connections (5-12A). A very large area has been provided for sports, a play area and picnic tables. Although the site does not have its own swimming pool, the beach is just a short walk away. There are 'Bengali' static tents for hire. A communal barbecue is available.

Facilities

One modern and heated toilet block. Washbasins in cabins and showers. Facilities for babies and disabled visitors. Laundry facilities. Bread and milk (high season). Snack bar/takeaway (July/Aug). Motorcaravan service point. Large field for football. Pétanque. Fenced play area. Internet access on request. Bicycle hire. Fishing. Off site: Beach. Kérity village with shops, restaurants and cafés. Riding 2 km. Golf 10 km.

Open: 1 April - 10 October.

Directions

From N12 St Brieuc bypass, take D786 north towards Paimpol. Village of Kérity is 3 km. south of Paimpol. Site is signed. GPS: 48.76966, -3.02209

Charges guide

Per unit incl. 2 persons	
and electricity	€ 15,40 - € 17,50
child (under 7 yrs)	€ 1,70 - € 2,20
dog	€ 1,30 - € 1,60

For latest campsite news, availability and prices visit
alanrogers.com

We can book this site for you! Call 01580 214000

alan rogers ◐ travel

Pénestin-sur-Mer
Camping le Cénic
F-56760 Pénestin-sur-Mer (Morbihan) T: 02 99 90 33 14. E: info@lecenic.com
alanrogers.com/FR56180

Le Cénic is attractively set amidst trees and flowers, providing activities for all tastes. An attractive covered aquatic complex has water slides, bridges, rivers and a jacuzzi, whilst the outdoor pool comes complete with water slide, 'mushroom' fountain and sunbathing areas. You may fish in the lake or use inflatables, watched by the peacock, geese and turkeys. There is a hall for table tennis and a range of indoor games. There are 310 pitches, 160 of which are for touring. Of these, 90 have electricity (6A), but long leads will be required. The area has much to offer from the beaches of La Mine d'Or, the harbour at Trébiguier-Pénestin, the Golf du Morbihan with its numerous islands, La Baule with its magnificent beach and the medieval city of Guérande to the unique Brière nature reserve.

Facilities
Good new toilet block includes washbasins in cabins, facilities for disabled visitors, baby room and laundry and dishwashing sinks. Separate laundry. Bar and shop (1/7-31/8). TV and games rooms (1/7-31/8). Indoor (15/4-15/9) and outdoor (1/7-31/8) swimming pools. Play area. Fishing. Off site: Riding 500 m. Bicycle hire 1 km. Sailing 2 km. Pénestin town 2 km. Sandy beaches 2.5 km. Golf 30 km.

Open: 1 May - 30 September.

Directions
From D34 (La Roche-Bernard), at roundabout just after entering Pénestin take D201 south (Assérac). After 100 m. take first turning on left. After 800 m. turn left and campsite is 300 m. on right down a narrow winding lane. GPS: 47.47910, -2.45643

Charges guide
Per unit incl. 2 persons	
and electricity	€ 18,00 - € 31,00
extra person	€ 4,50 - € 6,00
child (under 7 yrs)	€ 2,00 - € 3,00
dog	€ 1,50 - € 2,50

Covered Aquatic Centre (heated swimming pool, balneotherapy area, children's pool), outdoor pool, water chute, games room, bar, fishing in the lake.
Le Cénic offers a range of accommodation: static caravans, chalets to rent.

www.lecenic.com
56760 Pénestin-sur-Mer   **Tél: +33 (0)2 99 90 33 14**   **info@lecenic.com**
                                                                      Fax: +33 (0)2 99 90 45 05

Pénestin-sur-Mer
Camping des Iles
La Pointe du Bile, B.P. 4, F-56760 Pénestin-sur-Mer (Morbihan) T: 02 99 90 30 24
E: contact@camping-des-iles.fr alanrogers.com/FR56120

You will receive a warm, friendly welcome at this family run campsite. The owner, Madame Communal, encourages everyone to make the most of this beautiful region. Of the 184 pitches, 103 are for touring. Most are flat, hedged and of a reasonable size (larger caravans and American motorhomes are advised to book) and all have electricity. Some pitches have sea views and overlook the beach. There is direct access to cliff-top walks and local beaches (you can even walk to small off-shore islands at low tide). The attractive heated swimming pool complex provides a focal point for all ages. Most pitches for mobile homes and chalets are in a separate site across the road. Ideally placed with a ramp for launching small boats and sea fishing, although the tide does go out a long way.

Facilities
The new large central toilet block is spotlessly clean with washbasins in cabins and showers. Laundry facilities. Facilities for disabled campers, and baby room. Shop (all season). Bar and restaurant with takeaway (15/5-15/9). Pool complex (15/5-30/9). Bicycle hire. Riding. Activities and entertainment in July/Aug. Across the road in Parc des Iles (mobile home section of site): TV room, multisport pitch, tennis court and motorcaravan service point. No electric barbecues. Internet access in bar (charged). Off site: Windsurfing 500 m. Sailing 3 km. Golf 20 km.

Open: 2 April - 17 October.

Directions
From D34 (La Roche-Bernard), at roundabout just after entering Pénestin take D201 south (Assérac). Take right fork to Pointe-du-Bile after 2 km. Turn right at crossroads just before beach. Site is on left. GPS: 47.44543, -2.48396

Charges guide
Per unit incl. 2 persons	
and electricity	€ 19,50 - € 39,50
extra person (over 7 yrs)	€ 2,30 - € 5,80
child (0-7 yrs)	€ 1,00 - € 3,20
dog	€ 4,00

Pénestin-sur-Mer

Yelloh! Village Domaine d'Inly

Route de Couarne, B.P. 24, F-56760 Pénestin-sur-Mer (Morbihan) T: 02 99 90 35 09
E: info@yellohvillage-domaine-inly.com **alanrogers.com/FR56240**

This very large site is mainly taken up with mobile homes and cottages, some belonging to the site owner, some private and some belonging to tour operators. Most of these pitches are arranged in groups of 10 to 14 around a central stone circle with a water point in the middle. Of the 500 pitches, 100 are for touring units and all are large (150-200 sq.m) with a 10A electrical connection (Europlug). Most are level and are situated by the attractive lake at the bottom of the site where one can fish or canoe. Next to it is a riding school.

Facilities

One toilet block with facilities for disabled visitors, and a baby room. Laundry. Shop. Small, comfortable bar, with large screen satellite TV, attractive restaurant and takeaway (all season). Heated swimming pool complex with slide (outdoor 15/5-15/9, indoor all season). Games room. Play areas. Football pitch. Lake for fishing and canoeing. Riding. Bicycle hire. Internet access in reception. Off site: Town centre 2 km. Supermarket 1 km. Golf 25 km. Sailing and boat ramp 2.5 km. Beach 2 km.

Open: 3 April - 20 September.

Directions

From D34 from La Roche-Bernard, at roundabout just after entering Pénestin take D201 south, signed Assérac. After 100 m. take first turning on left (site signed) opposite Carrefour supermarket. After 650 m. turn right, again signed, and campsite is 400 m. on left. GPS: 47.471483, -2.467267

Charges guide

Per unit incl. 2 persons and electricity	€ 15,00 - € 39,00
extra person	€ 5,00 - € 6,00

Pleubian

Camping de Port la Chaine

F-22610 Pleubian (Côtes d'Armor) T: 02 96 22 92 38. E: info@portlachaine.com
alanrogers.com/FR22140

Michelle and Thierry Suquet offer a warm welcome to this comfortable, quiet, family site. In a beautiful location on the Presqu'île Sauvage between Paimpol and Perros-Guirec, attractive trees and shrubs provide a balance of sun and shade for the 200 pitches. Of these, 140 are for touring, all with electricity (long leads may be needed in places) and some also have water and drainage. Pitches are on grassy terraces on the gradual descent towards the bay and the sea (a sandy bay with rocks). Most terraces have a slight slope, so those with motorcaravans will need to choose their pitch carefully.

Facilities

Two renovated toilet blocks are comfortable and fully equipped. Washbasins in cabins, British and Turkish style toilets. Cabins for families and disabled visitors. Washing machines and dryer. Bar, snacks and takeaway (2/7-20/8). Bread and croissants (all season). Heated swimming pool (1/6-4/9). Play area. Games room. Pétanque. Children's entertainer (July/Aug). Beach, fishing and sailing. WiFi in reception area. Off site: Bus 1 km. Village 2 km. for tennis, market, shops and restaurants. Good fishing and diving. Boat launching 1 km. Bicycle hire 2 km. Riding 6 km.

Open: 4 April - 20 September.

Directions

Pleubian is 37 km. north of Guingamp and 87 km. by road east of Roscoff. From D786 Lannion - Paimpol road, east of Tréguier turn north on D20 to Pleubian and on for 2 km. towards l'Armor Pleubian. Site signed to left. GPS: 48.8555, -3.1327

Charges 2011

Per unit incl. 2 persons and electricity	€ 16,60 - € 25,80
extra person	€ 3,60 - € 5,80
child (2-7 yrs)	€ 3,10 - € 3,80

Plobannalec-Lesconil

Yelloh! Village l'Océan Breton

Lieu dit le Manoir de Kerlut, F-29740 Plobannalec-Lesconil (Finistère) T: 02 98 82 23 89
E: info@yellohvillage-loceanbreton.com **alanrogers.com/FR29120**

L'Océan Breton is a comfortable site in the grounds of a manor house on a river estuary near Pont l'Abbé. The campsite itself has neat, modern buildings and is laid out on flat grass providing 240 pitches (90 for touring units). All have electricity connections, some also have water and drainage and around ten pitches have hardstanding. One area is rather open with separating hedges planted, the other part being amongst more mature bushes and some trees which provide shade. Site amenities are of good quality. The old 'Manoir' is still open to the public and is used during the high season as a crêperie. A Yelloh! Village member.

Facilities

Three good toilet blocks (one new) with washbasins all in cabins, facilities for babies and disabled visitors. Laundry. Shop. Takeaway. Large modern bar with TV (satellite) and entertainment all season. Two swimming pools (one covered and heated). Sauna, solarium and small gym. Play area. Tennis. Bicycle hire. Off site: Beach 2 km. Fishing 2 km. Riding 5 km.

Open: 28 May - 19 September.

Directions

From Pont l'Abbé, on D785, take D102 road towards Lesconil. Site is signed on the left, shortly after the village of Plobannalec. GPS: 47.81234, -4.22105

Charges 2011

Per unit incl. 2 persons and electricity	€ 15,00 - € 40,00
extra person	€ 5,00 - € 7,00

For latest campsite news, availability and prices visit

alanrogers.com

Pléneuf Val André
Campéole les Monts Colleux

Campé●le

26 rue Jean Lebrun, F-22370 Pléneuf Val André (Côtes d'Armor) T: 02 96 72 95 10
E: monts-colleux@campeole.com alanrogers.com/FR22380

Les Monts Colleux is a member of the Campéole group with an unusual town centre location in Le Val André. The site, however, has a hilltop setting and some pitches have fine views of the sea. This was formerly a municipal site and is well managed with well kept hedges and pitches. The reception area and shop have been added recently, although the wash blocks are older. Pitches are generally flat, although, given its hillside location, there are a number of sloping pitches. The 115 pitches all have electrical connections (10A). Although there is no swimming pool on site, there is a large covered municipal pool adjacent with limited free access for campers. Around 71 pitches are occupied by mobile homes, chalets and fully equipped bungalow tents (available for rent). The nearest beach is close – just 300m, and boats can be launched nearby. An attractive golf course is 1km. distant. Val André is an attractive resort and the town centre is just 300m from the site. There are many activities there during the high season, including weekly free jazz concerts.

Facilities	Directions
Play area. Bouncy castle. Shop. Snack bar. Takeaway meals. Games/TV room. Activity and entertainment programme. Tourist information. Mobile homes and chalets for rent. Off site: Municipal covered swimming pool adjacent. Val André centre 300 m. Golf 1 km. Nearest beach 300 m. Fishing.	Approaching from the east (St Malo and Dinard) on the D786, bypass Erquy and continue to Pléneuf Val André and then to Le Val André. Follow signs to 'Piscine Municipale' – the site is adjacent. GPS: 48.5894, -2.5508

Open: 1 April - 30 September.

Charges guide

Per unit incl. 2 persons and electricity	€ 15,10 - € 22,00

Plouescat
Village Center Baie du Kernic

Villagecenter

Rue de Pen An Theven, F-29430 Plouescat (Finistère) T: 04 99 57 21 21. E: resa@village-center.com
alanrogers.com/FR29440

This is a large site close to the beach near Plouescat and only 15 minutes from the popular beach resort of Roscoff. At present the site is still in the process of renovation, although the indoor heated pool is now open. The new owners, the Village Center Group, have plans for a new bar, reception area and a pool complex and upgrades to the rest of the site, and when completed this will be a good, lively site in an interesting location. There are 256 rough grass pitches separated by hedges with 143 for touring, only 45 with electricity.

Facilities	Directions
Three adequate but tired toilet blocks. Motorcaravan services. Shop. Bar, snack bar, restaurant (July/Aug). Outdoor swimming and paddling pools, covered pool (all season). Games/TV room. Organised activities (July/Aug). Bicycle hire. Internet. Off site: Fishing, beach, sailing 100 m. Bicycle hire 3 km. Golf 30 km. Tennis. Watersports. Thalassotherapy. Casino.	Site is on the D788 between Brignogan Plage and Roscoff, well signed from Plouescat centre. GPS: 48.65868, -4.21744

Open: 27 May - 18 September.

Charges guide

Per unit incl. 2 persons and electricity	€ 14,00 - € 22,00
extra person	€ 3,00 - € 5,00
dog	€ 3,00
No credit cards.	

Plouézec

Camping le Cap Horn

Port Lazo, F-22470 Plouézec (Côtes d'Armor) T: 02 96 20 64 28. E: lecaphorn@hotmail.com
alanrogers.com/FR22320

Le Cap Horn is in a magnificent setting with exceptional views of the Bay of Paimpol and the Ile de Bréhat. The enthusiastic owners are keen to make visitors welcome at their site which is well positioned for exploring the Goëlo Coast, Paimpol and the Pink Granite Coast. The campsite is in two sections and slopes down to the beach. The upper section is mostly devoted to mobile homes and is reached by a road or a series of steep steps, the lower section is for tourers. There are 149 pitches with 115 good sized grass pitches for touring (90 with 6A electricity).

Facilities	Directions
Two toilet blocks include facilities for campers with disabilities but site is not ideal for those with walking difficulties. Small shop. Bar, restaurant with takeaway and terrace with views over the bay (July/Aug). Heated swimming pool, paddling pool (1/6-15/9). Play area. Boules. Fishing. Watersports. Sports area. Bicycle hire, Organised activities (July/Aug). Internet. Off site: Beach 100 m. Riding 6 km. Golf 12 km.	From Saint Brieuc take D786 north to Paimpol (par la Côte). Site is at Plouézec, south of Paimpol, well signed from D786. GPS: 48.759792, -2.962795

Open: 7 April - 30 September.

Charges guide

Per unit incl. 2 persons	€ 14,00 - € 21,00
incl. electricity (6A)	€ 17,00 - € 25,00
extra person	€ 4,00 - € 5,50
child (under 7 yrs)	€ 3,00 - € 5,00

Plouhinec

Camping Moténo

Route du Magou'r, F-56680 Plouhinec (Morbihan) T: 02 97 36 76 63. E: camping-moteno@wanadoo.fr
alanrogers.com/FR56440

This site is situated on the east side of the river d'Etel just before it enters the sea. The grass pitches are of average size, hedged and shaded by large trees. Of the 256 pitches, 181 are occupied by mobile homes, mostly for rent. The new aqua park complex with covered and open areas is superb and includes slides, flumes and various pools. The beach is easily accessible, just 800 m. away, as is the little port facing Etel which can be reached by a regular ferry service. Plouhinec, the nearest town, is 5 km. by road where you will find shops and restaurants. A little further is the large town of Lorient.

Facilities	Directions
Three toilet blocks (only one open when we visited in June) are old and poorly maintained. Washing machines and dryer. Shop and bar (July/Aug). New aqua complex. Multisport court. Gym. Bicycle hire. Play area. Entertainment (July/Aug). Off site: Beach 800 m. Ferry to Etel for bars and shopping. Nearby towns of Lorient, Auray and the Quiberon peninsular.	From Plouhinec, southeast of Lorient, take the D781 in the direction of Carnac. Site is signed on right in 4 km. Follow signs for Plage. GPS: 47.66457, -3.22098

Open: 5 April - 13 September.

Charges guide

Per unit incl. 2 persons and electricity	€ 18,20 - € 26,00
extra person (over 7 yrs)	€ 3,60 - € 6,00
child (0-7 yrs)	€ 2,50 - € 4,30

Ploumanach

Yelloh! Village le Ranolien

Ploumanach, F-22700 Perros-Guirec (Côtes d'Armor) T: 02 96 91 65 65. E: info@yellohvillage-ranolien.com
alanrogers.com/FR22080

Le Ranolien has been attractively developed around a former Breton farm – everything here is either made from, or placed on or around the often massive pink rocks. Of the 520 pitches only 110 are for touring, mostly large and flat, but some quite small and all with electricity and some with water and drainage. The rest of the site is taken up with mobile homes and chalets for hire and several tour operators. The site is on the coast, with beaches and coves within walking distance and there are spectacular views from some pitches.

Facilities	Directions
The main toilet block (heated in cool weather) has washbasins in cabins, mostly British style WCs, good showers, some spacious and with washbasins. Facilities for disabled visitors. Laundry. Motorcaravan service point. Supermarket and gift shop. Restaurant, crêperie and bar (all open all season). Indoor and outdoor swimming pool complex. Wellness centre. Disco in high season. Minigolf. Games room. Play area. Cinema. Gym and steam room. Internet and WiFi (charged). Mobile homes for hire. Off site: Beach 150 m. Bicycle hire 3 km. Boat launching and sailing 1.5 km. Riding 3 km. Golf 10 km.	From Lannion take D788 to Perros-Guirec. Follow signs to Centre Ville past main harbour area, then turn right along coast road (signed Centre Ville par la Corniche and Trégastel). Continue through north of town and on to La Clarté. After a sharp left hand bend site is immediately on the right. GPS: 48.82798, -3.47623

Open: 9 April - 18 September.

Charges 2011

Per unit incl. 2 persons and electricity	€ 15,00 - € 41,00
extra person	€ 5,00 - € 8,00
child (3-7 yrs)	free - € 5,00

For latest campsite news, availability and prices visit

alanrogers.com

Poullan-sur-Mer

Flower Camping Caravaning le Pil-Koad

Route de Douarnenez, F-29100 Poullan-sur-Mer (Finistère) T: 02 98 74 26 39. E: info@pil-koad.com
alanrogers.com/FR29060

Pil-Koad is an attractive, family run site just back from the sea near Douarnenez in Finistère. It has 190 pitches on fairly flat ground, marked out by separating hedges and of quite good quality, though varying in size and shape. With 88 pitches used for touring units, the site also has a number of mobile homes and chalets. All pitches have electrical connections and the original trees provide shade in some areas. A large room, the 'Woodpecker Bar', is used for entertainment with discos and cabaret in July/Aug. Weekly outings and clubs for children are organised (30/6-30/8). A variety of beaches are within easy reach, with the coast offering some wonderful scenery and good walking.

Facilities

Two main toilet blocks in modern style include washbasins mostly in cabins and facilities for disabled visitors. Laundry facilities. Motorcaravan service point. Gas supplies. Small shop for basics (1/4-30/9). Bar, new restaurant and takeaway (all 1/6-31/8). Heated swimming and paddling pools (1/4-30/9, no Bermuda-style shorts). Tennis. Minigolf. Fishing. Bicycle hire. Playground.
Off site: Restaurants in village 500 m. Riding 4 km. Nearest sandy beach 5 km. Douarnenez 6 km.

Open: 4 April - 27 September.

Directions

Site is 500 m. east from the centre of Poullan on D7 road towards Douarnenez. From Douarnenez take circular bypass route towards Audierne; if you see road for Poullan sign at roundabout, take it, otherwise there is a sign at turn to Poullan from the D765 road. GPS: 48.0824, -4.40805

Charges guide

Per unit incl. 2 persons	
and electricity	€ 16,00 - € 30,80
extra person	€ 3,60 - € 5,10
child (2-7 yrs)	€ 2,30 - € 3,40

Quiberon

Camping Do Mi Si La Mi

31 rue de la Vierge, Saint Julien-Plage, F-56170 Quiberon (Morbihan) T: 02 97 50 22 52
E: camping@domisilami.com alanrogers.com/FR56360

Occupying a five-hectare site on the Quiberon Peninsula just 100 metres from the sandy beaches, this campsite has plenty to offer and is particularly quiet and laid back in low season. Of the 350 pitches, 194 are for touring and are set amongst high mature hedges giving plenty of shade and privacy; some have sea views. Long leads are required on a few pitches as hook-ups can be shared between three or four pitches. The excellent facilities for children are in a well fenced area and include climbing frames, bouncy castles and multisport courts. Treasure hunts and other activities are organised daily in high season. Staff at the well managed reception gave us excellent customer service and we enjoyed our stay on this site which is ideally situated for exploring this fascinating area.

Facilities

Seven sanitary blocks, with good hot showers. Separate laundry. Shop. Bar. TV room. Bouncy castles. Multisport courts. Children's club. Off site: Bar, restaurant, supermarket 50 m. Beaches 100 m. Bicycle hire 100 m. Town centre 2 km. Golf, riding 3 km.

Open: 1 April - 2 November.

Directions

From the N165 Vannes-Lorient dual carriageway south of Auray, take the exit for Carnac/Ploemel. Continue southwest on D768 through the town of Plouharmel following signs for Quiberon. About 25 km. from the N165 but before reaching the town of Quiberon, the site is signed to the left at St Julien Plage. GPS: 47.49974, -3.12026

Charges guide

Per unit incl. 2 persons	
and electricity	€ 16,80 - € 25,50
extra person	€ 3,10 - € 4,40
child (under 7 yrs)	€ 1,80 - € 2,70

For latest campsite news, availability and prices visit

alanrogers.com

Quiberon

Camping Bois d'Amour

Allée de Dianee, F-56170 Quiberon (Morbihan) T: 02 40 60 17 40. E: info@homair.com

alanrogers.com/FR56520

Le Bois d'Amour faces toward Belle Ile and lies just 150 m. from the attractive, sandy Goviro beach at the southern end of the Quiberon peninsula. There are 290 pitches here, of which around 110 are for touring units, most with electricity. Other pitches are occupied by mobile homes and chalets (available for rent). On-site amenities include a large outdoor pool and a separate children's pool. Quiberon is explored by bicycle and these are available to rent on site. In high season, a regular programme of activities and entertainment is organised, including activities for children. Thalassotherapy is very popular in this region and specialist centres are available at both Quiberon and nearby Carnac. Quiberon is otherwise renowned for its sardine production, the origins of which date back to the early 19th century. Nowadays, it is home to many excellent seafood restaurants and tourism has long since replaced fishing as the primary activity. Belle Ile lies 14 km. to the south of Quiberon and is the largest island off the Breton coast. Regular ferries ply there from Quiberon.

Facilities	Directions
Bar/snack bar. Shop. Takeaway food. Swimming pool. Children's pool. Gym. Cycle hire. Games room. Playground. Activity and entertainment programme. Tourist information. Mobile homes and chalets for rent. Off site: Nearest beach 150 m. Fishing. Cycle tracks. Tennis. Quiberon. Carnac. Excursions to Belle Ile.	From Auray (RN 165) take the southbound D768 to Plouharnel and on to Quiberon. Upon arrival in Quiberon, follow signs to 'Thalassotherapie' and then the site. GPS: 47.47634, -3.110364
Open: 1 April - 15 October.	**Charges 2011** Contact the site.

My outdoor holiday at : **Le Bois d'Amour** ***

Check availabilities or find more campsites in Brittany on our website : www.homair.co.uk or by phone on : 00 33 442 204 725

Rochefort-en-Terre

Camping de Moulin Neuf

Chemin de Bogeais, F-56220 Rochefort-en-Terre (Morbihan) T: 02 97 43 37 52. E: ian.hetherington@orange.fr

alanrogers.com/FR56100

This quiet family site is in wooded countryside, 600 m. from the town. Ian and Norma Hetherington have worked hard to develop Moulin Neuf into a neat, tidy and organised site. There are 72 pitches (60 for tourers, 44 with 10A electricity) of good size (120 sq.m) on neat grass, with two levels. The top level, with a limited number of electrical hook-ups, is flat and pitches are divided by young shrubs. The entrance is here and reception is located just beyond the security gate. The lower level is partly sloping with mature trees, shade and electricity on all pitches. Rochefort-en-Terre itself is a marvellous medieval town, beautifully preserved and only ten minutes walk from the site, with a wealth of art and craft workshops, antique shops and art galleries.

Facilities

The modern heated sanitary block is kept very clean and includes large, comfortable showers, cabins with washbasins and British and Turkish style WCs. Provision for disabled visitors. Baby room. Laundry facilities with washing lines. Bread delivered each morning. Heated swimming pool (1/6-31/8). Tennis court, table tennis, basketball, football area. Two play areas. Off site: Lake 500 m. with watersports. Shop 600 m. Riding and golf. Vannes and the beaches of Golfe du Morbihan.

Open: 15 May - 16 September.

Directions

From Redon take D775 Vannes road west for 25 km. Branch north on D774 signed Rochefort-en-Terre. Follow road past the lake on left, in 800 m. Turn left and follow sign to site. GPS: 47.69515, -2.34913

Charges guide

Per unit incl. 2 persons	€ 16,60 - € 19,00
incl. electricity	€ 21,10 - € 23,50
extra person	€ 4,80 - € 5,50
child (under 8 yrs)	€ 3,10 - € 4,00

Quimper

Castel Camping l'Orangerie de Lanniron

Château de Lanniron, F-29336 Quimper (Finistère) T: 02 98 90 62 02. E: camping@lanniron.com
alanrogers.com/FR29050

L'Orangerie is a beautiful and peaceful family site set in ten acres of a 17th-century, 38-hectare country estate on the banks of the Odet river, formerly the home of the Bishops of Quimper. The site has 199 grassy pitches (156 for touring units) of three types varying in size and services. They are on flat ground laid out in rows alongside access roads with shrubs and bushes providing pleasant pitches. All have electricity and 88 have three services. The original outbuildings have been attractively converted around a walled courtyard. Used by tour operators (30 pitches). With lovely walks within the grounds, the restaurant and the gardens are both open to the public and in spring the rhododendrons and azaleas are magnificent. The site is just to the south of Quimper and about 15 km. from the sea and beaches at Bénodet. The restoration of the park, including the original canal, fountains, ornamental 'Bassin de Neptune', the boathouse and the gardens is now complete. In addition to the golf course (9-hole) and driving range, a training bunker and pitching area have been created along with a second putting green. The Aqua park provides in excess of 600 sq.m. of heated water and includes balneotherapy, spa, jacuzzi, fountains, slides and games. These facilities are free of charge to campers.

Facilities

Excellent heated block in the courtyard and second modern block serving the top of the site. Facilities for disabled campers, and babies. Laundry. Motorcaravan services. Shop (15/5-9/9). Bar, snacks and takeaway. New restaurant. Swimming and paddling pools. Aqua park with waterfall, balnéo, spa, jacuzzi, fountains, water slides and games. Small play area. Tennis. Minigolf. Golf course (9 holes), driving range, two putting greens, training bunker and pitching area (weekly package available). Fishing. Archery. Bicycle hire. General reading and games rooms. TV/video room. Karaoke. Outdoor activities. Large room for indoor activities. Pony rides and tree climbing (high season). Internet access and WiFi. Off site: Two hypermarkets 1 km. Historic town of Quimper under 3 km. Golf, cycling, walking, fishing, canoeing, surfing and sailing nearby. Beach 15 km.

Open: 15 May - 15 September.

Directions

From Quimper follow Quimper Sud signs, then 'Toutes Directions' and general camping signs, finally signs for Lanniron. GPS: 47.97685, -4.11102

Charges guide

Per unit incl. 2 persons	
and electricity	€ 22,00 - € 38,60
extra person	€ 4,30 - € 7,50
child (2-9 yrs)	€ 2,80 - € 4,80
dog	€ 2,80 - € 4,50

Less 15% outside July/Aug.
Camping Cheques accepted.

For latest campsite news, availability and prices visit
alanrogers.com

Saint Briac-sur-Mer

Camping Emeraude

7 chemin de la Souris, F-35800 Saint Briac-sur-Mer (Ille-et-Vilaine) T: 02 99 88 34 55
E: camping.emeraude@wanadoo.fr alanrogers.com/FR35100

M. et Mme Giroux have, over the past 10 years, created a pleasant site with a French feel and some surprising features for such a compact site. Notably these include an attractive heated leisure pool with water slides, whirlpool and a paddling pool, safely separated from the main pool and with its own little slide. There are 71 level pitches for touring, separated by hedges or shrubs and all with electricity connection adjacent (6A). Beyond these are 121 mobile homes and chalets (65 for rent). Although in an urban setting, the sandy beaches of the attractive Côte Eméraude are only a short drive away. Saint Briac has a choice of shops, bars and restaurants and the resort of Dinard is only seven kilometres to the east. A bus service will take you there and you could then hop on the sea bus across to Saint Malo.

Facilities

Large toilet block with washbasins in cubicles and controllable showers. Facilities for disabled visitors. Baby room. Washing machine and dryer. Motorcaravan service points. Swimming pool (8/5-10/9). Shop and takeaway (all season). Bar (July/Aug). Games room. Excellent play area. Minigolf. Bicycle hire. Children's activities and evening entertainment for families (July/Aug). Gas barbecues only (available for hire). No twin-axle caravans or motorhomes. Off site: Beach, fishing, sailing and boat-launching 900 m. Golf 3 km. Shops, bars and restaurants nearby.

Open: 3 April - 19 September.

Directions

Saint Briac is 7 km. west of Dinard and 14 km. from Saint Malo by road. From ferry terminal follow signs for Dinard. Turn west onto D168. Keep west onto D603 and follow signs for 'Camping Eméraude par la côte' (avoids town centre); site is well signed from there. From other directions take D976/N176 and follow signs for Dinard. GPS: 48.62776, -2.130865

Charges guide

Per unit incl. 2 persons and electricity	€ 22,80 - € 29,60

CAMPING Emeraude ★★★
Saint-Briac sur mer / Bretagne

Camping Emeraude★★★

7, Chemin de la Souris - 35800 Saint Briac sur Mer - France
Tel. 0033 299 88 34 55 - camping.emeraude@wanadoo.fr - www.campingemeraude.com

Saint Cast-le-Guildo

Camping le Châtelet

Rue des Nouettes, F-22380 Saint Cast-le-Guildo (Côtes d'Armor) T: 02 96 41 96 33. E: chateletcp@aol.com
alanrogers.com/FR22040

Carefully developed over the years from a former quarry, Le Châtelet is pleasantly and quietly situated with lovely views over the estuary from many pitches. It is well laid out, mainly in terraces with fairly narrow access roads. There are 216 good-sized pitches separated by hedges, all with electricity and 112 with water and drainage. Some pitches are around a little lake (unfenced) which can be used for fishing. Used by three different tour operators (73 pitches). A 'green' walking area is a nice feature around the lower edge of the site and a path leads from the site directly down to a beach (about 200 m. but including steps).

Facilities

Four toilet blocks with access at different levels include washbasins in cabins and facilities for children. Three small toilet blocks on the lower terraces. Some facilities are closed outside July/Aug. Motorcaravan services. Heated swimming and paddling pools. Shop for basics, takeaway, bar lounge and general room with satellite TV and pool table. 'Zen' room for rest, meditation and massage sessions (high season). Games room. Play area. Organised games and activities in season. Dancing (June, July and Aug). Off site: Beach 200 m. Bicycle hire, riding and golf within 1.5 km.

Open: 24 April - 10 September.

Directions

Best approach is to turn off D786 road at Matignon towards St Cast; just inside St Cast limits turn left at sign for 'campings' and follow camp signs on C90. GPS: 48.63723, -2.26934

Charges guide

Per unit incl. 2 persons and electricity	€ 22,00 - € 42,00
extra person	€ 4,00 - € 7,00
child (2-14 yrs)	€ 3,00 - € 5,00
dog	€ 4,00

For latest campsite news, availability and prices visit
alanrogers.com

Saint Cast-le-Guildo

Castel Camping le Château de Galinée

La Galinée, F-22380 Saint Cast-le-Guildo (Côtes d'Armor) T: 02 96 41 10 56. E: chateaugalinee@wanadoo.fr
alanrogers.com/FR22090

Situated a few kilometres back from Saint Cast and owned and managed by the Vervel family, Galinée is in a parkland setting on level grass with numerous and varied mature trees. It has 273 pitches, all with electricity, water and drainage and separated by many mature shrubs and bushes. The top section is mostly for mobile homes. An attractive outdoor pool complex has swimming and paddling pools and two pools with a water slide and a 'magic stream'. A new indoor complex has now also been added and includes a swimming pool, bar, restaurant and large entertainment hall.

Facilities	Directions
The large modern sanitary block includes washbasins in private cabins, facilities for babies and disabled visitors. Laundry room. Shop for basics, bar and takeaway menu (all 25/5-4/9). Attractive heated pool complex (indoor 16/4 and outdoor 14/5-10/9) with swimming and paddling pools. New covered complex has heated swimming pool, bar, restaurant, entertainment hall and internet access. Tennis. Fishing. Off site: Beach and golf 3.5 km.	From D168 Ploubalay - Plancoet road turn onto D786 towards Matignon and St Cast. Site is very well signed 1 km. after leaving Notre Dame de Guildo. GPS: 48.58475, -2.25656

Open: 14 May - 10 September.

Charges 2011

Per unit incl. 2 persons and electricity	€ 21,70 - € 41,30
extra person	€ 4,00 - € 6,80

Camping Cheques accepted.

Saint Jouan-des-Guerets

Camping le P'tit Bois

Saint Malo, F-35430 Saint Jouan-des-Guerets (Ille-et-Vilaine) T: 02 99 21 14 30
E: camping.ptitbois@wanadoo.fr alanrogers.com/FR35040

On the outskirts of Saint Malo, this neat, family-oriented site is very popular with British visitors, being ideal for stopovers or for longer stays in this interesting area. Le P'tit Bois provides 274 large, level pitches with 114 for touring units. In two main areas, either side of the entrance lane, these are divided into groups by mature hedges and trees, separated by shrubs and flowers and with access from tarmac roads. Nearly all have electrical hook-ups and over half have water taps. There are site-owned mobile homes and chalets but this does mean that the facilities are open over a long season (for limited hours).

Facilities	Directions
Two fully equipped toilet blocks, include washbasins in cabins. Baby baths. Laundry rooms. Simple facilities for disabled campers. Motorcaravan service point. Small shop, bar (entertainment in July/Aug), snack bar with takeaway. Heated swimming pool, paddling pool and water slides (from 15/5). Indoor pool with Turkish baths and jacuzzi (all season). Playground. Multisport court. Tennis. Minigolf. No charcoal barbecues. Off site: Beach, fishing 2 km. Bicycle hire and riding 6 km. Golf 15 km.	St Jouan is west off the St Malo - Rennes road (N137) just outside St Malo. Site is signed from the N137 (take second exit for St Jouan on the D4). GPS: 48.60993, -1.98665

Open: 2 April - 11 September.

Charges guide

Per unit incl. 2 persons and electricity	€ 22,00 - € 40,00
extra person	€ 5,00 - € 8,00
child (1-6 yrs)	€ 3,00 - € 6,00

Saint Lunaire

Camping la Touesse

171 rue Ville Gehan, F-35800 Saint Lunaire (Ille-et-Vilaine) T: 02 99 46 61 13
E: camping.la.touesse@wanadoo.fr alanrogers.com/FR35060

This family campsite was purpose built and has been developed since 1987 by Alain Clément who is keen to welcome more British visitors. Set just back from the coast road, 300 metres from a sandy beach, it is in a semi-residential area. It is, nevertheless, a pleasant, sheltered site with a range of trees and shrubs. Of the 141 level, grass pitches in bays, 90 are for touring units, all with electricity. The plus factor of this site, besides its proximity to Dinard, is the fine sandy beach which is sheltered – so useful in early season – and safe for children. The owners speak English.

Facilities	Directions
The central toilet block is well maintained, heated in low season with all modern facilities (may be partially closed outside July/Aug). Baby bath. Toilet for disabled visitors. Laundry facilities. Motorcaravan service point. Shop for basics (1/4-20/9). Pleasant bar/restaurant with TV. Video games with snooker. Sauna. Internet access and WiFi (free) at reception. Bouncy castle. Off site: Buses 100 m. Sandy beach, fishing 300 m. Saling 400 m. Riding 500 m. Bicycle hire 1.5 km. Golf 3 km. Shops, bars and restaurants nearby.	From ferry terminal follow signs for Dinard. From other directions take D976/N176 and follow signs for Dinard. Turn west onto D168, then northwest onto D64 towards St Lunaire. Follow signs to campsite at La Fourberie east of town. GPS: 48.63084, -2.08418

Open: 1 April - 30 September.

Charges guide

Per unit incl. 2 persons and electricity	€ 16,80 - € 22,00
extra person	€ 4,20 - € 5,30
child (under 7 yrs)	€ 2,40 - € 3,00

No credit cards.

For latest campsite news, availability and prices visit

alanrogers.com

Saint Malo

Domaine de la Ville Huchet

Route de la Passagère, Quelmer, F-35400 Saint Malo (Ille-et-Vilaine) T: 02 99 81 11 83. E: info@villehuchet.com

alanrogers.com/FR35050

Domaine de la Ville Huchet was taken over a few years ago by the owners of Camping Les Ormes (FR35020). It has been transformed into a superb site with modern facilities and lots of character. The pitches are well laid out and of generous size, most with 6A electricity and some with shade. They are set around an old manor house (disused) at the centre of the site. A splendid pool complex with its slides and pirate theme is particularly exciting for children. A range of entertainment for young and old takes place in the spacious bar area and a new crêperie provides a range of food. This is a useful site, positioned on the edge of St Malo with easy access to the ferry terminal, old town and beaches. A bus service to take you into the town is 400 m. away.

Facilities

The sanitary blocks are modern and clean. Facilities for disabled visitors. Shop. Bar, crêperie and snack bar. Aqua park with water slides. Bicycle hire. Play area. Entertainment programme in peak season (including live bands). Off site: Aquarium 700 m. St Malo (beaches, ferry terminal and old town) 4 km.

Open: 10 April - 12 September.

Directions

From St Malo take D301 heading south. Join the D165 signed Quelmer and the site is well signed (2 km). GPS: 48.61507, -1.98782

Charges guide

Per unit incl. 2 persons and electricity	€ 21,00 - € 32,00
extra person	€ 3,80 - € 6,10
child (2-13 yrs)	€ 2,50 - € 3,70
dog	€ 3,10

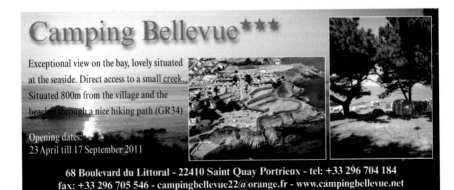

Saint Pierre-de-Quiberon
Flower Camping l'Océan
16 avenue de Groix, B.P. 18 Kerhostin, F-56510 Saint Pierre-de-Quiberon (Morbihan)
T: 02 97 30 91 29. E: info@relaisdelocean.com alanrogers.com/FR56470

L'Océan is a member of the Flower group and can be found just 100 m. from the nearest beach, halfway down the Quiberon peninsula. The site forms a part of a holiday complex that was established in 1925 and which also includes a hotel. There are 275 pitches which are generally well shaded, although some sunnier pitches are also available. A selection of mobile homes and fully equipped tents are for rent. In peak season, a varied entertainment programme is on offer, including traditional Celtic folk evenings and magic shows, as well as discos and concerts. The site's bar/restaurant 'Ty Mouss' is the focal point and specialises in pizzas and crêpes, as well as other light meals. The nearest beach is sandy and various activities take place there, including beach volleyball and children's games. Bicycle hire is available on site and there are miles of marked cycle tracks around the peninsula, and further afield, for example, to the prehistoric standing stones at Carnac.

Facilities
Sanitary facilities provide hot showers. Facilities for disabled visitors. Laundry facilities. Motorcaravan services. Shop, bar/restaurant and takeaway (all July/Aug). Multisports terrain. Fishing. Tennis. Bicycle hire. Canoe hire. Play area. TV/games room. Activity and entertainment programme. Mobile homes and equipped tents for rent. Internet access and WiFi (charged). Off site: Nearest beach 100 m. Riding 3 km. Golf 15 km. Cycle tracks. Prehistoric stones at Carnac.

Open: April - October.

Directions
Leave the N165 at the Quiberon exit and head south on the D768. Continue towards St Pierre-de-Quiberon, passing through Plouharnel. Site is at Kerhostin and is signed to the right, before St Pierre. GPS: 47.534327, -3.139558

Charges 2011
Per unit incl. 2 persons	
and electricity	€ 15,50 - € 24,50
extra person	€ 3,50 - € 5,00
child (2-7 yrs)	€ 2,20 - € 3,50

Camping Relais de l'Océan
**16 Avenue de Groix Kerhostin
BP18 - 56510 St. Pierre Quiberon**

Situated on the Presqu'lle de Quiberon (South Brittany), 30 meters from the sea on open terrain with many trees. Flower Camping de l'Océan is a perfect destination for your family holiday.

Flower Camping de l'Océan welcomes you from April till October for a relaxing holiday in the heart of the Morbihan (South Brittany)

Campsite is part of Camping Qualité

Information: 0033 297 30 91 29 / Reservations: www.relaisdelocean.com

---

Saint Quay-Portrieux
Camping Bellevue
68 boulevard du Littoral, F-22410 Saint Quay-Portrieux (Côtes d'Armor) T: 02 96 70 41 84
E: campingbellevue22@orange.fr alanrogers.com/FR22230

With magnificent coastal views, this attractive and well cared for site lives up to its name. Family owned for many years, it is situated on the outskirts of the popular seaside resort of St Quay-Portrieux and you will be made to feel most welcome by the owners. The 173 numbered touring pitches vary in size and 140 have 6A electricity. Some are separated by hedges, whilst others are in groups of four. Entertainment on site is limited but there is plenty to do and see around the area and great opportunities for exploring the Goëlo coast. Lazy hours could be spent gazing at the superb views of this spectacular part of the Brittany coast which can be seen from many of the Bellevue pitches. Further afield a days excursion could take you to Dinan, Dinard or the old walled town of St Malo. Some of the finest seafood can be found in this area of France.

Facilities
Two clean sanitary blocks provide both open and cubicled washbasins and controllable showers. Facilities for disabled visitors and babies. Laundry facilities. Motorcaravan service point. Shop for basics. Simple snack bar (1/7-31/8). Outdoor pool (1/6-18/9; no Bermuda shorts). Paddling pool. Volleyball. Boules. Play area. WiFi (free Jul/Aug). Off site: Within walking distance of St Quay-Portrieux with shops, bars, restaurants and casino. Bicycle hire 1 km. Riding 8 km. Golf 10 km.

Open: 30 April - 18 September.

Directions
From N12 St Brieuc by-pass, take D786 north towards Paimpol. Site is well signed northwest of St Quay-Portrieux, 13 km. from the bypass. GPS: 48.66277, -2.84443

Charges guide
Per unit incl. 2 persons	
and electricity	€ 17,00 - € 21,50
extra person	€ 4,00 - € 5,20
child (under 7 yrs)	€ 3,00 - € 3,30

For latest campsite news, availability and prices visit
alanrogers.com

Saint Pol-de-Léon

Camping Ar Kleguer

Plage Sainte Anne, F-29250 Saint Pol-de-Léon (Finistère) T: 02 98 69 18 81. E: info@camping-ar-kleguer.com

alanrogers.com/FR29040

Ar Kleguer is less than 20 minutes from the Roscoff ferry terminal in the heart of the Pays du Léon in north Finistère. One section of the site (used in high season) has a 'country' feel and incorporates a small domestic animal park. The main section is divided into several areas, some on terraces at the edge of the sea with spectacular views overlooking the Bay of Morlaix. There are 173 large and well kept pitches, 125 for touring units, all with 10A electricity connections. Of these, 125 are for touring units. This neat site is decorated with attractive flowers, shrubs and trees.

Facilities

Three modern, tiled toilet blocks are well maintained and kept clean. Facilities for babies, children and disabled visitors. Laundry room. Shop, bar and takeaway (July/Aug). Good heated pool complex with paddling pools and slide (20/6-5/9). Pool table. Tennis. Bicycle hire. Animal park. Play area. Activities for children and some entertainment in high season. Beach adjacent. Free WiFi. Off site: Restaurant at site entrance. Sailing and boat launching 1 km. Riding 4 km. Golf 7 km.

Open: Easter - 30 September.

Directions

Saint-Pol is 18 km. northwest of Morlaix just off the D58 Morlaix-Roscoff road. Site is best approached from south, leaving D58 on the D769 signed Saint-Pol Littoral. Turn right at Cemetery following signs for 'Plages et Port' and Campsites. Turn left along seafront to site at end. GPS: 48.69151, -3.96717

Charges guide

Per person	€ 4,00 - € 5,35
child (2-7 yrs)	€ 2,40 - € 3,65
pitch incl. electricity	€ 9,00 - € 10,00

Sarzeau

Camping la Ferme de Lann-Hoëdic

Rue Jean de la Fontaine, F-56370 Sarzeau (Morbihan) T: 02 97 48 01 73. E: contact@camping-lannhoedic.fr

alanrogers.com/FR56200

Camping la Ferme is an attractively landscaped site with flowering shrubs and trees. The 108 touring pitches, all with electricity (10A) are large and mostly level, with maturing trees which are beginning to offer some shade. The 20 pitches with mobile homes are in a separate area. The working farm produces cereal crops and the summer months are an interesting time for children to see the harvest in progress. Mireille and Tim, the owners, go out of their way to make this a welcoming and happy place to stay. Located in the countryside on the Rhuys Peninsula, Golfe du Morbihan, it is an ideal base for cycling, walking and water based activities. Since Camping la Ferme opened in 2002, it has developed into one of the prettiest campsites in the Morbihan region of France. A visitor remarked that it is like 'camping in a garden'. Ecology is taken very seriously with solar panels for water heating and a composting system that you are encouraged to use for any waste food.

Facilities

Two new, high quality toilet blocks with facilities for disabled visitors and babies. Washing machines and dryers. Bread delivery. Ice creams and soft drinks available at reception. Takeaway meals and traditional Breton 'soirées' (high season). Bicycle hire. Playground with modern well designed equipment. Pétanque. Internet access and free WiFi. Off site: Beach, fishing and boating 800 m. Sarzeau 2 km. Riding 2 km. Golf 6 km.

Open: 1 April - 31 October.

Directions

East of Vannes on the N165, join the D780 in the direction of Sarzeau. Exit D780 at the 'Super U'; roundabout south of Sarzeau, following signs for Le Roaliguen. Campsite is signed. GPS: 47.50745, -2.76092

Charges guide

Per unit incl. 2 persons and electricity	€ 15,60 - € 19,90
extra person	€ 3,50 - € 4,50
child (under 7 yrs)	€ 1,60 - € 2,10
dog	€ 1,20 - € 1,90

No credit cards. Camping Cheques accepted.

For latest campsite news, availability and prices visit

alanrogers.com

Sarzeau

Camping Manoir de Ker An Poul

Lieu-dit Penvins, F-56370 Sarzeau (Morbihan) T: 02 97 67 33 30. E: info@manoirdekeranpoul.com
alanrogers.com/FR56450

Le Manoir de Ker An Poul has an attractive location, close to the sea (700 m) in the southern Morbihan region. The old manor house is charming and the site has been developed in the grounds. This is quite a large site with around 350 pitches, around half of which are occupied by mobile homes and chalets. There is a large pool and aquagym is organised in peak season. Scuba diving lessons are available for children. Many other activities are on offer in high season, including evening entertainment and a children's club.

Facilities

Sanitary facilities include hot showers, washbasins in cabins and facilities for disabled visitors. Laundry facilities. Shop, bar and snack bar (all 1/7-31/8). Swimming and paddling pools. Games room. Tennis. Multisports pitch. Play area. Bicycle hire. Activity and entertainment programme. Off site: Nearest beach 700 m. Sarzeau 7 km. Cycle and walking tracks. Fishing. Morbihan gulf.

Open: 5 April - 27 September.

Directions

From Vannes, head south on D780 towards Sarzeau. At St Armel join the D199 (Route de Menez) to Penvins and site is clearly signed. GPS: 47.50542, -2.68325

Charges guide

| Per unit incl. 2 persons and electricity | € 23,00 - € 29,00 |
| extra person | € 5,50 |

Taden

Camping Municipal la Hallerais

4 rue de la Robardais, F-22100 Taden (Côtes d'Armor) T: 02 96 39 15 93. E: camping.la.hallerais@wanadoo.fr
alanrogers.com/FR22060

La Hallerais has a lot more to offer than most municipal sites. It is ideally located for exploring this fascinating area and is quite a short run from Saint-Malo and from the resorts of the Côte d'Armor. It is just outside the attractive old medieval town of Dinan, beyond and above the little harbour on the Rance estuary. There is a pleasant riverside walk to the port and up into the town. Of the 226 pitches, 107 are for touring, all with electricity (6A), water and drainage, and are mainly on level, shallow terraces, with trees and hedges giving a park-like atmosphere.

Facilities

Two good quality toilet blocks, one recently refurbished, include pushbutton showers, washbasins in cubicles and spacious cabins with shower and washbasin. Unit for disabled visitors. Launderette. Shop. Bar/restaurant with outside terrace and takeaway (all season). Swimming and paddling pools (15/5-30/9). Tennis. Minigolf. Play area. Fishing. Mobile homes for rent. Internet and WiFi. Off site: Riding 2 km. Bicycle hire 5 km. Beach, sailing and boat launching 15 km. Port with shops 3 km.

Open: 12 March - 13 November.

Directions

Dinan is due south of Saint-Malo (32 km. by road). From N176 (Avranches/Saint-Brieuc) take Taden exit north of Dinan, turn towards Taden and follow blue signs to site. GPS: 48.47148, -2.02284

Charges 2011

Per unit incl. 2 persons and electricity	€ 13,50 - € 19,80
extra person	€ 3,25 - € 3,85
child (under 7 yrs)	€ 1,37 - € 1,67

Taupont

Camping la Vallée du Ninian

Le Rocher, F-56800 Taupont (Morbihan) T: 02 97 93 53 01. E: info@camping-ninian.com
alanrogers.com/FR56160

M. and Mme. Joubaud have developed this peaceful family run site in central Brittany from a former farm and they continue to make improvements to ensure that their visitors have an enjoyable holiday. The level site falls into three areas – the orchard with 100 large, hedged pitches with electricity; the wood with about 13 pitches more suited to tents; and the meadow by the river providing a further 35 pitches delineated by small trees and shrubs, with electricity. The bar has as its centrepiece a working cider press with which M. Joubaud makes his own 'potion magique'.

Facilities

A central building houses unisex toilet facilities including washbasins in cubicles, large cubicle with facilities for disabled visitors and laundry area with washing machines, dryer and ironing board. Shop (July/Aug) selling bread. Small (7x12 m) heated swimming pool and children's pool with slide and fountain. Swings, slides and large trampoline. Trout fishing (permits from office). Off site: Riding 2 km. Bicycle hire, golf 7 km.

Open: 15 April - 15 September.

Directions

From Ploërmel follow signs to Taupont north on N8. Continue through Taupont turn left (east) signed Vallée du Ninian. Follow road for 3 km. to site on left. From Josselin follow signs for Hellean. Through village, sharp right after river Ninian bridge. Site is 400 m. on right. GPS: 47.96931, -2.47014

Charges guide

| Per unit incl. 2 persons and electricity (6A) | € 14,70 - € 17,50 |
| extra person | € 3,20 - € 4,00 |

Credit cards accepted in July/Aug. only.

Telgruc-sur-Mer

Camping le Panoramic

Route de la Plage-Penker, F-29560 Telgruc-sur-Mer (Finistère) T: 02 98 27 78 41
E: info@camping-panoramic.com alanrogers.com/FR29080

This medium sized, traditional site is situated on quite a steep, ten-acre hillside with fine views. It is personally run by M. Jacq and his family who all speak good English. The 200 pitches are arranged on flat, shady terraces, in small groups with hedges and flowering shrubs, and 20 pitches have services for motorcaravans. Divided into two parts, the main upper site is where most of the facilities are located, with the swimming pool, its terrace and a playground located with the lower pitches across the road. Some up-and-down walking is therefore necessary, but this is a small price to pay for such pleasant and comfortable surroundings. This area provides lovely coastal footpaths. The sandy beach and a sailing school at Trez-Bellec-Plage are a 700 m. walk. A Sites et Paysages member.

Facilities

The main site has two well kept toilet blocks with another very good block opened for main season across the road. All include British and Turkish style WCs, washbasins in cubicles, facilities for disabled visitors, baby baths, plus laundry facilities. Motorcaravan services. Small shop (1/7-31/8). Refurbished bar/restaurant with takeaway (1/7-31/8). Barbecue area. Heated pool, paddling pool and jacuzzi (1/6-15/9). Playground. Games and TV rooms. Tennis. Bicycle hire. WiFi. Off site: Beach and fishing 700 m. Riding 6 km. Golf 14 km. Sailing school nearby.

Open: 1 May - 15 September.

Directions

Site is just south of Telgruc-sur-Mer. On D887 pass through Ste Marie du Ménez Horn. Turn left on D208 signed Telgruc-sur-Mer. Continue straight on through town and site is on right within 1 km. GPS: 48.22409, -4.37186

Charges guide

Per unit incl. 2 persons and electricity	€ 25,10 - € 26,50
extra person	€ 5,00
child (under 7 yrs)	€ 3,00

Less 20% outside July/Aug.

Tinténiac

Camping Les Peupliers

F-35190 Tinténiac (Ille-et-Vilaine) T: 02 99 45 49 75. E: camping.les.peupliers@wanadoo.fr
alanrogers.com/FR35110

In the grounds of la Domaine de Besnelais, this little site has a very French feel. It is in a quiet area with wonderful opportunities for walking and cycling, with a flight of eleven locks on the attractive canal nearby. Of the 100 level, grassy pitches separated by hedges and bushes, 40 are for touring, all with electricity (10A). There are a couple of small fishing lakes. The site is close to the D137 Saint-Malo - Rennes expressway and could be used as a peaceful base from which to visit Dinan and Dinard, Mont -Saint-Michel and the bustling city of Rennes. The owners are now in their third year and are aiming to develop a truly 'green' site, creating little gardens and encouraging wildlife, particularly birds.

Facilities

The traditional toilet block is kept very clean and has mainly British style toilets, controllable showers and some washbasins in cubicles. Laundry room. Swimming and paddling pools (15/5-30/9, heated 15/6-15/9). Bar with terrace (limited hours in low season). Weekly themed evening and some children's activities in high season. Takeaway food (to order in low season). Friterie (July/Aug). Basic supplies in reception. Tennis. Minigolf. Pitch and putt. Boules. Fishing. Bicycle hire. Internet and free WiFi. Some mobile homes to rent (1/3-31/10). Off site: Riding 200 m. Golf 25 km. Beaches and sailing 30 km.

Open: 1 April - 30 September.

Directions

Tinténiac is 43 km. south of Saint Malo and 30 km. north of Rennes. Site is 2.5 km. south of village and is signed. From D137, leave at exit for Hédé and turn east then north towards Tinténiac. Site is 1.5 km. GPS: 48.310016, -1.821075

Charges guide

| Per unit incl. 2 persons and electricity | € 19,40 - € 21,10 |

For latest campsite news, availability and prices visit

alanrogers.com

Tredrez-Locquémeau

Camping les Capucines

Kervourdon, F-22300 Tredrez-Locquémeau (Côtes d'Armor) T: 02 96 35 72 28. E: les.capucines@wanadoo.fr
alanrogers.com/FR22010

A warm welcome awaits at Les Capucines which is quietly situated about a kilometre from the village of Saint Michel with its good, sandy beach and also very near Locquémeau, a pretty fishing village. This attractive, family run site has 100 pitches on flat or slightly sloping ground. All are well marked out by hedges, with mature trees and some more recently planted. There are 70 pitches with electricity, water and drainage, including ten for larger units. A good value restaurant/crêperie can be found at Trédrez; others at Saint Michel. A Sites et Paysages member.

Facilities	Directions
Two modern toilet blocks, clean and very well kept, include washbasins mainly in cabins, facilities for babies and disabled visitors. Laundry. Small shop for essentials (bread to order). Takeaway, bar with T. New covered and heated swimming pool (all season). Playground. Tennis. Minigolf. New multisport area. Chalets and mobile homes to rent. WiFi. Off site: Beach 1 km. Fishing 1 km. Riding 2 km. Golf 15 km.	Turn off main D786 road northeast of St Michel where site is signed, and 1 km. to site. GPS: 48.69274, -3.55663

Open: 27 March - 30 September.

Charges 2011

Per unit incl. 2 persons	
and electricity	€ 18,00 - € 27,00
extra person	€ 4,00 - € 5,50
child (under 7 yrs)	€ 2,90 - € 3,60

Trélévern

Camping de Port l'Epine

Venelle de Pors Garo, F-22660 Trélévern (Côtes d'Armor) T: 02 96 23 71 94
E: camping-de-port-lepine@wanadoo.fr   alanrogers.com/FR22130

Port l'Epine is a pretty little site in a unique situation on a promontory with direct access to the sea, and views across the attractive bay to Perros Guirec. There are 160 grass pitches, 101 for touring, all with electricity (16A) and some fully serviced. They are separated by attractive hedging and trees. The rest are used for mobile homes. This site is ideal for families with young children, though not for teenagers looking for lots to do! On the north side is a little port facing an archipelago of seven small islands.

Facilities	Directions
The original toilet block is well equipped and a second block has been refurbished in modern style with thermostatically controllable showers and washbasins in cubicles. Baby room. Facilities for disabled visitors. Modern launderette. Shop and bar (all season) restaurant with takeaway (1/7-31/8). Small heated swimming pool and paddling pool (May-Sept). Fenced play area near the bar/restaurant. Video games. Bicycle hire. Fishing and boat launching. Internet and WiFi in bar. Off site: Riding 2 km. Sailing 5 km. Golf 15 km. Useful small supermarket up hill from site. Many coastal paths to enjoy. Boat trips from Perros Guirec 10 km.	Trélévern is 14 km. northeast of Lannion and 70 km. by road east of Roscoff. From roundabout south of Perros Guirec take D6 towards Tréguier. After passing through Louannec, turn left at crossroads near Trélévern. Go through village following camping signs – Port l'Epine is then clearly marked as distinct from the municipal site. GPS: 48.81311, -3.38598

Open: Mid May - 11 September.

Charges guide

Per unit incl. 2 persons	
and electricity	€ 14,50 - € 30,00
with services	€ 17,00 - € 33,00
extra person	€ 5,00 - € 7,00
child (2-11 yrs)	€ 3,00 - € 5,00

Vannes-Meucon-Monterblanc

Camping du Haras

Aérodrome Vannes-Meucon, Kersimon, F-56250 Vannes-Meucon-Monterblanc (Morbihan) T: 02 97 44 66 06
E: contact@campingvannes.com   alanrogers.com/FR56150

Close to Vannes and the Golfe du Morbihan in southern Brittany, Le Haras is a small, family run, rural site that is open all year. There are 140 pitches, in a variety of settings, both open and wooded, the pitches are well kept and of a good size, all with electricity (4-10A) and most with water and drainage. Whilst M. Danard intends keeping the site quiet and in keeping with its rural setting, he provides plenty of activities for lively youngsters, including some organised games and evening parties.

Facilities	Directions
The two modern toilet blocks (heated in winter) provide a few washbasins in cabins and controllable showers. Facilities for babies and disabled visitors. Laundry facilities. No shop but basics are kept in the bar. Bar with snacks (May-Oct). Takeaway (July/Aug). Swimming pool with waves and slide (1/5-31/10). Play area. Animal park. Trampoline. Minigolf. Bicycle hire. Organised activities (high season). Off site: Riding 400 m. Fishing 3 km. Beach 15 km. Golf 25 km.	From Vannes on N165 take exit signed Pontivy and airport on the D767. Follow signs for airport and Meucon. Turn right on the D778, follow airport and yellow campsite signs. GPS: 47.730477, -2.72801

Open: All year.

Charges guide

Per unit incl. 2 persons	
and electricity (10A)	€ 19,00 - € 25,00
extra person	€ 4,00 - € 5,00
child (0-7 yrs)	€ 2,00 - € 3,00
dog	€ 3,00 - € 4,00

For latest campsite news, availability and prices visit

alanrogers.com

A striking area whose beauty lies not only in the landscape. Normandy is famed for its seafood, its medieval heritage and its role in turning around World War II on D-Day. Certain areas of Normandy remain untouched and wonderfully old fashioned.

DÉPARTEMENTS: 14 CALVADOS, 27 EURE, 50 MANCHE, 61 ORNE, 76 SEINE MARITIME

MAJOR CITIES: CAEN, ROUEN AND LE HAVRE

Normandy has a rich landscape full of variety. From the picturesque bay of Mont St Michel to the wild, craggy, granite coastline of the northern Cotentin, up through the rugged coastlines of La Manche to the long, sandy beaches of Calvados and chalk cliffs of the north. It boasts 270 miles of superb coastline including the Cotentin Peninsula, cliffs of the Côte d'Albâtre and the fine beaches and fashionable Second Empire resorts of the Côte Fleurie, plus a wealth of quiet villages and unspoilt countryside for leisurely exploration.

The history of Normandy is closely linked with our own. The famous Bayeux Tapestry chronicles the exploits of the Battle of Hastings and there are many museums, exhibitions, sites and monuments, including the Caen Memorial Museum, which commemorate operations that took place during the D-Day Landings of 1944.

Known as the dairy of France you'll also find plenty of fresh fish and seafood, rich cream, butter, and fine cheeses such as Camembert and Pont l'Evêque. The many apple orchards are used in producing cider and the well known Calvados, Normandy's apple brandy.

Normandy
Love the land. Live the life.

www.**normandy-tourism.org**

Places of interest

D-Day & the Battle of Normandy

Caen Memorial Museum.
Merville Franceville Battery.
Omaha Beach American Cemetery and Visitor Centre.
Landing Museum in Arromanches.

www.**normandiememoire.com**

Impressionism

Monet's House and Garden in Giverny.
Impressionist Museum in Giverny.
Rouen Fine Art Museum.
Malraux Museum in Le Havre.
Honfleur, cradle of impressionism.

www.**impressionism-normandy.com**

William the Conqueror

Bayeux Tapestry.
Falaise Castle.
Caen Ducal Castle.

Cider route

Pays d'Auge area of Calvados where the distinctive apple brandy and cider are produced. The circular route takes in the countryside around Cambremer and Beuvron-en-Auge through picturesque villages.

La Cité de la Mer

Situated on the site of the old Transatlantic Railway Terminal in Cherbourg, La Cité de la Mer is a new and unique tourist centre, of great interest both scientifically and culturally.

Cuisine of the region

Andouille de Vire: small chitterling (tripe) sausage.

Barbue au cidre: brill cooked in cider and Calvados.

Douillon de pommes à la Normande: baked apples in pastry.

Escalope Vallée d'Auge: veal sautéed and flamed in Calvados with cream and apples.

Teurgoule: rice pudding with cinnamon.

Tripes à la mode de Caen: stewed beef tripe with onions, carrots, leeks, garlic, cider and Calvados.

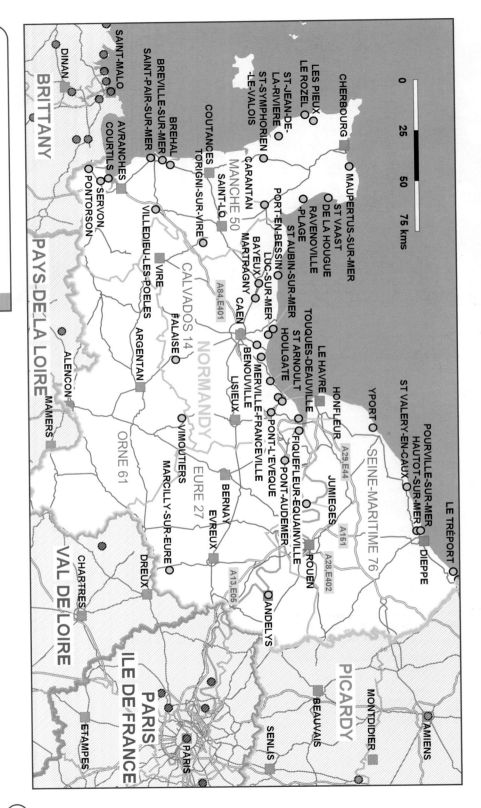

For latest campsite news, availability and prices visit
alanrogers.com

Andelys

Camping de l'Ile des Trois Rois

1 rue Gilles Nicolle, F-27700 Andelys (Eure) T: 02 32 54 23 79. E: campingtroisrois@aol.com
alanrogers.com/FR27070

523

One hour from Paris and 30 minutes from Rouen, l'Ile des Trois Rois has an attractive setting on the banks of the Seine, with a private fishing lake and is a haven of peace. It is overlooked by the impressive remains of the Château-Gaillard and would be ideal as an overnight stop or for longer. The site has been owned by the Francais family for the past few years and they live on site. Within walking distance of the town and shops, there are 210 spacious and partly shady grass pitches, all with electricity (long leads may be required for some). Water taps are rather scarce. There are also seven mobile homes for rent and 70 pitches occupied by private mobile homes/seasonal units. The Medieval Festival is held in Les Andelys during the last weekend in June. Bread and cakes are available 24 hours from a vending machine.

Facilities

Four small, unheated toilet blocks with British style toilets (no seats), showers and washbasins all in cubicles, dishwashing and laundry sinks. One has facilities for disabled campers, another has a laundry facility. Motorcaravan service area. Two heated swimming pools (15/5-15/9). Fishing in the Seine or in the private lake. Fenced play area. Entertainment. Bar and restaurant, evening entertainment (4/7-30/8). Bicycles and barbecues for hire. Satellite TV. Internet access and WiFi. Off site: Day trips to Paris and Rouen. Cycling and walking trails. Riding 5 km. Golf 9 km. Giverny 20 km.

Open: 15 March - 15 November.

Directions

From the A13 motorway, take exit 17 and join the D316 to Les Andelys. In Les Andelys follow signs to Evreux, and the campsite is just off the island before passing the bridge over the Seine.
GPS: 49.23592, 1.40064

Charges guide

Per unit incl. 2 persons	€ 16,00 - € 21,00
extra person	€ 5,50
child (under 3 yrs)	free
dog	€ 2,00

L'Ile des Trois Rois

The park Ile des Trois Rois is situated in the most beautiful bend of the Seine nearby Castle Gaillard in Normandy and is a haven of peace. Paris is situated of less than than an hour and Rouen is half an hour driving from the camp site. Facilities: two heated swimming pools, ping pong, camper service, bar and restaurant (high season) and play area

1, Rue Gilles Nicole - F-27700 Les Andelys - France - Tel. 0033 (0) 2 32 54 23 79
Fax 0033 (0) 2 32 51 14 54 - Email campingtroisrois@aol.com - www.camping-troisrois.com

Bayeux

Camping des Bords de l'Aure

Boulevard Eindhoven, F-14400 Bayeux (Calvados) T: 02 31 92 08 43. E: campingmunicipal@mairie-bayeux.fr
alanrogers.com/FR14020

Only a few kilometres from the coast and the landing beaches this site makes a very useful night stop on the way to or from Cherbourg, whether or not you want to see the tapestry. The 140 pitches are in two areas (many on hardstanding), well marked and generally of good size with electricity. The site is busy over a long season – early arrival is advised as reservations are not taken. There is a full time warden from 15/6-15/9, otherwise reception is open from 08.00-10.00 and 17.00-19.00. There may be some road noise on one side of the site.

Facilities

The two good quality toilet blocks have British and Turkish style WCs, washbasins in cabins in main block, and units for disabled visitors. Motorcaravan service point. Laundry room. Takeaway food and snacks. Two playgrounds. Reading room with TV. Games room. Off site: Large public indoor swimming pool adjoins site with children's pool and jacuzzi. Supermarket nearby (closes 20.00). Bicycle hire 1 km. Riding 5 km. Beach, golf or fishing 8 km.

Open: 1 May - 30 September.

Directions

Site is on the south side of northern ring road (D613) to town, and just west of the junction with the D516 to autoroute. GPS: 49.2839, -0.6976

Charges guide

Per unit incl. 2 persons and electricity	€ 14,65
extra person	€ 3,45
child (under 7 yrs)	€ 1,80
dog	free
Less 10% for stay over 5 days.	

For latest campsite news, availability and prices visit

alanrogers.com

Bénouville

Camping les Hautes Coutures

Avenue de la Côte de Nacre, F-14970 Bénouville (Calvados) T: 02 31 44 73 08
E: info@campinghautescoutures.com alanrogers.com/FR14060

Les Hautes Coutures is a pleasant site whose new owner has made considerable improvements to the leisure facilities so that it is now not only an ideal site for overnight stops (being just 4 km. from the Caen-Portsmouth ferry terminal) but also well worth considering for a longer stay. There are 120 good-sized grass touring pitches separated by mature hedges, all with electrical connections (4-10A). An area close to the canal has large, unmarked pitches. There are also around 150 mobile homes, 30 available to rent. The site is beside the Caen ship canal and a short walk along the footpath takes you to Pegasus Bridge and the Pegasus Memorial museum. In the other direction the path (and cycle track) goes to Ouistreham.

Facilities

Two toilet blocks include showers, washbasins in cabins (warm water). Facilities can be under pressure at peak times with variable hot water supply. Laundry facilities. Motorcaravan service point. Small shop, restaurant and takeaway (July/Aug). Bar (May-Sept). Attractive new pool complex with water slides and an outdoor pool linked to another with retractable roof (May-Sept). Small lounge/TV area and games room. Impressive new play area and outdoor fitness equipment. Multisport court. Children's club (July/Aug). Fishing. Minigolf. Boules. Off site: Pegasus Bridge and Memorial Museum short walk along canal path. Beach, sailing, boat launching, water-skiing and riding all 2-3 km. Golf 4 km.

Open: 1 April - 30 October.

Directions

Bénouville is 10 km. northeast of Caen. From northern ring road (N 814) at exit 3, take D515 towards Ouistreham (or follow car ferry signs from other points). After Bénouville (now the D514) take first exit and site entrance is ahead. From ferry take D514 towards Caen; in 4 km. take slip road for Bénouville and at T-junction turn left to site. (Owner awaits arrivals from evening ferry). GPS: 49.24948, -0.27217

Charges guide

Per unit incl. 2 persons and electricity	€ 34,30 - € 34,80
extra person	€ 9,40
child (2-7 yrs)	€ 5,50

★★★★
Les Hautes Coutures

Route de Ouistreham 14970 BENOUVILLE
Tel : 02 31 44 73 08   Fax : 02 31 95 30 80
E-mail : info@campinghautescoutures.com   Web site : www.campinghautescoutures.com

Bréhal

Camping La Vanlée

Rue des Gabions, F-50290 Bréhal (Manche) T: 02 33 61 63 80. E: contact@camping-vanlee.com
alanrogers.com/FR50220

A typical French beach holiday is on offer when you stay at La Vanlée. The resident manager who enthusiastically runs this municipal site on the outskirts of St. Martin de Bréhal is passionate about the area and the type of holiday offered by the site. There are 470 pitches, which are open, marked and numbered. All are on sandy grass and in some areas the ground is undulating. The roads around the site are tarmac but it is necessary to drive over grass to access most of the pitches. The swimming and paddling pools are a little dated without slide or flume, but there is direct access to the beach. Five toilet blocks are available in the high season with good facilities for children and visitors with disabilities.

Facilities

There are five toilet blocks, although only two were open at the time of our visit. Washbasins in open cabins with hot and cold water. Pushbutton showers. Good facilities for disabled campers. Washing and drying facilities. Shop, bar and takeaway (July/Aug). TV room, multi sport pitch, boules, games room (July/Aug). Activities programme for all age groups. Internet access. Torches useful. Off site: Golf and horse riding 500 m. Supermarket and shops at Bréhal 4 km. Bus service from site entrance (Jul/Aug).

Open: 1 May - 30 September.

Directions

From North or South on D971 enter Bréhal. Leave on D592, signed Camping La Vanlée. Entering St. Martin de Bréhal follow signs for 'camping-golf'. Continue alongside golf course directly to site. GPS: 48.908405, -1.564897

Charges guide

Per unit incl. 2 persons and electricity (6A)	€ 15,00 - € 18,20
extra person	€ 3,70 - € 4,55

For latest campsite news, availability and prices visit

alanrogers.com

Breville-sur-Mer

Kawan Village la Route Blanche

F-50290 Breville-sur-Mer (Manche) T: 02 33 50 23 31. E: larouteblanche@camping-breville.com

alanrogers.com/FR50150

La Route Blanche has a bright and cheerful atmosphere and Philippe and Corinne, the owners, are working continually to make an excellent site even better. The 140 pitches for touring are average in size, numbered, on well-cut grass and divided by young conifers. There are many shrubs and flowers and mature trees give shade to some areas. 67 pitches have 6/10A electricity and long leads may be necessary for some. Although the site does not have its own restaurant, there are five to choose from within a short distance. Three hundred and twenty square metres of swimming pool complex with exceptional facilities for people with disabilities will be enjoyed by all. If golf is your game, then you will not be disappointed. There is an 18-hole course and a nine-hole course only 400 m. away. The area has the highest tides in Europe and each visitor to the site is given a current tide timetable. The sandy beach is only 800 m. away and there are several walking routes way-marked through the dunes. A new building to house the bar will now be up and running. Corinne cooks moules and frites a couple of times in the high season for site visitors and on-site entertainment is arranged during July and August. Late arrivals are not accepted after 21.00 hours. WiFi is available all round the site.

Facilities

Well maintained sanitary facilities with British style toilets, washbasins in cabins and showers. Good provision for disabled visitors. Laundry and dishwashing facilities. Bread available all season. Bar and takeaway (July/Aug). Large swimming pool complex. Play area. Multisports court. Entertainment in high season. WiFi (charged). Off site: Golf opposite. Fishing 500 m. Riding 1 km. Boat trips to the Channel Islands and the Isles de Chausey from Granville. Le Mont St Michel. Cruises on board old tall ships. Shops, restaurants and supermarket at Donville -les-Bains 3 km.

Open: 1 April - 17 October.

Directions

Take D971 that runs between Granville and Coutance. Then one of the roads west to Breville-sur-Mer. The site is well signed.
GPS: 48.869658, -1.563873

Charges guide

Per unit incl. 2 persons and electricity	€ 22,00 - € 33,00
extra person	€ 4,50 - € 6,00
child (2-7 yrs)	free - € 4,80
dog	€ 2,50 - € 3,00

For latest campsite news, availability and prices visit

alanrogers.com

Carentan

Flower Camping Le Haut Dick

30 chemin du Grand Bas Pays, F-50500 Carentan (Manche) T: 02 33 42 16 89
E: contact@camping-lehautdick.com alanrogers.com/FR50240

Le Haut Dick is located at the heart of south Cotentin peninsula. On the banks of the Haut Dick canal, this is a simple campsite but offers all comforts required. It comprises 120 good-sized pitches which are flat, grassy and well divided by hedges. The village of Carentan is a 10 minute walk away and features a brand new pool complex. Le Haut Dick is an ideal departure point for visiting the Landing Beaches, such as Omaha Beach, and Arromanche. The famous Mont Saint-Michel is also a short drive.

Facilities

Sanitary buildings include showers, baby rooms and facilities for disabled visitors. Washing machine. Snack bar. Table tennis. Minigolf. Play area. Bicycle hire. Boules courts. Accommodation to rent.

Open: 1 April - 15 October.

Directions

Leave the A13 and follow the RN13 and then the E46 to Carentan. GPS: 49.309859, -1.238869

Charges guide

Per unit incl. 2 persons and electricity	€ 15,00 - € 17,00
extra person	€ 3,50
child (under 7 yrs)	€ 2,50
dog	€ 1,50

For latest campsite news, availability and prices visit
alanrogers.com

Courtils

Camping Saint Michel

35 route du Mont Saint Michel, F-50220 Courtils (Manche) T: 02 33 70 96 90
E: infos@campingsaintmichel.com alanrogers.com/FR50110

This delightful site is owned and run by an enthusiastic young couple, the Duchesnes. It is located in a peaceful, rural setting, yet is only 8 km. from the busy tourist attraction of Mont St Michel. The site has 100 pitches which include 43 for touring units and 30 for mobile homes to rent. Electricity connections (6A) are available to all pitches and many trees and shrubs provide a good amount of shade. From the restaurant and its terrace overlooking the pool, the site slopes gently down to a small enclosure of farm animals kept to entertain children and adults alike. Meet Nestor and Napoléon, the donkeys and Linotte the mare, as well as miniature goats, sheep, chickens and ducks. It is the intention of M. and Mme. Duschesne to maintain a quiet and peaceful site, hence there are no discos or organised clubs.

Facilities

Two small, well maintained toilet blocks have washbasins in cubicles and pushbutton showers. Separate laundry. Baby room. En-suite facilities for disabled visitors. Motorcaravan service point. Shop (all season) and bar (15/3-15/10). Restaurant and takeaway (15/6-10/9). Heated swimming pool (1/5-20/9). Animal farm. Play area. Games room. Bicycle hire. Internet access and WiFi in reception area. Off site: Fishing (sea) 2 km, (river) 6 km. Riding 9 km. Sailing 25 km. Beach 2 km. or for swimming 30 km.

Open: 11 February - 13 November.

Directions

Courtils is 8 km. east of Mont Saint-Michel. From south on A84 and from north on A84/N175 leave at junction 33/34 and follow signs for Mont Saint Michel (N175/D43) and Courtils. From St Malo take D137 south and join N176 east to Pontorson where it becomes N175. In 12 km. turn northwest on D43 signed Courtils. Site is through village on left. GPS: 48.627616, -1.416

Charges 2011

Per unit incl. 2 persons and electricity	€ 17,40 - € 23,40

Falaise

Camping Municipal du Château

3 rue du Val d'Ante, F-14700 Falaise (Calvados) T: 02 31 90 16 55. E: camping@falaise.fr
alanrogers.com/FR14100

The location of this site is really quite spectacular, lying in the shadow of the Château of William the Conqueror, within walking distance of the historic town of Falaise in the 'coeur de Normandie'. The site itself is small, with only 66 pitches (most with electricity) either beside the little river, on a terrace above or on gently sloping ground. With trees and hedges providing some shade as well as open grassed areas, this site has a rather intimate 'up-market' feel about it, different from the average municipal site. Charges are reasonable and the reception friendly.

Facilities

Although the sanitary facilities are dated, they are of good quality and kept clean. Free hot water to showers, washbasins in cubicles for ladies and laundry and dishwashing sinks (all closed overnight). Unit for disabled visitors (shower room and separate WC). Motorcaravan service point. Excellent new play area for younger children. New tennis courts and boules pitch. TV room. Fishing. Free WiFi access. Off site: Bicycle hire 300 m. Riding 500 m. Tree-top adventure park 17 km. Kayak club with canoe hire and river descent 19 km.

Open: 1 May - 30 September.

Directions

Falaise is 35 km. southeast of Caen on the route to Alençon and le Mans. Site on western side of town, well signed from ring road. From N158 heading south take first roundabout into Falaise and follow site signs through residential suburb to site. GPS: 48.89556, -0.20468

Charges guide

Per unit incl. 2 persons and electricity	€ 16,60
extra person	€ 3,80
child (3-12 yrs)	€ 2,70

For latest campsite news, availability and prices visit
alanrogers.com

Fiquefleur-Equainville

Camping du Domaine Catinière

Route de Honfleur, F-27210 Fiquefleur-Equainville (Eure) T: 02 32 57 63 51. E: info@camping-catiniere.com

alanrogers.com/FR27020

A peaceful, friendly site, close to the Normandy coast, in the countryside yet in the middle of a very long village, this site is steadily achieving a modern look, whilst retaining its original French flavour. In addition to 19 rental and 24 privately owned mobile homes, there are 87 pitches for touring units, plus a large open field for tents and units not needing electricity. Caravan pitches are separated, some with shade, others are more open and all have electricity hook-ups. The site is divided by well fenced streams, popular with young anglers. The site is a good base for visiting this part of Normandy. The pretty harbour town of Honfleur is less than 5 km. away and the nearby Vallée de la Risle is worth a visit. A Sites et Paysages member.

Facilities

Toilet facilities include mostly British style WCs, some washbasins in cubicles, and facilities for disabled visitors and babies. Washing machine and dryer. Reception with shop. Small bar/restaurant with regional dishes and snacks. Heated swimming pool with slides and flume (1/6-15/9). Two playgrounds. Trampoline. Children's farm. Boules. Barrier (card deposit). Off site: Large supermarket close to southern end of the bridge. Smaller supermarket in Beuzeville 7 km. Beach 7 km. Golf 15 km.

Open: 8 April - 19 September.

Directions

From the Pont de Normandie (toll bridge). Take first exit on leaving bridge (exit 3, A29) signed Honfleur. At roundabout turn left under motorway in direction of Le Mans and Alencon on D180. Take second exit on right after about 2.5 km, onto D22 towards Beuzeville. Site is on right after about 1 km. GPS: 49.40090, 0.30608

Charges 2011

Per unit incl. 2 persons	
and electricity	€ 20,00 - € 27,00
extra person	€ 4,00 - € 6,00
child (under 7 yrs)	€ 3,00 - € 4,00
dog	€ 2,00

Credit cards accepted (minimum of € 70).

Hautot-sur-Mer

Camping la Source

Petit Appeville, F-76550 Hautot-sur-Mer (Seine-Maritime) T: 02 35 84 27 04. E: info@camping-la-source.fr
alanrogers.com/FR76040

This friendly, attractive site with a new heated pool is just four kilometres from Dieppe and is useful for those using the Newhaven-Dieppe ferry crossing either as a one night stop-over or for a few days' break before heading on. The 120 pitches (54 with electricity 10A) are flat and there is some shade. There are good hardstandings for motorcaravans. The site is quietly located in a valley with the only disturbance from the occasional passing train. A fast-flowing small river runs along one border (not protected for young children).

Facilities	Directions
A good, clean single toilet block (unisex) includes washbasins in cubicles and mainly British style WCs. Unit for disabled campers, but unmade gravel roads may cause problems. Laundry facilities. Motorcaravan service point. Small bar and terrace. Swimming pool. Playing field. TV and games rooms. Fishing. Bicycle hire. Mobile homes (3) for rent. Off site: Supermarket in Dieppe. Baker in the village. Riding 2 km. Beach 3 km. Golf 4 km.	From Dieppe follow D925 west to Fécamp. At foot of descent at traffic lights in Petit Appeville turn left. From west, turn right (signed D153 St Aubin). Just after railway, turn left under bridge and ahead on narrow road (limited passing places). Site is shortly on the left. GPS: 49.89846, 1.05694

Open: 15 March - 15 October.

Charges guide

Per unit incl. 2 persons and electricity	€ 20,70 - € 23,70
extra person	€ 4,90 - € 5,40
Camping Cheques accepted.	

Honfleur

Camping la Briquerie

Equemauville, F-14600 Honfleur (Calvados) T: 02 31 89 28 32. E: info@campinglabriquerie.com
alanrogers.com/FR14180

La Briquerie is a large, neat municipal site on the outskirts of the attractive and popular harbour town of Honfleur. Very well cared for and efficiently run by a family team, the site has 420 pitches, many of which are let on a seasonal basis. There are also 130 hedged touring pitches. All have electricity (5/10A), water and drainage. Among the main attractions here are the splendid swimming complex with indoor and outdoor pools, and the close proximity to Honfleur where one can watch the fishing boats from the quay or browse the work of the artists who display their paintings in the galleries around the town.

Facilities	Directions
Two toilet blocks with washbasins in cubicles and showers. Good facilities for disabled visitors. Laundry room. Restaurant (July/Aug). Takeaway (1/6-15/9). Bar (1/6-30/9). Small shop (July/Aug). Large pool complex with two flumes (15/5-15/9). Sauna. Jacuzzi. Fitness room. Boules. Minigolf. Multisport pitch. TV. Internet and WiFi. Off site: Supermarket adjacent. Riding and bicycle hire 1 km. Beach 2 km. Fishing 5 km. Golf 7 km.	Site is well signed from Honfleur on D579, beside the Intermarché on D62. GPS: 49.39735, 0.20849

Open: 1 April - 30 September.

Charges guide

Per unit incl. 2 persons, electricity, water and drainage	€ 20,80 - € 26,80
extra person	€ 5,40 - € 7,40
child (2-7 yrs)	€ 3,00 - € 4,00
No credit cards.	

Houlgate

Camping de la Vallée

88 rue de la Vallée, F-14510 Houlgate (Calvados) T: 02 31 24 40 69. E: camping.lavallee@wanadoo.fr
alanrogers.com/FR14070

Camping de la Vallée is an attractive site with good, well maintained facilities, situated on the rolling hillside above the seaside resort of Houlgate. The original farmhouse building has been converted to house a bar/brasserie and a comfortable TV lounge and billiards room overlooking the pool. The site has 373 pitches with 98 for touring units. Large, open and separated by hedges, all the pitches have 4/6A electricity and some also have water and drainage. Part of the site is sloping, the rest level, with gravel and tarmac roads. Shade is provided by a variety of well kept trees and shrubs.

Facilities	Directions
Three good toilet blocks include washbasins in cabins, mainly British style toilets, facilities for disabled visitors and baby bathrooms. Laundry facilities (no washing lines allowed). Motorcaravan services. Shop (from 1/5). Bar. Snack bar with takeaway in season (from 15/5). Heated swimming pool (1/5-30/9; no shorts). Games room. Playground. Bicycle hire. Entertainment in Jul/Aug. Internet access. Only one dog per pitch. Off site: Riding 500 m. Beach, town, fishing 1 km. Golf 2 km.	From A13 take exit for Cabourg and follow D400 to Dives-sur-Mer, then D513 (Houlgate/Deauville) until you reach the sea front. After 1 km. at lights turn right and follow site signs to campsite on right in about 1 km. GPS: 49.2940, -0.0683

Open: 1 April - 30 September.

Charges guide

Per unit incl. 2 persons and electricity (4A)	€ 21,00 - € 30,00
extra person	€ 5,00 - € 6,00
Camping Cheques accepted.	

For latest campsite news, availability and prices visit

alanrogers.com

Jumièges

Camping de la Forêt

Rue Mainberthe, F-76480 Jumièges (Seine-Maritime) T: 02 35 37 93 43. E: info@campinglaforet.com

alanrogers.com/FR76130

This is a pretty family site with a friendly, relaxed atmosphere. It is located just 10 km. from the A13 Paris - Caen autoroute. Cars and smaller motorcaravans can approach by ferry across the River Seine (not caravans). Formerly a municipal site, it has recently been taken over by the Hoste family. The 111 grassy pitches (84 for tourers) are attractively located in woodland. Many pitches have some shade and all have 10A electrical connections. There is a separate area for tents. The site organises some activities in high season and these include treasure hunts and guided walks.

Facilities	Directions
Two modern toilet blocks, maintained to a good standard with British toilets, some basins in cubicles and preset showers. Baby room. Facilities for disabled visitors. Laundry facilities. Motorcaravan service point. Shop. Baker calls daily. Small swimming pool and paddling pool (heated 1/6-15/9). Playground. Boules. Games room. Bicycle hire. Chalets and mobile homes to let. Off site: Bar/restaurant 600 m. Riding and golf 8 km. **Open:** 11 April - 25 October.	From A29, exit 8, follow Yvetot - Pont de Brotonne. Before bridge, turn left and follow signs for Le Trait and Jumièges. Site clearly signed. GPS: 49.43487, 0.82897

Charges guide

Per unit incl. 2 persons and electricity	€ 21,00 - € 23,50
extra person	€ 4,50

Le Rozel

Camping Le Ranch

F-50340 Le Rozel (Manche) T: 02 33 10 07 10. E: contact@camping-leranch.com

alanrogers.com/FR50230

Le Ranch is a pleasantly situated, family run site with direct access to a long and wide sandy beach that extends to some 3 km. The reception area is well presented and has a small shop that stocks all the basic provisions. An outdoor pool complex has a large heated pool, paddling pool and a small separate pool with water slides. The whole area is surrounded by clear screening and incorporates ample space with sun loungers for soaking up the sunshine. Access to site is controlled by a magnetic key, which is also used to activate the showers in the splendid sanitary block. Touring pitches are large and well defined by small hedges; some are on raised terraces but are easily accessed.

Facilities	Directions
One modern heated toilet block was spotlessly clean. Sinks in closed cabins and showers operated by barrier entry key. Baby changing area. Facilities for disabled visitors. Laundry and dishwashing area. Shop for basics and beach toys. Bar with TV, pizzeria. Games area with pool table, electronic games and table tennis. Outdoor pool complex with heated pool. Children's play area. Exercise machines. Boules. TV in bar. Barbecue areas. WiFi (charged). Off site: Restaurant by site entrance. Riding and bicycle hire 4 km. Fishing and golf 15 km. **Open:** 1 April - 30 September.	Heading to or from Cherbourg on D650, 3 km. South of Les Pieux take D62 signed Le Rozel. D62 leads directly to the site which is well signed. GPS: 49.480199, -1.842055

Charges guide

Per unit incl. 2 persons and electricity	€ 21,60 - € 32,20
extra person	€ 4,20 - € 6,50
child (3-11 yrs)	€ 3,00 - € 5,00
dog	€ 2,10 - € 2,30

Le Tréport

Camping Municipal les Boucaniers

Rue Pierre Mendès France, F-76470 Le Tréport (Seine-Maritime) T: 02 35 86 35 47

E: camping@ville-le-treport.fr **alanrogers.com/FR76110**

This is a large, good quality, municipal site which has undergone redevelopment. It has an attractive entrance and some floral displays, tarmac roads and site lighting. The 193 touring pitches (176 with electricity 6A: some long leads necessary) are on level grass, some with dividing hedges, and trees to provide a little shade. There are 22 good quality wooden chalets for rent, and some privately owned mobile homes. A small unit acts as shop, bar and takeaway all season, the baker calls daily in high season, and every day except Monday in low season.

Facilities	Directions
Three well equipped sanitary blocks (one can be heated) provide mainly British style WCs, washbasins in cubicles, preset hot showers, with new facilities for small children and disabled visitors in one block. Multisport court. Minigolf. Boules. Max 2 dogs on site. Off site: Tennis, football and gymnasium nearby. Fishing, golf and beach 2 km. Riding 3 km. Markets at Le Tréport (Mon and Sat) and at Eu (Fri). **Open:** 1 April - 30 September.	From D925 Abbeville - Dieppe road take D1915 towards Le Tréport centre. At new roundabout take first exit to right and site entrance is 150 m. on the right in rue Pierre Mendès-France. GPS: 50.05772, 1.38870

Charges guide

Per unit incl. 2 persons and electricity	€ 20,60
extra person	€ 4,00
child (3-12 yrs)	€ 2,80

For latest campsite news, availability and prices visit

alanrogers.com

Les Pieux

Kawan Village le Grand Large

F-50340 Les Pieux (Manche) T: 02 33 52 40 75. E: info@legrandlarge.com
alanrogers.com/FR50060

Le Grand Large is a well established, quality family site with direct access to a long sandy beach and within a 20 km. drive of Cherbourg. It is a neat and tidy site with 147 touring pitches divided and separated by hedging giving an orderly, well laid out and attractive appearance. A separate area has 40 mobile homes for rent. The reception area is at the entrance (with a security barrier) and the forecourt is decorated with flower beds. To the rear of the site and laid out in the sandhills is an excellent play area with swings, slides and climbing frame. Not surprisingly the sandy beach is the big attraction. The length of units is restricted to eight metres to prevent any problems accessing pitches. Roads around the site are tarmac and many of the delightful plants and shrubs that you see bordering these carry name tags in four languages. The pleasant views from the site stretch across the bay to the tip of the Cherbourg peninsula. Every effort is made at Le Grand Large to attract and cater for families with young children, so noisy entertainment is not an option. Most of the pitches have electricity, water and drainage and the site owner hopes that this will extend to all pitches in the near future. Plans are also in place to replace the showers in all the cubicles.

Facilities

Two well maintained toilet blocks, the main one modern with washbasins in cubicles and some family rooms. WCs are mostly to the outside of the building. Provision for disabled visitors. Baby bathroom. Laundry area. Motorcaravan services. Shop for basics, bar (all season). Restaurant and takeaway (3/7-28/8). Swimming and paddling pools (24/4-19/9). Play area. Tennis. Boules. Fishing. TV room. Some entertainment (July/Aug). WiFi (charged). Off site: Bicycle hire and riding 5 km. Golf 15 km. Two supermarkets in Les Pieux. Day trips by ferry to the Channel Islands (May-Sept) from nearby Diellete.

Open: 10 April - 19 September.

Directions

From Cherbourg port take N13 south for about 2 km. Branch right on D650 (previously D904) signed Cartaret. Continue for 18 km. to Les Pieux. Take D4 in town and turn left just after 'Super U' supermarket. Follow site signs via D117/517. GPS: 49.49452, -1.84246

Charges guide

Per unit incl. 2 persons and electricity	€ 21,00 - € 35,00
extra person	€ 4,50 - € 7,00
child (under 18 yrs)	€ 3,00 - € 4,00

Luc-sur-Mer

Camping la Capricieuse

2 rue Brummel, F-14530 Luc-sur-Mer (Calvados) T: 02 31 97 34 43. E: info@campinglacapricieuse.com
alanrogers.com/FR14170

La Capricieuse is situated on the edge of the delightful small seaside town of Luc-sur-Mer. It is an ideal location for visiting the D-Day landing beaches, which are just a few minutes drive from the Ouistreham car ferry. This immaculate site has 204 touring pitches of varying sizes, most are on level grass with hedges and a variety of trees giving some shade; 105 have electricity and 52 also have water and drainage. Although the site does not have its own shop, bar or restaurant, these can be found within walking distance in Luc-sur-Mer.

Facilities

Three modern toilet blocks with washbasins in cubicles and showers are kept very clean. Fully equipped facilities for disabled visitors. Laundry and dishwashing facilities. Motorcaravan service point. Large TV room. Games room with WiFi. Adventure playground (unfenced). Tennis. Boules. Off site: Fishing and bicycle hire nearby. Beach 200 m. Riding 3 km. Public transport outside main gate.

Open: 1 April - 30 September.

Directions

Take the D514 from Ouistreham car ferry and head west to Luc-sur-Mer. Campsite is well signed from the western end of St Luc. GPS: 49.31797, -0.35780

Charges guide

Per unit incl. 2 persons and electricity	€ 19,05
extra person	€ 4,55

For latest campsite news, availability and prices visit

alanrogers.com

Marcilly-sur-Eure

Domaine de Marcilly

Route de Saint-Andre-de-l'Eure, F-27810 Marcilly-sur-Eure (Eure) T: 02 37 48 45 42
E: domainedemarcilly@wanadoo.fr alanrogers.com/FR27060

Just between Ile de France and Normandy, less than an hour's drive from Paris, Domaine de Marcilly is beautifully located in a 15 hectare park, surrounded by pine, oak and birch trees. Although most pitches are dedicated to mobile homes, this park also welcomes motorcaravans and each pitch has a picnic table. Leisure facilities include a swimming pool and two tennis courts. There are paths and cycle routes through the parkland and surrounding countryside, as well as riding and fishing. The site is well located for exploring the northern Loire and both Chartres and Paris are within easy reach. The département of the Eure is less well known but has much of interest, including the cathedral city of Evreux and Monet's gardens at Giverny.

Facilities

The sanitary block provides hot showers, washbasins, laundry room and facilities for disabled visitors. Washing machine. Motorcaravan service point. Heated swimming pool (1/6-30/9). Boules. Tennis. Internet point. TV room. Animation and entertainment during high season. WiFi. Off site: Local shops 900 m. Riding 3 km. Golf 10 km. Canoeing. Walking and cycling routes.

Open: All year.

Directions

From Paris A13, A12 exit onto N12 for Houdan, take exit Goussainville, Havelu, Bu, then Marcilly. Site is on the D52 in the direction of St Andre.
GPS: 48.8252, 1.3237

Charges guide

Per unit incl. 2 persons	€ 18,00 - € 21,00
child (3-10 yrs)	€ 2,50 - € 3,00
electricity	€ 3,00

For weekends and holidays in Normandy
Come and discover the Domaine de Marcilly on
the borders of Ile de France and Normandy

Route de Saint-Andre de l'Eure - F-27810 Marcilly sur Eure - France
Tel.: 02 37 48 45 42 - Fax: 02 37 48 51 11
Email: domainedemarcilly@wanadoo.fr - www.domainedemarcilly.com

Martragny

Castel Camping le Château de Martragny

F-14740 Martragny (Calvados) T: 02 31 80 21 40. E: chateau.martragny@wanadoo.fr
alanrogers.com/FR14030

Martragny is an attractive site in a parkland setting adjoining the château. Close to D-Day beaches, it is also convenient for the ports of Caen and Cherbourg, and has the facilities and charm to encourage both long stays and stopovers. The pleasant lawns surrounding and approaching the château take 160 units, with electricity connections for 140. Most pitches are divided by either a small hedge or a few trees. Bed and breakfast (en-suite) accommodation is available in the château all year (reservation essential). Madame de Chassey takes great pride in the site and takes care that peace and quiet is preserved. This is a perfect place for a quiet relaxing holiday yet only 12 km. from the sea, the wartime landing beaches, the excellent museum at Arromanche, the Bayeux tapestry or the Calvados 'cider route'.

Facilities

Three modernised sanitary blocks include washbasins in cabins, sinks for dishes and clothes and two baby baths. Disabled visitors are well catered for. Good laundry. Shop (all season). Takeaway food and bar (24/5-10/9). Swimming pool (20x6 m) and paddling pool heated in poor weather. Play areas. Tennis. Minigolf. Games and TV room. Fishing. Off site: Riding 1 km. Beach 15 km. Golf 20 km.

Open: 1 May - 12 September.

Directions

Site is off the N13, 8 km. southeast of Bayeux. Take Martragny exit from dual carriageway.
GPS: 49.24941, -0.60237

Charges 2011

Per unit incl. 2 persons and electricity	€ 29,50 - € 33,50
extra person	€ 6,50 - € 7,50
child (under 7 yrs)	€ 3,00 - € 3,50
dog	free
Camping Cheques accepted.	

For latest campsite news, availability and prices visit
alanrogers.com

Maupertus-sur-Mer

Castel Camping Caravaning l'Anse du Brick

Route du Val de Saire, F-50330 Maupertus-sur-Mer (Manche) T: 02 33 54 33 57
E: welcome@anse-du-brick.com alanrogers.com/FR50070

A friendly, family site, l'Anse du Brick overlooks a picturesque bay on the northern tip of the Cotentin peninsula, eight kilometres east of Cherbourg port. This quality site makes a pleasant night halt or an ideal longer stay destination for those not wishing to travel too far. Its pleasing location offers direct access to a small sandy beach and a woodland walk. This is a mature, terraced site with magnificent views from certain pitches. Tarmac roads lead to the 117 touring pitches (all with 10A electricity) which are level, separated and mostly well shaded by many trees, bushes and shrubs. Beyond the site lie miles of walking tracks through gorse-covered hills which, together with a stark rock face, surround the site and make it a sheltered suntrap. A gourmet restaurant is conveniently located just outside the site gates.

Facilities

New sanitary facilities are kept spotlessly clean and are well maintained. British style toilets, washbasins mainly in cubicles and pushbutton showers. Provision for disabled visitors. Laundry area. Motorcaravan service point. Shop (1/4-30/9). Restaurant and bar/pizzeria (1/5-10/9). Heated swimming pool (1/5-15/9). Tennis. Play area. Organised entertainment in season. Miniclub (6-12 yrs). Bicycle and kayak hire. Off site: Fishing 100 m. Riding 4 km. Golf 10 km.

Open: 1 April - 30 September.

Directions

From Cherbourg port follow signs for Caen and Rennes. After third roundabout, take slip road to right, under road towards Bretteville-en-Saire (D116). From southeast on N13 at first (Auchan) roundabout, take slip road to right towards Tourlaville (N13 car ferry), ahead at next roundabout, right at third lights on D116 to Bretteville. Continue for 7 km. Site signed to right. GPS: 49.66715, -1.48704

Charges guide

Per unit incl. 2 persons and electricity	€ 19,60 - € 44,50
extra person	€ 4,10 - € 7,20
child (3-12 yrs)	€ 3,20 - € 5,30

Merville-Franceville

Camping les Peupliers

Allée des Pins, F-14810 Merville-Franceville (Calvados) T: 02 31 24 05 07. E: asl-mondeville@wanadoo.fr
alanrogers.com/FR14190

Les Peupliers is run by friendly, family managers who keep this site attractive and tidy. It is just 300 metres from a long, wide, sandy beach. The touring pitches, of which there are 85, are on level open ground, all with 10A electricity. Those in the newest part are hedged but, with just a few trees on the edge of the site, there is little shade. The campsite amenities are near the entrance, housed in neat modern buildings. An animation programme for children and various activities are organised in high season. This site is ideally located for visiting Caen, Bayeux and the traditional seaside towns of Deauville and Trouville.

Facilities

Two excellent heated toilet blocks with washbasins in cabins and showers. Good facilities for disabled visitors and for babies. Laundry room. Small shop, bar with terrace and takeaway (all July/Aug). Heated outdoor swimming pool and paddling pool (May-Sept). Play area. Games room. Entertainment in high season. WiFi. Off site: Fishing, riding and golf all within 1 km. Bicycle hire 2 km. Public transport 400 m.

Open: 1 April - 31 October.

Directions

From Ouistreham take the D514 to Merville-Franceville. Site is well signed off Allée des Pins. From Rouen on A13 (exit 29B), take D400 to Cabourg then the D514 to Merville-Franceville. GPS: 49.28326, -0.17053

Charges guide

Per unit incl. 2 persons and electricity	€ 20,10 - € 26,80
extra person	€ 5,55 - € 6,90

THE MERVILLE BATTERY

The Merville Battery, a German army strongpoint in the Atlantic Wall, was situated at the eastern flank of the allied invasion of 6 June 1944.
Bombed ineffectively many times, it was neutralised by the British 9th Parachute Battalion after an incredible attack.
On this totally preserved historic site, an educational trail winds between the different bunkers and invites you to learn the story of the Merville Battery.
Every 20 minutes, you can experience "total immersion". Sound, light smoke and odours will convey you for a few short minutes into the hell that was the bombardment and the attack on the Battery.

The 9ᵗʰ Battalion
The Parachute Regiment

MUSÉE DE LA BATTERIE DE MERVILLE
Place du 9è Bataillon
14810 MERVILLE-FRANCEVILLE
Tél : 02 31 91 47 53
E-mail : museebatterie@wanadoo.fr
Web : www.batterie-merville.com

For latest campsite news, availability and prices visit

alanrogers.com

Merville-Franceville

Camping le Point du Jour

Route de Cabourg, F-14810 Merville-Franceville-Plage (Calvados) T: 02 31 24 23 34
E: camp.lepointdujour@wanadoo.fr alanrogers.com/FR14210

Camping le Point du Jour has a very French flavour and is an ideal location for family holidays as it has direct access to a fine sandy beach. There are 142 pitches bordered by shrubs and hedging, including 20 occupied by mobile homes and chalets (ten for hire). Although there are quite a few seasonal units, most have to be removed for high season. All touring pitches have 10A electricity, including those on the sea dyke looking down onto the beach. Facilities are simple, but there is a smart new heated pool with retractable roof.

Facilities

Two toilet blocks (one heated) provide washbasins in cubicles, pushbutton showers, and fairly basic facilities for babies and for disabled visitors. Laundry facilities. Motorcaravan service points. All-purpose room has small bar (serving basic drinks and snacks except in very low season), projector for films and football matches, pool table and exercise machines. Play area. Bicycle hire. Bread delivery. Entertainment and activity programme in high season. Internet access and WiFi in reception area. Off site: Fishing 0.5 km.

Open: 1 March - 15 November.

Directions

From A13 motorway at junction 29 take the D400 towards Dives-sur-Mer and bear left on D400a to Cabourg. Follow signs for Merville Franceville along D514. Site is on right in 2 km. From Ouistreham Car Ferry (16 km) follow signs for Caen and turn east on D514 over Pegasus Bridge and through Merville to site on left. GPS: 49.28319, -0.19098

Charges guide

Per unit incl. 2 persons	€ 20,00 - € 29,40
extra person	€ 4,80 - € 7,80

Pont-Audemer

Camping Caravaning des Etangs Risle-Seine

19 route des Etangs, Toutainville, F-27500 Pont-Audemer (Eure) T: 02 32 42 46 65.
E: camping@ville-pont-audemer.fr alanrogers.com/FR27010

This attractive and well maintained site is owned by the Pont-Audemer Council and run by an enthusiastic manager. It is well laid out with 61 hedged pitches on level grass and electricity connections for 28 of them. Fishing and watersports are possible as the site is positioned next to some large lakes, but swimming is not allowed. In high season a shuttle bus goes to Pont-Audemer where you will find shops, restaurants and a good swimming complex.

Facilities

Two well equipped and maintained toilet blocks with facilities for disabled visitors. They include washbasins in cabins and preset showers. Laundry and dishwashing facilities. Bar area with terrace (soft drinks only as there is no alcohol licence, visitors may bring their own). Bread and milk available. Paddling pool. Playing field. TV. Bicycle hire. Fishing. Takeaway food and courtesy bus (high season).

Open: 15 March - 15 November.

Directions

Approaching from north or south on D810, at the bridge over the River Risle, turn to the west on south side of river and travel 1.5 km. on rue des Etangs. Site is well signed. GPS: 49.3666, 0.48739

Charges guide

Per unit incl. 2 persons and electricity (10A)	€ 16,25 - € 17,70
extra person	€ 3,05
child (under 7 yrs)	€ 1,65

Pont-l'Evêque

Castel Camping du Brévedent

Le Brévedent, F-14130 Pont-l'Evêque (Calvados) T: 02 31 64 72 88. E: contact@campinglebrevedent.com
alanrogers.com/FR14090

Le Brévedent is a well established, traditional site with 144 pitches (109 for tourists, 31 used by tour operators) set in the grounds of an elegant 18th-century hunting pavilion. Pitches are either around the fishing lake, in the lower gardens (level), or in the old orchard (gently sloping). Most have electricity. It is an excellent holiday destination within easy reach of the Channel ports and its peaceful, friendly environment makes it ideal for mature campers or families with younger children (note: the lake is unfenced). Reception provides vast tourist information and English is spoken.

Facilities

Three toilet blocks include washbasins in cubicles and facilities for disabled visitors. Laundry facilities. Motorcaravan service point. Shop (baker delivers daily). Bar open evenings. Restaurant (24/5-19/9). Takeaway (1/5-25/9). Heated swimming and paddling pools (1/5-25/9). Playground. Minigolf. Boules. Games room. Fishing. Clubroom. Internet access. TV and library. Rowing. Bicycle and buggy hire. Entertainment and children's club (high season). Dogs are not accepted. Off site: Riding 1 km. Tennis. Golf 12 km. Beach 25 km.

Open: 28 April - 23 September.

Directions

Pont-l'Evêque is due south of Le Havre. Le Brévedent is 13 km. southeast from Pont-l'Evêque: take D579 toward Lisieux for 4 km. then D51 towards Moyaux. At Blangy le Château continue ahead on D51 to Le Brévedent. GPS: 49.22525, 0.30438

Charges guide

Per person	€ 5,20 - € 6,70
child (1-12 yrs)	€ 2,20 - € 4,50
pitch	€ 7,00 - € 9,00
electricity	€ 2,45 - € 3,20

For latest campsite news, availability and prices visit
alanrogers.com

Pontorson

Kawan Village Haliotis

Chemin des Soupirs, F-50170 Pontorson (Manche) T: 02 33 68 11 59. E: camping.haliotis@wanadoo.fr
alanrogers.com/FR50080

The staff at this beautiful campsite offer a warm welcome to visitors. Situated on the edge of the little town of Pontorson, the site has 152 pitches, including 118 for touring units. Most have 16A electricity and 34 really large ones also have water and drainage. Excellent private sanitary facilities are available on 12 'luxury' pitches. The comfortable reception area incorporates a pleasant bar opening onto the swimming pool terrace. The site is attractively laid out and includes a Japanese garden. Haliotis (which takes its name from a large shell) is next to the river Couesnon and it is possible to walk, cycle or canoe along the river to Mont Saint-Michel, 9 km. away. An auberge at half-distance could provide a welcome break! A good bus service is available from close to the site entrance to all major towns in the area.

Facilities

Well equipped heated toilet block with controllable showers and washbasins in cubicles. Good facilities for disabled visitors incorporating baby room. Laundry facilities. Bar where breakfast is served. Bread to order. Heated swimming pool with jacuzzi and separate paddling pool. Sauna and solarium. Good fenced play areas. Trampoline. Pétanque. Archery. Games room. Tennis court. Golf practice range. Multisport court. Outdoor fitness equipment. Bicycle hire. Fishing in the River Couesnon. Japanese garden and animal park. Club for children. Internet access in bar and WiFi throughout (both free). Off site: Local services including large supermarket, bars, restaurants and takeaways in Pontorson within easy walking distance. Riding 3 km. Bay 10 km. Beach 30 km.

Open: 18 March - 14 November.

Directions

Pontorson is 22 km. southwest of Avranches and is by-passed by the N176 which links with D137 from Saint Malo to the west and (via N175) with A84 (Caen - Rennes) to the east. Site is 300 m. north of the town centre and is well signed. NB. Entrance is on rue du Général Patton. Sat nav users should follow signs! GPS: 48.55836, -1.51429

Charges 2011

Per unit incl. 2 persons and electricity	€ 19,00 - € 24,50
with individual sanitary facility	€ 22,50 - € 30,00
extra person	€ 5,00 - € 6,00
child (under 12 yrs)	€ 2,00 - € 3,50

Camping Cheques accepted.

Camping ★★★ Haliotis
Located at 5mn from Mont-Saint-Michel along a river
NORMANDIE

Tel : +33(0)2 33 68 11 59   Fax : +33(0)2 33 58 95 36
info@camping-haliotis-mont-saint-michel.com

Port-en-Bessin

Sunêlia Port'land

Chemin du Castel, F-14520 Port-en-Bessin (Calvados) T: 02 31 51 07 06. E: campingportland@wanadoo.fr
alanrogers.com/FR14150

The Gerardin family will make you most welcome at Port'land, now a mature site lying 700 m. to the east of the little resort of Port-en-Bessin, one of Normandy's busiest fishing ports. The 300 pitches are large and grassy with 202 available for touring units, including 128 with 15A electricity. There is a separate area for tents without electricity. The camping area has been imaginatively divided into zones, some overlooking small fishing ponds and another radiating out from a central barbecue area. An attractive modern building houses reception and the good amenities which include a shop and a bar/restaurant with fine views over the Normandy coastline. A member of the Sunelia group.

Facilities

The two sanitary blocks are modern and well maintained. Special disabled facilities. Heated swimming pool (covered in low season) and paddling pool. Bar, restaurant, takeaway (all season). TV and games room. Multisports pitch. Fishing. Play area. WiFi . Off site: Nearest beach 4 km. 27-hole Omaha Beach International golf course adjacent. Fishing 600 m. Bicycle hire and riding 10 km. D-Day beaches. Colleville US war cemetery. Bayeux.

Open: 1 April - 3 November.

Directions

Site is clearly signed off the D514, 4 km. west of Port-en-Bessin. GPS: 49.3463, -0.7732

Charges 2011

Per unit incl. 2 persons and electricity	€ 20,50 - € 32,00
extra person	€ 5,00 - € 8,00
child (2-10 yrs)	€ 3,00 - € 5,00
dog	€ 3,00

For latest campsite news, availability and prices visit
alanrogers.com

Pourville sur Mer

Camping le Marqueval

1210 rue de la Mer, F-76550 Pourville sur Mer (Seine-Maritime) T: 02 35 82 66 46
E: contact@campinglemarqueval.com **alanrogers.com/FR76010**

Le Marqueval is a well established, family site of 290 pitches, located close to the seaside town of Hautot-sur-Mer, and has been developed around three small lakes (one unfenced, suitable for fishing). There are 60 grass pitches for touring units, all of a good size, separated by hedges and 40 with electrical connections (6A). The majority of the pitches are used for privately owned mobile homes. Leisure amenities include a swimming pool and smaller children's pools. The site's bar also functions as a snack bar and during the high season evening entertainment is occasionally organized here. The site's owners will be happy to recommend places of interest in the area and these include Dieppe, with its old town, and the stylish resort of Le Tréport. This stretch of the Normandy coastline is well known for its towering white cliffs and fine sandy beaches. There are some superb coastal walks along the clifftops and quiet lanes, ideal for exploration by cycle.

Facilities

The single toilet block is at the entrance to the site. Motorcaravan service point (charge). Snack bar. Swimming pool. Fishing (charged). Playground. Entertainment and activity programme. Mobile homes for rent. Off site: Nearest beach 1.2 km. Riding 1.5 km. Tennis. Cycle and walking tracks. Dieppe 5 km. St Valery -en-Caux (fishing port). Supermarket in Dieppe.

Open: 17 March - 15 October.

Directions

Head west from Dieppe on the D925 as far as Hautot-sur-Mer. Then turn right onto the D153 towards Pourville. Site is well signed from here. GPS: 49.9088, 1.0406

Charges guide

Per unit incl. 2 persons	
and electricity	€ 16,50 - € 22,50
extra person	€ 4,00 - € 6,50

CAMPING LE MARQUEVAL** - 1210 RUE DE LA MER - 76550 POURVILLE SUR MER
TEL: 0033 235 82 66 46 - FAX: 0033 234 00 02 82
CONTACT@CAMPINGLEMARQUEVAL.COM - WWW.CAMPINGLEMARQUEVAL.COM

Ravenoville-Plage

Kawan Village le Cormoran

Ravenoville-Plage, F-50480 Sainte Mère-Eglise (Manche) T: 02 33 41 33 94. E: lecormoran@wanadoo.fr
alanrogers.com/FR50050

This welcoming, environmentally friendly, family run site, close to Cherbourg and Caen, is situated just across the road from a long sandy beach. It is also close to Utah beach and is ideally located for those wishing to visit the many museums, landing beaches and remembrance gardens of WW2. On flat, quite open ground, the site has 100 good size pitches on level grass, all with 6A electricity. Some extra large pitches are available. The well kept pitches are separated by mature hedges and the site is decorated with flowering shrubs. A covered pool, sauna and gym are among recent improvements. These facilities, plus a shop, comfortable bar and takeaway are open all season. This modern, clean and fresh looking campsite caters for both families and couples and would be ideal for a holiday in this interesting area of France. The country roads provide opportunities for exploring on foot or by bike.

Facilities

Four well maintained toilet blocks, one heated, are of varying styles and ages. Laundry facilities. Shop. Bar and terrace. Snacks and takeaway. Outdoor pool (1/6-15/9, unsupervised). New covered pool, sauna and gym. Play areas. Tennis. Boules. Entertainment, TV and games room. Billiard golf. Playing field with archery (July/Aug). Hairdresser and beauty therapist. Bicycle and shrimp net hire. Riding (July/Aug). Communal barbecues. WiFi (charged). Off site: Beach 20 m. Golf 3 km.

Open: 2 April - 25 September.

Directions

From N13 take Ste Mère-Eglise exit and in centre of town take road to Ravenoville (6 km), then Ravenoville-Plage (3 km). Just before beach turn right and site is 500 m. GPS: 49.46643, -1.23533

Charges guide

Per unit incl. 1 or 2 persons	
and electricity	€ 20,00 - € 32,00
extra person	€ 4,00 - € 7,50
child (5-10 yrs)	€ 2,00 - € 3,00

Larger pitches available (extra charge).

For latest campsite news, availability and prices visit

alanrogers.com

Saint Arnoult

Camping la Vallée de Deauville

Avenue de la Vallée, F-14800 Saint Arnoult (Calvados) T: 02 31 88 58 17. E: contact@camping-deauville.com
alanrogers.com/FR14200

Close to the traditional seaside resorts of Deauville and Trouville, this large, modern site is owned and run by a delightful Belgian couple. With a total of 450 pitches, there are many mobile homes, both for rent and privately owned, and 150 are used for touring units. These pitches are level, of a reasonable size and mostly hedged, and 60 have 10A electricity connections. A brand new pool complex complete with flumes, lazy river, jacuzzi and fun pool makes an attractive focal point near the entrance and there is a large fishing lake. The bar and restaurant are large and comfortable and there is a very good shop on the site. Several of the World War Two Normandy landing beaches are easily accessible from the site and the well equipped reception area holds plenty of information on these. Markets are plentiful and a different one can be visited each day. The area is well served by public transport and a bus stops just by the gate en route to Trouville and Deauville where you can enjoy the vast expanse of beach or perhaps rub shoulders with a celebrity or two. The wide sandy beaches of this coast are 3 km. With the various new developments at this site, it promises to be a good choice in the Deauville and Caen area.

Facilities

Two heated toilet blocks with showers and washbasins in cubicles. Good facilities for babies and disabled visitors. Laundry facilities. Small shop, bar and restaurant (high season). Takeaway (all season). New swimming pool complex. Good play area and play room. Entertainment in high season. WiFi (charged). Off site: Beach 3 km. Golf and riding 2 km. Bicycle hire 3 km.

Open: 1 April - 31 October.

Directions

From the north, take the A29, then the A13 at Pont l'Eveque. Join the N177 (Deauville/Trouville) and after 9 km. take the D27 signed St Arnoult. Site is well signed on edge of village. GPS: 49.32864, 0.086

Charges guide

Per unit incl. 2 persons	
and electricity	€ 20,40 - € 34,00
extra person	€ 5,40 - € 9,00
child (0-7 yrs)	€ 3,00 - € 5,00
dog	€ 2,40 - € 4,00

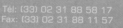

Saint Aubin-sur-Mer

Yelloh! Village la Côte de Nacre

Rue du Général Moulton, F-14750 Saint Aubin-sur-Mer (Calvados) T: 02 31 97 14 45
E: info@yellohvillage-cote-de-nacre.com alanrogers.com/FR14010

La Côte de Nacre is a large, commercial site with many facilities, all of a high standard. This could be an ideal holiday location for families with older children and teenagers. Two thirds of the site is given over to mobile homes and there are four tour operators on the site. The touring pitches are reasonable, both in size and condition. With pleasant, well cared for flowerbeds, there is some hedging to the pitches, but not much, and a few trees, so little shade. There is a 'state of the art' pool complex which includes a covered pool (with lifeguards in attendance).

Facilities

One open toilet block has showers and washbasins in cubicles. Laundry room. Bar, restaurant and takeaway. Pool complex with outdoor and indoor pools, slides, etc. Play area. Library. Games room. Children's club. Multisports area. Ice skating. Off site: Town 1 km.

Open: 2 April - 26 September.

Directions

Travel west from Ouistreham on D514 to St Aubin-sur-Mer. Site is well signed, just off the main road in a residential area. GPS: 49.322333, -0.387333

Charges guide

Per unit incl. 2 persons and electricity	€ 20,00 - € 44,00
extra person	€ 5,00 - € 8,00

Saint Jean-de-la-Riviere

Yelloh! Village les Vikings

4 rue des Vikings, Saint Jean-de-la-Rivière, F-50270 Barneville-Carteret (Manche) T: 04 66 73 97 39
E: info@yellohvillage-lesvikings.com alanrogers.com/FR50200

Les Vikings is located close to the attractive resort of Barneville-Carteret on the western side of the Cherbourg peninsula. The site is just 400 m. from a sandy beach. There are 250 pitches of which around 70 are reserved for touring, the rest being occupied by mobile homes and chalets, some of which are for rent. Pitches are grassy and of a reasonable size. Most of the site's amenities are grouped around the entrance and these include a swimming pool (covered and heated), a restaurant/pizzeria and bar as well as a grocery shop. During the whole season, various activities are organised including discos and karaoke evenings.

Facilities

Shop. Bar. Restaurant, snack bar and takeaway. Swimming pool. Games room. Play area. Activity and entertainment programme. Mobile homes for rent. Off site: Supermarket. Trips to the Channel Islands and D-day beaches. Mont St-Michel.

Open: 27 March - 4 October.

Directions

From Cherbourg, head southwest on the D650 to Barneville-Carteret. Site is at St Jean-de-la-Rivière, just to the south of the town and clearly signed. GPS: 49.3641, -1.75347

Charges guide

Per unit incl. 2 persons and electricity	€ 15,00 - € 39,00
extra person	€ 5,00 - € 7,00
child (3-7 yrs)	free - € 5,00

Saint Pair-sur-Mer

Castel Camping le Château de lez Eaux

Saint Aubin-des-Préaux, F-50380 Saint Pair-sur-Mer (Manche) T: 02 33 51 66 09. E: bonjour@lez-eaux.com
alanrogers.com/FR50030

Set in the spacious grounds of a château, Lez Eaux lies in a rural situation just off the main route south, under two hours from Cherbourg. There are 229 pitches of which 113 are for touring, all with electricity (5/10A) and 70 fully serviced. Most of the pitches are of a very good size, partly separated by trees and shrubs on either flat or very slightly sloping, grassy ground overlooking Normandy farmland or beside a small lake (with carp and other fish). There is a considerable tour operator presence, but these units by no means dominate, being generally tucked away in their own areas.

Facilities

Three modern clean toilet blocks include hot showers and washbasins in cabins, facilities for children and babies, and for disabled visitors. Shop, small bar, snacks and takeaway (all from 1/5). Small heated swimming pool and indoor tropical-style fun pool (from 1/5, no T-shirts or Bermuda-style shorts). Play area. Tennis. Games and TV rooms. Bicycle hire. Lake fishing. Torches useful. Internet access and WiFi (charged). Only one dog per pitch. Off site: Beach 4 km. Riding 5 km. Golf 7 km. Markets in Granville and Avranches (Sat), St Pair (Thu).

Open: 1 April - 15 September.

Directions

Lez Eaux is just to the west of the D973 about 17 km. northwest of Avranches and 7 km. southeast of Granville. Site is between the two turnings east to St Aubin-des-Préaux and well signed. GPS: 48.79778, -1.52498

Charges guide

Per unit incl. 2 persons and electricity	€ 21,00 - € 47,50
extra person	€ 8,00
child (under 7 yrs)	€ 6,00
dog	free

For latest campsite news, availability and prices visit
alanrogers.com

Saint Symphorien-le-Valois

Camping l'Etang des Haizes

43 rue Cauticotte, F-50250 Saint Symphorien-le-Valois (Manche) T: 02 33 46 01 16
E: info@campingetangdeshaizes.com alanrogers.com/FR50000

This is an attractive and very friendly site with a swimming pool complex with a four-lane slide, jacuzzi and a paddling pool. L'Etang des Haizes has 160 good sized pitches, of which 100 are for touring units, on fairly level ground and all with electricity (10A). They are set in a mixture of conifers, orchard and shrubbery, with some very attractive, slightly smaller pitches overlooking the lake and 60 mobile homes inconspicuously sited. The fenced lake has a small beach (swimming is permitted), with ducks and pedaloes, and offers good coarse fishing for huge carp (we are told!). There are good toilet and shower facilities where children and campers with disabilities are well catered for. Monsieur Laurent, the friendly owner of the site, who speaks excellent English, has recently had an outdoor fitness park installed consisting of eight different pieces of equipment all designed to exercise different parts of the body in the fresh air. This is a good area for walking and cycling and an eight kilometre round trip to experience the views from Le Mont de Doville is a must. Just one kilometre away is La Haye-du-Puits with two supermarkets, restaurants and a market on Wednesdays. A good sandy beach is within 10 km. at Bretville sur Ay and in July and August you can try your hand at archery or water polo.

Facilities

Two well kept and modern unisex toilet blocks have British style toilets, washbasins in cabins, units for disabled visitors, and two family cabins. Small laundry. Motorcaravan services. Milk, bread and takeaway snacks available (no gas). Snack bar/bar with TV and terrace. Swimming pool complex (all amenities 20/5-10/9). Play areas. Bicycle hire. Pétanque. Organised activities including treasure hunts, archery, water polo and food tasting (5/7-25/8). Well stocked tourist information cabin. WiFi is available around the reception area (charged). Off site: Riding 1 km. Beach 10 km. Walking (routes well signposted). Cycling. Normandy landing beaches 30 km.

Open: 1 April - 15 October.

Directions

Site is just north of La Haye-du-Puits on the primary route from Cherbourg to Mont St-Michel, St Malo and Rennes. It is 24 km. south of N13 at Valognes and 29 km. north of Coutances: leave D900 at roundabout at northern end of bypass (towards town). Site signed on right. GPS: 49.2954, -1.55494

Charges guide

Per unit incl. 2 persons and electricity	€ 16,00 - € 37,00
extra person (over 4 yrs)	€ 5,00 - € 7,00
dog	€ 1,00 - € 2,00

Saint Vaast-la-Hougue

Camping la Gallouette

F-50550 Saint Vaast-la-Hougue (Manche) T: 02 33 54 20 57. E: contact@camping-lagallouette.fr

alanrogers.com/FR50010

Claudine and Jean Luc Boblin will give you a warm welcome at their seaside campsite which is ideally placed for visiting Barfleur, Ste Mère-Eglise and the Normandy landing beaches. There are 183 level pitches in total, 119 of which are for touring and all have 6/10A electricity. Some are separated by hedges and there are many colourful flower beds, shrubs and trees but little shade. A light and airy bar faces onto a terrace and swimming pool and there is also a state-of-the-art multisport court. The site is close to the cross-channel ferry terminal at Cherbourg. Saint Vaast-la-Hougue is a busy fishing port with freshly caught fish on sale and a good choice of fish restaurants. Just a couple of hundred yards from the site on a Saturday morning finds you in the midst of a bustling, traditional French market.

Facilities

Three modern sanitary blocks, one open and two enclosed, have British style toilets, showers and washbasins (some in cabins). Area for disabled visitors and for babies. Laundry facilities. Small shop. Snack bar. Bar with terrace. Swimming pool. Multisports court. Play area. Pétanque. WiFi in reception and bar (charged). Entertainment in high season. Off site: Beach 300 m. Shops and restaurant in St Vaast. Riding 5 km. Golf 12 km. Fishing. Sailing. Boat trips to Ile de Tatihou.

Open: 1 April - 30 September.

Directions

The D902 runs between Barfleur and Valognes on the eastern side of the Cherbourg peninsula. About half way along at Quettehou take the D1 to St Vaast. Site signed on right on entering town. GPS: 49.58400, -1.26783

Charges guide

Per unit incl. 2 persons	
and electricity (6A)	€ 19,35 - € 26,10
extra person	€ 4,60 - € 6,00
child (1-10 yrs)	€ 2,90 - € 3,60
animal	€ 1,80

Saint Valery-en-Caux

Camping Municipal d'Etennemare

Hameau d'Etennemare, F-76460 Saint Valery-en-Caux (Seine-Maritime) T: 02 35 97 15 79

alanrogers.com/FR76090

This comfortable, neat municipal site is two kilometres from the harbour and town, 30 km. west of Dieppe. Quietly located, it has 116 pitches of which 49 are available for touring units. The grassy pitches are all on a slight slope, all with electricity (6A), water and drainage, but there is very little shade. Reception is open all day in July and August, but in low season the site is closed 12.00-15.00 daily and all day Wednesday: there is a card-operated security barrier. The site is close to the municipal sports complex with tennis and football field, and there are shops and restaurants in the bustling town and a casino, pools and plenty of entertainment along the seafront.

Facilities

Two modern, clean and well maintained sanitary buildings are side by side, one containing showers and the other, more recently refitted, has toilets, both open and cubicle washbasins and facilities for disabled visitors. Both blocks can be heated in winter. Dishwashing and laundry sinks. Washing machines. Small shop (July/Aug). Playground. Off site: Hypermarket 1.5 km. Harbour and beach (pebbles) 2 km.

Open: All year.

Directions

From Dieppe keep to D925 Fécamp road (not through town). At third roundabout turn right on D925E towards hypermarket. From Fécamp turn left on D925E as before. Take first right (site signed) to site on left in 1 km. GPS: 49.8585, 0.7046

Charges guide

Per unit incl. 2 persons and electricity	€ 13,40
extra person	€ 2,75
child (under 10 yrs)	€ 1,75

For latest campsite news, availability and prices visit

alanrogers.com

Servon

Campéole Saint Grégoire

Campé●le

F-50170 Servon (Manche) T: 02 33 60 26 03. E: saint-gregoire@campeole.com

alanrogers.com/FR50190

This small rural site is simple and well cared for. Modestly sized pitches are in groups of three or four with very little indication of pitch boundaries. Shrubs and well trimmed hedges are planted throughout. Thirty of the 88 pitches are occupied by chalets and mobile homes. One building houses all of the facilities which are modern, bright and of a high standard. A reasonable car journey will take you to Le Mont St Michel, St Malo or Avranches.

Facilities	Directions
One modern sanitary block has washbasins in cabins and controllable showers. Baby room. Very good facilities for disabled visitors. Washing machine. Takeaway (July/Aug). Small swimming pool (15/6-15/9). Boules. Play area (3-8 yrs). Torches required. Off site: Several beaches can be reached by car. Mont St Michel. St Malo. Avranches.	On the RN175 from Avranches towards St Malo, take exit for Servon on the right. Site is on the right in 200 m. GPS: 48.59703, -1.41316

Open: 1 April - 30 September.

Charges guide

Per unit incl. 2 persons and electricity	€ 15,10 - € 20,40

Torigni-sur-Vire

Camping le Lac des Charmilles

Route de Vire, F-50160 Torigni-sur-Vire (Manche) T: 02 33 56 91 74
E: contact@camping-lacdescharmilles.com **alanrogers.com/FR50170**

The very friendly new owners have recently acquired this former municipal site and have already made some outstanding changes. Situated next to a lake on the outskirts of Torigni-sur-Vire (1 km) and surrounded by farmers' fields, the 39 touring pitches are divided by mature hedges giving plenty of privacy. Additions have included an exceptional new bar and restaurant with an attractive wooden terrace, a new sanitary block providing the most modern facilities and a multisport court along with trampolines and a bouncy castle. So, although still lacking some facilities, the first-class additions already installed make this a great choice if visiting this area. There are plans to increase the number of pitches and with so much unused land much more may be achieved over the coming months and years.

Facilities	Directions
Two sanitary blocks including one new central block with excellent facilities including those for disabled visitors. Bar/restaurant with full menu and takeaway. Outdoor swimming pool (heated 15/6-15/9). TV, table tennis, go-karts, pétanque, multisport court, trampoline, bouncy castle. Motorcaravan service point. Large units accepted. Off site: Fishing 200 m. Village with shops, bars, banks etc. 1 km. Canoes 5 km. Riding 13 km. Golf 30 km. Beaches of Normandy 45 mins.	Exit the A84 Caen - Rennes motorway at junction 40 and head north on the N174 towards St Lô. The campsite is on your right just before you enter the town of Torigni-sur-Vire. GPS: 49.02851, -0.97190

Open: 1 April - 15 October.

Charges guide

Per unit incl. 2 persons and electricity	€ 17,80 - € 20,80
extra person	€ 3,90
child (0-6 yrs)	€ 2,90
dog	€ 1,50

Camping Cheques accepted.

Etapes Normandes is a small group of just three campsites, all well placed for enjoying some of Normandy's finest sights, as well as immersing yourself in the laid-back lifestyle of this tranquil, rural region.

The verdant, rolling pastures, the wide sandy beaches and the wonderful rich cuisine are yours to enjoy.

Camping le Lac des Charmilles

Route de Vire
F-50160 Torigni-sur-Vire

Tel: 02 33 56 91 74
contact@camping-lacdescharmilles.com
www.camping-lacdescharmilles.com

Flower Camping Le Haut Dick

30 chemin du Grand Bas Pays
F-50500 Carentan

Tel: 02 33 42 16 89
contact@camping-lehautdick.com
www.camping-lehautdick.com

Flower Camping les Chevaliers

2 impasse Pré de la Rose
F-50800 Villedieu-les-Poêles

Tel: 02 33 61 02 44
contact@camping-deschevaliers.com
www.camping-deschevaliers.com

Etapes Normandes

In Their Own Words...

We will look after you

You are assured a warm and friendly welcome at each of our 3* campsites. We enjoy what we do and are proud of our campsites and we want you to have a great holiday with us!

We recognise that our visitors have different requirements, so we ensure facilities are open all season: enjoy a drink in our friendly bars, a takeaway meal or a simple snack, and not just in high season.

We invest in quality

Whether it's heated swimming pools, modern play equipment for the children and all weather multi-sports pitches, we aim to provide you with great standards. We invest in our campsites and ensure that our mobile homes are never more than five years old.

We ensure plenty to do

Wherever you stay, you will find we are situated near to some wonderful sights and activities. Maybe you fancy a memorable visit to experience the ancient drama of Mont St Michel or the vast, moving D-Day Beaches; not to mention numerous boat trips, châteaux, zoos, museums, and of course endless sandy beaches.

www.etapesnormandes.com

Touques - Deauville

Camping des Haras

Chemin du Calvaire, F-14800 Touques - Deauville (Calvados) T: 02 31 88 44 84
E: campingdesharas@orange.fr alanrogers.com/FR14270

Les Haras is located in Touques, just outside the stylish resort of Deauville. This is a mature site with grassy and well shaded pitches. A number of mobile homes are available for rent. Leisure amenities include a heated pool (July and August) with a separate children's pool and spa bath. There is a bar and snack bar, with many other restaurants in nearby Deauville. The sandy beaches of Deauville and its neighbour, Trouville, are deservedly renowned and are likely to be the main appeal here. The site is open for a long season and may appeal as a short break destination. The Duke of Morny, half brother of Napoleon III, founded Deauville in 1861 and inaugurated the Deauville-La Touques race course in 1864, even before the church was built! The resort quickly grew around the race course and is still one of the most important in France. Indeed, Les Haras translates as a stud farm. Golf is also popular here and the Barriere club has a fine location, overlooking the town.

Facilities

Bar and snack bar. Swimming pool and children's pool. Playground. Games room. Mobile homes for rent.
Off site: Shops and restaurants in Deauville and Trouville. Golf. Riding.

Open: 1 March - 30 October.

Directions

Site is south of Trouville. Approaching from A132 motorway, continue on D677 towards Trouville and Deauville. On reaching Touques, take eastbound D62 (Route d'Honfleur) and the site is well signed. GPS: 49.349567, 0.111711

Charges guide

Per unit incl. 2 persons	
and electricity	€ 23,00 - € 35,00
extra person	€ 6,00 - € 9,00
child (2-7 yrs)	€ 4,00 - € 5,00

Near Deauville, 2 km from the beaches, visit us to enjoy the panoramic view of the country of Auge with their horses in the green meadows. You will appreciate the peace and the serinity of a raised and spacious campsite where the family can enjoy the life in fresh-air, with good activities, facilities and various possibilities the regio offers you.

Chemin du Calvaire · F-14800 Touques · Deauville · France
Tél: +33 231 88 44 84 · contact@camping-des-haras.com
www.camping-des-haras.com

Villedieu-les-Poêles

Flower Camping les Chevaliers

2 impasse Pré de la Rose, F-50800 Villedieu-les-Poêles (Manche) T: 02 33 61 02 44
E: contact@camping-deschevaliers.com alanrogers.com/FR50180

This pleasant site is situated less than a five minute walk from the attractive and interesting town of Villedieu-les-Poêles with its history of metalwork shops and foundries. There are five museums to visit, three of which are close by. This former municipal site is undergoing many modernisations and so far the sanitary facilities have been renovated and a heated outdoor swimming pool added. The 84 touring pitches are separated by low hedges and there are many mature trees giving plenty of shade. There are plenty of electrical connections (8A). A small river runs alongside the site which is safely fenced with a gate for access.

Facilities

Two sanitary blocks provide adequate facilities. One main block situated behind reception has all modern facilities, the other centrally located with toilets and sinks only. Shop. Bar and restaurant with terrace. Takeaway snacks and pizzas. Swimming pool (15/6-15/9). Multisport court. Purpose-built skateboard park. Playground with bouncy csatle and trampoline. Go-karts and bicycle hire.
Off site: Shops, bars and restaurants in town 500 m.

Open: 1 April - 15 October.

Directions

From the A84 Rennes - Caen motorway, take exit 37 and head east on the D524 to Villedieu-les -Poêles. Follow signs for the Office de Tourisme and continue on, keeping the Office and Post Office on the left. The campsite is 200 m. on the left. GPS: 48.83665, -1.21697

Charges 2011

Per unit incl. 2 persons	
and electricity	€ 18,00 - € 24,90
extra person	€ 3,50 - € 4,50
child (0-6 yrs)	€ 2,90 - € 4,00

For latest campsite news, availability and prices visit
alanrogers.com

Vimoutiers

Camping Municipal la Campière

Boulevard du Docteur Dentu, F-61120 Vimoutiers (Orne) T: 02 33 39 18 86. E: mairie.vimoutiers@wanadoo.fr
alanrogers.com/FR61010

This small, well kept site is situated in a valley to the north of the town, which is on both the Normandy Cheese and Cider routes. Indeed the town is famous for its cheese and has a Camembert Museum, five minutes walk away in the town centre. The 40 pitches here are flat and grassy, separated by laurel hedging and laid out amongst attractive and well maintained flower and shrub beds. There is some shade around the perimeter and all pitches have electricity.

Facilities

The single central sanitary block is clean and heated, providing open washbasins, good sized, well designed showers, children's toilets and a bathroom for disabled visitors. Dishwashing and laundry facilities under cover. Off site: No shop but a large supermarket is 300 m. Tennis courts and a park are adjacent. Restaurant, water sports facilities and riding 2 km.

Open: May - October.

Directions

Site is on northern edge of town, signed from main Lisieux - Argentan road next to large sports complex. GPS: 48.932557, 0.196643

Charges guide

Per unit incl. 2 persons	
and electricity	€ 12,95 - € 13,40
extra person	€ 2,59 - € 3,10
child (0-10)	€ 1,55 - € 1,85
dog	€ 1,13 - € 1,35

Reductions for 7th and subsequent days.

Yport

Flower Camping la Chênaie

Rue Henry Simon, F-76111 Yport (Seine-Maritime) T: 02 35 27 33 56
E: camping.yport@flowercampings.com **alanrogers.com/FR76170**

La Chênaie is a small campsite with just 70 pitches. The pitches are set on open ground and might not offer the privacy you may be looking for. The site is set in the heart of the Albâtre coast and is 800 m. from the beach. It offers a very tranquil environment. Yport is a small seaside town renowned for its fishermen's houses and beautiful 19th-century villas. It is an authentic, traditional fishing village with lovely views out to sea. The village of Etretat is nearby where its famous cliffs inspired the paintings of Claude Monet and Gustave Courbet.

Facilities

Sanitary buildings with showers. Toilets for disabled visitors. Bakery. Table tennis. Boules. Library. TV room. Play area.

Open: 1 April - 29 September.

Directions

Yport is located between Etretat and Fécamp. From Le Havre (42 km), go through Sainte Adresse and take the D79 to the D940, then through Etretat. Turn left on la Route des Hogues, then turn left, then first right and continue along Chemin des Acres. From Paris (200 km) use the A13. Exit at Pont de Brotonne, signed Fécamp. Go through Fécamp, then follow signs to Etreta. GPS: 49.732805, 0.320682

Charges guide

Per unit incl. 2 persons	
and electricity	€ 15,00 - € 17,00
extra person	€ 3,00 - € 4,00
child (2-7 yrs)	€ 2,00 - € 2,50
dog	free

For latest campsite news, availability and prices visit

alanrogers.com

Nord-Pas de Calais, with its lush countryside and market towns, is much more than just a stopover en-route to or from the ports. The peaceful, rural, unspoilt charms of the region provide a real breath of fresh air.

DÉPARTEMENTS: 59 NORD, 62 PAS DE CALAIS

MAJOR CITIES: LILLE AND ARRAS

Nord-Pas de Calais is jam-packed with history, culture, seaside resorts and bustling towns and cities. A region known for its hospitality, it most recently found fame among the French as the setting for the box office hit comedy 'Bienvenue chez les Ch'tis', mocking northern and southern stereotypes while portraying the region as the friendly and welcoming place that it is.

Nord-Pas de Calais offers a large range of sporting activities, a variety of landscapes and historic sites and museums that will captivate all visitors. Stay for a day or for a week, within a few hours you could be a million miles from home. This is a region where good living is an everyday event.

It is certainly a region that will surprise and delight: traditional fairs and festivals where you too can join in the fun; long, sandy expanses of coast where you can try your hand at sand-yachting, the undulating countryside with its lush, green meadows and vivid blue and yellow fields of flax and rapeseed, bustling towns with their colourful markets and festive night life, and of course a warm welcome everywhere.

Tourism in
Nord-Pas de Calais

Places of interest

Lille
For shopping and culture.

The Opal Coast
Cap Blanc Nez and Cap Gris Nez and
seaside resorts.

Arras
Its squares and Flemish architecture.

Boulogne-sur-Mer
Nausicaa: unique sea centre offers insights
into the world's seas and oceans.

Roubaix
Museum La Piscine.

Avesnois
Le Quesnoy and the Regional Natural Park.

Saint-Omer
Audomarois Marshland.

Le Cateau-Cambrésis
Matisse Museum.

Lewarde
Coalmine museum.

Cassel
French Flanders hills.

Cuisine of the region

In the Nord and Pas de Calais region, you
can enjoy good French gastronomy as
well as regional dishes that must be tasted
in typical regional restaurants, called
'estaminets'. Cheese, beers, sweets…
the region has plenty to offer gourmets.

Hochepot: A thick Flemish soup with virtually
everything in it but the kitchen sink.

Carbonade flamande: Beef in a beer and
gingerbread sauce served with French fries.

Waterzooï: A cross between soup and stew,
usually of fish or chicken.

Langue de Lucullus: Foie gras with thin slices
of ox tongue.

Maroilles and Vieux Lille: cheeses.

Waffles

*Images © (left to right, top to bottom): Matthieu Langrand; Pascal Morès;
Jean-Pierre Duplan; Samuel Dhote; Samuel Dhote; Matthieu Langrand*

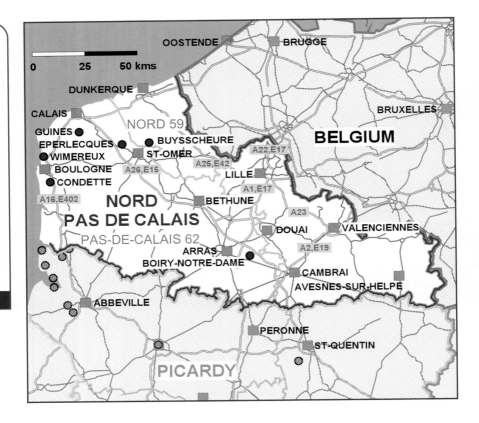

Boiry-Notre-Dame

Camping la Paille Haute

145 rue de Sailly, F-62156 Boiry-Notre-Dame (Pas-de-Calais) T: 03 21 48 15 40. E: la-paillehaute@wanadoo.fr

alanrogers.com/FR62080

Quietly situated in a small village overlooking beautiful countryside and easily accessed from the A1 and A26 autoroutes, this site makes an ideal overnight stop, whilst at the same time being a good base from which to explore the city of Arras and its surroundings. There are 100 pitches here, 65 for touring and all with 6/10A electricity. Some pitches are on open, level grass with lovely views over the countryside, and others are by the site's small fishing lake. You can be sure of a warm welcome here from the friendly owner, who is working hard still developing areas of the site. In high season there is a heated outdoor pool, together with paddling pool, and a bar serving snacks and a self-service salad bar. Situated by the pool is an outdoor bar and pizza oven, and entertainment is organised for all ages.

Facilities

One modern, basic toilet block, unisex. Extra toilets by pool. One toilet/shower room for disabled visitors. Washing machine and dryer under canopy. Motorcaravan service point. Bar and snacks. Swimming pool (15/6-15/9). Poolside bar and pizza oven. TV in bar. Fishing pond. Playground. Boules. Internet access. Entertainment. Off site: Supermarket 500 m. City of Arras with Flemish architecture, and network of cellars and tunnels spreading beneath the town centre. WW1 Canadian memorial at Vimy Ridge.

Open: 1 April - 31 October.

Directions

From A1 take exit 15 and D939 southeast. Follow signs for Boiry-Notre-Dame. From A26 take exit 8 and D939 northwest following signs for Boiry -Notre-Dame. From village follow camping signs to site. GPS: 50.273533, 2.948667

Charges guide

Per unit incl. 2 persons	€ 15,00 - € 18,00
extra person	€ 3,00 - € 3,50
child (under 7 yrs)	€ 2,00 - € 2,50
electricity (6A)	€ 3,00

For latest campsite news, availability and prices visit

alanrogers.com

Buysscheure

Camping Caravaning la Chaumière

529 Langhemast Straete, F-59285 Buysscheure (Nord) T: 03 28 43 03 57
E: camping.LaChaumiere@wanadoo.fr alanrogers.com/FR59010

This is a very friendly, pleasant site, in the département du Nord with a strong Flanders influence, There is a real welcome here. Set just behind the village of Buysscheure, the site has 29 touring pitches separated by trees and bushes. Each pair shares a light, electricity connections, water points and rubbish container. Access from narrow site roads can be difficult, although once on site there are several pitches available for extra large units. A small, fenced fishing lake contains some large carp. A bonus is that Bernadette works for the local vet and can arrange all the documentation for British visitors' pets.

Facilities

Modern unisex toilet facilities are simple and few in number, with two WCs, one shower and one washbasin cabin. Facilities for disabled visitors may also be used (toilet and separate washbasin/shower room). Dishwashing and laundry facilities. Motorcaravan services. Basic chemical disposal. Bar (daily) and restaurant (weekends only, all day, in season). Dog exercise area. Heated outdoor pools (July/Aug). Play area. Minigolf. Archery. Fishing. WiFi (free). Off site: Local market (Monday) at Bergues. St Omer. Beach 30 km. Lille 60 km.

Open: 1 April - 30 September.

Directions

From Calais take N43 (St Omer) for 25 km. Just beyond Nordausques take D221 left (Watten). In Watten turn left for centre, then right on D26 (Cassel). Soon after Lederzeele site signed to right. On reaching Buysscheure turn left, then right, site signed. Single track road (1 km) with bend. GPS: 50.80152, 2.33924

Charges guide

Per unit incl. 2 persons and electricity	€ 19,00 - € 20,00

No credit cards.

Condette

Caravaning du Château d'Hardelot

21 rue Nouvelle, F-62360 Condette (Pas-de-Calais) T: 03 21 87 59 59. E: campingduchateau@libertysurf.fr
alanrogers.com/FR62040

Within about 15 minutes drive of Boulogne and only 5 minutes by car from the long sandy beach at Hardelot, this modern site has 70 pitches with around 50 for touring units, the rest occupied by long stay and units to rent. Pitches are of varying size on level grass, all with access to electricity (10A). Hedging plants between the pitches are maturing well and there is shade from mature trees around the site. With friendly and accommodating owners, this site provides a useful overnight stop, but it is also an excellent base for longer stays. British visitors enjoy the welcome they receive here and return year after year.

Facilities

Modern sanitary facilities in two small units (one heated) include large hot showers and baby bath (all spotless). Laundry facilities (washing machine and dryer). Motorcaravan services. Excellent playground and entertainment for children in season. Small fitness room. WiFi (charged). Off site: English-run pub/restaurant within walking distance. Fishing 800 m. Riding 1 km. Bicycle hire, golf and boat launching 3 km.

Open: 1 April - 31 October.

Directions

South of Boulogne, take N1 Amiens (Paris) road, then on the outskirts take the right fork for Touquet-Paris Plage (D940). Continue for 5 km. passing signs for Condette, then turn right at new roundabout (site signed). Continue to next roundabout and turn right again to site. GPS: 50.6466, 1.6256

Charges guide

Per unit incl. 2 persons and electricity	€ 20,00 - € 25,50

No credit cards.

Eperlecques

Kawan Village Château du Gandspette

133 rue de Gandspette, F-62910 Eperlecques (Pas-de-Calais) T: 03 21 93 43 93
E: contact@chateau-gandspette.com alanrogers.com/FR62030

This spacious family run site, in the grounds of a 19th-century château, conveniently situated for the Channel ports and tunnel, provides overnight accommodation together with a range of facilities for longer stays. There are 110 touring pitches, all with electric hook-ups, intermingled with 20 privately owned mobile homes and caravans, with a further 18 for hire. Pitches are delineated by trees and hedging. Mature trees form the perimeter of the site, through which there is access to woodland walks.

Facilities

Two sanitary blocks with a mixture of open and cubicled washbasins. Good facilities for disabled campers and babies. Laundry facilities. Motorcaravan service point. Bar, grill restaurant and takeaway (all 1/5-15/9). Swimming pools (15/5-15/9). Playground. Multisport court. Tennis. Pétanque. Children's room. Entertainment in season. WiFi in bar area (charged). Off site: Supermarket 1 km. Fishing 3 km. Riding, golf 5 km. Beach 30 km.

Open: 1 April - 30 September.

Directions

From Calais follow D943 (St Omer) for 25 km. Southeast of Nordausques take D221 (east). Follow site signs for 5-6 km. From St Omer follow D943 to roundabout at junction with D300. Turn right on D300 (Dunkirk). After 5 km. turn left on D221. Site is 1.5 km. on right. GPS: 50.81924, 2.17753

Charges guide

Per unit incl. 2 persons and electricity	€ 17,00 - € 27,00

Camping Cheques accepted.

We can book this site for you!
Call 01580 214000

alan rogers travel

For latest campsite news, availability and prices visit

alanrogers.com

Guînes

Castel Camping Caravaning la Bien-Assise

D231, F-62340 Guînes (Pas-de-Calais) T: 03 21 35 20 77. E: castels@bien-assise.com

alanrogers.com/FR62010

A mature and well developed site, the history of La Bien-Assise goes back to the 1500s. There are 198 grass pitches mainly set among mature trees with others on a newer field. Connected by gravel roads and of a good size (up to 300 sq.m), shrubs and bushes divide most of the pitches. Being close to Calais, the Channel Tunnel exit and Boulogne, makes it a good stopping point en-route, but it is well worth a longer stay. The site can have heavy usage at times (when maintenance can be variable). Used by tour operators (40 pitches).

Facilities

Three well equipped toilet blocks provide many washbasins in cabins, mostly British style WCs and provision for babies, laundry and dishwashing. The main block is in four sections, two unisex. Motorcaravan service point. Shop. Restaurant. Bar/grill and takeaway (evenings from 1/5). TV room. Pool complex (1/5-20/9) with toboggan, covered paddling pool and outdoor pool. Play areas. Minigolf. Tennis. Bicycle hire. Free WiFi in bar area. Off site: Riding 3 km. Fishing 8 km. Beach 12 km.

Open: 25 April - 20 September.

Directions

From ferry or tunnel follow signs for A16 Boulogne. Take exit 11 (Frethun, Gare TGV) and RD215 (Frethun). At first roundabout take third exit (Guînes). Pass under the TGV. In Frethun take RD246 towards Guînes and St Tricat and at roundabout take exit for Guînes. Pass through St Tricat and Hames Boucres, and in Guines follow site signs.
GPS: 50.86632, 1.85698

Charges guide

Per unit incl. 2 persons and electricity	€ 23,00 - € 31,50
extra person	€ 4,50 - € 6,50

Wimereux

Camping l'Eté Indien

Hameau Honvault, F-62930 Wimereux (Pas-de-Calais) T: 03 21 30 23 50. E: ete.indien@wanadoo.fr

alanrogers.com/FR62120

L'Eté Indien is a new site located near the resort of Wimereux, a little to the north of Boulogne. It offers a quiet and tranquil environment in which to enjoy your holiday – apart from some train noise (every 30 minutes, daytime only). Pitches for touring and camping are furthest from the entrance and vary in size. All have electrical connections (10A). In keeping with its Wild West theme, there is a small village of four Indian 'teepees' for rent, as well as more conventional mobile homes and chalets. The swimming pool and children's pool are a fair distance from the touring pitches. Other amenities include a fishing pond and a snack bar, Le Jardin de l'Eté Indien. The site lies at the heart of the Côte d'Opale, which boasts over 130 km. of coastline. Wimereux is an old-fashioned resort with plenty of shops and restaurants, and is renowned as a centre for kite surfing and speed sailing.

Facilities

Two toilet blocks include facilities for babies and disabled visitors. Laundry. Small shop. Bar. Snack bar and takeaway. Motorcaravan services. Swimming pool. Children's pool. Play area with trampoline. Boules. Games room. Internet access and WiFi. Bicycle hire. Fishing pond. Off site: Wimereux, Le Touquet, Boulogne and the Nausicaa museum. Cité de l'Europe shopping complex at Calais. Beach 1 km. Riding adjacent. Golf 1.5 km.

Open: All year.

Directions

From the A16 take exit 32 (Wimereux) and follow signs to Wimereux (D96 and D940). After 1.5 km. turn right. Site is well signed from here and is located on the left, close to a riding centre. Approach is rather narrow, with speed ramps and is poorly surfaced. GPS: 50.75142, 1.60728

Charges guide

Per unit incl. 2 persons and electricity	€ 15,50 - € 20,00
extra person	€ 3,20 - € 4,00
child (under 13 yrs)	€ 2,00 - € 2,50

For latest campsite news, availability and prices visit

alanrogers.com

Insurance Service

High quality, low cost insurance you can trust

Price Beater
GUARANTEE*

Caravan Insurance
SAVE UP TO 60%

We've been entrusted with readers' campsite-based holidays since 1968, and they have asked us for good value, good quality insurance.

We have teamed up with Shield Total Insurance – one of the leading names in outdoor leisure insurances – to bring you peace of mind and huge savings. Call or visit our website for a no obligation quote – there's no reason not to – and trust us to cover your valued possessions for you.

* Price Beater **GUARANTEE**
Motorhomes and Static Caravans
We guarantee to beat any genuine 'like for like' insurance renewal quote by at least £25. Subject to terms & conditions.

- Caravans - **Discounts up to 60%**
- Park Homes - **Fantastic low rates**
- Cars - *COMING SOON*

Instant quote
Call **0844 824 6314**

alanrogers.com/insurance

The birthplace of Gothic architecture in France with no less than six cathedrals, this region between Lille and Paris is still predominantly rural with deep river valleys, forests of mature beech and oak, peaceful lakes and sandy beaches providing plenty of contrast.

DÉPARTEMENTS: 02 AISNE, 60 OISE, 80 SOMME

MAJOR CITY: AMIENS

France itself was born in this northern province located between the Marne and the Somme rivers, for it was here that the Franks – ancestors of the French – first settled. Picardy tends to be a region that most people travel through and this was the invaders' route. Evidence of this is visible in the 17th-century defensive citadels designed by Vauban at the end of a long period of conquests by English kings and Burgundian dukes. From a more recent age, acres of immaculately tended war graves are a sobering reminder of two Great Wars. Almost every village between Arras and Amiens has its memorial. Two of the most important sites to discover are the Museum of the Great War at Péronne and the Somme Trench museum at Albert.

Picardy's coastline is the least urbanised in all France with mile upon mile of beautiful sandy beaches and dunes – great for windsurfing, sand yachting, sailing, swimming and building castles. Do not miss the lovely village of Saint Valéry-sur-Somme, where William the Conquerer left for Great Britain, the magnificent 'Baie de Somme' or the largest bird park in Europe, the Marquenterre, the Forest of Compiègne and the 'Crowned Mountain' of Laon.

PICARDIE

www.**picardietourisme.com/en**
campingpicardy.co.uk

Création Skertzo pour Amiens Métropole

Places of interest

Abbeville

Church of St Vulfran, Bagatelle Château, Baie de Somme nature reserve.

Amiens

Notre Dame cathedral, impressive for its size and richly sculpted façade and the stone carvings of the choir; monument to the 1918 Battle of the Somme; remarkable 'Hortillonnages' (water gardens) and interlocking canals.

Aisne

Surrounded by 60 fortified churches.

Chantilly

Château of Chantilly with a 17th-century stable with a 'live' Horse Museum.

Compiègne

Seven miles east of the town is Clairière de l'Armistice. The railway coach here is a replica of the one in which the 1918 Armistice was signed and in which Hitler received the French surrender in 1942.

Laon

12th-century cathedral, First World War trenches, Vauclair Abbey.

Marquenterre

One of Europe's most important bird sanctuaries.

Parks

Over 70 parks and gardens to discover and in certain rose gardens: the Rose of Picardy.

www.**fleur-et-jardin-picardie.com**

Cuisine of the region

Fresh fish and seafood is popular.

Ficelles Picardes: ham pancakes with mushroom sauce.

Flamiche au maroilles: puff pastry tart with maroilles cheese.

Soupe des Hortillons: soup made with fresh vegetables from Amiens Hortillons

Papillottes d'agneau: lamb from the Baie de Somme with passe-pierres and basil butter

Soissoulet: baked beans from Soissons cooked with smoked sausages and lamb

Chantilly cream

Images © (this page, left to right, top to bottom): Benjamin Teissèdre; Anne-Sophie Flament; Anne-Sophie Flament; Jean-Pierre Gilson

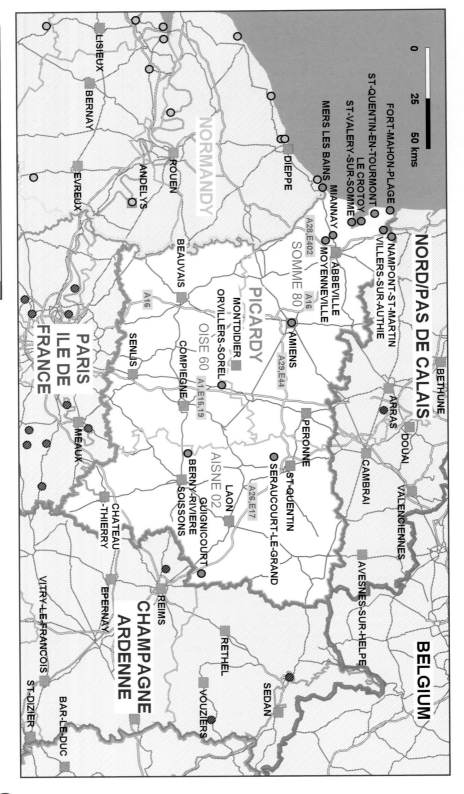

For latest campsite news, availability and prices visit
alanrogers.com

Amiens

Camping Parc des Cygnes

111 avenue des Cygnes, F-80080 Amiens (Somme) T: 03 22 43 29 28. E: camping.amiens@wanadoo.fr
alanrogers.com/FR80100

This 3.2 hectare site has been completely levelled and attractively landscaped. Bushes and shrubs divide the site into areas and trees around the perimeter provide some shade. The 145 pitches are for touring, with five mobile homes for rent. All pitches are grassed with plenty of space on the tarmac roads in front of them for motorcaravans to park in wet conditions. There are 81 pitches with 10A electricity, of which 37 also have water and drainage and further water points can be accessed throughout the rest of the site. The site is just a few minutes from the N1, the A16 Paris-Calais motorway and the A29/A26 route to Rouen and the south, so it is useful as a stop-over being about 50 km. from the ports. Amiens itself is an attractive cathedral city where you can eat out on the waterfront of the Venice of the North or take a boat trip around the 'floating gardens' of Les Hortillonnages. Information is available and reduced prices are offered for visits to these historical locations as the site is a Somme Battlefields Partner. A Sites et Paysages member.

Facilities	Directions
Two toilet blocks (both open when site is busy) with separate toilet facilities but unisex shower and washbasin area. Baby bath. Facilities for disabled visitors. Reception building also has toilets, showers and washbasins (heated when necessary). Laundry facilities. Shop (open on request all season), bar and takeaway (7/5-12/9; weekends only in low season). Games and TV room. Bicycle hire. Fishing. Off site: Golf and riding 12 km. Beaches 70 km.	From A16, leave at exit 20. Take the Rocade Nord (northern bypass) to exit 40, follow signs for Amiens Longpré. At roundabout take second exit to Parc de Loisirs, then right to site (signs all the way). For sat nav use rue du Grand Marais. GPS: 49.920916, 2.258833

Open: 1 April - 14 October.

Charges guide

Per unit incl. 2 persons	
and electricity	€ 19,10 - € 24,80
extra person	€ 6,00
child (4-12 yrs)	€ 5,00
dog	€ 2,10

Parc des Cygnes★★★★
Camping & Caravaning, Cottages

For quality holidays!

PARC DES CYGNES
CAMPING & CARAVANING
★★★★
Le camping au cœur d'Amiens

Camping Qualité

111 Avenue des Cygnes - 80080 AMIENS
Tél.: +33 (0)3 22 43 29 28
Fax: +33 (0)3 22 43 59 42
E-mail: camping.amiens@wanadoo.fr
Web: www.parcdescygnes.com
GPS: 49.920916 / 2.258833

Berny-Riviere

Caravaning la Croix du Vieux Pont

F-02290 Berny-Riviere (Aisne) T: 03 23 55 50 02. E: info@la-croix-du-vieux-pont.com
alanrogers.com/FR02030

Located on the banks of the River Aisne, la Croix du Vieux Pont is a very smart, modern 34-hectare site offering a high standard of facilities. Many pitches are occupied by mobile homes and tour operator tents, but there are 60 pleasant touring pitches, some on the banks of the Aisne. Maintained to a high standard, the excellent amenities include four heated swimming pools, one indoors with a waterslide and jacuzzi. At the heart of the site is a well stocked fishing lake which is also used for pedaloes and canoes. There are two tennis courts, an amusement arcade and volleyball court. Coach trips are organised regularly to Paris, Parc Asterix and Disneyland.

Facilities	Directions
The six toilet blocks are modern and kept very clean, with washbasins in cabins and free hot showers. Laundry facilities. Facilities for disabled visitors. Large supermarket. Bar, takeaway and good value restaurant (most amenities 1/4-30/9). Swimming pool complex (covered pool 1/4-30/10, outdoor 1/5-30/9). Play area. Fishing. Bicycle hire. Apartments to let. Off site: Riding 100 m. Golf 30 km.	From Compiegne take N31 towards Soissons. At Vic-sur-Aisne turn right, towards Berny-Riviere and site is on right after 400 m. GPS: 49.40487, 3.12840

Open: 8 April - 31 October.

Charges guide

Per unit incl. 2 persons	
and electricity	€ 21,50 - € 24,00
incl. 4 persons	€ 30,50 - € 33,00
Camping Cheques accepted.	

For latest campsite news, availability and prices visit
alanrogers.com

Fort-Mahon-Plage

Camping le Royon

1271 route de Quend, F-80120 Fort-Mahon-Plage (Somme) T: 03 22 23 40 30. E: info@campingleroyon.com

alanrogers.com/FR80040

This busy site, some two kilometres from the sea, has 397 pitches of which 116 are used for touring units. Most are near the entrance, some are set amongst the mobile homes. They are of either 95 or 120 sq.m, marked, numbered and divided by hedges and are arranged either side of the access roads. Electricity (6A) and water points are available to all. The remaining 281 pitches are used for mobile homes. The site is well lit, fenced and guarded at night (€ 30 deposit for barrier card). Entertainment is organised for adults and children in July/Aug when it will be very full.

Facilities

Four toilet blocks provide unisex facilities with British and Turkish style WCs and washbasins in cubicles. Units for disabled visitors. Baby baths. Laundry facilities. Shop (15/3-1/11). Gas supplies. Mobile takeaway calls evenings in July/Aug. Clubroom and bar (15/3-1/11). Heated, open air and covered pools. Open air children's pool and sun terrace. Play area. Games room with TV. Multisport court. Tennis. Boules. Bicycle hire. Internet access and WiFi. Off site: Fishing, riding, golf and watersports centre within 1 km. Public transport nearby (July/Aug).

Open: 15 March - 1 November.

Directions

From A16 exit 24, take D32 around Rue (road becomes D940 for a while) then continues as D32 (Fort-Mahon-Plage). Site is on right after 19 km. GPS: 50.33229, 1.5796

Charges guide

Per unit incl. up to 3 persons and electricity	€ 18,00 - € 30,00
extra person (over 1 yr)	€ 7,00
dog	€ 3,00

Guignicourt

Camping Municipal Guignicourt

14 bis rue des Godins, F-02190 Guignicourt (Aisne) T: 03 23 79 74 58. E: mairie-guignicourt@wanadoo.fr

alanrogers.com/FR02060

This very pleasant little municipal site has 100 pitches, 20 for long stay units and 80 for touring units. These two sections are separated by the main facilities on a higher terrace. Pitches are generally large and level, although you might need an extra long electricity lead for some, but there are few dividing hedges. Pitches along the river bank have most shade, with a few specimen trees providing a little shade to some of the more open pitches. On a quiet evening you are likely to hear the site's nightingales. The town is quite attractive and is worthy of an evening stroll.

Facilities

The modern sanitary unit has British and Turkish style toilets, washbasins (cold only except for the one in a cubicle), pushbutton hot showers, dishwashing and laundry sinks. Playground. Boules. Fishing. Off site: The town has all services including a supermarket and bank. Golf 3 km. Beach 15 km. Good train service into Reims with its spectacular cathedral.

Open: 1 April - 30 September.

Directions

Guignicourt is about 20 km. north of Reims, just east of the A26, junction 14. The site is well signed from D925 in the village. GPS: 49.4320, 3.9704

Charges guide

Per person	€ 2,20
child (under 12 yrs)	€ 1,50
pitch incl. electricity	€ 11,10 - € 13,20
animal	€ 1,50

Le Crotoy

Kawan Village le Ridin

Lieu-dit Mayocq, F-80550 Le Crotoy (Somme) T: 03 22 27 03 22. E: contact@campingleridin.com

alanrogers.com/FR80110

Le Ridin is a popular family site in the countryside just 2 km. from Le Crotoy with its beaches and marina, and 6 km. from the famous bird reserve of Le Marquenterre. The site has 162 pitches, including 40 for touring, the remainder are occupied by mobile homes and chalets (for rent). There is some shade. The pitches and roads are unsuitable for large units. The site amenities are housed in beautifully converted barns across the road and these include a heated pool, fitness centre, bar/restaurant and bicycles for hire. Reception staff are helpful and will advise on local excursions.

Facilities

Toilet blocks are heated in cool weather and provide good showers and special facilities for children. Laundry facilities. Motorcaravan service point. Restaurant/bar. Small shop. Swimming and paddling pools. Fitness centre. Games room. Play area. TV room. Bicycle hire. Entertainment and activity programme in high season. WiFi (free). Off site: Golf 2 km. Fishing and riding 3 km. Birdwatching 6 km.

Open: 1 April - 7 November.

Directions

From A16 (Calais - Abbéville) take exit 24 and follow signs to Le Crotoy. At roundabout on arrival at Le Crotoy turn towards St Férmin, then second road on right. GPS: 50.23905, 1.63182

Charges guide

Per unit incl. 2 persons and electricity	€ 19,50 - € 30,00
extra person	€ 5,30 - € 5,80
child (2-7 yrs)	€ 4,30 - € 4,80

For latest campsite news, availability and prices visit

alanrogers.com

Mers-les-Bains

Flower Camping le Rompval

Lieu dit Blengues, F-80350 Mers-les-Bains (Somme) T: 02 35 84 43 21
E: lerompval@baiedesommepleinair.com alanrogers.com/FR80220

Le Rompval is a former municipal site located in the pleasant seaside resort of Mers-les-Bain, around 25 km. west of Abbeville, at the mouth of the River Bresle. There are 135 pitches here and these are grassy and of a good size. Most are equipped with electricity (13A). Around 10 pitches are occupied by chalets (available for rent). The site boasts some interesting architecture and a number of amenities including a small shop and takeaway food service and a heated, covered pool and paddling pool. The nearest beach is 2.5 km. distant. This is a great sweep of sand, ideal for sand yachting and windsurfing. Mers is an attractive resort with all normal services, including a supermarket. It is closely linked with its neighbours, Eu and Le Tréport.

Facilities

Shop. Takeaway. Tourist information. Play area. Activity programme (high season). Chalets for rent. WiFi (free). Off site: Nearest beach 2.5 km. Mers-les-Bains (attractive seaside resort with Belle Epoque villas). Clifftop walks. Supermarket. Windsurfing and sand yachting. Riding 3 km. Golf and fishing 5 km.

Open: 1 April - 7 November.

Directions

Approaching from the north, leave the A16 motorway at exit 23 (Abbeville Nord). Briefly join the southbound A28 and then take D925 to Eu. Here, head west on D1015 to Mers-les-Bains and follow signs to the site. GPS: 50.077262, 1.414474

Charges guide

Per unit incl. 2 persons and electricity	€ 20,00 - € 24,00

Miannay

Camping le Clos Cacheleux

Route de Bouillancourt, F-80132 Miannay (Somme) T: 03 22 19 17 47. E: raphael@camping-lecloscacheleux.fr
alanrogers.com/FR80210

Le Clos Cacheleux is a well situated campsite of six hectares bordering woodland in the park of the Château Bouillancourt which dates from the 18th century. The site was first opened in July 2008. It is 11 km. from the Bay of the Somme, regarded as being amongst the most beautiful bays in France. There are 100 very large, grassy pitches (200 sq.m) and all have electricity hook-ups and water points. The aim of the owners is to make your stay as enjoyable as possible by providing high quality services and activities. Visitors have access to the swimming pool, bar and children's club of the sister site – Le Val de Trie (20 m). A Sites et Paysages member.

Facilities

The single sanitary block is clean and well maintained. Facilities for disabled visitors. Baby room. Laundry room with washing machine and dryer. Motorcaravan service point. At the sister site: shop (all season), bar with terrace (1/4-15/10), library and TV room, restaurant and takeaway (26/4-4/9). Play area. Boules. Picnic tables. Freezer for ice packs. Barbecue hire. Bicycle hire. Fishing pond. Caravan storage. There is also a covered pool (15/4-30/9) on the sister site and a second sanitary block with family showers plus children's facilities. Off site: Village 1 km. Hypermarket in Abbéville. Riding 4 km. Sandy beaches of the Picardy coast 12 km. Golf 9 km. Riding 14 km.

Open: 15 March - 15 October.

Directions

From the A28 at Abbéville take the D925 towards Eu and Le Tréport; do not go towards Moyenville. Turn left in Miannay village on the D86 towards Toeufles. The road to Bouillancourt-sous-Miannay is on the left after 2 km. and site is signed in the village. GPS: 50.08352, 1.71343

Charges guide

Per unit incl. 2 persons and electricity	€ 18,50 - € 24,80
extra person	€ 3,10 - € 5,10
child (under 7 yrs)	€ 1,90 - € 3,10
dog	€ 0,80 - € 1,30

See advertisement on page 112.

For latest campsite news, availability and prices visit

alanrogers.com

Moyenneville

Camping le Val de Trie

Rue des Sources, Bouillancourt-sous-Miannay, F-80870 Moyenneville (Somme) T: 03 22 31 48 88
E: raphael@camping-levaldetrie.fr alanrogers.com/FR80060

Le Val de Trie is a natural countryside site in woodland, near a small village. The 100 numbered, grassy pitches are of a good size, divided by hedges and shrubs with mature trees providing good shade in most areas, and all have electricity (6A) and water. It can be very quiet in April, June, September and October. If there is no-one on site, just choose a pitch or call at farm to book in. This is maturing into a well managed site with modern facilities and a friendly, relaxed atmosphere. It is well situated for the coast and also the cities of Amiens and Abbeville. There are good walks around the area and a notice board keeps campers up to date with local market, shopping and activity news. English is spoken. The owners of Le Val de Trie have recently opened a new campsite nearby, Le Clos Cacheleux (FR80210), where larger units can be accommodated.

Facilities

Two clean, recently renovated sanitary buildings include washbasins in cubicles, units for disabled visitors, babies and children. Laundry facilities. Microwave. Shop (from 1/4), bread to order and butcher visits in season. Bar with TV, snack bar with takeaway (23/4-4/9). Room above bar for children. Covered heated swimming pool with jacuzzi (15/4-30/9). Outdoor pool for children (26/4-10/9). WiFi in bar area (free). Off site: Riding 4 km. Golf 10 km. Beach 12 km.

Open: 1 April - 15 October.

Directions

From A28 take exit 2 near Abbeville and D925 to Miannay. Turn left on D86 to Bouillancourt-sous -Miannay: site is signed in village.
GPS: 50.08539, 1.71499

Charges guide

Per unit incl. 2 persons	
and electricity	€ 18,50 - € 24,80
extra person	€ 3,10 - € 5,10
child (under 7 yrs)	€ 1,90 - € 3,10
dog	€ 1,80 - € 2,00

Nampont-Saint Martin
Kawan Village la Ferme des Aulnes

1 rue du Marais, Fresne-sur-Authie, F-80120 Nampont-Saint Martin (Somme) T: 03 22 29 22 69
E: contact@fermedesaulnes.com alanrogers.com/FR80070

524

This peaceful site, with 120 pitches, has been developed on the meadows of a small, 17th-century farm on the edge of Fresne and is lovingly cared for by its new enthusiastic owners, Marie and Denis Lefort and their hard working team. Restored outbuildings house reception and the facilities, around a central courtyard that boasts a fine heated swimming pool. A new development includes a bar and entertainment room. Outside, facing the main gate, are 20 large level grass pitches for touring. There is also an area for tents. The remaining 22 touring pitches are in the main complex, hedged and fairly level. Activities are organised for children and there are indoor facilities for poor weather. From here you can visit Crécy, Agincourt, St Valéry and Montreuil (where Victor Hugo wrote Les Misérables). The nearby Bay of the Somme has wonderful sandy beaches and many watersports.

Facilities

Both sanitary areas are heated and include washbasins in cubicles with a large cubicle for disabled campers. Dishwashing and laundry sinks. Shop. Piano bar and restaurant. Motorcaravan service point. TV room. Swimming pool (16x9 m; heated and with cover for cooler weather). Jacuzzi and sauna. Fitness room. Aquagym and balneotherapy. Playground. Boules. Archery. Rooms with Play Stations and videos. Internet café. WiFi (free). Shuttle service to stations and airports. Off site: Private lake fishing (free) 2 minutes away. River fishing 100 m. Golf 1 km. Riding 8 km.

Open: 1 April - 1 November.

Directions

From Calais, take A16 to exit 25 and turn for Arras for 2 km. and then towards Abbeville on N1. At Nampont-St Martin turn west on D485 and site will be found in 2 km. GPS: 50.33645, 1.71285

Charges guide

Per unit incl. 2 persons and electricity	€ 27,00 - € 33,00
extra person	€ 7,00
child (under 7 yrs)	€ 4,00
dog	€ 4,00

Camping Cheques accepted.

For latest campsite news, availability and prices visit
alanrogers.com

Orvillers-Sorel

Aestiva Camping de Sorel

Rue Saint-Claude, F-60490 Orvillers-Sorel (Oise) T: 03 44 85 02 74. E: contact@aestiva.fr

alanrogers.com/FR60020

Aestiva Camping de Sorel is located north of Compiègne, close to the A1 motorway and is ideal as an overnight stop. The site has 80 large grassy pitches, of which 50 are available for touring, all with electrical connections (three with water and waste water). The original farm buildings have been carefully converted to house the site's amenities including a bar, TV room and the toilet facilities. The site is open for a long season but most amenities are only open from April to September. The site is, however, close to the village of Sorel with its shops and restaurants. There are four mobile homes for rent.

Facilities

Toilet block with facilities for children and disabled visitors. Motorcaravan service point. Small shop. Bar, snack bar and takeaway (15/5-15/10). TV room. Play area. Boules. Hairdressing service. Bicycle hire. WiFi. Off site: Tennis. Riding 5 km. Fishing 2 km. Golf 7 km. Compiègne 15 km.

Open: 1 February - 14 December.

Directions

Take exit 11 from the A1 motorway (Lille - Paris) and join the northbound N17. Site is signed to the right on reaching village of Sorel after around 8 km. GPS: 49.56688, 2.70841

Charges guide

Per unit incl. 2 persons and electricity	€ 16,50 - € 18,00
extra person	€ 6,00

Camping Cheques accepted.

Saint Quentin en Tourmont

Camping Caravaning le Champ Neuf

Rue du Champ Neuf, F-80120 Saint Quentin en Tourmont (Somme) T: 03 22 25 07 94
E: contact@camping-lechampneuf.com **alanrogers.com/FR80020**

Le Champ Neuf was started in 1995 and all the charming family are now involved. It is located in the Bay de Somme in a country location near the sea. There are 157 pitches with 34 for touring, of which 30 are in a new field with the remainder scattered amongst more permanent mobile homes. All pitches are on level grass with 6A electricity. The site is only 75 minutes from Calais, 18 km. off the motorway. This is a quiet site with home cooking and soirées, and with the famous Marquenterre bird reserve next door, bird-watching enthusiasts will appreciate the dawn chorus and migrating birds. An excellent covered pool complex has been added, including a flume, jacuzzi and pool for toddlers.

Facilities

Four unisex toilet blocks have showers, washbasins in cubicles, family cubicles and facilities for disabled visitors. Laundry facilities. Motorcaravan service point. Bar, entertainment area and snack bar. Play area. TV. Games room. Covered, heated pool complex including slides, jacuzzi and children's pool. Fitness room. Sauna. Multisport court. WiFi in bar area (free). Off site: Shops, restaurants and bars in Rue 7 km.

Open: 1 April - 1 November.

Directions

From A16 exit 24, take D32 towards and around Rue. At second roundabout take second exit on D940, then left on D4 for 1.5 km. before turning right on D204 to Le Bout des Crocs. Site is signed to the left. GPS: 50.26895, 1.60263

Charges guide

Per unit incl. 2 persons and electricity	€ 19,00 - € 29,00
extra person	€ 5,00 - € 6,50

Saint Valery-sur-Somme

⌐**524**

Camping Airotel Le Walric

Route d'Eu, F-80230 Saint Valery-sur-Somme (Somme) T: 03 22 26 81 97. E: info@campinglewalric.com

alanrogers.com/FR80150

A clean, well-kept and managed site, Le Walric is about 75 minutes from Calais. A former municipal site, it has been completely updated with a new bar and snack bar, a pool complex, two play areas and entertainment in high season. There are 263 well laid out, large and level grass pitches. Of these, 47 with electricity connections are for touring with the remainder used for a mix of new mobile homes and semi-residential caravans. The site's situation on the outskirts of the town make it an ideal holiday location. Medieval Saint Valery is renowned for its association with William the Conqueror.

Facilities

Two heated toilet blocks include British style WCs, washbasins in cubicles and showers. Facilities for disabled visitors. Laundry room with baby changing. Motorcaravan service point. Shop. Bar with snacks and TV (1/4-1/11). Heated outdoor pool (1/5-15/9). Play areas. Tennis. Volleyball. Boules. Children's club and entertainment (July/Aug). Internet access (charged). Off site: Shops, restaurants, bars in St Valery. Bicycle hire and beach 2 km.

Open: 1 April - 1 November.

Directions

From A16 exit 24, follow D32 across N1. At the roundabout take D235 to Morlay; turn left on the D940 and continue around Saint-Valery until second roundabout where take first exit on D3 to site on right. GPS: 50.1838, 1.61791

Charges guide

Per unit incl. 3 persons and electricity	€ 18,00 - € 30,00
extra person	€ 7,00
child (under 1 yr)	free

For latest campsite news, availability and prices visit

alanrogers.com

Saint Valéry-sur-Somme

Castel Camping le Château de Drancourt

B.P. 80022, F-80230 Saint Valéry-sur-Somme (Somme) T: 03 22 26 93 45. E: chateau.drancourt@wanadoo.fr
alanrogers.com/FR80010

This is a popular, busy and lively site within easy distance of the Channel ports, between Boulogne and Dieppe. There are 356 pitches in total, of which 130 are occupied by several tour operators; 30 units for rent, and 26 privately owned. The 170 touring pitches are on level grass, of good size, some in shade and others in the open, all with electricity (10A). The site is well landscaped and, in spite of the numbers in high season, does not feel overcrowded. It can be dusty around the reception buildings and the château in dry weather.

Facilities

Three toilet blocks include washbasins in cubicles, family bathrooms and facilities for disabled visitors. Laundry facilities. Shop, restaurant and takeaway, several bars (all Easter-mid Sept). TV rooms, one for children. Games room. Heated pools, one indoor, one outside (1/6-15/9) and paddling pool. Tennis. Golf practice range. Minigolf. Bicycle hire. Fishing. Large field for ball games and kite flying. WiFi in bar area (charged). Off site: Beach 14 km. Riding 15 km. Golf 30 km. Many traffic-free cycle paths.

Open: Easter - 1 November.

Directions

Site is 2.5 km. south of St Valery and signed from the D940 Berck - Le Tréport road. Turn south on D48 Estreboeuf road. Turn immediately left to Drancourt and site. GPS: 50.15281, 1.63614

Charges guide

Per unit incl. 2 persons and electricity	€ 17,00 - € 35,00
extra person	€ 4,50 - € 7,50
child (under 5 yrs)	€ 3,50 - € 5,20

Seraucourt-le-Grand

Camping Caravaning du Vivier aux Carpes

10 rue Charles Voyeux, F-02790 Seraucourt-le-Grand (Aisne) T: 03 23 60 50 10
E: camping.du.vivier@wanadoo.fr **alanrogers.com/FR02000**

Vivier aux Carpes is a small quiet site, close to the A26, two hours from Calais, so is an ideal overnight stop but is also worthy of a longer stay. The 59 well spaced pitches, are at least 100 sq.m. on flat grass with dividing hedges. The 40 for touring units all have electricity (6A), some also with water points, and there are special pitches for motorcaravans. This is a neat, purpose designed site imaginatively set out with a comfortable feel. The enthusiastic owners and manager speak excellent English and are keen to welcome British visitors.

Facilities

The spacious, clean toilet block has separate, heated facilities for disabled visitors, used by other campers in winter. Laundry facilities. Motorcaravan service point (fresh water for large vans is charged). TV/games room. Small play area. Bicycle hire. Pétanque. Fishing (about € 5.50 p/day). Gates close 22.00, office open 09.00-21.30. Rallies welcome. WiFi (free). Off site: Village has post office, doctor, chemist and small supermarket. Large supermarket in Gauchy 6 km. Markets in St Quentin and Gauchy. Riding 5 km. Golf 12 km.

Open: 1 March - 31 October.

Directions

Leave A26 (Calais - Reims) at exit 11. Take D1 left towards Soissons for 4 km. Take D8, on entering Essigny-le-Grand (4 km) turn sharp right on D72 signed Seraucourt-le-Grand (5 km). Site signed. GPS: 49.78217, 3.21403

Charges guide

Per unit incl. 2 persons and electricity	€ 19,00
extra person	€ 4,00
child (under 10 yrs)	€ 3,00

Discounts for students with tents. No credit cards.

Villers-sur-Authie

Kawan Village Caravaning le Val d'Authie

20 route de Vercourt, F-80120 Villers-sur-Authie (Somme) T: 03 22 29 92 47. E: camping@valdauthie.fr
alanrogers.com/FR80090

In a village location, this well organised site is fairly close to several beaches, but also has its own excellent pool complex, small restaurant and bar. The owner has carefully controlled the size of the site, leaving space for a leisure area with an indoor pool complex. There are 170 pitches in total, but with many holiday homes and chalets, there are only 60 for touring units. These are on grass, some are divided by small hedges, with 6/10A electric hook-ups, and ten have full services.

Facilities

Good toilet facilities, some unisex, include shower and washbasin units, washbasins in cubicles, and limited facilities for disabled campers and babies. Shop (not Oct). Bar/restaurant (5/4-12/10; hours vary). Swimming and paddling pools (with lifeguards in July/Aug). Playground, club room with TV. Weekend entertainment in season. Multisport court, beach volleyball, football, boules and tennis court. Internet room. Fitness room including sauna (charged). WiFi in office. Off site: Shops, banks and restaurants in Rue 6 km.

Open: 1 April - 10 October.

Directions

Villers-sur-Authie is about 25 km. NNW of Abbéville. From A16 junction 24 take N1 to Vron, then left on D175 to Villers-sur-Authie. Or use D85 from Rue, or D485 from Nampont St Martin. Site is at southern end of village at road junction. GPS: 50.31357, 1.69488

Charges guide

Per unit incl. 2 persons	€ 19,00 - € 25,00
extra person	€ 6,00
child (2-6 yrs)	€ 3,00
electricity (6/10A)	€ 5,00 - € 8,00

For latest campsite news, availability and prices visit
alanrogers.com

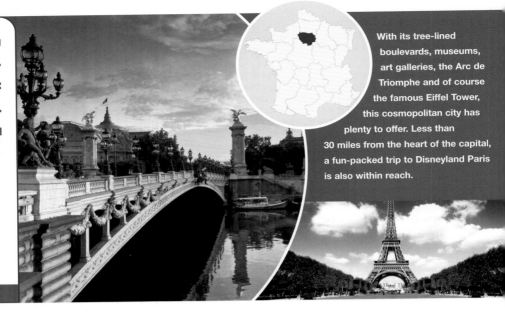

With its tree-lined boulevards, museums, art galleries, the Arc de Triomphe and of course the famous Eiffel Tower, this cosmopolitan city has plenty to offer. Less than 30 miles from the heart of the capital, a fun-packed trip to Disneyland Paris is also within reach.

DÉPARTEMENTS: 75 PARIS, 77 SEINE-ET-MARNE, 78 YVELINES, 91 ESSONE, 92 HAUTS-DE-SEINE, 93 SEINE-ST-DENIS, 94 VAL DE MARNE, 95 VAL D'OISE

MAJOR CITIES: PARIS, VERSAILLES, IVRY, MELUN, NANTERRE, BOBIGNY, CRETEIL AND PONTOISE

One of the most chic and culturally rewarding cities in the world, Paris has something for everyone. The list of things to do is virtually endless and could easily fill many holidays with window shopping, the Eiffel Tower, Notre Dame, Montmartre, trips on the Seine, pavement cafés and the Moulin Rouge, the list goes on.

As a peaceful retreat, you can relax and enjoy the lush scenery of surrounding hills and secret woodlands of the Ile de France. Square bell towers in gentle valleys, white silos on endless plains of wheat; soft and harmonious landscapes painted and praised by La Fontaine, Corot and all the landscape painters. Paris is surrounded by forests: Fontainebleau, Compiègne, Saint-Germain-en-Laye, and majestic châteaux such as Fontainbleau and Vaux-le-Vicomte.

Disneyland Resort Paris provides a great day out for all the family with two fantastic theme parks with over 70 attractions and shows to choose from. On the outskirts of Paris is Parc Astérix. with one of Europe's most impressive roller-coasters.

Places of interest

Fontainebleau: château and national museum, history of Napoléon from 1804-1815.

Malmaison: château and national museum.

Meaux: agricultural centre, Gothic cathedral, chapter house and palace.

Paris: obviously! The list of places is too extensive to include here.

St Germain-en-Laye: château, Gallo-roman and Merovingian archaeological museum.

Sèvres: ceramics museum.

Thoiry: château and Parc Zoologique, 450-hectare park with gardens and African reserve containing 800 animals.

Versailles: Royal Castle, Royal Apartments, Hall of Mirrors, Royal Opera and French History Museum.

Cuisine of the region

Although without a specific cuisine of its own, Paris and Ile de France offer a wide selection of dishes from all the regions of France. Paris also has a wide choice of foreign restaurants, such as Vietnamese and North African.

www.new-paris-idf.com
info@nouveau-paris-idf.com
(0)1 44 50 19 98

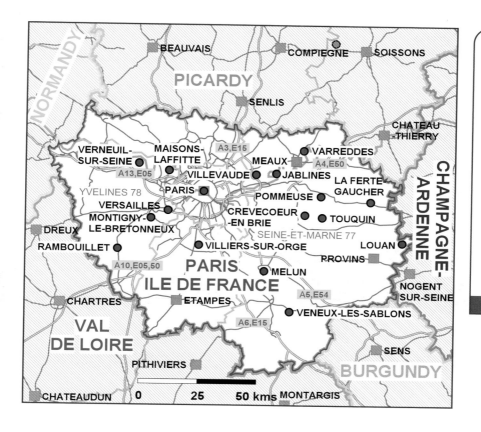

Crèvecoeur-en-Brie

Caravaning des 4 Vents

Rue de Beauregard, F-77610 Crèvecoeur-en-Brie (Seine-et-Marne) T: 01 64 07 41 11. E: f.george@free.fr
alanrogers.com/FR77040

This peaceful, pleasant site has been owned and run by the same family for over 35 years. There are around 200 pitches, with many permanent or seasonal units, however, there are 130 spacious grassy pitches for tourists, well separated by good hedges, all with 6A electricity and a water tap shared between two pitches. The whole site is well landscaped with flowers and trees everywhere. This is a great family site with pool and games facilities located at the top end of the site so that campers are not disturbed. Crèvecoeur celebrates the 'feast of small villages' on 21/22 June each year. Central Paris is just a 40 minute train ride from the nearest railway station (8 km), Disneyland is just 16 km. by road.

Facilities

Three modern sanitary units (heated in cooler weather) provide British style WCs, washbasins (mainly in cubicles) and pushbutton showers. Facilities for disabled visitors. Laundry facilities. Motorcaravan service point. In high season (July/Aug) a mobile snack bar and pizzeria (open 16.00-23.00), and a baker (07.30-11.00). Well fenced, circular swimming pool (16 m. diameter; June to Sept). Playground, games room, volleyball court, billiard hall and boules court. Riding (high season). Off site: La Houssaye 1 km. Fontenay Tresigny 5 km.

Open: 1 March - 1 November.

Directions

Crèvecoeur is just off the D231 between A4 exit 13 and Provins. From north, pass obelisk and turn right onto the C3 in 3 km. From south 19 km. after junction with N4, turn left at signs to village. Follow site signs. GPS: 48.75063, 2.89708

Charges 2011

Per unit incl. 2 persons and electricity	€ 27,00
extra person (over 5 yrs)	€ 6,00

For latest campsite news, availability and prices visit
alanrogers.com

Jablines

International de Jablines

Base de Loisirs, F-77450 Jablines (Seine-et-Marne) T: 01 60 26 09 37. E: welcome@camping-jablines.com
alanrogers.com/FR77030

Jablines is a modern site which, with the leisure facilities of the adjacent 'espace loisirs', offers an interesting, if a little impersonal, alternative to other local sites. Man-made lakes provide opportunities for many water-based activities. The Grand Lac is said to have the largest beach on the Ile-de-France. The site itself has 150 pitches, of which 141 are for touring units. Most are of a good size, often slightly sloping, with gravel hardstanding and grass, accessed by tarmac roads and marked by fencing panels and shrubs. All have 10A electrical connections, 60 have water and waste connections. The whole complex close to the Marne has been developed around old gravel workings. Whilst staying on the campsite, admission to the Base de Loisirs is free. Water activities include catamaran sailing, windsurfing, water boarding, canoeing, fishing and supervised bathing, plus a large equestrian centre, an orienteering course, a multisport court and mountain-bike trails. In high season the activities at the leisure complex are supplemented by a bar/restaurant and a range of very French style group activities.

Facilities

Two toilet blocks, heated in cool weather, include pushbutton showers, some washbasins in cubicles. Dishwashing and laundry facilities. Motorcaravan service point (charged). Shop (9/4-5/11). Play area. Internet point in reception. Ticket sales for Disneyland and Parc Astérix. Mobile homes for rent. Off site: Bar/restaurant adjacent (500 m) at Base de Loisirs with watersports, riding, tennis and minigolf. Fishing, horse riding, bicycle hire, beach, boat launching all 500 m. Golf 15 km.

Open: 9 April - 5 November.

Directions

From A4 Paris-Rouen turn north on A104. Take exit 8 on D404 Meaux/Base de Loisirs Jablines. From A1 going south, follow signs for Marne-la-Vallée using A104. Take exit 6A Clay-Souilly on N3 (Meaux). After 6 km. turn south on D404 and follow signs. GPS: 48.91378, 2.73451

Charges 2011

Per unit incl. 2 persons	
and electricity	€ 24,00 - € 27,00
extra person	€ 6,00 - € 7,00

Camping Cheques accepted.

L'international de Jablines - www.camping-jablines.com - Tel: 0160260937

Base de loisirs de Jablines-Annet (77450)

La Ferté Gaucher

Flower Camping la Ferté Gaucher

Route de Saint Martin-des-Champs, F-77320 La Ferté Gaucher (Seine-et-Marne) T: 01 64 20 20 40
E: info@flowercampings-la-ferte-gaucher.com alanrogers.com/FR77150

La Ferté Gaucher is an attractive town in the valley of the Grand Morin, a tributary of the Marne. The site is a member of the Flower group and extends over four hectares of parkland. There are 199 grassy pitches with 149 available for touring, all of a good size and with electrical connections. The river runs through the site but is well fenced. The bar/restaurant has an imaginative menu with barbecues arranged in fine weather. Occasional evening entertainment is organised during the peak season. Shops, bars and restaurants are within walking distance.

Facilities

Two very traditional sanitary blocks (desperately in need of renovation) provide basic facilities including pushbutton showers, some washbasins in cubicles and a mix of British and Turkish-style WCs. Facilities for disabled visitors. Motorcaravan service point. Good little bar and restaurant with takeaway (all season). Fishing. Play area. Occasional entertainment and activities. Mobile homes for rent. Off site: Tennis and swimming pool adjacent. Bicycle hire 600 m. Riding 12 km. Golf 30 km. Disneyland 55 km.

Open: 1 March - 30 November.

Directions

From A4 autoroute, leave at exit 16 (Crécy-la-Chapelle). Take D934 southeast through Coulommiers to la Ferté Gaucher. In town centre look for signs for 'Camping Municipal' or 'Ensemble Sportif'. Site is on D14 towards St Martin-des-Champs. GPS: 48.78232, 3.31205

Charges guide

Per unit incl. 2 persons	
and electricity	€ 15,00 - € 26,00
extra person	€ 3,00 - € 4,00

For latest campsite news, availability and prices visit

alanrogers.com

Louan

Yelloh! Village Paris/Ile-de-France

Route de Montaiguillon, F-77560 Louan (Seine-et-Marne) T: 04 66 73 97 39
E: info@yellohvillage-paris-iledefrance.com alanrogers.com/FR77140

Formerly known as la Cerclière, this Yelloh! Village site to the east of Paris lies at the heart of the Montaiguillon forest, around 50 km. from Disneyland Paris and 80 km. from the city itself. This 11-hectare site contains 220 pitches, of which 40 are currently for touring units and 72 for mobile homes and chalets of which 20 are privately owned. The current pitches are well shaded, although some are rather small and only a few have electricity. The site boasts some impressive amenities including a swimming pool with water slides, as well as a balnéotherapy pool.

Facilities

Six toilet blocks, but when we visited only three were in use with quite a walk from some pitches. Provision was fairly basic with limited facilities for disabled visitors, motorcaravans and chemical disposal. Shop. Bar. Restaurant. Takeaway. Swimming pool complex with slides. Balneotherapy pool. Multisports pitch. Bicycle hire. Tennis. Fishing. Overhead cable runway for over 8 year olds (charged). Pony rides (charged). Activity and entertainment programme. Play area. Internet access and WiFi (charged). Off site: Disneyland Paris 50 km.

Open: 26 April - 6 September.

Directions

Take exit 16 from the A4 (Paris-Metz) and join the N34. Continue as far as la Ferté Gaucher and then turn right to join the southbound D204. Upon reaching the N4 turn left and then right on to the D15 to Villiers St Georges. Continue on D60 to Louan Villegruis Fontaine from where site is currently signed as la Cerclière. GPS: 48.63095, 3.49193

Charges guide

Per unit incl. 2 persons and electricity	€ 14,00 - € 35,00

Maisons-Laffitte

Camping Caravaning International

1 rue Johnson, F-78600 Maisons-Laffitte (Yvelines) T: 01 39 12 21 91. E: ci.mlaffitte@wanadoo.fr
alanrogers.com/FR78010

This site on the banks of the Seine is consistently busy, has multilingual, friendly reception staff and occupies a grassy, tree covered area bordering the river. There are 351 pitches, with 57 occupied by mobile homes and 70 used by tour operators, plus two areas dedicated to tents. Most pitches are separated by hedges, are of a good size with some overlooking the Seine (unfenced access), and all 195 touring pitches have electricity hook-ups (6A). The roads leading to the site are a little narrow so large vehicles need to take care. Train noise can be expected.

Facilities

Three sanitary blocks, two insulated for winter use and one more open (only used in July/Aug). Facilities are clean, with constant supervision necessary due to volume of visitors. Provision for visitors with disabilities. Laundry and dishwashing areas. Motorcaravan service point. Self-service shop. Restaurant/bar. Takeaway food and pizzeria (all open all season). TV in restaurant, table tennis, football area. Internet point. Off site: Sports complex adjoining. Riding 500 m. Bicycle hire 5 km.

Open: 27 March - 31 October.

Directions

Best approached from A13 or A15 autoroute. From A13 take exit 7 (Poissy) and follow D153 (Poissy), the D308 (Maisons-Laffitte), then site signs on right. From A15 exit 7 take D184 towards St Germain, after 11 km. turn left on D308 (Maisons-Laffitte). Follow site signs. GPS: 48.9399, 2.14589

Charges 2011

Per unit incl. 2 persons and electricity	€ 26,70 - € 32,20

Melun

Kawan Village la Belle Etoile

Quai Joffre, la Rochette, F-77000 Melun (Seine-et-Marne) T: 01 64 39 48 12. E: info@campinglabelleetoile.com
alanrogers.com/FR77070

Alongside the River Seine, this site has an overall mature and neat appearance, although the approach road is somewhat off-putting with several industrial plants. However, you will discover that La Belle Etoile enjoys a pleasant position with pitches to the fore of the site within view of the barges which continually pass up and down. The 170 touring pitches, 130 with 6A electricity connections, are on grass and laid out between the many shrubs and trees. There are ten units for hire. A friendly, family run site with pleasant and helpful English speaking owners, it is ideally situated for visiting Fontainebleau and Paris.

Facilities

The toilet blocks are not new but they are kept very clean and the water is very hot. Laundry room. Baby bath. Facilities for disabled visitors (shower, washbasin and WC). Motorcaravan service point. Small bar, snacks, shop and takeaway (all 1/7-29/8). Heated outdoor swimming pool (1/5-15/9). Play area. Bicycle hire. Tickets for Disney and Vaux le Vicomte. Off site: Fontainebleau and Paris. Bus to connect with trains 100 m. Fishing 100 m.

Open: 27 March - 17 October.

Directions

Travelling north on RD606 Fontainebleau - Melun road, on entering La Rochette, pass petrol station on left. Turn immediately right into Ave de la Seine. At end of road turn left to site on left in 500 m. GPS: 48.52502, 2.66940

Charges guide

Per unit incl. 2 persons	€ 20,00 - € 23,00
Camping Cheques accepted.	

For latest campsite news, availability and prices visit

alanrogers.com

Montigny-Le-Bretonneux

Campéole Parc Etang

Base de Loisirs, F-78180 Montigny-Le-Bretonneux (Yvelines) T: 01 30 58 56 20. E: parc-etang@campeole.com
alanrogers.com/FR78080

This site is close enough to Paris to go there for day trips but, on the other hand, it is secluded enough to allow visitors a peaceful, quiet stay away from the bustle which is Paris. The site has 500 pitches stretching over 12 hectares and is located next to a leisure park – ideal for cyclists and joggers. Numerous trees provide shade whilst sun worshippers can also find pitches to suit their needs. Most of the 100 touring pitches are divided by hedges and have electricity hook-ups (French style plug 6/10A).

Facilities

Five toilet blocks include facilities for disabled visitors but none for children/families. They are rather dilapidated with showers, washbasins in cabins, British and Turkish style toilets. No laundry. Motorcaravan service point. Bar serving basic snacks. Bread to order from reception (no shop). Play area with bouncy castle. Off site: Large supermarket close by. Versailles 7 km. Paris 1 hour by car. Fishing 800 m.

Open: All year.

Directions

From the A12 motorway take exit for St Quentin en Yvelines. Join N10 and follow signs to 'Centre Commercial', then 'base de loisirs'. GPS: 48.7895, 2.03361

Charges guide

Per unit incl. 1 or 2 persons	€ 11,00 - € 14,20
extra person	€ 4,00 - € 5,50
electricity	€ 4,00

Paris

Camping du Bois de Boulogne

2 allée du Bord de l'eau, F-75016 Paris (Paris) T: 01 45 24 30 00. E: camping-boulogne@stereau.fr
alanrogers.com/FR75020

A busy site and the nearest to the city, set in a wooded area between the Seine and the Bois de Boulogne. The site is quite extensive but nevertheless becomes very full with many international visitors, with noise well into the night, despite the rules. There are 510 pitches of varying size (including mobile homes and a few chalets) of which 280 are marked, with electricity (10A), water, drainage and TV aerial connections. The site has undergone a huge improvement and development programme including the refurbishment of toilet blocks. Reservations are made – if not booked, arrive early in season (mornings).

Facilities

Most toilet blocks have British style WCs, washbasins in cubicles and showers with divider and seat (warm water throughout). All these facilities suffer from heavy use in season. One laundry room. Five motorcaravan service points. Shop. Bar and restaurant. Bar open 07.00-24.00 most times and until 02.00 in high season. Pizza bar and takeaway. Small Playground. Information service. Off site: Fishing 1 km. Bicycle hire 2 km.

Open: All year.

Directions

Site is on east side of Seine between the river and the Bois de Boulogne, just north of the Pont de Suresnes. Easiest approach is from Port Maillot. Traffic lights at site entrance. Follow signs closely and use a good map. GPS: 48.86829, 2.23545

Charges guide

Per unit incl. 2 adults, 2 children and electricity	€ 26,60 - € 39,90
extra person	€ 4,60 - € 6,80
child (under 7 yrs)	€ 2,40 - € 3,20

Pommeuse

Camping le Chêne Gris

24 place de la Gare de Faremoutiers, F-77515 Pommeuse (Seine-et-Marne) T: 01 64 04 21 80
E: info@lechenegris.com alanrogers.com/FR77020

This site is being progressively developed by a Dutch holiday company. A principal building houses reception on the ground floor and also an airy restaurant/bar plus a takeaway. Of the 350 pitches, 30 are for touring, many of which are on aggregate stone, the rest (higher up the hill on which the site is built) being occupied by over 230 mobile homes and 85 tents belonging to a Dutch tour operator. Terraces look out onto the heated leisure pool complex and an adventure-type play area for over-fives, whilst the play area for under-fives is at the side of the bar with picture windows overlooking it.

Facilities

One toilet block with pushbutton showers, washbasins in cubicles and a dishwashing and laundry area. At busy times these facilities may be under pressure. A second block is to be added. Facilities for disabled visitors. Bar, restaurant, takeaway and swimming pool complex (all season). Off site: Shops, bars and restaurants within walking distance. Fishing and riding 2 km.

Open: 20 April - 8 November.

Directions

Pommeuse is 55 km. east of Paris. From A4 at exit 16 take N34 towards Coulommiers. In 10 km. turn south for 2 km. on D25 to Pommeuse; site on right after level-crossing. Also signed from south on D402 Guignes - Coulommiers road, taking D25 to Faremoutiers. GPS: 48.808213, 2.993935

Charges 2011

Per unit incl. 2 persons and electricity	€ 25,00 - € 44,00
extra person	€ 2,50 - € 5,00
child (3-11 yrs)	€ 2,50 - € 3,00
Camping Cheques accepted.	

For latest campsite news, availability and prices visit

alanrogers.com

Rambouillet

Huttopia Rambouillet

Rue du Château d'Eau, F-78120 Rambouillet (Yvelines) T: 01 30 41 07 34. E: rambouillet@huttopia.com
alanrogers.com/FR78040

This pleasant site is now part of the Huttopia group whose philosophy is to 'rediscover the camping spirit'. It is in a peaceful forest location beside a lake, with good tarmac access roads and site lighting. The 146 touring pitches, 100 with electrical connections, are set among the trees and in clearings. As a result, shade is plentiful and grass sparse. The main area is kept traffic-free but there is a section for motorcaravans and those who need or prefer to have their car with them. The result is a safe, child-friendly site. There is an 'espace nature' with 40 huge pitches for campers. As part of their efforts to be environmentally friendly, Huttopia have built a natural swimming pool – the water is filtered by reeds and it was used for the first time in 2008 and passed the stringent tests of France's Ministry of Health. The opening date each year depends on how quickly the reeds do their work, but it will certainly be open from June to September. From your pitch, you can stroll out into the forest and there are many good cycle routes and footpaths in the area. Rambouillet itself is an interesting town and Chartres and Versailles are within easy reach. It is possible to visit Paris by rail (a 30 minute journey) and the Mobilis 'transport package' ticket is available from the railway station.

Facilities

The brand new sanitary block has controllable showers, some washbasins in cubicles and a number of more spacious 'family' cubicles. Facilities for disabled visitors. Laundry facilities. Three outlying 'rondavels' each with two family rooms. Motorcaravan service point. Small shop (all season) selling basics plus bar/restaurant with terrace (weekends in low season and daily in July and August). Games room with TV. Free internet and WiFi. Play area. 'Natural' swimming pool (June-Sept, earlier if possible). Bicycle hire. Fishing. Children's and family activities with a 'natural' theme (July-Aug). No American motorhomes or twin-axle caravans. Off site: Riding 5 km. Lake with beach 15 km. Golf 15 km. Sailing 20 km. Shops, bars and restaurants in town plus large supermarket nearby.

Open: 25 March - 6 November.

Directions

Rambouillet is 52 km. southwest of Paris. Site is southeast of town: from N10 southbound take Rambouillet/Les Eveuses exit, northbound take Rambouillet centre exit, loop round (site signed) and rejoin N10 southbound, taking next exit. Pass under N10, following signs to site in 1.7 km.
GPS: 48.62638, 1.84375

Charges guide

Per unit incl. 2 persons and electricity	€ 17,50 - € 26,20
extra person	€ 5,50 - € 6,90
child (2-7 yrs)	€ 3,00 - € 4,30
dog	€ 4,00

Touquin

Camping les Etangs Fleuris

Route Couture, F-77131 Touquin (Seine-et-Marne) T: 01 64 04 16 36. E: contact@etangs-fleuris.com

alanrogers.com/FR77090

This is a pleasant, peaceful site which has a very French feel. The 90 touring pitches are grouped on level ground around the attractive lakes, all with electricity (10A) and water, separated by hedges and with shade from mature trees. The life of the site centres round a smart bar/function room which doubles as the reception and shop, as well as the lakes and an attractive, irregularly shaped pool. The lakes are home to some sizeable carp as well as being restocked daily with trout (fishing € 5 for half a day). Ideal base to visit Paris (50 km) and Disneyland (23 km) and to provide a practical alternative to the busier sites nearer the centre.

Facilities

A fairly simple, heated toilet block has pushbutton showers and open washbasins (with dividers and hooks) for men but mainly in cubicles for ladies. No facilities for disabled visitors. Another heated block is only opened when site is very busy. Laundry facilities. Motorcaravan service area. Shop for basics in bar (1/4-15/9). Heated pool with paddling section (15/4-15/9). Takeaway meals and snacks (15/5-13/8). Internet access and WiFi. Multisports pitch. Minigolf. Trampoline. Off site: Riding 5 km. Golf 15 km. Zoo 5 km.

Open: 4 April - 15 September.

Directions

Touquin is off the D231, 21 km. from exit 13 of the A4 motorway and 30 km. northeast of Provins. From D231 follow signs for Touquin, then Etangs Fleuris. Site is 2.5 km. west of village.
GPS: 48.733054, 3.046978

Charges 2011

Per unit incl. 2 persons and electricity	€ 19,00
extra person	€ 9,50
child (2-10 yrs)	€ 4,00
dog	€ 1,50

CAMPING Les Etangs Fleuris★★★
Camping Qualité
Only 25 minutes from Disneyland Resort Paris!
CAMPING Les Etangs Fleuris★★★ • Route de la Couture • 77131 Touquin
Tél.: +33 164 04 16 36 • Fax: +33 164 04 12 28
E-mail: contact@etangs-fleuris.com • www.etangs-fleuris.com
GPS location: 48.733054 / 3.046978

Varreddes

Le Village Parisien

Route de Congis (D121), F-77910 Varreddes (Seine-et-Marne) T: 01 64 34 80 80
E: contact@villageparisien.com alanrogers.com/FR77050

If you are intending to visit Disneyland, this site is ideally situated 12 km. away. Tickets can be purchased at the site and taxi travel can be arranged. The site has 224 pitches and is reasonably well cared for with mature hedges dividing the pitches. There are about 50 used for touring units and these vary both in size and quality. Access on some could be difficult for larger units. Le Village Parisien is unfortunately rather dominated by the large number of seasonal pitches (80%). The three toilet blocks are old and only just adequate. There is a reasonably large swimming pool (unheated). The opening of the facilities, such as the bar and shop are somewhat erratic and depends on the numbers on the site and whether it is a school or public holiday.

Facilities

Three toilet blocks (old and in need of refurbishment). Dishwashing and laundry facilities. Small shop and takeaway. Bar with entertainment and TV. Swimming and paddling pools (unheated). Tennis. Play area. Fishing. Bicycle hire. Tickets and taxis for Disneyland. Off site: Golf 10 km.

Open: 15 March - 1 November.

Directions

Heading south on the A1 towards Paris, turn southeast on N330 at Senlis. Head towards Meaux, then turn left on D405 for Varreddes. Site is well signed from here (about 2 km).
GPS: 49.002938, 2.941412

Charges guide

Per unit incl. 2 persons and electricity	€ 19,00 - € 29,00
extra person (over 4 yrs)	€ 4,00
dog	free
Camping Cheques accepted.	

For latest campsite news, availability and prices visit

alanrogers.com

Veneux-les-Sablons

Camping les Courtilles du Lido

Les Courtilles du Lido, chemin du Passeur, F-77250 Veneux-les-Sablons (Seine-et-Marne) T: 01 60 70 46 05
E: lescourtilles-dulido@wanadoo.fr   alanrogers.com/FR77130

Les Courtilles du Lido is a well established, family-run site located just outside the 14th-century village of Moret-sur-Loing on the edge of the Forêt de Fontainebleau. There are 180 well shaded grassy pitches with 10A electricity, dispersed throughout the five-hectare terrain. A good range of amenities includes a pool and an 18-hole minigolf course, as well as a pizzeria and bar. There are 17 mobile homes for rent. Paris lies 55 km. to the north and can be accessed by either the A5 or A6 motorways or by rail from the local station (within walking distance). Some train noise can be heard from the site. The close proximity of Fontainebleau, just 5 km. distant, is, of course, a major attraction and the town merits repeated visits. The château was once the home of the kings of France. Fontainebleau's golf course is the second oldest in France and many other activities are possible in the area, including rock climbing and 25 km. of walking and cycle trails through the forest.

Facilities

A single toilet block provides adequate facilities. No facilities for children or disabled visitors. Shop, Pizzeria, bar and takeaway (all season). Outdoor swimming pool (15/5-22/9). Play area. Games room. Motorcaravan services. Minigolf. Short tennis. Boules. Internet access and free WiFi. Off site: Moret-sur-Loing (an attractive Gallo-Roman village) 2 km. Fishing 500 m. Canoeing. Golf 10 km. Riding 15 km. Fontainebleau 5 km. River cruises 5 km. Paris 55 km.

Open: 3 April - 20 September.

Directions

Site is close to the point where the Loing joins the Seine. From Fontainebleau take the southbound N6 (towards Sens). Upon arrival at Veneux les Sablons follow signs for Moret-sur-Loing and then St Mammès. Final approach is through a tunnel. Site is well signed. GPS: 48.38321, 2.80303

Charges guide

Per unit incl. 2 persons and electricity	€ 16,00 - € 22,00
extra person	€ 4,00
child (under 10 yrs)	€ 3,00 - € 8,50

Camping Les Courtilles du Lido - Chemin du Passeur - 77250 Veneux les Sablons
Tel: 0033 160 70 46 05 - Fax: 0033 164 70 62 65
E-mail: lescourtilles-dulido@wanadoo.fr - www.les-courtilles-du-lido.fr

Verneuil-sur-Seine

Camping le Val de Seine

Base de Loisirs, chemin du Rouillard, F-78480 Verneuil-sur-Seine (Yvelines) T: 01 39 28 16 20
E: vds78@orange.fr   alanrogers.com/FR78050

This is an excellent little site, completely refurbished to high standards and located in a large leisure and country park on the western outskirts of Paris. Campers have free access to the huge country park (800 m. from site) with its three large lakes, one with a beach for swimming, others for sailing and pedalo hire. The site has 87 pitches in two sections, one end for campers (mainly groups) with its own toilet block, the other for caravans and tents. Here there are 37 level pitches, all but four with electricity (6A), water and drainage. There is some aircraft and train noise.

Facilities

Two modern toilet blocks have controllable showers and some washbasins in cubicles. Facilities for disabled visitors (touring area). Dishwashing provision. Small block for children plus baby room (camping area). Laundry facilities. Motorcaravan service point. Reception sells bread (to order) and basics. Country park with lakes, fishing, sailing, many other sports facilities, a self-service restaurant and brasserie. Tennis, Minigolf. Communal barbecue in camping area. Off site: Riding adjacent. Golf 7 km. Paris 20 mins by train, 30 mins by car.

Open: 15 April - 30 September.

Directions

From A13 take exit 8 (Meulan-les Mureaux). Follow signs for 'Base de Loisirs du Val de Seine'. Go through Les Mureaux and bear right on D154 towards Verneuil. At roundabout turn left (signed 'Base de Loisirs') to site. GPS: 48.99643, 1.9601

Charges guide

Per unit incl. 2 persons and electricity	€ 14,50 - € 16,60
extra person (over 4 yrs)	€ 3,25 - € 3,75
dog	€ 2,00

For latest campsite news, availability and prices visit

alanrogers.com

Versailles

Huttopia Versailles

31 rue Berthelot, F-78000 Versailles (Yvelines) T: 01 39 51 23 61. E: versailles@huttopia.com

alanrogers.com/FR78060

This Huttopia site is rather different. When the French owners visited Canada and experienced 'back to nature' camping, they were so impressed that they decided to introduce the idea to France. This is a little like camping as it used to be, but with some big differences. Gone are the formal pitches with neatly trimmed hedges and instead there are 148 of ample size, arranged informally among the trees, 93 with electricity (10A) and 14 with water and drainage as well. The terrain is as nature intended with very little grass and much of it steep and rugged (there are plans to introduce some terracing). Long electricity leads are required and be prepared to use blocks and corner steadies on many pitches, most of which have good shade. All the site buildings are designed and built to fit into the natural concept. Wooden huts, tents and gypsy style caravans can be rented. This is a different but popular site that will suit campers who, while still wanting their creature comforts, like to be in more natural surroundings.

Facilities

Three well designed toilet blocks (wood cabin style) are evenly dispersed around the site and provide basic facilities. Special bivouacs set up for cooking and washing up. Restaurant with takeaway food (May-Sept). Bar (all season). Games room. Simple swimming and paddling pools (May-Sept). Playground. Bicycle hire. Children's club. Off site: Versailles and its château (tickets can be purchased at the site). Hiking. Cycling trails. Fishing 1 km. Golf 3 km. Riding 5 km. Paris 20 minutes by RER express train from Versailles.

Open: 25 March - 6 November.

Directions

From the front of the château of Versailles take the Avenue de Paris and the site is signed after 2 km. GPS: 48.78967, 2.15633

Charges guide

Per unit incl. 2 persons	
and electricity	€ 27,85 - € 40,95
extra person	€ 6,20 - € 8,70
child (2-7 yrs)	€ 3,00 - € 4,50
dog	€ 4,00

Villevaudé

Camping Club le Parc de Paris

Rue Adèle Claret, Montjay la Tour, F-77410 Villevaudé (Seine-et-Marne) T: 01 60 26 20 79
E: info@campingleparc.fr alanrogers.com/FR77110

This rural, sloping site (open all year) is conveniently situated as an overnight stop or for a visit to Disneyland or to Paris. The 200 largely level, grassy touring pitches all have access to 6A electricity, though some areas have yet to be fully prepared for use. There are 100 mobile homes for rent. The new owners have ongoing plans for improving the site. A ten minute drive takes you to a station on a Metro (RER) line to Paris and there is free parking. Disneyland and Parc Astérix are easily reached via the motorways.

Facilities

The three toilet blocks have some washbasins in cabins, mainly British-style toilets and pushbutton showers. Facilities for young children and disabled visitors. Laundry. Motorcaravan service point. Bar, snack bar and takeaway. Play area. Games area. TV room. Internet access in reception and WiFi throughout (charged). Off site: Fishing, riding and golf 6 km. Paris 20 km. Disneyland 20 km. Parc Astérix 40 km.

Open: All year.

Directions

From the north: A1 Paris, join A104 Marne la Vallée and leave at exit 6B onto N3. After Claye-Souilly turn right on D404 towards Villevaudé and follow signs to site on left. From the south: A4 Reims, Metz, Nancy, join A104 Lille and take exit 8 to join D404 towards Claye-Souilly and Villevaudé then follow signs to site on right after village. GPS: 48.91282, 2.67465

Charges guide

Per unit incl. 2 persons	
and electricity	€ 21,00 - € 29,00
extra person	€ 4,00 - € 7,00
child (3-11 yrs)	€ 3,00 - € 5,00

Villiers-sur-Orge

Camping le Beau Village de Paris

1 voie des Prés, F-91700 Villiers-sur-Orge (Essonne) T: 01 60 16 17 86. E: le-beau-village@wanadoo.fr
alanrogers.com/FR91010

This is a pleasant, typically French campsite just 25 km. south of Paris and conveniently located at the centre of a triangle formed by the A6 motorway, the N20/A10 to Orleans and the N104 east/west link road 'La Francilienne'. Half of its 100 pitches are occupied on a seasonal basis by Parisians or by mobile homes to rent; the remainder are touring pitches, all hedged and with 10A electricity. Trees provide some shade. Reception, in a traditionally-styled building, also has a pleasant little bar, a games room and an attractive terrace with wooden tables, benches, thatched canopies and a stone-built barbecue.

Facilities

Three toilet blocks, heated as required, have controllable showers and some washbasins in cabins. The main block has been refurbished and has a baby changing room and laundry facilities. A second (older) block has adequate facilities for disabled visitors, the third is in a Portacabin with some additional washbasins outside in a very tired row of cubicles. Small bar (open high season and on demand). Games room. WiFi in reception area (free sessions). Adventure play area. Free loan of canoes. Boules. Off site: Station with trains to Paris (in 20 mins) 700 m. Tennis and football adjacent. Restaurants and shops nearby. Golf, riding 2 km. River beach and sailing 3 km. Boat launching 4 km.

Open: All year.

Directions

Villiers-sur-Orge is 25 km. south of Paris. From the A6 leave at exit 6 (Savigny-sur-Orge). Turn southwest, follow signs for Quartier Latin on D25 then right at roundabout on D35 to Villiers-sur-Orge. Turn left immediately after river on Voie des Prés along river bank to site on left. From A10 turn east on N104. From N104 take N20 north. From N20 at Ballainvilliers take exit for La Ville du Bois on D35 southeast to Villiers-sur-Orge. In village (foot of hill), turn right, then as above. GPS: 48.65527, 2.30409

Charges 2011

Per unit incl. 2 persons and electricity	€ 18,00 - € 20,00
extra person	€ 4,50 - € 5,00
child (0-7 yrs)	€ 2,25 - € 2,50
animal	€ 2,00

For latest campsite news, availability and prices visit
alanrogers.com

The varied landscapes of Champagne-Ardenne include dense forests, vineyards and winding rivers. The whole area is dotted with fascinating ancient churches and castles, towns and villages.

DÉPARTEMENTS: 08 ARDENNES, 10 AUBE, 51 MARNE, 52 HAUTE-MARNE

MAJOR CITY: REIMS, TROYES

Situated on the flatlands of Champagne are the most northerly vineyards in France where special processing turns the light, dry wine into 'le Champagne'. Nowhere else in the world are you allowed to make sparkling wine and call it Champagne. Reims and Epernay are the centres for the wine trade. It is not the names of the vineyards that have become famous but those of the shippers, such as Moët & Chandon and Veuve Clicquot.

Champagne-Ardenne is a very rich cultural land which offers, from the Belgian border to the gates of Burgundy, a rich heritage and diverse sites which shouldn't be missed: the cathedral of Reims, a listed UNESCO World Heritage Site, the largest fortified castle in Europe in Sedan, the picturesque medieval alleys of Troyes, the loft of Renoir in Essoyes or the all new Memorial of General de Gaulle in Colombey-les-Deux-Eglises. Nature is all around: meanders of the Meuse River deeply embanked in the Ardennes Massif, the great lakes of Champagne between Saint-Dizier and Troyes, hiking trails leading into deep forests. A wonderful preserved environment ideal for getting in touch with nature.

CHAMPAGNE ARDENNE

TOURISME

www.**tourisme-champagne-ardenne.com**

Champagne

Perching Bar in Verzy

Perched over 18 feet high in a tree, the Perching Bar enjoys an exceptional view over the plains of Champagne. The bar offers a large choice of great brands and wine growers' champagnes.

www.perchingbar.eu

Cellier Saint-Pierre

In the heart of Troyes, opposite the cathedral, discover a unique place and taste different wines and fine liquors.

www.celliersaintpierre.fr

Cycling

La Voie Verte Trans-Ardennes

Running along the spectacular Meuse River valley, the Trans-Ardennes cycle path offers an easy 85 km. ride between Charleville-Mézières and Givet, near the Belgian border. The route passes through the beautiful landscape of the Ardenne massif from north to south.

www.ardennes.com

Les Voies Vertes du Lac du Der

Several 'green tracks' run through the Pays du Der: the loop around the lake (38 km) mainly uses the dykes and offers panoramic views of the 4,800 ha. lake. The loop can be extended to reach Saint-Dizier (12 km), Montier-en-Der (12 km) and Vitry-le-François (20 km).

www.lacduder.com

Heritage

Reims Cathedral

The Cathedral of Notre Dame de Reims, built in the 13th century is a masterpiece of Gothic art and one of the most important buildings of the European Middle Ages. In 2011 the 8th centenary will be celebrated.

www.reims-tourisme.com

Mémorial du Général De Gaulle

The new General De Gaulle Memorial is equipped with the most modern techniques to celebrate the history of Charles de Gaulle and of France in the 20th century.

www.memorial-charlesdegaulle.fr

Champagne and land
AUTHENTIC FLAVOURS

- Let your imagination enjoy this unique vineyard.
- Follow the slopes for unexpected walks.
- Visit the oldest cellars.
- Discover the secret of the most mythical of wines.
- Enjoy its exuberant effervescence !

A region full of history where our love of good things is second nature which amateurs and professionals love share throughout the year. There is a 350 miles Champagne Route to discover. Behind every slope and each vinta legends and secrets are transmitted from generation to generation. Come and shed light on the mystery of bubbles.

Don't wait anymore, find all the information on
www.champagne-ardenne-tourism.co.uk
To organise your next tasting

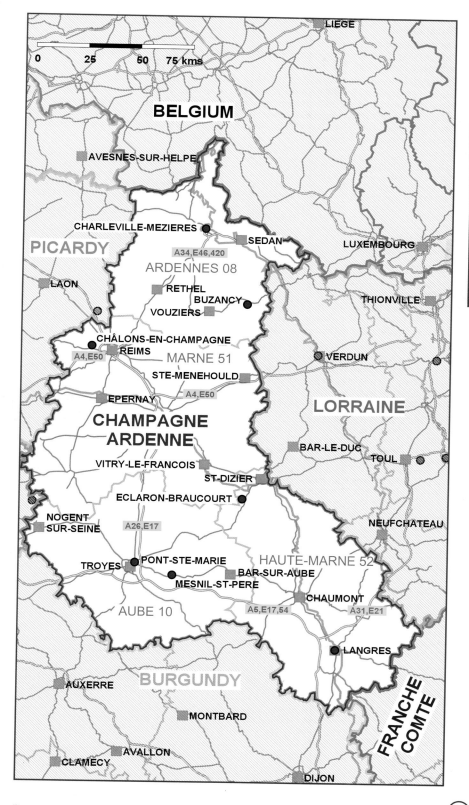

For latest campsite news, availability and prices visit
alanrogers.com

Buzancy

Camping la Samaritaine

Rue des Etangs, F-08240 Buzancy (Ardennes) T: 03 24 30 08 88. E: info@campinglasamaritaine.com

alanrogers.com/FR08040

A delightful new site in the heart of the Ardennes. It is peacefully situated just outside the village beside a stream. There may be some high season noise from a nearby lake, where you can swim or fish. Flowers decorate the entrance and bushes and saplings separate the pitches. The 101 numbered touring pitches all have electricity (10A) and are on level grass off hard access roads. They vary in size up to 130 sq.m. 55 have water and drainage and there are small wooden containers for waste. There are also ten mobile homes and nine chalets for rent.

Facilities

Sanitary facilities provide private cabins. Baby bath. Facilities for disabled visitors. Laundry facilities. Motorcaravan service point. Bread delivered daily. A few essentials are kept in reception. Snack bar/takeaway (20/6-31/8). Large recreation room with games and tables. Play area. Boules. Accompanied walks and entertainment programme (high season). Off site: Restaurant in village.

Open: 1 May - 20 September.

Directions

Buzancy is about 22 km. east of Vouziers on the RD947 towards Stenay and Montmédy. Site is just over 1.5 km. from centre of village down a small road. Well signed. GPS: 49.42640, 4.94010

Charges guide

Per unit incl. 2 persons and electricity	€ 16,50 - € 18,50
extra person	€ 3,00 - € 3,50
child (under 10 yrs)	€ 2,00 - € 2,50
No credit cards.	

Châlons-en-Champagne

Camping de Châlons-en-Champagne

Rue de Plaisance, F-51000 Châlons-en-Champagne (Marne) T: 03 26 68 38 00
E: camping.mairie.chalons@wanadoo.fr alanrogers.com/FR51020

The location of Châlons, south of Reims and near the A4 and A26 autoroutes, about 200 miles from Calais and Boulogne, makes this an ideal stopover. This site on the southern edge of town is an example of a good municipal site. The wide entrance with its neatly mown grass and flower beds sets the tone for the rest of the site; 96 of the 148 pitches, accessed from tarmac roads, are on a gravel base with the rest on grass. All have electricity (10A). The generously sized gravel pitches are separated by hedges. The newest area of pitches overlooks the small lake.

Facilities

Two toilet blocks (one can be heated) include washbasins in cabins, baby room and hairdressing station. Facilities for disabled visitors. Laundry and dishwashing facilities. Refuse bins. Bread to order. Bar (20/5-30/9), snack bar and takeaway (1/6-30/9). Gas supplies. Games and TV rooms. Playground. Minigolf, tennis, volleyball, boules, mini-football. Motorcaravan service point. Off site: Bus stop. Fishing. Horse riding 1 km. Golf 15 km.

Open: 2 April - 31 October.

Directions

From north on A4, take La Veuve exit (27) onto N44 which by-passes town. Leave at last exit (St Memmie), follow camping signs. From south on A26, take exit 18 on N77 and towards town. Site well signed 'Camping', (south of town on D60). GPS: 48.9359, 4.3832

Charges guide

Per unit incl. 2 persons and electricity	€ 18,90
extra person	€ 5,15
child (under 16 yrs)	€ 2,50
vehicle	€ 3,45

Charleville-Mezieres

Camping Municipal du Mont Olympe

Rue des Paquis, F-08000 Charleville-Mezieres (Ardennes) T: 03 24 33 23 60
E: camping-charlevillemezieres@wanadoo.fr alanrogers.com/FR08010

Attractively situated alongside the Meuse River, within easy walking distance across a footbridge to the centre of the pleasant large town, this site was completely rebuilt in 2002. It now offers excellent facilities, with 129 grass pitches, all with electricity (10A), water and waste water connections. There are 66 from 108 to 219 sq.m. in size, 49 up to 106 sq.m. and seven hardstandings for motorcaravans.

Facilities

Two heated buildings provide first class showers, private cabins, baby rooms and facilities for disabled visitors. Well equipped laundry room. Motorcaravan service point. Shop (July/Aug). Play area. TV and games room. Barbecues allowed at communal area only. Off site: Municipal pool next door. Boat trips on the river. Attractive town centre close by. Bicycle hire 1 km. Golf 20 km.

Open: 1 April - 1 October.

Directions

Site north of Charleville on island of Montcy St Pierre. From north D988/D1 follow river, over bridge, then immediately left. From southeast (A203/N51/N43) take 'centre' exit, head for 'gare' then follow Avenue Forest north and sharp left after bridge. Site is 150 m. on from old site. GPS: 49.7790, 4.7207

Charges guide

Per unit incl. 2 persons and electricity	€ 15,31 - € 17,61
extra person	€ 3,35
child (2-10 yrs)	€ 1,70

For latest campsite news, availability and prices visit

alanrogers.com

Eclaron-Braucourt

Flower la Presqu'île de Champaubert

F-52290 Eclaron-Braucourt (Haute-Marne) T: 03 25 04 13 20. E: ilechampaubert@free.fr
alanrogers.com/FR52010

This site is situated beside what is said to be the largest man-made inland lake in Europe (4,800 ha.), the Lac du Der Chantecoq. This provides superb facilities for windsurfing, sailing, etc. and even for swimming from a 100 m. beach alongside the site (lifeguard in main season). The site itself is on the shores of the lake, with 195 fairly level grassy pitches of a good size, 70 for tourers, all with electrical connections (7A) and many with hardstanding. They are separated by hedges and trees that also provide a fair amount of shade. The general appearance and the views across the lake are very attractive.

Facilities

The current toilet block, although old, is fully equipped and clean. Laundry facilities. Motorcaravan service point. Small shop for essentials in reception area. Bar/restaurant. New toilet block and a new heated swimming pool are planned. Playground. Bicycle hire. Fishing. Mobile homes for rent. Off site: Beach for swimming. Miles of walking and cycle tracks. Birdwatching. Sailing and windsurfing on Lac de Der. Montier-en-Der with shops, restaurants and ATM 10 km.

Open: 3 April - 11 September.

Directions

From St Dizier, take D384 past Eclaron to Braucourt and follow signs to the site (3 km). GPS: 48.55425, 4.79235

Charges guide

Per unit incl. 2 persons	
and electricity	€ 15,00 - € 31,00
extra person	€ 4,00 - € 5,00
child (3-7 yrs)	free - € 5,00
dog	€ 4,00

Eclaron-Braucourt

Yelloh! Village en Champagne

F-52290 Eclaron-Braucourt (Haute-Marne) T: 04 66 73 97 39
E: info@yellohvillage-en-champagne.com **alanrogers.com/FR52050**

Formerly known as Les Sources du Lac, this Yelloh! Village site is located close to the village of Eclaron and has direct access to the Lac du Der. This is a very large lake with 77 km. of shoreline and is home to over 270 species of birds. Part of the lake is an ornithological reserve but a wide range of water based activities are on offer in other areas. These include including fishing, windsurfing and sailing, and a separate area is reserved for motor boats. There are just 30 touring pitches here and around 120 mobile homes and chalets for rent.

Facilities

Two toilet blocks include facilities for babies. The facilities may be under pressure at busy times. Shop (July/Aug). Bar. Restaurant. Takeaway. Swimming pool. Paddling pool. Direct access to the lake and beach. Play area. Bicycle hire. Fishing. Ornithological activities. Activity and entertainment programme. Off site: Riding 10 km. Walking and cycle trails. Fishing. The 'Champagne route'. Grange aux Abeilles (bee barn) at Giffaumont Champaubert.

Open: 1 May - 30 September.

Directions

Take the southbound N44 from Chalons-en -Champagne as far as Vitry-le François and then join the eastbound N4 as far as St Dizier. From the St Dizier ring road take the D384 towards Montier-en -Der and upon reaching Eclaron-Braucourt follow signs to the site. GPS: 48.57213, 4.84891

Charges guide

Per unit incl. 2 persons	€ 15,00 - € 30,00
extra person (over 3 yrs)	€ 4,00 - € 5,00
child (3-7 yrs)	free - € 5,00

Langres

Kawan Village Lac de la Liez

Peigney, F-52200 Langres (Haute-Marne) T: 03 25 90 27 79. E: campingliez@free.fr
alanrogers.com/FR52030

Managed by the enthusiastic Baude family, this excellent lakeside site is near the city of Langres. Only 10 minutes from the A5, Camping Lac de la Liez provides an ideal spot for an overnight stop en route to the south of France. There is also a lot on offer for a longer stay. The site provides 131 fully serviced pitches, some with panoramic views of the 250 hectare lake with its sandy beach and small harbour where boats and pedalos may be hired. Ideal for swimming and watersports, access to the lake is down steps and across quite a fast road (in total 150 m).

Facilities

Two toilet blocks have all facilities in cabins (only one is open in low season). Facilities for disabled visitors and babies. Laundry facilities. Motorcaravan services. Shop, bar and restaurant (with takeaway food). Indoor pool complex with spa and sauna. Heated outdoor pool (15/6-15/9). Games room. Playground. Extensive games area. Tennis (free in low season). WiFi. Off site: Lake with beach. Boat and bicycle hire and cycle tracks around lake. Fishing 100 m. Riding 5 km. Golf 40 km.

Open: 1 April - 15 October.

Directions

From Langres take the N19 towards Vesoul. After 3 km. turn right, straight after the large river bridge, then follow site signs. GPS: 47.87022, 5.37627

Charges guide

Per unit incl. 2 persons	
and electricity	€ 22,00 - € 31,00
extra person	€ 6,00 - € 8,00
child (2-12 yrs)	€ 3,00 - € 4,50
dog	€ 3,00
Camping Cheques accepted.	

We can book this site for you! Call 01580 214000 alan rogers travel

For latest campsite news, availability and prices visit
alanrogers.com

Langres

Camping Navarre

9 boulevard Maréchal de Lattre de Tassigny, F-52200 Langres (Haute-Marne) T: 03 25 87 37 92
E: campingnavarre@free.fr alanrogers.com/FR52060

Camping Navarre is a small municipal site of 66 pitches, with the advantage of being located in a unique position within the town of Langres. The pitches here are grassy, well shaded and of a good size, mostly with electrical connections. The site's toilet block has all the usual facilities and is a new building of architectural merit. Although there are few amenities on site, the town centre is just a short walk away with a wide selection of shops, cafés and restaurants. Langres, with its 3.5 km. of ancient ramparts and imposing towers, is classified as one of the 50 most beautiful towns in France and makes a popular overnight stop. For those choosing to spend longer in the Haute-Marne, the surrounding countryside, Lac de la Liez (resulting from the construction of the Marne - Saône canal) and the Marne valley are well worth exploration. The Liez sailing school offers opportunities for windsurfing, sailing, and canoe and pedalo hire.

Facilities

Modern, heated toilet block with facilities for disabled visitors. Washing machines. Play area. WiFi (free, near reception). Off site: Langres centre. Lac de la Liez 5 km. Fishing (river) 3 km. Cycle and walking tracks.

Open: 15 March - 31 October.

Directions

Langres is close to the intersection of the A5 and A31 motorways. Leave either motorway and head for the town centre. Site is well signed.
GPS: 47.86085, 5.33029

Charges guide

Per unit incl. 2 persons and electricity	€ 12,10 - € 14,10
extra person	€ 2,30 - € 2,70
child (2-13 yrs)	€ 1,20 - € 1,40

For a one-night stop or a longer stay in the historical city of Langres the campsite Navarre is ready to welcome you with a brand new toilet block

Camping Navarre • 9, Boulevard Marechal de Lattre de Tassigny • 52200 Langres
Tél./fax: 0033 (0)325 87 37 92 • E-mail: campingnavarre@free.fr • www.campingnavarre.fr

For latest campsite news, availability and prices visit
alanrogers.com

Mesnil Saint Père

Kawan Resort Lac d'Orient

Rue du Lac, F-10140 Mesnil Saint Père (Aube) T: 03 25 40 61 85. E: info@camping-lacdorient.com
alanrogers.com/FR10020

Le Lac d'Orient opened in 2009 and is one of the first Kawan Resorts, a new group of campsites in attractive rural locations and equipped with a good range of leisure amenities. The site can be found at the centre of the large Forêt d'Orient natural park and is just 100 m. from the Lac d'Orient which is ideal for all manner of watersports. Previously, a small municipal site, Kawan Resort Lac d'Orient has been rebuilt and offers a new restaurant, bar and takeaway, as well as a heated indoor pool and outdoor swimming pools with slides, all in one complex with the reception and the shop. The pitches here are large and are semi-shaded with mature trees. There are 135 pitches, a few occupied by mobile homes and chalets. All pitches have electrical connections and some also offer water and drainage.

Facilities

One new, purpose built toilet block and one totally refurbished, both of a high standard. Facilities for disabled visitors. Laundry facilities. Motorcaravan services (outside site). Restaurant, bar and takeaway (1/4-1/10). Shop (1/4-1/10). Heated indoor pool (1/4-1/10) and outdoor swimming pools with slides (1/5-1/10). Paddling pool. Spa bath. TV room. Play area. Multisport court. Only one dog per pitch accepted. Off site: Troyes centre 20 km. Lac d'Orient 100 m. Windsurfing and sailing. Canoe and pedalo hire. Fishing. Cycle and walking tracks.

Open: 26 March - 30 September.

Directions

Mesnil Saint-Père is close to the intersection of the A5 and A26 motorways, 20 km. east of Troyes. From the north, leave the A26 at exit 23 and join the eastbound D619, signed Lac d'Orient. Turn left on D43 following signs to Mesnil Saint-Père and then site. From the south on the A5 take exit 22, the D443 to Vendeuvre then D619 towards Troyes. After 9 km. turn right to Mesnil Saint-Père and signs to site. GPS: 48.254856, 4.341359

Charges 2011

Per unit incl. 2 persons and electricity	€ 25,00 - € 34,00
extra person	€ 6,00 - € 8,00
child (under 7 yrs)	€ 3,00 - € 4,00
Camping Cheques accepted.	

Pont-Sainte-Marie

Camping Municipal de Troyes

7 rue Roger Salengro, F-10150 Pont-Sainte-Marie (Aube) T: 03 25 81 02 64. E: info@troyescamping.net
alanrogers.com/FR10010

This municipal campsite, within the Troyes city boundary and about 2 km. from the centre, has been taken over by two young enthusiastic managers who are turning it into an attractive place to stay. Their plans include adding a heated pool for 2010. There are 110 level grassy pitches (six with hardstanding), all for tourers, mostly equally shaded and open. Electricity connections and water points are to be improved for the 2010 season. Being on one of the main routes from Luxembourg to the southwest of France, and on the main route from Calais to the Mediterranean, Troyes makes a good night stop. As the old capital of the Champagne region, it is also a delightful city, with a marvellous mediaeval centre and interesting museums, and is well worth a longer stay.

Facilities

Two modern toilet blocks contain British style WCs, washbasins and preset showers. Facilities for disabled visitors. Motorcaravan services. Washing machines and dryer. Shop for basics. Gas supplies. Restaurant, snack bar and takeaway (15/5-15/9). TV room. Games room. Playground. Minigolf. Boules. Bicycle hire. Off site: Bus to Troyes centre 100 m. Supermarket 100 m. Other shops, restaurants, bars, ATM 300 m. Riding 8 km.

Open: 1 April - 15 October.

Directions

From all routes follow signs for Troyes and Pont-Sainte-Marie (just north of the old city centre), then signs for Camping Municipal. Site is on the Chalons road no. 77. GPS: 48.31124, 4.09683

Charges guide

Per person	€ 4,80
child (2-11 yrs)	€ 3,35
pitch	€ 7,00
electricity (5A)	€ 2,80

For latest campsite news, availability and prices visit
alanrogers.com

The Vosges Massif, green in summer and covered with snow in winter, large lakes and ponds, the Route des Crêtes and three regional nature parks. A large region with beautiful panoramas to explore on foot, by bicycle or on four wheels.

DÉPARTEMENTS: 54 MEURTHE-ET-MOSELLE, 55 MEUSE, 57 MOSELLE, 88 VOSGES

MAJOR CITIES: NANCY AND METZ

In 2010 the city of Metz joined the greatest international capitals of modern art with the opening of the Centre Pompidou-Metz, a building of extravagant architecture. The contrast with the cathedral of Saint-Etienne and the city's historic yellow stone buildings couldn't be greater. Nancy, the other important city, boasts a World Heritage Site with the famous Stanislas Square and is renowned for its Art Nouveau architecture and decorations.

Lorraine is also a region of historical events and sites commemorating the military past, that are both impressive and moving. The way of life in Lorraine consists of a subtle mix of French elegance and influences from over the borders (being the only French region bordering three other countries). The gastronomy reflects this in a delicious way: quiche lorraine, excellent yellow plums eaten on their own, in jam, in pastry, in liqueurs and in many other culinary specialities.

La Lorraine
tourisme-lorraine.fr

Nature

The blue line of the Vosges

The line of the horizon in green and blue can be admired from the Route des Crêtes, which runs past the mountain tops of the Vosges Massif.

Gastronomy

Le caviar de Bar-le-Duc

The name of the jam made of currants deseeded with a goose quill since 1344!

Macaroons of Nancy and Boulay

Fine mix of almonds, sugar and egg white.

Le Crillon des Vosges

Rhubarb wine, from very dry to very mellow!

Vittel and Contrexéville

Famous for their mineral waters and thermal springs.

Places of interest

Le plan incliné de Saint-Louis-Arzviller

Unique in Europe, a spectacular lift for boats.

Military memorials

Impressive citadels of Bitche and Montmédy.

Verdun with red zone, underground citadel and memorial.

The charnel house of Douaumont and the great works of the Maginot Line.

Images © (left to right, top to bottom): M Laurent; M Laurent; M Laurent; M Ehrhard; Nancy; Centre Pompidou-Metz, avril-mai 2010 © Shigeru Ban Architects Europe et Jean de Gastines Architectes, avec Philip Gumuchdjian Architectes pour la conception du projet lauréat du concours / Metz Métropole / Centre Pompidou-Metz / Photo Roland Halbe

BELGIUM
LUXEMBOURG

LUXEMBOURG

GERMANY

THIONVILLE

A30

SAARBRUCKEN

A4,E25,50

SARREGUEMINES

VERDUN

A4,E50

METZ

FRANCALTROFF

MEUSE 55

A31,E21,E23

MOSELLE 57

LORRAINE

SARREBOURG

ALSACE

BAR-LE-DUC

NANCY
VILLERS-LES-NANCY

TOUL
VILLEY-LE-SEC

LUNEVILLE

MEURTHE-ET-MOSELLE 54

A31,E21

NEUFCHATEAU

ST-DIE-DES-VOSGES

HERPELMONT

CORCIEUX

SANCHEY

GRANGES-
SUR-VOLOGNE

REHAUPAL
LE THOLY

VOSGES 88

LA BRESSE

CHAUMONT

SAULXURES-SUR-MOSELOTTE

BUSSANG

ST-MAURICE-SUR-MOSELLE

THANN

CHAMPAGNE
ARDENNE

LANGRES

FRANCHE
COMTE

LURE

VESOUL

0   25   50 kms

For latest campsite news, availability and prices visit
alanrogers.com

Bussang

Kawan Village Domaine de Champé

14 rue des Champs-Navés, F-88540 Bussang (Vosges) T: 03 29 61 61 51. E: info@domaine-de-champe.com

alanrogers.com/FR88050

Bordered by the Moselle river, surrounded by the mountains of the Vosges and located just off the town square, this site is open all year making it a good base from which to explore in summer, and ideal for skiing in winter, when you might be tempted to rent one of the 12 chalets. Domaine de Champé is a level site with 110 touring pitches, all with electricity (4-12A), spread over a fairly large area on both sides of a tributary stream, so some are quite a distance from the facilities. There are two heated pools, one large outside and a smaller one inside. The village boasts a Theatre of the People, founded in 1895, giving shows in July and August. The Casino is open all year and is very popular.

Facilities

Two sanitary units, one behind reception, one more central, are adequate rather than luxurious and include two family rooms. Facilities for disabled campers. Motorcaravan services. Bar, restaurant (all year), takeaway (high season). Swimming pools (outdoor 1/5-30/9, indoor all year). Wellness centre (charged) including sauna, hammam and relaxation room. Tennis. Two large play areas. Internet access and WiFi (charged). Off site: Skiing 3 km. Lake fishing 3.5 km. Riding 4 km. Skiing 3 km. Shops and all other services at Le Thillot 10 km.

Open: All year.

Directions

Bussang is about midway between Remiremont and Mulhouse on N66, almost due north of Belfort. Site is signed from town centre.
GPS: 47.888617, 6.85715

Charges guide

Per unit incl. 2 persons	
and electricity	€ 22,00 - € 31,00
extra person	€ 5,00 - € 8,00
child (4-10 yrs)	€ 3,00 - € 5,00

Camping Cheques accepted.

Corcieux

Yelloh! en Vosges Domaine des Bans

Rue James Wiese, F-88430 Corcieux (Vosges) T: 03 29 51 64 67. E: info@yellohvillage-domaine-des-bans.com

alanrogers.com/FR88080

Domaine des Bans is a large, busy holiday village with plenty of opportunities to be busy and open all year. There is a very high percentage of static and tour operator units, but room for about 80 touring units. These pitches are numbered, vary in size and are scattered around the campsite with some on low terraces. Most have good shade and all have electricity, water and drainage. Some are tucked away in quiet areas, with others closer to where activities take place. Not ideal for short stays, it is better as a base for exploring the varied and interesting countryside.

Facilities

Three functional toilet blocks provide all necessary facilities including for disabled visitors and babies. Shop and bar (30/5-15/9). Restaurant (1/5-15/9). Takeaway (30/4-15/9). Large swimming pool complex (outdoor 1/6-15/9, indoor 1/5-15/9). Playground and area for ball games. Tennis. Minigolf. Archery. Bicycle hire. Riding. Three lakes for fishing and boating. High season entertainment including discos (soundproof room). 'Goats' Castle' with about two dozen goats. Internet access. WiFi.

Open: 26 April - 6 September.

Directions

Corcieux is about 25 km. south of St Dié. From St Dié - Gérardmer road (N415, then D8), turn west on D60 just north of Gerbépal to Corcieux. Site is signed and is just south of the town.
GPS: 48.16903, 6.88028

Charges guide

Per unit incl. 2 persons	
extra person	€ 15,00 - € 39,00
child (3-7 yrs)	€ 5,00 - € 7,00
	free - € 7,00

Corcieux

Camping Au Clos de la Chaume

21 rue d'Alsace, F-88430 Corcieux (Vosges) T: 03 29 50 76 76. E: info@camping-closdelachaume.com

alanrogers.com/FR88120

This pleasant site is within walking distance of the town, on level ground with a small stream adjacent. The friendly family owners, who are British and French, live on site and do their best to ensure campers have an enjoyable and relaxing stay. There are 100 level grassy pitches of varying sizes and with varying amounts of sun and shade. All have electricity hook-ups (6/10A) and some are divided by shrubs and trees. There are some chalets and caravan holiday homes on the site, which boasts an attractive, well fenced, new swimming pool and a small adventure style playground. A Sites et Paysages member.

Facilities

Two units (one newly refurbished) provide well maintained facilities including a dual-purpose room for families and disabled visitors. Laundry with washing machines and dryers. Motorcaravan service point. Reception keeps basic supplies (July/Aug). New swimming pool (June -Sept). Play area. Games room. Boules. Volleyball. WiFi. Off site: Bicycle hire 800 m. Riding 2 km. Fishing 3 and 10 km. Golf 30 km. Corcieux market (Mondays).

Open: 30 April - 18 September.

Directions

Corcieux is 17 km. southwest of St Dié-des-Vosges. Site is on the D60, east of town centre, by the town boundary sign. GPS: 48.16826, 6.89025

Charges 2011

Per unit incl. 2 persons	
and electricity	€ 16,00 - € 20,80
extra person	€ 4,80
child (2-7 yrs)	€ 3,00

For latest campsite news, availability and prices visit

alanrogers.com

Francaltroff

Parc Résidentiel de la Tensch

F-57670 Francaltroff (Moselle) T: 03 87 01 79 04. E: tensch@tensch.com

alanrogers.com/FR57090

La Tensch is a large leisure park located south of St Avold in the Moselle département. The park has been developed around three lakes and fishing is understandably very popular here, although many watersports are also possible, including windsurfing, canoeing and jet skiing. Although there are 100 touring pitches, this is primarily a 'parc résidentiel' with a few mobile homes and chalets for rent, as well as residential units. Many footpaths lead around the lakes passing picnic areas and well designed playgrounds. There are two swimming pools, one especially for children with a water slide. There is plenty to do in the park with a tennis court, skate park, trampolines and a minigolf course. St Avold is a large town with an interesting old centre. To the north of the town, Europe's largest American military cemetery can be found and the town enjoys close links with the USA. The southern parts of the Moselle are heavily forested and offer some excellent opportunities for cycling and walking.

Facilities

Shop. Bar/restaurant. Takeaway. Swimming pool. Children's pool. Pedaloes. Canoe hire. Bicycle hire. Tennis. Trampolines. Play area. Games room. Activity and entertainment programme. Mobile homes and chalets for rent. Off site: Riding. Fishing. Cycle and walking tracks. St Avold.

Open: 20 March - 19 December.

Directions

Leave the A4 autoroute at exit 39 for St Avold and head south on D633 to St Avold. Continue south on D22 to Francaltroff and the site is clearly signed. GPS: 48.96083, 6.77444

Charges guide

Per unit incl. 2 persons and electricity	€ 25,60
extra person	€ 3,80
child (3-7 yrs)	€ 1,80
dog	€ 1,00

Granges-sur-Vologne

Camping la Sténiole

1 le Haut Rain, F-88640 Granges-sur-Vologne (Vosges) T: 03 29 51 43 75. E: steniole@wanadoo.fr

alanrogers.com/FR88110

Set in a lovely rural area in the heart of the Vosges massif, this attractive site is run by a dedicated young couple who are constantly improving the site and its facilities. There are 70 pitches, either separated by hedges or beside the water. A small river has been used to form a small lake for fishing and swimming and a series of separate ponds (water quality is checked regularly). An atmosphere of relaxation is encouraged and the whole family can have a good time here. At an altitude of 720 m. there is easy access to 160 km. of paths and tracks for walking and cycling. In winter cross-country skiing is possible locally, with Alpine skiing available at Gérardmer 20 minutes away. There are apartments and studios to rent at the site.

Facilities

A new toilet block now supplements the original, and with further facilities in the main building provides all necessities including 4 private cabins. Washing machines and dryers. Bar. Restaurant (July/Aug). Takeaway (1/6-30/8). Internet access on the terrace. Lake swimming. Fishing. Games room with TV and library. Play area. Tennis. Apartments and mobile homes to rent. Off site: Woods and hills for walking and cycling. Riding 5 km. Bicycle hire 10 km. Golf 30 km.

Open: 1 May - 30 September.

Directions

Take the N420 from Epinal to Gérardmer then the D423 to Granges. There are two sites not far away from each other. GPS: 48.1217, 6.8284

Charges guide

Per unit incl. 2 persons and electricity	€ 15,00 - € 17,00
extra person	€ 3,50
child (under 8 yrs)	€ 2,50
dog	€ 1,00

For latest campsite news, availability and prices visit

alanrogers.com

Herpelmont

Camping Caravaning Domaine des Messires

1 rue des Messires, F-88600 Herpelmont (Vosges) T: 03 29 58 56 29. E: mail@domainedesmessires.com
alanrogers.com/FR88070

Nestling in woods beside a lake, des Messires is a haven of peace and perfect for nature lovers – not just birds and flowers but beavers, too. The Vosges is famous for its mountains and you can easily cross the Col de Schlucht to the Moselle vineyards and the medieval villages like Riquewihr with their old walls and storks on chimneys. The 110 good-sized and fully-serviced pitches are on grass over stone, with some directly by the lakeside, excellent for fishing. When the day is over, enjoy a leisurely meal at the restaurant overlooking the lake or just relax over a glass of wine. There are also 22 mobile homes for rent. For the more active, canoes are available free of charge in low season; swim in the lake or visit the nearby partner site for a swim in their pool. Should the weather be inclement, try some of the old-fashioned wooden games, play indoor minigolf or watch the satellite TV in the lounge with its open fire, near the bar. You are going to be spoilt for choice. Groups are catered for in an area away from the main touring section, but still overlooking the lake at one end of the campsite.

Facilities

The fully equipped, modern, airy toilet block includes all washbasins in cabins, provision for disabled visitors (key from reception), baby room and laundry. Bar and restaurant overlooking the lake (both 1/5-1/10). Takeaway (1/5-1/10). Two small play areas. Games and TV room. Canoeing and lake swimming. Programme of activities for children and adults in high season. WiFi (charged). Off site: Weekly markets in nearby Bruyères, Corcieux and St Dié. Riding and golf 12 km.

Open: 23 April - 18 September.

Directions

From Épinal, exit N57 on N420 for St Dié and follow signs until you pick up signs for Bruyères. Lac du Messires is signed as you leave Bruyères on D423, at Laveline go south to Herpelmont and site. GPS: 48.1787, 6.74309

Charges guide

Per unit incl. 2 persons and electricity	€ 18,00 - € 25,50
extra person	€ 4,00 - € 6,50
child (6-12 yrs)	€ 3,00 - € 5,00

Domaine des Messires ****
1 la Feigne
88600 Herpelmont
Tel 03 29 58 56 29
www.domainedesmessires.com

La Bresse

Domaine du Haut des Bluches

5 route des Planches, F-88250 La Bresse (Vosges) T: 03 29 25 64 80. E: hautdesbluches@labresse.fr
alanrogers.com/FR88210

Le Haut des Bluches is attractively located in the rolling hills of the Vosges and is close to the ski resorts of Gérardmer and Xonrupt-Longemer. The site is open most of the year with skiing possible in winter and it is a good base for nature lovers in summer. There are 140 slightly uneven and sloping grass/gravel pitches informally laid out in groups on terraces. These include 108 for touring, all with electricity (4/8/13A), long leads and rock pegs advised. Special areas of hardstanding for motorcaravans include some electricity hook-ups. Although there is little organised on the site, La Bresse (4 km) has a wide range of activities on offer. The swimming pool in La Bresse is free in high season for campers under 12 years old and there is also a luge and skating rink.

Facilities

Two well appointed, modern, heated toilet blocks include cabins with WC, basin and shower. Facilities for babies and campers with disabilities. Motorcaravan services. Small shop (bread to order) and bar (all year). Restaurant and takeaway (high season and weekends in low season). Games/TV room. Play area. Multisport court. Boules. Internet. Off site: Several ski resorts, 5-8 km. La Bresse with shops, bars, restaurants, museums and market 4 km.

Open: All year excl. November to mid December.

Directions

La Bresse is 25 km. south of Gérardmer on the D486. At the eastern end of the town turn south on Route des Planches. Site is signed, entrance in 350 m. GPS: 47.998986, 6.918324

Charges 2011

| Per unit incl. 2 persons and electricity | € 13,60 - € 22,80 |
| extra person | € 3,00 |

For latest campsite news, availability and prices visit
alanrogers.com

Le Tholy
Camping de Noirrupt
5 chemin de l'Etang, F-88530 Le Tholy (Vosges) T: 03 29 61 81 27
E: info@jpvacances.com alanrogers.com/FR88030

An attractive, modern, family-run site, Camping de Noirrupt has a commanding mountainside position with some magnificent views especially from the upper terraces. This is a very comfortable and high quality site and one that is sure to please. The tarmac site road winds up through the site with pitches being terraced and cars parked in separate small car parks close by. The 70 lawn-like tourist pitches are generally spacious, and the whole site is beautifully landscaped and divided up with many attractive shrubs, flower beds, decking and trees. Paved paths and steps take more direct routes between levels.

Facilities
Two very modern buildings at different levels, plus a small unit behind reception, all immaculate with modern fittings. Washbasins in cubicles, facilities for babies, children and disabled campers. Washing machines and dryer. Shop. Bar, snack bar and takeaway (4/7-20/8). Swimming pool (15x10 m. 1/6-15/9). TV room (1/6-15/9). Tennis. Organised activities in high season include wagon rides for children and accompanied hikes in the mountains. WiFi (charged). Heated chalets for rent. No double-axle caravans or American RVs. Off site: Riding 300 m. Fishing 2 or 5 km. Le Tholy with its supermarket and other services 2 km. Gérardmer with banks 10 km. Golf 30 km.

Open: 1 May - 15 October.

Directions
From Gérardmer take D417 west towards Remiremont. In Le Tholy turn right on D11, continue up hill for 2 km., and site is signed to your left.
GPS: 48.0889, 6.728483

Charges guide
Per unit incl. 2 persons and electricity	€ 23,70 - € 25,70
extra person	€ 5,80
child (under 7 yrs)	€ 3,30
dog	€ 1,50

Metz
Camping Municipal de Metz-Plage
Allée de Metz-Plage, F-57000 Metz (Moselle) T: 03 87 68 26 48. E: campingmetz@mairie-metz.fr
alanrogers.com/FR57050

As this site is just a short way from the autoroute exit and within easy walking distance for the city centre, it could make a useful night stop if travelling from Luxembourg to Nancy or for a longer stay if exploring the area. By the Moselle river, the 151 pitches are on fairly level grass and most are under shade from tall trees. 65 pitches are fully serviced and 84 have electricity (10A). Tent pitches have a separate area beside the river. The new Pompidou-Metz Art Centre is well worth a visit, if only to see the building's wonderful architecture.

Facilities
The two sanitary blocks, one newer than the other, are acceptable if not luxurious. Facilities for disabled visitors. Baby room. Laundry and dishwashing facilities. Motorcaravan service point. Shop. Bar, restaurant and takeaway. Hardstanding pitches for over night stops for motorcaravans without electricity. WiFi (free). Bicycle hire. Fishing (permits for sale). Off site: Indoor pool adjacent (free entry). Riding 5 km. Golf 8 km.

Open: 24 April - 5 October.

Directions
From autoroute take Metz-Nord-Pontiffray exit (no. 33) and follow the site signs.
GPS: 49.12402, 6.16917

Charges guide
Per unit incl. 2 persons and electricity	€ 18,00
extra person	€ 3,00
child (4-10 yrs)	€ 1,50
dog	€ 0,50

Rehaupal

Camping du Barba

45 le village, F-88640 Rehaupal (Vosges) T: 03 29 66 35 57. E: barba@campingdubarba.com

alanrogers.com/FR88100

Located in the refreshing and beautiful Haute-Vosges region, this small, very pleasant campsite is owned and run by a dedicated couple. There is room for 50 units on well tended, unmarked grass where you pitch where you like. This creates a very relaxed, natural environment with hedges and mature trees providing shelter and shade. The site is in the heart of the village with an auberge next door for fine wines and good food, including local specialities. The surrounding hills offer 150 km. of marked walking and bike trails. Gérardmer and the Valley of the Lakes are just 15 minutes away.

Facilities

The single toilet block, built in chalet style, is of a high standard and should be sufficient. Washing machine and dryer. Bread delivered. Auberge next door for meals and takeaway (to order) and small shop. Off site: Supermarket 5 km. Walking, cycling, skiing and fishing. Riding 6 km.

Open: 1 May - 1 October.

Directions

From Gérardmer follow signs to Rehaupal. Site is very well signed. GPS: 48.11892, 6.73130

Charges guide

Per unit incl. 2 persons	
and electricity	€ 14,80 - € 17,50
extra person	€ 3,60
child (under 7 yrs)	€ 2,00

Saint Dié-des-Vosges

Kawan Village Vanne de Pierre

5 rue du camping, F-88100 Saint Dié-des-Vosges (Vosges) T: 03 29 56 23 56. E: vannedepierre@orange.fr

alanrogers.com/FR88130

La Vanne de Pierre is a neat and attractive site with 118 pitches, many of which are individual with good well trimmed hedges giving plenty of privacy. There are 13 chalets and mobile homes (for rent) and a few seasonal units, leaving around 101 touring pitches, all multi-serviced with water, drainage and electricity hook-up (6/10A). The reception building has been recently refitted and provides a well stocked small shop plus a restaurant/bar with a takeaway facility (all year but opening hours may vary). A small L-shaped outdoor swimming pool (max depth 1.5 m) is well fenced and a programme of children's entertainment is arranged in July and August. The city centre is an easy 2 km. cycle ride or a level walk alongside the river. Places to visit include the St Dié Cathedral, Museum Pierre-Noël and Liberty Tower.

Facilities

Main unit is heated with good facilities including washbasins in cubicles. Three family rooms each with WC, basin, and shower and two similar units fully equipped for disabled campers. Dishwashing and laundry rooms. A second, older unit (opened July/Aug). Shop. Bar/restaurant and takeaway. Swimming pool (1/4-30/9, weather permitting). Internet access. Gas supplies. Bicycle hire. Nordic walking is organised. Off site: Golf, tennis, archery and riding all 1 km. Fishing. Supermarkets.

Open: All year.

Directions

Site is east of St Dié on north bank of river Meurthe and south of D82 to Nayemont les Fosses. Site is well signed. GPS: 48.2858, 6.96898

Charges guide

Per unit incl. 2 persons	
and electricity	€ 22,00 - € 31,00
extra person	€ 5,00 - € 8,00
child (4-10 yrs)	free - € 5,00
Camping Cheques accepted.	

Saint Maurice-sur-Moselle

Camping les Deux Ballons

17 rue du Stade, F-88560 Saint Maurice-sur-Moselle (Vosges) T: 03 29 25 17 14
E: stan@camping-deux-ballons.fr alanrogers.com/FR88010

Les Deux Ballons is in a narrow valley near the source of the River Moselle in the Vosges. The 168 pitches (150 fully serviced, 4-15A electricity) are on stoney ground or grass, some under trees and others in the open by a stream that runs through the site. Wild birds are abundant, including kingfishers. Try an exhilarating walk to the top of the nearby Ballon d'Alsace (1250 m), or drive and walk the last half mile. Theatre lovers should visit Bussang (6 km) and see the large wooden People's Theatre, built in 1895 and still performing in July and August every year; you will marvel at the raked stage and the enormous backstage areas which may be visited at any time.

Facilities

Two new up-to-date toilet blocks (open all season) and two older ones (high season only). Facilities for disabled campers and babies. Laundry. Motorcaravan service point. Gas supplies. Bar, snack bar and takeaway (all July/Aug). Large heated swimming pool with slide and children's pool (15/6-31/8). Walks, fishing, boules. TV. Internet point and WiFi (charged). Tennis. Bicycle hire. Off site: Shops and restaurant nearby. Riding 3 km.

Open: 10 April - 15 September.

Directions

Site is on main N66 Le Thillot - Bussang road on western edge of St Maurice behind Avia filling station (entrance partly obscured - keep a look out). GPS: 47.85517, 6.81108

Charges guide

Per unit incl. 2 persons	
extra person	€ 16,30 - € 27,20
child (2-7 yrs)	€ 5,35 - € 5,60
	€ 4,00
No credit cards (on-line bookings excepted).	

We can book this site! Call 01580 214000

alanrogers travel

We can book this site for you! Call 01580 214000

alanrogers travel

For latest campsite news, availability and prices visit
alanrogers.com

Sanchey

Kawan Village Lac de Bouzey

19 rue du Lac, F-88390 Sanchey (Vosges) T: 03 29 82 49 41. E: lacdebouzey@orange.fr

alanrogers.com/FR88040

Open all year, Camping Lac de Bouzey is 8 km. west of Épinal, at the start of the Vosges Massif. The 160 reasonably level grass pitches are separated by very tall trees and some hedging giving varying amounts of shade. There are 121 for touring, all with electricity (6-10A) and 100 fully serviced. They are on a gently sloping hillside above the lake and have views over the lake and its sandy beaches. In high season there is entertainment for all ages, especially teenagers and the site will be very lively. English is spoken.

Facilities

The refurbished toilet block includes a baby room and one for disabled visitors (some up- and down-hill walking). Small, heated area in main building with toilet, washbasin and shower is used in winter. Laundry facilities. Motorcaravan service point. Shop, bar, restaurant and takeaway. Heated pool (1/5-30/9). Fishing. Riding. Games room. Archery. Bicycle hire. Internet access. Soundproof room for cinema shows and discos (high season). Lake beach, bathing and boating. Off site: Golf 8 km.

Open: All year.

Directions

Site is 8 km. west of Épinal on the D460. From Épinal follow signs for Lac de Bouzey and Sanchey. At western end of Sanchey turn south, site signed. GPS: 48.16692, 6.35990

Charges guide

Per unit incl. 2 persons and electricity	€ 23,00 - € 34,00
extra person	€ 6,00 - € 10,00

Camping Cheques accepted.

Saulxures-sur-Moselotte

Base de Loisirs du Lac de la Moselotte

Les Amias B.P. 34, F-88290 Saulxures-sur-Moselotte (Vosges) T: 03 29 24 56 56
E: lac-moselotte@ville-saulxures-mtte.fr   alanrogers.com/FR88090

This neat, well run, spacious lakeside site, part of a leisure village complex, has 105 grassy pitches with 72 for touring. All have electricity (10A) and 25 of these also have water and a drain. They are individually hedged and a variety of young trees give only a little shade. The site is fully fenced with a security barrier with a key used for the gates to the lakeside. The adjacent Base de Loisirs has a wide variety of activities on offer and the area is very good for walking and cycling. This is a good base for both summer and winter.

Facilities

The heated toilet block has key entry, controllable hot showers, some washbasins in cubicles and good facilities for babies and disabled campers. Laundry facilities. Shop (July/Aug). Bread to order. Bar/snack bar and terrace (all year). Bicycle hire. Play area. Outdoor skittle alley. Entertainment programme (July/Aug). Base de Loisirs adjacent with lake (swimming supervised July/Aug), sandy beach, play area, climbing wall, fishing, archery and hire of pedaloes, canoes and kayaks. 30 chalets for rent. Off site: Saulxures-sur-Moselotte 1.5 km. with shops, bars and restaurants. Riding 2 km. Golf 15 km. Skiing 15 km.

Open: All year.

Directions

Saulxures-sur-Moselotte is 20 km. east of Remiremont. From Remiremont take D417 east (St Amé), then right (southeast) on D43 towards La Bresse for 10.5 km. Turn left into Saulxures (site signed), entrance on right by lake after 700 m. GPS: 47.95273, 6.75212

Charges guide

Per unit incl. 2 persons and electricity	€ 17,00 - € 20,00
extra person	€ 4,00 - € 5,00
child (4-10 yrs)	€ 2,40 - € 3,00

Verdun

Camping les Breuils

Allée des Breuils, F-55100 Verdun (Meuse) T: 03 29 86 15 31. E: contact@camping-lesbreuils.com

alanrogers.com/FR55010

Thousands of soldiers of many nations are buried in the cemeteries around this famous town, and the city is justly proud of its determined First World War resistance. Les Breuils is a neat, attractive site beside a small fishing lake and close to the town and Citadel. It provides 166 flat pitches of varying sizes on two levels (144 for touring units), many with shade. Separated by trees or hedges, they are beside the lake and 120 offer electricity connections (6A) – long leads will be necessary for some. The 'citadelle souterraine' is well worth a visit and is within walking distance of the site.

Facilities

Two sanitary blocks are a mixture of old and new, including washbasins in cabins for ladies. Laundry facilities. Facilities for disabled visitors and babies. Cleaning variable. Motorcaravan services. Shop (1/5-30/9). Restaurant (1/6-20/8), bar (evenings 1/5-30/9). Swimming pool (200 sq.m.) and children's pool (1/6-31/8). Fenced gravel play area. Multisports complex. Off site: Bicycle hire, town 1 km. Riding 5 km.

Open: 1 April - 30 September.

Directions

The RN3 forms a sort of ring road round the north of the town. Site is signed from this on the west side of the town (500 m. to site). GPS: 49.15404, 5.36573

Charges guide

Per person	€ 4,20 - € 5,80
child (2-10 yrs)	€ 3,00 - € 3,70
pitch	€ 3,00 - € 5,00
electricity (6A)	€ 4,00

Credit cards accepted (minimum € 15).

Villers-les-Nancy

Campéole le Brabois

Campéole

Avenue Paul Muller, F-54600 Villers-les-Nancy (Meurthe-et-Moselle) T: 03 83 27 18 28
E: brabois@campeole.com alanrogers.com/FR54000

This former municipal site is within the Nancy city boundary and 5 km. from the centre. Situated within a forest area, there is shade in most parts and, although the site is on a slight slope, the 185 good-sized, numbered and separated pitches are level. Of these, 160 pitches have electrical connections (5/15A) and 30 also have water and drainage. Being on one of the main routes from Luxembourg to the south of France, Le Brabois makes a good night stop. However, Nancy is a delightful city in the heart of Lorraine and well worth a longer stay. There are many attractions in the area including the interesting 18th-century Place Stanislas (pedestrianised) and 11th-century city centre. The British manager has a wide range of tourist literature, publishes a monthly English newsletter and is pleased to help plan visits and day trips. Horse racing takes place every two weeks at the Nancy race track next to the campsite, and good wine is produced nearby.

Facilities

Six sanitary blocks provide a mix of British and Turkish style WCs and some washbasins in cubicles. Facilities for babies and disabled visitors. Laundry facilities. Motorcaravan service point. Shop. Bread to order. Restaurant with bar and small shop (15/6-31/8). Library. Playground. Off site: Restaurants, shops 1 km. Walking and cycling. Regular buses to Nancy.

Open: 1 April - 15 October.

Directions

From autoroute A33 take exit 2b for Brabois and continue for 500 m. to 'Quick' restaurant on left. Turn left, pass racetrack to T-junction, turn right and after 400 m. turn right on to site entrance road. GPS: 48.66440, 6.14330

Charges guide

Per unit incl. 2 persons	
and electricity	€ 13,60 - € 18,70
extra person	€ 4,00 - € 5,60
child (2-6 yrs)	free - € 3,60
Credit cards minimum € 15.	

Campéole
CAMPSITES AND RENTALS

LORRAINE

Le Brabois***
Peaceful, ideal to visit Nancy
(Stanilas square).
Amenities, pitches and
accommodations of high quality.

54600 Villers Les Nancy - Tel.: +33-383-2718-28 - www.campeole.co.uk / brabois@campeole.com

Villey-le-Sec

Camping de Villey-le-Sec

34 rue de la Gare, F-54840 Villey-le-Sec (Meurthe-et-Moselle) T: 03 83 63 64 28
E: info@campingvilleylesec.com alanrogers.com/FR54010

This neat campsite is a popular overnight stop, but the area is worth a longer stay. Villey-le-Sec has its own fortifications, part of the defensive system built along France's frontiers after the 1870 war, and a long cycle track passes near the site. On a bank of the Moselle river, there are 96 level grassy marked touring pitches, with electricity (6/10A) and plenty of water taps. There are also individual water taps and waste water drainage for eight of these pitches. Another area without electricity accommodates 11 tents. Just outside the site is an overnight stopping place for motorcaravans.

Facilities

Two modern toilet blocks (one heated) contain British style toilets, washbasins in cabins and controllable showers. Facilities for disabled campers and babies. Motorcaravan services. Washing machine and dryer. Bar/restaurant. Shop. Snack bar and takeaway (all 15/4-20/9). Playground. Playing field. Table tennis. Boules. Fishing. Off site: Riding 2 km. Rock climbing 4 km. Golf 15 km.

Open: 1 April - 30 September.

Directions

Villey-le-Sec is 7 km. east of Toul. Leave A31 west of Nancy at exit 15 and after 1 km. at roundabout (Leclerc supermarket) take D909 to Villey-le-Sec. In village follow signs 'Camping' to the right. At bottom of hill turn left to site in 300 m. GPS: 48.65281, 5.99151

Charges guide

Per unit incl. 2 persons	
and electricity (6A)	€ 17,20 - € 19,20
extra person	€ 3,40
child (0-7 yrs)	€ 2,30

Lying between the Rhine and the Vosges mountains, to the north and east Alsace shares a border with Germany, to the south with German-speaking Switzerland and to the west with Lorraine and Franche Comté.

DÉPARTEMENTS: 67 BAS-RHIN, 68 HAUT-RHIN

MAJOR CITY: STRASBOURG

Nestled between the Vosges to the west and the Rhine to the east, Alsace is called the crossroads of Europe because of its situation at the very heart of Europe. Although it is the smallest French region, Alsace is big in qualities thanks to its world famous cuisine, its remarkably rich history, its strong cultural identity and, of course, its characteristic wines. Alsace invites you to discover its treasures all year round, from feudal castles to Romanesque churches, from its woodframed houses to the romantic ruins perched on the peaks of the Vosges, from the narrow streets of ancient districts to the superb collections to be found in the region's museums.

Wend your way between plains, forests, vineyards and valleys, along country lanes or all the way up to the summits of the Vosges Mountains: Alsace offers a wealth of surprises just waiting to be discovered. As well as being the ideal region for walking holidays – Alsace features over 16,000 km. of hiking paths – the region also offers many holiday opportunities for lovers of horse riding, biking, canoeing and climbing.

tourism-alsace.com
ALSACE

ALSACEZ-VOUS!
Experience the Alsace way of life

Places of interest

Strasbourg

Former Roman city has a town centre entirely listed as Unesco World Heritage. You can explore the city by riverboat, tram, bicycle and on foot.

Colmar

Historic centre with half-timbered houses, canals and flowers, with a vast pedestrian area and a town of art, e.g. the Unterlinden Museum in a beautiful 13th-century convent.

Mulhouse

Former industrial city is now renowned for its technical museums. The National Automobile Museum is fascinating.

Nature

Nideck waterfalls

At an altitude of 534 m, the romantic Nideck waterfalls are part of a marvellously preserved natural site. They offer an outstanding site for hiking and rambling, which is easily accessible.

The Donon

Grandfontaine

As the high point of the Basses-Vosges (1,009 m), the Donon is chiefly famous for the reconstructed Roman temple on its peak, but also includes many remains from the region's mystical past.

The Munster Valley

Situated in the Ballons des Vosges Regional Nature Park, the Munster Valley offers a wealth of attractions guaranteed to delight lovers of nature, fine food, arts and crafts and sports.

Cuisine of the region

Beckenoffe (Baeckeoffe): a hotpot of potatoes, lamb, beef, pork and onions, cooked in local wine.

Choucroute: sauerkraut with peppercorns, boiled ham, pork, Strasbourg sausages and boiled potatoes.

Chou farci: stuffed cabbage.

Foie gras: goose liver.

Tarte a l'oignon Alsacienne: onion and cream tart.

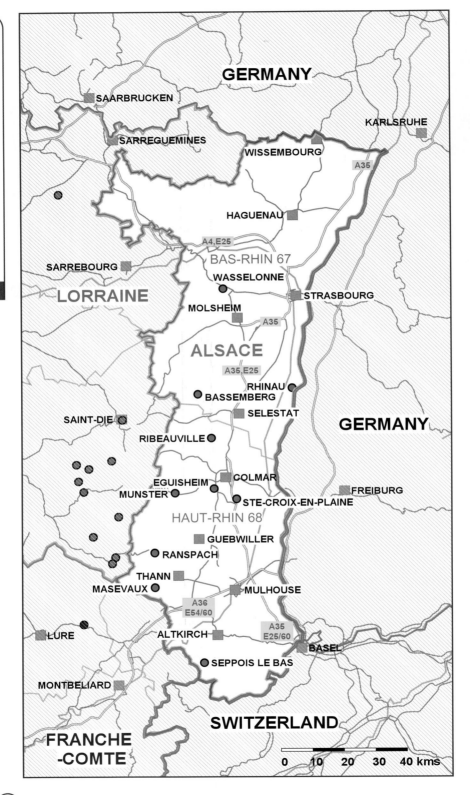

For latest campsite news, availability and prices visit
alanrogers.com

Bassemberg

Campéole le Giessen

Route de Villé, F-67220 Bassemberg (Bas-Rhin) T: 03 88 58 98 14. E: giessen@campeole.com

alanrogers.com/FR67070

Campé●le

Le Giessen is a member of the Campéole group and can be found at the foot of the Vosges mountains, with easy access to many of the best loved sights in Alsace. Although there is no pool on site, a large complex, comprising an indoor and outdoor pool with a water slide, can be found adjacent to the site, with free admission for all campers. Pitches here are grassy and of a good size, mostly with electrical connections. A number of mobile homes and fully equipped tents are available for rent. Various activities are organised in high season including a children's club and disco evenings. Nearby places of interest include the magnificent fortified castle of Haut-Koenigsbourg, as well as the great cities of Strasbourg and Colmar. This is a good base for exploring the Vosges and the Route du Vin (bicycle hire in the village). The site's friendly managers will be pleased to recommend possible itineraries.

Facilities

Multisport court. Bar. Play area. Tourist information. Activities and entertainment. Mobile homes and equipped tents for rent. Off site: Swimming pool complex adjacent. Tennis. Rollerblading rink. Hiking and mountain biking. Bicycle hire. Riding. Strasbourg 50 km.

Open: 1 April - 18 September.

Directions

Leave the A35 autoroute at exit 17 (Villé) and follow the D697 to Villé. Continue south on D39 to Bassemberg from where the site is well indicated. GPS: 48.33722, 7.28862

Charges guide

Per unit incl. 2 persons and electricity	€ 15,10 - € 24,50

Eguisheim

Camping des Trois Châteaux

10 rue du Bassin, F-68420 Eguisheim (Haut-Rhin) T: 03 89 23 19 39. E: camping.eguisheim@wanadoo.fr

alanrogers.com/FR68040

The village of Eguisheim is on the Alsace 'Route du Vin' to the west of Colmar. The three châteaux from which the site gets its name are clearly visible on the distant hills. Being close to the village, Les Trois Châteaux is busy and popular. Flowers, shrubs and trees, and well tended grass areas make this a very pleasant place. The 121 pitches, 115 with electricity (6/10A), are either on a slight slope or a terrace, and are marked and numbered, most with good shade. Around 80% of pitches have some gravel hardstandings, most of irregular shape and size. The facilities of the fascinating village of Eguisheim are close and the site is well located for exploring this delightful part of Alsace.

Facilities

The single heated sanitary block in the centre of the site has hot showers and warm water only to washbasins. Some washbasins in cubicles and facilities for disabled visitors. Motorcaravan service point. Playground. Bicycle hire. Off site: Fishing 3 km. Golf, riding 10 km.

Open: 1 April - 20 October.

Directions

Eguisheim is just off the N83 and the site is well signed in the village. GPS: 48.04255, 7.29989

Charges guide

Per unit incl. 2 persons	€ 11,50 - € 13,00
extra person	€ 3,50 - € 4,00
child (0-12 yrs)	€ 0,10 - € 2,50
electricity (6/10A)	€ 3,00 - € 5,00
dog	€ 1,50 - € 2,00

For latest campsite news, availability and prices visit

alanrogers.com

Masevaux

Camping de Masevaux

3 rue du Stade, F-68290 Masevaux (Haut-Rhin) T: 03 89 82 42 29. E: camping-masevaux@tv-com.net

alanrogers.com/FR68030

Masevaux is a pleasant little town in the Haut-Rhin département of Alsace, just north of the A36 Belfort - Mulhouse motorway. The neatly mown 110 pitches for tourists are on level grass, of reasonable size, marked by trees and hedges, and all have electricity (3/6A). Most are well shaded with good views of the surrounding hills. The pleasant and helpful Scottish managers, who take pride in the site, would like to welcome more British visitors. A good choice for one night or a longer stay to explore this interesting region, and an ideal destination for serious walkers.

Facilities

A modern, well designed and well equipped sanitary block has most washbasins in private cabins. Baby room. Laundry. Café/bar serving snacks. Baker calls in high season. Ice-creams and soft drinks from reception. TV room, small library. Boules. Play area. Tennis (extra charge). Fishing. Off site: Supermarket, restaurants and indoor pool. Market in Masevaux Wednesdays. Bicycle hire 300 m. Golf 7 km. Riding 10 km.

Open: All Year.

Directions

From D466 in Masevaux follow signs for Belfort and then 'Camping Complexe Sportif'. GPS: 47.7782, 6.9909

Charges guide

Per unit incl. 2 persons and electricity	€ 15,40
extra person	€ 3,90
child (2-16 yrs)	€ 1,60 - € 2,30
dog	€ 0,50

Munster

Village Center le Parc de la Fecht

Route de Gunsbach, F-68140 Munster (Haut-Rhin) T: 04 99 57 21 21. E: resa@village-center.com

alanrogers.com/FR68100

Part of the Village Center Group, this site has 228 pitches, some of which are occupied by mobile homes and chalets. The 139 touring pitches are on two levels in woodland and heavily shaded. Electricity (6A) is available to all but long leads may be necessary. A fast flowing river borders the length of the site on one side. This part of the Vosges is beautiful and great for walking or mountain-biking. The site is not far from the famous wine routes of Alsace and close to historic Colmar and the medieval villages with storks nesting on chimneys.

Facilities

Two toilet blocks. Small play area for children. Mobile homes for rent. Off site: Supermarket, shops and restaurants in Munster. Riding 10 km. Swimming pool with water slides. Extensive walking and cycle (mountain bike) opportunities. Many picturesque Alsatian villages.

Open: 15 December - 13 March and 15 June - 11 September.

Directions

Site is 1 km east of the town centre on D10 and is well signed. GPS: 48.04325, 7.15118

Charges guide

Per unit incl. 2 persons and electricity	€ 14,00 - € 16,00
extra person	€ 3,00 - € 4,00

Ranspach

Flower Camping les Bouleaux

8 rue des Bouleaux, F-68470 Ranspach (Haut-Rhin) T: 03 89 82 64 70 E: contact@alsace-camping.com alanrogers.com/FR68140

Les Bouleaux is a well maintained site with 100 pitches of a rather small size (80 sq.m), although they are flat and grassy. The site is open all year round, although the outdoor swimming pools and the shop are only opened during the high season. The site is ideally situated if you are coming by motorbike or are planning to go paragliding or skiing. Les Bouleaux is set in the heart of the Thur valley, at the foot of the Vosges mountains. It offers many possibilities for outdoor activities such as climbing, playing golf, hiking and fishing, to name just a few. Also recommended is a visit at the Wesserling park and its beautiful gardens which were established in 1699!

Facilities

Sanitary buildings with showers. Snack bar. Outdoor swimming pools. Table tennis. Boules. Volleyball. Minigolf. Accommodation to rent.

Open: All year.

Directions

Leave the A31 and follow signs for Epinal on the E23. Approching Epinal follow the E512 towards Mulhouse. Continue on the E512 until Ranspach. Drive on 700 m. on the 'route national', then turn right on Rue des Bouleaux to the site. GPS: 47.880743, 7.010334

Charges guide

Per unit incl. 2 persons and electricity	€ 15,50
extra person	€ 4,00
child (under 10 yrs)	€ 3,50
dog	€ 1,70

Rhinau

Camping la Ferme des Tuileries

1 rue des Tuileries, F-67860 Rhinau (Bas-Rhin) T: 03 88 74 60 45. E: camping.fermetuileries@neuf.fr
alanrogers.com/FR67040

Close to the German border, this ten-hectare, family run site has 150 large open pitches, hardstanding for 15 motorcaravans and room for 50 seasonal caravans. The site buildings have a traditional external appearance but modern interiors. Welcoming reception staff will provide information about the site and the local area. A small lake with two water slides is used for swimming, fishing and boating (divided into two areas) and there is also a small unsupervised swimming pool (hats compulsory). A newly built restaurant and bar are at the lakeside. A ferry crosses the Rhine river into Germany from 1 km. away.

Facilities

Three modern, bright and cheerful blocks with the normal facilities. Two washing machines and two dryers. Controllable showers. Family bathroom at no extra charge. Fully equipped facilities for disabled visitors. Motorcaravan services. Newly built restaurant and bar. Small lake for swimming, fishing, boating, two water slides. Swimming pool (unguarded) open July/Aug. Tennis. Pétanque. Minigolf. Dogs are not accepted. Off site: Supermarket 500 m. Ferry across the Rhine.

Open: 1 April - 30 September.

Directions

Coming from Colmar (A35) take exit 14 (Kogenheim -Benfeld-Erstein) then the N83 to exit for Benfeld -Rhinau, following site signs. From Strasbourg on the A35 take exit 7 (Erstein-Fegersheim) then the N83. GPS: 48.321, 7.698

Charges guide

| Per unit incl. 2 persons and electricity | € 11,90 - € 13,70 |
| extra person | € 3,50 |

No credit cards or cheques.

Ribeauvillé

Camping Municipal Pierre de Coubertin

23 rue de Landau, F-68150 Ribeauvillé (Haut-Rhin) T: 03 89 73 66 71. E: camping.ribeauville@wanadoo.fr
alanrogers.com/FR68050

The fascinating medieval town of Ribeauvillé on the Alsace Wine Route is within walking distance of this attractive, quietly located site. Popular and well run, it has 226 touring pitches, all with 16A electricity and some separated by shrubs or railings. There are tarmac and gravel access roads. This is a site solely for touring units – there are no mobile homes or seasonal units here. The small shop is open daily for most of the season (hours vary) providing bread, basic supplies and some wines. Only breathable groundsheets are permitted.

Facilities

Large, heated block provides modern facilities with washbasins in cubicles. Baby facilities. Large laundry and dishwashing rooms. A smaller unit at the far end of the site is opened for July/Aug. Very good facilities for disabled campers at both units. Shop (Easter-Oct). Excellent adventure style play area with rubber base. Tennis. Boules. TV room. WiFi (free) on all pitches. Off site: Outdoor pool (June-Aug). Bicycle hire 200 m. Fishing 500 m. Golf 12 km.

Open: 15 March - 15 November.

Directions

Ribeauvillé is 13 km. southwest of Sélestat and site is well signed. Turn north off the D106 at traffic lights by large car park, east of the town centre. GPS: 48.19482, 7.33654

Charges 2011

Per unit incl. 2 persons and electricity	€ 15,50 - € 16,50
extra person	€ 4,00
child (0-7 yrs)	€ 2,00
dog	€ 1,00

Saint Croix-en-Plaine

Camping Clair Vacances

Route de Herrlisheim, F-68127 Saint Croix-en-Plaine (Haut-Rhin) T: 03 89 49 27 28
E: clairvacances@wanadoo.fr alanrogers.com/FR68080

Clair Vacances is a very neat, tidy and pretty site with 130 level pitches of generous size which are numbered and most are separated by trees and shrubs. All have electricity connections (8-13A) and ten are fully serviced with water and drainage. The site has been imaginatively laid out with the pitches reached from hard access roads. This is a quiet family site. The friendly couple who own and run it will be pleased to advise on the attractions of the area. The site is 1 km. from the A35 exit, not far from Colmar in the region of Alsace, a popular and picturesque area.

Facilities

Two excellent, modern toilet blocks include washbasins in cabins, well equipped baby rooms and good facilities for disabled visitors. Laundry facilities. Swimming and paddling pools (heated) with large sunbathing area (15/6-15/9). Playground. Community room. Archery in high season. Camping Gaz. Dogs are not accepted. No barbecues or football. American motorhomes and twin axle caravans are not accepted. Off site: Colmar with restaurants and shops is not far away.

Open: Week before Easter - 15 October.

Directions

Site is signed from exit 27 of the A35 on D1, halfway between Saint Croix-en-Plaine and Herrlisheim. GPS: 48.01606, 7.35016

Charges guide

Per unit incl. 2 persons and electricity	€ 15,50 - € 25,00
extra person	€ 4,00 - € 7,00
child (0-7 yrs)	free - € 3,00
child (8-12 yrs)	€ 3,00 - € 6,00

For latest campsite news, availability and prices visit

alanrogers.com

Seppois-le-Bas

Village Center les Lupins

1 rue de la Gare, F-68580 Seppois-le-Bas (Haut-Rhin) T: 04 99 57 21 21. E: contact@village-center.com
alanrogers.com/FR68120

Only ten kilometres from the Swiss border and within walking distance of a small village (800 m), this is a very attractive site. It has 142 grass touring pitches, which are not separated and 25 chalets to rent. Attractive trees have been planted throughout the site. The main site building houses reception, a small shop, two pool tables and a television and used to be the old local railway station (1910-1970). A very pleasant, small, fenced swimming pool is guarded in July and August, as is a playground for small children. In the south of the Alsace region, this quiet site is a fine base for walks into the forest and hills. The site is a member of the Village Center group.

Facilities

One good toilet block provides plenty of facilities in a traditional style. A second block is older but with similar facilities. Cabins for disabled visitors. Free hot water. Small shop. bar and terrace. Swimming pool. Play area. Internet access. Off site: Village 800 m. Restaurant across the road. Forest walks.

Open: 24 June - 4 September.

Directions

Leave Belfort - Basel (CH) autoroute at Grandvillars. From Colmar/Strasbourg to Altkirch-Férette and Seppois-le-Bas. Leave A36 at Burnhaupt (exit 14) and take D103 towards Dannemarie, then the D7b to Seppois. From there follow signs to site. GPS: 47.53913, 7.17998

Charges guide

Per unit incl. 2 persons and electricity	€ 14,00 - € 16,00

Wasselonne

Camping Municipal Wasselonne

Route de Romanswiller, F-67310 Wasselonne (Bas-Rhin) T: 03 88 87 00 08
E: camping-wasselonne@wanadoo.fr alanrogers.com/FR67050

A good quality municipal site with a resident warden. Facilities include a well stocked small shop, a crêperie in season and the added bonus of free admission to the superb indoor heated swimming pool adjacent to the site. There are 80 tourist pitches and around 20 seasonal units, on grass with a slight slope, all with electricity hook-ups (10A). Four new rental chalets are in a separate fenced area and there are six new private chalets. This could be an excellent base from which to visit Strasbourg. A full programme of events is offered in the town by the Tourist Office, including welcome evenings, guided tours, concerts, musical festivals, food tasting evenings.

Facilities

The single, large, and well maintained sanitary unit has unisex facilities with ample sized showers and washbasins in cubicles. Laundry facilities and covered dishwashing sinks. No specific facilities for disabled visitors but the rooms are spacious and should be accessible to many. Excellent drive-over motorcaravan service point. Off site: Heated pool, hotel with restaurant, tennis courts, plus athletics stadium all adjacent. Supermarket 500 m. Fitness trail, riding 1 km.

Open: 15 April - 15 October.

Directions

Wasselonne is 25 km. west of Strasbourg. Site lies southwest of town centre on D224 towards Romanswiller, and is well signed. GPS: 48.6377, 7.4318

Charges guide

Per unit incl. 1 person	€ 7,30 - € 7,70
extra person	€ 3,40 - € 3,60
child (0-10 yrs)	€ 1,80 - € 1,90
electricity	€ 3,00
animal	€ 0,50 - € 0,60

For latest campsite news, availability and prices visit
alanrogers.com

Want independent campsite reviews at your fingertips?

You'll find them here...

Over 3,000 in-depth campsite reviews at **www.alanrogers.com**

With over one hundred of France's finest châteaux, this is a region to inspire the imagination. Stunning châteaux, peaceful gardens, fine food and wine, the Loire Valley has it all.

DÉPARTEMENTS: 18 CHER, 28 EURE-ET-LOIR, 36 INDRE, 37 INDRE-ET-LOIRE, 41 LOIR-ET-CHER, 45 LOIRET

MAJOR CITIES: ORLÉANS, BLOIS AND TOURS

In 2000, UNESCO gave official recognition to the Loire Valley for its architectural heritage combined with its exceptional unspoilt nature. The region is remarkable for its monumental architecture and the quality of its urban sites. Nowhere else in Europe do you find such a density of Renaissance castles or such quality of urban facades built on the riverbanks: Chambord, Amboise, Villandry, Chenonceau, all dotted along the Loire River and its tributaries. The Loire à Vélo long-distance cycle trail offers a delightful way to get back to nature and enjoy the unspoilt river banks, beautiful villages and historic cities.

Known as the Garden of France, the Loire's mild climate and fertile landscape of soft green valleys, lush vineyards and fields of flowers makes it a favourite with visitors. Renowned for its wines, with hundreds to choose from, all are produced from vineyards stretching along the main course of the River Loire. Cities such as Blois and Tours are elegant with fine architecture and museums, and Paris is only one hour by TGV.

Région Centre
Loire Valley

 www.**visaloire**.com

Architectural & Cultural Heritage

Amboise
Château, Leonardo da Vinci museum.

Beauregard
Château with Delft tiled floors.

Blois
Château with architecture from Middle Ages to Neo-Classical periods.

Chambord
Renaissance château.

Chaumont-sur-Loire
A world renowned International Garden Festival.

Chartres
Cathedral with stained glass windows.

Chinon
Old town, Joan of Arc museum.

Orléans
Holy Cross cathedral, house of Joan of Arc.

Sancerre
Its vineyard and the Maison des Sancerre.

Sully-sur-Loire
A medieval fortress home to a number of tapestries, paintings, sculptures and pieces of furniture.

Tours
Renaissance and Neo-Classical mansions, cathedral of St Gatien.

Villandry
Famous Renaissance gardens.

Outdoor activities

Balloon Flights
France Montgolfières.

Cycling
www.**cycling-loire.com**

Cuisine of the region

Wild duck, pheasant, hare, deer and quail are classics, and freshwater fish such as zander, perch and eel are favourites.

Specialities
Rillettes, Rillons de Tours, Pâté de Chartres, mushrooms, green lentils of Berry and five different designations of origin (AOC) of goat's cheese are found in the region.

The home-made pears, 'Poires tapées à l'ancienne', the result of long and meticulous drying, served with salted dishes, pastries or ice cream.

Tarte Tatin: a succulent upside-down tart of caramelised apples and pastry.

Almond Pithiviers: puff pastry pie.

Images © (left to right, top to bottom): C Mouton; JD; S Le Donne; CL; C Mouton; C Mouton

For latest campsite news, availability and prices visit
alanrogers.com

Aubigny sur Nère

Flower Camping les Etangs

Route de Sancerre, F-18700 Aubigny-sur-Nère (Cher) T: 02 48 58 02 37
E: camping.aubigny@orange.fr alanrogers.com/FR18010

Les Etangs is a site of 100 pitches, close to the Sancerre vineyards and the lakes of the Sologne. A member of the Flower group, this site extends over 2 hectares and borders a small lake (suitable for fishing). Pitches are large and grassy (most have electrical connections). There are chalets available for rent. The town of Aubigny-sur-Nère is very close (1 km) and has a close attachment with Scotland, thanks to the 'Auld Alliance'. The town is the only one in France to celebrate French/Scottish friendship on Bastille Day. Bring your bicycle as there are many tracks running through the surrounding forests. A covered municipal swimming pool is 50 m. from the site (a charge is made). Various activities are organised on site during the high season, including special events for children. There is much to see in the area, including the châteaux on the Route Jacques Coeur, the great Gothic cathedral at Bourges and the medieval château at Sully-sur-Loire.

Facilities

Two heated toilet blocks are a good provision and are well located. Bar (high season). Play area. Fishing (permit required). Activity and entertainment programme. WiFi (free). Chalets and tents for rent. Off site: Aubigny-sur-Nère 1 km. Walking and cycle tracks. Swimming pool 50 m. (with aqua-gym). Riding 20 km. Sancerre vineyards.

Open: 1 April - 30 September.

Directions

Aubigny is southeast of Orléans. Approaching from the north (Orléans) on the A71 autoroute take exit 4 for Salbris and head east on D724 and D924 until Aubigny. Take the D923 towards Sancerre and site is 1 km. GPS: 47.48435, 2.45703

Charges guide

Per unit incl. 2 persons and electricity	€ 13,90 - € 17,80
extra person	€ 2,60 - € 4,00
child (2-7 yrs)	€ 2,00 - € 2,50
dog	free

Ballan-Miré

Camping de la Mignardière

22 avenue des Aubépines, F-37510 Ballan-Miré (Indre-et-Loire) T: 02 47 73 31 00. E: info@mignardiere.com
alanrogers.com/FR37010

Southwest of the city of Tours, this site is within easy reach of several of the Loire châteaux, notably Azay-le-Rideau. There are also many varied sports amenities on the site or very close by. The site has 177 numbered pitches of which 139 are for touring units, all with electricity (6/10A) and 37 with drainage and water. Pitches are of a good size on rather uneven grass with limestone gravel paths (which are rather 'sticky' when wet). The barrier gates (coded access) are closed 22.30-07.30. Reservation is essential for most of July/August. The site's facilities are supplemented by a small 'parc de loisirs' just across the road which provides a bar and refreshments, pony rides, minigolf, small cars, playground and other amusements.

Facilities

Three toilet blocks include washbasins in private cabins, a unit for disabled visitors, baby bath and laundry facilities. Motorcaravan service point. Shop. Takeaway. Two large, heated swimming pools (one covered). Paddling pool. Tennis. Bicycle hire. Off site: Attractive lake 300 m. Family fitness run. Fishing 500 m. Riding 1 km. Golf 3 km. Tours centre 8 km.

Open: 1 April - 25 September.

Directions

From A10 autoroute take exit 24 and D751 towards Chinon. Turn right after 5 km. at Campanile Hotel following signs to site. From Tours take D751 towards Chinon. GPS: 47.35509, 0.63408

Charges guide

Per unit incl. 2 persons	€ 14,00 - € 29,00
extra person	€ 4,00 - € 5,30
child (2-10 yrs)	€ 2,60 - € 3,20

For latest campsite news, availability and prices visit

alanrogers.com

Candé-sur-Beuvron

Kawan Village la Grande Tortue

3 route de Pontlevoy, F-41120 Candé-sur-Beuvron (Loir-et-Cher) T: 02 54 44 15 20
E: grandetortue@wanadoo.fr **alanrogers.com/FR41070**

In the region that the Kings of France chose to build their most beautiful residences, this pleasant, shady site has been developed in the surroundings of an old 800 hectare forest, just 1 km. from the banks of the Loire river. For those seeking a relaxing holiday, it provides 169 touring pitches (the majority of more than 100 sq.m), all with 10A electricity and includes 58 fully serviced pitches. The friendly family owners continue to develop the site with a new multisport court and an attractive swimming pool complex. During July and August, they organise a programme of trips including canoeing and horse riding excursions, as well as twice weekly concerts and shows. La Grande Tortue is very well placed for visiting the châteaux of the Loire or the cities of Orléans and Tours. It is located on the long distance 'Loire à vélo' cycle track and this leads from the site to Chaumont, Blois and Chambord, with over 300 km. of marked cycle tracks in the surrounding area. There are some good restaurants close at hand, although the site restaurant is also recommended with a range of good value meals in a pleasant environment.

Facilities

Three sanitary blocks offer British style WCs, washbasins in cabins and pushbutton showers. Facilities for disabled visitors in one block. Laundry facilities. Motorcaravan service point. Shop, terraced bar and restaurant with reasonably priced food and drink plus a takeaway service (all 2/4-15/9). Covered, heated swimming pool (2/4-15/9) and two shallower pools for children (15/5-30/9). Trampolines, a ball crawl with slide and climbing wall, two bouncy inflatables. Club for children (July/Aug). Multisport court. Bicycle hire. Off site: Walking and cycling. Fishing 500 m. Golf 10 km. Riding 12 km. Châteaux at Blois 10 km, Chambord 20 km, Chenonceau 20 km.

Open: 2 April - 25 September.

Directions

Site is just outside Candé-sur-Beuvron on D751, between Amboise and Blois. From Amboise, turn right just before Candé, then left into site. GPS: 47.4900069, 1.2583208

Charges 2011

Per unit incl. 2 persons and electricity	€ 22,00 - € 32,50
extra person	€ 6,75 - € 9,00
child (3-9 yrs)	€ 3,75 - € 5,75
dog	€ 3,70

Camping Cheques accepted.

Chemillé-sur-Indrois

Camping les Coteaux du Lac

Base de Loisirs, F-37460 Chemillé-sur-Indrois (Indre-et-Loire) T: 02 47 92 77 83
E: lescoteauxdulac@wanadoo.fr alanrogers.com/FR37150

This former municipal site has been completely refurbished to a high standard and is being operated efficiently by a private company owned by the present enthusiastic manager, Thiery Licois. There are 49 touring pitches, all with electricity (10A) and individual water tap; four have hard standing for motorcaravans. At present there is little shade apart from that offered by a few mature trees, but new trees and bushes have been planted and flower beds are to be added. In a few years this promises to be a delightful site; meanwhile it is smart and very well tended. The site is in pleasant countryside above a lake and next to a rapidly developing Base de Loisirs with watersports provision and a bar/restaurant. There is a good, well-equipped little swimming pool with paddling area securely separated from the main pool (open and heated 1/6-30/9). The site is near the town of Loches which has an attractive château, and is an easy drive from Tours and from the many châteaux along the Loire and the Indre, including Chenonceaux.

Facilities

Excellent sanitary block with controllable showers, some washbasins in cabins and en-suite facilities for disabled visitors. Laundry facilities. Reception sells a few basic supplies and bread can be ordered. Swimming and paddling pools. Playing field. Play equipment for different ages. Chalets to rent (15) are grouped at far end of site, Off site: Fishing 100 m. Lakeside beach, sailing and other water sports 200 m. Riding 4 km. Golf 15 km.

Open: 1 May - 30 September.

Directions

Chemillé-sur-Indrois is 55 km. southeast of Tours and 14 km. east of Loches, just off the D760 from Loches to Montrésor. Site is to the north of this road and is signed just west of Montrésor.
GPS: 47.15786, 1.15986

Charges guide

Per unit incl. 2 persons	€ 13,30 - € 18,30
extra person	€ 3,90 - € 5,00
child (2-9 yrs)	€ 2,20 - € 3,40
electricity	€ 3,90

For latest campsite news, availability and prices visit
alanrogers.com

Château de Chenonceau

Property of the Crown, then a royal résidence, Château Chenonceau is an exceptional site, due to the originality of its design and historical role.

Tél. : +33 (0)2 47 23 90 07
info@chenonceau.com

www.chenonceau.com

Cheverny

Camping les Saules

Route de Contres (D102), F-41700 Cheverny (Loir-et-Cher) T: 02 54 79 90 01
E: contact@camping-cheverny.com alanrogers.com/FR41100

Set in the heart of the châteaux region, les Saules has recently been revitalised and re-opened by a local family. The tastefully renovated traditional reception buildings in their lakeside setting give a very pleasant welcome. There are 166 good sized, level pitches with 149 available for touring units. All have shade from the many trees on the site, 150 have electrical connections (a few will require leads longer than 25 m), and there are ample water taps. Cheverny is considered to have the best interior and furnishings of all the châteaux in the Loire region, and many others are within easy reach. A Sites et Paysages member.

Facilities

Two sanitary blocks with toilets, showers, washbasins in cubicles and facilities for disabled visitors. Laundry facilities. Motorcaravan service point. Gas supplies. Shop. Restaurant (July/Aug). Bar. Snack bar and takeaway. Swimming and paddling pools. TV/social room with toys, board games, books. Two play areas. Large grass area for ball games. Minigolf (free). Fishing. Bicycle hire. Internet and WiFi. Off site: Golf 3 km. Riding 3 km.

Open: 1 April - 30 September.

Directions

From Cheverny take D102 south towards Contres. Site is on the right after about 2 km.
GPS: 47.50000, 1.46113

Charges guide

Per unit incl. 2 persons	
and electricity	€ 19,50 - € 29,00
extra person	€ 4,50
child (4-10 yrs)	€ 2,00

Chinon

Camping de l'Ile Auger

Quai Danton, F-37500 Chinon (Indre-et-Loire) T: 02 47 93 08 35. E: camping-ile-auger@hotmail.fr
alanrogers.com/FR37070

This traditional municipal-style site is well placed for exploring the old medieval town of Chinon and lies alongside the River Vienne opposite the impressive castle which was once the home of England's Henry II and includes a museum to Joan of Arc. A five minute walk over the bridge takes you to the town centre. The 277 level pitches are numbered but not separated and trees provide some shade. All have electricity (long leads needed in places). Nearby are châteaux at Azay le Rideau and Villandry and the abbey at Fontevraud.

Facilities

Hot water is provided to showers and basins in two blocks near the entrance and in a small block at the far end of the site. WCs here are mainly British style. Three small blocks around the rest of the site, provide additional WCs (many Turkish style) and basins with cold water. Motorcaravan service point. Laundry facilities. Playground. Boules court. Fishing. Canoes. Barrier locked 22.00-07.00. A warden lives on site. Off site: Town with shops, bars and restaurants 500 m. Tennis. Indoor and outdoor swimming pools nearby. Bicycle hire, boat launching 100 m. River beach (no swimming) 1 km. Riding 10 km.

Open: 1 April - 31 October.

Directions

Chinon is 45 km. southwest of Tours. From A85 at exit 9 (Chinon) follow D749 for 10 km. and turn south on D751 for 3 km. Turn east on D751E then north towards town centre. Follow one-way system, cross traffic coming out of town at bridge and continue ahead to campsite entrance on right. From A10 exit 25 take D760 to Chinon, then as above. GPS: 47.16433, 0.23327

Charges guide

Per unit incl. 2 persons and electricity	€ 10,45 - € 11,85

Combreux

Camping Hortus, l'Etang de la Vallée

Vitry aux Loges, F-45530 Vitry Aux Loges (Loiret) T: 02 38 36 35 94. E: info@camping-hortus.com
alanrogers.com/FR45070

Camping l'Etang de la Vallée is a member of the new Hortus group and lies deep within the massive Forêt d'Orléans and close to the Etang de la Vallée. There are 180 level, stony/grassy pitches with 176 for touring and all fully serviced (6A electricity). Some are separated by hedges and many have some shade. A bar/snack bar and a large sandy beach (lifeguard in high season) are on the opposite side of the road alongside the lake. Rowing boats, canoes and bicycles can be hired in the high season. There are many miles of cycle trails through the woods and along the roads waiting to be explored. Fishing, boating and bathing from the sandy beach are popular at the lake opposite the site and fishing lessons are available. There are some fine, less well known châteaux to visit east of Orléans such as Chamerolle and Châteauneuf-sur-Loire. Châteauneuf has shops, bar and restaurants and is only 15 km. away. Orléans, a much larger and more famous city known for its association with Joan of Arc, at 40 km. is easily accessible for a day trip.

Facilities

Two adequate toilet blocks with all necessary facilities, including facilities for campers with disabilities. Washing machine, laundry sinks. Play area. Tourist information. Off site: Fishing, sandy beach, canoes, boats, bicycle hire (high season), bar/snack bar (1/4-30/9), beach volleyball (all opposite site alongside lake). Golf 20 km. Shops, bars, restaurants, château at Châteauneuf-sur-Loire 15 km. Orléans 40 km. Walking and cycle tracks through forest.

Open: 1 April - 1 October.

Directions

From Orléans, take N60 east to Châteauneuf-sur-Loire exit. Take D10 and D137 north to Vitry-aux-Loges. Follow signs to Etang de la Vallée and site. GPS: 47.958555, 2.281557

Charges guide

Per unit incl. 2 persons and electricity	€ 15,00 - € 20,00
dog	€ 2,00

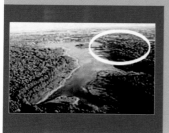

We can book this site for you!
Call 01580 214000
alan rogers travel

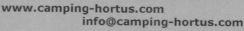

Gien

Kawan Village les Bois du Bardelet

Route de Bourges, Le Petit Bardelet, F-45500 Gien (Loiret) T: 02 38 67 47 39. E: contact@bardelet.com
alanrogers.com/FR45010

This attractive, high quality and lively site, ideal for families with young children, is in a rural setting and well situated for exploring the less well known eastern part of the Loire Valley. Two lakes (one for boating, one for fishing) and a pool complex have been attractively landscaped in 12 hectares of former farmland, blending old and new with natural wooded areas and more open field areas with rural views. There are 260 large, level grass pitches with 130 for touring units. All have 8A or 16A electricity, 20 have water and waste water and some are hard standing. The communal areas are based in attractively converted former farm buildings with a wide range of leisure facilities. A weekly family club card can be purchased to make use of the many activities on a daily basis (some high season only). Excursions are organised to Paris, famous châteaux and vineyards plus several riverboat trips. The site is an easy cycle ride from the nearest château town of Gien which has a range of shops, bars, restaurants and museums plus a Wednesday market. There are many opportunities to relax on site including the indoor pool, jacuzzi and excellent children's indoor water play area.

Facilities

Two toilet blocks include facilities for disabled visitors and babies. Washing machines, dryers. Minimart (1/4-11/9). Bar, snack bar, takeaway, (all 1/4-11/9). Full restaurant (high season and weekends). Heated outdoor pool (1/5-31/8). Heated indoor pool and children's pool with purchased club card (1/4-11/9). Aquagym, fitness and jacuzzi room. Games area. Archery. Canoeing and fishing. Tennis. Minigolf. Boules. Bicycle hire. Playground. WiFi (charged). Off site: Supermarket 5 km. Riding 7 km. Golf 25 km. Walking and cycling routes.

Open: 1 April - 30 September.

Directions

Leave A77 Autoroute (exit 19 Gien). Take D940 (signed Bourges) to Gien, cross river Loire, continue D940 for 5 km. At junction with D53 (site signed) turn right and right again to cross D940 (no left turn). Follow signs for 1.5 km. to site.
GPS: 47.64152, 2.61528

Charges 2011

Per unit incl. 2 persons and electricity	€ 24,00 - € 32,00
extra person (over 2 yrs)	€ 4,90 - € 6,50
child (2-5 yrs)	free - € 6,50
dog	€ 4,00

Less 15-25% in low seasons (20-40% for over 60s). Discount of 25% for 2 week stay, 30% for 3 week stay, outside 10/7 to 14/8.

Francueil-Chenonceau

Camping le Moulin Fort

F-37150 Francueil-Chenonceau (Indre-et-Loire) T: 02 47 23 86 22. E: lemoulinfort@wanadoo.fr
alanrogers.com/FR37030

Camping le Moulin Fort is a tranquil, riverside site with British owners, John and Sarah Scarratt. The 130 pitches are enhanced by trees and shrubs offering plenty of shade and 110 pitches have electricity (6A). From the snack bar terrace adjacent to the restored mill building a timber walkway over the mill race leads to the unheated swimming pool and paddling pools. The site is ideal for couples and families with young children, although the river is unfenced. There is occasional noise from trains passing on the opposite bank of the river. All over the campsite, visitors will find little information boards about local nature (birds, fish, trees and shrubs), about the history of the mill and fascinating facts about recycling. The owners are keen to encourage recycling on the site. The picturesque Château of Chenonceau is little more than 1 km. along the Cher riverbank and many of the Loire châteaux are within easy reach, particularly Amboise and its famous Leonardo de Vinci museum.

Facilities

Two toilet blocks with all the usual amenities of a good standard, include washbasins in cubicles, baby baths and facilities for disabled visitors. Motorcaravan service point. Shop, bar (limited hours), restaurant and takeaway (all 28/5-18/9). Swimming pool (25/5-18/9). Excellent play area. Minigolf. Pétanque. Games room and TV. Library. Fishing. Bicycle and canoe hire. In high season regular family entertainment including wine tasting, quiz evenings, activities for children, light-hearted games tournaments and live music events. WiFi in bar area. Please note that dogs must be kept on a lead at all times. Off site: Boat launching 2 km. River beach 4 km. Riding 12 km. Golf 20 km. Trains to Tours 1.5 km.

Open: 1 April - 30 September.

Directions

Site is 35 km. east of Tours off the D976 Vierzon road. From A85 at exit 11 take D31 towards Bléré and turn east on D976 (Vierzon) for 7 km. then turn north on D80 (Chenonceau) to site. From north bank of Cher (D140/D40) turn south on D80 to cross river between Chenonceau and Chisseaux. Site on left just after bridge. GPS: 47.32735, 1.08936

Charges 2011

Per unit incl. 2 persons and electricity	€ 18,00 - € 26,00
extra person	€ 3,00 - € 5,00
child (4-12 yrs)	€ 3,00 - € 4,00
dog	€ 2,00 - € 3,00

For latest campsite news, availability and prices visit
alanrogers.com

Mesland

Yelloh! Village Parc du Val de Loire

155 route de Fleuray, F-41150 Mesland (Loir-et-Cher) T: 02 54 70 27 18. E: parcduvaldeloire@wanadoo.fr

alanrogers.com/FR41010

Between Blois and Amboise, quietly situated among vineyards away from the main roads and towns, this site is nevertheless centrally placed for visits to the châteaux; Chaumont, Amboise and Blois (21 km) are the nearest in that order. There are 150 touring pitches of reasonable size, either in light woodland marked by trees or on open meadow with separators. All the pitches have electricity (10A) and 50 of them also have water and drainage. Sports and competitions are organised in July/August with a weekly disco and dance for adults, and opportunities for wine tasting are arranged weekly. There are local walks and bike rides on marked paths (free maps available). Nearby there are balloon and helicopter flights over the Loire valley. New, experienced owners have recently taken over the site.

Facilities

Three original toilet blocks of varying ages are barely acceptable. One unit is very old and only open in July/Aug. Units for disabled visitors and babies. Laundry facilities. Motorcaravan services. Shop with bakery (July/Aug). Bar, restaurant, snack service, pizzeria and takeaway (all 8/4-11/9). TV and recreation rooms. Three swimming pools, one heated and covered (outdoor 25/4-11/9; covered 8/4-11/9), one larger one with slide and flume. Balneo. Tennis. Three playgrounds, one adventure type. Bicycle hire. Minigolf. Barbecue area. Off site: Golf 5 km. Fishing 7 km. Horse riding and boat launching 10 km.

Open: 8 April - 11 September.

Directions

From A10 exit 18 (Château-Renault, Amboise) take D31 south to Autrèche (2 km). Turn left on D55 for 3.5 km. In Darne-Marie Les Bois turn left and then right onto D43 to Mesland. Follow site signs. Or, from south, site signed from Onzain.
GPS: 47.51002, 1.10481

Charges guide

Per unit incl. 2 persons large pitch (120-170 sq.m)	€ 14,00 - € 24,00
with services	€ 22,00 - € 32,00
extra person	€ 4,50 - € 7,00
child (4-14 yrs)	€ 3,50 - € 6,20

Tel +332 5432 2048

-15%
till end 2011

www.franceballoons.com
Quote discount code
ALRG11

Muides-sur-Loire

Camping Château des Marais

27 rue de Chambord, F-41500 Muides-sur-Loire (Loir-et-Cher) T: 02 54 87 05 42
E: chateau.des.marais@wanadoo.fr alanrogers.com/FR41040

The Château des Marais campsite is in a good spot for visiting the chateau at Chambord (its park is impressive) and the other châteaux in the Vallée des Rois. The site provides 133 large touring pitches, all with electricity, water and drainage and with ample shade, is situated in the oak and hornbeam woods of its own small château. An excellent swimming complex offers pools with two slides, two flumes and a lazy river. A new 'wellness centre is a recent addition. English is spoken and the reception from the enthusiastic owners and the staff is very welcoming. Used by tour operators (90 pitches).

Facilities

Four modern sanitary blocks have good facilities including some large showers and washbasins en-suite which may be suitable for visitors with disabilities. Washing machines and dryers. Motorcaravan service point. Shop and takeaway. Bar/restaurant with large terrace. Swimming complex with heated and unheated pools, slide and cover. New wellness spa centre. Bicycle and go-kart hire. Games room. Fishing pond. Excursions to Paris, an entertainment programme and canoe trips organised in high season. Internet access (free). Off site: Riding 5 km. Golf 12 km. Muides-sur-Loire (five minutes walk).

Open: 8 May - 15 September.

Directions

From A10 autoroute take exit 16 to Mer. Turn left off the N152 to cross the Loire. Turn right to join the D951. Opposite car park in centre of Muides-sur-Loire, turn left onto D103. Site is signed off the D103 to the southwest of the village, 600 m. from junction with D112. GPS: 47.66580, 1.52877

Charges guide

Per unit incl. 2 persons and electricity (6/10A)	€ 30,00 - € 42,00
extra person	€ 8,00
child	free - € 7,00

Credit cards accepted for amounts over € 80.

Pierrefitte-sur-Sauldre

Leading Camping les Alicourts

Domaine des Alicourts, F-41300 Pierrefitte-sur-Sauldre (Loir-et-Cher) T: 02 54 88 63 34
E: info@lesalicourts.com alanrogers.com/FR41030

A secluded holiday village set in the heart of the forest and with many sporting facilities and a super spa centre, Parc des Alicourts is midway between Orléans and Bourges, to the east of the A71. There are 490 pitches, 150 for touring and the remainder occupied by mobile homes and chalets. All pitches have electricity connections (6A) and good provision for water, and most are 150 sq.m. (min. 100 sq.m). Locations vary from wooded to more open areas, thus giving a choice of amount of shade. All facilities are open all season and the leisure amenities are exceptional. The Senseo Balnéo centre offers indoor pools, hydrotherapy, massage and spa treatments for over 18s only (some special family sessions are provided). An inviting outdoor water complex (all season) includes two swimming pools, a pool with wave machine and a beach area, not forgetting three water slides. Competitions and activities are organised for adults and children including a high season club for children with an entertainer twice a day, a disco once a week and a dance for adults. Member of Leading Campings Group.

Facilities

Three modern sanitary blocks include some washbasins in cabins and baby bathrooms. Laundry facilities. Facilities for disabled visitors. Motorcaravan services. Shop. Restaurant. Takeaway in bar with terrace. Pool complex. Spa centre. 7 hectare lake (fishing, bathing, canoes, pedaloes). 9-hole golf course. Adventure play area. Tennis. Minigolf. Boules. Roller skating/skateboarding (bring own equipment). Bicycle hire. Internet access and WiFi (charged).

Open: 29 April - 9 September.

Directions

From A71, take Lamotte Beuvron exit (no 3) or from N20 Orléans to Vierzon turn left on to D923 towards Aubigny. After 14 km. turn right at camping sign on to D24E. Site signed in 4 km.
GPS: 47.54398, 2.19193

Charges guide

Per unit incl. 2 persons and electricity	€ 19,00 - € 42,00
extra person	€ 7,00 - € 10,00
child (1-17 yrs)	free - € 8,00
dog	€ 5,00 - € 7,00

Reductions for low season longer stays.

Poilly-lez-Gien

Les Roulottes des Bords de Loire

Rue des Iris, F-45500 Poilly-lez-Gien (Loiret) T: 02 38 67 12 50. E: info@roulottes-bords-de-loire.com
alanrogers.com/FR45050

The pitches at this site are used exclusively for mobile home, chalet or other types of accommodation. For full details please see our PRL section starting on page 538.

Poilly-lez-Gien
Camping Touristique de Gien

Rue des Iris, F-45500 Poilly-lez-Gien (Loiret) T: 02 38 67 12 50. E: camping-gien@wanadoo.fr

alanrogers.com/FR45030

This open, attractive, well cared for site lies on the bank of the Loire with views of the town of Gien and its château. It has a long river frontage, which includes a good expanse of sandy beach. There are 200 well-sized, level, grassy touring pitches with 150 for touring. All have 4/10A electricity, 18 have water and drainage (between two). Some are shaded by mature trees and many have good views over the river. The bar and restaurant, with a large outdoor area, are open to the public. Soirées with different themes are held at least weekly in July and August. No twin-axle caravans. The town of Gien, with its shops, bars, restaurants and château, is within a kilometre just across the bridge. A long distance cycle path passes the entrance. This is an excellent base for exploring the eastern end of the Loire valley, and Gien has a festival celebrating the heritage of this part of the Loire at Ascensiontide, which is well worth a visit. The tourist office organises a wide range of activities both sporting and cultural. There is a regular bus service to Orléans an ancient city well known for its association with Joan of Arc.

Facilities

Three toilet blocks, one heated, and one new with an en-suite unit for disabled visitors. Laundry. Bar and restaurant (1/4-30/9), both open to the public. Shop 20 m. outside gates (all year). Swimming pool and paddling pools (15/6-15/9). Play area and grassed games area. Minigolf. Bicycle and pedal cart hire. Canoe hire. Fishing. Large sandy beach. Some organised activities (July/Aug). Off site: Children's club on beach. Town centre less than 1 km. Hypermarket 1 km. Riding 2 km. Golf 25 km. Many sporting activities, excursions and visits can be arranged from the site or the tourist office.

Open: 1 March - 7 November.

Directions

Leave A77 Autoroute (exit 19 Gien). Take D940 (signed Bourges) to Gien, follow signs to Centre Ville and cross the river Loire. Immediately, at traffic lights, turn west D951 signed Pouilly-lez-Gien. Fork right to site in 300 m. on right. GPS: 47.68229, 2.62315

Charges guide

Per unit incl. 2 persons and electricity	€ 21,50 - € 25,00
extra person	€ 6,00
child (under 12 yrs)	€ 4,00
dog	€ 2,00

Rillé

Huttopia Rillé

Lac de Rillé, F-37340 Rillé (Indre-et-Loire) T: 02 47 24 62 97. E: rille@huttopia.com

alanrogers.com/FR37140

Huttopia Rillé is situated by a lake in a forest and the aim is to provide a traffic-free environment. Cars are left in a carpark outside the barrier (allowed on site to unload and load) and new arrivals must park outside and gain an entry code from reception. There are 104 large touring pitches, all with electricity (10A), 24 with water and waste water. They vary in size and are numbered in groups amongst the trees but are not marked. Heated swimming pool and terrace overlooking the lake. Accommodation for hire.

Facilities

The central toilet block has family rooms (with showers and basins), washbasins in cubicles and facilities for disabled visitors (shower/basin plus separate toilet) but there are no ramps and access for wheelchairs is very difficult. Another smaller block has separate showers, washbasins and slightly better facilities for disabled visitors. Motorcaravan service point. Heated swimming pool with paddling area (May-Sept). Play area. Fishing. Canoes on lake. Communal barbecue areas. Max. 1 dog. Off site: Nature reserve at lake. Riding 6 km. Golf 15 km.

Open: 22 April - 6 November.

Directions

Rillé is 40 km. west of Tours. From D766 Angers - Blois road at Château la Vallière take D749 southwest. From N152 Tours - Angers road go northwest at Langeais on D57. In Rillé turn west on D49. Site is on right in a short distance.
GPS: 47.45811, 0.2192

Charges guide

Per unit incl. 2 persons and electricity	€ 19,55 - € 35,65
extra person	€ 5,20 - € 6,90
child (2-7 yrs)	€ 3,10 - € 4,60

Saint Père-sur-Loire

Camping Hortus, Le Jardin de Sully

1 route d'Orléans (D60), Sully-sur-Loire, F-45600 Saint Père-sur-Loire (Loiret) T: 02 38 36 35 94
E: info@camping-hortus.com alanrogers.com/FR45040

Across the river from Sully-sur-Loire with its imposing château, this site makes a comfortable base for exploring this part of the Loire valley. Open all year, there are 100 varying sized, level stony/grassy pitches with 80 for touring, all with 10A electricity, water and drainage. They are mostly arranged in groups of six surrounded by low hedging with a few trees giving just a little shade. Between the main area and the river there is an extra area for tents; with shady, undelineated pitches but few electric points. Many pitches have views over the river but, unfortunately, not of the town or its château. Much work is being done to improve the site including new small inflatable swimming and paddling pools, a bar and an open-air restaurant. Improvements are also planned for the very small, basic toilet block in the centre of the site, which at present may be overstretched in the high season. The other, larger toilet block near the entrance is some way from most of the pitches. A full entertainment programme is planned for the high season. Access is easy for large outfits.

Facilities

Two modern, well equipped toilet blocks. One near the entrance is heated, with a suite for visitors with disabilities. Second block in centre of site is small with open-air showers. Small shop. Bar and open-air restaurant and takeaway (1/5-30/9). Small, heated, covered swimming pool and separate paddling pool (1/5-30/9). Fishing. Bicycle hire. Games/TV room. Minigolf. Boules. Play areas. WiFi. Off site: Town and château 1.5 km. Two supermarkets 2 km. Golf 2 km. Riding 4 km.

Open: All year.

Directions

From Orléans take N60 then the D952 east towards Gien. Turn south on D948 for Sully-sur-Loire. In St Père-sur-Loire, at roundabout just before river bridge, turn west on D60 signed St Benoit-sur-Loire. Site is 800 m. on left. GPS: 47.77106, 2.36214

Charges guide

Per unit incl. 2 persons and electricity	€ 15,00 - € 25,00
extra person	€ 3,00 - € 4,00

Saint Satur

Flower Camping les Portes de Sancerre

Quai de Loire, F-18300 Saint Satur (Cher) T: 02 48 72 10 88
E: camping.sancerre@flowercampings.com alanrogers.com/FR18020

The site is situated on the banks of the Loire, just a few miles from the A77 motorway and as such is well placed as an overnight stopover point. However it should also be considered for longer stays as it is close to the medieval town of Sancerre which is perched high on a hill and surrounded by vine covered slopes. Visit the village of Chavignol where you can taste the wine and cheese direct from the producer. There are facilities for tennis, canoeing and bicycle hire just outside the site and a baker is just five minutes walk.

Facilities

One toilet block with toilets, washbasins and showers. Baby room. Facilities for disabled visitors (separate). No motorcaravan service point but pitches specifically for them. Water taps in short supply. Laundry facilities. Small shop with limited stock at reception. Small play area. Communal barbecue area. Boules. Off site: Baker nearby. Supermarket in Saint Satur. Marina and boat launching 300 m. Minigolf and bar just outside rear gate. Swimming pool in Saint Satur. Golf 6 km. Tourist information office in town. Bourges 30 km.

Open: 1 April - 30 September.

Directions

Leave A77 at exit 24 and join the D4 signed Saint Satur. Cross the river Loire and immediately turn right into Rue Quai de Loire. Site is 300 m. along this road on the right. GPS: 47.34209, 2.86565

Charges guide

Per unit incl. 2 persons	
and electricity	€ 13,50 - € 16,00
extra person	€ 3,00 - € 4,00
child (2-7 yrs)	€ 2,00 - € 2,50
dog	free

Senonches

Huttopia Senonches

Etang de Badouleau, avenue de Badouleau, F-28250 Senonches (Eure-et-Loir) T: 04 37 64 22 35
E: senonches@huttopia.com alanrogers.com/FR28140

Huttopia Senonches is hidden away in the huge Forêt Dominiale de Senonches and in keeping with other Huttopia sites, combines a high standard of comfort with a real sense of backwoods camping. There are 101 touring pitches here, some with electricity (6/10A). The pitches are very large ranging from 100 sq.m. to no less than 300 sq.m. There are also 25 Canadian style log cabins and tents available for rent. A good range of on-site amenities includes a shop and a bar/restaurant. The chlorine free natural pool, with terrace, overlooks a lake and is open from early July until September. The forest can be explored on foot or by cycle (rental available on site) and beyond the forest, the great city of Chartres is easily visited, with its stunning Gothic cathedral, widely considered to be the finest in France.

Facilities

The toilet blocks are modern and are heated in low season, with special facilities for disabled visitors. Shop (all season). Bar, snack bar and takeaway (limited in low season). Swimming pool. Fishing. Play area. Bicycle hire and horse riding. Entertainment and activity programme. Tents, Cahuttes and chalets for rent. Gas barbecues only. Max. 1 dog. Off site: Riding 4 km. Senonches (good selection of shops, bars and restaurants). Cycle and walking tracks. Chartres.

Open: 22 April - 6 November.

Directions

Approaching from Chartres, use the ringroad (N154) and then take the D24 in a northwesterly direction. Drive through Digny and continue to Senonches, from where the site is well signed.
GPS: 48.5533, 1.04146

Charges guide

Per unit incl. 2 persons	
and electricity	€ 18,00 - € 34,00
extra person	€ 4,00 - € 5,50
child (2-7 yrs)	€ 2,50 - € 3,60

Sainte Maure-de-Touraine

Castel Camping Parc de Fierbois

F-37800 Sainte Catherine de Fierbois (Indre-et-Loire) T: 02 47 65 43 35
E: contact@fierbois.com alanrogers.com/FR37120

Parc de Fierbois has an impressive entrance and a tree-lined driveway and is set among 250 acres of lakes and forest in the heart of the Loire Valley. In all, there are 420 pitches including 125 for touring units, the remainder being used by tour operators and for chalets and mobile homes. Of the 125 touring pitches, mostly level and separated by low hedging or small trees, all have electricity (10A). The other pitches are small or medium in size, many unmarked and some sloping and in the shade. This is a lively family holiday site. There is a super pool complex and a sandy beach on the shores of the lake.

Facilities

Three toilet blocks with British style WCs, hot showers and washbasins in cubicles. Baby room. Dishwashing and laundry facilities. Motorcaravan service point. Shop, bar, restaurant, takeaway. Water complex (pools, slides). Indoor heated pool. Indoor entertainment and games bar. Tennis. Pétanque. Minigolf. Bicycle hire. Go-karts and electric cars. Gym. Fishing. Pedaloes, canoeing and entertainment (July/Aug). Off site: Riding 10 km.

Open: 16 May - 9 September.

Directions

Travelling south on N10 from Tours, go through Montbazon and on towards St Maure and Chatellerault. Site signed 16 km. outside Montbazon near Ste Catherine. Turn off main road. Follow site signs. From A10 autoroute use St Maure exit and turn north up N10. GPS: 47.1487, 0.6548

Charges guide

Per unit incl. 2 persons	€ 16,00 - € 48,00
extra person	€ 7,00 - € 9,00

Sonzay

Kawan Village l'Arada Parc

525

Rue de la Baratière, F-37360 Sonzay (Indre-et-Loire) T: 02 47 24 72 69. E: info@laradaparc.com
alanrogers.com/FR37060

A good, well maintained site in a quiet location, easy to find from the motorway and popular as an overnight stop. Camping l'Arada Parc is an attractive family site nestling in the heart of the Touranelle countryside between the Loire and Loir valleys. The 73 grass touring pitches all have electricity and 19 have water and drainage. The clearly marked pitches, some slightly sloping, are separated by trees and shrubs some of which are now providing a degree of shade. An attractive, heated pool is on a pleasant terrace beside the restaurant. Entertainment, themed evenings and activities for children are organised in July/August. This is a new site with modern facilities which include a superb new covered pool and fitness room. The campsite is situated in the heart of 'château country' so you will have the opportunity to visit Villandry, Azay-le-Rideau and Langeais. Why not try the vineyards too? Chinon, Vouvray, Touraine and Amboise – you'll be spoilt for choice!

Facilities

Two modern toilet blocks provide unisex toilets, showers and washbasins in cubicles. Baby room. Facilities for disabled visitors (wheelchair users may find the gravel access difficult). Laundry facilities. Shop, bar, restaurant and takeaway (all season). Motorcaravan service point. Outdoor swimming pool (no Bermuda-style shorts; 1/5-15/9). Heated, covered pool (all season). Fitness room. Small play area. Games area. Boules. TV room. Bicycle hire. Internet access. WiFi throughout site. Footpath to village. Off site: Tennis 200 m. Fishing 500 m. Golf 12 km. Riding 14 km.

Open: 26 March - 1 November.

Directions

Sonzay is northwest of Tours. From the new A28 north of Tours take the exit to Neuillé-Pont-Pierre which is on the N138 Le Mans - Tours road. Then take D766 towards Château la Vallière and turn southwest to Sonzay. Follow campsite signs. GPS: 47.625963, 0.452843

Charges guide

Per unit incl. 2 persons and electricity (10A)	€ 18,60 - € 27,10
extra person	€ 4,00 - € 5,10
child (2-10 yrs)	€ 3,50

Camping Cheques accepted.

For latest campsite news, availability and prices visit
alanrogers.com

Suèvres

Castel Camping Château de la Grenouillère

RN152, F-41500 Suèvres (Loir-et-Cher) T: 02 54 87 80 37. E: la.grenouillere@wanadoo.fr

alanrogers.com/FR41020

Château de la Grenouillère is a comfortable site with good amenities. It is set in a 28 acre park and the 275 pitches are in three distinct areas. The majority are in a wooded area, with about 60 in the old orchard and the remainder in open meadow, although all pitches are separated by hedges. There is one water point for every four pitches and all have electric hook-ups (10A). Additionally, there are 14 fully serviced pitches with a separate sanitary block in the outbuildings of the château.

Facilities

Three sanitary blocks are modern and well appointed, including some washbasins in cabins. Laundry facilities. Shop. Bar. Pizzeria/takeaway. Restaurant and grill takeaway. Swimming complex of four pools (one covered) and slide. Spa and wellness. Whirlpool, jacuzzi, sauna, massage. Tennis. Games room. Internet point. Bicycle and canoe hire (July/Aug). Fishing. Off site: Suèvres 3 km. Riding, and watersports 5 km. Golf 10 km.

Open: 17 April - 11 September.

Directions

Site is between Suèvres and Mer on the north side of the N152 and is well signed.
GPS: 47.68557, 1.48686

Charges guide

Per unit incl. 2 persons and electricity	€ 26,00 - € 39,00
incl. full services	€ 30,00 - € 45,00
extra person	€ 5,00 - € 8,00
child (under 7 yrs)	€ 3,00 - € 6,00
dog	€ 4,00

Trogues

Camping du Château de la Rolandière

F-37220 Trogues (Indre-et-Loire) T: 02 47 58 53 71. E: contact@larolandiere.com

alanrogers.com/FR37090

This is a charming site set in the grounds of a château. The owners, Ghislain and Sabine Toulemonde, offer a very warm welcome. There are 50 medium sized, flat or gently sloping pitches, separated by hedges. Most have 6A electricity and water taps nearby and parkland trees give shade. There is a large chalet for hire and the château and adjoining buildings contain rooms to let. The site has a pleasant swimming pool with a sunny terrace and paddling pool, minigolf and an area for ball games, swings and slides. The site is close to both the A10 and the N10, so is convenient for an overnight break. However it certainly merits a longer stay as it is a delightfully peaceful spot from which to visit the châteaux at Chinon, Loches, Villandry or Azay-le-Rideau and the villages of Richelieu and Crissay-sur-Manse. There are interesting excursions to gardens and grottoes, and in nearby Azay-le-Rideau, to the wicker craftsmen's workshops. A Sites et Paysages member.

Facilities

The toilet block is older in style, but refurbished to provide good facilities with modern showers, washbasin and laundry areas around central British style WCs. Provision for disabled visitors. Small shop for basics. Bar with terrace. Snacks and takeaway (July/Aug). Swimming pool (15/5-30/9). Minigolf. Play area. Fitness room. TV lounge. WiFi. Off site: Fishing 1 km. on River Vienne. River beach and boat launching 4 km. Golf 15 km. Bicycle hire 25 km. Restaurant 4 km. St Maure 7 km.

Open: 23 April - 24 September.

Directions

Trogues is 40 km. southwest of Tours on the D760 Loches - Chinon road. Site is east of village, 5 km. west from exit 25 on A10 at St Maure-de-Touraine. Entrance is signed and marked by a model of the château. GPS: 47.10767, 0.51052

Charges guide

Per unit incl. 2 persons and electricity	€ 20,50 - € 28,50
extra person	€ 4,50 - € 6,00
child (under 10 yrs)	€ 2,50 - € 3,50
animal	€ 2,00 - € 3,00
No credit cards.	

Trogues

Village Center le Parc des Allais

Les Allais, F-37220 Trogues (Indre-et-Loire) T: 04 99 57 21 21. E: contact@village-center.com
alanrogers.com/FR37130

Village Center le Parc des Allais is a mainly residential site situated in the heart of the Loire Valley. It is convenient for exploring the surrounding countryside and the region's world class châteaux. The site lies within a 16 hectare park and borders an attractive lake. It has a new indoor and outdoor pool complex overlooking the Vienne River. Of the 198 pitches there are only 25 small pitches for touring (10A electricity), separated by hedges and with good shade, all near the entrance.

Facilities

Two basic toilet blocks with facilities for campers with disabilities. Shop, bar, takeaway (31/3-13/10). Restaurant (July/Aug). Swimming pool complex, indoor and outdoor pools, slides, paddling pool (15/4-15/10). Miniclub. Theme evenings. Entertainment (July/Aug). Minigolf. Tennis. Boules. Fishing. Bicycle hire. Boat and go-kart rental (July/Aug). Play area. Fitness facilities. Games room. Internet. Motorcaravan services outside entrance.
Off site: Countryside and châteaux of the Loire region. Futuroscope (45 minutes). Tours (less than an hour). Caves. Wine Route. Riding 3 km. Golf 30 km.

Open: 8 April - 2 October.

Directions

South of Tours leave A10 autoroute at exit 25 signed Ste Maure de Touraine. Take D970 west for about 3 km. Turn south on D58 to Pouzay. Turn west on D109 to site. It is between Pouzay and Trougues. GPS: 47.099233, 0.504183

Charges guide

Per unit incl. 2 persons and electricity	€ 23,00 - € 29,86
extra person	€ 4,00 - € 5,00
child (under 12 yrs)	€ 3,00 - € 4,00

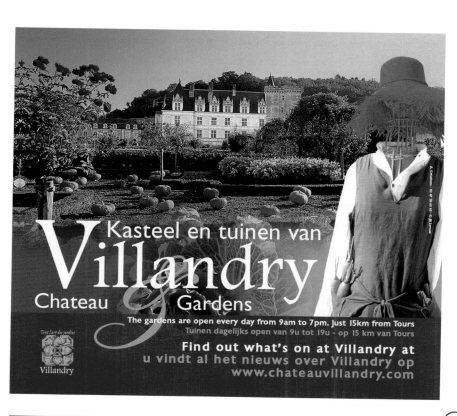
For latest campsite news, availability and prices visit
alanrogers.com

The Pays de la Loire covers the area of western France to the south of Brittany and Normandy. It lies along the lower stretches of the river Loire, the longest river in France, downstream from the châteaux of the Val de Loire region.

DÉPARTEMENTS: 44 LOIRE-ATLANTIQUE, 49 MAINE-ET-LOIRE, 53 MAYENNE, 72 SARTHE

Strictly speaking, the département of 85 Vendée is also part of this region. Because of its importance as a holiday destination for British visitors, we have featured it separately in this guide.

MAJOR CITIES: ANGERS, NANTES, LE MANS AND SAUMUR

Pays de la Loire is one of the regions created in the late 20th century to serve as an administrative zone of influence for its capital, Nantes. The Pays de la Loire is home to many great monuments, such as the castles of Angers, Laval and Mayenne and the Château des Ducs de Bretagne at Nantes, the Royal Fontevraud Abbey and the old city of Le Mans. It also contains many natural parks including the Brière, the Poitou marshes and Les Alpes Mancelles.

The region has become very popular with British visitors involving no more than a day's drive from the Channel ports. It includes 450 km. of Atlantic coastline that offers long, sandy beaches, rugged creeks, islands such as the Ile de Noirmoutier and the Ile d'Yeu, resorts such as La Baule, contrasting with the lush green countryside through which flows the River Loire.

At the region's heart lies Angers, the capital of the historic province of Anjou, home to the feudal warlords and the Plantagenet kings of England. To the southeast, the Vendée, is a peaceful holiday area very popular with summer visitors.

paysdelaloire.co.uk
Brimming with holiday ideas

Cities

Nantes
Castle, the Machines of the Ile de Nantes and the gigantic elephant.

Angers
Art town, medieval castle and tapestries, cathedral.

Laval
Castle, Douanier Rousseau art gallery, boat trips on the Mayenne.

Le Mans
Car museum, old town, cathedral.

Saumur
13th-century castle, Cadre Noir National School of Horse Riding, wine cellars and Mushroom Museum.

Loire Wines

Famous vineyards to discover
Muscadet, Saumur-Champigny, Anjou Rouge, Coteaux du Layon.

www.**vinsvaldeloire.fr**

Castles and Monuments

Fontevraud
12th-century Royal abbey, one of the largest cloister cities of Europe.

Brissac
15th-century castle, still inhabited.

Le Lude
Fine example of early Renaissance architecture and delightful garden, still inhabited.

Adventure Parks

Terra Botanica in Angers
40 attractions and presentations, offering a multi-dimensional experience of plant life from all six continents.

www.**terrabotanica.fr**

Escal'Atlantic in Saint Nazaire
Almost life-size reconstruction of an ocean liner inside the former submarine base recreates the life of the ocean ships of yesterday.

www.**escal-atlantic.com**

Le Grand Parc du Puy du Fou (Vendée)
A whirlwind of shows and entertainment in several villages, each representing a different era.

www.**puydufou.com**

Specialities of the Region

Beurre blanc: a buttery sauce that goes well with fish.

Rillauds d'Anjou: muscadet-flavoured sausages of cooked pork belly.

Curé Nantais and Port-Salut: local cheeses.

Pâté aux prunes: sugary pastry filled with plums.

Brioche: confectionery, spécialité de Vendée

Cointreau: orange liqueur.

Images © (left to right, top to bottom): P Baudry; J P Klein; A Laurioux; B Rivière; M Thiery; A Laurioux

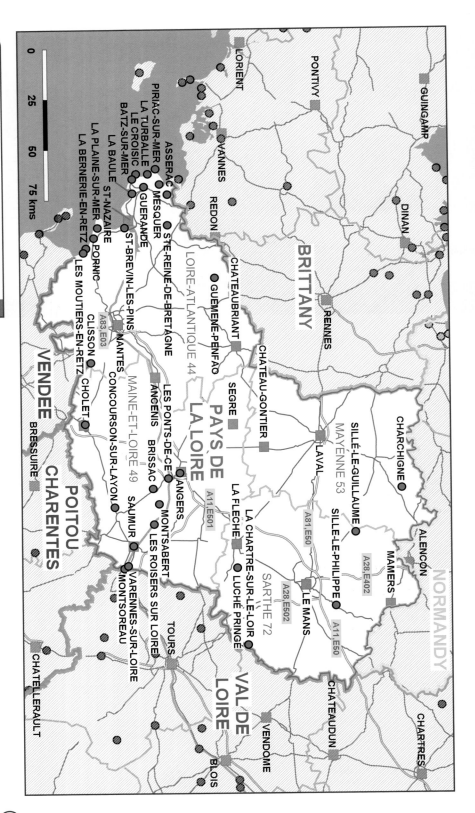

For latest campsite news, availability and prices visit
alanrogers.com

Angers

Camping du Lac de Maine

Avenue du Lac de Maine, F-49000 Angers (Maine-et-Loire) T: 02 41 73 05 03. E: camping@lacdemaine.fr
alanrogers.com/FR49000

The Lac de Maine campsite is situated in the heart of the Anjou region. Most of the 141 level touring pitches are part grass and part gravel hardstanding, with the remainder all gravel. All have water, a drain and electricity (6/10A). The main entrance has a height restriction of 3.2 metres, although there is an alternative gate for higher vehicles. This is a useful site, open for a long season and only five minutes from the centre of Angers. With wide access roads, it is also suitable for American RVs. This site has the advantage of being at the southern end of the Parc de Loisirs du Lac de Maine. The adjacent 100 acre lake has a sandy beach for swimmers, windsurfing, sailing and pedaloes available, while the parkland provides tennis courts and a nature reserve.

Facilities

Two sanitary blocks, one which can be heated and includes some washbasins in cubicles. British style WCs (no seats). Facilities for babies and visitors with disabilities. Laundry facilities. Motorcaravan service point. Reception stocks gas. Restaurant/bar (both 15/6-15/9). Heated L-shaped swimming pool (1/6-15/9). Spa. Petanque. Bicycle hire. Internet point. Barrier card deposit (€ 20). Off site: Lake beach 500 m. Fishing 1 km. Riding 3 km. Golf 5 km.

Open: 25 March - 10 October.

Directions

Site is just west of Angers near the N23 (Angers - Nantes road). Turn south at signs for Quartier de Maine and Lac de Maine. Follow signs for Pruniers and Bouchemaine. Site on D111 and signed. GPS: 47.45434, -0.59619

Charges guide

Per unit incl. 2 persons	€ 11,85 - € 17,00
extra person	€ 3,00
child (under 13 yrs)	€ 2,00
electricity (10A)	€ 3,40
animal	€ 2,00

Camping Cheques accepted.

Camping du Lac de Maine ☆☆☆☆
Discover this pretty campsite nestling in the heart of the Anjou wine region, close to the historic town of Angers and a beautiful vast 100 ha lake.
Openingdates: 25/03 to 10/10/2011
Mobile homes and bungalows for rent
Heated Swimming Pool, Paddling pool, SPA, Restaurant, Bar, Takeaway, Bike hire, Internet Facilities (WiFi)...
Avenue du Lac de Maine - F-49000 Angers - Tel: 0033 (0)2.41.73.05.03
Fax: 0033 (0)2.41.73.02.20 - camping@lacdemaine.fr - www.camping-angers.fr

Assérac

Flower Camping Domaine du Pont Mahé

Pont Mahé, F-44410 Assérac (Loire-Atlantique) T: 02 40 01 74 98. E: contact@pont-mahe.com
alanrogers.com/FR44400

La Grande Brière is a vast area of marshland to the north of the Loire estuary. This is an area rich in flora and fauna, arguably best explored using the traditional punts (chalands). Domaine du Pont Mahé is a seaside site to the north of the Brière. Of the 81 pitches, 36 are for touring and the remainder are occupied by mobile homes (27 for rent). Pitches are generally well shaded and of a good size. The site's covered swimming pool is a focal point and is attractively surrounded by a terrace with straw parasols. Bicycle hire is on offer and a number of cycle tracks run close to the site.

Facilities

Sanitary facilities include hot showers and washbasins in cabins. Facilities for disabled visitors. Laundry facilities. Shop. Bar. Takeaway. Covered swimming pool. Children's pool. Play area. Games room. Bicycle and canoe hire. Activity and entertainment programme. Mobile homes and equipped tents for rent. Off site: Nearest beach 250 m. Grande Brière natural park. Fishing. Cycle tracks. La Baule (18 km).

Open: 1 April - 31 October.

Directions

Leave the N165 at Arzal exit and head south on the D139 (which becomes the D83) as far as Assérac. Head west here on D82 to Pont Mahé and site is well signed. GPS: 47.44737, -2.45043

Charges guide

Per unit incl. 2 persons and electricity	€ 14,00 - € 25,00
extra person	€ 3,00 - € 4,00
child (2-7 yrs)	€ 2,00 - € 3,00
dog	€ 3,00

Brissac

Camping de l'Etang

Route de Saint-Mathurin, F-49320 Brissac (Maine-et-Loire) T: 02 41 91 70 61. E: info@campingetang.com

alanrogers.com/FR49040

At Camping de l'Etang many of the 124 level touring pitches have pleasant views across the local countryside. Separated and numbered, some have a little shade and all have electricity with water and drainage nearby. 21 are fully serviced. A small bridge crosses the river Aubance which runs through the site (well fenced) and there are two lakes where fishermen can enjoy free fishing. The site has its own vineyard and the wine produced can be purchased on the campsite. The adjacent Parc de Loisirs is a paradise for young children with many activities (free for campers). A Sites et Paysages member.

Facilities

Three well maintained toilet blocks provide all the usual facilities. Laundry facilities. Baby room. Disabled visitors are well catered for. Motorcaravan service point. The farmhouse houses reception, small shop and takeaway snacks (July/Aug) when bar is closed. A bar/restaurant serves crêpes, salads, etc. (evenings July/Aug). Swimming pool (heated and covered) and paddling pool. Fishing. Play area. Bicycle hire. Evening entertainment in high season. WiFi. No electric barbecues. Off site: Golf and riding 10 km. Sailing 25 km.

Open: 15 May - 15 September.

Directions

Brissac-Quincé is 17 km. southeast of Angers on D748 towards Poitiers. Do not enter the town but turn north on D55 (site signed) in direction of St Mathurin. GPS: 47.3611, -0.4353

Charges guide

Per unit incl. 2 persons	€ 18,00 - € 30,00
extra person	€ 4,00 - € 5,00
child (3-10 yrs)	€ 2,00 - € 3,00

Batz-sur-Mer

Campéole les Paludiers

Rue Nicolas Appert, F-44740 Batz-sur-Mer (Loire-Atlantique) T: 02 40 23 85 84. E: paludiers@campeole.com

alanrogers.com/FR44360

Campéole

Les Paludiers, part of the Campéole group, is pleasantly situated at Batz-sur-Mer, a typical Breton village between La Baule and the fortified town of Guérande. The site has 300 pitches, with 150 used for touring units on sandy ground, marked and divided by shrubs. There are 70 with 10A electricity. The remainder of the pitches are occupied by mobile homes and canvas bungalows. At the rear of the modern reception building there is a bar and games room. Outside a patio area overlooks a small heated pool and a play area for children. Entertainment is provided for both children and adults in the high season. This site is ideal for families with young children, with a good pool and a safe environment for play. The added bonus here is the close proximity of a lovely sandy beach – just five minutes walk. The drive along the Côte Sauvage to Le Croisic is quite spectacular.

Facilities

Three modern toilet bocks each with good facilities for disabled visitors and a baby room. Laundry facilities. Shop with limited but essential stocks. Bar and snacks (1/7-31/8). Swimming and paddling pools (15/5-15/9). Play area. Games room. Barbecues are only permitted in a dedicated area. Off site: Beach 100 m. Fishing 500 m. Golf, bicycle hire and riding 1 km. Town centre 800 m. Salt marshes and coastal walking paths.

Open: 5 April - 23 September.

Directions

From Nantes take the N171 to St Nazaire and then the D213 towards Guérande. At the D774 follow signs to Batz-sur-Mer, continue through village and take exit from the roundabout into rue Nicolas Appert. Site entrance is on the left. GPS: 47.2788, -2.4913

Charges guide

Per unit incl. 2 persons and electricity	€ 17,10 - € 26,60

Charchigné

Camping le Malidor

F-53250 Charchigné (Mayenne) T: 02 43 00 11 12. E: lemalidor@gmail.com
alanrogers.com/FR53020

This attractive, small, rural site is surrounded by farmland and it provides a real taste of the French countryside. The three private lakes provide great fishing and only a short walk away a path leads to the village where you will find the local bakery and restaurant. There are 27 pitches, 17 for touring, all with 10A electricity. They are terraced and divided by mature hedges. Fly pitches are allowed by prior arrangement with the manager, to within three metres of the main lake for the keen fisherman. The beautiful surrounding countryside is well worth exploring and this site is a perfect place from which to do so. Large units are accepted. Fishing gear and bait are available.

Facilities	Directions
One sanitary block provides good facilities including a disabled access shower. Bar and restaurant (all year). Play area, boules, darts and pool table plus a hall for groups up to 90. Fishing on all three lakes, Minigolf and nice walks in the local area. New facilities in 2010 include a fishing platform for wheelchair users. Off site: Village with bar/restaurant and shop 500 m. Horse riding 3.5 km. Beaches 20 km and golf 25 km.	From A81 (Rennes - Le Mans) take exit 3 for Laval. Head northeast on N162 to Mayenne. Then take N12 in the same direction towards Alençon for 20 km. Just before Javron turn left on D33 to Cherchigné. Then follow signs to site just before Cherghigné. GPS: 48.41857, -0.40141

Open: Said to be all year, but check before visiting.

Charges guide

Per unit incl. 2 persons and electricity	€ 15,00
extra person	€ 2,00

Cholet

Centre Touristique Lac de Ribou

Allée Léon Mandin, F-49300 Cholet (Maine-et-Loire) T: 02 41 49 74 30. E: info@lacderibou.com
alanrogers.com/FR49120

Situated just 58 km. southeast of Nantes and a similar distance from the River Loire at Angers and Saumur, this could be a useful place to break a journey or to spend a few days relaxing. Camping Lac de Ribou, with the adjacent Village Vacances, forms a holiday complex in pleasant parkland next to an extensive lake on the outskirts of the busy market town of Cholet. 162 touring pitches are on undulating land (some are sloping), divided by hedges and with mature trees providing shade on many; most have electricity (10A) and 115 also have individual water taps and drainage.

Facilities	Directions
One sanitary block with preset showers and washbasins in cabins. Facilities for disabled visitors. Motorcaravan service points. Small shop (July/Aug). Bar and snack bar with takeaway (July/Aug). Large heated swimming pool plus smaller pool with slide and paddling pool (1/6-30/9). Play area. Full programme of activities (July/Aug). Cabaret evenings. Night club (high season). WiFi (with deposit). Off site: Fishing and small beach (no swimming) 500 m. Supermarket 2 km. Riding 5 km. Golf 7 km.	From Cholet ring road east of town, turn east on D20 towards Maulévrier and Mauléon. At roundabout by Leclerc supermarket, take first exit signed to site which is signed 'Parc de Loisirs de Ribou' all around the town. GPS: 47.036367, -0.843733

Open: 1 April - 30 September.

Charges guide

Per unit incl. 1 or 2 persons and electricity	€ 10,00 - € 22,00
extra person	€ 3,00 - € 5,00
No credit cards.	

Clisson

Camping Municipal du Moulin

Route de Nantes, F-44190 Clisson (Loire-Atlantique) T: 02 40 54 44 48
alanrogers.com/FR44020

This good value, small site is conveniently located on one of the main north – south routes on the edge of the interesting old town of Clisson. A typical municipal site, it is useful for short stays. There are 45 good sized, marked and level pitches with electricity and divided by hedges and trees giving a good degree of privacy and some shade. There is also an unmarked area for small tents. A barbecue and camp fire area is to the rear of the site above the river where one can fish or canoe (via a steep path).

Facilities	Directions
The fully equipped toilet block, cleaned each afternoon, includes some washbasins in cabins and others in a separate large room, with hot and cold water. Unit for disabled visitors. Dishwashing and laundry facilities. Bread delivered daily. Table tennis, volleyball, and small playground. No double axle or commercial vehicles accepted. Off site: Supermarket with cheap fuel just across the road. Bicycle hire, riding 5 km. Sailing 15 km. Golf 30 km.	From N249 Nantes - Cholet road, take exit for Vallet/Clisson and D763 south for 7 km. then fork right towards Clisson town centre. At roundabout after passing Leclerc supermarket on your right take second exit (into site). GPS: 47.09594, -1.28271

Open: Mid April - mid October.

Charges guide

Per unit incl. 1 person and electricity	€ 7,77 - € 8,20
extra person	€ 2,42 - € 2,55
child (0-7 yrs)	€ 1,61 - € 1,70
No credit cards.	

For latest campsite news, availability and prices visit
alanrogers.com

Concourson-sur-Layon

Camping Caravaning la Vallée des Vignes

La Croix Patron, F-49700 Concourson-sur-Layon (Maine-et-Loire) T: 02 41 59 86 35
E: Campingvdv@wanadoo.fr alanrogers.com/FR49070

The enthusiasm of the English owners here comes across instantly in the warm welcome received by their guests. Bordering the Layon river, the 50 good sized touring pitches are reasonably level and fully serviced (10A electricity, water tap and drain). Five pitches have a hardstanding for cars. Attractions include an enclosed bar and restaurant, a generously sized sun terrace surrounding the pool and high season activities for children and adults. These include wine tasting, competitions and treasure hunts. An ideal base for visiting the châteaux of the Loire and the many caves and vineyards.

Facilities

The toilet block includes washbasins in cabins, and dishwashing facilities. Baby room. Facilities for disabled visitors. Laundry facilities. Bar (from 15/5 or on request) serving meals, snacks and takeaway (from 15/5). Swimming and paddling pools (from 15/5). Playground, games area and football pitch. Volleyball, basketball, minigolf. Internet access. Fishing. Caravan storage. Pets corner with goats, chickens and rabbits. Off site: Zoo and rose gardens at Doué-la-Fontaine. Grand Parc Puy du Fou.

Open: 15 April - 30 September.

Directions

Site signed off D960 Doué - Vihiers road, just west of Concourson-sur-Layon. GPS: 47.17431, -0.34730

Charges guide

Per unit incl. 2 persons and electricity	€ 21,50 - € 27,00
extra person	€ 5,00 - € 9,00
child (2-12 yrs)	€ 3,00 - € 4,00
dog	€ 3,00

Special offers available.

Guémené-Penfao

Camping l'Hermitage

36 ave du Paradis, F-44290 Guémené-Penfao (Loire-Atlantique) T: 02 40 79 23 48
E: contact@campinglhermitage.com alanrogers.com/FR44130

L'Hermitage is a pretty wooded site set in the Vallée du Don and would be useful for en-route stops or for longer stays. The enthusiastic staff, even though their English is a little limited, provide a warm welcome and maintain this reasonably priced site to a good standard. There are 110 pitches of which 80 are a good size for touring and camping. Some are formally arranged on open, level grass pitches, whereas others are informal amongst light woodland. Electricity (6A) is available to all (a long lead may be useful). Both Nantes and Rennes are 30 minutes away, La Baule with its beaches is 40 minutes.

Facilities

A clean and well serviced toilet block includes some washbasins in cabins with warm water. Laundry and dishwashing sinks under cover (cold water but a hot tap is provided). Smallish pool, paddling pool and slide, nicely maintained and carefully fenced. Small play area. Petanque. Games room with video games.
Off site: Leisure complex with indoor pool opposite. Fishing 500 m. Village 1 km. for all facilities. Riding 2 km. Many walking trails.

Open: 1 April - 31 October.

Directions

Exit N137 at Derval (signed Châteaubriant) but take D775 for Redon. Guémené-Penfao is about 13 km. Watch for site signs before village centre. Site is on the outskirts in a semi-residential area to the northeast. GPS: 47.62595, -1.8181

Charges guide

Per unit incl. 2 persons	€ 12,00
extra person	€ 3,50
child (under 7 yrs)	€ 2,50
electricity	€ 2,90
dog	€ 1,00

Guérande

Le Domaine de Léveno

Route de Sandun, F-44350 Guérande (Loire-Atlantique) T: 02 40 24 79 30. E: domaine.leveno@wanadoo.fr

alanrogers.com/FR44220

525

There have been many changes to this extensive site over the past years and considerable investment has been made to provide some excellent new facilities. The number of mobile homes and chalets has increased considerably, leaving just 38 touring pitches. However, these are mainly grouped at the far end of the site and are rather worn with little grass. Pitches are divided by hedges and trees which offer a good deal of shade and all have electricity (10A). Access is tricky to some and the site is not recommended for larger units. Twin axle caravans and American motorhomes are not accepted. This site has exceptional facilities for entertaining the young.

Facilities

Main refurbished toilet block offers preset showers, washbasins in cubicles and facilities for disabled visitors. Laundry facilities. Small shop selling basics and takeaway snacks. Restaurant, bar (all Apr-Sept). Indoor pool. Heated outdoor pool complex (15/5-30/9). Fitness room. Excellent, safe play area. Multisport court and crazy golf. Extensive programme of activities and events (high season). WiFi in bar (free). Off site: Large hypermarket 1 km. Fishing 2 km. Beach, golf and riding all 5 km.

Open: 4 April - 30 September.

Directions

Site is less than 3 km. from the centre of Guérande. From D774 and from D99/N171 take D99E Guérande by-pass. Turn east following signs for Villejames and Leclerc hypermarket and continue on D247 to site on right. GPS: 47.33352, -2.3906

Charges guide

Per unit incl. 2 persons, electricity and water	€ 18,00 - € 35,00
extra person	€ 3,00 - € 7,00
dog	€ 3,00 - € 5,00

La Baule

Camping les Ajoncs d'Or

Chemin du Rocher, F-44500 La Baule (Loire-Atlantique) T: 02 40 60 33 29. E: contact@ajoncs.com

alanrogers.com/FR44170

This site is situated in pine woods, 1.5 km. on the inland side of La Baule and its beautiful bay. A well maintained, natural woodland setting provides a wide variety of pitch types (just over 200), some level and bordered with hedges and tall trees to provide shade and many others that maintain the natural characteristics of the woodland. Most pitches have electricity and water nearby and are usually of a larger size. A central building provides a shop and open friendly bar that serves snacks and takeaways. The English speaking Bazillails family (the owners) who live on site will welcome you to their campsite.

Facilities

Two good quality sanitary blocks are clean and well maintained providing plenty of facilities including a baby room. Washing machines and dryers. Shop and bar (July/Aug). Snack bar (July/Aug). Good sized swimming pool and paddling pool (1/6-5/9). Sports and playground areas. Bicycle hire. Reception with security barrier (closed 22.30-07.30). Off site: La Baule. Beach 1.5 km. Fishing and riding 1.5 km. Golf 3 km.

Open: 1 April - 30 September.

Directions

From N171 take exit for La Baule les Pins. Follow signs for La Baule Centre, then left at roundabout in front of Carrefour supermarket and follow site signs. GPS: 47.28950, -2.37367

Charges guide

Per unit incl. 2 persons and electricity	€ 18,00 - € 24,00
extra person	€ 5,25 - € 7,00
child (2-7 yrs)	€ 2,25 - € 3,00

La Chartre-sur-le-Loir

Camping du Vieux Moulin

Chemin des Bergivaux, F-72340 La Chartre-sur-le-Loir (Sarthe) T: 02 43 44 41 18. E: camping@lachartre.com

alanrogers.com/FR72070

Le Vieux Moulin is a pleasant family site, located on the banks of the Loir, close to the pretty town of La Chartre-sur-le Loir, to the south east of Le Mans. Pitches here are grassy and of a good size. There are also a number of mobile homes and fully equipped tents available for rent. On-site amenities include a heated swimming pool, a paddling pool and a sports field. Canoeing is popular here and canoes can be rented on site. The site becomes livelier in peak season with a limited entertainment and activity programme, including a children's club and occasional karaoke evenings.

Facilities

Traditional sanitary block provides pushbutton showers and some washbasins in cubicles. Facilities for disabled visitors. Washing machine and dryer. Motorcaravan service point. Small shop, restaurant and takeaway with licence (weekends and July/Aug). Swimming and paddling pools (1/6-20/9). Fishing. Canoeing. Bicycle hire. Large sports field. Play area. Tourist information. Mobile homes and equipped tents for rent. Internet access and free WiFi. Off site: Village 1 km. Lake 4 km.

Open: 1 May - 20 September.

Directions

From A28 exit 26, head east to Château du Loir, turn south on the D938/D338 (Caen - Tours road) and cross the Loir. Then head northeast on the D305 to La Chartre-sur-le Loir. After one-way system follow signs to the site, turning left immediately after crossing river. GPS: 47.7324, 0.57095

Charges guide

Per unit incl. 2 persons and electricity	€ 11,90 - € 18,20
extra person	€ 2,70 - € 3,60

For latest campsite news, availability and prices visit

alanrogers.com

La Bernerie-en-Retz

Camping les Ecureuils

24 avenue Gilbert Burlot, F-44760 La Bernerie-en-Retz (Loire-Atlantique) T: 02 40 82 76 95
E: camping.les-ecureuils@wanadoo.fr alanrogers.com/FR44050

Just 350 metres from both the sea and the centre of the little town of La Bernerie, Les Ecureuils is a family run site. The sandy beach here is great for children; swimming is restricted to high tide, since the sea goes out a long way although at low tide a shallow lagoon remains which is perfect for young children. The site has 167 touring pitches, all with electricity (10A) close by and 19 with their own water tap and drain. There are also 80 mobile homes and chalets for rent and a further 70 privately owned. The site prides itself on its pool complex with heated leisure and swimming pools including three water slides and a flume. The fishing port of Pornic is worth a visit, as is the Ile de Noirmoutier, just 35 km. south.

Facilities

Four toilet blocks are in traditional French style; some have controllable showers and washbasins in cubicles. Facilities for disabled visitors are not all easily accessible. Baby room. Bar with terrace (15/6-31/8), also selling bread (1/7-31/8). Snack bar and takeaway (July/Aug). Swimming pools (15/5-15/9). Playground. WiFi in bar area. Off site: Shops, restaurants and bars 350 m. Also beach, fishing, sailing and boat launching. Golf, riding and bicycle hire 6 km.

Open: 1 May - 15 September.

Directions

La Bernerie-en-Retz is 5 km. south of Pornic and 26 km. south of the Saint Nazaire bridge. From the D213/D13 (St Nazaire - Noirmoutier) turn west on D66 to La Bernerie. Site is signed to right by railway station before reaching town.
GPS: 47.0845, -2.036667

Charges guide

Per unit incl. 2 persons and electricity	€ 19,00 - € 34,00
extra person	€ 4,00 - € 6,50
child (0-10 yrs)	free - € 5,00

CAMPING LES ECUREUILS***

24, Avenue Gilbert Burlot - 44760 La Bernerie-en-Retz
Tel: 0033(0) 240 82 76 95 - Fax: 0033(0) 240 64 79 52
E-mail: camping.les-ecureuils@wanadoo.fr - Internet: www.camping-les-ecureuils.com

La Plaine-sur-Mer

Camping la Tabardière

F-44770 La Plaine-sur-Mer (Loire-Atlantique) T: 02 40 21 58 83. E: info@camping-la-tabardiere.com
alanrogers.com/FR44150

Owned and managed by the Barré family, this campsite is pleasant, peaceful and immaculate. It will suit those who want to enjoy the local coast and towns but return to an 'oasis' for relaxation. However, it still provides activities and fun for those with energy remaining. The pitches are mostly terraced and care needs to be taken in manoeuvring caravans into position – although the effort is well worth it. The pitches have access to electricity and water taps are conveniently situated nearby. The site is probably not suitable for people using wheelchairs. Whilst this is a rural site, its amenities are excellent with covered swimming pool, paddling pool and a water slide, volleyball, tennis, boules and a very challenging 18-hole minigolf to keep you occupied, plus a friendly bar. The beautiful beaches are 3 km. with the fishing harbour town, Pornic, some 5 km, ideal for cafés, restaurants and evening strolls. A Sites et Paysages member.

Facilities

Two good, clean toilet blocks are well equipped and include laundry facilities. Motorcaravan service point. Shop, bar, snacks and takeaway (high season). Good sized covered swimming pool, paddling pool and slides (supervised). Playground. Minigolf. Volleyball and basket-ball. Half size tennis courts. Boules. Fitness programme. Overnight area for motorcaravans (€ 13 per night). Off site: Beach 3 km. Sea fishing 3 km. Golf, riding and bicycle hire all 5 km.

Open: 4 April - 27 September.

Directions

Site is well signed, situated inland off the D13 Pornic - La Plaine-sur-Mer road. GPS: 47.140767, -2.15052

Charges guide

Per unit incl. 2 persons	€ 15,00 - € 26,70
extra person	€ 3,70 - € 6,40
child (2-9 yrs)	€ 2,75 - € 4,35
dog	€ 3,20
electricity (3/8A)	€ 3,30 - € 4,80
Camping Cheques accepted.	

La Plaine-sur-Mer
Camping le Ranch
Les Hautes Raillères, F-44770 La Plaine-sur-Mer (Loire-Atlantique) T: 02 40 21 52 62
E: info@camping-le-ranch.com **alanrogers.com/FR44240**

This is a pleasant, family-run campsite with a friendly atmosphere, close to the beaches of the Jade Coast between Pornic and St Brévin-les-Pins, yet not right on the seashore. The 94 touring pitches all have access to electricity (6A) although on some a long cable may be required; these occupy the central part of the site, with the fringe areas taken up by mobile homes and chalets, 18 for rent and 74 privately owned (although 30 of these are also available for rent in high season). The rows of pitches are separated by well-kept hedges, and small trees mark the corners of most plots. In high season there is a very lively atmosphere and at less busy times it is almost certainly a very peaceful site. A pleasant bar and terrace overlook the attractive pool complex with a swimming pool and paddling pool, together with water slides and a flume. Linked to the bar is a large barn with stage and dance floor, which at other times is a games room and an indoor volleyball court. The central area, with boules, gives the site a very French ambience.

Facilities

The central sanitary block has preset showers and washbasins in cubicles. Facilities for disabled visitors. Baby room. Further small toilet block. Heated swimming pool complex with slides and flume (1/5-15/9). Bar has small shop selling bread, basics and camping gaz. Good takeaway (July/Aug). Activities for children and entertainment and sports events for families in high season. Off site: Beach 800 m. Bicycle hire 1.5 km. Boat launching 3 km. Fishing 5 km. Sailing 3 km. Riding 4 km. Golf 6 km.

Open: 1 April - 30 September.

Directions

La Plaine-sur-Mer is 16 km. south of the St Nazaire bridge. Site is on D96 5 km. northeast of the town. From D213 (Route Bleue) just south of St Michel -Chef-Chef turn southwest on D96 towards La Plaine. Site on left in about 2 km.
GPS: 47.155216, -2.1649

Charges guide

Per unit incl. 2 persons	
and electricity	€ 17,00 - € 28,50
extra person	€ 3,10 - € 5,50
child (under 8 yrs)	€ 2,10 - € 3,40
dog	€ 2,20 - € 2,90

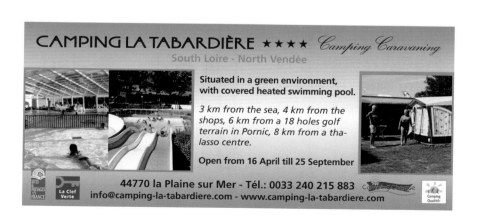

For latest campsite news, availability and prices visit
alanrogers.com

La Turballe

Camping le Parc Sainte-Brigitte

Domaine de Bréhet, chemin des Routes, F-44420 La Turballe (Loire-Atlantique) T: 02 40 24 88 91

E: saintebrigitte@wanadoo.fr **alanrogers.com/FR44040**

Le Parc Sainte-Brigitte is a well established site in the attractive grounds of a manor house, three kilometres from the beaches. It is a spacious site with 150 good pitches, 110 with electricity, water and drainage. Some are arranged in a circular, park-like setting near the entrance, others are in wooded areas under tall trees and the remainder are on more open grass in an unmarked area near the pool. This is a quiet place to stay outside the main season, whilst in high season, it can become very busy. One can walk around many of the areas of the estate that are not used for camping; there are farm animals to see and a carp fishing lake will be popular with anglers. In high season it is mainly used by families with its full share of British visitors. The nearby seaside town of La Baule with its 'chic' shops is worth visiting as is the old medieval walled town of Guérande. With beaches only three kilometres away, this site has something for everyone.

Facilities

The main toilet block, supplemented by a second block, is of good quality. They include washbasins in cabins and two bathrooms. Laundry facilities and lines provided. Motorcaravan services. Small shop. Pleasant restaurant/bar with takeaway (both 15/5-15/9). Heated swimming pool with retractable roof and paddling pool. Playground. Bicycle hire. Boules. TV room and traditional 'salle de réunion'. Fishing. WiFi (free). Off site: Riding 2 km. Nearest beach 3 km. Golf 15 km.

Open: 1 April - 1 October.

Directions

Entrance is off the busy La Turballe-Guérande D99 road, 3 km. east of La Turballe. A one-way system operates - in one lane, out via another. GPS: 47.34253, -2.47168

Charges guide

Per unit incl. 2 persons, water, waste water and electricity	€ 29,80
extra person	€ 6,30
child (under 7 yrs)	€ 5,00

No credit cards.

PARC SAINTE-BRIGITTE

★ ★ ★ ★ N.N.

De Luxe Camping Site

HEATED SWIMMING POOL

Close to the fishing village of LaTurballe and neighbouring beaches. 10 km from the well-known resort of La Baule. The charm of the countryside with the pleasures of the seaside. Sanitary facilities as in a first class hotel. Heated and covered swimming pool (approximately 200 m² water and 200 m² covered terrace around it). The cover can be retracted during warm weather. Children's pool.

campingsaintebrigitte@wanadoo.fr
www.campingsaintebrigitte.com

La Turballe

Camping la Falaise

1 boulevard de Belmont, F-44420 La Turballe (Loire-Atlantique) T: 02 40 23 32 53
E: info@camping-de-la-falaise.com alanrogers.com/FR44340

La Falaise is a simple site enjoying direct access to a wide sandy beach. There are 150 pitches of which 67 are available to tourers with water and electricity. Other pitches are occupied by mobile homes or chalets (some to rent). The pitches are of a reasonable size but are unshaded and tend to be very sandy. This is a quiet site in low season becoming much livelier in July and August. There are relatively few amenities on site but nearby La Turballe has a good selection of shops and restaurants. In high season, a takeaway food service is available. There is one main building housing reception and washing and toilet facilities. La Turballe is a bustling fishing port and nearby Guérande, on the edge of the Grande Brière natural park, merits a visit with its excellent market.

Facilities

Central toilet block (predominantly Turkish style toilets). Bar, restaurant and takeaway (1/6-15/9). Play area (unfenced). Mobile homes and chalets for rent. Direct access to the beach. Off site: Shops 300 m. Fishing. Boat launching 500 m. Golf 2 km. Riding 10 km. Walking and cycle trails. Shops and restaurants in La Turballe 2 km.

Open: 1 April - 31 October.

Directions

Take the D99 from Guérande to La Turballe and then continue towards Piriac sur Mer. Bypass La Turballe and the site is on this road after a further kilometre. GPS: 47.353833, -2.517333

Charges guide

Per unit incl. 2 persons and electricity	€ 20,60 - € 31,40
extra person (over 4 yrs)	€ 4,35 - € 5,00
dog	€ 2,30 - € 2,95

Camping La Falaise

2 entrance to the beach, on 400 m distance from the fisher harbour and marina. The center is at 600 meters distance, you will find a supermarket at 400 meter distance. La Falaise is near various places of interest. The mediaeval city of Guérande, ferries to the islands, the Parc Naturel Régional de Brière and the Côte Sauvage.

1 Boulevard de Belmont - 44420 La Turballe - Tel: 0033 240 23 32 53 - Fax: 0033 240 62 87 07
E-mail: camping-de-lafalaise@orange.fr - www.camping-la-falaise.com

Les Moutiers-en-Retz

Flower Camping les Brillas

Le Bois des Tréans, F-44760 Les Moutiers-en-Retz (Loire-Atlantique) T: 02 40 82 79 78
E: info@campinglesbrillas.com alanrogers.com/FR44310

You are assured of a warm welcome from M. and Mme. Perret, the owners of this site. The small number of touring pitches are on grass, hedged and small. The larger pitches are being taken up by mobile homes of which there is a much higher ratio compared to touring pitches. This could be a useful base for visiting Pornic and St Nazaire where there are many tourist attractions. The reception, bar and restaurant are housed in the same modern building as the sanitary facilities. Care should be taken on the approach road to the site which is a long narrow lane with no passing places.

Facilities

The toilet block is clean but basic and includes a mix of English and Turkish style toilets and preset showers. Good facilities for disabled visitors. Dishwashing and laundry facilities. Bar and restaurant with limited menu. Shop in bar. Large games area. Small unfenced play area. Basic swimming pool. Bicycle hire. Entertainment (July/Aug). Off site: Fishing and sailing 3 km. Riding 5 km. Golf 12 km.

Open: 1 April - 30 October.

Directions

Site is 1.5 km. from Les Moutiers. Heading northwest from Les Moutiers on D97 turn right onto Route du Bois des Treans. Site well signed. GPS: 47.07166, -2.00433

Charges guide

Per unit incl. 2 persons and electricity	€ 13,00 - € 22,50
extra person	€ 2,50 - € 5,50
child (under 7 yrs)	free - € 3,00
child (under 18 yrs)	€ 1,50 - € 4,00

For latest campsite news, availability and prices visit

alanrogers.com

Le Croisic
Camping de l'Océan

15 route de la Maison Rouge, F-44490 Le Croisic (Loire-Atlantique) T: 02 40 23 07 69
E: camping-ocean@wanadoo.fr alanrogers.com/FR44210

526

Camping de l'Océan is situated on the Le Croisic peninsula, an attractive part of the Brittany coastline. Out of a total of 400 pitches, 80 are available for tourers with the remainder being taken by mobile homes either privately owned or for rent. The pitches are level and 80-100 sq.m. in size (they were rather worn when we visited). The leisure facilities, which include a restaurant, bar and pool complex, are of an excellent standard. This site, probably more suitable for families with young teenagers, can be very lively in high season with a wealth of activities and entertainment for all ages. Sports are well catered for and there are tournaments in high season. After an excellent meal in the restaurant you can enjoy different entertainment on most evenings in July and August. The site is within walking distance of the Atlantic Ocean and white sandy beaches are just 150 m. away.

Facilities

Five adequate toilet blocks include facilities for disabled visitors. Washing machines and dryers. Good restaurant and bar. Takeaway. Shop. Motorcaravan service point. Swimming pool complex comprising an indoor pool, outdoor pool and paddling pool. Volleyball. Football. Basketball. Tennis. Bicycle hire. Off site: Market (most days). Le Croisic for shops, bars and restaurants. Sailing, riding and golf.

Open: 3 April - 30 September.

Directions

From Le Pouliguen, travel west on N171 to Le Croisic. Site is well signed from here and found in about 1.5 km. GPS: 47.29752, -2.53593

Charges guide

Per unit incl. 2 persons	
and electricity	€ 20,50 - € 49,00
extra person	€ 4,00 - € 8,00
child (2-7 yrs)	€ 2,00 - € 6,50
dog	€ 2,00 - € 6,50

Les Ponts-de-Cé

Camping Hortus, l'Ile du Château

Avenue de la Boire Salée, F-49130 Les Ponts-de-Cé (Maine-et-Loire) T: 02 38 36 35 94

E: info@camping-hortus.com alanrogers.com/FR49110

This could be a very useful site for those wishing to visit Angers and tour the surrounding vineyards and châteaux from a no-nonsense campsite offering good value for money. Just five kilometres from the city centre, the site is on an island in the Loire, though sadly one arm of the river is now dry in summer because of reservoirs upstream. A camping field (25 pitches without electricity) overlooks this, while the main area has 89 touring pitches on generally level ground, with lots of mature trees offering shade, separated by hedges and all with electricity (6A). It is well tended by its friendly managers who are keen to welcome more British visitors.

Facilities

The main sanitary block is traditional, kept clean and offers reasonable provision. Mainly seatless WCs, with some Turkish, some washbasins in cabins and preset showers. Facilities for disabled visitors. Baby bath. Laundry facilities. Motorcaravan service point. Small shop selling basics (bread can be ordered). Open air bar with snacks and takeaway (all 1/7-31/8). Small children's play area. Basketball. Minigolf. Boules. Bicycle hire. Adjacent open-air leisure pool, tennis courts and football field. Free access to the pool (code). WiFi. Security barrier.
Off site: Takeaway pizza, bus stop, fishing, canoe/kayak hire, all 200 m. Supermarket, bars and restaurant nearby.

Open: 7 April - 31 October.

Directions

Les Ponts-de-Cé is just off the N260 Angers eastern bypass. Take exit west onto D4 signed Ponts-de-Cé and Bouchemaine. In 1.5 km. turn south on N160 signed to town centre and campsite. After about 1 km. turn right at post office, next to a small roundabout into campsite road. Road is narrow and may be difficult for large units. You are advised not to use sat nav on final approach.
GPS: 47.424583, -0.5291

Charges guide

Per unit incl. 2 persons	€ 15,00 - € 20,00
extra person	€ 3,00 - € 4,00

Les Rosiers-sur-Loire

Flower Camping Val de Loire

6 rue Sainte-Baudruehe, F-49350 Les Rosiers-sur-Loire (Maine-et-Loire) T: 02 41 51 94 33

E: contact@camping-valdeloire.com alanrogers.com/FR49180

This former municipal site on the outskirts of a village on the River Loire between Saumur and Angers has 84 touring pitches, all with electricity (5/10A), individual water taps and waste water drainage. A further 28 pitches are used for mobile homes, mostly for hire. Recent additions include a pleasant little bar with a terrace and an adjacent marquee used for games and entertainment. There are two new heated swimming pools, one covered, the other surrounded by sunbathing terraces and with a large (linked) paddling pool. In July/August there is a busy programme of activities.

Facilities

The main sanitary block is modern with controllable showers and washbasins in cubicles. Two older blocks and a new Portacabin unit provide additional facilities. The main block has facilities for disabled visitors and a fully equipped laundry room. Bar with TV serves snacks and fresh bread to order (July/Aug). Covered pool (1/4-30/9). Outdoor pool (1/5-15/9). Children's activities, daytime events and outings, and evening entertainment in season. Play area. Games room. Minigolf. Tennis. Bicycle hire. Off site: Fishing 800 m. Riding 2 km. Golf 15 km. Boat launching 1 and 15 km. Bakery, shops, supermarket, bar and restaurant and buses in village 800 m.

Open: 1 April - 30 September.

Directions

Les Rosiers is 17 km. northwest of Saumur. From A85 motorway at exit 1 take southbound D144 to Beaufort-en-Vallée, then continue south on D59. Site is signed to right on approach to village. From D952 Saumur-Angers road turn north in village to site on left in 800 m. GPS: 47.35877, -0.22604

Charges guide

Per unit incl. 2 persons	€ 14,00 - € 20,00
extra person	€ 4,00 - € 5,00
child (2-10 yrs)	€ 3,00 - € 4,00
electricity	€ 4,00

For latest campsite news, availability and prices visit
alanrogers.com

Luché-Pringé

Camping La Chabotière

Place des Tilleuils, F-72800 Luché-Pringé (Sarthe) T: 02 43 45 10 00. E: contact@lachabotiere.com
alanrogers.com/FR72100

This is a delightful little municipal site on the River Loir, just a few steps from the main square of an interesting village classed as a 'Petite Cité de Caractère'. There are 85 pitches, 65 for touring and all with access to electricity and the remainder used for wooden chalets and canvas 'bungalows' for rent. The main part of the site down by the river is kept vehicle free in July and August, ensuring a safer and quieter environment. A child-proof gate leads out onto the river bank and footpath. There are many opportunities for walking, cycling and sightseeing in the area.

Facilities

The traditional toilet block is well maintained and clean with pushbutton showers and some washbasins in cubicles. Baby room and washbasins for children. Facilities for disabled visitors. Washing machines and dryer. Motorcaravan service point. Quiet room with tables for cards games plus free Internet access (adults only). Free WiFi in reception area. Adventure play area. Large sports field. Bicycle hire. Fishing. Activities for children and in the evening. Chalets for rent. Off site: Espace de Loisirs (July/Aug) at entrance: supervised swimming and paddling pools (unheated), minigolf, tennis, bar with games, and hire of boats, canoes and pedaloes. Shops in village. Boat launching 500 m. Lake with beach 7 km.

Open: 1 April - 15 October.

Directions

Luché-Pringé is 40 km. south of Le Mans. From A11 between Le Mans and Angers, leave at exit 10 or 11 and head eastwards to La Flèche, then north on D323 towards Le Mans. At Clermont-Créans turn east on D13 to Luché-Pringé. In main square (ignore earlier campsite sign) turn sharp right then left, signed 'Minigolf' then site. GPS: 47.70252, 0.07364

Charges 2011

Per unit incl. 2 persons	
and electricity	€ 10,60 - € 13,88
extra person	€ 2,30 - € 3,50
child (under 10 yrs)	€ 1,40 - € 1,80
dog	€ 1,50

Mesquer

Camping le Château du Petit Bois

1820 route de kerlagadec, F-44420 Mesquer (Loire-Atlantique) T: 02 40 42 68 77
E: info@campingdupetitbois.com   alanrogers.com/FR44270

This pleasant campsite is located in the wooded grounds of a small château. The 125 good-sized touring pitches, all with electricity (3 or 6A) have varying degrees of shade and a few are in the open for those who like a sunny plot. Reception is housed in a wooden chalet and is welcoming and informative. The Marin family and their staff are friendly and helpful and the site is very well run. On site there is an attractive swimming pool complex: a heated main pool and paddling pool, and a separate pool with two good water slides which is only open when the pool is supervised. The sea is just over a kilometre away, as is the village of Mesquer and nearby are the salt marshes which produce the famous Sel de Guérande.

Facilities

The main sanitary block has preset showers and open style washbasins together with some cubicles with controllable shower and a washbasin. Dishwashing and laundry facilities. Facilities for disabled visitors. Combined bar, snack bar and takeaway. Small shop selling bread and basics (July/Aug). Pool complex with heated main pool, paddling pool and pool with water slides (only open when supervised). Activities (all July/Aug). WiFi in bar (free). Off site: Fishing, bicycle hire nearby. Golf 12 km.

Open: 1 April - 30 October.

Directions

From N165 Nantes-Vannes road, leave at exit 15 towards La Roche Bernard, turn left to join D774 towards La Baule. 8 km. after Herbignac, turn right on D52 to St Molt and Mesquer. Site is on D52 just west of village. GPS: 47.399016, -2.471316

Charges guide

Per unit incl. 2 persons	€ 13,00 - € 22,20
extra person	€ 4,90 - € 6,40
child (3-7 yrs)	€ 3,40 - € 4,40
electricity (3/6A)	€ 4,40 - € 5,40

Montsabert

Yelloh! Village Parc de Montsabert

Montsabert, F-49320 Coutures (Maine-et-Loire) T: 02 41 57 91 63
E: info@yellohvillage-parcdemontsabert.com alanrogers.com/FR49060

This extensive site has recently been taken over by a friendly French couple who already have plans for improvements. It has a rural atmosphere in the shadow of Montsabert château, from where visiting peacocks happily roam in the spacious surroundings. The main features are the heated swimming pool (with cover) and the adjoining refurbished, rustic style restaurant. There are 111 large, well marked touring pitches, divided by hedges and all with water tap, drain and electricity (10A). Picnic tables are provided. The site is used by several small tour operators (12 pitches). Partially wooded by a variety of trees, this site offers the peace of the countryside.

Facilities

The main toilet block can be heated and has washbasins and bidets in cabins and a baby room. Laundry facilities. A second block serves the pool and another provides more WCs. Shop, bar and takeaway. Restaurant. Heated pool (no Bermuda style shorts) and paddling pool. Sports hall. Minigolf. Tennis. Play area. Bicycle hire. Entertainment (high season). Archery. Riding. Max. 2 dogs.
Off site: Canoeing nearby. Fishing 5 km. Golf 8 km.

Open: 10 April - 12 September.

Directions

Coutures is on the D751 to Saumur. From A11 take exit 14 and follow signs for Cholet/Poitiers, then Poitiers on D748. At Brissac-Quincé turn NE on D55 and in 5 km. turn right to Coutures. Montsabert is north of village. GPS: 47.3744, -0.3469

Charges guide

Per unit incl. 2 persons	€ 15,00 - € 29,00
extra person	€ 4,00 - € 5,00
child (3-7 yrs)	free - € 5,00

Montsoreau

Kawan Village l'Isle Verte

Avenue de la Loire, F-49730 Montsoreau (Maine-et-Loire) T: 02 41 51 76 60. E: isleverte@cvtloisirs.fr
alanrogers.com/FR49090

This friendly, natural site, with pitches overlooking the Loire, is just 200 m. from the nearest shop, bar and restaurant in Montsoreau, and is an ideal base from which to explore the western Loire area. Most of the 90 shaded, level and good-sized tourist pitches are separated by low hedges but grass tends to be rather sparse during dry spells. All have electricity (16A). Excellent English is spoken in the reception and bar/restaurant. Attractions within walking distance include the château, troglodyte caves (used for traditional mushroom production) and restaurant, wine tasting in the cellars nearby, and a Sunday market in the town. Fishermen are particularly well catered for at Isle Verte, there being an area to store equipment and live bait (permits are available in Saumur). Cyclists and walkers could also be in their element here. For the less energetic, there is a bus service into Saumur with its château and other historic buildings, and all its shops, bars and restaurants. Trains or buses are available in Saumur to take you on to other towns along the Vallée de la Loire. Just 5 km. south of Montsoreau is the fascinating 12th-century Abbaye Royale de Fontévraud.

Facilities

A single building provides separate male and female toilets. Washbasins, some in cabins, and showers are unisex. Separate facilities for disabled campers. Baby room. Laundry facilities. Motorcaravan service point. Bar and restaurant(1/5-30/9). Swimming and paddling pools (25/5-30/9). Small play area. Table tennis, volleyball and boules. Fishing. Boat launching. WiFi (charged).
Off site: River beach 300 m. Bicycle hire and sailing 1 km.

Open: 1 April - 30 September.

Directions

Montsoreau is 12 km. southeast of Saumur on the D947 towards Chinon. Site is clearly signed on left along the road into town. GPS: 47.21820, 0.05265

Charges 2011

Per unit incl. 2 persons and electricity	€ 18,50 - € 22,50
extra person	€ 3,00 - € 4,00
child (5-10 yrs)	€ 2,00 - € 2,50
Camping Cheques accepted.	

For latest campsite news, availability and prices visit
alanrogers.com

Piriac-sur-Mer

Camping Parc du Guibel

F 526

Route de Kerdrien, F-44420 Piriac-sur-Mer (Loire-Atlantique) T: 02 40 23 52 67. E: camping@parcduguibel.com
alanrogers.com/FR44070

This very large site, situated in an extensive wood, describes itself as 'un hôtel de plein air' and prides itself on its spaciousness and its trees. A keen birdwatcher told the owner that he had seen 50 different species of birds. There are 450 pitches of which 307 are for touring scattered among the 14 hectares of woodland, mainly shaded but some in clearings. One section at the top of the site across a minor road is always quiet and peaceful. 110 pitches have electricity (3, 6 or 10A) of which 67 also have a water tap and drainage. There are also 134 mobile homes and chalets for rent. A long room houses the bar, snack bar with takeaway and a small restaurant together with an electronic games area. A small shop sells bread and a few basics. A new pool complex of 500 sq.m. includes a slide, flume and a paddling pool. A programme of activities and entertainment for children and adults is organised in high season. The sea is just over a kilometre away and nearby are the salt marshes producing the famous 'sel de Guérande'.

Facilities

Five sanitary blocks: the newest is smart and well equipped, with controllable showers and washbasins. Two others have been partially refurbished to the same standards. Facilities for disabled visitors. Baby room. Laundry facilities. Motorcaravan service point. New swimming pool complex with slide, flume and paddling pool (1/5-15/9). Bar, snackbar, takeaway and restaurant (July/Aug only). WiFi in reception (free). Off site: Riding 400 m. Fishing 1 km. Beach 1.2 km. Sailing 3.5 km.

Open: 1 April - 30 September.

Directions

On N165 from Vannes, leave at exit 15 towards La Roche Bernard, turn left to join D774 towards La Baule. 8 km. after Herbignac, turn right on D52 to St Molt and Mesquer towards Piriac. Do not take the coast road but turn left on D52. Site signed on right in 3 km. GPS: 47.38616, -2.51029

Charges guide

Per unit incl. 2 persons and electricity (10A)	€ 15,00 - € 24,90
child (under 7 yrs)	€ 2,00 - € 3,80

Pornic

Camping le Patisseau

29 rue du Patisseau, F-44210 Pornic (Loire-Atlantique) T: 02 40 82 10 39. E: contact@lepatisseau.com
alanrogers.com/FR44100

Le Patisseau is situated in the countryside just a short drive from the fishing village of Pornic. It is a relaxed site with a large number of mobile homes and chalets, and popular with young families and teenagers. The 102 touring pitches, all with electrical connections (6A), are divided between the attractive 'forest' area with plenty of shade from mature trees and the more open 'prairie' area. Some are on a slight slope and access to others might be tricky for larger units. A railway runs along the bottom half of the site with trains several times a day, (but none overnight) and the noise is minimal. The Morice family work very hard to maintain a friendly atmosphere.

Facilities

The modern heated toilet block is very spacious and well fitted; most washbasins are open style, but the controllable showers are all in large cubicles which have washbasins. Also good facilities for disabled visitors and babies. Laundry rooms. Shop (1/7-30/8). Bar, restaurant and takeaway (all season). Indoor heated pool with sauna, jacuzzi and spa (all season). Small heated outdoor pools and water slides (1/6-30/9). Play area. Multisport court. Bicycle hire. WiFi in bar area. Off site: Fishing and beach 2.5 km. Riding, golf, sailing and boat launching all 5 km.

Open: 3 April - 11 November.

Directions

Pornic is 19 km. south of St Nazaire bridge. Access to site is at junction of D751 Nantes - Pornic road with the D213 St Nazaire - Noirmoutier 'Route Bleue'. From north take exit for D751 Nantes. From south follow D751 Clion-sur-Mer. At roundabout north of D213 take exit for Le Patisseau and follow signs to site. GPS: 47.118833, -2.072833

Charges guide

Per unit incl. 2 persons and electricity (6A)	€ 25,00 - € 39,00
extra person	€ 3,00 - € 8,00

Pornic

Camping EléoVic

Route de la Pointe St-Gildas, Préfailles, F-44770 Pornic (Loire-Atlantique) T: 02 40 21 61 60
E: contact@camping-eleovic.com alanrogers.com/FR44230

This is a well situated site overlooking the sea on the attractive Jade Coast west of Pornic. There are 70 touring pitches which are rather worn, some with wonderful views of the sea, and a similar number of mobile homes, many of which are available for rent. All pitches have access to electricity (10A), though on some you may need a long cable. Much of the ground is sloping, so a really level pitch may not be available and access for larger units to some pitches may be tricky. The site has so much to offer, however, that any extra effort that may be needed to get installed is likely to be quickly forgotten. There is an excellent covered, heated pool (with paddling pool) which has a canopy that can be opened up in good weather. A path from the site leads directly to a small rocky cove where you can gather oysters and mussels freely at low tide. Other wider sandy beaches are a short distance away.

Facilities

Central sanitary block has spacious preset showers and washbasins in cabins. Facilities for disabled visitors. Excellent room for dishwashing and laundry. Further facilities are in the pool building and another smaller block. Good restaurant (July-Aug; not Wednesdays) with small bar and terrace. Fitness room. Playground. Boules. Children's activities and entertainment and sporting events for families (high season). Bicycle hire. Off site: Sailing and boat launching 800 m. Riding 3 km. Golf 7 km.

Open: 3 April - 26 October.

Directions

From north on D213 (Route Bleue) turn southwest just south of St Michel-Chef-Chef on D96 to La Plaine-sur-Mer and follow signs for Préfailles. From Pornic take D13 to La Plaine but do not enter town. Follow signs for Préfailles. Continue on D313 past village towards La Pointe Saint-Gildas and at 50 km. sign turn left, then left again to site on right. GPS: 47.132616, -2.2315

Charges guide

| Per unit incl. 2 persons and electricity | € 20,80 - € 36,00 |
| extra person | € 4,90 - € 8,30 |

Route de la pointe St Gildas - 44770 Préfailles
Loire Atlantique - Bretagne sud
Tel: 0033 240 21 61 60 - E-mail: accueil@camping-eleovic.com
www.camping-eleovic.com

★★★★
camping-caravaning

The campsite Eleovic with its direct access to the beach, overhang the bay of Bourgneuf and made in front of the island of Noirmoutier.
Relaxation and user-friendliness are gathered to spend pleasant holidays!

Pornic

⌐ 526

Camping de la Boutinardière

Rue de la Plage de la Boutinardière 23, F-44210 Pornic (Loire-Atlantique) T: 02 40 82 05 68
E: info@laboutinardiere.com alanrogers.com/FR44180

This is truly a holiday site to suit all the family whatever their ages, just 200 m. from the beach. It has 250 individual good sized pitches, 100-120 sq.m. in size, many bordered by three metre high, well maintained hedges for shade and privacy. All pitches have electricity available. It is a family owned site and English is spoken by the helpful, obliging reception staff. Beside reception is the excellent site shop and across the road is a complex of indoor and outdoor pools, paddling pool and a twin toboggan water slide. On site there are sports and entertainment areas.

Facilities

Toilet facilities are in three good blocks, one large and centrally situated and two supporting blocks. Washbasins are in cabins. Laundry facilities. Shop. New bar, restaurant, terrace complex. Three heated swimming pools, one indoor (Apr-Sept), a paddling pool and water slides (15/5-22/9). Games room. Sports and activity area. Playground. Minigolf. Fitness equipment and sauna. Off site: Sandy cove 200 m. Golf, riding, sea fishing, restaurants, cafés, fishing harbour, boat trips, sailing and windsurfing, all within 5 km.

Open: 3 April - 28 September.

Directions

From north or south on D213, take Nantes D751 exit. At roundabout (with McDonalds) take D13 signed Bemarie-en-Retz. After 4 km. site is signed to right. Note: do NOT exit from D213 at Pornic Ouest or Centre. GPS: 47.09150, -2.05133

Charges guide

Per unit incl. 2 persons and electricity	€ 20,00 - € 43,00
extra person	€ 3,50 - € 8,00
child (under 8 yrs)	€ 2,50 - € 6,00

For latest campsite news, availability and prices visit
alanrogers.com

Sainte Reine-de-Bretagne

Kawan Village du Deffay

B.P. 18 Le Deffay, Sainte Reine-de-Bretagne, F-44160 Pontchâteau (Loire-Atlantique) T: 02 40 88 00 57
E: campingdudeffay@wanadoo.fr alanrogers.com/FR44090

A family managed site, Château du Deffay is a refreshing departure from the usual formula in that it is not over organised or supervised and has no tour operator units. The 142 good sized, fairly level pitches have pleasant views and are either on open grass, on shallow terraces divided by hedges, or informally arranged in a central, slightly sloping wooded area. Most have electricity. The facilities are located within the old courtyard area of the smaller château that dates from before 1400. A significant attraction of the site is the large, unfenced lake which is well stocked for fishermen and even has free pedaloes for children. The landscape is wonderfully natural and the site blends well with the rural environment of the estate, lake and farmland which surround it. Alpine type chalets overlook the lake and fit in well with the environment and the larger château (built 1880 and which now offers B&B) stands slightly away from the camping area but provides a wonderful backdrop for an evening stroll. The site is close to the Brière Regional Park, the Guérande Peninsula, and La Baule and is just 20 minutes drive from the beach.

Facilities

The main toilet block is well maintained, if a little dated, and well equipped including washbasins in cabins, provision for disabled visitors and a baby bathroom. Laundry facilities. Shop, bar, small restaurant with takeaway (1/5-20/9). Covered, heated swimming pool (at 28°C when we visited) and paddling pool (all season). Play area. TV. Animation in season. Torches useful. Off site: Golf 7 km. Riding 10 km. Beach 25 km.

Open: 1 May - 30 September.

Directions

Site is signed from D33 Pontchâteau - Herbignac road near Ste Reine. Also signed from the D773 and N165-E60 (exit 13). GPS: 47.44106, -2.15981

Charges guide

Per unit incl. 2 persons	
and electricity	€ 18,10 - € 27,80
extra person	€ 3,30 - € 5,50
child (2-12 yrs)	€ 2,30 - € 3,80
Camping Cheques accepted.	

For latest campsite news, availability and prices visit
alanrogers.com

Saumur

Camping de Chantepie

Saint Hilaire-Saint Florent, F-49400 Saumur (Maine-et-Loire) T: 02 41 67 95 34. E: info@campingchantepie.com
alanrogers.com/FR49020

On arriving at Camping de Chantepie with its colourful, floral entrance, a friendly greeting awaits at reception, set beside a restored farmhouse. The site is owned by a charitable organisation which provides employment for local people with disabilities. Linked by gravel roads (which can be dusty), the 150 grass touring pitches are level and spacious, with some new larger ones (200 sq.m. at extra cost – state preference when booking). All pitches have electricity (6/10A) and are separated by low hedges of flowers and trees which offer some shade. This is a good site for families. The panoramic views over the Loire from the pitches on the terraced perimeter of the meadow are stunning and from here a footpath leads to the river valley. Leisure activities for all ages are catered for in July/August by the Chantepie Club, including wine tastings, excursions and canoeing. A Sites et Paysages member.

Facilities

The toilet block is clean and facilities are good with washbasins in cubicles, new showers (men and women separately) and facilities for disabled visitors. Baby area. Laundry facilities. Shop, bar, terraced café and takeaway (all 15/6-31/8). Covered and heated pool, outdoor pool and paddling pool. Play area with apparatus. Terraced minigolf, TV. Video games. Pony rides. Bicycle hire. WiFi (charged). Off site: Fishing 500 m. Golf and riding 2 km.

Open: 15 May - 15 September.

Directions

St Hilaire-St Florent is 2 km. west of Saumur. Take D751 (Gennes). Right at roundabout in St Hilaire-St Florent and on until Le Poitrineau and campsite sign, then turn left. Continue for 3 km. then turn right into site road. GPS: 47.29381, -0.14264

Charges guide

Per unit incl. 2 persons	€ 18,00 - € 30,00
extra person	€ 4,00 - € 6,00
child (3-10 yrs)	€ 2,00 - € 3,00

Saumur

Kawan Village Ile d'Offard

Bvd. de Verden, Ile d'Offard, F-49400 Saumur (Maine-et-Loire) T: 02 41 40 30 00. E: iledoffard@cvtloisirs.fr
alanrogers.com/FR49080

This site occupies a prime position on an island in the River Loire within walking distance of the centre of the historic town of Saumur. The 207 touring pitches are mainly on grass with plenty of shade provided by mature trees. Twelve hardstandings nearer the entrance can be rather dusty in dry weather. 150 pitches have access to electricity (10A) and some also have water and drainage. Ile d'Offard is useful as an overnight stop on the journey south (or north) but it is also an excellent base from which to visit the numerous châteaux in the region. Indeed, the château and other historic buildings of Saumur, as well as its shops, bars and restaurants, are within walking distance. From the town buses and trains will take you to many of the other delightful towns of the Loire Valley. On site, an attractive modern bar and restaurant, serving varied (if slightly pricey) food overlook a heated pool with paddling and spa pools.

Facilities

Three unisex sanitary blocks, one heated in winter, with provision for disabled visitors. One block has a well equipped laundry. The others are only open in high season. Motorcaravan services. Restaurant and bar (1/5-30/9) with takeaway. Heated swimming, paddling and spa pools (15/4-30/9). Internet access and WiFi (charged). Play area. Some activities and a children's club, wine tastings, etc. in high season. Off site: River beach, sailing and bicycle hire all 1 km. Golf and riding 10 km.

Open: 1 March - 15 November.

Directions

From north and A85 exit 3, take D347 south (Saumur). After 2.5 km. go left at roundabout signed 'Saumur touristique'. Follow old road towards river and town. Cross bridge onto island and immediately go left at roundabout. GPS: 47.25762, -0.06100

Charges 2011

Per unit incl. 2 persons and electricity	€ 20,00 - € 33,00
extra person	€ 5,00 - € 6,00
Camping Cheques accepted.	

Saint Brévin-les-Pins

Camping le Fief

57 chemin du Fief, F-44250 Saint Brévin-les-Pins (Loire-Atlantique) T: 02 40 27 23 86. E: camping@lefief.com

alanrogers.com/FR44190

If you are a family with young children or lively teenagers, this could be the campsite for you. Le Fief is a well established site only 800 m. from sandy beaches on the southern Brittany coast. It has a magnificent 'aqua park' with outdoor and covered swimming pools, paddling pools, slides, river rapids, fountains, jets and more. The site has 174 pitches for touring units (out of 405). Whilst these all have 5A electricity, they vary in size and many are worn and may be untidy. There are also 183 mobile homes and chalets to rent and 48 privately owned units. This is a lively site in high season with a variety of entertainment and organised activity for all ages. This ranges from a miniclub for 5-12 year old children, to 'tonic days' in a state-of-the-art wellness centre with aquagym, jogging and sports competitions, and to evening events which include karaoke, themed dinners and cabaret. There are plenty of sporting facilities for active youngsters.

Facilities

One excellent new toilet block and three others of a lower standard. Laundry facilities. Shop (1/6-31/8). Bar, restaurant and takeaway (3/4-26/9) with terrace overlooking the pool complex. Outdoor pools, etc. (1/5-15/9). Covered pool (all season). Wellness centre. Play area. Tennis. Pétanque. Archery. Games room. Internet access. Organised entertainment and activities (weekends Apr-June, daily July/Aug). Bicycle hire. Off site: Beach 800 m. Bus stop 1 km. Riding 1 km. Golf 15 km. Planète Sauvage safari park.

Open: 3 April - 3 October.

Directions

From the St Nazaire bridge take the fourth exit from the D213 signed St Brévin-l'Océan. Continue over first roundabout and bear right at the second to join Chemin du Fief. The site is on the right, well signed. GPS: 47.23486, -2.16757

Charges guide

Per unit incl. 2 persons	
and electricity	€ 22,00 - € 43,00
extra person	€ 5,00 - € 9,00
child (0-7 yrs)	€ 2,50 - € 4,50
dog	€ 3,00 - € 7,00
No credit cards.	

For latest campsite news, availability and prices visit

alanrogers.com

Sillé-le-Guillaume

Camping Indigo les Molières

Sillé Plage, F-72140 Sillé-le-Guillaume (Sarthe) T: 02 43 20 16 12. E: molieres@camping-indigo.com

alanrogers.com/FR72040

Les Molières is an attractive recent addition to the Indigo group. It can be found close to Sillé-le-Guillaume, around 30 km. north of Le Mans. There are 120 large shady pitches here, most equipped with electrical connections (10A). A large lake of 32 hectares is ideal for sailing and windsurfing, and the forested surrounds of the Parc Naturel Régional provide an excellent environment for cycling or walking. Swimming is also popular from the large sandy beach. The Maison du Lac et de la Forêt is an interesting centre with information about the area. In high season, a little tourist train trundles around the lake.

Facilities

Direct access to lake. Sailing. Fishing. Bicycle hire. Play area. Tourist information. Max. 1 dog. Off site: Walking and cycling tracks. Le Mans 30 km.

Open: 30 April - 26 September.

Directions

From Le Mans head north on D338 and then the D304 to Sillé-le-Guillaume. Then follow signs to the Parc Naturel Régional and the site. GPS: 48.203383, -0.127667

Charges guide

| Per unit incl. 2 persons | € 11,50 - € 13,30 |
| extra person | € 2,90 - € 3,20 |

Sillé-le-Philippe

Castel Camping le Château de Chanteloup

Chanteloup, F-72460 Sillé-le-Philippe (Sarthe) T: 02 43 27 51 07. E: chanteloup.souffront@wanadoo.fr

alanrogers.com/FR72030

An attractive and peaceful site close to Le Mans, Chanteloup is situated in the park of a 19th-century château in the heart of the Sarthe countryside. There are 100 pitches all with 6A electricity although long leads will be required in some places. Some are in the woods, many are around the edges of the lawns and completely open, and a few overlook the lake, so there are differing degrees of shade throughout the site. This lack of regimentation enhances the atmosphere and feeling of spaciousness in the grounds surrounding the old château. Tours of the grounds and the village by pony and cart can be arranged.

Facilities

All sanitary facilities are in the château outbuildings and are well maintained and kept very clean. Washbasins are in cabins. Dishwashing and laundry facilities. Small shop, takeaway and restaurant with covered outdoor seating (all 5/7-24/8). Bar (all season). Swimming pool (all season). Play area (parental supervision essential). Games room, volleyball, table tennis. Organised activities (high season). WiFi. Off site: Riding 7 km. Golf 10 km. Tennis club in Le Mans.

Open: 28 May - 31 August.

Directions

Sillé-le-Philippe is 18 km. northeast of Le Mans on the D301 to Bonnétable. From autoroute take exit 23, follow signs for Le Mans and Tours, then Le Mans and Savigné l'Evêque. Site is to the east just off main road and signed on southern edge of Sillé. GPS: 48.10586, 0.34108

Charges 2011

| Per unit incl. 2 persons and electricity | € 26,90 - € 43,40 |
| extra person | € 6,30 - € 11,50 |

Charges are higher during Le Mans 24 hr race week.

Varennes-sur-Loire

Castel Camping l'Etang de la Brèche

5 impasse de la Brèche (RN152), F-49730 Varennes-sur-Loire (Maine-et-Loire) T: 02 41 51 22 92 E: mail@etang-breche.com alanrogers.com/FR49010

The Saint Cast family have developed l'Etang de la Brèche with care and attention. The site provides 116 large, level touring pitches with shade from trees and bushes. Less shaded areas are used for recreation. There are electrical connections to all pitches (some long cables may be required), with water and drainage on 63 of them. The restaurant, bar and terrace, also open to the public, provides a social base and is popular with British visitors. The pool complex includes one with a removable cover, one outdoor, and one for toddlers. The site is situated on a 25-hectare estate, four kilometres northeast of Saumur on the edge of the Loire behind the dykes.

Facilities

Three toilet blocks, modernised to good standards, include facilities for babies with two units for visitors with disabilities. Washing up sinks and laundry. Shop and epicerie. Restaurant, pizzeria and takeaway. Heated swimming pools. Tennis. Multisport pitch. Go-karts. Minigolf. Bicycle hire. General room, games and TV rooms. Internet point. Varied sporting and entertainment programme (10/7-25/8). Pony riding. Child-minding is arranged in afternoons. Torch useful. Off site: Golf 7 km.

Open: 30 April - 15 September.

Directions

Site is 100 m. north off the main N152, about 4 km. northeast of Saumur on the north bank of the Loire. GPS: 47.24731, -0.00048

Charges guide

Per unit incl. 2 persons and electricity	€ 16,00 - € 36,50
with water and drainage	€ 18,00 - € 39,00
extra person	€ 5,00 - € 8,00
child (4-10 yrs)	€ 3,00 - € 4,00

For latest campsite news, availability and prices visit

alanrogers.com

It's not only the fine beaches that make this holiday region so appealing – sleepy fishing harbours, historic ports and charming towns all create a great holiday atmosphere.

Vendée

DÉPARTEMENT: VENDÉE

MAJOR CITY: LA ROCHE-SUR-YON

The Vendée is located along the Atlantic coast, south of the river Loire, between the towns of Nantes and La Rochelle, and is less than 400 miles from the UK. Access to the Vendée is simple, with the airports of Nantes and La Rochelle only an hour away and frequently served from London and other cities. Travel by train and by road are just as easy.

The Vendée has so much to offer. If you could just choose one feature, you would probably pick the marvellous fine sandy beaches. The local micro-climate rivals the sunshine hours of the south of France and the variety of sporting and leisure activities means you can holiday in the Vendée all year round. The unique, flat landscapes of this family destination are ideal for discovery by bike. There are hundreds of châteaux, abbeys and medieval forts plus numerous parks and gardens; plenty to keep a busy family entertained throughout your holiday!

VENDÉE
Tourisme

Nature

Le Marais Poitevin

Encircled by forests and great medieval abbeys, the Poitevin Marshes (also called the 'Green Venice') occupy an area that was once a marine gulf dotted with islands and limestone peninsulas.

The Vendée Bocage

To the north, Le Bocage is a hilly landscape and a mosaic of cultivation and grassland, punctuated by coloured hedges separating hamlets and isolated farms.

Attractions

In the Vendée more than 100 tourist and cultural sites can be visited.

Adventure park Le Puy du Fou

A whirlwind of shows and entertainment in the ambience of centuries gone by: the games of the Roman circus, the Viking attacks, the jousting tournaments, the musketeer combats, the ancestral art of falconry, the skills of craftsmen and the street theatre. In the evening enjoy the greatest night spectacle in the world: Cinéscénie.

Outdoor activities

By the sea and on the lakes

Sailing, windsurfing, surfing, kitesurfing, wave-skiing, catamaran, sand-sailing and speed-sailing.

Cycling

Over 800 km. of cycle paths to explore this beautiful region.

Cuisine of the region

Locally-produced meat and poultry include Charolais beef, salt-marsh lamb, duck from Challans and foie gras. Seafood includes sole sablaise cooked with lemon, barbecued sardines from Saint Gilles Croix-de-Vie, baked white tuna or mussels from the Baie de l'Aiguillon cooked in white wine.

Samphire: a seaweed herb that grows on the edges of the salt marshes.

Bonnottes: potatoes with the taste of hazel nuts, served for a few days each year in France's best restaurants.

Angles

Camping le Clos Cottet

Route de la Tranche-sur-Mer, F-85750 Angles (Vendée) T: 02 51 28 90 72
E: contact@camping-clos-cottet.com alanrogers.com/FR85950

Le Clos Cottet is an attractive family site, based around an old Vendéen farm. This is a lively site in high season with activities for children and the whole family, including regular discos and karaoke evenings, as well as many sports tournaments. There are 196 pitches here, all of which have reasonable shade. Many of them are occupied by mobile homes and chalets, but 70 are available for touring, all with electricity (10A). In high season (July and August) a free shuttle bus service runs to the nearest beach (6 km). On site, a fine swimming pool complex provides a large outdoor pool with water slides and a heated indoor pool plus a sauna and Turkish bath. Angles is a pretty village with a good range of shops and restaurants. Les Sables d'Olonne lies to the northwest and is a stylish resort with a long sandy beach and a popular zoo. The Vendée offers a wide variety of well-documented tourist attractions, whilst days out could include a trip to the impressive historical theme park Le Puy du Fou or in complete contrast a leisurely punt along the shaded waterways of the Marais Poitevin (La Venise Verte).

Facilities

Two traditional toilet blocks provide pre-set showers and washbasins in cubicles. Baby room. En suite unit for disabled visitors. Hot water to dishwashing and laundry sinks. Washing machine and dryer. Motorcaravan service point. Shop, plus bar with snack bar and takeaway (July/Aug). Pool complex (all season). Sauna. Fitness room. Play area. Multisport court. Sports field. Minigolf. Fishing lake. Activity and entertainment programme (July/Aug plus holiday weekends). Free WiFi in bar area. Mobile homes and chalets for rent. Off site: Angles village centre 1.5 km. Riding 5 km. Nearest beach, sailing 6 km. Cycle and walking tracks. Puy du Fou 75 km.

Open: 5 April - 20 September.

Directions

Angles is 34 km south of La Roche sur Yon. From A87 Cholet/La Roche sur Yon leave at exit 32 for La Tranche sur Mer and follow D747 towards La Tranche. Site is south of Angles and is well signed to the right. GPS: 46.39239, -1.40365

Charges guide

Per unit incl. 2 persons	
and electricity	€ 18,00 - € 29,00
extra person	€ 4,00 - € 6,00
child (under 4 yrs)	€ 2,50 - € 4,00

Avrillé

Castel Camping Domaine des Forges

Rue des Forges, F-85440 Avrillé (Vendée) T: 02 51 22 38 85. E: contact@campingdomainedesforges.com
alanrogers.com/FR85930

Le Domaine des Forges has recently been acquired by Cathy and Thierry Pacteau. They already have experience in owning a caravan site, and it is their intention to create a prestige site with the highest quality of services. Arranged in the beautiful grounds of a 16th century manor house, the 250 touring pitches are generous in size (170-300 sq.m) and fully serviced including 32A electricity, internet access and cable TV. The owners' aim is to eventually develop a residential site and there are already mobile homes and chalets on site for viewing. Plans for the future include an indoor pool. An area of hardstanding pitches for motorcaravans, a fitness room and a TV room opened in 2010.

Facilities

Two toilet blocks with facilities for disabled visitors and babies. Laundry facilities. Shop (1/7-31/8). Bar (15/6-15/9), restaurant (all year) and takeaway (15/6-15/9). Heated outdoor pool (15/5-15/9). Tennis. Minigolf. Fishing lake. Off site: Village 400 m. Les Sables d'Olonne 25 km. Vendée beaches 7 km. Golf de la Domangère and Golf Port Bourgenay at 20mn (special price with the campsite).

Open: All year.

Directions

Travel south from La Roche-sur-Yon on the D747 for about 21 km. At the D19, turn right for Avrille (about 6 km). At junction with the D949 turn right and first right again into rue des Forges. Site at the end of the road. GPS: 46.47609, -1.49454

Charges guide

Per unit incl. 2 persons, electricity, water and waste water	€ 16,00 - € 32,00
extra person	€ 2,00 - € 6,00
child (2-6 yrs)	free - € 4,00
animal	€ 3,00 - € 4,00

LES CASTELS
Hôtellerie de Plein Air

Camping Domaine des Forges

Open all year
Very comfortable pitches of 220 m²
Member of 'Les Castels'

• Rue des Forges • F-85440 Avrillé • Tél: 0033 2 51 22 38 85 •
contact@campingdomainedesforges.com • www.campingdomainedesforges.com

For latest campsite news, availability and prices visit
alanrogers.com

Bois-de-Céné

Camping le Bois Joli

2 rue de Châteauneuf, F-85710 Bois-de-Céné (Vendée) T: 02 51 68 20 05
E: contact@camping-le-boisjoli.com alanrogers.com/FR85510

A warm welcome is given by the English speaking owners, Martine and Eric Malard, who make every effort to ensure that your stay is enjoyable. On site is a small, attractive lake with fishing and a large sports field. Next to the small swimming pool and paddling pool are a pleasant bar with terrace and a dancing area. There are 152 pitches of which 91 are for touring units, all with electricity; water taps may be less close. The site has 24 mobile homes for rent, including one equipped for disabled visitors, and there are 37 which are privately owned.

Facilities

Three toilet blocks, one modern, one small but functional and one very basic, although a replacement is planned for 2011. All are unisex with washbasins in cubicles. Laundry facilities. Facilities for disabled vistors. Motorcaravan service point. Bar serving simple meals (all season) with evening entertainment and takeaway service (July/Aug and busy weekends). Play area. Tennis. Bicycle hire. WiFi (charged). Off site: Riding 5 km. Beach 18 km.

Open: 1 April - 15 October.

Directions

Bois de Céné is 47 km. southwest of Nantes. Site is south of the village where the D58 from Challans meets the D21 and D28 and is signed.
GPS: 46.93382, -1.88791

Charges guide

Per unit incl. 2 persons and electricity	€ 14,80 - € 19,20
extra person	€ 4,20 - € 5,20
child (1-6 yrs)	€ 3,00 - € 4,00

Brem-sur-Mer

Camping Caravaning le Chaponnet

Rue du Chaponnet (N16), F-85470 Brem-sur-Mer (Vendée) T: 02 51 90 55 56
E: campingchaponnet@wanadoo.fr alanrogers.com/FR85480

This well established, family run site is within five minutes' walk of Brem village and 1.5 km. from a sandy beach. The 81 touring pitches are level with varying amounts of grass, some with shade from mature trees. Pitches are separated by tall hedges and serviced by tarmac or gravel roads and have frequent water and electricity points (long leads may be required). Tour operators have mobile homes and tents on 100 pitches and there are 146 other mobile homes and chalets, over half available for rent. The heated swimming pool complex also has a jacuzzi, slides and a children's pool, together with a sauna and fitness centre. It is overlooked by the spacious bar and restaurant/snack bar. Entertainment and activities for all ages are organised in high season with a children's club and daytime family activities (Sun-Fri) and entertainment every evening. Brem has a number of shops, bars and restaurants, two small supermarkets and a weekly market; neighbouring Brétignolles provides a wider range of opportunities for shopping and eating out and has two thriving markets each week.

Facilities

The five sanitary blocks including a more airy one central to the main touring area, are well maintained with washbasins in cubicles, and some showers and basins with controllable water temperature. Facilities for babies and disabled visitors. Laundry facilities. Bar (June-Sept), snack bar and takeaway (1/6-31/8). Indoor and outdoor heated pools. Waterslide, jacuzzi and sauna. Play area with space for ball games. Tennis. Bicycle hire. WiFi in bar/pool area (charged). Activities and entertainment (July/Aug). Off site: Shops and bus stops 200 m. Beach and sailing 1.5 km. Fishing 2 km. Riding 4 km.

Open: 2 April - 30 September.

Directions

Brem is on the D38 St Gilles - Les Sables d'Olonne road. From A87 at La Roche continue on D160 towards Les Sables d'Olonne. Take exit for La Mothe-Achard and Brétignolles-sur-Mer. Follow the D54 to Brem-sur-Mer. Site is clearly signed.
GPS: 46.60433, -1.83244

Charges guide

Per unit incl. 3 persons and electricity	€ 25,70 - € 36,80
extra person	€ 4,60 - € 6,40
child (under 5 yrs)	€ 2,70 - € 3,90

For latest campsite news, availability and prices visit

alanrogers.com

Brem-sur-Mer

Camping l'Océan

Rue des Gabelous, F-85470 Brem-sur-Mer (Vendée) T: 02 51 90 59 16. E: contact@campingdelocean.fr
alanrogers.com/FR85110

Set amongst grapevines and fir trees, Camping l'Océan is only 600 metres from a beautiful sandy beach while the village centre is also within walking distance. A warm welcome awaits you at the modern reception area which is well stocked with local information. The 90 touring pitches, all with electric connections reasonably close, are of a good size, separated by bushes (and in some cases vines) and with some mature trees providing shade. They are centrally located close to the entrance and you are largely unaware of the 260 mobile homes (120 available to rent) on either side.

Facilities

A modern toilet block serves the touring area plus a smaller, older block. Preset showers, British style WCs, and washbasins in cubicles. Separate toilet and shower for visitors with disabilities. Laundry facilities. Shop, bar, snack bar and takeaway (July/Aug and busy weekends). Heated swimming pool (15/6-15/9) with slide. Heated indoor pool (all season). Fitness room. Bicycle hire. Play areas. WiFi (charged). Activities and entertainment. Clubs for children and teenagers (July/Aug). Off site: Beach 600 m. Fishing 1 km. Supermarkets 1.2 km. Sailing 2 km.

Open: 1 April - 31 October.

Directions

Brem is 35 km. west of La Roche-sur-Yon and is on the D38 coast road. From A87 at La Roche continue on D160 towards Les Sables d'Olonne. Take exit for La Mothe-Achard and Brétignolles-sur-Mer. Follow D54 to Brem-sur-Mer. Site is to north of village on D38 to Brétignolles and is signed to the west.
GPS: 46.601654, -1.84404

Charges guide

Per unit incl. 2 persons	€ 15,00 - € 22,00
incl. electricity (10A)	€ 17,00 - € 25,00
extra person	€ 4,00 - € 5,00

Château-d'Olonne

Camping les Fosses Rouges

8 rue des Fosses Rouges, F-85180 Château d'Olonne (Vendée) T: 02 51 95 17 95
E: info@camping-lesfossesrouges.com alanrogers.com/FR85860

A family run site, Les Fosses Rouges was created in 1968 on the fields owned by the present owner's grandfather. Since it was built, the site has been surrounded by urban development, but nevertheless it is still a good value and well presented, if compact, site. There are 205 well hedged pitches of small to average size, most with some shade and electricity (10A). Some 45 are used for mobile homes, both private and to rent. There are also some seasonal or long stay tourers. There is a good swimming pool and a separate sports and games area. The site offers some low key entertainment in the main season. Nearby are the zoo and seashell museum at Les Sables d'Olonne, the fascinating salt pans and the museum of modern art at the Abbaye Sainte-Croix.

Facilities

Four colourful toilet blocks in traditional style are evenly distributed around the site. Washbasins in cubicles for ladies, push button showers. Facilities for disabled visitors. Washing machine at two blocks. Bar and takeaway (1/7-31/8). Shop (15/5-30/9). Motorcaravan service point. Swimming pool (heated, open all season and covered when necessary). Playground. Tennis. Minigolf. Giant chess. Open air stage for animation. Internet access (July/Aug). Communal barbecue areas. Off site: ATM at supermarket 1 km. Fishing 1 km. Golf and riding 4 km. Boat launching 5 km.

Open: 8 April - 30 September.

Directions

Site is southeast of Les Sables d'Olonne between the D949 and the sea. From large roundabout by supermarket on D949 turn towards sea on Avenue Dugay Trouin (signed La Pironnière). Continue straight on at mini-roundabout and in 150 m. turn left into rue des Fosses Rouges to site in 500 m.
GPS: 46.47932, -1.74123

Charges guide

Per unit incl. 2 persons and electricity	€ 16,00 - € 19,60
extra person	€ 2,80 - € 3,60
child (under 7 yrs)	€ 1,40 - € 1,80
dog	free - € 1,60

Camping les Fosses Rouges • 8, Rue des Fosses Rouges • F-85180 Château d'Olonne
Tel. (33) 2 51 95 17 95 • ww.camping-lesfossesrouges.com • info@camping-lesfossesrouges.com

Bretignolles-sur-Mer

Chadotel Camping la Trévillière

1 Rue de Bellevue, F-85470 Bretignolles-sur-Mer (Vendée) T: 02 51 90 09 65. E: info@chadotel.com

alanrogers.com/FR85310

In a pleasant rural setting, la Trévillière is on the edge of the little resort town of Bretignolles. There are 200 pitches, 110 for tourers, all with access to water and electricity (long leads rquired in places). Some are level, some sloping; all are separated by hedges or low bushes either with shade or more open. Although just 2 km. from the nearest beach and less than 5 km. from the Plage des Dunes (one of southern Vendée's best beaches), la Trévillière has a more 'laid-back' feel than many other sites in the area, particularly in low season.

Facilities

Three traditional toilet blocks, a little tired in parts, include washbasins in cubicles, pushbutton showers, a unit for disabled visitors and a baby room with bath, shower and toilet. Laundry facilities. Bar (1/5-30/9). Small shop (15/6-10/9). Snack bar with takeaway (1/6-10/9). Heated pool with slide and paddling pool. Play area. Minigolf. Max. 1 dog. Off site: Shops, restaurants and bars 1 km. Beach 2 km. Fishing, sailing and riding all 3 km. Golf 10 km. Saint Gilles Croix-de-Vie (8 km).

Open: 3 April - 1 November.

Directions

Brétignolles is on the D38 coast road. From north, after St Gilles go through Brétignolles-La Sauzaie (left fork) and before reaching Brétignolles turn left on sharp right hand bend, heading for water tower. Site on right in 800 m. From south, after Brétignolles, turn right (sign Ecoles), then left. Site signed to left after stadium. GPS: 46.63632, -1.85844

Charges guide

Per unit incl. 2 persons	€ 15,40 - € 29,50
extra person	€ 5,80

Coëx

RCN Camping la Ferme du Latois

F-85220 Coëx (Vendée) T: 02 51 54 67 30. E: info@rcn-lafermedulatois.fr

alanrogers.com/FR85770

Originally a simple 'camping á la ferme', this site has been developed by a Dutch organisation into an extensive, very well equipped and well maintained campsite. Naturally a very high proportion of its clientèle is Dutch, but the owners maintain a very French ambience and are keen to attract more British visitors. Located round two attractive fishing lakes, the 199 pitches, most available for touring, are spacious and attractively laid out with plenty of grass, hedges and trees, some young, some mature. All have electricity and a few are very large. There are 22 mobile homes for rent.

Facilities

Two large sanitary blocks have excellent toilets, showers and washbasins in cubicles. Good facilities for disabled visitors, babies and children. Two smaller blocks provide additional facilities. Laundry room. Small shop. Bar with terrace. Restaurant. Swimming pool with slides. Play area. Bicycle hire. Fishing lakes. WiFi (charged) around bar area. Internet point. Max. 1 dog. Off site: Golf and riding 3 km. Beach 12 km. Shops, bars and restaurants in Coëx 2 km.

Open: 9 April - 1 October.

Directions

Coëx is 29 km. west of La Roche-sur-Yon via the D938 to Aizenay, then the D6 St Gilles Croix-de-Vie road. Site is south of the village just off the D40 to La Chaize-Giraud and is clearly signed. GPS: 46.677033, -1.76885

Charges guide

Per unit incl. 2 persons and electricity	€ 18,25 - € 39,50
incl. 6 persons	€ 23,25 - € 52,00

Jard-sur-Mer

Camping les Ecureuils

Route des Goffineaux, F-85520 Jard-sur-Mer (Vendée) T: 02 51 33 42 74. E: contact@camping-ecureuils.com

alanrogers.com/FR85210

Les Ecureuils is a wooded site in a quieter part of the southern Vendée. It is undoubtedly one of the prettiest sites on this stretch of coast, with an elegant reception area, attractive vegetation and large pitches separated by low hedges with plenty of shade. Of the 261 pitches, some 128 are for touring units, each with water and drainage, as well as easy access to 10A electricity. This site is popular with tour operators (54 pitches). Jard is rated among the most pleasant and least hectic of Vendée towns. The harbour is home to some fishing boats and rather more pleasure craft.

Facilities

Two toilet blocks, well equipped and kept very clean, include baby baths, and laundry rooms. Small shop (bread baked on site). Snack bar and takeaway (1/6-15/9). Bar with snacks. Good sized L-shaped pool and separate paddling pool (30/5-15/9). Indoor pool and fitness centre (all season). Club for children (July/Aug). Bicycle hire. Internet access. Gas barbecues only. Dogs are not accepted. Off site: Beach 400 m.

Open: 4 April - 26 September.

Directions

From Les Sables d'Olonne take the N949 towards Talmont-St Hilaire. Keep right in the centre (D21 towards Jard). From la Roche-sur-Yon follow the D474 and the D49 towards Jard-sur-Mer. From the village follow signs 'Autre campings' or Camping les Ecureuils. Site on the left. GPS: 46.4113, -1.5896

Charges guide

Per unit incl. 2 persons	€ 23,00 - € 30,00
extra person	€ 5,00 - € 6,90

For latest campsite news, availability and prices visit

alanrogers.com

Jard-sur-Mer

Chadotel Camping l'Océano d'Or

58 rue Georges Clémenceau, B.P. 12, F-85520 Jard-sur-Mer (Vendée) T: 02 51 33 05 05. E: info@chadotel.com
alanrogers.com/FR85270

This site should appeal to families with children of all ages. It is very lively in high season but appears to be well managed, with a full programme of activities (it can therefore be noisy, sometimes late at night). The site is only 1 km. from the excellent beach. There are 430 flat, grass and sand pitches of which 40% are occupied by tour operators and mobile homes. The 260 for touring units, all with 6A electricity, are quite large (about 100 sq.m). Some are separated by high hedges, others are more open with low bushes between them. There are shops, bars and restaurants, and a weekly market in Jard-sur-Mer.

Facilities

Four rather dated, unisex toilet blocks include washbasins all in cabins (cleaning and maintenance is variable). Laundry facilities. Shop (1/6-10/9). Bar and snack bar (1/6-10/9, limited hours outside high season). Swimming pool (heated 20/5-20/9) with slides, waterfalls and children's pool. Walled (three sides) play area. Tennis. Pétanque. Minigolf. Electric barbecues are not allowed. Max. 1 dog. Off site: Beach within walking distance.

Open: 9 April - 25 September.

Directions

Site is on the D21 Talmont-St Hilaire - Longeville sur Mer, just east of the turning to the town centre. GPS: 46.42075, -1.5694

Charges guide

Per unit incl. 2 persons	
and electricity	€ 15,40 - € 29,90
extra person	€ 5,80
child (2-13 yrs)	€ 3,80

La Barre-de-Monts

Campéole la Grande Côte

Route de la Grande Côte, F-85550 La Barre-de-Monts (Vendée) T: 02 51 68 51 89
E: grande-cote@campeole.com alanrogers.com/FR85840

A site that lives up to its name, this one is very large, with 727 pitches. However, 245 are occupied by Bengali tents to rent, 60 by private caravans and 29 by tour operators. There are still 394 numbered touring pitches in rows, all with 10A electricity and spread over undulating sand dunes with sparse grass under pine trees. The site is served by eight fairly modern and fairly well maintained toilet blocks around the site. Some of the terraced pitches at the rear of the site have views of the impressive bridge onto the Ile de Noirmoutier, and there is direct access to a sandy beach via a gate. Also on site is an outdoor heated swimming pool. In July and August, the site offers clubs for children of all ages whilst adults can enjoy themed tapas, karaoke, cabaret, and aquagym. Whilst in high season this site is very busy, in low season it is rather quiet with only the pool and the playground open. Footpaths lead from the site to the village of Fromentine where there are shops and services plus the historic 19th century Estacade and an old Lighthouse. You can also buy oysters and other seafoods.

Facilities

Eight toilet blocks, all of a similar design, include some washbasins in cubicles, seatless toilets, baby bath, and a good unit for disabled campers. One laundry room. Outdoor swimming pool (15/5-30/9). Shop for bread and basics. Bar and takeaway (1/7- 31/8). Playgrounds, trampoline and bouncy castle. Entertainment and clubs for children (1/7-31/8). Multi-sports court. Boules. Bicycle hire. No charcoal barbecues. Supplement for double axle caravans. Off site: Fishing, sailing 50 m. Golf 15 km. Riding 2 km. Boat launching 25 km. Nearby is Ecomuseum du Oaviaud.

Open: 31 March - 16 September.

Directions

Site is on the mainland at the approach to the Ile de Noirmoutier. From the north via Bourgneuf-en-Retz take D758 to Beauvoir-sur-Mer, then d22 to La Barre-de-Monts. Continue through town ignoring road to Fromentine. At town boundary turn right on D38b (slightly oblique turn), signed Ile de Noirmoutier. In 500 m, straight on at roundabout for about 1 km. then right signed Grand Côte and Fromentine. Take next left for 1 km. to site (entrance on right). GPS: 46.8858, -2.1477

Charges guide

Per unit incl. 2 persons	€ 17,10 - € 26,60

For latest campsite news, availability and prices visit
alanrogers.com

La Chapelle-Hermier

Camping le Pin Parasol

Lac du Jaunay, F-85220 La Chapelle-Hermier (Vendée) T: 02 51 34 64 72. E: contact@campingpinparasol.fr

alanrogers.com/FR85680

Tucked away in the Vendée countryside yet just 15 minutes' drive from the beach, the site enjoys a pleasant rural setting above the Lac du Jaunay, well away from the bustle of the coast. There are 233 good sized touring pitches, all with electricity (10A) and 32 with water tap and drainage. Some have shade, others are in the open with maturing hedges and trees. The enthusiastic family owners are very hands-on and the facilities are of a high standard, most notably the elegant entrance and reception building, and the pool area with its excellent indoor pool, jacuzzi, steam room and fitness suite.

Facilities

Four toilet blocks include hot showers, washbasins in cabins and facilities for babies and disabled visitors. Washing machines and dryers. Shop and bar with terrace (15/5-25/9). Takeaway (July/Aug). Heated outdoor pool with paddling pool and slides (15/6-15/9). Indoor pool (all season). Play areas. Multisport pitch. Boules. Bicycle hire. Entertainment in high season. Fishing. Tennis. New internet and WiFi system. Off site: Golf 5 km. Riding 10 km. Beaches and sailing 12 km. Brétignolles 12 km.

Open: 23 April - 25 September.

Directions

La Chapelle-Hermier is 26 km. west of La Roche-sur-Yon. Site is to the south of the D42 La Chapelle-Hermier - l'Aiguillon-sur-Vie road, 2 km. east of the junction with the D40 Coëx-La Chaize - Giraud road and is well signed. GPS: 46.66622, -1.75528

Charges guide

Per unit incl. 2 persons and electricity	€ 16,50 - € 32,50
extra person	€ 4,50 - € 6,50
child (0-10 yrs)	€ 3,00 - € 3,50

La Guérinière

Camping le Caravan'ile

1 rue de la Tresson B.P. 4, La Guérinière, F-85680 Ile de Noirmoutier (Vendée) T: 02 51 39 50 29
E: contact@caravanile.com alanrogers.com/FR85620

This well appointed, family run site on the island of Noirmoutier has direct access across a dune and an extensive sandy beach, although swimming is only possible at high tide. It has a good pool and leisure complex, and a variety of entertainment is arranged in high season. Most of the 103 reasonably-level touring pitches are on sand beneath the dune. All have electricity (5A) and are separated by bushes and the occasional maturing tree; there is little shade. The site has a very French ambience, with many privately-owned mobile homes, plus 90 for rent.

Facilities

Three very clean sanitary blocks with preset shower and washbasins in cabins. Facilities for babies and disabled visitors. Laundry facilities. Small supermarket at entrance (15/4-15/9). Bar, snack bar and takeaway (15/4-15/9 but only school holidays and busy weekends until mid-June). Heated indoor pool with sauna, jacuzzi, steam room and solarium. Outdoor pool (15/5-15/9; heated July/Aug). Play area. Games room WiFi (charged) in bar area.

Open: 15 March - 15 November.

Directions

At La Barre des Monts, take D38 across bridge to island and continue to fifth roundabout. Take exit for La Guérinière and immediately turn left to site. GPS: 46.96631, -2.216073

Charges guide

Per unit incl. 2 persons incl. 8A electricity	€ 16,00 - € 26,00
	€ 17,50 - € 27,50
extra person	€ 3,40 - € 6,50
child (2-7 yrs)	€ 2,30 - € 4,00

La Guérinière

Camping les Moulins

54 rue des Moulins, F-85680 La Guérinière (Vendée) T: 02 51 39 51 38. E: contact@camping-les-moulins.com

alanrogers.com/FR85625

New owners have completely transformed this site on the Ile de Noirmoutier, making it an ideal choice for a seaside holiday. It is on the edge of a forest with direct access across dunes to a pleasant sandy beach. One area has 177 touring pitches on generally level ground and separated by hedges; most have electricity and a few also have water and drainage. Two other areas have an impressive range of well-equipped tented accommodation, fully in keeping with the forest setting. The heated pool has two paddling pools and a jacuzzi, whilst the bar also serves a full range of meals and snacks.

Facilities

Two modern, well equipped sanitary blocks provide unisex, preset showers and washbasins (all in cubicles). Baby bath and changing station, and good facilities for disabled visitors. Laundry facilities. Motorcaravan service point. Bar/restaurant and takeaway (July/Aug plus weekends May-Sept). Heated pool complex with paddling pools and jacuzzi (15/4-15/9). Wellness suite. Small gym. Internet room plus Wifi (charged). Small theatre. Multisport court. Pétanque. Bicycle hire. Off site: Small supermarket outside entrance. Riding 5 km. Noirmoutier en l'Ile 6 km.

Open: 1 April - 30 September.

Directions

The Ile de Noirmoutier is 70 km. southwest of Nantes. At la Barre des Monts take D38 across bridge to island and continue to fifth roundabout. Take exit for La Guérinière and immediately turn left to site. GPS: 46.966233, -2.217173

Charges guide

Per unit incl. 2 persons and electricity	€ 28,00 - € 51,00
extra person	€ 4,00 - € 7,00
child (5-9 yrs)	€ 3,00 - € 5,00

For latest campsite news, availability and prices visit

alanrogers.com

La Tranche-sur-Mer

Camping Baie d'Aunis

10 rue du Pertuis Breton, F-85360 La Tranche-sur-Mer (Vendée) T: 02 51 27 47 36
E: info@camping-baiedaunis.com alanrogers.com/FR85870

This very popular site has direct access to a sandy beach through a pedestrian gate (with key code) and across a car park. The town centre is also only 500 m. away. Shady and level, there are 150 individual pitches, all with electricity (10A). A good number of pitches are on a gravel base and a few are suitable only for smaller units. There are chalets and mobile homes (19) to rent. On site amenities include a heated swimming pool and a good restaurant and bar. This is a popular seaside resort with 13 km. of good quality sandy beaches. All have first aid posts, lifeguards in season and dogs are forbidden on the sands. From the pier by the Centre Nautique, just 50 m. from the site's rear pedestrian gate, you can catch ferries to the islands of Aix and Ré and to the larger resort of La Rochelle across the bay. You can also learn to fly or take pleasure flights from the aerodrome behind the town.

Facilities

The main centrally located sanitary unit is large, of a good quality and very well appointed. A smaller, simpler unit is at the far end of the site. British style WCs, washbasins in cubicles, provision for babies and disabled visitors. Laundry room at each block. Motorcaravan service point. Bar/restaurant and takeaway (1/5-10/9, w/ends only in low season). Outdoor swimming pool (10x20 m; heated May-Sept). Playground. TV room. Animals are not accepted in July/Aug. Off site: La Tranche is a major sail-boarding centre, with teaching facilities in a special lagoon, plus a surf school. Beach, bicycle hire, sea fishing all within 50 m. Town 500 m. Golf 38 km. Riding 12 km.

Open: 30 April - 19 September.

Directions

La Tranche-sur-Mer is 35 km. south of La Roche-sur-Yon. From La Roche-sur-Yon take 0747 to La Tranche. At roundabout (D747 and D1046) carry straight on to next roundabout and turn right towards town centre. At next (new) roundabout continue straight on to site on left (well signed). GPS: 46.34638, -1.43184

Charges guide

Per unit incl. 2 persons and electricity	€ 23,30 - € 31,00
extra person	€ 5,35 - € 6,35
child (under 5 yrs)	€ 3,25 - € 3,55
dog (not 1/7-31/8)	€ 2,20

CAMPiNG BAiE D'AUNiS★★★★

Camping Baie d'Aunis | 10, Rue du Pertuis Breton | 85360 La Tranche sur Mer
Tel: 0033 (0) 251 27 47 36 | Fax: 0033 (0) 251 27 44 54
info@camping-baiedaunis.com | www.camping-baiedaunis.com

La Tranche-sur-Mer

Camping du Jard

123 boulevard Maréchal de Lattre de Tassigny, F-85360 La Tranche-sur-Mer (Vendée) T: 02 51 27 43 79
E: info@campingdujard.fr alanrogers.com/FR85020

Camping du Jard is a well maintained site between La Rochelle and Les Sables d'Olonne. First impressions are good, with a friendly welcome from M. Marton or his staff. The 160 touring pitches, all with electricity and 60 also with water and drainage, are level and grassy; many are hedged by bushes and a large variety of trees provide shade in places. An impressive pool complex has a heated outdoor pool with toboggan and paddling pool, plus an indoor pool with jacuzzi. The site is 700 m. from a sandy beach with many shops and restaurants nearby.

Facilities

Three toilet blocks (only one open in low season). Basic facilities for babies and disabled visitors. Controllable showers in one block (planned in others) and some washbasins in cabins. Laundry facilities. Motorcaravan service point. Shop (1/6-10/9), restaurant and bar (25/5-10/9). Heated outdoor pool (from 25/5); heated indoor pool (all season). Sauna, solarium and fitness room. Tennis. Minigolf. Bicycle hire. Internet point. Free WiFi around bar. No American motorhomes. No pets. Off site: Beach 700 m. Fishing 1 km. Sailing 3 km.

Open: 26 April - 15 September.

Directions

From A87 Cholet/La Roche-sur-Yon leave at exit 32 for La Tranche sur Mer and take D747 to La Tranche. Turn east following signs for La Faute-sur-Mer along bypass. Take exit for La Grière and then turn east to site. GPS: 46.34836, -1.38738

Charges guide

Per unit incl. 2 persons, water and electricity	€ 25,50 - € 34,90
extra person	€ 4,50 - € 5,50
child (under 5 yrs)	€ 3,00 - € 4,00

For latest campsite news, availability and prices visit

alanrogers.com

Landevieille

Camping Pong

Rue du Stade, F-85220 Landevieille (Vendée) T: 02 51 22 92 63. E: info@lepong.com

alanrogers.com/FR85130

A comfortable family run site, in a rural situation close to St Gilles Croix-de-Vie, and just 5 km. from the coast at Brétignolles. Camping Pong has 229 pitches of which 177 are for tourers. All are of a good size and have electricity; most also have a water tap and drainage. The bar, snack bar, function room, games room, gym and shop are in a neat group of buildings next to the reception. The original area around the small fishing lake has mature trees, whilst in the newer section, trees and shrubs are developing well.

Facilities	Directions
A modern, well equipped sanitary blocks serves the main touring area and provides controllable showers, washbasins in cabins, facilities for disabled visitors, baby room and laundry. The older blocks are of a more traditional style. Shop (July/Aug). Bar plus snack bar and takeaway (15/6-15/9). Heated pool with jacuzzi, toboggan and paddling pool (from 15/5). Small gym. Bicycle hire. Fishing. Activities and entertainment (July/Aug). Wifi. Off site: Lac du Jaunay 2.5 km. Beach and riding 5 km.	Landevieille is 32 km. west of La Roche-sur-Yon via the A87/D160 Les Sables road; take exit for La Motte Achard and follow D12 for St Gilles Croix-de-Vie. Site is on the edge of Landevieille and is signed from the D12 and from the D32 (Challans - Les Sables d'Olonne) GPS: 46.64231, -1.79935

Open: 1 April - 15 September.

Charges guide

Per unit incl. 2 persons and electricity	€ 16,00 - € 24,00
extra person	€ 3,20 - € 4,90

Le Perrier

Domaine le Jardin du Marais

208 route de Saint-Gilles, F-85300 Le Perrier (Vendée) T: 02 51 68 09 17. E: info@lejardindumarais.eu

alanrogers.com/FR85635

A delightful, family campsite situated, as its name suggests, in a country setting on the edge of the marshes. It is beautifully kept and has excellent facilities including a well-stocked shop, a pleasant bar/restaurant and a good pool complex. The enthusiastic and hard-working owners are keen to welcome more British visitors who will be sure of a warm welcome. Of the 120 pitches, 52 are available for touring: the established pitches offer some shade and have electricity and water nearby; a new area offers large pitches with electricity, water and drainage, but bushes and trees have yet to mature. The beaches are just seven kilometres away. For shops, bars and restaurants you can use the nearby village of Le Perrier or head for the resorts of Saint Jean-de-Monts or Saint Hilaire-de-Riez where there are also large supermarkets and a frequent markets. Just south of Saint Hilaire is the busy fishing port and resort of Saint Gilles Croix-de-Vie where you can have a drink or a meal on the quayside, wander along the pedestrianised shopping streets or admire the yachts in the thriving marina.

Facilities	Directions
Two bright, modern sanitary blocks provide hot showers and washbasins in cubicles. Baby room. En-suite facility for disabled visitors. Laundry facilities. Motorcaravan services arranged. Shop, bar/restaurant and takeaway (all season, on demand). Outdoor pool with paddling pool (15/6-15/9). Indoor heated pool (15/4-15/9). Solarium. Fitness room. Play area. Free fishing on small lake (fenced and gated). Daytime activities and evening entertainment (July/Aug). Games area. Bicycle hire. Internet point. WiFi (charged) in bar area. Off site: Riding 4 km. Beach and sailing 7 km. Golf 8 km. St Jean-de-Monts 8 km.	Le Perrier is 51 km. northwest of La Roche-sur-Yon and 11 km. southwest of Challans. Site is 2 km. to the south on the D59 to Le Pissot and St Gilles; from the new route of the D753 Challans - St Jean-de-Monts road turn south on D59 and site is on right in 300m. GPS: 46.80133, -1.980656

Open: 1 April - 2 October.

Charges guide

Per unit incl. 2 persons and electricity	€ 19,80 - € 29,50
extra person	€ 4,90 - € 6,90
dog (max. 2)	€ 3,50

For latest campsite news, availability and prices visit

alanrogers.com

Les Sables-d'Olonne

Chadotel Camping les Roses

Rue des Roses, F-85100 Les Sables-d'Olonne (Vendée) T: 02 51 33 05 05. E: info@chadotel.com

alanrogers.com/FR85450

Les Roses has an urban location, with the fashionable town centre and lovely beach of Les Sables just a short walk away. It has an informal air with the 210 pitches arranged interestingly on a knoll. Mature trees give good shade to some areas. There are 90 touring pitches of varying sizes, all with access to water and electricity (long cables may be needed). The site has 120 mobile homes and chalets, some for rent and some owned by a tour operator. Roads around the site can get crowded in high season.

Facilities

Three fairly basic toilet blocks have pushbutton showers, washbasins in cubicles, a unit for disabled visitors, a baby room, washing machines and dryers. Simple bar and takeaway and small shop (10/6-15/9). Small, heated, outdoor pool with water slide and paddling pool (15/5-15/9). Volleyball, basketball and pétanque. Play area. Bicycle hire. Gas barbecues only (for hire). WiFi in bar area (charged). Max. 1 dog. Off site: Beach 500 m. Golf, riding, karting, watersports, zoo, fishing all within 5 km.

Open: 3 April - 7 November.

Directions

From end of A87 Cholet/La Roche sur Yon at exit 33, continue on D160 to Les Sables ring road. At eastern end of ring road in Château d'Olonne (at the 'Géant Casino' roundabout), turn west along Avenue d'Aquitaine towards town centre. Site is signed to left at small rounabout.
GPS: 46.49167, -1.76517

Charges guide

Per unit incl. 2 persons and electricity	€ 18,50 - € 31,00
extra person	€ 3,80 - € 5,80

Longeville-sur-Mer

Camping le Petit Rocher

1250 avenue de Docteur Mathevet, F-85560 Longeville-sur-Mer (Vendée) T: 02 51 90 31 57
E: info@campinglepetitrocher.com **alanrogers.com/FR85000**

A former municipal site, Le Petit Rocher is now under the same management (M. Guignard) as another local campsite, Les Brunelles. With its seaside location set in a pine forest, there is an air of peace and tranquillity. Although the area is undulating, the 150 good size touring pitches are flat and arranged in terraces throughout the wooded area. Electricity hook-ups are available (Euro style plugs) and there are adequate water points. A grassy play area for children is thoughtfully situated in a hollow, but has limited equipment. A fun pool was added in 2008.

Facilities

Three new, spacious sanitary blocks are clean and well maintained with showers, British style WCs. Facilities for disabled visitors. Washing machine and dryer. Bar, restaurant and takeaway (July/Aug). Tennis court. New heated outdoor pool (28/5-17/9). Max. 1 dog. Off site: Beach 200 m. Bars, restaurant, and small shops nearby. Riding and bicycle hire 2 km. Boat launching 11 km. Fishing 15 km. Golf 20 km.

Open: 28 May - 17 September.

Directions

From Longeville-sur-Mer follow signs for Le Rocher towards La Tranche-sur-Mer. Turn right at first roundabout, following campsite signs to site on right.
GPS: 46.403767, -1.507183

Charges guide

Per unit incl. 2 persons and electricity	€ 16,00 - € 25,00
extra person	€ 3,00 - € 5,00

Longeville-sur-Mer

Camping le Zagarella

Route de La Tranche, F-85560 Longeville-sur-Mer (Vendée) T: 02 51 33 30 60. E: zagarella@franceloc.com

alanrogers.com/FR85010

This pleasant campsite is set in a wooded, six-hectare area, a 1300-metre walk from the beach (or 1.5 km. by road). Scattered among the 130 mobile homes (110 to rent) are 70 touring pitches, which are of a reasonable size, though the site is probably unsuitable for larger units. On well-drained grass and shaded, the pitches are hedged and all have water and electricity. An impressive landscaped pool complex with indoor and outdoor pools, includes water slides paddling pool and a pirate-themed adventure area. Nearby is a large adventure playground with a huge bouncy castle.

Facilities

Three well maintained, if rather drab, toilet blocks include washbasins in cubicles and free preset showers. Separate baby room and facilities for disabled visitors. Laundry facilities. Shop (from 25/5). Bar (from 20/5). Restaurant and takeaway. Outdoor heated pool (from 1/6) and indoor pool (all season). Adventure playground. Multisport court. Tennis. Bicycle hire. Free WiFi in bar area. Only gas barbecues permitted. Off site: Beach 1300 m. Riding 1 km. Sailing 1.5 km. Fishing 10 km. Golf 30 km. Shops, bars and restaurants in Longeville 3 km.

Open: 1 May - 30 September.

Directions

Longeville-sur-Mer is 32 km south of La Roche-sur-Yon. Site is 3 km south of the town on D105 to La Tranche-sur-Mer. From A87 Cholet/La Roche leave at exit 32 for La Tranche and take D747 to La Tranche. Turn northwest on D105 for 8.5 km. to site on right (between La Conche and Le Rocher).
GPS: 46.40390, -1.48810

Charges guide

Per unit incl. 2 persons and electricity	€ 16,00 - € 33,00
extra person	€ 4,70 - € 8,00

For latest campsite news, availability and prices visit

alanrogers.com

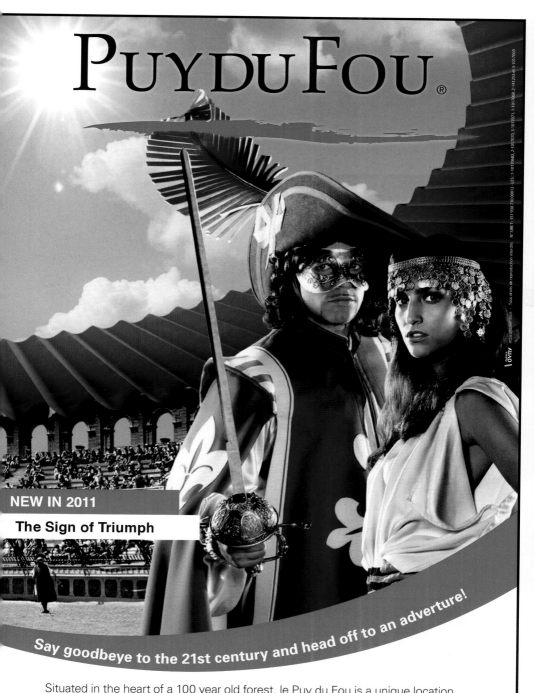

Longeville-sur-Mer

Camping les Brunelles

Le Bouil, F-85560 Longeville-sur-Mer (Vendée) T: 02 51 33 50 75. E: camping@les-brunelles.com

alanrogers.com/FR85440

This is a well managed site with good facilities and a programme of high season entertainment for all the family. A busy site in high season, there are plenty of activities to keep children happy and occupied. In 2007 Les Brunelles was combined with an adjacent campsite to provide 600 pitches of which 200 are for touring; all have electricity and 20 of the new touring pitches also have water and waste. All are in excess of 100 sq.m. to allow easier access for larger units. On the original Les Brunelles site, the touring pitches are all level on sandy grass and separated by hedges, away from most of the mobile homes.

Facilities

Four old, but well maintained and modernised toilet blocks have British and Turkish style toilets and washbasins, both open style and in cabins. Laundry facilities. Shop, takeaway and large modern, airy bar (all season). Covered pool with jacuzzi (all season). Outdoor pool with slides (21/5-24/9). Tennis. Bicycle hire. Max. 1 dog. Off site: Riding 3 km. Golf 20 km. Sandy beach 900 m. St Vincent-sur-Jard 2 km.

Open: 2 April - 24 September.

Directions

From D21 (Talmont - Longueville), between St Vincent and Longueville, site signed south from main road towards coast. Turn left in Le Bouil. Site is 800 m. on left. GPS: 46.41330, -1.52313

Charges guide

Per unit incl. 2 persons	€ 21,00 - € 35,00
extra person	€ 5,00 - € 8,00

Camping Cheques accepted.

Noirmoutier-en-l'Ile

Camping Indigo Noirmoutier La Vendette

23 allée des Sableaux, Bois de la Chaize, F-85330 Noirmoutier-en-l'Ile (Vendée) T: 02 51 39 06 24
E: noirmoutier@camping-indigo.com **alanrogers.com/FR85720**

Located in woodland and on dunes along a two kilometre stretch of sandy beach just east of the attractive little town of Noirmoutier on the island of the same name, this could be paradise for those who enjoy a simple campsite in a natural setting. On land belonging to France's forestry commission, this site is operated by Huttopia whose aim is to adapt to the environment rather than take it over. The 420 touring pitches, all with electricity, are situated among the pine trees and accessed along tracks. Those on the sand dunes have fantastic views across the Baie de Bourgneuf. They cost a few euros extra – if you are lucky enough to get one. Cars are only allowed in these areas on arrival and departure. There are no mobile homes, but Indigo have installed 80 large, and well equipped canvas tents on wooden bases for rent. Nearby are salt marshes, an aquarium and a water theme park, and there are opportunities to walk, cycle, sail and windsurf. The island is reached by a bridge, but the more adventurous can still do it the old way and cross the causeway.

Facilities

Five sanitary blocks currently provide basic facilities including preset showers and some washbasins (with warm water) in cubicles. The central one is larger and more modern, and another has been refurbished with controllable showers and washbasins, although these are open-style. Facilities for babies and disabled visitors. Laundry facilities. Basic motorcaravan services point. Play area. Bicycle hire. Free internet point in reception. WiFi planned for 2011. Off site: Noirmoutier en l'Ile 2 km. Riding 4 km. Sailing 5 km. Golf 25 km.

Open: 1 April - 9 October.

Directions

At La Barre des Monts, take D38 across bridge to island and continue 20 km. to Noirmoutier en l'Ile. Go through town past three sets of traffic lights and at roundabout turn right following blue signs to 'Campings'. Site is ahead at roundabout in about 2 km. GPS: 46.9969, -2.2201

Charges guide

Per unit incl. 2 persons and electricity	€ 20,10 - € 26,00
extra person	€ 5,20 - € 6,00
child (2-7 yrs)	€ 2,00 - € 2,60

Olonne-sur-Mer

Camping la Loubine

1 route de la Mer, F-85340 Olonne-sur-Mer (Vendée) T: 02 51 33 12 92. E: camping.la.loubine@wanadoo.fr
alanrogers.com/FR85030

On the edge of a forest and just 1.8 kilometres from a sandy beach, La Loubine is a busy campsite close to Les Sables d'Olonne. The 60 grass touring pitches are mostly shaded, all with electricity and with water points nearby. Mobile homes and chalets, many for rent, and tour operator tents occupy the remaining 300 pitches. The focal point is an excellent restaurant with an attractive covered terrace and bar with an entertainment area for karaoke and discos, plus a patio overlooking the splendid pool complex with its water slides and heated indoor pool. The camping areas have lots of trees and hedges, some quite high, providing plenty of shade when it is sunny, but perhaps making things a bit dark if it isn't. A shuttle bus to the beach operates in high season, the area has a network of cycle tracks and there are occasional buses to Les Sables and Saint Gilles from close by. Olonne-sur-Mer has shops, bars, restaurants and a hypermarket, whilst ten minutes away is fashionable Les Sables with its fine sandy beach and a wider range of options for dining and shopping.

Facilities

Four fairly basic and mostly rather tired toilet blocks (cleaning variable) have British style WCs, washbasins in cubicles and controllable showers. Facilities for disabled visitors. Laundry facilities. Shop, bar, restaurant and takeaway (15/5-15/9). Outdoor pools and heated indoor pool (all season). Tennis. Fitness room. Minigolf. Play area. Bicycle hire. Free WiFi in bar area. Internet (charged). Shuttle bus to beach (July/Aug). No dogs in high season. Off site: Riding 200 m. Canoeing 1 km. Beach 1.8 km. Golf 4 km. Fishing 6 km. Olonne-sur-Mer 4 km.

Open: 2 April - 25 September.

Directions

Site is off D80 coast road between Olonne-sur-Mer and Brem-sur-Mer, clearly signed at small roundabout. From La Roche-sur-Yon via A87/D160, turn west on D949 Les Sables ring road then north on D32 to Olonne-sur-Mer, Site is signed to left in town centre. GPS: 46.54626, -1.80556

Charges guide

Per unit incl. 2 persons	€ 15,50 - € 27,50
extra person	€ 3,25 - € 5,10
electricity (6A)	€ 3,70

Camping La Loubine

Traditional-style facilities set in the grounds of an old farm only 1800 m from the beach; La Loubine is a lively site with one of the best pool complexes in the area. (1 heated indoor pool with 3 waterslides, whirlpool bath and sauna).

Bar - Restaurant - Take Away - Shop - Tennis Court - Crazy Golf - Playground - Fitness Room - Multi Sport Pitch - Bicycle Hire - Entertainment in high season.

1, Route de la Mer - 85340 Olonne Sur mer - France
Tel.: 0033 (0)2 51 33 12 92 - Fax: 0033 (0)2 51 33 12 71

camping.la.loubine@wanadoo.fr
www.la-loubine.fr

Olonne-sur-Mer

Domaine de l'Orée

13 route des Amis de la Nature, F-85340 Olonne-sur-Mer (Vendée) T: 02 51 33 10 59. E: loree@free.fr
alanrogers.com/FR85180

On the edge of a national forest, close to marshes and a bird sanctuary, and just 1,800 m. from a fine sandy beach, Domaine de l'Orée will provide ample opportunities for an active holiday whether in the impressive pool complex, using the many sports facilities, venturing out onto the network of footpaths and cycle tracks or just going to the beach. The 53 touring pitches are level and separated by bushes; all have electricity (16A) and 40 also have a water tap and drainage. The remaining 243 pitches are occupied by chalets and mobile homes, many available for rent.

Facilities

Two blocks providing a little tired but adequate sanitary facilities with British style WCs, hot showers and washbasins in cabins. Baby bath. Basic facilities for disabled visitors. Laundry facilities. Small shop, bar with TV, snack bar and takeaway (all from 1/5). Heated outdoor swimming pool and fun pool with slides (from 1/5) plus heated indoor swimming pool with jacuzzi (all season). Play areas. Trampolines. Tennis. Bicycle hire. Free WiFi in bar and pool area. Off site: Riding 50 m. Canoeng 500 m. Beach 1.8 km. Golf 6 km. Olonne-sur-Mer 5 km.

Open: 11 April - 13 September.

Directions

Olonne-sur-Mer is 5 km. north of Les Sables d'Olonne. Site is on D80 coast road between Olonne-sur-Mer and Brem-sur-Mer. From La Roche-sur-Yon via A87/D160, turn west on D949 Les Sables Ring Road then north on D32 to Olonne-sur-Mer. Site is signed to left in town centre. GPS: 46.54979, -1.80159

Charges guide

Per unit incl. 1 or 2 persons	€ 15,30 - € 26,60
extra person	€ 3,00 - € 5,50
electricity	€ 3,00 - € 4,00

For latest campsite news, availability and prices visit

alanrogers.com

Saint Gilles-Croix-de-Vie

Chadotel le Domaine de Beaulieu

Rue du Parc, Givrand, F-85800 Saint Gilles-Croix-de-Vie (Vendée) T: 02 51 55 59 46. E: info@chadotel.com

alanrogers.com/FR85490

Domaine de Beaulieu has an open airy feel in a semi-rural setting on the edge of the village of Givrand, a short drive from a good sandy beach and from the fishing port and resort of St Gilles. The 125 touring pitches all with electricity and water nearby, are pleasantly laid out and separated by hedges or bushes; most have shade from mature trees, others are more open. A little stream in an unfenced cutting runs through the site. There are 130 mobile homes, most for rent, and tour operators occupy 100 pitches.

Facilities

Three well maintained toilet blocks include preset showers, washbasins in cubicles, baby room, unit for disabled visitors and laundry facilities. Shop (15/6-10/9). Bar and takeaway (15/5-10/9). Restaurant (15/6-31/8). Heated outdoor swimming pool with water slides, toboggan, paddling pool and jacuzzi (15/5-15/9). Play area. Multisport terrain. Minigolf. Tennis. Bicycle hire. WiFi (charged) in bar area. Off site: Restaurant 500 m. Beach 1.5 km. Fishing 3 km. Riding 4 km. Sailing 5 km. Golf 7 km.

Open: 2 April - 24 September.

Directions

St Gilles-Croix-de-Vie is 45 km. west of La Roche-sur-Yon on the D38 coast road. Site is signed from roundabout at Givrand, at southern end of Saint Gilles bypass, 7 km. north of Brétignolles. GPS: 46.67094, -1.90387

Charges guide

Per unit incl. 2 persons and electricity (10A)	€ 15,40 - € 29,50
extra person	€ 5,80

Saint Hilaire-de-Riez

Camping la Puerta del Sol

Chemin des Hommeaux 7, F-85270 Saint Hilaire-de-Riez (Vendée) T: 02 51 49 10 10
E: info@campinglapuertadelsol.com alanrogers.com/FR85080

A short distance away from the busy coast, Puerta del Sol could suit not only families with teenage children to entertain, but also those seeking a more peaceful and relaxing holiday. Of the 216 pitches, 70 are available for touring units, each with electricity, water and drainage; they are level with dividing hedges and there is plenty of shade from mature trees. The remaining pitches are occupied by mobile homes and wooden chalets, 66 available for rent. A pleasant bar with snack bar, takeaway and small shop overlooks the pool and terrace.

Facilities

Two toilet blocks have a mixture of Turkish and British style WCs, washbasins in cabins and controllable showers. Baby bath. Facilities for disabled visitors. Laundry facilities. Shop, bar snack bar and takeaway (1/5-15/9). Heated swimming pool with slide and paddling pool (1/5-30/9) and indoor pool from 1 April 2011. Play area. Tennis. Bicycle hire. Games room. Library. Internet room. Fitness suite. Sauna and jacuzzi. WiFi in bar area (charged). Very large motorhomes not accepted. Off site: Riding 2 km. Beach 5 km. Fishing, sailing and boat launching 10 km. Golf 15 km.

Open: 1 April - 30 September.

Directions

St Hilaire-de-Riez is 45 km northwest of La Roche-sur-Yon. Site is 6 km. to the north. At Le Pissot, 7 km. north of St Gilles Croix-de-Vie on D38 to St Jean-de-Monts, turn north on D59 (Le Perrier). Site is signed to the right in 2 km. GPS: 46.7645, -1.9572

Charges guide

Per unit incl. up to 2 persons and services	€ 22,00 - € 32,00
extra person	€ 5,00 - € 6,50
child (under 7 yrs)	€ 2,50 - € 4,50

Saint Hilaire-de-Riez

Camping les Ecureuils

100 avenue de la Pège, F-85270 Saint Hilaire-de-Riez (Vendée) T: 02 51 54 33 71
E: info@camping-aux-ecureuils.com alanrogers.com/FR85230

Of the seaside sites on the Vendée, Les Ecureuils has to be one of the best, run by a friendly and most helpful family. Just 300 m. from a superb beach, the site is ideally situated for exploring from Les Sables d'Olonne to Noirmoutier. Developed on what was originally a farm, there are 215 pitches (42 for touring units). On sandy grass, all have electricity (6A, Euro adaptors avalable), water and drainage. Well kept hedges and mature trees give shade and privacy, although some more open pitches are also available for sun lovers. The site is popular with British tour operators (60%).

Facilities

The two main sanitary blocks are spacious, and include some washbasins in cubicles, and facilities for babies and disabled visitors. Laundry facilities. Small shop (1/5-4/9). Restaurant. Large, airy bar with screened terrace. Pool complex including pool for small children with its own mini aqua park, large heated pool, and water slide with separate splash pool. Indoor pool, paddling pool and jacuzzi. Off site: Beach 300 m. Bicycle hire 200 m. Fishing 4 km. Riding 5 km. Golf and sailing 6 km.

Open: 1 May - 11 September.

Directions

Driving south D38 (St Jean-de-Monts - St Gilles), turn right at L'Oasis hotel/restaurant in Orouet (6 km. outside St Jean-de-Monts), signed Les Mouettes. After 1.5 km. at roundabout turn left (St Hilaire-de-Riez). Site is 500 m. on left. GPS: 46.7361, -2.0095

Charges guide

Per unit incl. 2 persons and electricity	€ 26,60 - € 36,00
extra person	€ 5,00 - € 6,25

Saint Hilaire-de-Riez

Camping Caravaning la Ningle

Chemin des Roselières 66, F-85270 Saint Hilaire-de-Riez (Vendée) T: 02 51 54 07 11
E: campingdelaningle@wanadoo.fr alanrogers.com/FR85350

At Camping La Ningle you are guaranteed to receive a warm welcome from M. et Mme. Guibert, who have established a very pleasant campsite with a friendly, family atmosphere. There are 155 pitches, 60 available for touring units. All are fully serviced (electricity 6/10A, water and drainage). Pitches are spacious with dividing hedges and all have some shade. The nearest beach is a 600 m. walk through a pine forest, but there are also three small heated swimming pools on site. This site is well situated to explore the beautiful port of St Gilles-Croix-de- Vie, with its abundance of restaurants (where seafood is served direct from the morning's catch) and pedestrianised shopping area with a variety of individual boutiques.

Facilities

Two clean toilet blocks include some washbasins in cubicles. Toilet/shower room for disabled visitors and large family shower room. Laundry facilities. Bread (July/Aug). Takeaway three evenings per week. Bar (July/Aug). Main swimming pool, larger children's pool, paddling pool and slide (15/5-10/9). Fitness suite. Tennis court. Games field. Games room. Fishing lake. Children's activities (July/Aug), and regular petanque and tennis competitions. WiFi in bar area. Off site: Small supermarket and takeaway 200 m.

Open: 20 May - 10 September.

Directions

Driving south on D38 (St Jean-de-Monts - St Gilles), turn right at L'Oasis hotel/restaurant in Orouet, signed Les Mouettes. After 1.5 km. at roundabout, turn left (St Hilaire-de-Riez). Pass two campsites, then next left, signed La Ningle.
GPS: 46.7447, -2.0044

Charges guide

Per unit incl. 2 persons and electricity	€ 17,50 - € 31,90
extra person	€ 3,10 - € 4,80
child (under 7 yrs)	€ 1,65 - € 2,90

Saint Hilaire-la-Forêt

Camping des Batardières

F-85440 Saint Hilaire-la-Forêt (Vendée) T: 02 51 33 33 85
alanrogers.com/FR85390

Camping des Batardières is a haven of tranquility on the edge of an unspoilt village, yet just 5 km. from the sea. It is an attractive, unsophisticated little site, lovingly maintained by its owners for more than 25 years. Many visitors return year after year. There are 75 good-sized pitches (a few up to 130 sq.m) and all are available for touring units (there are no mobile homes and no tour operators!) All have easy access to water and electricity (6A, or 2A for tents). Otherwise there are few facilities on site.

Facilities

The sanitary block is kept very clean and visitors are encouraged to keep it that way (no shoes in the shower cubicles, for instance). Some washbasin and shower combination cubicles. Laundry facilities. Tennis court. Play area and field for games, kite flying etc. Not suitable for American motorhomes or twin axle caravans. Off site: Village shop and bar 200 m. Jard-sur-Mer 5 km. Bicycle hire 3 km. Fishing 5 km. Golf 16 km.

Open: 27 June - 2 September.

Directions

From Les Sables d'Olonne take D949 (la Rochelle) towards Talmont-St Hilaire and Luçon. 7 km. after Talmont turn right on D70 to St Hilaire-la-Forêt. Site signed to the right approaching village.
GPS: 46.4486, -1.5286

Charges 2011

Per unit incl. 2 persons and electricity	€ 23,50
extra person	€ 3,00
dog	€ 1,50

No credit cards.

Saint Jean-de-Monts

Campéole Dornier

Route de la Tonnelle, F-85160 Saint Jean-de-Monts (Vendée) T: 02 51 58 81 16. E: dornier@campeole.com

alanrogers.com/FR85960

Le Dornier is an extensive site, located on land belonging to the French forestry commission and close to the popular resort of St Jean-de-Monts. The site has direct access to a superb sandy beach and also has a good sized heated swimming pool. The 229 touring pitches, all with electricity available, are mostly sandy and of a reasonable size. A range of chalets, fully equipped bungalow tents and mobile homes are available for rent including some models specially adapted for campers with disabilities. The site has a small bar and snack bar (July/Aug) just along the road. There is also a small supermarket and a large bar and restaurant close by. The site can become quite lively in high season with a daily children's club and a wide range of daytime activities and evening entertainment, including concerts and discos. However, touring pitches are well scattered on this vast site, so it should be possible to ask to be located well away from these events if desired. A number of cycle tracks pass through the woods close to the site. St Jean is a well equipped resort with dozens of restaurants, cafés and other attractions.

Facilities

Two sanitary blocks have recently been refurbished to a very high standard with modern preset showers, washbasins in cubicles, and excellent facilities for babies, children and disabled visitors. Laundry facilities. Motorcaravan service point. Other blocks still await refurbishment. Direct beach access. Heated swimming pool and paddling pool (8/5-11/9, supervised July/Aug). Bicycle hire. Archery. Multisport court. Snack bar adjacent. Play area. Entertainment programme (July/Aug). WiFi (charged). Off site: Beach 300 m. Golf and riding 3 km.

Open: 1 April - 11 September.

Directions

The site is 6 km. north of St Jean-de-Monts on the D38 towards Notre Dame-de-Monts. Turn west at the roundabout at Les Tonnelles where site is signed and is on right in 300 m. GPS: 46.8094, -2.1208

Charges guide

Per unit incl. 2 persons	
and electricity	€ 17,10 - € 26,60
extra person	€ 4,50 - € 7,10
child (2-6 yrs)	free - € 4,40
dog	€ 2,50 - € 3,20

Saint Jean-de-Monts

Camping les Places Dorées

Route de Notre-Dame-de-Monts, F-85160 Saint Jean-de-Monts (Vendée) T: 02 51 59 02 93

E: contact@placesdorees.com alanrogers.com/FR85280

Les Places Dorées is, in high season, a busy, popular site with a lively programme of activities and entertainment. At other times it is quieter, but has still plenty to offer. There are 288 grassy pitches, of which just 60 are available for touring units, the quietest being towards the back of the site. Those nearer the leisure complex can be noisy in high season with the bar and disco closing late. Pitches are separated by hedges and there is some shade from maturing trees. A 20 minute walk will take you to a long sandy beach.

Facilities

Three toilet blocks are beginning to show their age, but seem to be kept clean. Preset showers and washbasins in cubicles. Facilities for disabled visitors. Laundry facilities. Bread to order. Bar/restaurant (July/Aug and busy weekends). Snack bar and takeaway. Outdoor pool complex with slides, jacuzzi and waterfall. Covered, heated pool. Spa facilities. Gym. Activities, entertainment and children's club (July/Aug). WiFi (charged) in bar area. Max. 1 small dog. Off site: Fishing 500 m. Beach 800 m. Riding 1 km. Saint-Jean-de-Monts 4 km.

Open: 15 June - 11 September.

Directions

Saint-Jean-de-Monts is 55 km. northwest of La Roche-sur-Yon. Site is 4 km. north of St Jean-de-Monts on the D38 St Jean-de-Monts - Notre Dames-de-Monts road on the eastern side, almost opposite L'Abri des Pins. GPS: 46.80993, -2.10992

Charges guide

Per unit incl. 3 persons	
and electricity	€ 23,70 - € 35,50
extra person	€ 3,80 - € 6,50

No credit cards.

Saint Jean-de-Monts

Camping la Yole

Chemin des Bosses, Orouet, F-85160 Saint Jean-de-Monts (Vendée) T: 02 51 58 67 17
E: contact@la-yole.com alanrogers.com/FR85150

La Yole is an attractive and well run site, 2 kilometres from a sandy beach. It offers 356 pitches, some of which are occupied by tour operators and mobile homes to rent. There are 164 touring pitches, most with shade and separated by bushes and trees. A newer area at the rear of the site is more open. All the pitches are of at least 100 sq.m. and have electricity (10A), water and drainage. The pool complex includes an outdoor pool, a paddling pool, slide and an indoor heated pool with jacuzzi. There are also new gym facilties. Entertainment is organised in high season. This is a clean and tidy site, ideal for families with children and you will receive a helpful and friendly welcome.

Facilities

Two toilet blocks include washbasins in cabins and facilities for disabled visitors and babies. A third block has a baby room. Laundry facilities. Shop (15/5-5/9). Bar, restaurant and takeaway (1/5-15/9). Outdoor pool and paddling pool. Indoor heated pool with jacuzzi (all season, no shorts). Gym centre. Play area. Club room. Tennis. Games room. Entertainment in high season. WiFi. Gas barbecues only. Max. 1 dog. Off site: Beach, bus service, bicycle hire 2 km. Riding 3 km. Fishing, golf and watersports 6 km.

Open: 4 April - 29 September.

Directions

Site is signed off the D38, 6 km. south of St Jean-de-Monts in the village of Orouet. Coming from St Jean-de-Monts turn right at l'Oasis restaurant towards Mouette and follow signs to site. GPS: 46.75659, -2.00792

Charges guide

Per unit incl. 2 persons	
and electricity	€ 16,00 - € 30,50
extra person	€ 3,70 - € 6,50
child (under 9 yrs)	free - € 5,20
dog	€ 4,00 - € 5,00

Camping Cheques accepted.

Hot Spot WiFi

Camping La Yole ★★★★

Camping Cheque

Wake up to the sound of birdsong in a wooded park of 17 acres with four star comfort. Space, security, informal atmosphere: la yole, tucked away between fields and pine trees, only 2 km from the beach.

– Chemin des Bosses - Orouet - F 85160 Saint Jean de Monts –
– Tel: 0033 251 58 67 17 - Fax: 0033 251 59 05 35 –
– contact@la-yole.com / www.la-yole.com –

Saint Jean-de-Monts
Camping la Forêt

190 chemin de la Rive, F-85160 Saint Jean-de-Monts (Vendée) T: 02 51 58 84 63
E: camping-la-foret@wanadoo.fr **alanrogers.com/FR85360**

Camping La Forêt is an attractive, well run site with a friendly family atmosphere, thanks to the hard working owners M. and Mme. Jolivet. It provides just 63 pitches with 39 for touring units. They are of a reasonable size and surrounded by mature hedges; all have water and electricity, and some also have drainage. A variety of trees provides shade to every pitch. There are 13 mobile homes for rent and one tour operator on site (11 pitches), but their presence is not intrusive and the site has a quiet and relaxed atmosphere.

Facilities

The central toilet block includes hot showers and washbasins in cubicles. Laundry facilities. Baby bath. Facilities for disabled visitors. Motorcaravan waste tanks can be emptied on request. Basic provisions sold in reception. Takeaway (15/5-15/9). Small heated swimming pool (15/5-15/9). Games room with TV. WiFi throughout (charged). Play area. Bicycle hire. Only gas and electric barbecues allowed. No American motorhomes.
Off site: Beach 400 m. Sailing 1 km. Golf 2 km. Riding 3 km. Shop, bar and restaurant within 2 km.

Open: 1 May - 28 September.

Directions

Saint Jean-de-Monts is 55 km. northwest of La Roche-sur-Yon. The site is 6 km. north of St Jean just off the D38 towards Notre Dame-de-Monts. At southern end of Notre Dame, turn west at sign for site and Plage de Pont d'Yeu. Bear left and site is on left in about 200 m. GPS: 46.80807, -2.11384

Charges guide

Per unit incl. 2 persons and electricity	€ 21,90 - € 31,90
extra person	€ 3,50 - € 5,00

Saint Jean-de-Monts
Camping Caravaning le Bois Joly

46 route de Notre-Dame-de-Monts, B.P. 507, F-85165 Saint Jean-de-Monts (Vendée) T: 02 51 59 11 63
E: campingboisjoly@wanadoo.fr **alanrogers.com/FR85780**

This is an attractive, family run holiday site with Indoor and outdoor pool complexes and 385 pitches, most of which are fully serviced. Of these 202 are taken by mobile homes or chalets, leaving 183 good sized, hedged pitches with 10A electric hook-ups for touring units. Grassy and level, these are served by tarmac roads and four fresh, clean, modern, toilet blocks. A good family holiday location, there are lots of activities and entertainment in July and August. The indoor pool is open all season, the L-shaped outdoor pool complex has a 'menhirs' theme and attractive flower beds. There are four toboggans, a paddling pool and a raised solarium deck. On site there are several small playgrounds for younger children, plus a very large and comprehensive adventure playground. The river behind the site offers opportunities for fishing or canoeing.

Facilities

Four modern toilet blocks with controllable showers, washbasins in cubicles. Facilities for babies and disabled visitors. Laundry facilities. One block is heated for low season. Bar and snack bar. Takeaway (July/Aug). Indoor pool. Outdoor pools (15/6-15/9). Sauna, solarium and gym. Playgrounds. Multisport court. Pétanque. TV room. Games room. Events, entertainment and canoeing on site in July/Aug. River fishing. Motorcaravan service point. Safety deposit boxes. No charcoal barbecues allowed. No double axle caravans accepted. Off site: Golf 2 km. Riding and tennis 500 m. Bicycle hire 1.5 km. Beach and boat launching 1.5 km. Shops and restaurants within 2 km.

Open: 9 April - 25 September.

Directions

Site is at the northern end of St Jean-de-Monts, on the eastern side of the D38, about 300 m. north of junction (roundabout) with the D51.
GPS: 46.79915, -2.0744

Charges 2011

Per unit incl. 2 persons and electricity	€ 18,00 - € 32,00
extra person	€ 2,00 - € 5,00
child (1-7 yrs)	€ 1,00 - € 2,50
dog	€ 1,50 - € 3,00

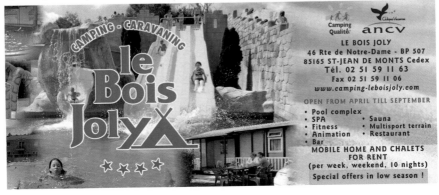

Saint Jean-de-Monts

Camping Plein Sud

246 route de Notre-Dame-de-Monts, F-85160 Saint Jean-de-Monts (Vendée) T: 02 51 59 10 40
E: info@campingpleinsud.com **alanrogers.com/FR85590**

Plein Sud is a small, friendly site, immaculately kept and with a very French ambience. Of the 110 grassy pitches separated by hedges, 40 are available for touring. They are of a reasonable size and all have electricity and water; most also have drainage. Twenty pitches have site-owned mobile homes, cabins or tents for rent, the rest have privately-owned mobiles. The touring pitches at the far end of this long, narrow site are particularly peaceful, Only 800 m. away, via another campsite across the road and through a strip of forest, is a long stretch of safe, sandy beach.

Facilities	Directions
Two immaculate sanitary blocks provide pushbutton showers and washbasins in cabins. Good facilities for disabled visitors. Baby room. Laundry facilities. Bar with terrace (July/Aug). Heated pool with paddling pool. Play areas. Multisport court. Bread and milk to order (high season). Takeaways (Tues-Sun). Bicycle hire. Pony and trap rides. Family entertainment (July/Aug). WiFi planned. Off site: Beach 800 m. Fishing 2 km.	Saint Jean-de-Monts is 55 km. northwest of La Roche-sur-Yon. Site is about 4 km. north of the town on the D38 towards Notre Dame-de-Monts, on the right almost opposite Camping L'Abri des Pins. GPS: 46.809805, -2.109557

Open: 1 May - 15 September.

Charges guide

Per unit incl. 2 persons	€ 12,00 - € 24,00
incl. 6A electricity	€ 14,00 - € 28,00

Saint Jean-de-Monts

Campéole les Sirènes

Campé●le

Avenue des Demoiselles, F-85164 Saint Jean-de-Monts (Vendée) T: 02 51 58 01 31
E: sirenes@campeole.com **alanrogers.com/FR85970**

Les Sirènes is a large campsite located in the forest behind the popular resort of St Jean-de-Monts. The nearest beach, just 700 m. away, is long and sandy, shelving very gradually into the sea. Pitches here here vary considerably; some, ideal for tents, are among the tall pine trees whilst others are on flat ground but still with shade provided by a variety of younger trees. Most have electrical connections and water taps nearby. A number of equipped tents and mobile homes (including specially adapted models for disabled visitors) are available for rent. On-site amenities include a swimming pool and separate children's pool, a multi-sport pitch and archery. This is a lively site in high season with plenty going on, including a daily children's club and regular sporting competitions. Evenings, however, are generally quiet, with just a weekly 'soirée dansante'. Les Sirènes has a good location with easy pedestrian access to the beach, and to lively Saint Jean-de-Monts with a good choice of shops, bars and restaurants.

Facilities	Directions
Several small, fairly basic sanitary blocks (in low season only the main block is open). A refurbishment programme is in progress. Some modern preset showers and mainly open-style washbasins (a few in cabins) with only cold water. Washing machines and dryers. Shop, takeaway (July/Aug). Heated swimming pools (1/6-11/9. Multisport pitch. Bicycle hire. Bouncy castle. Archery. Play area. Children's club and activities programme (July/Aug). Tourist information. WiFi (charged) around reception. Mobile homes and equipped tents for rent. Off site: Restaurant at site entrance. Beach 700 m. Golf, riding, sailing and water sports 3 km. Fishing 10 km.	From southern end of D38/D38bis Saint Jean bypass turn north on D38 Route des Sables towards town. At next roundabout go left on D123 Avenue Valentin, signed La Plage. Bear right at second roundabout, then after 1.2 km. turn right at roundabout along ave des Mimosas into ave des Demoiselles. Site is signed and is on right in 400 m. GPS: 46.780083, -2.055881

Open: 1 April - 11 September.

Charges guide

Per unit incl. 2 persons and electricity	€ 17,10 - € 26,60
extra person	€ 4,50 - € 7,10
child (2-6 yrs)	free - € 4,40

For latest campsite news, availability and prices visit

alanrogers.com

Saint Julien-des-Landes

Flower Camping la Bretonnière

F-85150 Saint Julien-des-Landes (Vendée) T: 02 51 46 62 44. E: camp.la-bretonniere@wanadoo.fr

alanrogers.com/FR85850

An attractive, modern site on a family farm surrounded by beautiful peaceful countryside, this site is sure to please. With 150 pitches in an area of six hectares, there is plenty of space for everyone. There are 101 touring pitches, 28 tour operator tents and 17 alpine style chalets, spread around several fields, some quite open, others with some shade from perimeter hedges. The grassy pitches are all of a really generous size with electricity (12/16A). Two swimming pools, one covered, the other outdoor, are surrounded by a pleasant terrace, with the bar and reception close by. Also on site is a lovely large fishing lake (unfenced) with a pleasant walk all around. The bar and takeaway operate in July/August, ices and basic tinned food items are available from reception and there is a really good motorcaravan service point. The village of Saint Julien is 2.5 km. and the larger town of La Mothe-Achard is 7 km.

Facilities

Five modern, clean and well appointed toilet blocks are spread evenly around the site, with baby rooms and facilities for disabled visitors at two blocks. Motorcaravan service point. Bar, snack bar and takeaway (July/Aug). Covered swimming pool (15.5x7 m) and outdoor pool (11x5 m) open June-Sept. WiFi around bar and reception. Playgrounds. Games/TV room. Tennis. Boules. Fishing lake. Caravan storage. Off site: Village 2.5 km. La Mothe-Achard 7 km. Golf 12 km. Riding 2 km. Boat launching 4 km.

Open: 1 April - 15 October.

Directions

Saint Julien-des-Landes is 18 km. northeast of Les Sables d'Olonne and 5 km. northwest of La Mothe-Achard. From La Mothe-Achard take D12 west (Bretignolles-sur-Mer), pass through St Julien and after 2 km. take first turn right (site signed). Site is 500 m. GPS: 46.64463, -1.73328

Charges 2011

Per unit incl. 2 persons and electricity	€ 14,00 - € 26,90
extra person	€ 3,50 - € 4,50
child (2-7 yrs)	€ 2,50 - € 3,50
dog	€ 2,00

www.la-bretonniere.com

Saint Julien-des-Landes

Castel Camping Caravaning la Garangeoire

F-85150 Saint Julien-des-Landes (Vendée) T: 02 51 46 65 39. E: info@garangeoire.com

alanrogers.com/FR85040

La Garangeoire is a stunning campsite, situated some 15 km. inland near the village of St Julien-des-Landes. Set in 200 ha. of parkland surrounding the small château of La Garangeoire of which there is an outstanding view as you approach through the gates. With a spacious, relaxed atmosphere, the main camping areas are on either side of the old road which is edged with mature trees. The 357 pitches, all named after birds, are individually hedged, some with shade. They are well spaced and are especially large (most 150-200 sq.m), most with electricity (8A) and some with water and drainage also.

Facilities

Ample, first class sanitary facilities. All have washbasins in cabins. Facilities for babies and disabled visitors. Laundry facilities. Motorcaravan service point. Shop, full restaurant and takeaway (10/5-22/9) with bars and terrace (all season). Pool complex with a new covered pool, water slides, fountains and a children's pool. Play field with play equipment. Games room. Tennis courts. Bicycle hire. Minigolf. Archery. Riding (July/Aug). Fishing and boating. Bouncy castle. Trampolines. Quadricycles (on payment). Off site: Golf 10 km. Beaches 15 km.

Open: 9 April - 24 September.

Directions

Site is signed from St Julien; entrance is to the east off the D21 road, 2.5 km. north of St Julien-des-Landes. GPS: 46.66387, -1.71346

Charges 2011

Per unit incl. 2 persons and electricity	€ 17,50 - € 37,00
extra person	€ 4,50 - € 7,90
child (under 10 yrs)	€ 2,50 - € 4,30
dog	€ 3,00 - € 4,00

Camping Cheques accepted.

For latest campsite news, availability and prices visit

alanrogers.com

Saint Julien-des-Landes

Village de la Guyonnière

La Guyonnière, F-85150 Saint Julien-des-Landes (Vendée) T: 02 51 46 62 59. E: info@laguyonniere.com

alanrogers.com/FR85260

La Guyonnière is a spacious, rural site. It is Dutch owned but English is spoken and all visitors are made very welcome. The pitches are arranged on eight different fields, each being reasonably level and seven having a toilet block. There are 270 mostly large pitches (225 sq.m) with a mix of sun and shade. Some are open, others are separated by a tree and a few bushes. All have access to electricity connections and 86 are occupied by mobile homes and chalets. A new pool complex includes an outdoor pool with a 'wild water river' and a heated indoor pool with a waterfall. Bar and restaurant facilities are housed in original farm buildings attractively converted. Entertainment is provided in the bar on high season evenings. This is a perfect place for families, with large play areas on sand and grass, and a paddling pond with shower. Visitors with disabilities are made especially welcome with a range of facilities (for example, a lift in the pool and special scooters to rent). Being in the country, it is a ideal for cyclists and walkers with many signed routes from the site. A pleasant 500 m. walk takes you to the Jaunay lake where fishing is possible (permits from the village), canoeing (life jackets from reception) and pedaloes to hire. There are no tour operators and, needless to say, no road noise. This site is popular for many reasons, the main one being the relaxed atmosphere.

Facilities

Modern toilet blocks. Most cubicles are quite small. Washbasins are in cubicles. Provision for disabled visitors (including lift in the pool, scooters to rent). Laundry facilities. Shop. Bar with TV and pool table (both 1/5-15/9). Restaurant (15/6-15/9). Pizzeria with takeaway (1/5-29/9). New pool complex with outdoor pool and 'wild water river' and covered pool with waterfall. Paddling pool. Play areas, sand pit. Tennis. Bicycle hire. Car wash. WiFi. Off site: Riding 3 km. Golf 8 km. Beaches 10 km.

Open: 25 April - 25 September.

Directions

Site is signed off the D12 road (La Mothe Achard - St Gilles Croix-de-Vie), about 4 km. west of St Julien-des-Landes. The site is about 1 km. from the main road. GPS: 46.65273, -1.74987

Charges 2011

Per unit incl. 2 persons	
and electricity	€ 18,00 - € 36,90
extra person	€ 4,90 - € 6,00
child (3-9 yrs)	€ 3,30 - € 3,90
animal	€ 3,50

Less 10-20% outside high season.

For latest campsite news, availability and prices visit

alanrogers.com

Saint Laurent-sur-Sèvre

Camping le Rouge Gorge

route de la verrie, F-85290 Saint Laurent-sur-Sèvre (Vendée) T: 02 51 67 86 39
E: campinglerougegorge@wanadoo.fr alanrogers.com/FR85890

A family run site, Le Rouge-Gorge is open all year. There are 72 touring pitches, plus some units for rent and privately owned caravans and chalets. The site does accept a small number of workers' units. Slightly sloping and undulating pitches are on grass in a garden-like setting and a small wildlife pond (fenced) is in the centre of the site. It would make a suitable base from which to visit the spectacles of Puy de Fou and the steam railway which runs from Mortagne-sur-Sèvre to Les Herbiers. This is also an excellent stop-over for those heading to and from southern France and Spain, or the ski-resorts. Two similar nicely fitted toilet blocks (only one heated and open in low season), and a small (16 x 8 m) fenced and gated outdoor pool. A small epicerie has bread and basic foods.

Facilities

Two toilet blocks, one can be heated, with washbasins in cubicles and facilities for disabled campers and babies. Laundry with washing machine and dryer. Motorcaravan service point. Bar and shop (bread and basic provisions) (1/7-31/8). Takeaway (15/6-15/9). Swimming pool (1/6-30/9). Some low key family entertainment in high season. Boules. Charcoal barbecues are not permitted. TV room. WiFi. Off site: Fishing 500 m. Riding 2 km. Steam railway passes close to site.

Open: All year.

Directions

Saint Laurent-sur-Sèvre is about 10 km. due south of Cholet, just south of the N149. Site is on D111 west of town towards la Verrie, entrance at top of hill on right. GPS: 46.9585115, -0.9033567

Charges guide

Per unit incl. 2 persons	
and electricity	€ 17,00 - € 26,00
extra person	€ 3,90
child (under 10 yrs)	€ 2,50
dog	€ 1,75

Talmont-Saint Hilaire

Yelloh! Village le Littoral

Le Porteau, F-85440 Talmont-Saint-Hilaire (Vendée) T: 02 51 22 04 64. E: info@campinglelittoral.com
alanrogers.com/FR85250

One hundred metres from the sea, five minutes from Les Sables d'Olonne, Le Littoral is situated on the South Vendée coast. It has been fully modernised over recent years by the Boursin family. The site's 483 pitches are mainly used for mobile homes and chalets, but there are 80 touring pitches, hedged, of a good size and all with water, electricity and drainage. The site has a heated outdoor pool complex with outdoor and indoor pools. The minimarket, bar and restaurant are open all season with frequent themed evenings and lots of entertainment and activities in high season. There is direct access from the site to a spectacular cove with wonderful sea views.

Facilities

Three sanitary blocks have both British and Turkish style WCs, showers and washbasins in cubicles. Baby rooms. Facilities for disabled visitors. Laundry facilities. Fridge hire. Shop, bar, restaurant and takeaway, pizzeria and crêperie. Indoor pool (all open all season). Outdoor pool complex with slides (14/5-10/9). Bicycle hire. Multisport court. Tennis. Excellent play areas. Games room with TV. Club for younger children (all season). Activities, entertainment and excursions. July/Aug and holiday weekends. Internet access and free WiFi in bar area. Minibus to beach and town. Off site: Sea fishing 200 m. Riding 500 m. Beach 3 km. Sailing 5 km. Golf 10 km.

Open: 2 April - 12 September.

Directions

From La Roche sur Yon on A87/D160 turn east on Ring Road and continue on D949 towards Talmont. Soon after end of dual carriageway site is signed to the south opposite a market garden; in 3.5 km turn right to site in 300 m. GPS: 46.451633, -1.702017

Charges guide

Per unit incl. 2 persons	
and electricity	€ 15,00 - € 40,00
extra person	€ 5,00 - € 6,00
child (3-7 yrs)	free - € 6,00
dog	€ 4,00

For latest campsite news, availability and prices visit

alanrogers.com

On the Atlantic coast, between the châteaux of the Loire Valley and the Bordeaux vineyards, lies Poitou-Charentes, one of the sunniest parts of the French western coast. Its mild climate – 2,250 hours of sunshine per year – makes it popular with visitors from early spring to late autumn.

DÉPARTEMENTS: 16 CHARENTE, 17 CHARENTE-MARITIME, 79 DEUX SÈVRES, 86 VIENNE

MAJOR CITIES: POITIERS, LA ROCHELLE, COGNAC

Three hundred miles of coastline with fine sandy beaches backed by fragrant pine forests, lively resorts such as La Rochelle and Royan, and the islands of Oléron, Aix and Ré attract many holiday makers, particularly the French themselves. The scenery inland is in marked contrast: vast horizons and wooded valleys, the vineyards of Cognac, the Poitou fens and Marais Poitevin, the soothing tranquility of canals, the valley of Vienne and the foothills of Charente.

Farming is important to the economy; wheat, corn and cattle are raised. Industries produce machinery, chemicals and dairy products. The region is renowned as the home of Cognac – such famous names as Martell, Hennessy and Rémy Martin line the river Charente around the towns of Cognac and Jarnac where the spirit is distilled.

The capital of the region and capital of the Vienne département, is the city of Poitier. Situated on high ground at the confluence of the Clain and Boivre rivers, the city commands the so-called gate of Poitou, a gap 44 miles (71 km) wide between the mountains south of the Loire River and the Massif Central that serves as the connecting link between northern and southern France.

Places of interest

Angoulême: hilltop town surrounded by ramparts, cathedral, Renaissance château.

Cognac: the most celebrated 'eau de vie' in the world, cellars, Valois castle.

Marais Poitevin: marshes also known as the 'Green Venice'.

Poitiers: Palais de Justice, Notre Dame la Grande Romanesque church, old city.

La Rochelle: port, Porte de la Grosse Horloge (clock gate), Museum of the New World.

Saint Savin: 17th-century abbey, mural painting.

Cuisine of the region

Fish predominates, both fresh water (eel, trout, pike) and sea water (shrimps, mussels, oysters).

Bouilliture (bouilleture): eel stew with shallots and prunes in Sauvignon white wine.

Boulaigou: thick sweet or savoury pancake.

Bréjaude: cabbage, leek and bacon soup.

Cagouilles: snails from Charente.

Casserons en matelote: squid in red wine sauce with garlic and shallots.

Farcidure: a dumpling (poached or sautéed).

Farci Poitevin: paté of cabbage, spinach and sorrel, encased in cabbage leaves.

Mouclade: mussels cooked in wine, egg yolks and cream, served with Pineau des Charentes.

www.visit-poitou-charentes.com
crt@poitou-charentes-vacances.com
(0)5 49 50 10 50

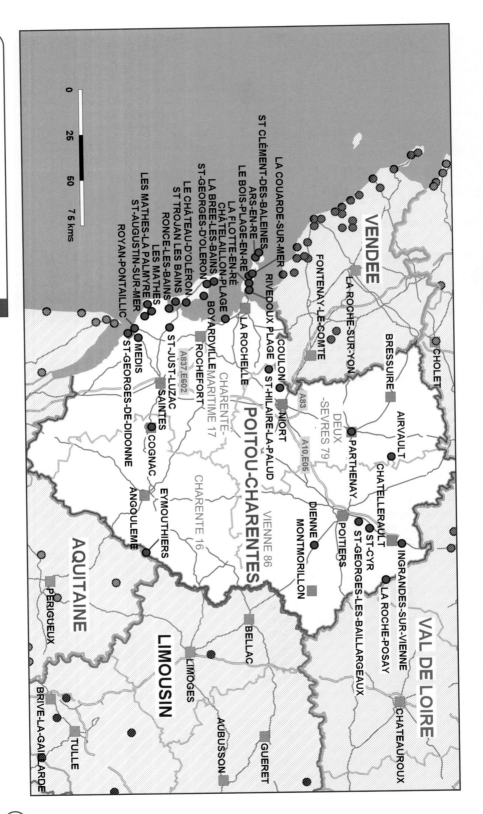

For latest campsite news, availability and prices visit

alanrogers.com

Ars-en-Ré

Camping le Cormoran

Route de Radia, Ars-en-Ré, F-17590 Ile de Ré (Charente-Maritime) T: 05 46 29 46 04. E: info@cormoran.com
alanrogers.com/FR17260

On the outskirts of Ars-en-Re, Le Cormoran offers a quiet rural holiday. Touring pitches vary in size and are a mixture of sand and grass. Large units may be advised to call ahead. There are 33 pitches for touring units (all with 10A electricity) and the clean sanitary facilities are a mix of modern and traditional. A small comfortable bar and restaurant are located next to the pleasant pool. Being close to the local oyster beds and with numerous cycle paths which include routes through a nature reserve this campsite is popular with families of all ages. Although rural, the campsite is only 500 m. from the sea. During July and August children's clubs and evening entertainment are organised. The village of Ars-en-Ré is only 800 m. away and a local market is held regularly during the season.

Facilities

One traditional toilet block and one modern unit provide good facilities. Washbasins are mainly in cabins. Provision for disabled visitors. Laundry. Motorcaravan services. Bar, restaurant and takeaway meals (4/4-15/9). Swimming pool (unheated). Fitness centre. Tennis. Games room. Play area. Entertainment programme in high season. Bicycle hire. WiFi. Off site: Nearest beach 500 m. Ars-en-Ré 800 m. Fishing 500 m. Boat launching 1 km. Riding 3 km. Golf 10 km.

Open: 4 April - 26 September.

Directions

Cross the toll bridge from La Rochelle onto the Ile de Ré and continue on D735 to Ars-en-Ré from where site is well signed. GPS: 46.21121, -1.5298

Charges guide

Per unit incl. 2 persons	
and electricity	€ 23,00 - € 48,70
extra person	€ 5,50 - € 12,25
child (1-9 yrs)	€ 3,50 - € 12,25
dog	€ 2,80 - € 5,70

For latest campsite news, availability and prices visit
alanrogers.com

Airvault

Camping de Courte Vallée

8 rue de Courte Vallée, F-79600 Airvault (Deux-Sèvres) T: 05 49 64 70 65. E: camping@caravanningfrance.com

alanrogers.com/FR79020

This small and beautifully landscaped site is family run. Set in 10 acres of parkland close to the Thouet river, it is within walking distance of Airvault (the birthplace of Voltaire). In the heart of rural France and off the main tourist tracks, the site offers tranquility and a warm and friendly atmosphere in surroundings maintained to the highest standards. There are 64 grass pitches, many with electricity, water and drainage which makes the site ideal for a long stay to explore the area. Nearby are Puy du Fou, Fontevraud Abbey, Doué la Fontaine zoo and the châteaux of Saumur and Oiron.

Facilities

A modern unisex block has spacious cubicles for showers and washbasins, and shower and WC cubicles for disabled visitors, all kept to a very high standard of cleanliness. Laundry facilities. Reception sells frites, snacks, a selection of beers and wine and ice cream. Internet access. Swimming pool. Boules. Play area. Caravan storage. Wine tasting events and barbecues. Coffee bar. Off site: Airvault (birthplace of Voltaire) is a 10-15 minute walk. Fishing 300 m. Riding 8 km.

Open: 15 March - 31 October.

Directions

From D938 (Parthenay-Thouars) take D725 Airvault. On approaching village turn left over bridge. At the T-junction turn sharp left, second exit at roundabout, left at junction to site on left. Note: caravans are not allowed in village. GPS: 46.833056, -0.148333

Charges 2011

Per unit incl. 2 persons	€ 29,00 - € 33,00
extra person	€ 7,00 - € 8,00
No credit cards.	

Boyardville

Camping Signol

121 avenue des Albatros, F-17190 Boyardville (Charente-Maritime) T: 05 46 47 01 22. E: contact@signol.com

alanrogers.com/FR17600

Occupying an 8 hectare site, just 800 metres from the sandy beaches, this campsite has plenty to offer. Of the 300 pitches, 107 are for touring and are set amongst high pine trees and one metre high hedges give plenty of shade and privacy; some have sea views. The pitches are generous (80-120 sq.m) although access to some is tight and may not be suitable for larger units. Levelling blocks are required on some. Electricity (6A) is available to all, although long leads are required occasionally as hook-ups can be shared between three or four pitches. There may be a short walk to the water supply.

Facilities

Three modern, fully equipped toilet blocks provide washbasins and showers in cubicles. They also include facilities for visitors with disabilities, and for children. Laundry. Motorcaravan services. No shop. Bar/snack bar, terrace, takeaway, breakfast service. Two swimming pools (21/5-24/9). Play area. Boules. Children's club and evening entertainment (from 1/7). WiFi. Dogs are not accepted in July/Aug. No barbecues (communal area provided). Mobile homes and chalets to hire. Off site: Beach 800 m. Sailing and windsurfing. Fishing. Riding. Cycle and walking trails.

Open: 1 May - 12 September.

Directions

Cross the viaduct and continue on the D26 to Dolus and turn right on D126 signed Boyardville. Continue on this road for 6 km. until the canal bridge at the edge of the town. Cross bridge and turn immediately sharp right along the quayside. Site signed from here. GPS: 45.96807, -1.24456

Charges guide

Per unit incl. 2 persons	
and electricity	€ 22,00 - € 34,60
extra person	€ 5,00 - € 8,50
Credit cards accepted.	

Cognac

Camping de Cognac

Boulevard de Châtenay, route de Sainte-Sévère, F-16100 Cognac (Charente) T: 05 45 32 13 32
E: info@campingdecognac.com **alanrogers.com/FR16050**

Situated close to the historic town of Cognac, this municipal site is set in a rural area next to the Charente river. It has 168 pitches, 160 for touring caravans and 8 mobile homes which are all available for rent. All have 6A electricity and a water tap but no drain. The pitches are separated by shrubs and hedging, and access for large units on this site is good with tarmac or gravel roads all around. This area is naturally very suitable for people who enjoy brandy, with all the famous Cognac houses offering tours for visitors to see how the drink is made and learn of its history.

Facilities

Two well equipped, fairly modern toilet blocks (access by steps) include children's toilets and washing machines. Separate ground level facilities for disabled visitors. Motorcaravan services. Small swimming pool. Shop. Snack bar and takeaway. Fishing. Play area. Minigolf. Double axle caravans not accepted. Off site: Bicycle hire 2 km. Riverside walks. Town 2.3 km. Golf 5 km.

Open: 26 April - 30 September.

Directions

Site is to the north of the town beside the river on the D24 to St Sévère. GPS: 45.70916, -0.31289

Charges guide

Per unit incl. 2 persons	
and electricity	€ 13,00 - € 20,00
extra person	€ 4,00 - € 5,50
child (2-12 yrs)	€ 3,50 - € 4,00
Less for stays over 7 days.	

For latest campsite news, availability and prices visit

alanrogers.com

Châtelaillon-Plage

Camping Au Port-Punay

Allée Bernard Moreau, les Boucholeurs, F-17340 Châtelaillon-Plage (Charente-Maritime)
T: 05 46 56 01 53. E: contact@camping-port-punay.com alanrogers.com/FR17340

Au Port-Punay is a friendly, well run site just 200 metres from the beach and 3 km. from the centre of the resort of Chatelaillon-Plage. There are 136 touring pitches laid out on well trimmed grass, with many mature poplars and low shrubs. The site has a well stocked shop, open all season and a small bar and restaurant open mid June - mid September. A heated swimming pool has a separate gated area for paddling. There is a good range of activities available and in high season some entertainment is arranged. This is a family run site (Famille Moreau) and the son of the family speaks excellent English, as does his Dutch wife. Rochefort to the south and La Rochelle to the north are well worth a visit (buses from outside the site), as is the nearby town of Châtelaillon-Plage, which has an all-year covered market and, in summer, a street market every day. Au Port-Punay has just one large toilet block, centrally positioned on the site, with very good facilities.

Facilities

One large toilet block with good facilities including washbasins in cubicles and large shower cubicles. Facilities for disabled visitors and babies. Washing machines. Shop. Bar, restaurant and takeaway (15/6-12/9). Swimming pool (heated May-Sept). Games area. Play area. Bicycle hire. Internet access. WiFi. Off site: Beach 200 m. Châtelaillon-Plage 3 km. by road, 1.5 km. along the seafront on foot or bike. Buses to Rochefort and La Rochelle from outside site. Riding 2 km. Golf 10 km.

Open: 22 April - 25 September.

Directions

From N137 (La Rochelle - Rochefort) take exit for Châtelaillon-Plage. At first roundabout follow sign for town centre. At 2nd roundabout turn left. Follow signs to site at seaside hamlet of Les Boucholeurs. Drive to the sea wall then turn left through village to site. The road has traffic-calming measures and can be narrow in places. GPS: 46.05480, -1.08340

Charges guide

Per unit incl. 2 persons	
and electricity	€ 20,90 - € 32,00
extra person	€ 4,90 - € 5,90
child (0-3 yrs)	€ 3,30 - € 4,30

Coulon

Camping de la Venise Verte

178 route des Bords de Sèvre, F-79510 Coulon (Deux-Sèvres) T: 05 49 35 90 36
E: accueil@camping-laveniseverte.fr alanrogers.com/FR79040

This family run site on the edge of the Sevre Nortaise and the Marais Poitevin is ideal for short or long stays. With canoe and bicycle hire on site you have no excuse for not exploring the local area. In the Deux-Sèvres, the department of discovery, so named because it has two rivers named Sevre, the Noirtaise and Nantaise, the Venise Verte provides an excellent site. There are 140 flat pitches here with 100 used for touring units, the remainder occupied by mobile homes. The pitches are of a good size, all with 10A electricity, water and drainage and with some shade. A Sites et Paysages member.

Facilities

Modern toilet facilities are of a high standard with free showers. Washing machine and dryer. Motorcaravan services. Restaurant/bar. Takeaway on request. Swimming pool (1/7-31/8). Play area. Bicycle and canoe hire. Boules area. Barbecues are not permitted. Off site: Coulon 1.0 km. and boat trips in the Marais. Ideal for walking, fishing, cycling or canoeing. Fishing 200 m. Golf and riding 15 km.

Open: 1 April - 30 October.

Directions

From Niort take N11 towards La Rochelle. Turn on the D3 towards Sansais and then north on D1 (Coulon). At traffic lights head towards 'centre ville' (Coulon) at mini-roundabout turn slightly right. Follow Sevre Noirtaise for 1.5 km. to site right. GPS: 46.31492, -0.60835

Charges guide

Per unit incl. 2 persons	
and electricity	€ 18,00 - € 29,00
extra person	€ 4,00 - € 6,00

For latest campsite news, availability and prices visit
alanrogers.com

Dienné

Camping Domaine de Dienné

F-86410 Dienné (Vienne) T: 05 49 45 87 63. E: info@domaine-de-dienne.fr

alanrogers.com/FR86120

This is without doubt a wonderful site and unique in what it offers. It concentrates on your well being and provides all the facilities you could wish for in achieving that aim. The site extends over 47 hectares but there are just 30 pitches for touring units and these are on large generous plots of 250 sq.m. All have their own water supply, drainage and 10A electricity and access for even the largest of units will not cause a problem. The accommodation to rent includes gypsy style caravans, tree houses, yurts, a gite and cottages, which are all of superb quality and again on large plots. Domaine de Dienne cannot fail to impress from the moment you arrive.

Facilities

Restaurant. Heated swimming pools. Health and fitness centre. Hairdressing salon. Horse riding centre. Mountain biking. Adventure park. Climbing tower. Children's games. Walking trails. Fishing. Cooking lessons. WiFi. Off site: Poitiers airport 25 km. Futuroscope. Crocodile Planet. Monkey Park. Historical sites and castles.

Open: All year.

Directions

From Poitiers take the N147 towards Limoges. After the village of Fleure the site is well signed. GPS: 46.445028, 0.559294

Charges guide

Per unit incl. 2 persons and electricity	€ 25,00 - € 43,00

Eymouthiers

Castel Camping les Gorges du Chambon

Eymouthiers, F-16220 Montbron (Charente) T: 05 45 70 71 70. E: info@gorgesduchambon.fr

alanrogers.com/FR16020

This is a wonderful Castels site with 28 hectares of protected natural environment to be enjoyed in the rolling Perigord Vert countryside. The 90 pitches are extremely generous in size (150 sq.m), mostly level and enjoy a mixture of sunshine and shade. There are 85 with water and 10A electricity, the remaining five are fully serviced. The spaciousness is immense, with fine walks through the woodlands and around the grounds. Flora, fauna and wildlife are as nature intended. Here you can feel at peace and enjoy precious moments of quiet. There has been much work done with the ecology association. The songs of the birds can be heard against the backdrop of water flowing gently down a small river on one side of the campsite. The different types of birds that can be found here are numerous. Guided walks are a feature. Les Gorges du Chambon is arranged around a restored Charentaise farmhouse and its outbuildings. A converted barn provides space for the restaurant and bar and the food is excellent, at a reasonable price. There is a pleasant swimming pool together with a paddling pool. There is also a sand beach area along the river and canoes can be hired on the site. The site owners are friendly and very helpful and want you to enjoy your time at their site.

Facilities

Traditional style blocks include facilities for disabled visitors. Laundry facilities. Basic shop. Bar, restaurant and takeaway (all season). Swimming pool, children's pool. Play area. Games room, TV and library with English books. Tennis. Archery. Minigolf. Bicycle and canoe hire. Organised activities July/Aug, children's club, youth disco, teenagers' corner. Internet access. Dogs are not accepted. Off site: Private fishing (free) 6 km, with licence 200 m. Golf 6 km. Riding 6 km. Sailing 20 km. Visits are organised to local producers and day trips (low season).

Open: 23 April - 17 September.

Directions

From N141 Angoulême - Limoges road at Rochefoucauld take D6 to Montbron village. Follow D6 in direction of Piegut-Pluviers and site is signed to the north on D163 on entering La Tricherie. GPS: 45.6598, 0.557667

Charges 2011

Per unit incl. 2 persons and electricity	€ 18,40 - € 31,90
Camping Cheques accepted.	

Ingrandes-sur-Vienne

Castel Camping le Petit Trianon

Saint-Ustre, 1 rue du Moulin de Saint-Ustre, F-86220 Ingrandes-sur-Vienne (Vienne) T: 05 49 02 61 47
E: chateau@petit-trianon.fr alanrogers.com/FR86010

A family-owned site for many years, Le Petit Trianon is situated halfway between Tours and Poitiers. It enjoys a countryside position within the lovely grounds of an 18th century château. Visitors to the site often return several times after their first visit for the calm and tranquil atmosphere here. There are 99 pitches all with electricity (10A), set in seven hectares which gives a real sense of spaciousness. Plants are well tended and shade is provided in parts by the many attractive trees. Access around the site is good and large units are accepted by prior arrangement.

Facilities	Directions
The sanitary facilities include washbasins in cabins, some washbasin and shower units, baby baths, washing machines and dryer. Facilities for disabled visitors. Motorcaravan service point. Shop. Snack bar. Takeaway. Heated swimming pool and paddling pool. Playground. Minigolf. Badminton, croquet, volleyball and boules. Satellite TV. Reading room. Bicycle hire. Bread making. Internet access. WiFi. Caravan storage. Off site: Restaurant 50 m. Tennis 2 km. Fishing 3 km. Riding 15 km. Local markets. Futuroscope.	Take the N10 to Ingrandes sur Vienne and take the D75 in the direction of Oyre. Follow D121 to St Ustre (1.5 km) and site is then well signed. GPS: 46.885533, 0.586133

Open: 20 May - 20 September.

Charges guide

Per person	€ 7,00
child (3-6 yrs)	€ 3,50
pitch incl. electricity (5/10A) and vehicle	€ 12,40 - € 12,80
dog	€ 2,10

La Brée-les-Bains

Camping Antioche d'Oléron

Route de Proires, F-17840 La Brée-les-Bains (Charente-Maritime) T: 05 46 47 92 00
E: info@camping-antiochedoleron.com alanrogers.com/FR17570

Situated to the northeast of the island, Camping Antioche is quietly located within a five minute walk of the beach. There are 130 pitches, of which 73 are occupied by mobile homes and 57 are for touring units. The pitches are set amongst attractive shrubs and palm trees and all have electricity (10A), water and a drain. A new pool area which comprises two swimming pools (heated), two jacuzzis, two paddling pools and a raised sunbathing deck, is beautifully landscaped with palms and flowers. A small bar, restaurant and takeaway offer reasonably priced food and drinks. The site becomes livelier in season with regular evening entertainment and activities for all the family. With specially prepared trails for cycling, oyster farms and salt flats to visit, the Ile d'Oléron offers something for everyone. Bresnais market, selling local produce and products, is within easy access on foot and is held daily in high season.

Facilities	Directions
The single sanitary block is of a good standard and is kept clean and fresh. Facilities for disabled visitors. Laundry. Motorcaravan services. Bar, restaurant and snack bar (weekends only May and June, daily July/Aug). Swimming and paddling pools. Games room. Play area. WiFi. Bicycle hire (July/Aug). Off site: Beach 150 m. Fishing 150 m. Riding 1.5 km. Golf 7 km.	Cross the bridge on the D26 and join the D734. After St Georges turn right onto the D273E1 towards La Brée-les-Baines. At T-junction turn left from where the campsite is signed. GPS: 46.02007, -1.35764

Open: 1 April - 30 September.

Charges guide

Per unit incl. 2 persons and electricity	€ 21,15 - € 35,15
extra person	€ 7,10
child (1-14 yrs)	€ 3,70
dog	€ 4,00

For latest campsite news, availability and prices visit

alanrogers.com

La Couarde-sur-Mer

Camping la Tour des Prises

Route d'Ars, F-17670 La Couarde-sur-Mer (Charente-Maritime) T: 05 46 29 84 82. E: camping@lesprises.com

alanrogers.com/FR17630

La Tour des Prises is a friendly, family site close to the village of La Couarde-sur-Mer on the southern side of the Ile de Ré. There are 140 pitches here, around 50 of which are occupied by fully equipped mobile homes and chalets (available for rent). The 88 touring pitches are of a good size and are mostly equipped with electricity (16A). The site is just 600 m. from a fine sandy beach, the plage des Prises. Cycling is particularly popular on the island, thanks to the quality and extent of its cycle tracks, one of which passes adjacent to the site. English is spoken at reception. On-site amenities include a covered swimming pool, a shop and takeaway pizzas. La Couarde is a pleasant resort with 5 km. of beaches, backed by dunes and a pine forest.

Facilities

Two unisex toilet blocks provide good facilities and are kept clean and fresh, with washbasins in cubicles and seatless WCs. Baby room and facilities for visitors with disabilities. Laundry. Basic motorcaravan service point. No bar/restaurant or takeaway. Pizza van (Tues, Thurs and Sun). Small shop (1/6-15/9). Heated, covered swimming pool. Children's pool. Adult entertainment and children's club in high season. WiFi (free). Games room. Play area. Bicycle hire. Tourist information. Mobile homes and chalets to rent. No barbecues or washing lines.
Off site: Nearest beach 600 m. Fishing 600 m. Sailing 1 km. Walking and cycling tracks. Ecomuseum. Riding.

Open: 1 April - 30 September.

Directions

From La Rochelle, cross the toll bridge to the Ile de Ré (D735) and follow signs to St Martin and then La Couarde-sur-Mer. Do not tow/drive through village. Stay on D375 towards Ars-en-Ré. After 3 km. follow site signs on your right.
GPS: 46.204451, -1.446301

Charges guide

Per unit incl. 2 persons	
and electricity	€ 20,20 - € 40,20
extra person	€ 3,70 - € 8,20
child (0-7 yrs)	€ 2,57 - € 4,70
dog	€ 1,20 - € 3,00

La Flotte-en-Ré

527

Camping la Grainetière

Route de Saint Martin, F-17630 La Flotte-en-Ré (Charente-Maritime) T: 05 46 09 68 86
E: la-grainetiere@orange.fr alanrogers.com/FR17280

A truly friendly welcome awaits you from the owners, Isabelle and Eric, at La Grainetière. It is a peaceful campsite set in almost three hectares of pine trees which provide some shade for the 65 touring pitches of various shapes and sizes. There are also 50 well-spaced chalets for rent. Some pitches are suitable for units up to seven metres (these should be booked in advance). There are no hedges for privacy and the pitches are sandy with some grass. Ample new water points and electricity (10A) hook-ups (Euro plugs) serve the camping area. The site is well lit.

Facilities

The unisex sanitary block is first class, with washbasins in cubicles, showers, British style WCs, facilities for children and visitors with disabilities. Shop. Takeaway. New swimming pool (heated all season) and jacuzzi. Bicycle hire. Fridge hire. TV room. Charcoal barbecues are not permitted. Off site: Beach and sailing 2 km. Bar and restaurant 2 km. Fishing and boat launching 2 km. Riding 3 km. Golf 10 km.

Open: 1 April - 30 September.

Directions

Follow camping signs from La Flotte, 1 km. from the village. GPS: 46.18755, -1.344933

Charges guide

Per unit incl. 2 persons	
and electricity	€ 19,00 - € 30,00
extra person	€ 5,00 - € 7,50
child (0-7 yrs)	€ 2,50 - € 3,50
dog	€ 2,50 - € 3,00

La Grainetière

Between St. Martin harbor and la Flotte. All kinds of shops at proximity. Isabelle and Eric welcome you in a wooded park. Friendly family atmosphere.

Route de Saint Martin - 17630 La Flotte - Ile de Ré - France - Tel: 0033 (0)5 46 09 68 86
Fax: 0033 (0)5 46 09 53 13 - lagrainetiere@orange.fr - www.la-grainetiere.com

For latest campsite news, availability and prices visit

alanrogers.com

La Roche-Posay

Camping le Riveau

Route de Lesigny, F-86270 La Roche-Posay (Vienne) T: 05 49 86 21 23. E: info@camping-le-riveau.com

alanrogers.com/FR86050

Camping Le Riveau is set in 8 hectares and has direct access to the Creuse river on which fishing and canoes are popular. There are 200 pitches, of which 30 are used for mobile homes to rent. The touring pitches include 19 with hardstanding, ideal for motorcaravans and with services nearby. Access around the site is good for larger units. The pitches are all large and 16A electricity is available. This is a good, well run site in very natural surroundings. There is a sense of spaciousness at this site where you can relax in a convivial atmosphere.

Facilities

Two fully equipped, heated toilet blocks, one in each section. Excellent facilities for disabled visitors and children. Bar and snack bar. Swimming and paddling pools. Play area. Games room. Fishing. Canoes. Boules. Riding. Barbecues are not permitted. Entertainment in high season. Off site: Shops, restaurants, etc. 1 km. Golf 3 km.

Open: 2 April - 16 October.

Directions

Site is signed from the D725 town bypass, turning north at roundabout onto D5 towards Lesigny. Site is 50 m. on right. GPS: 46.799646, 0.80945

Charges 2011

Per unit incl. 2 persons and electricity	€ 16,90 - € 22,30
extra person	€ 4,00 - € 5,40

No credit cards.

Le Bois Plage en Ré

Campéole les Amis de la Plage

F-17580 Le Bois Plage en Ré (Charente-Maritime) T: 05 46 09 24 01. E: es-amis-de-la-plage@campeole.com

alanrogers.com/FR17610

Les Amis de la Plage, a former municipal site, is now a member of the Campéole group and located on the southern side of the Ile de Ré, at Le Bois Plage-en-Ré. The site has direct access to a superb sandy beach (across sand dunes). This is a large site with 243 pitches, some of which are occupied by mobile homes, chalets and fully equipped tents. The 169 touring pitches are sandy with varying degrees of shade (some are rather small). Most have electrical connections (10A). There is a small shop on site for essentials, as well as a snack bar/pizzeria, and the island's largest market is held daily, just 500 m. from the site. The Ile de Ré is well known for its cycle tracks and a number of these pass close to the site. It has to be the best way to explore the island (rental service close to site). We also recommend the Maison du Platin, an interesting ecomuseum, dedicated to the Ile de Ré's heritage and traditions. Back on the mainland, a visit to La Rochelle is a must, with its unique maritime heritage and stunning architecture. A small electric bus provides a free daily service to Amis de la Plage.

Facilities

Three toilet blocks (one closed low season) provide some washbasins in cubicles and facilities for disabled visitors and children. Laundry. Motorcaravan service point. No shop, but bread to order daily. Play area with bouncy castle. Boules. Table tennis. Activity and entertainment programme (high season). Tourist information. Direct access to beach. Communal Barbeque area. Mobile homes, chalets and tents for rent. WiFi (charged). Off site: Swimming pool and Bar/restaurant near site entrance (charged). Market 500 m. Bicycle hire 1 km. Riding 3km. Cycle and walking tracks. Tennis. Canoeing (on the island's marshes).

Open: 1 April - 30 September.

Directions

From La Rochelle, cross the toll bridge and take D201 along the southern coast of the island until you reach Le Bois Plage-en-Ré, and then follow signs to the campsite. GPS: 46.177401, -1.386514

Charges guide

Per unit incl. 2 persons and electricity	€ 16,60 - € 23,10
extra person	€ 3,50 - € 5,50
child (2-6 yrs)	free - € 3,30
dog	€ 2,00

Le Bois-Plage-en-Ré

Camping Club de la Bonne Etoile

Route de Gros Joncs á Saint-Martin, F-17580 Le Bois-Plage-en-Ré (Charente-Maritime) T: 05 46 09 10 16
E: camping-bonne-etoile@wanadoo.fr alanrogers.com/FR17510

La Bonne Etoile lies close to the centre of the Ile de Ré and is just 1 km. from a sandy beach. This site is open for most of the year and offers a range of mobile homes and chalets to rent as well as 6 sandy grass touring pitches. All have 10A electricity. The site is not recommended for very large units (over 7 m). This is a lively site in peak season with regular discos and karaoke evenings along with various games and competitions. Both the indoor and outdoor swimming pools are heated all season (April-November). A bar and restaurant located beside the pool area offer good, reasonably priced food and drink. There are over 87 km. of cycle tracks, several of which run close to the site.

Facilities

Two old traditional sanitary blocks offer basic facilities. Small shop (all year). Restaurant/bar. Takeaway (April-Sept). Swimming pool. Play area. Games room. TV room. Internet access and WiFi. Off site: Sandy beach 1 km. Cycle trails. Fishing.

Open: 20 January - 31 December.

Directions

After toll bridge turn left on the D735. Continue for 10 km. and at roudabout turn right onto the D201E2. After 300 m. turn right at campsite sign. Site is at the end of the road.
GPS: 46.182252, -1.369536

Charges guide

Per unit incl. 2 persons and electricity	€ 21,50 - € 43,50
extra person	€ 4,70 - € 7,00
child (under 7 yrs)	€ 2,60 - € 4,50
dog	€ 5,00

Le Château-d'Oléron

Airotel Oléron

Domaine de Montravail, F-17480 Le Château-d'Oléron (Charente-Maritime) T: 05 46 47 61 82
E: info@camping-airotel-oleron.com alanrogers.com/FR17060

This family run site on the outskirts of Le Château d'Oléron has very good facilities, including a superb equestrian centre, a full range of sporting activites and an attractive heated pool complex. This is a mature site with about 210 pitches of a good size, with varying degrees of shade provided by trees and shrubs. It is well laid out and most of the 70 touring pitches have electricity (10A), 4 with individual water and drainage. The remaining pitches are used for mobile homes of which 70 are for rent. A full entertainment programme is provided in high season. Visitors can enjoy exploring the island with its fine sandy beaches on the Atlantic coast. There are miles of flat tracks on the island for walking, cycling or horse riding. The equestrian centre offers courses up to a week in length for riders ranging from novice to experienced and runs all year round.

Facilities

Two modern toilet blocks with facilities for disabled visitors and babies. Washing machine and dryer. Motorcaravan service point. Shop. Bar, restaurant and takeaway (15/6-15/9). Heated swimming and paddling pools. Equestrian centre. Playground. Multisport court. Tennis. Minigolf. Fishing. Canoe hire. Bicycle hire. TV and games room. Internet access. WiFi. Off site: Supermarket. Local markets. Zoo. Aquarium.

Open: Easter - 30 September.

Directions

Cross the bridge onto the island and continue on D26. At second roundabout turn right, marked Dolus and Le Château. Proceed 500 m. and take first right, marked Campings. Site is 1 km. on the right.
GPS: 45.88207, -1.20648

Charges guide

Per unit incl. 2 persons	€ 13,50 - € 22,00
extra person	€ 4,00 - € 6,50
electricity (8A)	€ 3,90
dog	€ 2,50

For latest campsite news, availability and prices visit

alanrogers.com

Le Château-d'Oléron

Camping la Brande

Route des Huitres, F-17480 Le Château-d'Oléron (Charente-Maritime) T: 05 46 47 62 37
E: info@camping-labrande.com alanrogers.com/FR17220

A quality environmentally-friendly site, run and maintained to the highest standard, La Brande offers an ideal holiday environment on the delightful Ile d'Oléron, famed for its oysters. La Brande is situated on the oyster route and close to a sandy beach. Pitches here are generous and mostly separated by hedges and trees, the greater number for touring outfits. All are on level grassy terrain and have electricity hook-ups, some are fully serviced. The many activities during the high season, plus the natural surroundings, make this an ideal choice for families. A feature of this site is the heated indoor pool (28°) open all season. The Barcat family ensures that their visitors not only enjoy quality facilities, but Gerard Barcat offers guided bicycle tours and canoe trips. This way you discover the nature, oyster farming, vineyards and history of Oléron, which is joined to the mainland by a 3 km. bridge.

Facilities

Three clean sanitary blocks have spacious, well equipped showers and washbasins (mainly in cabins). Baby facilities. Excellent facilities for visitors with disabilities. Private facilities (shower, basin and toilet) to rent. Laundry rooms. Motorcaravan service point. Superb restaurant/takeaway and bar (July/Aug). Shop (July/Aug). Heated indoor swimming pool (all season). Jacuzzi. Sauna. Good playground. Games room. Football field, tennis, minigolf, fishing and archery. Bicycle hire. Canoe hire. Free WiFi. New building for children. Off site: Beach 300 m. Sailing 2 km. Riding 6 km. Golf 7 km.

Open: 20 March - 14 November.

Directions

After crossing bridge to l'Ile d'Oléron turn right towards Château d'Oléron. Continue through village and follow sign for Route des Huitres. Site is on left after 2.5 km. GPS: 45.90415, -1.21525

Charges guide

Per unit incl. 2 persons and electricity	€ 20,00 - € 42,00
extra person	€ 5,00 - € 8,00
dog	€ 3,00

Camping Cheques accepted.

Les Mathes

Camping l'Orée du Bois

225 route de la Bouverie, la Fouasse, F-17570 Les Mathes (Charente-Maritime) T: 05 46 22 42 43
E: info@camping-oree-du-bois.fr alanrogers.com/FR17050

L'Orée du Bois has 388 pitches of about 100 sq.m. in a very spacious, pinewood setting. There are 150 for touring units, mainly scattered amongst the permanent chalets and tents. They include 40 large pitches with hardstanding and individual sanitary facilities. Pitches are on flat, fairly sandy ground, separated by trees, shrubs and hedges and all have electrical connections (6A). The forest pines offer some shade. A family site, a good aqua-park is amongst the amenities. The site is lively in high season when it can be noisy but it is tranquil in low season. The site is used by several tour operators.

Facilities

Four main toilet blocks include some washbasins in cabins. Three have a laundry and facilities for disabled visitors. Shop. Excellent bar, restaurant, crêperie and takeaway service (1/5-13/9). Heated swimming pools (1/5-13/9), water slide and paddling pool (trunks, not shorts). Play areas. Tennis court, boules, football and basketball. Games room and TV lounge. Bicycle hire. Discos. Entertainment in July/Aug. Internet access. Barbecues in special areas only. WiFi. Off site: Riding 300 m. Fishing 4 km. Golf 5 km.

Open: 1 May - 13 September.

Directions

From north follow D14 La Tremblade. At the roundabout before Arvert turn on D268 (Les Mathes, La Palmyre). Site is on the right in Fouasse. From south, at Royan take D25 (La Palmyre). In town turn north to Les Mathes. At first roundabout in Les Mathes follow sign (Fouasse, La Tremblade). Site is on the left after 2 km. GPS: 45.7326, -1.1785

Charges guide

| Per unit incl. 2 persons | € 18,00 - € 50,50 |
| extra person | € 8,00 |

Camping Cheques accepted.

For latest campsite news, availability and prices visit

alanrogers.com

Les Mathes-La Palmyre

Camping la Clé des Champs

1188 route de la Fouasse, F-17570 Les Mathes-La Palmyre (Charente-Maritime) T: 05 46 22 40 53

E: contact@cledeschamps.com **alanrogers.com/FR17540**

Situated on the edge of the large Forêt de la Coubre and around 1.5 km. from the village of Les Mathes, La Clé des Champs has 128 grass touring pitches (90 sq.m). Set amongst avenues of small trees, most have electricity. This quiet campsite is flat, with 167 mobile homes (51 available to rent, the others privately owned) well positioned at the top end of the site. A new toilet block has been added which can be heated in cool weather. The swimming pool can be covered by a polythene stucture in low season and a bar and shop are open from mid-June to September. Various cycle tracks lead through the forest to the beaches of the Côte Sauvage. These stretch for 70 km. and sandy beaches alternate with rocky coves. The nearby zoo at La Palmyre, with over 1,600 animals, is France's second largest. La Palmyre is a stylish resort with many cafes and restaurants, as well as a fine sandy beach.

Facilities

New toilet block, heated in cool weather. Washing machine. Shop. Bar. Snack bar and takeaway (mid June-Sept). Swimming pool. Paddling pool. Games room. Play area. Bicycle hire. Activity and entertainment programme (July/Aug). WiFi. Mobile homes for rent. Off site: Nearest beach 4 km. Les Mathes village 1.5 km. (good range of shops and restaurants). Riding centre nearby. Minigolf 800 m.

Open: 28 March - 31 October.

Directions

From Saujon take the D14 heading northwest towards La Tremblade. At Arvert head south on the D141 to Les Mathes. Beyond the village, head right on the Route de la Fouasse and the site is on the right after a further 500 m. GPS: 45.72098, -1.17149

Charges guide

Per unit incl. 2 persons and electricity (6/10A)	€ 14,90 - € 26,70
extra person	€ 3,30 - € 4,70
child (2-7 yrs)	€ 2,60 - € 3,70

Covered heated swimming pool - Animation
Mobile homes for rent - Multisports terrain - Minigolf

La Clé des Champs ★★★

1188 route de la Fouasse • 17570 Les Mathes • Tél : 05 46 22 40 53
fax : 05 46 22 56 96 • www.la-cledeschamps.com
E-mail : contact@la-cledeschamps.com or : contact@la-cle-des-champs.net

Les Mathes-La Palmyre

Siblu Camping Bonne Anse Plage

La Palmyre, F-17570 Les Mathes-La Palmyre (Charente-Maritime) T: 05 46 22 40 90

E: bonneanseplage@siblu.fr **alanrogers.com/FR17040**

On the edge of the Forêt de la Coubre, just beyond La Palmyre, Bonne Anse Plage is attractively set amongst pines, just a short stroll from a tidal inlet, and just 600 m. from the mouth of the Gironde estuary. This is a spacious, gently undulating site, and is now owned by the Siblu group. There are 850 level, marked pitches, of which around half are for touring units (all with electricity). Most are well shaded, the ones nearer the sea less so and are rather sandier. The reception, restaurant and bar with a spacious outdoor terrace and an impressive pool complex form the social focus. The pool complex also features several giant water slides.

Facilities

Seven well maintained toilet blocks include facilities for disabled visitors and babies. Motorcaravan service point. Shopping centre. Restaurant and bar. Takeaway food. Large pool complex with water slides (including a junior chute). Playground. Video games room. TV. Minigolf. Football. Trampolines. Bicycle hire. Climbing wall. Entertainment and activities in high season. Internet access. Gas barbecues only. Off site: Supervised, safe beaches 500 m. Fishing, riding 1 km. Zoo 1 km.

Open: 1 May - 19 September.

Directions

Leave A10 autoroute at Saintes. Head for Royan (N150). In Royan take signs for La Palmyre (D25). At La Palmyre roundabout follow signs for Ronce-les-Bains. Site is 1 km. on left. GPS: 45.69810, -1.19976

Charges guide

Per unit incl. 3 persons and electricity	€ 37,60 - € 44,80
extra person (over 1 yr)	€ 7,60 - € 9,20

For latest campsite news, availability and prices visit

alanrogers.com

Les Mathes-La Palmyre

Camping Caravaning Monplaisir

26 avenue de la Palmyre, F-17570 Les Mathes-La Palmyre (Charente-Maritime) T: 05 46 22 50 31
E: campmonplaisir@aol.com alanrogers.com/FR17110

Monplaisir provides a small, quiet haven in an area with some very hectic campsites. It is ideal for couples or families with young children. Quite close to the town and set back from the road, the entrance leads through an avenue of trees, past the owners' home to a well kept, garden-like site with many trees and shrubs. There are 114 level, marked pitches and all but a few have electrical connections (6A); long leads may be required. On 14 there are caravans for rent and a modern building provides flats and studios for rent. Larger units would find this site difficult to navigate.

Facilities

The toilet block has some washbasins in cabins and facilities for disabled visitors. Laundry facilities. Ice pack service in reception. Bread delivered daily. TV, games room and library. Heated swimming pool and paddling pool (early May-30/9). Small play area. Winter caravan storage. Off site: Supermarket short walk. Minigolf adjacent (owned by the site). Fishing 500 m. Riding 1 km. Golf 5 km.

Open: Easter - 1 October.

Directions

Follow D25 to La Palmyre. In town, turn north to Les Mathes. At roundabout turn right to town centre. Site on left. From north on D14 (La Tremblade) turn onto D268 (Les Mathes and La Palmyre) at roundabout just before Arvert. Keep straight on to Les Mathes, road becomes D141 and turn left (north) at roundabout. Site is 600 m. on left.
GPS: 45.71384, -1.15939

Charges guide

Per unit incl. 2 persons	€ 17,00
incl. 3 persons	€ 19,50
extra person	€ 5,00
electricity	€ 3,00

Médis

Camping le Clos Fleuri

8 impasse du Clos Fleuri, F-17600 Médis (Charente-Maritime) T: 05 46 05 62 17. E: clos-fleuri@wanadoo.fr
alanrogers.com/FR17160

Camping Le Clos Fleuri really does live up to its name. The profusion of different trees and the lawns and flower beds give this small site a very rural atmosphere. There is always a warm welcome from the Devais family who created this pretty site in 1974. The 123 touring pitches are mostly of generous size (a little uneven in places). They vary from being in full sun to well shaded and 100 have electrical connections. The bar/restaurant is a converted barn providing a cool haven on hot days and a very convivial venue for evening gatherings and entertainment. There is occasional noise from light aircraft. The surrounding countryside is very pleasant with crops of sunflowers, wheat and maize, while beaches of all sorts are within easy reach. All in all the Clos Fleuri combines a great deal of charm, beauty and friendliness with a location from which the attractions of the Charente-Maritime may be discovered.

Facilities

Toilet facilities are kept clean. One block is segregated male and female, the other is unisex with each unit in its own cubicle. Facility for disabled visitors. Baby baths. Laundry facilities. Small pool and paddling pool. Sauna. Shop (5/7-15/9). Restaurant (11/7-31/8) and bar (5/7-15/9). In high season there are twice weekly soirées and boules and archery competitions. Minigolf. WiFi. Large units should call in high season to check there is space. Off site: Médis 2 km.

Open: 1 June - 18 September.

Directions

Médis is on the N150 from Saintes, halfway between Saujon and Royan. Drive into village. Site signed to south at various points in Médis and is about 2 km. outside village. GPS: 45.63011, -0.9458

Charges guide

Per unit incl. 2 persons	€ 18,90 - € 28,00
extra person	€ 6,00 - € 8,00
child (2-7 yrs)	€ 4,00 - € 5,50
electricity (5/10A)	€ 3,00 - € 6,00
dog	€ 2,50 - € 3,30

Parthenay

Kawan Village du Bois Vert

14 rue Boisseau, le Tallud, F-79200 Parthenay (Deux-Sèvres) T: 05 49 64 78 43
E: campingboisvert@orange.fr alanrogers.com/FR79050

Bois Vert is a former municipal site, now operated by a campsite group although so far it has changed little. There are 88 pitches of which 74 are for touring, all with electricity (10A) and 30 also with water and drainage. There are 15 mobile homes to rent. Pitches are separated by hedges and there are mature trees providing some shade. The site is on the Thouet river and although there is a secure fence, there is a steep drop to the river bank. Walkways along both sides and a footbridge close by enable you to walk into the old walled town. The medieval city of Parthenay is a place of art and history. It is the capital of the Gatine region, an agricultural area renowned for its sheep, farming, dairy products, apple orchards and cattle breeding. This is an ideal destination close to the Marais Poitevan and Venise Verte. In medieval times the city was also one of the stops on the pilgrims' route to Santiago de Compostela.

Facilities

Two toilet blocks, one with unisex toilets, showers and washbasins in cubicles, and scheduled for refurbishment for 2011. The second was closed when we visited. Dishwashing and laundry sinks. Facilities for disabled visitors, including new mobile homes. Bar with snack bar and takeaway (1/5-30/9). Small shop. Bread to order. Breakfast available at the bar. Heated swimming pool. TV. Badminton. Boules. Bicycle hire. Small play area. Security barrier. Tickets available for Futuroscope and Puy du Fou. Off site: Motorcaravan service point adjacent. Fishing 100 m. Base de Loisirs nearby. Riding and golf 15 km.

Open: 1 April - 31 October.

Directions

Parthenay is 50 km. west of Poitiers (and the A10) via the N149 to Bressuire and Nantes. Site is southwest of the town at Le Tallud on the D949 La Roche-sur-Yon road. Take ring road and site is on right as you join D949. GPS: 46.6414, -0.2672

Charges guide

Per unit incl. 2 persons	€ 15,50 - € 21,00
incl. electricity	€ 19,00 - € 24,50
extra person	€ 4,50 - € 5,50
child (5-10 yrs)	€ 2,00 - € 2,50

Rivedoux Plage

Campéole

Campéole le Platin

125 avenue Gustave Perreau, F-17940 Rivedoux Plage (Charente-Maritime) T: 05 46 09 84 10
E: platin@campeole.com alanrogers.com/FR17560

Located at the gateway to the Ile de Ré, Le Platin is just a short walk from the pleasant village of Rivedoux Plage where there are several good restaurants and shops. In high season a small market is held every morning in the village square. A long, narrow site, the beach is on one side and the main road on the other. It is divided into small avenues with around 20 pitches in each. All have 8/10A electricity and most are shaded, although the pitches nearest the beach have little shade (but the best views). Of the 200 pitches, 50 are used for canvas bungalows for hire, the rest are seasonal and for touring. Popular with motorcaravanners, Le Platin has a short stay area outside the barrier, and a bus stop 100 m. away makes it easy to explore the island and also to visit La Rochelle on the mainland. A cycle track runs alongside the site. Direct access onto the beach makes it an ideal spot for families, and sea fishing is a popular activity here. The beach is a hive of activity at low tide when the oyster beds are exposed.

Facilities

The toilet facilities here are a little below standard, although one block has good showers and an en-suite bathroom for disabled visitors. This is only the second year Campéole have been here, and there are plans for improvements. Small bar. Entertainment in high season. Off site: Bicycle hire 200 m.

Open: 1 April - 30 September.

Directions

After crossing the toll bridge from La Rochelle, continue on the D735 into Rivedoux Plage. Site is well signed on the right. GPS: 46.1588, -1.2708

Charges guide

| Per unit incl. 2 persons and electricity | € 19,50 - € 24,40 |
| extra person | € 4,10 - € 6,10 |

Ronce-les-Bains

Camping la Clairière

Rue des Roseaux, F-17390 Ronce-les-Bains (Charente-Maritime) T: 05 46 36 36 63

E: info@camping-la-clairiere.com **alanrogers.com/FR17480**

The site is attractively laid out with flowers, shrubs and trees and it is set away from the other campsites in the area and only 2.5 km. from the sea. It is tranquil and peaceful with a feeling of spaciousness due to its setting within 12 hectares. The 147 pitches are level, shady and have easy access for large units. There are mobile homes and chalets for rent. On-site facilities are impressive and include a covered pool (added in 2010) as well as a large outdoor aquapark with water slides). The gym here is well equipped with a good range of muscular training equipment for the energetically minded. Massages are also on offer. The bar is close at hand for afterwards together with a restaurant and outside terrace. There is a stage for entertainment in high season with a programme of activities. A riding complex can be found just 100m from the site. The Ile d'Oléron is also close, and is one of the France's most important centres for oyster culture.

Facilities

Two modern sanitary blocks. Nursery for babies. No facilities for disabled visitors. Washing machines. Shop, bar, restaurant and takeaway. Two swimming pools, toddlers pool and 55 metre toboggan. Games room with pool tables, table football and electronic games. Exercise equipment. Children's club. Entertainment in July/Aug. Tennis, petanque, minigolf, basketball. Gas barbecues only. Off site: Riding 100 m. Cycle and walking tracks through the Foret de la Coubre. Ile d'Oléron. La Palmyre (famous zoo).

Open: 28 April - 15 September.

Directions

From roundabout at Les Mathes, take the D25 to La Palmyre. Take first right and follow the signs for the site. GPS: 45.772933, -1.166734

Charges guide

Per unit incl. 2 persons and electricity	€ 21,50 - € 32,50
extra person	€ 6,00 - € 8,50
child (2-10 yrs)	€ 4,00 - € 6,50

For latest campsite news, availability and prices visit

alanrogers.com

Royan-Pontaillac

Campéole

Camping Clairefontaine

6 rue du Colonel Lachaud, F-17200 Royan-Pontaillac (Charente-Maritime) T: 05 46 39 08 11
E: info@camping-clairefontaine.com alanrogers.com/FR17100

Camping Clairefontaine is situated on the outskirts of Royan, 300 m. from a golden sandy beach and casino. Although it is a busy area, the site is peaceful and relaxing. There are 300 pitches, of which 282 are available for touring. Electricity is available to all pitches, but some may require long leads. The site is mostly shaded and level with easy access to pitches. American motorhomes are accepted but care is needed on the entrance road to the site as it is not wide enough for two vehicles to pass. The reception area is large and welcoming and English is spoken. A programme of entertainment is provided in July and August and includes karaoke, singers and folk groups. There are many places of interest to visit, notably the nature reserves, the lighthouse at Cordouan, forests and the oyster beds of Marennes and Oléron.

Facilities

Two modern sanitary blocks. Good facilities for disabled visitors. Washing machines. Ironing room. Motorcaravan services. Shop. Bar. Restaurant with takeaway. Swimming and paddling pools. Four play areas. Tennis. Basketball. Entertainment in high season. Internet access.
Off site: Beach and sailing 300 m. Bicycle hire 350 m. Fishing 2 km. Riding and golf 10 km.

Open: 24 May - 12 September.

Directions

Exit Royan on Avenue de Pontaillac towards La Palmyre. Turn right at the casino on the front, up Avenue Louise. Site is on left after 200 m. and is signed. GPS: 45.631388, -1.050122

Charges guide

Per unit incl. 2 persons and electricity	€ 32,00 - € 35,00
extra person	€ 9,00 - € 9,50
child (2-10 yrs)	€ 5,00 - € 5,50
dog	€ 3,00

Saint Clément-des-Baleines

Camping la Plage

408 rue du Chaume, F-17590 Saint Clément-des-Baleines (Charente-Maritime) T: 05 46 29 42 62
E: info@la-plage.com alanrogers.com/FR17590

This campsite, a member of the Airotel group, can be found at the western end of the Ile de Ré, very close to the imposing Phare des Baleines and just 100m from a sandy beach. Pitches are of average size and most are equipped with 10A electricity. Good selections of mobile homes are available for rent. Leisure facilities here include an attractive pool with a wide sunbathing terrace, and a multisport terrain. The bar/restaurant is the focal point for the site and a range of activities and entertainment take place there throughout the high season, including a daily children's club.

Facilities

One unisex toilet block provides good facilities and is kept clean and fresh. Washbasins in cubicles. Baby room and facilities for disabled visitors. Laundry. Basic motorcaravan service point. Bar. Restaurant. Takeaway food. Small shop.(July/Aug). Heated swimming pool and children's pool. Jacuzzi. Sauna and fitness suite (free). Games room. Multisport terrain. Play area. Entertainment and activity programme. Bicycle hire. WiFi (charged). Mobile homes to rent. Tourist information. Only gas and electric barbecues allowed. Off site: Sandy beach 100 m. Phare des Baleines. Ars-en-Ré. Riding. Fishing.

Open: 4 April - 26 September.

Directions

From La Rochelle cross the toll bridge to the Ile de Ré. Continue on D735 to Ars-en-Ré and then to St Clement-des-Baleines and the Phare des Baleines. The site is well signed from here. Large units should take care when turning into site. GPS: 46.241186, -1.55345

Charges guide

Per unit incl. 3 persons and electricity	€ 41,60 - € 49,60
1 or 2 persons (low season)	€ 17,50 - € 26,00
child (0-10 yrs)	€ 3,50 - € 12,50
dog	€ 2,80 - € 5,80

Saint Augustin-sur-Mer

Le Logis du Breuil

F-17570 Saint Augustin-sur-Mer (Charente-Maritime) T: 05 46 23 23 45
E: camping.Logis-du-Breuil@wanadoo.fr   alanrogers.com/FR17190

The first impression on arrival at this impressive campsite is one of space. The site covers a 30 hectare expanse of farm pasture where (on different areas) cattle graze and children play. The 9 hectare camping areas are set among rows of mature and shady trees giving a dappled effect to the 320 grassy pitches. There are 250 with 3/10A electricity and all are very large with direct access to wide, unpaved alleys which lead on to the few tarmac roads around the site. The amenities are centred around the reception area and pool complex. The area around the site is very pleasant agricultural land and the beaches of the Atlantic coast are nearby. Also near are the oyster and mussel beds of Marennes and La Tremblade. The Gagnard family started the campsite over 25 years ago and obviously take great pride in what it has now become a peaceful, friendly and very pleasant campsite from which to explore a delightful holiday area.

Facilities

Four well maintained toilet blocks are spaced around the camping area. Laundry facilities. Excellent shop, bar, restaurant and takeaway. Swimming pools (20/5-15/9). No evening entertainment. Play area. Indoor games area. Bicycle hire. Tennis. Excursions organised. WiFi. Gites, mobile homes and chalets to rent. Off site: Beach 10 minute drive to St Palais-sur-Mer and La Grande-Côte. Sailing 5 km.

Open: 1 May - 30 September.

Directions

From A10 exit 35, take the N150 to Saujon and continue on the N150 to Royan. Take the D25 towards La Palmyre (Zoo), then turn right onto the D145 towards Saint Augustin. Site is signed and is 2 km. on the left. GPS: 45.67555, -1.094817

Charges 2011

Per unit incl. 2 persons and electricity	€ 18,97 - € 27,21
extra person	€ 4,08 - € 6,98
child (under 7 yrs)	€ 3,51 - € 5,11
dog	€ 2,00 - € 3,00

Saint Cyr

Flower Camping du Lac de Saint-Cyr

F-86130 Saint Cyr (Vienne) T: 05 49 62 57 22. E: contact@lacdesaintcyr.com

alanrogers.com/FR86090

This well organised, five-hectare campsite is part of a 300-hectare leisure park, based around a large lake with sailing and associated sports, and an area for swimming (supervised July/Aug). Land-based activities include tennis, two half courts, table tennis, fishing, badminton, petanque, beach volleyball, TV room, and a well equipped fitness suite, all of which are free of charge. The campsite has around 185 touring pitches, ten mobile homes and three 'yurts' (canvas and wooden tents) for rent. The marked and generally separated pitches are all fully serviced with electricity (10A), water and drainage. Spacious and very natural, this is a tranquil setting.

Facilities

The main toilet block is modern and supplemented for peak season by a second unit, although they do attract some use by day trippers to the leisure facilities. They include washbasins in cubicles, laundry facilities, and facilities for babies and disabled visitors. Shop, restaurant and takeaway (April-Sept). Playground on beach. Bicycle hire. Barrier locked 22.00-07.00 (€ 10 deposit for card). Off site: Riding 200 m. Golf 800 m. Watersports and numerous other leisure activities around the lake.

Open: 1 April - 30 September.

Directions

Saint Cyr is about midway between Châtellerault and Poitiers. Site signed to east of N10 at Beaumont along D82 towards Bonneuil-Matours, and is part of the Parc de Loisirs de Saint Cyr. GPS: 46.71972, 0.46018

Charges guide

Per unit incl. 2 persons	
and electricity	€ 14,50 - € 27,00
extra person	€ 3,00 - € 5,00
child (2-7 yrs)	€ 2,00 - € 3,00
animal	€ 1,50

Saint Georges-d'Oléron

Chadotel le Domaine d'Oléron

La Jousselinière, F-17190 Saint Georges-d'Oléron (Charente-Maritime) T: 05 46 76 54 97

E: contact@chadotel.com alanrogers.com/FR17470

This is a neat, well presented and well managed site where you will receive a warm and friendly welcome from Anneke and Freddy. It is set in a peaceful rural location between St Pierre and St Georges and is part of the Chadotel group. At present there are 70 pitches of which 40 are for touring. There are plans to include further touring pitches but at present the site appears quite spacious with facilities being under used. Pitches are generously sized (100-150 sq.m) and are mostly shaded. Level and easily accessible, all have 10A electricity. The site is surrounded by the Forest of Saumonards and is just 3 km. from the beach. The local port, shops and restaurants are also nearby. Boat trips are available around the island to see Fort Boyard, Chasson Lighthouse and the Château d'Oléron.

Facilities

Modern sanitary block with facilities for disabled visitors and babies. Washing machines. Ironing room. Snack bar. Bar with TV. Takeaway. Bread delivered daily. Swimming pool with slides. Adventure style play area. Six pétanque lanes. Bicycle hire. Organised entertainment two or three times a week in July/Aug. Gas barbecues only on pitches, communal areas for charcoal. Off site: Royan Zoo. Fishing and riding 2 km. Cycle trails. Golf 8 km.

Open: 3 April - 25 September.

Directions

Take D734 to St Pierre. Turn right in St Pierre after Le Clerc supermarket. At next roundabout turn left towards Le Bois Fleury. After passing airfield, turn right and left and site is on the left. GPS: 45.9674685, -1.3192605

Charges guide

Per unit incl. 2 persons	
and electricity	€ 15,80 - € 29,90
extra person	€ 5,80
child (2-13 yrs)	€ 3,80
dog	€ 3,00

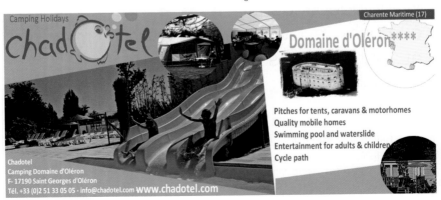

Saint Georges-d'Oléron

Camping les Gros Joncs

850 route de Ponthezieres, les Sables Vignier B.P. 17, F-17190 Saint Georges-d'Oléron (Charente-Maritime)
T: 05 46 76 52 29. E: info@les-gros-joncs.fr alanrogers.com/FR17070

Situated on the west coast of the island of Ile d'Oléron, Les Gros Joncs is owned and run by the Cavel family who work hard to keep the site up-to-date and of high quality. There are 50 or so touring pitches of a good size (some extra large) with tall pine trees providing a choice between full sun and varying degrees of shade. All have water and 10A electricity to hand. The main building not only houses a light and airy reception, but also a modern, beautifully presented bar and restaurant, a fully stocked and competitively priced shop, a luxurious indoor swimming pool and a magnificent spa. The indoor pool, with water jets and jacuzzi, has glass sides which in good weather are opened out onto an outdoor pool area where there are also water slides, a paddling area and plenty of sunbathing terraces. Both pools are heated. The luxurious spa offers hydrotherapy and beauty treatments, sauna, and a comprehensive fitness room. Much attention has been given to the needs of disabled visitors here, including chalets where space and equipment are specially adapted. All the amenities are of a standard unusual on a campsite.

Facilities

Traditional style toilet facilities are kept to a high standard. Laundry facilities. Motorcaravan services. Well stocked shop with bakery (1/4-15/9). Bar, restaurant and takeaway (all year). Indoor pool with first class spa and wellness centre (all year, with professional staff). Outdoor pool (heated, 1/4-15/9). Bicycle hire. Children's clubs (1/7-15/9). Internet access and WiFi. ATM. Barbecues are not permitted. Off site: Beach 200 or 400 m via a sandy path. Bus service from Chéray. Fishing 2 km. Riding 6 km. Golf 8 km.

Open: All year.

Directions

Cross the viaduct onto the Ile d'Oléron. Take D734 (St Georges-d'Oléron). At traffic lights in Chéray turn left. Follow signs for camping and Sable Vignier. Soon signs indicate directions to Les Gros Joncs. GPS: 45.95356, -1.37979

Charges guide

Per unit incl. 2 persons and electricity	€ 18,50 - € 45,50
extra person	€ 6,00 - € 11,80
child (0-7 yrs)	€ 2,70 - € 7,30
dog	€ 3,00

Les Sables Vignier - Route Côtière entre Domino et La Cotinière - 17190 Saint-Georges d'Oléron
Tél. : 05 46 76 52 29 - www.camping-les-gros-joncs.com

Saint Georges-de-Didonne

Camping Bois Soleil

2 avenue de Suzac, F-17110 Saint Georges-de-Didonne (Charente-Maritime) T: 05 46 05 05 94

E: camping.bois.soleil@wanadoo.fr **alanrogers.com/FR17010**

Close to the sea, Bois Soleil is a large site in three parts, with 165 serviced pitches for touring units and a few for tents. All the touring pitches are hedged and have electricity, with water and drainage between two. The main part, Les Pins, is attractive with trees and shrubs providing shade. Opposite is La Mer with direct access to the beach, some areas with less shade and an area for tents. The third part, La Forêt, is for caravan holiday homes. It is best to book your preferred area as it can be full mid June-late August. Excellent private sanitary facilities are available to rent, either on your pitch or at a block (subject to availability). There are a few pitches with lockable gates. The areas are all well tended and are cleared and raked between visitors. This lively site offers something for everyone, whether it be a beach-side spot or a traditional pitch, plenty of activities or the quiet life. Recent additions include a new toilet block and some accommodation to rent with sea views. The wide sandy beach is popular with children and provides a pleasant walk to the pretty town of Saint Georges-de-Didonne.

Facilities

Each area has one large and one small sanitary block. Heated block near reception. Cleaned twice daily, they include facilities for disabled visitors and babies. Launderette. Supermarket, bakery, beach shop (all 15/4-15/9). Restaurant, bar and takeaway (all 15/4-15/9). Swimming pool (heated 15/6-15/9). Steam room. Tennis. Bicycle hire. Play area. TV room and library. Internet terminal and WiFi. Charcoal barbecues not permitted. Dogs are not accepted 26/6-5/9. Off site: Fishing, riding 500 m. Golf 20 km.

Open: 2 April - 9 October.

Directions

From Royan centre take coast road (D25) along the seafront of St Georges-de-Didonne towards Meschers. Site is signed at roundabout at end of the main beach. GPS: 45.583583, -0.986533

Charges 2011

Per unit incl. 3 persons	
and electricity	€ 26,00 - € 50,00
extra person	€ 3,00 - € 8,50
child (3-7 yrs)	free - € 6,50
dog (not 26/6-5/9)	€ 3,00 - € 4,00

Camping Cheques accepted.

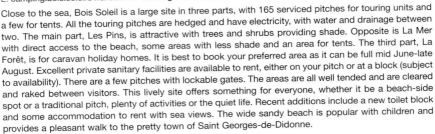

Saint Georges-d'Oléron

Camping l'Anse des Pins

Chemin du Râteau-Domino, F-17190 Saint Georges-d'Oléron (Charente-Maritime) T: 05 46 76 55 97

E: camping-apv@wanadoo.fr **alanrogers.com/FR17270**

Rock pools, sand dunes and spectacular sunsets, with sea views from many of the pitches, help to make this site attractive to those seeking an away from it all holiday in a quiet part of the island of the Ile d'Oléron. The campsite is arranged in three areas, some areas with good shade, others in full sun. There are 350 pitches including 137 for touring units, the remainder used for mobile homes. All pitches have electricity (3-10A) and 22 also have water and drainage. Across the road are the leisure facilities which include a complex of outdoor pools (unheated) with a toboggan and flume, and an indoor pool with a sauna. There is a bar and snack bar with takeaway and a small shop. Activities are organised for all (games, competitions) with some evening entertainment in high season. The nearest village (Domino) is about 500 m. away and has a daily market.

Facilities

Two main toilet blocks (plus two small blocks for high season use) with mainly British style toilets. Showers and washbasins in cabins. Laundry facilities. Gas supplies. Bar. Shop with limited takeaway and snack bar. Indoor pool (all season) and outdoor swimming and paddling pools (April-Sept). Play area. Activities in high season (1/7-31/8). Tennis. Boules. Bicycle hire. WiFi. Barbecues only permitted in a communal area. Off site: Beach 50 m. Bicycle hire 1 km. Riding 10 km. St Georges 5 km.

Open: April - October.

Directions

Cross the bridge onto Ile d'Oléron and follow D734 (St Dennis). In Chéray, turn left at traffic lights (signed Camping). Stay on this road to Domino (avoid side roads). Follow green signs to Rex and l'Anse des Pins Camping. Narrow roads. GPS: 45.97059, -1.3864

Charges guide

Per unit incl. 2 persons	
and electricity	€ 21,30 - € 35,20
extra person	€ 7,40 - € 8,00
child (0-4 yrs)	€ 3,70 - € 4,30
dog	€ 2,60

For latest campsite news, availability and prices visit

alanrogers.com

Bois Soleil

Camping ★★★★
Charente-Maritime

...urrounded by pine trees and a sandy beach on the ...tlantic Coast, with one direct access to the beach, Bois ...oleil proposes to you many attractions like tennis, ...bletennis, children playgrounds and entertainment. ...hops, take-away and snack-bar with big TV screen.

Spring and Summer

2, avenue de Suzac - 17110 ST GEORGES DE DIDONNE
Tel: 0033 546 05 05 94 - Fax: 0033 546 06 27 43
www.bois-soleil.com / e-mail: camping.bois.soleil@wanadoo.fr

Saint Georges-les-Baillargeaux

Kawan Village le Futuriste

F-86130 Saint Georges-les-Baillargeaux (Vienne) T: 05 49 52 47 52. E: camping-le-futuriste@wanadoo.fr

alanrogers.com/FR86040

Le Futuriste is a neat, modern site, open all year and close to Futuroscope. Its location is very convenient for the A10 and N10 motorway network. There are 112 individual, level, grassy pitches of a generous size and divided by flowering hedges. All pitches have electricity (6A) and 30 also have water and waste water connections. Pitches are mostly open although some do have the benefit of shade from trees. All are accessed via tarmac roads. There are lovely panoramic views from this site and the popular attraction of Futuroscope can be clearly seen. Large units are accepted by prior arrangement. There is a pleasant restaurant on site offering good food at reasonable prices. Entertainment takes place in the daytime rather than in the evenings. This site is ideal for a short stay to visit Futuroscope which is only 2 km. away but it is equally good for longer stays to see the region.

Facilities

Excellent, clean sanitary facilities in two heated blocks. Good facilities for disabled visitors and babies. Laundry facilities. Shop (1/5-30/9, bread to order). Bar/restaurant snack bar and takeaway (1/7-31/8). Two heated outdoor pools, one with slide and paddling pool (1/7-31/8). New covered pool (open from Feb 2011). Games room. TV. Boules. Multisport area. Lake fishing. Daily activities in season. Youth groups not accepted. Off site: Bicycle hire 500 m. Hypermarket 600 m. Futuroscope 2 km. Golf 5 km. Riding 10 km.

Open: All year.

Directions

From either A10 autoroute or N10, take Futuroscope exit. Site is east of both roads, off D20 (St Georges-les-Baillargeaux). Follow signs to St Georges. Site on hill; turn by water tower and site is on left.
GPS: 46.6644, 0.39463

Charges 2011

Per unit incl. 3 persons and electricity	€ 20,00 - € 27,00

Saint Georges-de-Didonne

Village Center les Catalpas

45 chemin d'Enlias, F-17110 Saint Georges-de-Didonne (Charente-Maritime) T: 04 99 57 21 21
E: contact@village-center.com alanrogers.com/FR17350

Camping les Catalpas is a member of the Village Center group and is located close to the Gironde estuary at St Georges de Didonne. Pitches are grassy and there is a choice between sunny and more shady options. A number of chalets are available for rent. On-site amenities include a swimming pool, children's paddling pool, a small shop and a snack bar. A large supermarket is just 3 minutes walk from the site. There are also some excellent beaches within a few minutes' walk of the site, and St Georges has all the amenities one would expect of a well established holiday resort.

Facilities

Two modern sanitary blocks with good facilities for disabled visitors and babies. Washing machines and dryers. Snack bar, pizzeria and bar (all season). Shop. Heated swimming pool with paddling pool. Games room. TV room. Internet access. Entertainment in July/Aug. Gas barbecues only on pitches. Chalets for rent. Off site: Nearest beach 10 minutes walk. Fishing. Golf.

Open: 24 June - 4 September.

Directions

From Royan take the southbound coast road (D25) to St Georges de Didonne. The site is located in parkland close to the Avenue d'Aquitaine and is well indicated. GPS: 45.61529, -0.99477

Charges 2011

| Per unit incl. 2 persons and electricity | € 16,00 - € 23,00 |
| extra person (over 5 yrs) | € 2,00 - € 5,00 |

Saint Just-Luzac

Castel Camping Séquoia Parc

La Josephtrie, F-17320 Saint Just-Luzac (Charente-Maritime) T: 05 46 85 55 55. E: info@sequoiaparc.com
alanrogers.com/FR17140

This is definitely a site not to be missed. Approached by an avenue of flowers, shrubs and trees, Séquoia Parc is a Castel site set in the grounds of La Josephtrie, a striking château with beautifully restored outbuildings and courtyard area with a bar and restaurant. Most of the 426 pitches are 140 sq.m. with 6/10A electricity connections and separated by mature shrubs providing plenty of privacy. The site has 300 mobile homes and chalets, with 126 used by tour operators. This is a popular site with a children's club and entertainment throughout the season and reservation is necessary in high season. The site itself is designed to a high specification with reception in a large, light and airy room retaining its original beams and leading to the courtyard area where you find the bar and restaurant. The pool complex with water slides, large paddling pool and sunbathing area is impressive. A new terraced area adjacent to the snack bar has been created so that you can buy a snack and then sit in a very pleasant garden setting with sunshades, to eat your meal. Member of Leading Campings Group.

Facilities

Three spotlessly clean luxurious toilet blocks, include units with washbasin and shower and facilities for disabled visitors and children. Large laundry. Motorcaravan service point. Gas supplies. Large supermarket. Boutique. Restaurant/bar and takeaway. Impressive swimming pool complex with water slides and large paddling pool. Massage parlour (July/Aug). Multisport pitch. Tennis. Games and TV rooms. Bicycle hire. Updated play areas. Pony trekking. Organised entertainment/excursions all season. Children's farm. WiFi in reception area (charged). Off site: Supermarket 5 km. Fishing 5 km. Golf 15 km.

Open: 14 May - 4 September (with all services).

Directions

Site is 5 km. southeast of Marennes. From Rochefort take D733 south for 12 km. Turn west on D123 to Ile d'Oléron. Continue for 12 km. Turn southeast on D728 (Saintes). Site signed, in 1 km. on left. From A10 at Saintes take D728 and leave this road by turning right shortly after St Just. Site signed. GPS: 45.81095, -1.06109

Charges 2011

Per unit incl. 2 persons and electricity	€ 20,00 - € 47,00
extra person	€ 7,00 - € 9,00
child (3-12 yrs)	€ 3,00 - € 5,00

Near Oléron island and its beaches

Aquapark of 2000 m²!

Kids club during whole season

Animations and horseriding

Bar restaurant Le Carrousel

Large pitches

Luxurious cottages, mobilehomes

Online bookings: **www.sequoiaparc.com**
17320 Saint Just-Luzac, France, tel.: +33 5 46 85 55 55

Open from 14/05 to 04/09/2011

For latest campsite news, availability and prices visit
alanrogers.com

Saint Hilaire-la-Palud

Camping le Lidon

F-79210 Saint Hilaire-la-Palud (Deux-Sèvres) T: 05 49 35 33 64. E: info@le-lidon.com

alanrogers.com/FR79060

Le Lidon is located within the Marais Poitevin, an enchanting region of over 400 km. of rivers, canals and fens lying to the west of Niort. This site has 132 grassy pitches scattered across 3 hectares, 116 for touring. The site's selection of rented accommodation includes fully equipped, Canadian style tents and chalets. The Marais Poitevin is undeniably best explored by canoe or punt and it is possible to rent these on site. During high season, an activity and entertainment programme is organised including a children's club and various family activities.

Facilities

Two toilet blocks (one closed in low season) with facility for disabled visitors and children. Shop, bar, snack bar. Bread to order. Laundry. Heated swimming pool (15/6-31/8). Bar/Restaurant. Takeaway. Games room. Play area. Motorcaravan service point. Direct access to river. Fishing. Bicycle and canoe hire. Entertainment and activities (July/Aug). Off site: Riding 2 km. Tennis 3 km. Golf 25 km. Vendée beaches 50 km.

Open: 3 April - 30 September.

Directions

St Hilaire la Palud lies midway between Niort and La Rochelle. From the north (Niort) leave A10 autoroute at exit 33 and head west on N248 as far as Epannes. Head north here on D1 to Sansais and then west on D3 to St Hilaire la Palud. Site signed to right just after village. GPS: 46.2838, -0.74345

Charges guide

Per unit incl. 2 persons	€ 20,10 - € 26,00
extra person	€ 5,20 - € 6,00

Saint Trojan-les-Bains

Camping Indigo Oléron

11 avenue des Bris, F-17370 Saint Trojan-les-Bains (Charente-Maritime) T: 05 46 76 02 39
E: oleron@camping-indigo.com alanrogers.com/FR17580

This four-hectare site is an attractive new addition to the Indigo group. It can be found close to the popular seaside resort of St Trojan-les-Bains on the south side of the island. There are 200 pitches, which vary in size, most of which have electrical connections. Indigo Oléron enjoys an attractive forest setting just 1 km. from the nearest sandy beach. The island is popular with cyclists and a track leads from the site to the village centre. In high season, a snack bar service is available as well as a very small shop - there is a Spar shop in the village. Oléron is the second largest French island (after Corsica) and is easily accessed thanks to the toll free bridge. The island's beaches are deservedly famous, backed by the large pine forest and surfing is also very popular here. The island (and nearby Marennes) is an important centre for oyster cultivation. Although quiet in low season, this site becomes much livelier during the peak months with occasional entertainment and activities.

Facilities

Two very modern toilet blocks provide washbasins in cabins, showers and British style toilets. Ramped facilities for disabled visitors. Laundry. Motorcaravan service point. Heated swimming pool (May-Sept). Small bar. Snack bar. Very small shop (mainly bread). Bicycle hire. Sandy play area with equipment for young children. Activity and entertainment programme. Barbecues allowed - gas or electric only. Tourist information. Max. 1 dog.
Off site: Nearest beach and fishing 0.5 km. Tourist train at St Trojan. Walking and cycling tracks. Riding 1 km. Supermarket 3 km.

Open: 2 July - 3 October.

Directions

From Marennes, cross the bridge to the Ile d'Oléron (D26) and then follow signs to St Trojan on D126. Drive through the shopping area to the second roundabout. Turn right and continue ahead. Follow alongside the railway track and where the road bends left, follow the road and the site is then on your left. GPS: 45.83152, -1.213882

Charges guide

Per unit incl. 2 persons and electricity	€ 17,10 - € 23,50
extra person	€ 3,30 - € 4,80
child (2-7 yrs)	€ 1,60 - € 2,70

Save up to 60% on your holiday

- **Over 600 campsites – all just £13.95 per night**
  (pitch +2 adults, inc electricity)
- **Maximum flexibility - go as you please**
- **29 Countries**
- **Fantastic Ferry Deals**

1 single price
£13.95
per night
for 2 people

Last year 250,000 people used nearly 1.6 million Camping Cheques and enjoyed half-price holidays around Europe. Make sure you don't miss out this year.

CALL NOW for your **FREE** Holiday Savings Guide
01580 214002

FOR FULL INFORMATION VISIT
www.campingcheque.co.uk

Holiday Savings
Guide 2011
www.campingcheque.co.uk

Fantastic
Ferry Offers

Burgundy is a wonderfully evocative region offering breathtaking châteaux and cathedrals, rolling hills and heady mountain views, vineyards and superlative cuisine, not to mention of course, a wide variety of world-renowned wines.

DÉPARTEMENTS: 21 CÔTE D'OR, 58 NIÈVRE, 71 SAÔNE-ET-LOIRE, 89 YONNE

MAJOR CITY: DIJON

In the rich heartland of France, Burgundy was once a powerful independent state and important religious centre. Its golden age is reflected in the area's magnificent art and architecture: the grand palaces and art collections of Dijon, the great pilgrimage church of Vézelay, the Cistercian Abbaye de Fontenay and the evocative abbey remains at Cluny, once the most powerful monastery in Europe.

However, Burgundy is best known for its wine, including some of the world's finest, notably from the great vineyards of the Côte d'Or and Chablis, and also for its sublime cuisine. You'll also notice how driving through the country villages is like reading a wine merchant's list with plenty of opportunities for tasting and choosing your wine.

The area is criss-crossed by navigable waterways and includes the Parc Régional du Morvan; good walking country amidst lush, rolling wooded landscape.

Burgundy

Places of interest

Church and Hill of Vézelay

The basilica of Sainte-Madeleine on the 'eternal hill' of Vézelay is an important place for pilgrims and starting point for the journey to Compostela.

www.**vezelaytourisme.com**

The Fontenay Abbey

Founded in 1118, the Fontenay Abbey offers a perfect image of what a large Cistercian monastery was all about.

www.**abbayedefontenay.com**

Museum Park Alesia

Discover the site of the battle of Alesia between the Romans of Julius Caesar and the Gauls of Vercingetorix. The new Museum Park building is planned to open in May 2011.

www.**alesia.com**

Activities

Burgundy à vélo

With 650 km. of 'voies vertes' and cycling routes, Burgundy is a real paradise for cyclists at all levels.

www.**burgundy-by-bike.com**

Festival Chalon dans la rue

The most important festival for street artists and performances in France has offered theatre, dance and circus for more than 20 years.

www.**chalondanslarue.com**

Tasting

Vineyards and caves

211 wine professionals adhere to the quality charter 'De Vignes en Caves'. Look out for this sign – wherever you see it, just knock on the door and your host will offer you a free tasting of at least one wine.

www.**burgundy-wines.fr**

Les Anis de Flavigny

Still made within the walls of an ancient abbey, these sweets conceal aniseed seeds at their heart. Discover their long and enchanting story.

www.**anis-flavigny.com**

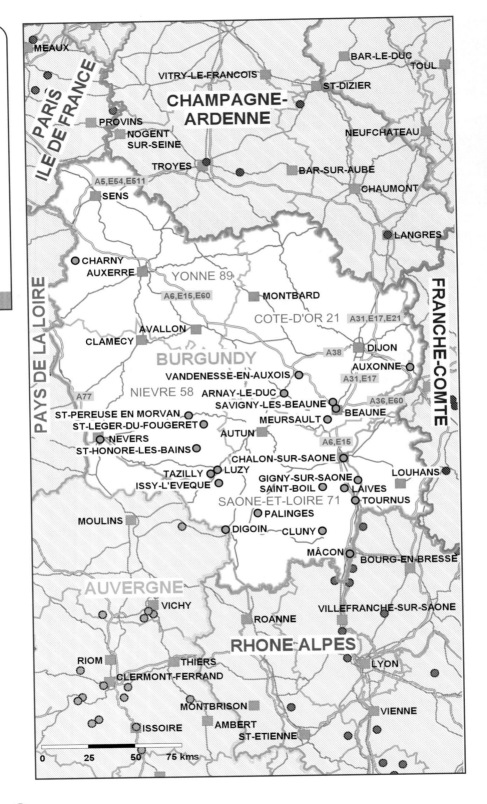

Auxonne

Camping de l'Arquebuse

Route d'Athée, F-21130 Auxonne (Côte d'Or) T: 03 80 31 06 89. E: camping.arquebuse@wanadoo.fr
alanrogers.com/FR21090

This is an all year round site located in the Northern Jura with a riverside setting on the Saône. l'Arquebuse has 100 level, unmarked pitches on grass, of which ten are occupied by mobile homes and chalets. All have 10A electricity and a variety of trees give shade to some pitches. Auxonne is close to both the A36 and A39 motorways and this site may prove a useful overnight stop. The site has a bar/restaurant, Le Pinocchio, and the adjacent 'base nautique' offers a good range of leisure activities, including canoeing, windsurfing, mountain biking as well as a large swimming pool. Auxonne is an attractive town, fortified by Vauban, and is renowned as the capital of the Saône valley. The town's most famous former occupant is Napoleon and he spent two years at the Auxonne military academy. Not surprisingly there are several monuments celebrating his time here!

Facilities

Basic toilet block, heated in winter, provides mostly Turkish style toilets and open washbasins. Washing machine. Small shop (1/5-31/10). Restaurant/bar (1/1-15/12). Pizzeria. Takeaway meals. Play area. TV room. WiFi. Chalets for rent. Off site: Swimming pool, windsurfing, canoeing, boat trips and fishing. Motorcaravan services. Fortified town of Auxonne with shops, bars and restaurants 1 km. Dijon 34 km.

Open: All year.

Directions

From the A39 autoroute take exit 5 and the N5 for about 6 km. to Auxonne. Site is signed to the left just before crossing the bridge over the Saône. Site is a few hundred metres. GPS: 47.19941, 5.38365

Charges guide

Per unit incl. 2 persons and electricity	€ 16,00 - € 17,90
extra person	€ 3,60
child (under 7 yrs)	€ 2,10
dog	€ 1,80

Camping l'Arquebuse ***
- 3 star campsite
- Open all year
- Wifi
- Washing machines and dryers
- Restaurant with terrace
- At the bank of the Saône
- Pool 10 metres from the campsite
- Shop
- Bungalow tents and mobile homes for rent
- Play area for children

Camping l'Arquebuse - Route d'Athée - 21130 Auxonne - Tel: 0033 (0)380 31 06 89 - Fax: 0033 (0)380 31 12 62
E-mail: camping.arquebuse@wanadoo.fr - www.campingarquebuse.com

Beaune

Camping Municipal les Cent Vignes

10 rue Auguste Dubois, F-21200 Beaune (Côte d'Or) T: 03 80 22 03 91
E: campinglescentvignes@mairie-beaune.fr alanrogers.com/FR21020

Les Cent Vignes is a very well kept site offering 116 individual pitches of good size, separated from each other by neat beech hedges high enough to keep a fair amount of privacy. Over half of the pitches are on grass, ostensibly for tents, the remainder on hardstandings with electricity for caravans. A popular site, within walking distance of the town centre, Les Cent Vignes becomes full mid June to early September but with many short-stay campers there are departures each day and reservations can be made. The Côte de Beaune, situated southeast of the Côte d'Or, produces some of the very best French wines. Beaune is also a city of art and has a charm all of its own and there are several 'caves' in the town just waiting to be visited.

Facilities

Two modern, fully equipped and well constructed sanitary blocks, one of which can be heated, should be large enough. Nearly all washbasins are in cabins. Laundry facilities. Shop, restaurant with takeaway (all 1/4-15/10). Playground. Sports area with tennis, basketball, volleyball and boules. TV room. Barbecue area. Off site: Centre of Beaune 1 km. Bicycle hire 1 km. Fishing, golf or windsurfing 4 km.

Open: 15 March - 31 October.

Directions

From autoroute exit 24 follow signs for Beaune centre on D2 road, camping signs to site in about 1 km. Well signed from other routes. GPS: 47.03304, 4.83911

Charges guide

Per unit incl. 2 persons and electricity	€ 15,90
extra person	€ 3,80
child (under 7 yrs)	€ 1,90

For latest campsite news, availability and prices visit
alanrogers.com

Châlon-sur-Saône

Camping du Pont de Bourgogne

Rue Julien Leneveu, Saint-Marcel, F-71380 Châlon-sur-Saône (Saône-et-Loire) T: 03 85 48 26 86
E: campingchalon71@wanadoo.fr alanrogers.com/FR71140

This is a well presented and cared for site, useful for an overnight stop or for a longer stay to explore the local area. It is close to the A6 Autoroute, and the interesting market town of Châlon-sur-Saône is only 2 km. There are 100 slightly sloping pitches (90 sq.m) all with 10A electricity, most on grass, but 30 have a gravel surface. They are separated by beech hedging, and a variety of mature trees gives varying amounts of shade. Many pitches overlook the river, a good spot to watch the passing boats. Access is easy for large outfits. The new central toilet block is of the highest standard and kept very clean. The bar, restaurant and terrace, close to the entrance and overlooking the river, have been recently extended. Takeaway meals are available from the bar all season but the restarant is open only in July and August. The site gets crowded in the third week of July during the Châlon street theatre festival. Across the river is a large municipal swimming pool. It is possible to walk or cycle alongside the river for several kilometres. A golf club and sailing club are within 1 km. Recent improvements include the large, covered terrace, new sanitary building and security barriers at the entrance and exit.

Facilities

Three toilet blocks, two traditional in style and fittings. The third is a superb modern building, including a children's bathroom, disabled bathroom and family shower. Motorcaravan services. Dishwashing facilities, laundry. No shop but essentials kept in the bar (bread to order). Modern bar/restaurant (July/Aug). Simple play area. Bicycle hire arranged. WiFi. Off site: Fishing and boat ramp 200 m. Municipal swimming pool 300 m. Golf, sailing 1 km. Riding 10 km. Châlon-sur-Saône with many shops, bars, banks etc.

Open: 1 April - 30 September.

Directions

From A6 exit 26 (Châlon-Sud), take N80 (signed Dôle) to second roundabout. Take fourth exit (signed Roseraie) and fork right (Les Chavannes). At traffic lights turn right (signed Roseraie) under bridge to site entrance 500 m. GPS: 46.78448, 4.87295

Charges guide

Per unit incl. 2 persons	€ 19,40 - € 24,70
extra person	€ 4,70 - € 5,90
child (under 7 yrs)	€ 3,30 - € 4,50
dog	€ 2,20 - € 2,50

Camping Cheques accepted.

Gigny-sur-Saône

Kawan Village Château de l'Epervière

528

F-71240 Gigny-sur-Saône (Saône-et-Loire) T: 03 85 94 16 90. E: domaine-de-leperviere@wanadoo.fr
alanrogers.com/FR71070

This popular and high quality site is peacefully situated in the wooded grounds of the 16th-century château, close to the A6 and near the village of Gigny-sur-Saône. It is within walking distance of the river where you can watch the river cruise boats on their way to and from Châlon-sur-Saône. There are 160 pitches in two separate areas, of which 100 are used for touring, all with 10A electricity. Some are on hardstanding and 30 are fully serviced. Some pitches, close to the château and fishing lake, are hedged and have shade from mature trees. The other area has a more open aspect. Red squirrels, ducks and the occasional heron can be found on the campsite and the pitches around the periphery are good for birdwatchers. The château's main restaurant serves regional dishes and there is a good range of takeaway meals. Gert-Jan, François and their team enthusiastically organise many activities, mainly for children, including wine tasting in the cellars of the château. Don't forget, here you are in the Maconnais and Châlonnaise wine regions, so arrange some visits to the local 'caves'.

Facilities

Two well equipped, very clean toilet blocks with all necessary facilities including those for babies and campers with disabilities. Washing machine/dryer. Basic shop (1/5-30/9). Restaurant with good menu and takeaway (1/4-30/9). Cellar with wine tasting. Converted barn with bar, large TV/games room. Unheated outdoor swimming pool (1/5-30/9) partly enclosed by old stone walls. Smaller indoor heated pool, jacuzzi, sauna (1/4-30/9). Play areas with paddling pool. Fishing. Bicycle hire. Motorcaravan services. WiFi. Off site: Boat launching 500 m. Riding 15 km. Golf 20 km. Historic towns of Châlon and Tournus, both 20 km. The Monday market of Louhans, to see the famous Bresse chickens 26 km.

Open: 1 April - 30 September.

Directions

From A6 heading south, take exit 26 Châlon-Sud, or from A6 heading north take exit 27 Tournus. Then N6 to Sennecey-le-Grand, turn east D18, signed Gigny. Follow site signs to site (6.5 km). GPS: 46.65485, 4.94463

Charges guide

Per unit incl. 2 persons and electricity	€ 23,40 - € 33,50
extra person	€ 5,70 - € 8,10
child (under 7 yrs)	€ 3,50 - € 5,60
dog	€ 2,40 - € 3,00

For latest campsite news, availability and prices visit

alanrogers.com

3 campsites in the heart of southern burgundy

www.campings-bourgogne.com

Holiday
in château park

www.domaine-eperviere.com

Discover Tournus

www.camping-tournus.com

www.camping-chalon.com

City campsite

Bourgondië

Charny

Flower Camping des Platanes

41 route de la Mothe, F-89120 Charny (Yonne) T: 03 86 91 83 60
E: campingdesplatanes@wanadoo.fr alanrogers.com/FR89070

Peacefully situated in the village of Charny, this is a tranquil, quiet site, yet within easy reach of the A6 autoroute and only 1.5 hours from Paris. The important archaeological site of Guédelon castle is nearby, the Chablis wines of the Yonne are ready for discovery and there are delightful walks around two local lakes. There are currently 82 level, grass pitches, all with 16A electricity. With 27 used for touring units (some now with water and waste water), the remainder are used for rented holiday homes and seasonal units. Charny has a very old covered market and opposite is a 17th-century hotel/restaurant. Many Parisians have second homes here to escape the bustle of the big city. Nearby is Joigny, the 'gateway to Burgundy' with its network of narrow streets, covered passageways and some fine examples of 15th- and 16th-century timbered houses.

Facilities

A modern, purpose-built, heated toilet block provides separate areas for men and women. Washbasins in cabins. Facilities for disabled visitors. Laundry. Motorcaravan service point. Bicycle and barbecue hire. Play area for under fives. Heated swimming pool. Off site: Fishing, riding, walking.

Open: 15 March - 31 October.

Directions

Leave A6 at exit 18 and follow D943 towards Montargis for 14 km. Turn left on D950 and site is on right at start of village. GPS: 47.891, 3.092

Charges guide

Per unit incl. 2 persons and electricity	€ 16,50
extra person	€ 3,00 - € 4,00
child (under 10 yrs)	€ 1,50 - € 2,00
dog	free - € 1,50

Cluny

Camping Municipal Saint-Vital

Rue des Griottons, F-71250 Cluny (Saône-et-Loire) T: 03 85 59 08 34. E: cluny-camping@wanadoo.fr
alanrogers.com/FR71030

Close to this attractive small town (300 m. walk) with its magnificent abbey (the largest in Christendom) and next to the municipal swimming pool (free for campers), this site has 174 pitches. On gently sloping grass, with some small hedges and shade in parts, electricity is available (long leads may be needed). Some rail noise is noticeable during the day but we are assured that trains do not run 23.30-07.00. In high season, on Friday evenings, there is a presentation of local produce in the 'salle de réunion'.

Facilities

Two sanitary buildings provide British and Turkish style WCs, some washbasins in cubicles and controllable showers. Dishwashing and laundry sinks. Washing machine, dryer and ironing board. Chemical toilet disposal. Shop. Off site: Fishing and bicycle hire 100 m. Riding 1 km. Wine routes, châteaux, churches. The excellent traffic-free cycle path from Cluny to Givry is highly recommended.

Open: 1 May - 30 September.

Directions

Site is east of town, by the D15 road towards Azé and Blanot. GPS: 46.43196, 4.66755

Charges guide

Per unit incl. 2 persons and electricity	€ 13,95
extra person	€ 6,90
child (under 7 yrs)	€ 2,25

Digoin

Camping de la Chevrette

Rue de la Chevrette, F-71160 Digoin (Saône-et-Loire) T: 03 85 53 11 49. E: info@lachevrette.com
alanrogers.com/FR71180

This pretty town site has been leased from the municipality for the last few years by an enthusiastic couple. There are 100 neat and tidy pitches which are delineated by hedges (even the pitches for tents) and flowers decorate the site. The level pitches include 75 with electricity (10A) for touring units, 23 for tents and two for caravan holiday homes for rent. At the far end of the site there is direct access to the Loire river and it is this aspect that attracts campers with canoes. The adjacent town swimming pool complex is free for campers. It incorporates a second large pool totally devoted to the sport of water jousting – seven in a boat!

Facilities

Four small toilet blocks, one with cold water only, each provide separate facilities for men and women and some washbasins in cabins. Washing machine and dryer. Facilities for disabled visitors. Small restaurant/snack bar (1/7-31/8). Swimming pool (adjacent 15/6-7/9). Club room with TV for bad weather. WiFi. Off site: Supermarkets, restaurants and bars in the town. Cycle paths along the canals. Nevers and its cathedral. Riding 3 km. Bicycle hire 15 km.

Open: 15 March - 15 October.

Directions

Digoin lies off the N79 and site is well signed from all directions. GPS: 46.47973, 3.96755

Charges 2011

Per unit incl. 2 persons and electricity	€ 3,20 - € 4,00
extra person	€ 1,90 - € 2,20
child (under 13 yrs)	€ 6,10 - € 6,50
dog	€ 3,40

Double-axle units are charged much more.

For latest campsite news, availability and prices visit

alanrogers.com

Issy-l'Évêque

Flower Camping de l'Etang Neuf

L'Etang Neuf, F-71760 Issy-l'Évêque (Saône-et-Loire) T: 03 85 24 96 05. E: info@issy-camping.com
alanrogers.com/FR71080

This well tended, tranquil campsite overlooking a lake, with views of a forest and the 19th-century Château de Montrifaut, is a real countryside haven for relaxation. The birdsong includes nightingales and golden orioles. The 61 marked, grass pitches have 6A electricity, a small hardstanding area for a car and are separated by a variety of maturing trees giving some shade. There is a separate area nearer the lake for tents. There is no organised entertainment but a play area and a fenced area of the lake, with beach for swimming and paddling plus plenty of space, will keep children happily amused.

Facilities

Two very clean sanitary blocks include washbasins in cabins. Dishwashing and laundry sinks. Washing machine, ironing board and baby room. Separate shower and toilet rooms for disabled visitors are in the lower block. Motorcaravan services. Bar (1/7-31/8). Bread and croissants to order. Boules. TV/games room. Internet access (WiFi). Off site: Minigolf just outside the site entrance. Riding or tennis 500 m. Nearest shops 1.2 km.

Open: 13 May - 15 September.

Directions

From N81 (Autun - Bourbon-Lancy) turn left onto D27/D25 just west of Luzy and continue for about 11 km. Turn right, D42 in centre of Issy-l'Évêque, signed to campsite. The road narrows slightly, entrance on the right. GPS: 46.70773, 3.96018

Charges 2011

Per unit incl. 2 persons and electricity	€ 16,50 - € 19,90
extra person	€ 3,00 - € 5,00

Laives

Camping la Heronnière

Lac de Laives, F-71240 Laives (Saône-et-Loire) T: 03 85 44 98 85. E: contact@camping-laheronniere.com
alanrogers.com/FR71120

Camping la Heronnière is a quiet relaxing site on the edge of a leisure lake in pleasant rolling woodland countryside. The 90 touring pitches are good sized, grassy and level. About half have shade, with electrical connections for 88 and there are plenty of water points. The site is within easy reach of Chalon-sur-Saône, Tournus and the Chalonnais vineyards and wine route. Cluny and the former industrial towns of Le Creusot and Montceau-les-Mines are each about 40 km. away.

Facilities

Well equipped modern sanitary block includes facilities for campers with disabilities. Snack bar (June-Aug). Covered area outside reception, with bread, drinks, ice cream, basic provisions and French breakfast. Heated outdoor pool. Boules. Bicycle hire. Fishing. Marquee with TV, board games. Playground. Off site: Lake swimming, grass area, beach, bar and restaurant 300 m. Exercise circuit, canoeing, windsurfing, pedaloes. Riding 10 km. Golf 15 km. Cluny, Chalon, Le Creusot and Montceau-les-Mines. Shops, etc. at Laives 4 km.

Open: 1 May - 15 September.

Directions

Leave N6 (Chalon-sur-Saône - Mâcon) at Sennecy-le-Grand (about 18 km. south of the centre of Chalon), taking D18 west to Laives (4 km). In centre of village, take right fork and continue along D18, 4 km. to the northwest. GPS: 46.67198, 4.8333

Charges guide

Per unit incl. 2 persons and electricity	€ 23,50
extra person	€ 5,00
child (under 7 yrs)	€ 3,40
dog	€ 1,50

Mâcon

Camping Municipal Mâcon

RN6, F-71000 Mâcon (Saône-et-Loire) T: 03 85 38 16 22. E: camping@ville-macon.fr
alanrogers.com/FR71010

A well cared for site worth considering as a stopover or for longer stays, as it is close to the main route south. The 266 good sized, level, grassy pitches, 190 with 5/10A electricity and 60 with fresh and waste water points, are easily accessed by tarmac roads. This is a pleasant site, remarkably quiet considering its location, and with a generally bright and cheerful ambience. Extra charge for outfits over 3.5 tonnes or with twin axles. Only gas and electric barbecues are permitted. Reservations are not accepted so in July and August, arrive by late afternoon to avoid disappointment. Some road and rail noise.

Facilities

Four well maintained toilet blocks, one new, others being refurbished. Facilities for campers with disabilities. Washing machine and dryer. Motorcaravan service point (with Fiamma sewage couplings). Shop/tabac, bar, takeaway and restaurant open midday and evenings. Heated swimming and paddling pools (campers only, 15/5-15/9). TV lounge. Playground. Free WiFi. Off site: Fishing 500 m. Golf, riding 10 km. Sports centre on banks of river close by. Supermarket 400 m. Centre of Mâcon 3 km. Bus passes site.

Open: 15 March - 31 October.

Directions

Site is on northern outskirts of Mâcon on main N6, 3 km. from the town centre, well signed (just south of A40 autoroute junction). GPS: 46.3021, 4.8325

Charges guide

Per unit incl. 2 persons with electricity (10A)	€ 15,30 - € 16,90 € 19,20 - € 21,40

For latest campsite news, availability and prices visit

alanrogers.com

We can book this site for you! Call 01580 214000

alan rogers ◉ travel

Meursault

Camping la Grappe d'Or

2 route de Volnay, F-21190 Meursault (Côte d'Or) T: 03 80 21 22 48. E: info@camping-meursault.com

alanrogers.com/FR21050

Meursault, the capital of the great white wines of Burgundy, is southwest of Beaune and Camping de la Grappe d'Or offers terraced pitches overlooking acres of vineyards. Most of the 125 touring pitches are flat, of varying sizes, and some have shade from mature trees. They all have 15A electrical connections. There is an outdoor pool and flume and, during July and August, aqua gym and other water activities are organised. There is a fenced play area for youngsters and, just across the road from the entrance, there are two tennis courts for campers.

Facilities

Sanitary facilities are in three blocks with some washbasins in cabins. Child/baby room. Facilities for visitors with disabilities. Laundry facilities. Shop. Bar, restaurant, takeaway (1/5-30/9). Swimming pool (15/6-15/9). Play area. Tennis. Bicycle hire. Off site: Golf or riding 7 km. Indoor pool 7 km. Fishing 8 km. Beaune 9 km.

Open: 1 April - 15 October.

Directions

Site is north of Meursault. Take N74 from Beaune and follow the sign for Meursault. Site is signed from town but not very clearly (tents with three arrows). GPS: 46.98574, 4.76858

Charges guide

Per unit incl. 2 persons and electricity	€ 17,00 - € 21,50
extra person	€ 3,00 - € 3,70

Camping Cheques accepted.

Nevers

Camping de Nevers

Rue de la Jonction, F-58000 Nevers (Nièvre) T: 06 84 98 69 79. E: info@campingnevers.com

alanrogers.com/FR58100

On the banks of the Loire in Nevers, facing the cathedral and the Palace of the Dukes across the river, this small site has 73 grass pitches. Of these, only two are used for caravan holiday homes. Half of the site is for tents and the other half are touring pitches with electricity (6/10A). This site would provide a good base for a short stay to explore the region with its famous Burgundy wines of Sancerre and Pouilly Fumé. The pitches are quite tight and are not suitable for larger units, but the site is ideal for those in motorcaravans or tents because of its proximity to the town.

Facilities

One modern toilet block has unisex toilets and bright, clean showers, which may be under pressure in high season. Baby area. Provision for disabled visitors. Laundry. Motorcaravan service point. Bar (all season) with snacks in high season. Off site: All the amenities of Nevers, including large stores. Boat launching 500 m Golf and riding 5 km.

Open: 9 April - 10 October.

Directions

From the east on the A77 take exit 37 and follow directions for 'centre ville' to site on the right just before bridge across the Loire. From the west (Bourges) on D976 follow sign for 'Nevers Centre' onto D907. After 3 km. before bridge turn right to site on left. Site closed 12.00-15.00 (no waiting place outside). GPS: 46.98209, 3.16098

Charges guide

Per unit incl. 2 persons and electricity	€ 16,80 - € 20,60
extra person	€ 2,00 - € 3,00

Camping Cheques accepted.

Saint Boil

Camping le Moulin de Collonge

Moulin de Collonge, F-71390 Saint Boil (Saône-et-Loire) T: 03 85 44 00 32. E: millofcollonge@wanadoo.fr

alanrogers.com/FR71050

This small campsite is situated on the wine route between Beaune and Cluny and close to the long cycle route through the Burgundy vineyards. This well run, family site offers an 'away from it all' situation and it will appeal to those seeking a quiet, relaxing environment in a garden-like setting. There are 61 small to average-sized, level, grassy pitches, with 50 for touring (6A electricity) although long leads may be required. Most pitches are well shaded by a wide variety of mature trees making access for tall outfits quite difficult. No twin-axle caravans or large outfits accepted.

Facilities

Well kept toilet facilities in a converted barn. Laundry facilities. Freezer for campers' use. Bread daily. Basic shop (1/5-30/9). Restaurant/pizzeria, snack bar. Covered swimming pool (all season). Playgrounds. Bouncy castle. Bicycle hire. Table tennis. Fishing. Pony trekking. WiFi. Off site: Riding 4 km. Châteaux, wine route, churches. 117 km. 'voie verte' cycle track.

Open: 1 April - 30 September.

Directions

From Chalon-sur-Saône, take N80 west 9 km. Turn south on D981 through Buxy (6 km). Continue south to Saint Boil (7 km) and site is signed at south end of the village. GPS: 46.64621, 4.69479

Charges guide

Per unit incl. 2 persons and electricity	€ 19,00 - € 23,60
extra person	€ 4,75 - € 5,80

For latest campsite news, availability and prices visit

alanrogers.com

Palinges

Camping du Lac

Le Fourneau, F-71430 Palinges (Saône-et-Loire) T: 03 85 88 14 49. E: camping.palinges@hotmail.fr
alanrogers.com/FR71110

Camping du Lac is a very special campsite and it is all due to M. Labille, the owner, who thinks of the campsite as his home and every visitor as his guest. The campsite has 40 pitches in total, 16 of which have 10A electricity and 16 are fully serviced. There are seven chalets to rent. The site is adjacent to a lake with a beach and safe bathing. Set in the countryside yet within easy reach of many tourist attractions, especially Cluny, the local Château Digoin and Mont St Vincent with distant views of Mont Blanc on a clear day. If you want to visit a specific place, then Monsieur knows exactly where you should go – he never recommends anything that he hasn't personally tried out. Monsieur Labille provides tables and chairs for tent campers and he freezes bottles of water for cyclists to take away (free of charge).

Facilities

The central sanitary block provides all necessary facilities including those for campers with disabilities – site is particularly well adapted for disabled visitors. Motorcaravan services. Washing machine and fridge. Bread and croissants to order. Boules. Play area. TV room. Sports field, lake beach and swimming adjacent. Off site: Bar/snack bar outside entrance (weekends only outside 1/7-31/8). Riding 8 km. Palinges is within walking distance, cycle and walking routes, museums, cruises on canals, châteaux, 'museographical' complex.

Open: 1 April - 30 October.

Directions

Palinges is midway between Montceau les Mines and Paray le Monial. From Montceau take the N70, then turn left onto D92 to Palinges. Follow campsite signs. Site is also well signed from D985 Toulon-sur-Arroux to Charolles road. GPS: 46.56124, 4.22546

Charges 2011

| Per unit incl. 2 persons and electricity | € 20,00 |
| extra person | € 3,50 |

No credit cards.

Saint Honoré-les-Bains

Camping des Bains

15 avenue Jean Mermoz, F-58360 Saint Honoré-les-Bains (Nièvre) T: 03 86 30 73 44
E: camping-les-bains@wanadoo.fr alanrogers.com/FR58010

You are assured of a warm welcome at this attractive family run site, situated within walking distance of the village, in an area of rolling countryside, woods, rivers and country villages and ideal for walking or cycling. The spacious 130 level grassed pitches (6A electricity, long leads advised) are mostly separated by hedges with mature trees offering varying amounts of shade. Adjacent to the site there is the 'thermal spa' with opportunities to 'take the waters' for a three day session or a full blown cure of three weeks! Reception has details. There is an excellent restaurant almost opposite the campsite entrance and a casino in the village. This site is situated in the heart of Burgundy and is ideal for exploring the Morvan Regional Park which is well known for its food and wine.

Facilities

Two main sanitary units have mostly British style WCs, washbasins in cabins and showers. Laundry facilities and baby bath. Facilities for disabled visitors. Bar provides food and a takeaway (1/4-30/9). Swimming pool, slide and paddling pool (15/6-15/9). Play area. Streams for children to fish. Minigolf. Games room. Entertainment for children (July/Aug). TV and DVDs. Internet access and WiFi (charged). Off site: St Honoré-les-Bains with shops, banks, bars and restaurants 800 m. Bicycle hire or riding 500 m. Fishing 5 km.

Open: 1 April - 25 October.

Directions

From Nevers, travel east on D978. 6 km. beyond Châtillon-en-Bazois turn right onto D985 to St Honoré-les-Bains. Site is signed on entering town. Care is needed at narrow site entrance. GPS: 46.90671, 3.82843

Charges guide

Per unit incl. 2 persons	€ 11,00 - € 16,00
extra person	€ 4,50
electricity (6A)	€ 3,50

Camping Cheques accepted.

For latest campsite news, availability and prices visit

alanrogers.com

Saint Léger-de-Fougeret

Camping l'Etang de la Fougeraie

Hameau de Champs, F-58120 Saint Léger-de-Fougeret (Nièvre) T: 03 86 85 11 85
E: campingfougeraie@orange.fr alanrogers.com/FR58040

This is a quiet and peaceful, spacious campsite laid out on a hillside deep in the Parc Naturel Régional du Morvan, with views over the lake, meadows and surrounding hills. The spring water lake is ideal for fishing and swimming. Therre is a small bar and restaurant serving good quality regional meals and a well stocked shop with local produce. There are 60 terraced pitches, with 57 for touring, 36 with electricity (6A). The site is not suitable for double-axle or large outfits or people with walking difficulties, as the site roads are steep and narrow. Large RVs are not accepted.

Facilities

Traditional and modern buildings with all necessary facilities and a heated family/disabled room lie at the top of the site, a fair distance uphill from some pitches. Washing machine and dryer. Shop. Bar and restaurant (1/5-30/9). WiFi. Lake swimming. Fishing. Playgrounds. Caravan storage. American RVs not accepted, site not really suitable for large units. Off site: Riding 2 km. Shops, bank with ATM and services 7 km.

Open: 1 April - 30 September.

Directions

St Léger de Fougeret is about 10 km. south of Château-Chinon. From Château-Chinon take the D27 south for 3 km, then fork right on D157 for 5.5 km. to St Léger. Continue through village, follow signs to site 1 km. GPS: 47.00587, 3.90548

Charges guide

Per unit incl. 2 persons and electricity	€ 16,20 - € 17,20
extra person	€ 5,00

Saint Pereuse-en-Morvan

Camping le Manoir de Bezolle

F-58110 Saint Pereuse-en-Morvan (Nièvre) T: 03 86 84 42 55. E: info@camping-bezolle.com

alanrogers.com/FR58030

Manoir de Bezolle is in the heart of Burgundy, well situated to explore the Morvan Natural Park and the Nivernais area and is open all year round. It has been attractively landscaped to provide a number of different areas, some giving pleasant views over the surrounding countryside. There are 100 spacious pitches with 84 for touring, most with 10A electricity (long leads advised). One area is set out on terraces and some pitches are slightly sloping. Many have good shade from a variety of magnificent trees. There is a good children's play area and three well stocked, small lakes for anglers. There is a good bar, restaurant and takeaway with an attractive terrace overlooking the large, heated swimming pools. The lower, level area is more suitable for those with walking difficulties. There are many small towns and villages to visit in an area renowned for its gastronomy and history.

Facilities

Two main toilet blocks provide washbasins in cabins, mostly British style WCs, baths, baby bath and provision for disabled visitors. A small unit contains two tiny family WC/basin/shower suites for rent. Facilities by the pools can be heated in winter. Laundry. Motorcaravan services. Shop. Bar and restaurant. Pizza and takeaway (all year). Internet point and WiFi (charged). Two heated pools (1/5-15/9). Large play area. Minigolf. Boules. Fishing. Off site: Châtillon-en-Bazois with bars, restaurants and shops 14 km. Interesting old towns and villages with their châteaux, museums and markets. Walking and cycling in the Morvan Regional Park.

Open: All year.

Directions

Site is between Nevers and Autun. Leave the D978, 13 km. east of Châtillon-en-Bazois (site signed) onto D11. Site is a few hundred metres on the right. GPS: 47.05877, 3.81716

Charges guide

Per unit incl. 2 persons and electricity	€ 19,00 - € 23,00
extra person	€ 5,00
child (0-6 yrs)	€ 4,00

Savigny-les-Beaune

Camping les Premier Pres

Route de Bouilland, F-21420 Savigny-les-Beaune (Côte d'Or) T: 03 80 26 15 06
E: mairie.savigny-les-beaune@wanadoo.fr **alanrogers.com/FR21030**

A former municipal site, now privately owned, this popular site is ideally located for visiting the Burgundy vineyards, for use as a transit site or for spending time in the town of Beaune. During the high season it is full every evening, so it is best to arrive by 4 pm. The 90 level pitches are marked and numbered, with electric hook-ups and room for an awning. Whilst the famed wine region alone attracts many visitors, Beaune, its capital, is unrivalled in its richness of art from times gone by. Narrow streets and squares are garlanded with flowers, pavement cafés are crammed with tourists and overlooking the scene is the glistening Hotel Dieu.

Facilities

Well kept sanitary facilities are housed in a modern building behind reception. Additional WCs and water points are conveniently placed towards the middle of the site. Motorcaravan service point. Ice available to purchase. Torch useful. Off site: Sunday market in the village 1 km. Beaune 7 km.

Open: 29 April - 30 September.

Directions

From A6 autoroute take exit 24 signed Beaune and Savigny-les-Beaune onto D2. Turn right towards Savigny-les-Beaune (3 km) and follow signs to site. GPS: 47.069, 4.803

Charges guide

Per person	€ 2,30
child (under 7 yrs)	€ 1,20
pitch	€ 3,20
electricity	€ 3,35

No credit cards.

Tazilly

Airotel Château de Chigy

Chigy, F-58170 Tazilly (Nièvre) T: 03 86 30 10 80. E: reception@chateaudechigy.com.fr
alanrogers.com/FR58050

This very spacious site (20 ha. for pitches and another 50 ha. of fields, lakes and woods) lies at the southern tip of the Morvan Regional Natural Park. The château houses the reception and apartments. Most of the facilities are nearby, and behind are 54 good sized, shaded and slightly sloping pitches, many uneven, all with electricity (6A). There is a large woodland area with paths, beyond which are 100 or so less shaded pitches, some of up to 150 sq.m. Most are slightly sloping and some are on low terraces, nearly all with electricity. Most have very good views. Fishing is possible in the lakes. In high season there are organised activities and entertainment, and a children's club meets twice a week.

Facilities

Two toilet blocks provide British style WCs, washbasins in cubicles, and showers but are a good distance from many pitches. A Portacabin has 4 cubicles, each with toilet, washbasin and shower (can be hired as private in July/Aug). Facilities for disabled visitors and babies. Laundry facilities. Gas supplies. Shop. Bar, restaurant and takeaway (July/Aug). Two outdoor pools, one with paddling pool (15/5-30/9). Swimming in lake. Covered pool. Games and TV rooms. Playground. Minigolf. Boules. All weather sports terrain. Playing field. Off site: Luzy 4 km. Riding 9 km.

Open: 26 April - 30 September.

Directions

Leave Autun on N81 southwest (signed Bourbon-Lancy) through Luzy (D973, signed Bourbon-Lancy). Site is signed to the left after about 4 km. GPS: 46.75746, 3.94478

Charges guide

Per unit incl. 2 persons	€ 16,00 - € 20,00
extra person	€ 5,00 - € 6,50
child (6-17 yrs)	€ 4,00 - € 5,50
electricity	€ 4,00
dog	free - € 2,00

Reductions during certain periods, for age 55+, and for longer stays.

For latest campsite news, availability and prices visit
alanrogers.com

Tournus

Camping de Tournus

14 rue des Canes, F-71700 Tournus (Saône-et-Loire) T: 03 85 51 16 58. E: info@camping-tournus.com

alanrogers.com/FR71190

This very well maintained, pleasant site is just a few minutes from the A6 autoroute, 200 metres from the River Saône and close to the interesting old market town of Tournus. It is ideal for a night halt but deserving of a longer stay. The surrounding area is well worth exploring with its beautiful scenery and many picturesque old towns and villages. The new owners have made some hardstanding pitches to complement the fairly level grassy pitches. All 90 pitches are for touring and 70 have 6A electricity. A few trees give some pitches varying amounts of shade. Access is very easy for big units.

Facilities

Two clean toilet blocks near the entrance provide all necessary facilities, including for campers with disabilities. Small café (no alcohol) also stocking daily necessities and bread to order (all season). Small play area. Internet terminal. Bicycle hire. Motorcaravan services planned. Off site: Fishing 100 m. Tournus, Saturday market, shops, bars, cafes, banks etc. short walk/bike ride alongside river. Municipal pool next door.

Open: 1 April - 30 September.

Directions

From the A6 take exit 12 for Tournus and the N6 south for just over 1 km. In Tournus (opposite railway station), turn left signed camping and follow signs to site, about 1 km. GPS: 46.574321, 4.909515

Charges guide

Per unit incl. 2 persons and electricity	€ 19,10 - € 23,90
extra person	€ 3,90 - € 4,90

Camping Cheques accepted.

Vandenesse-en-Auxois

Sunêlia Lac de Panthier

RD977b, F-21320 Vandenesse-en-Auxois (Côte d'Or) T: 03 80 49 21 94. E: info@lac-de-panthier.com

alanrogers.com/FR21000

Camping Lac de Panthier is an attractively situated lakeside site in the Burgundy countryside. It is in two distinct areas, the smaller section houses the reception, shop, restaurant, indoor pool and sauna. The second, larger area is 200 m. along the lakeside road and is where the other site activities take place and the outdoor pools can be found. The 207 pitches (153 for touring) all have electricity (6A) and are mostly on gently sloping grass, although in parts there are shallow terraces. The restaurant and some of the pitches have panoramic views over the lake which offers many watersports. Used by tour operators.

Facilities

Each area has two adequate unisex toilet blocks with provision for babies and disabled visitors. Shop, bar and restaurant. Games and TV rooms. Swimming pool, children's pool and slide. Indoor pool, sauna and gym. Fishing. Riding. Bicycle hire and canoe hire. Watersports. Entertainment and activities organised in high season and clubs for children and teenagers. Internet access on payment (WiFi, limited area). Trampolene. Off site: Boat excursions from Pouilly-en-Auxois (8 km). Riding and golf 10 km. Dijon, Autun and Beaune. Bus to Dijon and Poilly-en-Auxois 300 m.

Open: 9 April - 9 October.

Directions

From the A6 join the A38 and exit immediately at junction 24. Take N81 south towards Arnay Le Duc, over A6, shortly turn left on D977 for 5 km. Fork left for Vandenesse-en-Auxois. Through village on D977 for 2.5 km, turn left and site is on left. GPS: 47.23661, 4.62810

Charges 2011

Per unit incl. 2 persons	€ 19,00 - € 28,00
extra person	€ 5,00 - € 7,00
child (2-7 yrs)	€ 2,00 - € 4,00

Camping Cheques accepted.

Arnay le Duc

Camping de l'Etang de Fouché

Rue du 8 mai 1945, F-21230 Arnay le Duc (Côte d'Or) T: 03 80 90 02 23. E: info@campingfouche.com

alanrogers.com/FR21040

Useful as a stop en route to or from the Mediterranean or indeed for longer stays, this quite large but peaceful, lakeside site with its new bar/restaurant and swimming pool complex, can be very busy during the school holidays, and is probably better visited outside the main season. There are over 200 good sized pitches, on fairly level grass and all with 10A electricity (some with water). Many are hedged and offer a choice of shade or a more open aspect. In July/August there are regular activities for children and adults. A two-kilometre stroll around the lake is very pleasant.

Facilities

Two new toilet blocks and third one (totally refurbished) provide all the necessary modern facilities (male and female are separate). Facilities for disabled visitors. Baby room. Washing machines and dishwashing under cover. Shop, bar, restaurant, takeaway (all 15/5-15/9). TV/games room. New small heated outdoor swimming pool. Boules. Playground. Off site: Town centre 800 m. Lakeside beach with playground, water slides, pedaloes, canoes.

Open: 1 April - 15 October.

Directions

From A6 (exit 24) take D981, 16 km. to the town. Turn left on D906 for about 400 m. and site is signed to left. GPS: 47.13411, 4.49840

Charges guide

Per unit incl. 2 persons and electricity	€ 19,10 - € 24,30
extra person	€ 4,50 - € 5,90
child (2-10 yrs)	€ 2,30 - € 3,30

For latest campsite news, availability and prices visit

alanrogers.com

Been to any good campsites lately?
We have

You'll find them here...

The UK's market leading independent guides to the best campsites

Located to the south of Alsace, the historic province of Franche Comté boasts a varied landscape ranging from flat plains to dense woodlands, rugged dramatic mountains and limestone valleys.

DÉPARTEMENTS: 25 DOUBS, 39 JURA, 70 HAUTE-SAÔNE, 90 TERRITOIRE DE BELFORT

MAJOR CITY: BESANÇON

Franche Comté is really made up of two regions. The high valley of the Saône is wide, gently rolling farmland with a certain rustic simplicity, while the Jura mountains are more rugged with dense forests, sheer cliffs, craggy limestone escarpments and torrents of clear, sparkling water gushing through deep gorges. It is for this thrilling scenery that Franche Comté is best known. Nature lovers can climb, bike and hike in the mountains or explore the hills honeycombed with over 4,000 caves. The streams and lakes provide world-class fishing. The spa towns of Salins-les-Bains, Luxeuil-les-Bains and Lons-le-Saunier offer relaxation and a chance to 'take the waters'.

The region has a rich architectural heritage dating from many different periods, including medieval abbeys and châteaux and the chapel of Ronchamp built by Le Corbusier in 1954. Roman remains, fortresses perched on cliff tops and elegant towns can all be explored at leisure. The region's position, bordering Switzerland and close to Germany, is reflected in its culture and also the great diversity of architectural style in the many fine buildings.

Places of interest

Arbois
Pasteur family home and museum, museum of wine and wine growing.

Arc-en-Senans
Royal Saltworks.

Belfort
Sandstone lion sculpted by Bartholdi; memorial and museum of the French Resistance.

Besançon
Citadel with good views over the city.

Champlitte
Museum of folk art.

Dole
Lovely old town, Louis Pasteur's birthplace.

La Cluse-et-Mijoux
Joux castle.

Luxeuil-les-Bains
Tour des Echevins museum.

Montbéliard
Castle, historic town centre

Ornans
Little French Venice, Gustave Courbet birthplace, museum.

Ronchamp
Chapel of Notre-Dame du Haut designed by Le Corbusier.

Salins-les-Bains
Salt mines and tunnels and museum.

Sochaux
Peugeot Museum.

Cuisine of the region

Fish: Freshwater fish such as trout, grayling, pike and perch are local specialities.

Wine: The region has a rare wine known as vin de paille as well as vin jaune (deep yellow and very dry) and vin du jura, other Jura wine.

Brési: Wafer-thin slices of dried beef; many local hams.

Saucisse de Morteau: Fat pork sausage smoked over pine and juniper.

Poulet au vin jaune: Chicken, cream and morilles cooked in vin jaune.

Cheeses of the Region: The famous Comté, Morbier, Mont d'Or and others

Images: © CRT Franche Comté: 003 Régis Ravegnani, 293 Madeleine Vernay, 344 CIGC, 421 Cécile Ambacher, 467 Barbara Gris Pichot, 666 CIGC

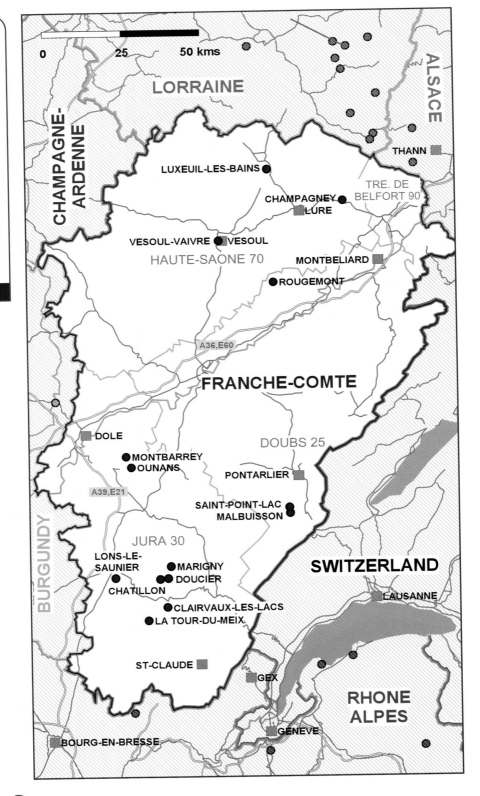

ALSACE

LORRAINE

CHAMPAGNE-ARDENNE

THANN

LUXEUIL-LES-BAINS

CHAMPAGNEY
LURE

TRE. DE
BELFORT 90

VESOUL-VAIVRE VESOUL

HAUTE-SAONE 70

MONTBELIARD

ROUGEMONT

A36,E60

FRANCHE-COMTE

DOLE

DOUBS 25

MONTBARREY
OUNANS

PONTARLIER

A39,E21

SAINT-POINT-LAC
MALBUISSON

JURA 30

SWITZERLAND

LONS-LE-SAUNIER

MARIGNY
DOUCIER

CHATILLON

CLAIRVAUX-LES-LACS

LA TOUR-DU-MEIX

LAUSANNE

ST-CLAUDE

GEX

RHONE
ALPES

GENEVE

BOURG-EN-BRESSE

BURGUNDY

For latest campsite news, availability and prices visit
alanrogers.com

Champagney

Camping Domaine les Ballastières

F-70290 Champagney (Haute-Saône) T: 03 84 23 11 22. E: contact@campinglesballastieres.com
alanrogers.com/FR70030

Within easy reach of the historic town of Belfort, Les Ballastières opened in 2008. The landscaping is becoming established and the 100 touring pitches are very large, level and easily accessible. Reception building also houses the bar and snack bar, while outside a patio with tables and chairs overlookings the pool and adjacent lake. The site has been designed with disabled campers in mind; although there is a sloping path down to the pool, a hoist has been installed, and one of the ten mobile homes has ramps.

Facilities

Two toilet blocks each with good facilities including those for disabled visitors, but may become stretched in high season. Washbasins in cabins. Laundry. Swimming and paddling pools (July/Aug). Shop (July/Aug), bar with TV and snackbar (all season). Special climbing facilities for children (3-11 yrs) with supervisor all season. Kayaks and canoes all season. Play area. Motorcaravan services. Off site: ATM 300 m. Ronchamp 4 km.

Open: 1 April - 31 October.

Directions

Site is 20 km. northwest of Belfort; from roundabout on east side of Ronchamp on D19, take the D4 eastwards for 2 km. Site is signed on the left. GPS: 47.706841, 6.671437

Charges guide

Per unit incl. 2 persons and electricity	€ 13,00 - € 20,50
dog	€ 1,50

Chatillon

Kawan Village Domaine de l'Epinette

15 rue de l'Epinette, F-39130 Chatillon (Jura) T: 03 84 25 71 44. E: info@domaine-epinette.com
alanrogers.com/FR39080

This site is set in charming wooded countryside on land sloping down to the river Ain, which is shallow and slow moving. There are 150 grassy pitches, 110 are available for touring units, some slightly sloping. These are arranged on terraces and separated by hedges and young bushes and trees, about half being shaded. Nearly all have electricity hook-ups, although some long leads are needed. Four pitches have hardstanding. There is an attractive swimming pool with a paddling pool. An activity club for children takes place in July/August. Guided canoe trips on the river start and finish at the campsite.

Facilities

Two modern toilet blocks. Unit for disabled visitors. Baby bath. Dishwashing and laundry sinks. Washing machine and dryer. Small shop for basics. Snack bar and takeaway (evenings). New reception, bar, TV room and shop. Swimming pool (heated 1/7-31/8). Playground. Boules. Direct river access river for swimming and canoeing. Off site: Riding 6 km. Golf 25 km. Shops in Doucier 6 km.

Open: 9 June - 15 September.

Directions

From Lons-le-Saunier take D471 eastwards towards Champagnole. After about 8 km. fork right onto D39 towards Doucier. After 11 km. at Chatillon turn right onto D151 south towards Blye. Site is less than 2 km. on the left. GPS: 46.65887, 5.72978

Charges guide

Per unit incl. 2 persons and electricity	€ 17,00 - € 27,00
extra person	€ 3,50 - € 4,50
Camping Cheques accepted.	

Clairvaux-les-Lacs

Yelloh! Village Fayolan

B.P. 52, F-39130 Clairvaux-les-Lacs (Jura) T: 04 66 73 97 39. E: info@yellohvillage-fayolan.com
alanrogers.com/FR39050

This large, spacious site is modern and well equipped. Backed by wooded hills, it is situated on the shores of Le Petit Lac amid the lakes and forests of the Jura, about a mile from the town of Clairvaux-les-Lacs. It is in two parts, with 516 pitches either on terraces overlooking the lake or on the flatter area near the shore. With 456 for touring units, all have electricity (10A) and 200 are fully serviced. The pitches are separated by hedges and mature trees giving most some shade. Many activities are organised on site, some in low season. Used by tour operators (130 pitches).

Facilities

Four modern well equipped toilet units. Baby room. Washing and drying machines. Shop. Restaurant. Bar. Snack bar/pizzeria and takeaway. Swimming pool complex with indoor pool (all season), outdoor pool (heated) 11/6-4/9). Fitness centre, sauna, steam bath, massage (16/5-2/9). Entertainment area. Playground. Organised activities, children's club. Internet access. Fishing. Beach sports area and lake swimming. Boules. Off site: Bicycle hire 800 m. Riding 15 km.

Open: 6 May - 4 September.

Directions

Clairvaux-les-Lacs is on the D678 about 23 km. southeast of Lons-le-Saunier. In Clairvaux follow signs for 'Lacs Campings' and Fayolan (1.5 km. southeast of town). GPS: 46.56438, 5.75621

Charges 2011

Per unit incl. 2 persons and electricity	€ 15,00 - € 42,00
extra person	€ 5,00 - € 7,00
child (3-7 yrs)	free - € 5,00
dog	€ 4,00

Doucier

Camping Domaine de Chalain

F-39130 Doucier (Jura) T: 03 84 25 78 78. E: chalain@chalain.com

alanrogers.com/FR39030

Doucier lies 25 km. east of Lons-le-Saunier among the wooded hills of the Jura and rather away from the main routes. This large, spacious site is in a parkland setting beside Lac de Chalain and is surrounded by woods and cliffs. Large areas are left for sports and recreation. The lake shelves gently but then becomes deep quite suddenly. The site also has an attractive, well equipped pool complex. There are 800 good-sized, level pitches with 462 for touring units, Most have electricity (7A) and there are varying amounts of shade. Booking is obligatory for caravans or motorcaravans over seven metres.

Facilities

Nine well equipped sanitary blocks with facilities for babies and disabled visitors. Shops (some high season only). Restaurant and bar. Takeaway, snacks (20/6-31/8). Swimming pool complex with heated indoor pool, outdoor pools with slide, sauna and spa (one entrance per day). Many large play areas. Fishing. Pedalo and bicycle hire. Sports activities including rock climbing, archery, aquagym. TV room. Disco, entertainment, organised activities. Dogs not permitted on lake beach. Off site: Riding 2 km. Golf 25 km.

Open: 29 April - 20 September.

Directions

Doucier is 25 km. east of Lons-le-Saunier. In village turn left off D39, site signed, entrance in 3 km. GPS: 46.66435, 5.81315

Charges guide

Per unit incl. 3 persons	
and electricity	€ 22,00 - € 36,50
extra person	€ 4,00 - € 6,00
child (4-15 yrs)	€ 3,00 - € 5,00
dog	€ 2,00

Doucier

Camping les Mérilles

Rue des 3 Lacs, F-39130 Doucier (Jura) T: 03 84 25 73 06. E: camping.lesmerilles@wanadoo.fr

alanrogers.com/FR39170

Camping les Mérilles is a small, good quality, family run campsite 500 m. from the small town of Doucier and only 2 km. from the beautiful Lac de Chalain. It has 96 good sized, level, grass pitches separated by hedging. A variety of trees give some shade. There are 73 pitches for touring with 16 having a private bathroom. All have electricity (6/10A). This site is a quieter alternative to the much busier sites near the lake. The surrounding area is well worth exploring and is well known for its lakes, waterfalls and caves. Owners of large outfits should phone ahead to reserve the larger pitches.

Facilities

One modern, well appointed and heated toilet block near reception, one older and very small block plus 16 private cabins to rent with certain pitches. Motorcaravan services. Basic shop and bar with TV (1/6-30/9). Takeaway (1/7-30/9). Outdoor heated pool and paddling pool (1/5-30/9). Playground. Bicycle hire. WiFi (free). Organised family activities (July/Aug). Off site: Doucier with small shops, bar and restaurant 500 m. Lac Chalain, indoor pool, beach and watersports 2 km.

Open: 1 April - 30 September.

Directions

Doucier is 25 km. east of Lons-le-Saunier. The site is 500 m. east of Doucier on the D39 with the entrance on the right. GPS: 46.65178, 5.77491

Charges guide

Per unit incl. 2 persons	
and electricity	€ 15,50 - € 18,90
incl. private bathroom	€ 19,10 - € 24,95
extra person	€ 3,80 - € 3,95
child (2-7 yrs)	€ 2,00 - € 2,30

La Tour-du-Meix

Camping de Surchauffant

Le Pont de la Pyle, F-39270 La Tour-du-Meix (Jura) T: 03 84 25 41 08. E: surchauffant@chalain.com

alanrogers.com/FR39020

With only 180 pitches, this site may appeal to those who prefer a more informal atmosphere, however it can be lively in high season. It is pleasantly situated above the beaches bordering the Lac de Vouglans, which can be reached quickly on foot directly from the site. The 133 touring pitches are of a reasonable size and are informally arranged, some are fully serviced and most have electricity (5A). They are divided by hedges and there is some shade. The lake offers a variety of watersports activities, boat trips, etc. and is used for fishing and swimming (guarded in high season as it shelves steeply). Two signed walks start from within 100 metres of the site entrance. English is spoken.

Facilities

The sanitary facilities are older in style and adequate rather than luxurious, but reasonably well maintained and clean when we visited. They include some washbasins in private cabins. Laundry. Heated swimming pool (200 sq.m), paddling pool and surround (15/6-15/9). Three playgrounds. Entertainment (July/Aug). Safety deposit boxes. Off site: Bicycle hire or riding 5 km. Restaurant, takeaway and shops adjacent.

Open: 24 April - 15 September.

Directions

From A39 take exit 7 and N1082 to Lons-le-Saunier. Continue south on D52 for about 20 km. to Orgelet. Site is by the D470, at La Tour-du-Meix, about 4 km. east of Orgelet. GPS: 46.5231, 5.67401

Charges guide

Per unit incl. 2 persons	
and electricity	€ 16,00 - € 23,00
extra person (over 4 yrs)	€ 3,00 - € 4,70

For latest campsite news, availability and prices visit

alanrogers.com

Lons-le-Saunier

Camping la Marjorie

640 boulevard de l'Europe, F-39000 Lons-le-Saunier (Jura) T: 03 84 24 26 94. E: info@camping-marjorie.com
alanrogers.com/FR39060

La Marjorie is a spacious site set on the outskirts of the spa town of Lons-le-Saunier with a long season. Bordering one area of the site are open fields and woodlands. It has 200 level pitches, 185 for touring units and 130 with electricity (6/10A). Some are on hardstanding and 37 are fully serviced. They are separated by well trimmed hedges interspersed with tall trees which gives privacy plus some shade. There is a cycle path from the site into town (2.5 km) and a mountain bike track behind the site. This is a good site for a long or short stay.

Facilities

Three well maintained toilet blocks, two modern and heated, Baby baths, facilities for disabled visitors. Small shop, small bar with takeaway meals (all 15/6-31/8). TV room. Small play area. Boules. Football field. Archery, canoeing and riding. Motorcaravan service point (charge). Bicycle hire. Off site: Swimming pool 200 m. (free for min. 5 day stay). Bus stop 400 m. Restaurants 500 m. Fishing 3 km. Riding 5 km. Golf 6 km. Caves and waterfalls 17 km.

Open: 1 April - 15 October.

Directions

Site is off the N1083 Lons-le-Saunier - Besançon road, just north of Lons. Follow signs for 'camping' and 'piscine'. GPS: 46.68437, 5.56843

Charges guide

Per unit incl. 2 persons	
and electricity	€ 15,30 - € 20,60
extra person	€ 2,90 - € 4,90
child (under 10 yrs)	€ 1,70 - € 3,20

Luxeuil-les-Bains

Domaine du Chatigny

14 rue du Gramont, F-70300 Luxeuil-les-Bains (Haute-Saône) T: 03 84 93 97 97
E: camping.ot-luxeuil@wanadoo.fr alanrogers.com/FR70010

An excellent example of a well cared for municipal site, du Chatigny is located on a hillside backing onto woods, yet is only a five minute walk from the centre of the interesting old spa town of Luxeuil-les-Bains. As the site has only recently been opened, all facilities are of a high quality and were very clean when we visited. There are 98 good sized, level or slightly sloping, grass pitches separated by young shrubs and trees with not much shade. Of the 78 touring pitches 52 have electricity (16A) and 26 are fully serviced. Some activities are organised on site, but a wide programme of events is offered within walking distance.

Facilities

One modern, heated toilet block is excellent and provides all necessary facilities. Motorcaravan services. Snack bar, swimming and paddling pool (open weekends June, Sept and every day July/Aug). Games/TV room. Tennis. Internet, WiFi. Off site: Fishing and riding 2 km. Golf 10 km. Spa town of Luxeuil-les-Bains with good range shops, bars, restaurants, casino, Saturday market and many organised events, 5 minutes walk.

Open: 1 April - 31 October.

Directions

There is no access for vehicles from the centre of Luxeuil-les-Bains. Bypass Luxeuil-les-Bains on the N57 and at supermarket (site signed) turn west into Rue Ste Anne. Bear right three times to site (900 m). GPS: 47.8236, 6.381667

Charges guide

Per unit incl. 2 persons	
and electricity	€ 17,00 - € 20,00
incl. full services	€ 18,50 - € 22,50
extra person	€ 2,00 - € 4,00

Malbuisson

Camping les Fuvettes

F-25160 Malbuisson (Doubs) T: 03 81 69 31 50. E: les-fuvettes@wanadoo.fr
alanrogers.com/FR25080

High in the Jura and close to the Swiss border, Les Fuvettes is a well established family site beside Lac Saint Point. The 320 reasonably sized grass pitches are separated by hedges and small trees with varying degrees of shade and many are slightly sloping. There are 250 for touring with 200 having electricity (4/6A). Only a few have views over the lake. The swimming pool complex is impressive with water slides and a separate children's pool. The site's bar/snack bar is housed in an attractive, steep roofed building and offers panoramic views across the lake.

Facilities

Three toilet blocks include facilities for babies and disabled campers. Shop. Bar and snack bar. Swimming pool with water slides, jacuzzi and paddling pool (from June). Play area. Minigolf. Archery. Bicycle hire. Sports pitch. Fishing (permit needed). Boat and pedalo hire. Games room. TV room. Children's club in peak season. Entertainment and excursion programme (July/Aug). Mobile homes and chalets for rent. Off site: Lake beach. Sailing school. Tennis. Riding 1 km. Bicycle hire 3 km.

Open: 1 April - 30 September.

Directions

From Besançon, head south on the N57 to just beyond Pontarlier. Take the D437 signed Lac St Point and Mouthe. The road skirts the lake and through Malbuisson. Site is on right at the end of the village. GPS: 46.79197, 6.29334

Charges guide

Per unit incl. 2 persons	
and electricity	€ 17,60 - € 26,10
extra person	€ 3,50 - € 5,20
child (under 7 yrs)	€ 1,80 - € 2,90

Marigny

Kawan Village la Pergola

1 rue des Vernois, F-39130 Marigny (Jura) T: 03 84 25 70 03. E: contact@lapergola.com

alanrogers.com/FR39040

Close to the Swiss border and overlooking the sparkling waters of Lac de Chalain, La Pergola is a good quality terraced site set amongst the rolling hills of the Jura. Neat and tidy, it is very well appointed, with 350 pitches, 100 for touring, mainly on grass and gravel and separated by small hedges. All have electricity (6A), water and drainage and some have shade from a variety of mature trees. The well-appointed bar/restaurant and terrace are next to the three swimming pools and the entertainment area, with good views over the lake. This is a good holiday base in high season for families. English is spoken.

Facilities

Three good quality and well appointed toilet blocks with all the necessary facilities including for disabled visitors and children. Motorcaravan services. Shop (1/6-15/9). Bar. Self-service restaurant. Pizzeria/takeaway (15/5-15/9). Pool complex, two pools heated. Good play areas and children's club. Archery. Boules. Lake swimming. Fishing. Pedaloes, canoes and small boats for hire. Evening entertainment with disco twice weekly. Internet and WiFi. Off site: Hang-gliding 2 km. Riding 3 km. Golf 25 km. Many marked walks and cycle trails in the area.

Open: 15 May - 15 September.

Directions

Doucier is 25 km. east of Lons-le-saunier. On outskirts of Doucier turn north onto D27, site signed. Site is 3 km. beside Lac de Chalain. GPS: 46.6771, 5.78094

Charges guide

Per unit incl. 2 persons and electricity	€ 21,00 - € 36,00
extra person	€ 5,50 - € 7,00
child (3-7 yrs)	free - € 5,50

Camping Cheques accepted.

Montbarrey

Flower Camping les Trois Ours

28 rue du Pont, F-39380 Montbarrey (Jura) T: 03 84 81 50 45. E: contact@camping-les3ours-jura.com

alanrogers.com/FR39150

This is a site for those seeking a shady, quiet and pleasant location. The adjacent River Loué will be an attraction for fishermen and river bathing is also possible. There are a number of mobile homes and chalets to rent, but there should be around 90 shady level grassy touring pitches all with electricity. During peak season, various activities are organised including canoeing trips and themed evenings. The new restaurant, with a river terrace, has been attractively decorated and has a varied and inviting menu.

Facilities

One sanitary block provides all the usual facilities. Good restaurant and bar with TV. Outdoor pool (1/6-15/9). Small adventure style playground. Boules. Small lake for fishing (free), river fishing (permit required). WiFi in bar area (charged). Off site: Riding and bicycle hire 3 km. Golf 13 km. Shops, ATM and services in Ounans 3 km.

Open: 1 April - 30 September.

Directions

From D472 Salins-les-Bains - Dole road, turn north on D11, 3.5 km. west of Ounans. Site is 3 km. on left just after river bridge. GPS: 47.011917, 5.6305

Charges guide

Per unit incl. 2 persons	€ 14,00 - € 20,50
extra person	€ 2,90 - € 5,00
child (2-7 yrs)	€ 1,90 - € 2,70

Ounans

Camping la Plage Blanche

3 rue de la Plage, F-39380 Ounans (Jura) T: 03 84 37 69 63. E: reservation@la-plage-blanche.com

alanrogers.com/FR39010

In the Jura, by the rippling waters of the River Loue, this spacious eight-hectare site has 220 pitches (193 for touring, 70 on the riverbank). All are large grassy and level with 10A electricity. In low season, this is a perfect site for couples; in high season it is ideal for family holidays with its children's club (5-11 years), two evening events per week in the bar/restaurant (DJ or live music), swimming pool, kayaking, canoeing, fishing, fly fishing and woodland walks in the site's own wood. La Plage Blanche is an excellent base for exploring Dole, Arbois and its vineyards and the famous Comté cheesemakers.

Facilities

Modern, well kept sanitary facilities (heated in low season) in three blocks, one renovated for 2011, include showers, washbasins in cabins and facilities for babies and campers with disabilities. Launderette. Motorcaravan service area. No shop but bread to order. Bar/restaurant with terrace (open all season). Swimming and paddling pools (1/5-30/9). Jacuzzi and sauna planned. Play area. Entertainment, activities and children's club (1/7-30/8). River fishing and fishing lake. Woodland walks. Canoeing. WiFi. Off site: Activities centre at site entrance. Bicycle hire 200 m. Shop 1.5 km. Supermarket 6 km. Riding 10 km.

Open: 1 April - 15 October.

Directions

Ounans is 20 km. southeast of Dole. From autoroute A36, exit 6 (Dole), take the N5 southeast to Mont-sous-Vaudrey (10 km). Bear left on D472 to Ounans (5 km). In Ounans take D71 north signed Montbarrey for 1 km. Turn left to site immediately after the river. GPS: 47.00284, 5.663

Charges guide

Per unit incl. 2 persons and electricity	€ 17,00 - € 22,00
extra person	€ 5,50
child (1-7 yrs)	€ 3,50
dog	€ 1,50

For latest campsite news, availability and prices visit

alanrogers.com

Rougemont

Castel Camping le Val de Bonnal

Bonnal, F-25680 Rougemont (Doubs) T: 03 81 86 90 87. E: val-de-bonnal@wanadoo.fr
alanrogers.com/FR25000

This is an impressive, generally peaceful, well managed site in a large country estate, designed to blend harmoniously with the surrounding countryside, well away from main roads and other intrusions. The site itself is very busy, with a wide range of activities and amenities. The 280 good sized, landscaped pitches (120 for touring) with electricity (6-10A) are separated by a mixture of trees and bushes. The main attraction must be the variety of watersports on the three large lakes and nearby river. The range of activities available in high season is almost inexhaustible, not to say exhausting!

Facilities

Four toilet blocks include washbasins in cabins, suites for disabled visitors and facilities for children and babies. Laundry facilities. Riverside restaurant, snack bar/takeaway, bar and terrace, shop (all 6/5-6/9). Swimming pool complex with water slides. Well equipped play areas. Sport and fitness facilities. Boules. Bicycle hire. Watersports. Fishing on the river and lake. Fitness suite. WiFi (charged). Off site: Rougemont 3.5 km. Golf 6 km. Riding 7 km. Day trips to Switzerland.

Open: 4 May - 4 September.

Directions

From Vesoul take D9 towards Villersexel. After about 20 km. turn right in Esprels signed Val-de-Bonnal. Continue for 3.5 km. to site on left. From autoroute A36, exit Baume-les-Dames; go north on D50, then D486 to Rougemont and follow site signs. GPS: 47.50698, 6.35487

Charges guide

Per unit incl. 2 persons and electricity	€ 25,00 - € 44,00
extra person	€ 6,70 - € 12,00

Saint Point-Lac

Camping Municipal de Saint-Point-Lac

8 rue du Port, F-25160 Saint Point-Lac (Doubs) T: 03 81 69 61 64. E: camping-saintpointlac@wanadoo.fr
alanrogers.com/FR25050

A good example of a municipal campsite in which the village takes a pride, this site is on the banks of a small lake with views to the distant hills. The 84 level, numbered pitches are on grass and 60 have electricity (16A). It is worth making a detour from the Pontarlier - Vallorbe road or for a longer stay. The village shop and restaurant are an easy 200 m. walk from the site entrance. Units over seven metres in length are not accepted.

Facilities

Well maintained, older style central sanitary block (partly refurbished) has British style WCs and free hot water. Suite for disabled visitors. Laundry facilities. Hot snacks and takeaway in high season (July/Aug). Fishing. Off site: Lakeside walk. Motorcaravan services opposite. Beach and swimming area. Pedalo hire. Bicycle hire 5 km.

Open: 1 May - 30 September.

Directions

From north, take D437 south of Pontarlier and keep on west side of the lake to the second village (Saint Point-Lac); from south exit N57 at Les Hopitaux-Neufs and turn west to lake. GPS: 46.8118, 6.3031

Charges guide

Per unit incl. 2 persons and electricity	€ 13,50 - € 15,00
extra person	€ 2,25 - € 2,75
child (4-10 yrs)	€ 1,25 - € 1,50
dog	€ 1,50

Vesoul-Vaivre

Camping International du Lac

Avenue des Rives du Lac, F-70000 Vesoul-Vaivre (Haute-Saône) T: 03 84 76 22 86
E: camping_dulac@yahoo.fr alanrogers.com/FR70020

This is one of the better examples of a town site and is part of a leisure park around a large lake. The campsite does not have direct access to the lake as it is separated by a security fence, but access is possible at the site entrance. There are 160 good sized, level, grass pitches, all with 10A electricity. Access is from hard roads and pitches are separated by shrubs and bushes. There is a large area in the centre of the site with a play area. A 5 km. path has been created around the lake for jogging, walking and cycling.

Facilities

Three good quality toilet blocks, one heated, are well spaced around the site and provide a mix of British and Turkish style WCs, washbasins and showers. Baby room. Two superb suites for disabled visitors. Washing machines and dryers. Motorcaravan service point. Baker calls daily (July/Aug); bread ordered from reception at other times. Entertainment (July/Aug). Bicycle hire. TV and games room. Boules. Internet access. Fishing. Off site: Bar and restaurant adjacent. Lake beach 100 m. Sailing 2 km. Riding 4 km.

Open: 1 March - 31 October.

Directions

On road D457 to west of Vesoul on route to Besançon, well signed around the town. GPS: 47.63054, 6.12946

Charges guide

Per person	€ 3,60
child (under 7 yrs)	€ 1,70
pitch	€ 3,50
incl. electricity	€ 5,50
vehicle	€ 2,70

For latest campsite news, availability and prices visit
alanrogers.com

This quiet and deeply rural province is right in the centre of France to the south of the tourist region of the Loire Valley. Unspoilt and thinly populated, it is unknown to many but by others is considered close to paradise.

DÉPARTEMENTS: 19 CORRÈZE, 23 CREUSE, 87 HAUTE-VIENNE

MAJOR CITIES: LIMOGES AND BRIVE-LA-GAILLARDE

On the western side of the Massif Central, this stunningly beautiful region of still lakes, fast flowing streams, gentle rolling valleys, such as the Dordogne valley, and forested hills has been one of the best kept secrets in France. Lush green meadows are grazed by the Limousin breed of cattle, numerous ancient villages and churches dot the landscape, as well as more imposing abbey churches and fortresses. The region's moorland has made it popular with horse breeders and the Anglo-Arab horse originated from the famous studs of Pompadour.

The city of Limoges, synonymous with porcelain production, produced the finest painted enamelware of Europe in the 16th and 17th centuries and today remains the porcelain capital of France. Aubusson is renowned for its beautiful and intricate tapestries.

But Limousin's appeal is above all the freedom of the countryside and it has not yet been discovered except by the discerning traveller. It is said that in Limousin a discovery awaits you at the end of every path and we consider this to be a fairly accurate description.

CORRÈZE | CREUSE | HAUTE-VIENNE

Nature

Le Lac de Vassivière

The largest lake of the Limousin has a special kind of magic: a distillation of landscapes, activities and contemporary art. Visit the Arts and Landscape Centre designed by architect Aldo Rossi or the Storytelling Festival.

www.lelacdevassiviere.com

Les Parc Naturels Régionaux

Two beautiful national parks: Périgord-Limousin offers a mosaic of surprising landscapes and Millevaches en Limousin, on the foothills of the Central Massif is an area also rich in cultural heritage.

www.parc-naturel-perigord-limousin.fr
www.pnr-millevaches.fr

The Valley of the Impressionists

In the middle of the 19th century, many painters followed the lead set by Claude Monet, to set up their easels along the valley of the Creuse. The ruins of Crozant were to be a focal point for landscape artists – and they are still today.

Outdoor activities

Walking

The region offers 6,000 km. of hiking paths in a beautiful, green, rolling landscape; ideal for a short outing with the family or a long march for the truly fit.

Cycling

A great choice of routes for all levels: flat roads on the highlands and hilly routes through mountains and valleys. Also good for mountain biking.

Canoeing

The Limousin is a region of unspoilt nature with plenty of water. For example, some 30 rivers are available for canoeing and there are many opportunities to rent boats.

Golf

Golf lovers can play ten courses, including five with 18 holes.

Argentat

Camping le Vaurette

Monceaux-sur-Dordogne, F-19400 Argentat (Corrèze) T: 05 55 28 09 67. E: info@vaurette.com

alanrogers.com/FR19090

You are assured of a warm welcome at this immaculate site, beautifully situated beside the shallow river Dordogne and just a few kilometres from Argentat. There are 120 large, gently sloping grass pitches, 118 for touring. Separated by a large variety of beautiful trees and shrubs offering varying amounts of shade, all have 6A electricity and many have good views over the river Dordogne as the pitches nearest the river are slightly terraced. The owners run an active campsite for all the family whilst maintaining an air of tranquillity (no radios). Excellent English is spoken.

Facilities

Two very clean traditional toilet blocks offer all the expected facilities, including those for disabled visitors. Further facilities are near the bar and heated pool. Motorcaravan service point. Shop and takeaway (July/Aug). Football. Gym. Badminton. Boules. Tennis. Fishing. River bathing. Accompanied canoe trips, walks and mountain bike rides. Organised activities for all the family (July/Aug) but no late night discos etc. WiFi. Off site: Argentat 9 km. Riding 15 km.

Open: 1 May - 21 September.

Directions

From the A20 or A89 take the exit for Tulle then the N120 to Argentat, onto the D12 towards Beaulieu. The site is on the left. GPS: 45.0464, 1.8821

Charges 2011

Per unit incl. 2 persons and electricity	€ 18,50 - € 28,50
extra person (over 2 yrs)	€ 3,50 - € 5,50
dog	€ 2,00 - € 3,50

For latest campsite news, availability and prices visit

alanrogers.com

Argentat

Sunêlia Au Soleil d'Oc

Monceaux-sur-Dordogne, F-19400 Argentat (Corrèze) T: 05 55 28 84 84. E: info@dordogne-soleil.com

alanrogers.com/FR19100

You will be assured of a very warm welcome, throughout the long season, at this attractive family run site set amongst a variety of tall trees on the banks of the river Dordogne. The 120 large, level, grass pitches, 80 for tourists, all with 6A electricity, are mostly separated by neatly trimmed shrubs and hedges. They are set out on two levels; the lower level nearer the river, with fewer static pitches, is some distance from the toilet facilities and sports area. This site should appeal to lovers of watersports and other activities, particularly in July and August when there is plenty to do for all the family.

Facilities

Two unisex toilet blocks offer all the facilities one would expect. Baby facilities. Shop. Bar. Restaurant and takeaway (1/6-30/9). Outdoor pool (1/5-15/10). New indoor pool planned. Motorcaravan service point. Bathing in the river Dordogne. Canoe hire and organised trips. Volleyball, football, pool table and electronic games. Archery. Minigolf. Fishing. Bicycle hire. Guided walks and bike rides. Entertainment programme (July/Aug). WiFi. Off site: River Dordogne. Argentat 4 km. Riding 15 km.

Open: 1 April - 1 November.

Directions

Leave Argentat on D12 heading southwest (Beaulieu). In 3.5 km. (village of Laygue) turn left across a single track bridge spanning the river Dordogne. Immediately turn left and site is a few hundred metres on left. GPS: 45.0753, 1.91699

Charges guide

Per unit incl. 2 persons	€ 14,50 - € 20,70
extra person	€ 3,80 - € 5,80
child (2-13 yrs)	free - € 3,90
dog	free - € 3,00

Camping Cheques accepted.

Aubazine

Campéole

Campéole le Coiroux

Centre Touristique du Coiroux, F-19190 Aubazine (Corrèze) T: 05 55 27 21 96. E: coiroux@campeole.com

alanrogers.com/FR19140

Le Coiroux, part of the Campéole group, is set in a picturesque location in the heart of a forest on the edge of a large leisure park and lake. There are 174 large pitches, 62 for touring all with 10A electricity. They are flat and grassy with small dividing hedges and trees giving shade. The large number of mobile homes and chalets on site are separate from the camping area and not intrusive. There is everything one needs for a family holiday at this site which caters for adults and children of all ages.

Facilities

One large modern very well equipped sanitary block with all necessary facilities including those for campers with disabilities and baby room. Washing machines and tumble dryers. Motorcaravan service point. Large heated swimming pool (1/5-30/9). Poolside bar, snack bar and large shop selling groceries, fruit and vegetables. Boules. Tennis. Organised activities for children, teenagers and adults throughout the day (July/Aug). Accommodation for hire (until 3/11). Off site: Leisure park (reduced fees charged). Excellent 27-hole golf complex 800 m. Lake fishing 300 m. Tree walking adventure course. Paintball. Rocamadour and many other tourist destinations are within 1 hour's drive.

Open: 1 April - 30 September.

Directions

Leave A20 exit 50 Brive centre, take N28 towards Tulle. At the village of Gare d'Aubazine turn right to Aubazine. Continue for 6 km. through village, take road to Chastang and follow signs to Parc Touristique du Coiroux about 4 km. GPS: 45.18633, 1.70775

Charges guide

Per unit incl. 2 persons and electricity	€ 15,10 - € 24,50
extra person	€ 4,00 - € 5,90
child (2-6 yrs)	free - € 3,90
dog	€ 2,00 - € 2,60

For latest campsite news, availability and prices visit
alanrogers.com

Beaulieu-sur-Dordogne

Flower Camping des Iles

Boulevard Rodolphe de Turenne, F-19120 Beaulieu-sur-Dordogne (Corrèze) T: 05 55 91 02 65
E: info@campingdesiles.fr alanrogers.com/FR19130

This is a very pleasant and well equipped site in a beautiful location on a small island in the river Dordogne. Camping des Iles is a very attractive family run site only five minutes walk away from the centre of the medieval town of Beaulieu-sur-Dordogne with its ancient streets, old churches, many shops and restaurants. This five-hectare site has 120 shady, grass pitches, 90 of which are available for touring, all with 10A electricity. The added bonus of its close proximity to the centre of the village makes this an ideal site for touring units.

Facilities

Three modern, clean toilet blocks. Baby room. Facilities disabled visitors. Laundry room. Motorcaravan service point. Heated pool (June-Sept), poolside bar, snacks. Boules. Canoe hire. Fishing. Children's entertainment (3-12 yrs) four days per week. Evening soirées two evenings per week. No shop or bread available on site. Off site: Pizzeria and takeaway 200 m. Tennis 600 m. Bicycle hire 8 km. Golf or riding 18 km. Gouffre de Padirac, Rocamadour, Collonges-la-Rouge (less than 1 hour). Caves, museums, several beautiful old villages.

Open: 7 April - 15 October.

Directions

The site is in the centre of the Beaulieu-sur-Dordogne on the D940. From Tulle turn right or from Montal turn left. Approach site with care through the narrow streets. Enter site through narrow archway. GPS: 44.979705, 1.840146

Charges guide

Per unit incl. 2 persons	€ 11,90 - € 19,90
with electricity	€ 14,90 - € 23,50
extra person	€ 3,90 - € 6,50
child (2-7 yrs)	free - € 3,00

Low season reductions.

Bonnac-la-Côte

Castel Camping le Château de Leychoisier

Domaine de Leychoisier, 1 route de Leychoisier, F-87270 Bonnac-la-Côte (Haute-Vienne) T: 05 55 39 93 43
E: contact@leychoisier.com alanrogers.com/FR87020

You will receive a warm welcome at this beautiful, family run 15th-century château site. It offers peace and quiet in superb surroundings. It is ideally situated for short or long stays being only two kilometres from the A20/N20 and ten kilometres north of Limoges. The large, slightly sloping and grassy pitches are in a parkland setting with many magnificent mature trees offering a fair amount of shade. Of the 90 pitches, 85 are for touring, 80 have 10A electricity and many have a tap, although long leads and hoses may be necessary. Explore the grounds and walk down to the four-hectare lake. The lake provides free fishing, boating, canoeing and a marked off area for swimming.

Facilities

The toilet block is very clean, but perhaps cramped at busy times. Some washbasins in cabins with good provision for disabled visitors. Washing machine. Basic food provisions. Restaurant (from 10/5). Bar, TV room and snack bar. Small swimming pool with sunbathing area (proper trunks, no shorts). Lake. Play area. Tennis and boules courts (in need of repair when we visited). Torch useful. Off site: Shop 2 km. Supermarket 5 km. Riding 7 km. Golf 20 km.

Open: 15 April - 20 September.

Directions

From A20, north of Limoges, take exit 27 (west) signed Bonnac-La-Côte. In village turn left and follow signs to site. GPS: 45.93299, 1.29006

Charges guide

Per person	€ 6,00 - € 7,50
child (under 7 yrs)	€ 4,00 - € 5,00
pitch	€ 9,00
electricity	€ 5,00
dog	€ 1,00

No credit cards.

Boussac

Castel Camping le Château de Poinsouze

Route de la Châtre, B.P. 12, F-23600 Boussac-Bourg (Creuse) T: 05 55 65 02 21
E: info@camping-de-poinsouze.com alanrogers.com/FR23010

Le Château de Poinsouze is a well established site arranged on the open, gently sloping, grassy park with views over the small lake and Château. It is an attractive, well maintained, high quality site situated in the unspoilt Limousin region. The 145 touring pitches, some with lake frontage, all have electricity (6-32A), water and drainage and 119 have sewerage connections. The site has a friendly family atmosphere with many organised activities in main season including dances, children's games and crafts. There are marked walks around the park and woods. This great site should ensure a stress-free, enjoyable holiday for all the family. Exceptionally well restored outbuildings on the opposite side of the drive house a shop, bar and a new restaurant serving excellent cuisine. All facilities are open all season. The pool complex has a new superb water play area for children with many fun fountains. The Château is not open to the public.

Facilities

High quality, sanitary unit with washing machines, dryer, ironing. Suites for disabled visitors. Motorcaravan services. Well stocked shop. Takeaway. Bar, internet and WiFi, two satellite TVs, library. Restaurant with new mini-bar for low season. Heated swimming pool, slide, children's pool and new water play area with fountains. Fenced playground. Pétanque. Bicycle hire. Free fishing in the lake, boats and lifejackets can be hired. Sports facilities. No dogs in high season (11/7-14/8). Off site: Boussac with its Thursday morning market 2.5 km. The massive 12th-/15th-century fortress, Château de Boussac, is open daily all year.

Open: 1 June - 4 September.

Directions

Boussac lies 35 km. west of Montluçon, between the A20 and A71 autoroutes. Site is 2.5 km. north of Boussac on D917 (towards La Châtre). GPS: 46.37243, 2.20268

Charges guide

Per unit incl. 2 persons and electricity	€ 19,00 - € 34,00
extra person	€ 3,00 - € 6,00
child (2-7 yrs)	€ 2,00 - € 5,00
dog	€ 3,00

For latest campsite news, availability and prices visit
alanrogers.com

Donzenac

Camping la Rivière

Route du Camping Louis Madrias, F-19270 Donzenac (Corrèze) T: 05 55 85 63 95
E: info@campingdonzenac.com alanrogers.com/FR19050

The Corrèze is less well known than the Dordogne to the immediate south, but it is a beautiful area deserving more attention. Donzenac is an attractive small town with a variety of shops, restaurants, etc. This former municipal site is situated on the outskirts, just under a mile from the centre (an uphill walk). The site is small and neat with 68 fairly large pitches on level grass, the majority with 10A electricity. A variety of trees and shrubs give some shade. The site is next door to the town tennis courts and swimming pool (open for July and August, and free to campers).

Facilities

Modernised sanitary facilities are very good and include a laundry room with washing machine and microwave. Baker calls in July/Aug. Bar (July/Aug). Games room. Boules. Minigolf. Play area. Fishing. WiFi in bar area. Double-axle caravans are not accepted. Off site: Riding 4 km. Golf 15 km.

Open: 1 April - 30 September.

Directions

At roundabout at southern end of Donzenac (D920) turn southwest onto D170 signed Ussac and La Rivière. Entrance to site is shortly on the right. GPS: 45.2187, 1.5187

Charges guide

Per unit incl. 2 persons	
and electricity	€ 16,60 - € 18,20
extra person	€ 4,30 - € 5,10
child (4-15 yrs)	free - € 3,70
dog	€ 1,50 - € 2,00
No credit cards.	

Neuvic

Camping Domaine le Mialaret

Route d'Egletons, F-19160 Neuvic (Corrèze) T: 05 55 46 02 50. E: info@lemialaret.com
alanrogers.com/FR19060

Mialaret is 4 km. from the village of Neuvic and only 6 km. from the Gorges of the Dordogne. It is set in the grounds of a 19th-century château, now a hotel and restaurant with a good reputation. Most pitches are set in a gently sloping parkland situation where 80 trees and many bushes have been planted. Some pitches are level and separated by small bushes, most have some shade and electricity. Entertainment and activities are organised in high season including Djembe drum workshops, a circus school, fishing lessons and evening concerts. In low season there are cooking courses with the chefs of the hotel. Also at that time of the year the owner has time to take customers on a conducted tour of the estate in his 4x4 vehicle. Ten pitches are used by a tour operator.

Facilities

Refurbished sanitary blocks give an adequate provision, one heated, facilities for disabled people, washing machines. Motorcaravan services. Shop with bread. Bar, snacks, takeaway. Dinner at hotel. Swimming pool with shallow area (15/6-15/9). Play areas. Tennis. Fishing. Off site: Village with shops and lake 4 km. Golf 4 km. Canoeing, cycling and riding trips organised.

Open: 1 April - 31 October.

Directions

From Clermont-Ferrand or Brives on the A89, take exit 23 for and follow signs for Neuvic (20 km). In Neuvic follow signs for La Mialaret (take first right after Ecomarché). Site is 4 km. GPS: 45.38242, 2.22910

Charges guide

Per unit incl. 2 persons	
and electricity	€ 21,00 - € 30,00
extra person	€ 5,00 - € 8,00
child (2-10 yrs)	free - € 5,00
dog	free
Camping Cheques accepted.	

For latest campsite news, availability and prices visit

alanrogers.com

Palisse

Camping le Vianon

F-19160 Palisse (Corrèze) T: 05 55 95 87 22. E: camping.vianon@wanadoo.fr

alanrogers.com/FR19080

You will receive a very warm welcome from the Dutch owners of this spacious and peaceful site and they speak excellent English. The site is tucked away in the lesser known, very beautiful Corrèze region yet it is only a few kilometres from the river Dordogne. This region is reputed to have the purest air in France. The grassy, slightly sloping pitches are of a good size in a natural woodland setting with tall trees offering shade and all have 16A electricity. The bar, restaurant and terrace overlook the swimming pool and sunbathing area and are open all season. One speciality is the fresh bread and croissants baked on site each morning. Activities are arranged for all the family when there are enough participants, but these do not continue too late in the evening.

Facilities

Modern toilet blocks with all the necessary facilities. Unit for disabled visitors. Bar. Restaurant, takeaway. Shop. Boules. Spacious play area. Bicycle hire. Lake fishing. Off site: Small town Neuvic with shops, restaurants 9 km. Large lake with water sports, swimming. Canoeing in the Dordogne (30 minutes). Riding and golf course at Neuvic. Marked walks and cycle rides.

Open: All year (telephone first October-April).

Directions

Leave A89 southwest of Ussel and take N89 towards Egletons. In about 7 km. just before Combressol, turn left on D47 signed Palisse and Camping le Vianon. Site entrance is on the left in 7 km. GPS: 45.42678, 2.20583

Charges guide

Per unit incl. 2 persons and electricity	€ 20,00 - € 29,35
extra person (over 2 yrs)	€ 4,00 - € 5,50
dog	€ 1,50 - € 2,00

Special rates for long stays.

Treignac

Flower Camping la Plage

La Plage, F-19260 Treignac (Corrèze) T: 05 55 98 08 54. E: camping.la.plage@wanadoo.fr

alanrogers.com/FR19030

La Plage is situated three kilometres from Treignac across the road from Lac des Bariousses. There are 130 large grassy pitches, 100 for touring all with 6A electricity. The site is well shaded and the flat pitches are terraced down the slope, all have easy access and many have views across the lake. Swimming and fishing are possible from the sandy beach. In high season there is a lifeguard on duty and all of the site's activities are centred on the beach and lake. There is a tunnel under the road from the site to the beach. This former municipal site is now owned by M. Francis who speaks good English.

Facilities

Two clean, spacious, basic toilet blocks with all necessary facilities including those for campers with disabilities. Washing machine. Small basic shop in high season selling wine and some local specialities. Motorcaravan service point. Snack bar on the beach (July/Aug). Fishing, canoes and pedaloes. Small children's games room. Library with English books. Organised activities on the beach (high season). Off site: Fishing in the Vézère river. Bicycle hire 200 m. Riding 10 km. Golf 30 km.

Open: 1 May - 15 September.

Directions

Leave Treignac on D940, direction Guéret, site is 3 km. on the left opposite Lac des Barriousses. GPS: 45.5596, 1.8134

Charges guide

Per person	€ 3,90 - € 4,10
child (3-7 yrs)	€ 2,30 - € 2,60
pitch	€ 4,20 - € 4,50
electricity (6A)	€ 2,80
dog	€ 1,20

For latest campsite news, availability and prices visit

alanrogers.com

Set in the heart of the Massif-Central, the Auvergne was formed by a series of volcanic eruptions and is a dramatic region of awe-inspiring, non-active volcanoes, lakes, sparkling rivers, green valleys and forests.

DÉPARTEMENTS: 03 ALLIER, 15 CANTAL, 43 HAUTE-LOIRE, 63 PUY-DE-DÔME

MAJOR CITY: CLERMONT-FERRAND

The Auvergne is a wonderful destination for nature lovers, for those who enjoy active outdoor pursuits or for people would like to relax at a spa resort.

The 'Parc Naturel Régional des Volcans d'Auvergne' – the Auvergne Volcano Park – is the largest national park in France and is a protected environment for exceptional flora and fauna. The mountains provide three classified downhill ski resorts and excellent cross-country skiing. A very wide range of outdoor activities is available. The ancient volcanoes have also provided ten thermal spa areas, five of which are among the leading thermal resorts in France.

For those interested in sightseeing, the region offers beautiful Romanesque churches, medieval castles, ruined fortresses and stiff black sculptures of the Madonna and child. Visit Vulcania, the European Volcano Park, and adults and children can learn about the fascinating science of volcanoes. The area was once fairly isolated and inward looking, but access is now much improved and roads are well engineered, so the region is now realising its potential as a holiday area.

Places of interest

Aurillac: old town, wax museum, archaeology museum.

Clermont-Ferrand: old city centre, 11th-12th-century Notre Dame du Port Basilica, 13th-century cathedral; known as 'ville noire' for its houses built in local black volcanic rock.

Le Mont-Doré: spa, winter sports, panoramic view.

Puy-de-Dôme: Gallo-Roman site, television tower and observatory.

Vichy: spa, natural spring park.

Volvic: lava quarry, Volvic springs.

Vulvania: 15 km. from Clermont-Ferrand, a unique experience that, until now, was reserved only for volcanologists. A scientific exploration park, designed for children and adults who want to discover and understand the fascinating world of volcanoes and the earth sciences.

Cuisine of the region

Local specialties include ham and andouille sausages, stuffed cabbage and bacon with lentils and cèpes (mushrooms). Le Puy is famed for its lentils and Vereine du Velay – yellow and green liqueurs made from over 30 mountain plants.

Aligot: purée of potatoes with Tomme de Cantal cheese, cream, garlic and butter.

Perdrix à l'Auvergnate: partridge stewed in white wine.

Potée Auvergnate: a stew of vegetables, cabbage, pork and sausage.

www.auvergne-tourisme.info.uk or
www.massifcentral-tourisme.com
documentation@crt-auvergne.fr
(0)4 73 29 49 99

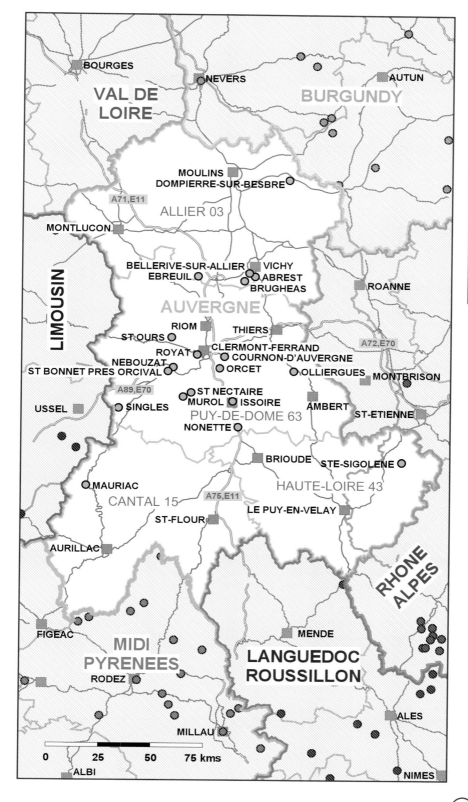

BOURGES

NEVERS

VAL DE LOIRE

BURGUNDY

AUTUN

MOULINS
DOMPIERRE-SUR-BESBRE

A71,E11

ALLIER 03

MONTLUCON

BELLERIVE-SUR-ALLIER   VICHY
EBREUIL   ABREST
BRUGHEAS

ROANNE

AUVERGNE

RIOM
ST OURS   THIERS

LIMOUSIN

CLERMONT-FERRAND
ROYAT   COURNON-D'AUVERGNE
NEBOUZAT   ORCET
ST BONNET PRES ORCIVAL   OLLIERGUES   MONTBRISON

A72,E70

A89,E70

ST NECTAIRE
MUROL   ISSOIRE   AMBERT
ST-ETIENNE

USSEL   SINGLES   PUY-DE-DOME 63
NONETTE

BRIOUDE   STE-SIGOLENE

MAURIAC   HAUTE-LOIRE 43

CANTAL 15   A75,E11

LE PUY-EN-VELAY

ST-FLOUR

AURILLAC

RHONE
ALPES

FIGEAC

MENDE

MIDI
PYRENEES

RODEZ

LANGUEDOC
ROUSSILLON

ALES

MILLAU

0   25   50   75 kms

ALBI

NIMES

For latest campsite news, availability and prices visit
alanrogers.com

Abrest

Camping de la Croix Saint Martin

Allée du Camping, 99 avenue des Graviers, F-03200 Abrest (Allier) T: 04 70 32 67 74

E: camping-vichy@orange.fr alanrogers.com/FR03110

La Croix Saint Martin is in Abrest on the edge of the attractive spa town of Vichy and close to the Bourbonnais mountains. The site is on the right bank of the Allier and extends over three hectares of wooded parkland. There are 90 level grassy pitches with 75 for touring and 45 with 10A electricity. They are separated by some hedging and a variety of mature trees give varying amounts of shade. Vichy's elegant parks are less than 30 minutes on foot and the town centre is only another ten minutes. Twin- axle caravans are not accepted. On-site amenities include a small swimming pool. Various activities are held on site during the peak season, including a children's club and occasional communal meals. Canoeing is popular on the Allier and in the high season.

Facilities	Directions
Adequate toilet block with all necessary facilities. Swimming pool (1/5-30/9). Fishing. Play area. Volleyball. Table tennis, tennis, boules. Children's miniclub (July/Aug). Tourist information. Motorcaravan services. Free WiFi. Off site: Vichy centre 40 minutes walk. Bus to Vichy. Canoeing, windsurfing, river bathing (3 km). Walking, cycling and riding in the Auvergne.	Abrest lies just south of Vichy. From town centre, head south D906 (Avenue de Thiers) to Abrest. Follow signs to site. GPS: 46.1073, 3.43747

Open: 1 April - 31 October.

Charges guide

Per unit incl. 2 persons and electricity	€ 14,00 - € 17,90
extra person	€ 3,50 - € 4,70
child (1-7 yrs)	€ 2,50 - € 3,00

Bellerive-sur-Allier

Camping Beau Rivage

Rue Claude Decloître, les Berges de l'Allier, F-03700 Bellerive-sur-Allier (Allier) T: 04 70 32 26 85

E: camping-beaurivage@wanadoo.fr alanrogers.com/FR03030

This well maintained, compact, urban site beside the River Allier is just over the water from the famous spa town of Vichy. It has recently been completely refurbished by the enthusiastic new owners (good English and Dutch spoken). There are 80 medium sized, reasonably level grass pitches with 47 for touring. Some have delightful views across the river to the beautiful Parc Napoléon beyond. They are separated by flowering shrubs and some tall hedging, and mature trees offer some shade. All pitches have electricity and 12 are fully serviced. On-site access is not easy for large outfits. Twin-axle caravans are not accepted. There are swimming and paddling pools and a separate toboggan.

Facilities	Directions
Very clean, modern airy sanitary facilities in individual cubicles in pleasantly decorated buildings. Fully equipped, including a baby room and facilities for campers with disabilities. Laundry facilities. Motorcaravan service point. Small bar with snacks (March-Oct). River fishing. Play area. Bicycles and pedaloes. Minigolf. Archery. Internet. WiFi (first hour free). Off site: Riding, canoeing and tennis nearby. Very close to the site are several bars and restaurants. Hypermarket within 1 km. Vichy 2 km.	From A71 exit 12 (Vichy), head east, A719 then D2209 to Bellerive-sur-Allier. Turn right at roundabout with fountains, follow signs to Berges des Allier, Campings and then Beau Rivage. Site is 3 km. GPS: 46.11567, 3.43012

Open: 1 April - 15 October.

Charges guide

Per unit incl. 2 persons and electricity (6A)	€ 15,70 - € 20,00
extra person	€ 4,10 - € 5,30
child (0-7 yrs)	€ 2,50 - € 4,00

Brugheas

Flower Camping la Roseraie

Route de Randan, F-03700 Brugheas (Allier) T: 04 70 32 43 33. E: camping.laroseraie@wanadoo.Fr

alanrogers.com/FR03120

La Roseraie is a family owned rural campsite near the village of Brugheas only 7 km. from the attractive spa town of Vichy. There are 80 large pitches with 54 for touring, all with 6A electricity. Some on the edge of the site are of open and have good views over the surrounding countryside. The others are separated by hedges and have heavy shade. A new building near the entrance houses reception, small bar, snack bar, takeaway and games/TV room. A paddling pool has been added to the existing swimming pool and toboggan. Although access is good, twin-axle caravans are not accepted.

Facilities	Directions
Basic shop, bar, snack bar and takeaway (mid May-mid Sept). Heated swimming pool, paddling pool and toboggan (mid May-mid Sept). Games room/TV. Play area. Archery. Bicycle hire. Minigolf. Entertainment and activity programme. WiFi. Off site: Vichy 7 km. Fishing, golf, river bathing, boating 5 km. Riding 2 km. Cycle and walking tracks. Puy de Dôme. Parc des Volcans. Le Pal theme park.	La Roseraie is on the D1093 between Clermont Ferrand and Vichy. The site is well signed, entrance opposite water tower, 7 km. from Vichy. GPS: 46.07961, 3.38213

Open: 1 April - 30 October.

Charges guide

Per unit incl. 2 persons and electricity	€ 14,90 - € 20,90
extra person	€ 2,50 - € 4,50
child (2-7 yrs)	€ 1,90 - € 2,50

For latest campsite news, availability and prices visit

alanrogers.com

Cournon-d'Auvergne

Camping le Pré des Laveuses

Rue des Laveuses, F-63800 Cournon-d'Auvergne (Puy-de-Dôme) T: 04 73 84 81 30
E: camping@cournon-auvergne.fr alanrogers.com/FR63230

A well equipped municipal site, le Pré des Laveuses is adjacent to a boating and fishing lake and its beach, alongside the River Allier, close to Cournon d'Auvergne and the A75 autoroute. This site will be busy in the high season due to its public bar/restaurant, new heated swimming pool complex, nearby activities and its proximity to Clermont Ferrand. There are 150 large, grassy, mostly level pitches with 120 for touring (all with 10A electricity, long leads advised). They are separated by neat hedges with mature trees giving some shade and many have pleasant views over the surrounding hills and the town, although hedging obscures views of the lake.

Facilities

Two modern toilet blocks with all necessary facilities, including those for campers with disabilities, possibly stretched when site busy. Washing machine and dryer. Public bar/restaurant with TV (June/Sept). New heated swimming pool complex. Children's room (TV). Play area. Boules. Overnight parking and services for motorhomes outside gate. WiFi (free). Many high season sporting and family activities, children's club. Off site: Lake, bathing, boating and free fishing (adjacent). Canoeing (high season) and free fishing in River Allier. Minigolf. Tennis. Excellent children's play and picnic areas, walks, bike rides in adjacent park. Cournon 2 km. Clermont Ferrand 12 km. Bicycle hire 2.5 km. Riding 10 km.

Open: 1 April - 31 October.

Directions

Site is 12 km. southeast of Clermont Ferrand. Leave autoroute A75 at exit 1, taking D212 to Cournon d'Auvergne. Site is well signed to east of town, beside River Allier. Follow Zone de Loisirs. GPS: 45.74019, 3.22266

Charges guide

Per unit incl. 2 persons	€ 14,50 - € 16,60
extra person	€ 4,20 - € 4,70
child (under 7 yrs)	€ 2,10 - € 2,60
electricity (10A)	€ 2,00 - € 3,10

Dompierre-sur-Besbre

Camping les bords de Besbre

F-03290 Dompierre-sur-Besbre (Allier) T: 04 70 34 55 57. E: camping.domaine@free.fr
alanrogers.com/FR03170

This immaculate, attractive and excellent value-for-money site has 67 level, partly shaded, individually hedged, grassy pitches, all with easy access. There are a few long stay units, leaving about 65 for tourists, all with electricity (10A) and most being fully serviced. It is located next to the municipal sports fields and is ideal for motorcaravans, being within easy walking distance of the town centre and supermarket (700 m). The warden is very proud of his efficiently run site and its award-winning floral displays. Twin-axle caravans are not accepted.

Facilities

Modernised, heated toilet blocks, very clean with all necessary facilities including provision for disabled visitors. Some washbasins in curtained cubicles for ladies. Washing machine. Excellent motorcaravan services. Charcoal barbecues are not permitted. Heated indoor swimming pool (all season). Off site: The small town has shops, restaurants and a Saturday market. Vallée de la Besbre has a wealth of activities, several rivers and small lakes nearby for fishing. Cycle tracks, footpaths, equestrian centres. Le Pal theme park and zoo 8 km.

Open: 15 May - 15 September.

Directions

Dompierre is 35 km. east of Moulins. Leave N79 at eastern end of Dompierre bypass, turn southwest on N2079 towards town. Entrance to sports complex and campsite is on left beyond D55 before the river bridge and town centre. GPS: 46.51564, 3.68434

Charges guide

Per unit incl. 2 persons and electricity	€ 8,90 - € 9,10
extra person	€ 2,30
child (5-12 yrs)	€ 1,40 - € 2,10
dog	free

For latest campsite news, availability and prices visit

alanrogers.com

Ebreuil

Camping de la Filature

Route de Chouvigny, F-03450 Ebreuil (Allier) T: 04 70 90 72 01. E: camping.filature@gmail.com

alanrogers.com/FR03010

Beside a fine fly fishing river, not far from the spa town of Vichy this spacious family campsite makes a good base for exploring the Auvergne, the nearby river gorges, châteaux, mountains and lakes. There are 80 spacious, grassy pitches, 74 for touring, in a parkland setting. Most have 6A electricity and some shade from mature trees. Many are directly by the river, which is clean, shallow and pleasant to play in. There is a deeper area for swimming 500 m. away. You will receive a warm welcome from the English owners, who also provide good value and very popular takeaway food. In May and June, the fields abound with wild flowers, some quite rare. Bird songs are many and varied. Listen for the songs of the nightingale and golden oriole, often heard but seldom seen. The quiet country roads are ideal for walking and cycling, especially mountain biking and for touring by car. The interesting village of Ébreuil with its Thursday market, is a just 15 minutes level stroll. Just west of the site are the gorges of the river Sioule, and the extinct volcanoes of the Puy de Dôme with the Vulcania Exhibition are well worth a visit.

Facilities

Clean, fully equipped sanitary facilities, bathroom and facilities for campers with disabilities. Laundry facilities. Small shop for essentials (1/5-30/9). Baker calls. Bar (15/5-30/9). Excellent takeaway (1/6-15/9). Barbecues and pizza nights organised in high season. River bathing and fishing. Large play areas. Minigolf. WiFi. Off site: Riding, canoeing, tennis, bicycle hire, motorhome services 500 m. Ébreuil with shops, bar, restaurants 1 km. Spa town of Vichy with large range of shops, bars, restaurants and sporting activities 30 km.

Open: 31 March - 1 October.

Directions

Site is well signed from exit 12 of A71 autoroute to Clermont Ferrand in the direction of Ébreuil. It is about 6 km. from the A71 and 1 km. west of Ébreuil beside the river on the D915 towards the Chouvigny gorges. GPS: 46.10877, 3.07338

Charges guide

Per unit incl. 2 persons and electricity	€ 20,50
extra person	€ 5,00
child (under 16 yrs)	€ 3,00
dog	free

Discounts of up to 50% in low season.

Issoire

Château Camping la Grange Fort

Les Pradeaux, F-63500 Issoire (Puy-de-Dôme) T: 04 73 71 02 43. E: chateau@lagrangefort.com

alanrogers.com/FR63040

This site has good, modern facilities, yet is oozing with character. It is very popular with the Dutch. The new reception is well stocked with tourist information and an internet access point. The cosy bar still has the old stable stalls and hay racks. The 120 pitches (90 for touring units) are of average size, mostly on grass but with some crushed stone hardstandings, and they are connected by rather narrow roads with limited play space for children. Some of the smaller pitches are in sunny fields around the castle, others in bays with hedges and trees. All have 6A electricity.

Facilities

Refurbished sanitary blocks have facilities for disabled visitors and a 'hydra shower'. Laundry room. Bread. Restaurant and takeaway (1/5-15/9). Bar (15/6-15/9). Indoor pool with sliding glass doors, sauna, massage table (15/4-15/10). Outdoor pools (15/6-1/10), grass sunbathing areas. New swimming pool (24.5x14.5 m) with jacuzzi. Play area, games room. Internet. WiFi. Tennis, minigolf, football, boules. Organised activities in season. Torches useful. Off site: Fishing 250 m. Riding 8 km.

Open: 10 April - 15 October.

Directions

From A75 autoroute take exit 13 onto D996 east towards Parentignat. At first roundabout take first exit on D999 new road (St Remy, La Vernet). At next roundabout take first exit (D34) and follow campsite signs. GPS: 45.50875, 3.28488

Charges guide

Per unit incl. 2 persons	€ 17,40 - € 24,50
extra person	€ 4,75 - € 6,10
child (under 10 yrs)	€ 3,70 - € 4,90
electricity	€ 3,25

Mauriac

Camping Caravaning le Val Saint-Jean

F-15200 Mauriac (Cantal) T: 04 71 67 31 13. E: valsaintjean@mauriac.fr
alanrogers.com/FR15030

Le Val Saint-Jean is set beside a lake in the heart of the département of Cantal. The campsite has 100 generously sized, slightly sloping, touring pitches (with 10A electricity), many with good views. It is organised for maximum privacy and you are never far from a sanitary block. Most of the activities are situated by the lake where you can use all the facilities of the leisure club (high season) including cycling, canoeing, kayaking and pedaloes. This less well known region is well worth exploring and the local gastronomy can be experienced in the village of Mauriac with its attractive architecture typical of the area. Salers, one of the most beautiful French towns is 20 km.

Facilities

The two toilet blocks are well equipped with hot water throughout, providing some washbasins in cabins, dishwashing sinks and a laundry room. Facilities for people with disabilities. Limited shop. Bar, snack bar and restaurant (all May-Sept). Play area and playing field. Activities organised for children in July/Aug.
Off site: Sandy beach. Lake fishing and swimming. Swimming pool (1/6-15/9). Golf. Guided walks. Mauriac village 1.6 km. Riding 3 km.

Open: 25 April - 27 September.

Directions

Mauriac is around 120 km. southwest of Clermont-Ferrand. Leave A89 autoroute at junction 23 (Ussel West), take D979 (Bort-les-Orgues) for 5 km. Turn right onto D982 (Mauriac) for 40 km. Follow site signs in town. GPS: 45.21867, 2.31588

Charges guide

Per unit incl. 2 persons	
and electricity	€ 17,10 - € 23,10
extra person	€ 4,40 - € 5,40
child (2-7 yrs)	free - € 3,30
dog	€ 1,50

Murol

Sunêlia la Ribeyre

Jassat, F-63790 Murol (Puy-de-Dôme) T: 04 73 88 64 29. E: info@laribeyre.com
alanrogers.com/FR63050

The friendly Pommier family have put much personal care into the construction of this site. There are 400 level, grassy pitches, of which 310 are for tourers and 200 of these have electricity (6/10A). Electricity, water and drainage are available for 71 pitches. A superb large indoor/outdoor water park includes slides, toboggan and lazy river and a small man-made lake at one end provides facilities for watersports. It is a great base for touring being only 1 km. from Murol, dominated by its ancient Château, 6 km. from St Nectaire and about 20 km. from Mont Dore and Puy de Sancy, the highest peak in the area. This site is a wonderful area for walking and cycling. Visit in May or June for fields of beautiful wild flowers and in September for the autumn colours.

Facilities

Six excellent, very clean modern toilet blocks with facilities for disabled visitors. Washing machines, dryers. Snack bar in peak season (1/6-31/8). Large indoor/outdoor water park (heated July/Aug). TV. Games room. Tennis. Fishing. Lake swimming and canoeing. Many organised activities in high season. Off site: Riding 300 m. Shops and restaurants and a large Wednesday market (high season) in Murol 1.5 km. Fishing and Bicycle hire 1 km. Fishing and watersports at Lac Chambon 3 km.

Open: 1 May - 15 September.

Directions

From A75 Autoroute, exit 6 signed St Nectaire. Continue to Murol, D978 then D996, several sites signed in town. Turn left up hill, D5, shortly turn right opposite car park, D618, site signed. Site is second on left. GPS: 45.56251, 2.93852

Charges 2011

Per unit incl. 2 persons	
and electricity	€ 25,05 - € 33,55
extra person	€ 5,75 - € 7,40
child (1-5 yrs)	€ 4,20 - € 5,85
dog (max.1)	€ 2,60 - € 2,80

For latest campsite news, availability and prices visit
alanrogers.com

Murol

Camping le Pré Bas

Lac Chambon, F-63790 Murol (Puy-de-Dôme) T: 04 73 88 63 04. E: prebas@campingauvergne.com

alanrogers.com/FR63070

Le Pré Bas is especially suitable for families and those seeking the watersports opportunities that the lake provides. Level, grassy pitches are divided up by mature hedging and trees and, with 106 mobile homes for rent, around 73 pitches are available for tourists, all with electricity (6A). A gate leads to the lakeside, where in high season there is windsurfing, pedaloes, canoes and fishing, and 50 m. away is a beach with supervised bathing and a snack bar. The site has a pool complex with heated swimming pools (one covered), a large slide and a paddling pool, plus a 'Family Center' covered area with sauna, jacuzzi and Turkish bath. The site is in the heart of the Parc des Volcans d'Auvergne. The cable car ride up to the Puy de Sancy, the highest peak in the area, provides superb views offering an excellent opportunity for trekking and mountain bike rides. Superb scenery abounds; wooded mountains rising to over 6,000 feet, flower filled valleys and deep blue lakes.

Facilities

Refurbished toilet building with facilities for disabled guests plus four smaller units. Washing machines, dryers, ironing, baby room. Motorcaravan services. Snack bar (10/6-10/9 and some weekends in low season). Three pools of different depths (20/5-10/9, lifeguard in July/Aug). Watersports, fishing in lake. Games room, table tennis, table football, pool, TV, library. Adventure style playground, football, basketball. Organised activities. WiFi. Max. 1 dog. Off site: Lakeside bars, restaurants, shops. Murol 4 km. St Nectaire famous for cheese. Puy-de-Dôme, hang gliding, Vulcania Exhibition.

Open: 1 May - 25 September.

Directions

Leave A75 autoroute at exit 6 and take D978 signed St Nectaire and Murol, then D996. Site is located on left, 3 km. west of Murol towards Mont Dore, at the far end of Lac Chambon. GPS: 45.57516, 2.91428

Charges guide

Per unit incl. 2 persons	
and electricity	€ 17,30 - € 28,40
extra person	€ 3,90 - € 6,30
child (under 5 yrs)	€ 2,60 - € 4,10
dog	€ 1,90 - € 2,10

Nébouzat

Camping les Domes

Les Quatre Routes de Nébouzat, F-63210 Nébouzat (Puy-de-Dôme) T: 04 73 87 14 06
E: camping.les-domes@wanadoo.fr alanrogers.com/FR63090

A popular site, it is ideally situated for exploring the beautiful region around the Puy de Dôme. The site has 65 small to medium sized pitches, most for touring, 50 with 10/15A electricity, separated by trees and hedges. Some pitches have a level, paved area ideal for caravans and motorcaravans. Rock pegs are advised. The attractive reception area comprising the office, a small shop for essentials (high season only) and a meeting room has local information and interesting artefacts. An added small attraction is a heated, covered swimming pool, which can be opened in good weather.

Facilities

Well appointed, clean toilet block, no special facilities for disabled visitors. Basic shop (baker calls). Breakfast, snacks. Boules, pool table, table football, table tennis, giant chess, drafts. Small play area. TV and games room. Off site: Fishing 100 m. Restaurant 200 m. Nebouzat 1.3 km. (shops etc). Riding 6 km. Hang gliding and parascending 8 km. (Puy de Dôme). Vulcania exhibition 15 minutes drive. Watersports 9 km. Golf 10 km. Clermont Ferrand 18 km.

Open: 1 May - 30 September.

Directions

Site is 18 km. southwest of Clermont Ferrand and is well signed from the roundabout at the junction of the D2089 and the D941A. It is a few hundred metres from the roundabout along the D216 towards Orcival. GPS: 45.72562, 2.89005

Charges guide

Per unit incl. 2 persons	€ 10,00
extra person	€ 6,50
electricity (10A)	€ 5,00

No credit cards.

For latest campsite news, availability and prices visit

alanrogers.com

Nonette

Camping les Loges

F-63340 Nonette (Puy-de-Dôme) T: 04 73 71 65 82. E: les.loges.nonette@wanadoo.fr
alanrogers.com/FR63140

A pleasant, spacious, rural site bordering the River Allier and close to the A75 autoroute. There are 126 good sized, level, grassy pitches offering plenty of shade, 100 for touring and all with 6A electricity. This site would suit those seeking a quieter holiday without too many organised activities. The river is good for bathing and canoeing and there are many walks and bike rides in the area. It is also well placed to explore the beautiful Auvergne countryside, the extinct volcanoes and the many attractive old towns and villages.

Facilities

Modern toilet blocks contain all the usual facilities. Small shop (July/Aug). Bar, restaurant, takeaway (mid June-mid Sept). TV room. Heated swimming pool with toboggan, paddling pool (June-Sept). Sauna, spa room (July/Aug). Volleyball. Play areas, play room. River fishing, bathing. Sunday evening dances in high season. Canoe trips. Off site: Walking and cycling routes. Riding 5 km. Small village of Nonette 3 km. Small range of shops at Saint Germain 5 km. Larger range of shops, restaurants etc in Issoire 13 km. Parc des Volcans, Volcania Exhibition.

Open: Easter - 13 October.

Directions

From A75 exit 17 (south of Issoire), turn left (D214) signed Le Breuil. Bypass Le Breuil, turn left (D123) signed Nonette. Cross river, turn left then immediately very sharp left just after roundabout (take care). Site is signed and entrance is 1 km. GPS: 45.47310, 3.27223

Charges guide

Per unit incl. 2 persons	€ 12,00 - € 16,20
extra person	€ 3,60 - € 4,60
child (2-7 yrs)	€ 2,40 - € 3,20
electricity (6A)	€ 3,50

Olliergues

Camping les Chelles

F-63880 Olliergues (Puy-de-Dôme) T: 04 73 95 54 34. E: info@camping-les-chelles.com
alanrogers.com/FR63220

A very rural, rustic site, les Chelles is run by enthusiastic Dutch owners. It is situated in the Parc Naturel Livradois, 25 km. south of Thiers, and is ideal for nature lovers and those seeking a quiet retreat. There are many marked walks and challenging cycle routes close by. There are 60 pitches with 50 slightly sloping grassy pitches for touring, some with views over the surrounding wooded hills (15A electricity, long leads advised). The pitches are naturally laid out on woodland terraces but not ideal for those with walking difficulties or for large or underpowered units due to the hilly terrain.

Facilities

Centrally placed basic toilet block. Washing machine and dryer. Motorcaravan service point (charge). Bar/restaurant (all season) with TV. Bread to order. Small swimming and paddling pools near small play area. Tennis. Boules. Bicycle hire (high season). Small fishing lake. Some activities for younger children, bike rides (high season). WiFi (charge). Off site: Olliergues 5 km. Thiers 25 km. Many challenging cycle rides and walks.

Open: 1 April - 30 October.

Directions

Olliergues is on D906 25 km. south of Thiers. On entering Olliergues bear left up hill, D37. Shortly turn sharp left on D87. In 1.5 km. at church turn right and shortly left to site. Well signed from Olliergues. GPS: 45.68987, 3.63336

Charges guide

Per unit incl. 2 persons and electricity	€ 15,80
extra person	€ 3,00
Low season 15% discount for 4 nights or more.	

Orcet

Camping le Clos Auroy

Rue de la Narse, F-63670 Orcet (Puy-de-Dôme) T: 04 73 84 26 97. E: info@campingclub.info
alanrogers.com/FR63060

You are assured a friendly welcome at Le Clos Auroy. It is a very well maintained and popular site, 300 metres from Orcet, a typical Auvergne village just south of Clermont Ferrand. Being close (3 km) to the A75, and open all year, it makes an excellent stopping off point on the journey north and south but you may be tempted to stay longer. The 90 good size pitches are on level grass, separated by very high, neatly trimmed conifer hedges, offering lots of privacy but not much shade. All have electricity (5/10A) and 25 are fully serviced. In winter only 20 pitches are available. Access is easy for large units.

Facilities

High quality, very clean toilet blocks. Washing machine, dryer. Motorcaravan services. Small shop (1/7-31/8), bar and takeaway (1/6-31/8). Heated pool, jacuzzi, large pool for children (15/5-15/9), terrace near bar (1/6-31/8). Playground. Coffee evenings. Tennis. Children's activities. Off site: Large playground nearby and riverside walk just outside gate. Village with shops and three wine 'caves' 300 m. Fishing and canoeing 500 m. Parc des Volcans with fantastic scenery, walking and cycling.

Open: 4 January - 1 November.

Directions

From A75 take exit 4 or 5 towards Orcet and follow campsite signs. It is just before the village. GPS: 45.70018, 3.16902

Charges guide

Per unit incl. 2 persons and electricity	€ 21,70 - € 27,70
extra person	€ 4,40 - € 5,60
child (4-10 yrs)	€ 3,10
Less for longer stays in low season. No credit cards.	

For latest campsite news, availability and prices visit

alanrogers.com

Royat

Camping Indigo Royat

Route de Gravenoire, F-63130 Royat (Puy-de-Dôme) T: 04 73 35 97 05
E: royat@camping-indigo.com alanrogers.com/FR63120

This is a spacious and attractive site sitting high on a hillside on the outskirts of Clermont Ferrand, but close to the beautiful Auvergne countryside. It has 191 terraced pitches on part hardstanding. There are 137 available for touring units, all with 10A electricity (long leads may be needed) and in addition five pitches offer water and drainage. The pitches are informally arranged in groups, with each group widely separated by attractive trees and shrubs. The bar and terrace overlook the irregularly shaped swimming pool, paddling pool, sunbathing area, tennis courts and play areas. Although very peaceful off season, the site could be busy and lively in July and August.

Facilities

Five well appointed toilet blocks, some heated. They have all the usual amenities but it could be a long walk from some pitches. Small shop (all season). Bar, restaurant and takeaway (July/Aug). Attractive heated swimming, paddling pools (27/5-18/9), sunbathing area. Tennis. Boules. Two grassy play areas. Organised entertainment in high season. Internet. Max. 1 dog. Off site: Royat 20 minutes walk. Bus service every 30 minutes in mornings. Clermont Ferrand, Puy-de-Dôme, Parc des Volcans, Vulcania exhibition. Fishing 2 km. Golf 3 km.

Open: 1 April - 29 October.

Directions

From A75 exit 2 (Clermont Ferrand) follow signs for Bordeaux (D799). At third roundabout exit left signed Bordeaux. Shortly take exit right then turn right, signed Ceyrat. Leaving Ceyrat, at traffic lights take D941C signed Royat and Puy-de-Dôme. At top of hill turn left (D5) site signed. Entrance 800 m. GPS: 45.7587, 3.05509

Charges guide

Per unit incl. 2 persons	€ 20,35 - € 26,85
extra person	€ 2,70 - € 5,50

Camping Cheques accepted.

Saint Bonnet près Orcival

Camping de la Haute Sioule

Route du Camping, F-63210 Saint Bonnet près Orcival (Puy-de-Dôme) T: 04 73 65 83 32
E: info@chalets-auvergne.info alanrogers.com/FR63210

This simple, small site is family run in a quiet, rural location in the heart of the beautiful Parc des Volcans. With good views over the surrounding hills, it is close to the Puy de Dôme and several winter and summer resorts. Developed from a farm with sheep and geese roaming freely until mid June, the site has 70 sloping, slightly uneven, grassy pitches with about 45 for touring (4-13A electricity, long leads needed). Access is not easy for motorhomes and large outfits. It would be a good base for touring the region but may be noisy in the high season due to the seasonal caravans.

Facilities

Central basic toilet block with mainly Turkish toilets. No facilities for campers with disabilities. Washing machine and dryer. Bar with TV, restaurant and snacks (all season). Play area for younger children. Minigolf. Boules. WiFi. Off site: St Bonnet 200 m. with some small shops, a restaurant and a bar. Orcival 4 km. with larger range shops etc. Vulcania exhibition. Winter ski resorts 20 km. Lakes. Fishing 5 km. Riding 7 km.

Open: 15 March - 1 November.

Directions

A75 just south of Clermont Ferrand at exit 2, signed Bordeaux and La Bourboule. Continue on D2089 until Les Quatre Routes. Turn left at roundabout, D216. Bear left to site entrance in just over 500 m. GPS: 45.7084, 2.86087

Charges guide

Per unit incl. 2 persons	€ 12,00
electricity (4-13A)	€ 2,70 - € 5,90

Saint Nectaire

Camping la Vallée Verte

Route des Granges, F-63710 Saint Nectaire (Puy-de-Dôme) T: 04 73 88 52 68. E: lavalleeverte@libertysurf.fr
alanrogers.com/FR63180

Vallée Verte is a very well tended, peaceful, good value campsite. Set in the heart of the beautiful Parc des Volcans d'Auvergne, it is only a short walk from the small spa town of Saint Nectaire and close to Lac Chambon with its sandy beach and some water sports. There are many other interesting towns and villages waiting to be explored. The site has 90 level grass pitches (5/8A electricity) with 74 for touring units. Separated by wooden rails or a variety of hedging, a mixture of trees gives shade to some of the pitches. Twin-axle caravans are not accepted.

Facilities

Excellent new toilet block with all necessary facilities including a superb room for families and campers with disabilities. Motorcaravan services. Shop, bar and restaurant with takeaway (all season). Play areas. Boules. Organised meals and walks in high season. Off site: St Nectaire with shops, bars, restaurants. Casino. Caves. Petrified fountains 500 m. Lac Chambon 6 km. Vulcania Exhibition. Puy-de-Dôme, Puy de Sancy.

Open: 15 April - 15 September.

Directions

Leave A75 at exit 6 south of Clermont Ferrand. Take the D978 then the D996 to St Nectaire. On entering St Nectaire turn left, D642 (site signed). Entrance is a few hundred metres. GPS: 45.57523, 2.99981

Charges guide

Per unit incl. 2 persons	€ 9,50 - € 13,50
extra person	€ 3,00 - € 4,60
electricity (5/8A)	€ 3,00 - € 3,50

For latest campsite news, availability and prices visit

alanrogers.com

Saint Ours

Camping Bel-Air

F-63230 Saint Ours (Puy-de-Dôme) T: 04 73 88 72 14. E: contact@campingbelair.fr

alanrogers.com/FR63160

This is an attractive, family run site. In traditional style, but with modern facilities, it has a rural location lying within the Parc des Volcans. There are 60 level grass pitches, 28 with 6/10A electricity, including three with hardstanding for larger motorcaravans and three chalets. The pitches are spaced around a wooded clearing, most with varying degrees of shade. This site is ideal for those seeking a peaceful holiday in a wonderful area for exploration – there are no activities here. Its position only 6 km. from the A89 autoroute makes it ideal for both short and long stays. Twin-axle caravans are not accepted.

Facilities

Modern well equipped toilet block with baby room and facilities for disabled visitors. Washing machine and dryer. Motorcaravan service point. Small shop (bread to order). Minigolf and boules. Gas and electric barbecues only (communal barbecue provided). Play area. WiFi in reception. Off site: Pontgibaud with shops, restaurants 3 km. Puy-de-Dôme 18 km. Vulcania Exhibition 8 km. Excellent area for touring on foot, bike or by car.

Open: 1 May - 30 September.

Directions

Leave A89 west of Clermont Ferrand at exit 26. Take D941 bypassing Pontgibaud. At roundabout turn left, D943 St Ours. Site shortly on left.
GPS: 45.84436, 2.87672

Charges guide

Per unit incl. 2 persons and electricity	€ 17,00
extra person	€ 4,60
child (under 10 yrs)	€ 2,70

No credit cards.

Sainte Sigolène

Kawan Village de Vaubarlet

Vaubarlet, F-43600 Sainte Sigolène (Haute-Loire) T: 04 71 66 64 95. E: camping@vaubarlet.com

alanrogers.com/FR43030

This peacefully located, spacious riverside family site has 131 marked, level, grassy, open pitches, with those around the perimeter having shade, all with electricity (6A). With 102 pitches for tourists, the remainder are occupied by site owned tents or mobile homes. Those who really like to get away from it all can use a small 'wild camping' area on the opposite side of the river with its own very basic facilities. This area is reached either by footbridge or a separate road access. The main site is separated from the river (unfenced) by a large field used for sports activities.

Facilities

Good, clean toilet blocks, baby room, washing machine, dryer. Two family bathrooms are also suitable for disabled people. WiFi. Small shop, bread. Takeaway, bar (all season). Attractive swimming pool, children's pool. Bicycle hire. Boules. Large games area. Playground. Activities in season include camp fire, music evenings, children's canoe lessons. Trout fishing. Bird watching. Off site: Shops in Ste Sigolène 6 km. Riding 15 km. Walks and cycle tracks from site.

Open: 1 May - 30 September.

Directions

Site is 6 km. southwest of Ste Sigolène on the D43 signed Grazac. Keep left by river bridge, site signed. Site shortly on right. GPS: 45.2163, 4.2124

Charges guide

Per unit incl. 2 persons and electricity	€ 16,50 - 22,00
extra person	€ 3,00 - € 4,00
child (2-7 yrs)	€ 2,25 - € 3,00

Less 15% outside July/Aug.
Camping Cheques accepted.

Singles

Camping le Moulin de Serre

Vallée de la Burande (D73), F-63690 Singles (Puy-de-Dôme) T: 04 73 21 16 06. E: moulindeserre@orange.fr

alanrogers.com/FR63080

Off the beaten track, this spacious and well maintained site is set in a wooded valley beside a river where one can pan for gold. It offers a good base for those seeking quiet relaxation in this lesser known area of the Auvergne. The 90 large pitches (55 for touring) are separated by a variety of trees and hedges giving good shade. Some pitches have hardstanding and all have electricity (5-10A), long leads may be necessary. Access around the site is easy but the narrow lanes leading to it are twisting which might prove difficult for larger units.

Facilities

Well appointed, clean toilet blocks (one heated) include excellent facilities for disabled people and babies. New communal barbecue. Heated swimming pool, terrace (8/6-28/9). Takeaway (July/Aug), bar/restaurant (July/Aug). Bread (19/5-16/9). Washing machine, dryer. Motorcaravan services. Large play area. Tennis. Canoe hire in high season. Organised activities (July/Aug). Off site: Lake for fishing 2 km. Château de Val 20 km. Spa town of La Bourboule 25 km. Riding.

Open: 9 April - 18 September.

Directions

Site is about 25 km. southwest of La Bourboule. Turn west off the D922 just south of Tauves at site sign. Follow site signs along the D29 and then the D73 for about 10 km. GPS: 45.54317, 2.54275

Charges 2011

Per unit incl. 2 persons and electricity	€ 13,75 - € 21,95
extra person	€ 2,35 - € 4,30
child (under 10 yrs)	€ 1,60 - € 2,95
dog	€ 1,05 - € 1,90

For latest campsite news, availability and prices visit

alanrogers.com

Want independent campsite reviews at your fingertips?

You'll find them here...

Over 3,000 in-depth campsite reviews at **www.alanrogers.com**

With a rich and varied landscape, the Rhône Alpes offers a spectacular region that includes the craggy gorges and scented hills of the Rhône Valley, the deep valleys and mountain slopes of the Savoy Alps and the forbidding Dauphiné Alps, all offering spectacular scenery.

DÉPARTEMENTS: 01 AIN, 07 ARDÈCHE, 26 DRÔME, 38 ISÈRE, 42 LOIRE, 69 RHÔNE, 73 SAVOIE, 74 HAUTE-SAVOIE

MAJOR CITIES; LYON, GRENOBLE

The Rhône valley holds areas of great interest and natural beauty. From the sun-baked Drôme, with its ever-changing landscapes and the isolated mountains of the Vercors to the deep gorges and high plateaux of the Ardèche, studded with prehistoric caves and lush valleys filled with orchards; and encompassing the vineyards of the Beaujolais and the Rhône Valley. For the energetic there are cycling, horse riding and even white-water rafting opportunities, while for the more leisurely inclined, the remote areas are a haven for bird watching and walking.

Lying between the Rhône Valley and the Alpine borders with Switzerland and Italy are the old provinces of Savoie and Dauphiné. This is an area of enormous granite outcrops, deeply riven by spectacular glacier hewn valleys. One of the world's leading winter playgrounds there is also a range of outdoor activities in the summer. Despite development, great care has been taken to blend the old with the new and many traditional villages still retain their charm and historical interest. For many, it is an opportunity to escape the crowds and enjoy some clean air, unusual wildlife, stunning views and hidden lakes.

Places of interest

Aix-les-Bains: spa resort on the Lac du Bourget, boat excursions to the Royal Abbey of Hautecombe.

Annecy: canal-filled lakeside town, 12th-century château, old quarter.

Beaujolais: vineyards and golden-stone villages.

Bourg-Saint-Maurice: centre of Savoie café society.

Chambéry: old quarter, Dukes of Savoie château, Savoie museum.

Chamonix: site of first Winter Olympics in 1924, world capital of mountain climbing.

Grenoble: University city, Fort de la Bastille.

Lyon: Gallo-Roman artifacts, Renaissance quarter, historical Fabric Museum, silk museum.

Vallon-Pont d'Arc: base from which to visit Gorges de l'Ardèche.

Cuisine of the region

Bresse (Poulet, Poularde, Volaille de): the best French poultry, fed on corn and when killed bathed in milk.

Farcement (Farçon Savoyard): potatoes baked with cream, eggs, bacon, dried pears and prunes.

Gratin Dauphinois: potato dish with cream, cheese and garlic.

Gratin Savoyard: another potato dish with cheese and butter.

Tartiflette: potato, bacon, onions and Reblochon cheese.

www.rhonealpes-tourism.co.uk
info@rhonealpes-tourisme.com
(0)4 72 59 21 59

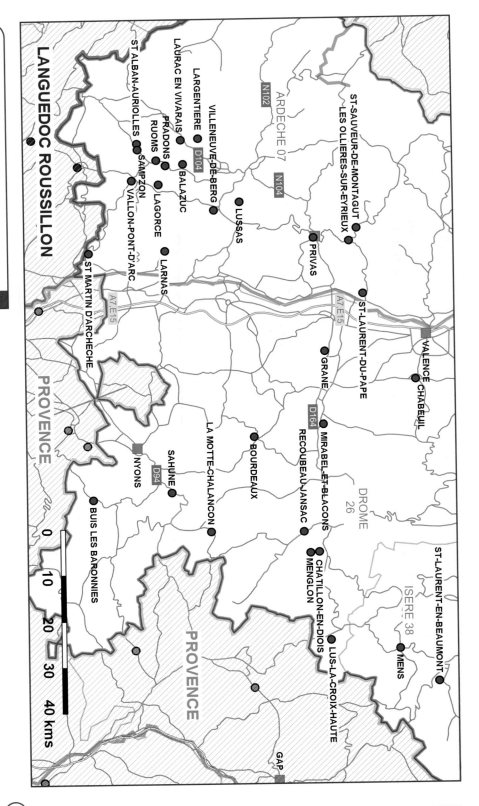

For latest campsite news, availability and prices visit

alanrogers.com

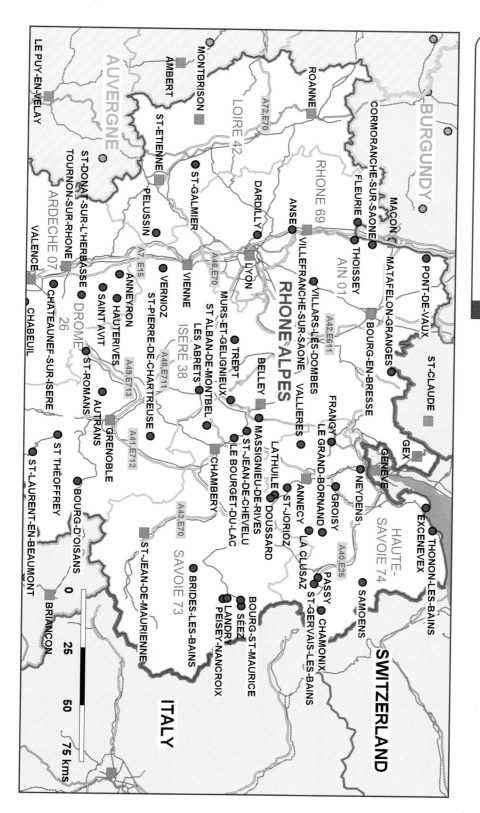

Anneyron

Flower Camping la Châtaigneraie

Route de Mantaille, F-26140 Anneyron (Drôme) T: 04 75 31 43 33. E: contact@chataigneraie.com

alanrogers.com/FR26140

La Châtaigneraie is a small, neat, terraced site run by a very friendly family (English is spoken). It is tucked away in the countryside high above the village of Anneyron with magnificent far-reaching views over the valley of the Rhône. There are 71 medium sized, slightly sloping, grassy pitches, 30 for touring away from the static units. They are separated by a variety of hedges and young trees providing varying degrees of shade and all have 6/10A electricity. Twin-axle caravans and large outfits are not admitted and only gas and electric barbecues are allowed on site. A range of activities is organised in the high season for families and younger children but there is little for the active teenagers. It will suit those seeking a quieter, relaxing family orientated site but is not ideal for those with walking difficulties.

Facilities

A well appointed and very clean toilet block has all the necessary facilities including those for campers with disabilities. Bar and small shop (all season). Good restaurant/takeaway with full menu at weekends and high season, otherwise a 'menu du jour'. Swimming and paddling pools (15/5-15/9). Short tennis. Two small play areas, TV and games room. Bicycle hire. Farmers' market twice a week. Entertainment for children and adults (July/Aug). WiFi internet access near bar. Off site: Marked walks and cycle tracks in the hills around. Fishing, riding and golf 3 km. Anneyron 3 km.

Open: 1 April - 30 September.

Directions

Leave A7 autoroute, exit 12, then N7 south for 7 km. Turn east, D1, to Anneyron (7 km). In the village turn right D161, signed Mantaille. In 3 km. turn right D301, signed Albon, to site immediately on right (well signed). GPS: 45.2547, 4.9039

Charges guide

Per unit incl. 2 persons	
and electricity	€ 16,50 - € 25,50
extra person	€ 4,00 - € 5,50
child (2-14 yrs)	€ 2,00 - € 4,00
dog	€ 2,00 - € 2,20

Anse

Camping les Portes du Beaujolais

Avenue Jean Vacher, F-69480 Anse (Rhône) T: 04 74 67 12 87. E: campingbeaujolais@wanadoo.fr

alanrogers.com/FR69030

Situated just off the A6 motorway at Anse, this campsite would make a good overnight stop. The good public transport from Anse also means that it could be used as a base for visiting Lyon. Despite some noise from the motorway and the mainline railway, this well run site has much to offer. It has good facilities with modern buildings of traditional design and materials. There are 150 formal pitches which are shady, level, numbered and marked, with neatly trimmed grass and hedges, and 10A electrical connections. Around 40% of the pitches are fully serviced. Some space is available for those who prefer to pitch in more simple and open surroundings.

Facilities

Modern toilet blocks include facilities for disabled visitors and baby rooms. Motorcaravan services. Washing machines. Shop (all season). Gas supplies. Bar, restaurant, takeaway (1/6-15/9). Swimming and paddling pools (1/5-30/9). Playground. Playing field. Tennis. Minigolf. Boules. Games room. Internet access and WiFi. Free loan of barbecues. Chalets, mobile homes and 3 tepees (sleeping up to 5 persons) to rent. Off site: Anse 1 km. Narrow gauge railway at exit. Fishing 200 m (permits sold on site). Boat launching 500 m. Riding 1.5 km. Sailing 1.5 km. Golf 2 km.

Open: 1 March - 31 October.

Directions

Leave the A6 at exit 32 and join the N6 to Anse. Site is signed from northern and southern ends of village. There are height limits on all approaches (3 or 3.2 m). GPS: 45.9405, 4.7268

Charges 2011

Per unit incl. 2 persons	
and electricity	€ 19,50 - € 23,00
extra person	€ 4,40 - € 4,80
child (2-7 yrs)	€ 3,40 - € 3,60
dog	€ 2,00
Camping Cheques accepted.	

For latest campsite news, availability and prices visit

alanrogers.com

Autrans

Kawan Village Au Joyeux Réveil

Le Château, F-38880 Autrans (Isère) T: 04 76 95 33 44. E: camping-au-joyeux-reveil@wanadoo.fr

alanrogers.com/FR38080

The superb, well organised summer and winter site is run by a very friendly family (English is spoken). It is on the outskirts of Autrans, high on a plateau (1,050 m) in the Vercors region close to a ski jump and short lift. There are 104 pitches with 70 for touring, electricity 6A in summer and 2-6A in winter. They are mainly on gently sloping grass, in a sunny location with fantastic views over the surrounding wooded mountains with small trees giving just a little shade. There is a new swimming pool area with two pools, one covered, a river and slide plus a separate paddling pool. Here the days can be very hot and sunny and the nights quite chilly. This site is ideally situated for many of the activities that this wonderful area has to offer – from walking, mountain biking and potholing in summer to downhill and cross-country skiing in winter, it is all there for you in magnificent scenery. The D531 and the D106 look a little daunting on the map and do involve a stiff climb but they are good roads and have no really difficult bends.

Facilities

The spotless toilet block is very well appointed, with underfloor heating and all the expected facilities. Another chalet-style building houses a bar with terrace, snack bar/takeaway (July/Aug). Two pools, one covered, toboggan for children, sunbathing area and a separate paddling pool. Small play area. TV room. Internet point and WiFi. Family entertainment (July/Aug). Off site: Autrans with a few shops 500 m. Fishing 200 m. Riding 300 m. Bicycle hire 500 m. Villard de Lans, supermarket, shops, restaurants, bars, ice rink and many other activities 16 km. Short ski lift is near the site and a shuttle bus runs (in winter) to the longer runs (5 km).

Open: 1 December - 31 March, 1 May - 30 September.

Directions

Leave A48, northwest of Grenoble, exit 13 (going south) or 3A (north). Follow N532 to Sassenage, turn west at roundabout, D531 to Lans-en-Vercors. At roundabout turn right, D106 Autrans. At roundabout in Autrans turn right (site signed) and very shortly right again. Site is on the left. This is the only route recommended for caravans and motorcaravans. GPS: 45.17517, 5.54762

Charges guide

Per unit incl. 2 persons	€ 22,50 - € 37,00
extra person	€ 5,00
child (under 6 yrs)	€ 3,50
Camping Cheques accepted.	

Balazuc

Camping le Chamadou

Mas de Chaussy, F-07120 Balazuc (Ardèche) T: 0820 366 197. E: infos@camping-le-chamadou.com

alanrogers.com/FR07620

La Chamadou is a delightful, well maintained and peaceful site run by an enthusiastic and friendly family. It is situated in the southern Ardèche, close to the medieval, perched village of Balazuc, not far from the river Ardèche. There are 86 slightly sloping grassy/stony pitches with 69 for touring (electricity 10A). They are separated by hedges and flowering shrubs with a variety of trees giving some shade. There are several small very clean toilet blocks with excellent facilities. A cosy restaurant and terrace have panoramic views. The narrow approach road makes access difficult for large outfits.

Facilities

Several small, well appointed and very clean toilet blocks have all the necessary facilities including those for campers with disabilities. Bar/TV (all season). Tiny shop. Restaurant and takeaway (July/Aug and some special occasions). Swimming pool, paddling pool, toboggan (all season). Good play area. Games room. Lake fishing. Canoe trips and bike hire organised. Only electric and gas barbecues allowed. Off site: Riding and bicycle hire 4 km.

Open: 1 April - 31 October.

Directions

Leave Aubenas on the D104, signed Alès. Shortly turn left on D579 signed Vallon-Pont-d'Arc. Bypass Vogüé, cross river and keep right. In 4.5 km. turn left at site sign along narrow lane to site in 2 km. GPS: 44.50778, 4.40347

Charges guide

Per unit incl. 2 persons	€ 17,00 - € 22,50
electricity (10A)	€ 4,00 - € 4,20

For latest campsite news, availability and prices visit

alanrogers.com

Bourdeaux

Camping les Bois du Chatelas

Route de Dieulefit, F-26460 Bourdeaux (Drôme) T: 04 75 00 60 80. E: contact@chatelas.com

alanrogers.com/FR26210

Located at the heart of the the Drôme Provençale, Les Bois du Chatelas is a quality family run site just 1.5 km. from the delightful village of Bourdeaux which offers some shops, cafés, etc. There are 126 level, good sized, terraced pitches, 76 for touring. They all have electricity, water and drainage. There is a superb swinming pool complex with indoor and outpools, toboggan, paddling pool, firness room, jacuzzi and sauna. Overlooking the pool area is a restaurant with superb views over the valley and hills beyond. Les Bois du Chatelas is a good choice for those seeking an active holiday. The long distance GR9 footpath passes through the site and there are very many walking and cycle routes close at hand. A popular aquagym is organised in the large outdoor pool in peak season, when there is a lively entertainment programme as well as a number of cycling and walking excursions. A member of Sites et Paysages.

Facilities

Two excellent heated toilet blocks (on upper and lower levels) with facilities for babies and visitors with disabilities (though not ideal for those with mobility problems). Shop. Bar. Restaurant/takeaway/pizzeria. Indoor and outdoor pools. Outdoor pool with water slide, waterfall, sauna, aquagym and jacuzzi. Sports pitch. Archery. Play area. Bicycle hire. Entertainment and excursion programme (July/Aug).WiFi in bar/terrace area. Off site: Bourdeaux 1.5 km. Dieulefit 12 km. Rafting and canoe trips. Riding 5 km. Fishing 1 km.

Open: 7 April - 30 September.

Directions

Leave A7 at exit 16 (Loriol). Take the D104 east to Crest. Leave Crest bypass at traffic lights, take the D538 south to Bourdeaux and continue towards Dieulefit for 1.5 km. Site is on the left (well signed). GPS: 44.57825, 5.12795

Charges guide

Per unit incl. 2 persons	€ 15,20 - € 29,80
extra person	€ 4,30 - € 7,00
child (2-7 yrs)	€ 3,30 - € 4,50
electricity (10A)	€ 4,30 - € 4,90

Camping Les Bois du Chatelas

Route de Dieulefit - F-26460 Bordeaux - Tél.: (33) 4 75 00 60 80 - Fax (33) 4 75 00 60 81
E-mail: contact@chatelas.com - www.chatelas.com

Bourg-d'Oisans

Camping à la Rencontre du Soleil

Route de l'Alpe d'Huez, F-38520 Bourg-d'Oisans (Isère) T: 04 76 79 12 22. E: rencontre.soleil@wanadoo.fr

alanrogers.com/FR38040

The Isère is an attractive and popular region with exceptional scenery. Bourg-d'Oisans lies in the Romanche valley 725 m. above sea level surrounded by high mountains. This compact site, pleasant, friendly and family run, nestles between two impressive mountain ranges, at the base of France's largest National Park, Le Parc des Ecrins. It is a real sun trap and gets very hot in summer. It is only 2 km. from the busy town of Bourg-d'Oisans. It has 73 level, hedged pitches of small to average size with mature trees offering good shade (43 for touring with 6/10A electricity). Rock pegs are advised. A Sites et Paysages member.

Facilities

Heated toilet block provides all the usual amenities, but no facilities for disabled visitors. Washing machine and dryer. Motorcaravan services. Bread to order. Restaurant and takeaway (all season). Room with TV, children's play room. Small, sheltered swimming pool (all season). Play area. Children's club. Activities in high season include walking, mountain biking. Off site: Supermarket 1 km. Fishing 5 km. Bicycle hire, riding 2 km. Canoeing, rafting, riding, hiking, climbing. Cable car at Alpe d'Huez.

Open: 1 May - 30 September.

Directions

From Grenoble bypass Bourg-d'Oisans on the N1091 towards Briancon. At end of bypass turn left at roundabout on D211 signed Alpe-d'Huez. Site is on left beyond Camping la Piscine and just before a sharp lefthand bend (so take care). GPS: 45.06547, 6.0394

Charges guide

Per unit incl. 2 persons and electricity	€ 18,55 - € 31,65
extra person	€ 1,95 - € 6,70

For latest campsite news, availability and prices visit

alanrogers.com

Bourg-d'Oisans

RCN Camping Belledonne

Rochetaillée, F-38520 Bourg-d'Oisans (Isère) T: 04 76 80 07 18. E: info@rcn-belledonne.fr
alanrogers.com/FR38100

This spacious site is now owned by the RCN group and many improvements are planned. It has 180 well drained, level, generous, grassy pitches, most for touring, all with electricity (6A). Beech hedges and abundant mature trees provide ample privacy and shade. A bar/restaurant with terrace (open all season) is next to an attractive pool complex, comprising two swimming pools (one covered and heated), a paddling pool and large sunbathing space surrounded by gardens and grassy areas. In July and August the site becomes quite lively with many organised activities. No twin-axle caravans are accepted and large outfits should phone ahead.

Facilities

Four well appointed sanitary blocks include baby rooms and facilities for disabled visitors. Shop. Bar/restaurant and takeaway (all open all season). TV/games room. Swimming and paddling pools (one covered and heated). Sauna. Tennis. Good play area, large meadow with fitness course. Football field. Bicycle hire (July/Aug). WiFi. Max. 1 dog. Off site: Riding 500 m. Fishing 4 km. Allemont, shops 2 km. Bourg-d'Oisans, shops, bars, restaurants and Saturday market 8 km. Cable car (high season).

Open: 23 April - 24 September.

Directions

Site is 8 km. west of Bourg-d'Oisans. From Grenoble take N85 to Vizille and then N91/D1091 towards Bourg-d'Oisans. In Rochetaillée branch left (site signed) onto D526, signed Allemont. Site is 250 m. on the right. GPS: 45.11423, 6.00765

Charges guide

Per unit incl. 2 persons and electricity	€ 18,90 - € 39,90
extra person (3 yrs and older)	€ 2,50 - € 4,90

Special offers for long stays, children and over 50's.

Bourg-d'Oisans

Camping le Colporteur

Le Mas du Plan, F-38520 Bourg-d'Oisans (Isère) T: 04 76 79 11 44. E: info@camping-colporteur.com
alanrogers.com/FR38140

The site is within a few minutes level walk of an attractive market town and ski resort, making this an ideal spot for motorcaravanners. There are 150 level grassy pitches, 120 for touring, including 10 hardstandings for motorhomes. All pitches have 15A electricity and rock pegs are advised. They are mostly separated by hedging and a variety of mature trees that offer some shade. There is no pool on site but campers have free entry to the adjacent municipal pool. In July and August the attractive bar/restaurant is the focal point for evening activities. Bourg-d'Oisans is in the largest national park in France. It is at an altitude of 700 m. and is surrounded by high mountains making it a real suntrap. The days can be very hot, especially in summer. The area is revered by serious cyclists as several mountain roads close by are regularly used by the Tour de France. This is an ideal base for exploring this scenic region with its abundance of wild flowers, old villages and rushing waterfalls; by car, on foot or by bike.

Facilities

Two large, clean toilet blocks are well equipped, modern and airy with all the necessary facilities including washbasins in cabins, baby room and en-suite room for disabled campers. Restaurant, bar and takeaway (mid June-end Aug). Games room. Boules. Small play area. Organised family activities (July/Aug). Off site: Shops, bars, restaurants in town. Supermarket 500 m. Ski resorts of Alpe-d'Huez (13 km) and Les Deux Alpes (19 km). Parc des Ecrins, cable cars (July/Aug).

Open: 17 May - 20 September.

Directions

Site is in Bourg-d'Oisans. From Grenoble follow the N91 into town and shortly after the road bears left in the town centre and then right (site signed). Follow signs to site, a few hundred metres.
GPS: 45.0526, 6.0355

Charges guide

Per unit incl. 2 persons and electricity	€ 23,10 - € 29,20
extra person	€ 4,70 - € 6,50
child (5-10 yrs)	€ 2,60 - € 4,50

Bourg-d'Oisans

Castel Camping le Château de Rochetaillée

Chemin de Bouthean, Rochetaillée, F-38520 Bourg-d'Oisans (Isère) T: 04 76 11 04 40
E: jcp@camping-le-chateau.com alanrogers.com/FR38180

Set in the grounds of the small château, with spectacular views, this site has recently been upgraded to provide high quality amenities. The grounds are shared with chalets and tents to rent, with these in a separate area. There are 97 touring pitches, all with 6/10A electricity hook-ups on level areas (some large) separated by hedges and trees. The site has an excellent heated swimming pool, a fitness room, sauna, bar/restaurant and takeaway food together with a small shop selling bread and basic groceries. The site is in the centre of an area ideal for walkers, cyclists and climbers.

Facilities

Three very good toilet blocks are colourful and very clean. Shower room with facilities for babies. Excellent, spacious facilities for disabled visitors. Small launderette. Freezer space. Shop, Bar, snacks, takeaway and restaurant (all 1/6-11/9). Heated swimming pool (1/6-11/9). Sauna, fitness room and jacuzzi (13/5-11/9). Climbing wall. Daily activities for children (July/Aug). Guided walks and other activities. Fishing. Safe hire. Barbecue area. Internet. WiFi. Off site: Bicycle hire 1.5 km. Riding 7 km.

Open: 13 May - 11 September.

Directions

South of Grenoble take exit 8 from A480 signed Stations de L'Oisans and follow the D1091 to Briançon. The site is signed just north of Rochetaillée. GPS: 45.11530, 6.00548

Charges 2011

Per unit incl. 2 persons and electricity	€ 22,40 - € 36,50
extra person	€ 5,40 - € 8,40
child (0-10 yrs)	€ 3,50 - € 5,30

Bourg-Saint-Maurice

Camping Caravaneige le Versoyen

Route des Arcs, F-73700 Bourg-Saint-Maurice (Savoie) T: 04 79 07 03 45. E: leversoyen@wanadoo.fr
alanrogers.com/FR73020

Bourg-St-Maurice is on a small, level plain at an altitude of 830 m. on the River Isère, surrounded by mountains. Le Versoyen attracts visitors all year round (except for a short time when they close). The site's 205 unseparated, flat pitches (180 for touring) are marked by numbers on the tarmac roads and all have electrical connections (4/6/10A). Most are on grass but some are on tarmac hardstanding making them ideal for use by motorcaravans or in winter. Trees give shade in some parts, although most pitches have almost none. Duckboards are provided for snowy and wet weather.

Facilities

Two acceptable toilet blocks can be heated, although the provision may be hard pressed in high season. British and Turkish style WCs. Laundry. Motorcaravan service facilities. Outdoor and covered pools (July/Aug). Heated rest room with TV. Small bar with takeaway in summer. Free shuttle in high season to funicular railway. Off site: Fishing or bicycle hire 200 m. Tennis and swimming pool 500 m. Riding 1 km. Golf 15 km. Cross-country ski track just behind the site.

Open: All year excl. 7/11-14/12 and 2/5-25/5.

Directions

Site is 1.5 km. east of Bourg-St-Maurice on CD119 Les Arcs road. GPS: 45.62248, 6.78475

Charges guide

Per unit incl. 2 persons and electricity	€ 16,10 - € 21,00
extra person	€ 4,00 - € 4,60
child (4-13 yrs)	€ 2,50 - € 4,40
dog	€ 0,50

Brides-les-Bains

Camping La Piat

Avenue du Comte Greyffie de Bellecombe, F-73570 Brides-les-Bains (Savoie) T: 04 79 55 22 74
E: contact@camping-brideslesbains.com alanrogers.com/FR73160

La Piat is a small family run campsite nestling at an altitude of 600 m. and surrounded by beautiful mountains. It is open for a long season and is only a few minutes walk from the small, attractive spa town of Brides-les-Bains. There are 80 often irregularly shaped, grass pitches laid out on low terraces with 73 for touring (electricity 6/10A, very long leads may be needed). On site access is good for large outfits but the final approach road is quite narrow. This site makes an ideal base for motorcaravans and those seeking a peaceful and relaxing holiday as there is no on-site entertainment.

Facilities

Two good, small toilet blocks, one quite new and there are plans to refurbish the other, with all necessary facilities including those for babies and disabled visitors. Bread etc. July/Aug. Motorcaravan services. Small play area. Boules. Off site: Spa town of Brides-les-Bains 500 m, with Casino, swimming pool, tennis, bars, restaurants, disco and a range of shops. Fishing 7 km. Golf or riding 13 km. Rafting. Canyoning. Many marked walks and cycle rides. Meribel 12 km. Courcheval 18 km.

Open: 9 April - 15 October.

Directions

Leave Albertville south on N90 to Moutier. Turn right, follow D915 to centre of Brides-les-Bains. Turn right by fountain, site signed. Site on right in 550 m. Approach from other direction is difficult and not recommended. GPS: 45.27162, 6.37703

Charges guide

| Per unit incl. 2 persons and electricity | € 11,35 - € 14,50 |
| extra person | € 2,90 - € 3,30 |

Buis-les-Baronnies

Camping Domaine de l'Ecluse

Bénivay, F-26170 Buis-les-Baronnies (Drôme) T: 04 75 28 07 32. E: camp.ecluse@wanadoo.fr
alanrogers.com/FR26200

Tucked away in the beautiful Drôme Provençale region, this quiet, rural site is situated high in the hills northeast of the Roman city of Vaison-la-Romaine. There are 75 level, stony pitches of average size, with 53 for touring (6A electricity, long leads necessary). They are separated by hedges and mature poplar trees giving varying amounts of shade. Rock pegs are advised. The attractive L-shaped swimming pool has a toboggan and sunbathing area. This site would make an ideal base for those who love serious hill-walking and biking. Visitors in June will be amazed by the variety of wild flowers and butterflies.

Facilities

Two toilet blocks with all the necessary modern facilities include rooms for babies and campers with disabilities. Small shop (May-Sept). Bar and restaurant (July/Aug). Takeaway (1/5-9/8). Swimming pool (April-Sept). Games field. Simple programme of events and some excursions (July/Aug). Gas barbecues only. Internet link via a cable. Max. 1 dog. Off site: Restaurant nearby. Bicycle hire, fishing and riding 8 km. Lake bathing 8 km. Historic villages of Buis les Baronies 8 km. Mollans 8 km. Vaison la Romaine 14 km.

Open: 5 April - 15 November.

Directions

Site is northeast of Vaison la Romaine. Only recommended access is via Buis le Baronnies. Just south of the village turn northwest on the D147 for 7 km. over the pass to Propiac. Turn right on the D347 and climb to site in 2 km. At entry, pull hard over to the right to take sharp left hand bend down slope. GPS: 44.28995, 5.1917

Charges guide

Per person	€ 3,50 - € 4,00
pitch	€ 5,50 - € 7,00
electricity (6A)	€ 3,20

Chabeuil

Le Grand Lierne

B.P. 8, F-26120 Chabeuil (Drôme) T: 04 75 59 83 14. E: contact@grandlierne.com
alanrogers.com/FR26030

In addition to its obvious attraction as an overnight stop, fairly convenient for the A7 autoroute, this site provides a pleasant base to explore this little known area between the Ardèche and the Vercors mountains and the Côtes du Rhône wine area. It has 198 marked, stony pitches, 45 for touring units (6/10A electricity), separated by hedges and oak trees which offer varying amounts of shade. The site has an attractive pool complex with several pools including a new covered heated pool for bathing in poor weather. They are surrounded by terraces with loungers for sunbathing.

Facilities

Two sanitary blocks, one refurbished in 2008, with modern facilities including those for disabled campers. Washing machines, dryers. Motorcaravan services. Shop. Restaurant and terrace (1/7-31/8). Bar/takeaway (all season). Fridge rental. Four pools (all season), one covered and heated. Paddling pool, water slide, toboggans and lazy river. Playgrounds. Entertainment programme in high season. WiFi. Only gas and electric barbecues are permitted. Dogs are not accepted in high season. Off site: Golf 3 km. Bicycle hire 4.5 km.

Open: 18 April - 26 September (with all services).

Directions

Site signed from Chabeuil about 11 km. east of Valence. Best approached from south side of Valence via Valence ring road. D68 to Chabeuil. Site is off D125 to Charpey, 5 km. from Chabeuil, well signed. GPS: 44.91572, 5.065

Charges guide

Per unit incl. 2 persons and electricity	€ 20,00 - € 39,00
extra person	€ 4,70 - € 7,00
child (2-7 yrs)	€ 3,50 - € 4,50

Chamonix

Camping de la Mer de Glace

200 chemin de la Bagna, les Praz, F-74400 Chamonix (Haute-Savoie) T: 04 50 53 44 03
E: info@chamonix-camping.com alanrogers.com/FR74150

This attractive site is convenient for Chamonix but is in a tranquil setting away from its hustle and bustle. The buildings are of typical regional timber construction, decorated with traditional painted flower designs. Set in a large level clearing, with a view of the Mont Blanc range, it has been kept as natural as possible without a pool, restaurant, bar or disco and is well suited to those looking for quiet and relaxation. The area is rich in trails for walking and mountain biking and many pass nearby. There are 150 pitches of varying sizes, most with shade and 75 have electricity connections (10A).

Facilities

Three sanitary blocks with facilities for disabled visitors. Washing machine, dryer. Motorcaravan services. Bread. Pizza van twice weekly in July/Aug. Meeting room, snack room. Small playground for young children. Free internet and WiFi access. Off site: Fishing and golf 500 m. Bicycle hire 1 km. Riding 5 km. Shops, etc. 700 m. in Les Praz or 1.5 km. in Chamonix. Free bus/train pass in locality.

Open: 29 April - 2 October.

Directions

From Chamonix take N506 northeast towards Les Praz. After 1 km. site signed to right. NOTE: the first two signs direct you under a 2.4 m. high bridge. Continue to a small roundabout at Les Praz, turn right and follow signs. GPS: 45.93805, 6.89267

Charges 2011

Per unit incl. 2 persons and electricity	€ 21,60 - € 25,60

For latest campsite news, availability and prices visit
alanrogers.com

Chamonix

Camping l'Ile des Barrats

185 chemin de l'Ile des Barrats, F-74400 Chamonix (Haute-Savoie) T: 04 50 53 51 44
E: campingiledesbarrats74@orange.fr alanrogers.com/FR74160

L'Ile des Barrats is a delightful neat, tidy, small and tranquil site. It is within easy walking distance of the beautiful town of Chamonix, although there are bus and train services close by if needed. There are 53 slightly sloping, grassy pitches all for touring mostly separated by small hedges and a variety of trees offering some shade. All have electricity (5/10A) and 32 have water and a drain. This is an ideal site for those wishing to roam the mountain trails and for those seeking a peaceful and relaxing holiday in a most superb setting. Twin-axle caravans are not accepted.

Facilities

A modern, clean toilet block offers all necessary facilities, including those for disabled visitors. Covered picnic area with table and benches, ideal for those with small tents. Motorcaravan services. Store room for mountaineers. Mobile shop in July/Aug. No organised activities. Off site: Baker 500 m. Chamonix 800 m. level walk (high class summer and winter resort with colourful Saturday market). Hang-gliding, funicular railway, cable cars and chair lifts nearby.

Open: 15 May - 1 October.

Directions

On entering Chamonix from Geneva, turn left at first roundabout after turn off for the Mont Blanc Tunnel (follow signs for Hospital). Shortly, at next roundabout, turn left and site is on right opposite hospital. GPS: 45.9143, 6.8615

Charges guide

Per person	€ 6,40
pitch incl. car	€ 7,90
electricity (5/10A)	€ 3,30 - € 4,30
No credit cards.	

Châtillon-en-Diois

Flower Camping Lac Bleu

Quartier la Touche, F-26410 Châtillon-en-Diois (Drôme) T: 04 75 21 85 30. E: info@lacbleu-diois.com
alanrogers.com/FR26150

This spacious and peaceful site is run by a very friendly family who have made many improvements to the site with many more in the pipeline. It lies in a beautiful valley surrounded by mountains, south of the Vercors National Park. The 199 pitches (76 for touring) are level with rough grass, slightly uneven and separated by a variety of trees offering some shade (rock pegs advised). All have electricity (10A). At the centre of the site is a lake of 2.5 hectares with warm clean water fed by springs, making it ideal for swimming and fishing. A good bar, restaurant and terrace overlook the lake and there is plenty of space for children to play. No dogs. Only gas and electric barbecues. A covered swimming pool was added recently. An evening stroll around the lake is recommended. The site is near the very small Bez river and not far from the interesting and ancient small town of Die, the home of the famous Clairette de Die – a sparkling wine mentioned in dispatches by the Romans around 40AD.

Facilities

Two clean toilet blocks one new, the other refurbished, with all the necessary facilities. Baby room. Facilities for disabled campers. Bar/restaurant, takeaway. TV/games room (all season). Covered heated swimming pool and paddling pool (all season). Motorcaravan service point. Play area. Ffishing. Bicycle hire. WiFi in bar/terrace area (charged). Only gas and electric barbecues allowed. Off site: Riding 7 km. Medieval villages (Châtillon 2 km).

Open: 1 April - 30 September.

Directions

Take D93 southeast from Die, signed Gap. After about 5 km. turn left on D539 signed Châtillon-en-Diois. After 4.5 km. bear right onto D140, site signed. Site shortly on left. GPS: 44.6824, 5.44795

Charges guide

Per unit incl. 2 persons and electricity	€ 15,30 - € 25,20
extra person	€ 2,50 - € 4,10
child (2-7 years)	€ 2,50 - € 4,10

Châteauneuf-sur-Isère

Camping le Soleil Fruité

Les Peches, F-26300 Châteauneuf-sur-Isère (Drôme) T: 04 75 84 19 70. E: contact@lesoleilfruite.com
alanrogers.com/FR26220

Le Soleil Fruité is a new site conveniently located a little to the north of Valence, only 6 km. from the Autoroute. The site lies amidst a large fruit farm with peaches, apricots and olives with views over the Ardèche mountains. Campers are invited to pick fruit and there is a twice weekly market featuring the farm's produce. There are 137 large, level, grassy pitches with 100 for touring (electricity 6A).They are separated by small shrubs and young trees giving little shade. Twin-axle caravans are not allowed on site. Only gas and electric barbecues. Dogs are not accepted iin July and August.

Facilities

Excellent, clean toilet block with facilities for babies and disabled visitors. Bar, TV/snack bar, small shop (all season). Swimming pool with jacuzzi. Paddling pool (all season). Play area. Bicycle hire. WiFi (free). Motorhome services. Table tennis, trampolines. Twice weekly market in high season. Entertainment for under 10s and excursion programme (July/Aug). Off site: Canoeing on the River Drôme. Minigolf. Covered pool. Health club with steam bath and massage. Golf 5 km.

Open: 28 April - 15 September.

Directions

Leave A7 Autoroute exit 14 (Valence Nord) take the N7 north for 2 km. Turn right, D877, site signed. After 2 km. turn left, then left at roundabout, then left again to site. GPS: 45.002716, 4.895514

Charges guide

Per unit incl. 2 persons	€ 15,90 - € 23,45
extra person	€ 4,95 - € 6,65
child (under 13 yrs)	free - € 4,85
electricity (6A)	€ 4,00

Cormoranche-sur-Saône

Camping du Lac

Base de Loisirs, les Luizants, F-01290 Cormoranche-sur-Saône (Ain) T: 03 85 23 97 10
E: contact@lac-cormoranche.com alanrogers.com/FR01090

Situated in a region famous for its wines, gastronomy and picturesque old villages, this site is part of the 42-hectare, landscaped recreation park that surrounds a tree lined lake. The 117 generous pitches are level, grassed and enclosed by hedges, all with electricity and drainage. A small dam divides the lake into two areas, one for swimming, the other larger part for fishing (also permitted at night) and boating. To the far side of the park is a TGV railway track. During the day the trains are fairly frequent, but there are no night services and the daytime noise is a moderate rumble. The reception office has a good selection of tourist information on a region lined with the wine routes of Beaujolais, Macon and Bourgogne. In addition, this is the region of Bresse chickens and freshwater fish and in the surrounding picturesque towns and villages there are many good restaurants, the most famous being that of Georges Blanc in Vonnas.

Facilities

Modern sanitary building provides free preset showers and (a little small), washbasins in cabins. Facilities for disabled visitors. Laundry room with washing machine. Motorcaravan service point. Small shop (order bread for following morning). Bar and restaurant with takeaway, overlooking lake. Lake swimming with a separate area for small children. Off site: Macon, Bourg-en-Bresse and the village of Perouges.

Open: 1 April - 30 September.

Directions

Site is 5 km. south-southwest of Macon on the eastern site of the Saône. It is well signed from all directions 'Base de Loisirs'. If approaching from the west via Creches, there is a 2.6 m. height restriction. GPS: 46.25167, 4.8261

Charges guide

Per person	€ 4,10 - € 5,00
child (2-12 yrs)	€ 1,60 - € 2,50
pitch incl. electricity	€ 5,80 - € 8,50

BASE DE LOISIRS DU LAC
CAMPING ★★★★
To rent - Chalets - Mobile Homes - Tipis
SNACK - BAR - ANIMATION
01290 Cormoranche-sur-Saône
00 33-(0)3-85-23-97-10
www.lac-cormoranche.com

COMMUNAUTE DE COMMUNES
CANTON DE PONT-DE-VEYLE

PARIS
MACON c'est ici
LYON

For latest campsite news, availability and prices visit
alanrogers.com

Dardilly

Camping Indigo Lyon

Porte de Lyon, Allee du Camping, F-69570 Dardilly (Rhône) T: 04 78 35 64 55
E: lyon@camping-indigo.com alanrogers.com/FR69010

This is a modern overnight site just off the A6 autoroute. Kept busy with overnight trade, reception and the café (in main season) open until quite late. There are 185 separate numbered plots all with 6/10A electricity and 140 of these also provide water and waste water drainage. Those for caravans are mostly on hardstandings on a slight slope, with another small grassy part, while those for tents are on a flatter area of grass. A very large commercial centre has been developed just outside the site, with eight hotels, restaurants, a supermarket, petrol station, etc. There is some road noise. Lyon is a very attractive city, especially noted for the excellence of its food, and well worth a visit. A bus stop for the centre (8 km) is nearby (timetables in reception).

Facilities

Three sanitary blocks, one heated, have free hot water (solar heated) and washbasins in cabins. Baby changing facilities and washing machines. Bar open at weekends in low season and daily in July and August. Takeaway provision on Friday and Saturdays. Motorcaravan service point. Swimming and paddling pools (1/6-18/9, supervised and free). Playground. TV room. Games room. Reading room (books and local information). Boules. Picnic and barbecue area. Off site: Riding 2 km. Golf 12 km.

Open: All year.

Directions

Travelling south, do not take A46 motorway around Lyon, continue on A6, take exit Limonest, Dardilly, Porte de Lyon. About 8 km. north of Lyon tunnel; turn left for Porte de Lyon (well signed).
GPS: 45.82035, 4.7604

Charges guide

Per unit incl. 2 persons	
and electricity	€ 20,40 - € 25,20
extra person	€ 4,10 - € 4,40
child (2-7 yrs)	€ 2,40 - € 3,00

Camping Cheques accepted.

In a beautiful natural park, at the gateway to the famous city of Lyon

Camping INDIGO

LyON ★★★★

«Wood & canvas» tents, mobile-homes and gipsy caravans to rent

Bar-restaurant with a huge underhung terrace, TV and playroom, swimming pool, grassy pitches, excellent public transport connections to visit Lyon

Allée du camping - Porte de Lyon - 69570 Lyon
Tel : +33 (0)4 78 35 64 55

www.camping-indigo.com

Doussard

Camping International le Lac Bleu

Route de la Plage, F-74210 Doussard (Haute-Savoie) T: 04 50 44 30 18. E: contact@camping-lac-bleu.com
alanrogers.com/FR74180

This lakeside site has its own beach and jetty and a short walk brings you to the lake ferry. The site has breathtaking views, a swimming pool (a 'fun pool' was added in 2010) and 220 pitches divided by privet and beech hedges. This site is perfect for walking, cycling or sailing and in low season provides a tranquil base for those just wishing to relax. In high season it will be busy and popular. The proximity of the public lakeside area which is often used as a festival venue could be either a source of noise or an exciting place to be depending on your point of view. When we visited the music stopped at 23.00. A nearby cycle track on a disused railway to Annecy gives a level 16 km. ride with mountains on the left and the lake to the right. In high season there is a children's club for the under eights. The bar has a thriving takeaway (roast whole chickens and pizza) and an 'al fresco' eating area.

Facilities

Three toilet blocks are of a high standard with free showers. Good provision for babies and disabled visitors. Bar (15/5-15/9) and integral small shop. Takeaway. Swimming pool (15/5-15/9). Bicycle hire. Boat launching (sailing lessons and boat hire nearby). Multisports pitch. Private beach. Off site: Small supermarket 100 m. Hypermarket 4 km. Village close with bars and restaurants. Fishing 100 m. Riding and golf 7 km.

Open: 1 April - 25 September.

Directions

Site is 16 km. south of Annecy on Route d'Albertville, well signed. GPS: 46.317367, 6.362967

Charges guide

Per unit incl. 2 persons	
and electricity	€ 20,50 - € 35,50
extra person (over 3 yrs)	€ 4,00 - € 6,20
dog	€ 2,90 - € 4,30

For latest campsite news, availability and prices visit

alanrogers.com

Doussard

Campéole la Nublière

30 allée de la Nublière, F-74210 Doussard (Haute-Savoie) T: 04 50 44 33 44. E: nubliere@wanadoo.fr
alanrogers.com/FR74190

If you are looking for large pitches, shady trees, mountain views and direct access to the lakeside beach, this site is for you. There are 271 touring pitches of which 243 have electrical hook-ups (6A). This area is very popular and the site is very likely to be busy in high season. There may be some noise from the road and the public beach. La Nublière is 16 km. from old Annecy and you are spoilt for choice in how to get there. Take a ferry trip, hire a sailing boat or pedalo, or walk or cycle along the traffic free track towards the town. The local beach and sailing club are close and there is a good restaurant on the site perimeter. Across the road from the site are tennis courts and boules pitches. The site is perfect for walking, cycling or sailing and in low season provides a tranquil base for those just wishing to relax in natural surroundings on the edge of a nature reserve.

Facilities

Large clean sanitary blocks include free hot showers and good facilities for disabled visitors. Laundry. Shop (1/5-15/9). Restaurant on site perimeter (closed Mondays). Children's club (3/7-26/8) for 4-8 yrs. Safe deposit. Off site: Small supermarket adjacent to site. Good watersports area within 70 m. Access to town beach from site. Fishing 100 m. Golf and riding 4 km. Bicycle hire 7 km.

Open: 28 April - 18 September.

Directions

Site is 16 km. south of Annecy on Route d'Albertville, well signed. GPS: 45.7908, 6.2197

Charges guide

Per unit incl. 2 persons and electricity	€ 17,10 - € 26,60
extra person	€ 4,50 - € 6,80
child (2-6 yrs)	free - € 4,30

Campéole

CAMPSITES AND RENTALS

La Nublière***

At the shore of Lac d'Annecy, direct acces to the beach and nautic base, with mountains all around. Pitches and accommodations of high quality.

74210 Doussard - Tel.: +33-450-4433-44 - www.campeole.co.uk / nubliere@campeole.com

Route de la Plage - 74210 Doussard
Tel: 0033 450 44 30 18
Fax: 0033 450 44 84 35
contact@camping-lac-blue.com
www.camping-lac-blue.com

Welcome to Camping Le Lac Bleu!
The whole team here will ensure that you have a great holiday on the shores of Lake Annecy on a wonderful site at the heart of the French Alps. You'll be sure to enjoy the fine beach and swimming pool, and, of course, a stunning natural setting which is the ideal place for outstanding holidays! This really is a great spot too for all watersports - waterskiing, windsurfing, sailing, pedaloes and much more.

Doussard

Camp de la Ravoire

Bout-du-Lac, route de la Ravoire, F-74210 Doussard (Haute-Savoie) T: 04 50 44 37 80
E: info@camping-la-ravoire.fr alanrogers.com/FR74040

La Ravoire is a high quality site, 800 m. from Lake Annecy, noted for its neat and tidy appearance and the quietness of its location in this popular tourist region. The 112 level pitches are on well mown grass with some shade and separated by small shrubs and some hedging. The 90 pitches for touring (21 with water and drain) have electricity (5-15A). Those looking for a campsite in this attractive region without the 'animation' programmes that many French sites feel are necessary, will find this a peaceful base. Take to the back roads and explore the ancient villages and wonderful countryside. Access to the banks of the lake is a walk away (across a busy road).

Facilities

Very good toilet block, facilities for disabled visitors, laundry room, washing machines, dryers and irons. Bar, snack bar, takeaway. Shop. Outdoor pool, water slide and paddling pool. All open all season. Good play area. Sports areas. Off site: Fishing, boat launching, bicycle hire 1 km. Riding 6 km. Golf 8 km. Good restaurants on the lakeside, shops in Doussard and Annecy. Cycle track (20 km) almost to Annecy passes close by. Canyoning and hang-gliding close. Boat trips.

Open: 15 May - 7 September.

Directions

Site is signed from N508 Annecy - Albertville road. About 13 km. south of Annecy, at traffic lights in Brédannaz, turn right (site signed) and then immediately left. Site on left in about 1 km. GPS: 45.80256, 6.20977

Charges 2011

Per unit incl. 2 persons	
and electricity	€ 24,50 - € 34,10
extra person	€ 5,00 - € 6,50
child (2-15 yrs)	€ 2,50 - € 4,50

Camping Cheques accepted.

Excenevex

Campé**o**le

Campéole La Pinède

F-74140 Excenevex Plage (Haute-Savoie) T: 04 50 72 85 05. E: pinede@campeole.com
alanrogers.com/FR74280

La Pinède is a member of the Campéole group and has direct access to Excenevex beach, the only naturally sandy beach on Lake Geneva. The site has a pleasant woodland setting and pitches are of a good size, all with electricity (10A). Mobile homes, chalets and fully equipped tents are available for rent (including specially adapted units for wheelchair users). There is a supervised bathing area on the beach, which shelves gradually, and a small harbour (suitable only for boats with a shallow draught). Other amenities include a shop and takeaway food service, as well as an entertainment marquee and children's play area. There is plenty of activity here in high season with a children's club and regular discos and karaoke evenings. Geneva is 25 km. distant and other possible excursions include Thonon-les-Bains with its weekly market and, of course, boat trips on Lake Geneva. Dramatic mountain scenery is close at hand, notably the spectacular Dent d'Oche (2,222 m) and the Gorges du Pont du Diable.

Facilities

Lake beach. Takeaway food. Play area. Bouncy castle. Activities and entertainment programme. Tourist information. Mobile homes, chalets and equipped tents for rent. Off site: Geneva 25 km. Thonon-les-Bains 15 km. Hiking and cycle tracks. Riding. Golf

Open: 11 April - 11 September.

Directions

From Geneva head along the south side of the lake on the D1005 as far as Massongy and shortly beyond here take the northbound D324 to Excenevex. The site is well indicated from here. GPS: 46.34492, 6.35808

Charges guide

Per unit incl. 2 persons	
and electricity	€ 17,10 - € 26,60

For latest campsite news, availability and prices visit

alanrogers.com

Fleurie

Camping Municipal la Grappe Fleurie

La Lie, F-69820 Fleurie (Rhône) T: 04 74 69 80 07. E: camping@fleurie.org

alanrogers.com/FR69020

With easy access from both the A6 autoroute and the N6, this site is ideally situated for night stops or indeed for longer stays to explore the vineyards and historic attractions of the Beaujolais region. Virtually surrounded by vineyards, but within walking distance (less than 1 km) of the pretty village of Fleurie, this is an immaculate small site, with 85 separated touring pitches. All are grassed and fairly level with the benefit of individual access to water, drainage and 10A electrical connections. A baker calls each morning (07.30-08.30). Wine tasting is arranged twice weekly in high season. Restaurant and shopping facilities are available in the village.

Facilities

Sanitary facilities in two blocks have British and Turkish style toilets and very satisfactory shower and washing facilities (showers closed 22.00-07.00). Facilities for disabled visitors. Two cold showers are provided for those wishing to cool down in summer. Washing machine and dryer. Outdoor swimming pool (15x7 m). Small playground. Only gas or electric barbecues are allowed. Off site: Fleurie 600 m. Fishing 10 km.

Open: Late March - end October.

Directions

From N6 at Le Maison Blanche/Romanech-Thorins, take D32 to village of Fleurie from where site is signed. GPS: 46.1879, 4.69916

Charges guide

Per unit incl. 2 persons and electricity	€ 12,90 - € 16,00
extra person	€ 4,70 - € 5,70
child (5-10 yrs)	€ 3,20 - € 3,70

Frangy

Camping le Chamaloup

Contamine Sarzin, F-74270 Frangy (Haute-Savoie) T: 04 50 77 88 28. E: camping@chamaloup.com

alanrogers.com/FR74240

Le Chamaloup is a neat and tidy site run by a very friendly family. It is situated midway between the lakes of Annecy, Geneva and de Bourget and only ten minutes from the A40 autoroute making it an ideal centre for exploring this beautiful region. There are only 60 level, grass pitches which are separated by small trees. Mature trees give varying amounts of shade. The 43 pitches for touring units (with 10A electricity) are well separated from authentic wooden chalets for rent. The emphasis here is on quiet family holidays with occasional soirées in the high season. Although access is easy for large units, twin-axle caravans are not accepted.

Facilities

Two modern toilet blocks with all necessary facilities including those for campers with disabilities. Bar, restaurant, takeaway (July/Aug). Heated swimming and paddling pools. Games/TV room. Some organised family activities (July/Aug). Internet access (WiFi). Off site: Riding 4 km. Golf, bicycle hire, lake beach, windsurfing, boat ramp 15 km. Frangy with small range of shops, bars, restaurants 4 km. Annecy 23 km. Geneva 34 km.

Open: 1 May - 15 September.

Directions

Leave A40 autoroute at exit 11, signed Frangy. Take N508 14 km. southeast, and after bypassing Frangy, site is on the left in 4 km. GPS: 46.01061, 5.97621

Charges guide

Per unit incl. 2 persons and electricity	€ 23,50 - € 26,00
extra person	€ 4,50 - € 5,50
child (1-12 yrs)	€ 3,50
dog	€ 2,00

Groisy

Camping Moulin Dollay

206 rue du Moulin Dollay, F-74570 Groisy (Haute-Savoie) T: 04 50 68 00 31. E: moulin.dollay@orange.fr

alanrogers.com/FR74170

Nestling between Annecy (15 km) and Geneva (35 km), this spacious site is a gem with only 45 pitches, 30 for touring. The friendly and enthusiastic owner has worked hard to develop this site to a high standard. The large to very large, level, grass pitches are partially separated by hedging and a variety of trees provide some shade. All pitches have 6A electricity and rock pegs are recommended. As there are only a few activities organised for youngsters on site it is perhaps better suited to those who would appreciate a peaceful site in a parkland setting alongside a rushing stream.

Facilities

Spacious, well appointed, heated toilet block, including facilities for disabled visitors and a baby room. Washing machine, dryer. Motorcaravan services. Bar, TV corner. Large open play and sports area. Fishing and bathing in shallow river. Off site: Some shops, restaurants, bank and supermarkets at Groisy 1 km. Interesting little town of Thorens-Glières with its 11th-century château 5 km. Annecy with wide range of facilities 12 km. Lake Annecy and watersports 15 km. Riding 4 km. Golf 6 km.

Open: 1 May - 30 September.

Directions

Site is north of Annecy. Heading north on N1203 Annecy - Bonneville road, turn right on D2 signed Thorens-Glières and site, then immediately right again. Site is 300 m. GPS: 46.00238, 6.19079

Charges 2011

Per unit incl. 2 persons and electricity	€ 18,00 - € 22,00
extra person	€ 5,00

No credit cards.

For latest campsite news, availability and prices visit

alanrogers.com

Grâne

Kawan Village Les Quatre Saisons

Route de Roche-sur-Grâne, F-26400 Grâne (Drôme) T: 04 75 62 64 17. E: contact@camping-4-saisons.com

alanrogers.com/FR26110

This small, terraced site, open all year, nestles in the hillsides of the lower Drôme valley close to the Vercors Mountains. With its 82 pitches (71 for touring units), at present it provides mainly overnight accommodation but it is worth a longer stay. The pitches are level and stony, of variable size, cut out of the hillside and reached by a one-way system on tarmac roads. All pitches have electricity (6A), some with water and drain. The modern main building houses reception on the top floor, with other facilities below, and provides commanding views across the valley towards Crest and the Vercors.

Facilities

Good sanitary facilities include baby room, en-suite facilities for disabled visitors (but site is very sloping and not suitable for wheelchairs). Washing machine. Bar (1/5-30/9). TV room. Small swimming pool (1/5-15/9). Play area. Only electric and gas barbecues are allowed on the pitch. Trampoline. Off site: Village nearby with shops catering for most needs. Fishing 1 km. Riding 3 km. Crest. Bicycle hire 2/3 km.

Open: 1 April - 30 September.

Directions

From A7 exit 17, or the N7 at Loriol, take the D104 towards Crest. After 8 km. in Grâne take the D113 south. Site is on left about 600 m. beyond the village. GPS: 44.7277, 4.9265

Charges 2011

Per unit incl. 2 persons	
and electricity	€ 18,00 - € 29,00
extra person	€ 5,00
child (under 6 yrs)	€ 3,50
dog	free

Camping Cheques accepted.

Les 4 Saisons Camping et Caravanning★★★★

Only 10 minutes from exit 16 of the A7 highway. Ideal for a stop-over or a longer stay in a quiet and relaxing environment with lovely well situated pitches with a nice view on the Vercors. The campsite is perfectly located for cyclists and walkers. Lovers of antiquity will love the magnificent high situated villages.

Route de Roche sur Grâne - 26400 Grane
Tél. 0031 (0)4 75 62 64 17 - Fax 0031 (0)4 75 62 69 06
E-mail contact@camping-4-saisons.com

www.camping-4-saisons.com

Hauterives

Flower Camping Le Château

5 route de Romans, F-26390 Hauterives (Drôme) T: 04 75 68 80 19. E: camping-hauterives@orange.fr

alanrogers.com/FR26360

Le Château is a former municipal campsite which is now run by the friendly and very helpful, Valérie and Franck. It is a family oriented site set an hour south of Lyon near the motorway. In high season activities are organised for the whole family. This site comprises 137 touring pitches and 13 used for accommodation to rent, well spread over and area of 4 ha. There is also a dedicated area for tent campers near the entrance of the site. The pitches are of a good size and kept neat and tidy. Le Château is located within walking distance of the village of Hauterives.

Facilities

Sanitary buildings include showers. Facilities for disabled visitors. Dishwashing sinks. Restaurant. Outdoor pools (salt water) and children's pool. Table tennis. TV room. Playground. Library. Boules. Accommodation to rent.

Open: 1 April - 30 September.

Directions

Leave the A7 at exit 12 (Chanas) and take the third exit from roundabout (D519 for Grenoble and Beaurepaire). At Beaurepaire take the D538 and go through Lens Lestang, then Hauterives. At roundabout by the church, turn left for Romans. Site is 200 m. on the left. GPS: 45.252796, 5.026717

Charges 2011

Per unit incl. 2 persons	
and electricity	€ 14,50 - € 25,30
extra person	€ 3,80 - € 5,00
child (2-7 yrs)	free - € 3,20
dog	€ 2,00 - € 2,20

For latest campsite news, availability and prices visit

alanrogers.com

La Clusaz

Camping le Plan du Fernuy

Route des Confins, F-74220 La Clusaz (Haute-Savoie) T: 04 50 02 44 75. E: info@plandufernuy.com
alanrogers.com/FR74090

This neat and open site has separate summer and winter seasons. It has 80 average sized, stony, grassy, pitches, 58 for tourists with electricity and 22 fully serviced. There are good mountain views but little shade, rock pegs essential. The site's crowning glory is an excellent indoor heated pool with large windows looking out on to the mountains. This is a good site for skiing in winter (with access to a ski-tow from the campsite and a free bus to other centres). In summer it is a good base for walking and cycling with other sporting opportunities nearby.

Facilities

Very good heated sanitary provision. Baby room. Facilities for disabled visitors. Washing machine and dryer. Drying room for ski clothing and boots. Motorcaravan services. Small shop and bar, snacks, takeaway. Games, TV room. Heated indoor pool and paddling pool. Skiing from site and ski excursions organised. Off site: Shops and restaurants in village 2 km. Riding 800 m. Golf, bicycle hire and fishing 1.5 km.

Open: 4 June - 4 September, 18 December - 24 April.

Directions

From Annecy take D909 to La Clusaz and at roundabout turn towards Les Confins. Site is on right after 2 km. (well signed). It is best to avoid using D909 from Flumat particularly with caravans or motorhomes. GPS: 45.90922, 6.45203

Charges guide

Per unit incl. 2 persons	€ 20,00 - € 24,00
incl. electricity (4-13A)	€ 23,50 - € 32,00
extra person	€ 5,50 - € 6,50

Winter prices are higher.

La Motte Chalancon

Camping la Ferme de Clareau

Route de Die (RD 61), F-26470 La Motte Chalancon (Drôme) T: 04 75 27 26 03
E: campingfermeclareau@wanadoo.fr alanrogers.com/FR26300

La Ferme de Clareau is a very spacious site located at the heart of La Drôme Provençale, close to the pretty village of La Motte Chalancon with superb views over the surrounding hills. There are 50 very large, sloping, unmarked pitches, some under trees and others in a large meadow with no access roads. Most have electricity though very long leads may be needed. The site is situated within a sheep farm and one side stretches along the River Oule (good for bathing and fishing). Access is difficult for large outfits. Gas and electric barbecues only. The old farm buildings have been sensitively restored and now house the site's snack bar/takeaway selling local produce (including Pre Chorier, a naturally leavened bread), close to the new swimming pool. La Motte Chalancon is a delight to explore with its unique covered streets (calades). There are innumerable walking and cycling opportunities in the area and the campsite organises family hikes, as well as various sports tournaments and games for children. Further afield, the Vercors and Ardèche ranges are both within easy access.

Facilities

Three basic toilet blocks. Snack bar (farmhouse breakfasts available). Swimming pool (min 1.2 m). Direct access to river. Vast play area. Table tennis. Games room (no TV). Low key entertainment and activity programme. Fully equipped tents for rent. WiFi at reception. Off site: La Motte Chalancon 1 km. Fishing (river). Picnic area and lake with bathing 6 km. Maison des Vautours wildlife centre. Cycle and walking tracks.

Open: 16 April - 18 October.

Directions

From Nyons take D94 northeast for 26 km. Just before Rémuzat turn north, D61 through La Motte Chalancon. Shortly turn right across bridge (site signed) climb narrow lane to farm house on right. GPS: 44.48022, 5.39458

Charges guide

Per unit incl. 2 persons and electricity	€ 11,60 - € 15,50
extra person	€ 3,40 - € 4,60

No credit cards.

For latest campsite news, availability and prices visit
alanrogers.com

Lagorce

Castel Domaine de Sévenier

F-07150 Lagorce (Ardèche) T: 04 75 88 29 44. E: domainedesevenier@orange.fr

alanrogers.com/FR07660

The pitches at this campsite are used exclusively for mobile home accommodation. For full details please see our PRL section starting on page 538.

Landry

Camping Caravaneige l'Eden

F-73210 Landry (Savoie) T: 04 79 07 61 81. E: info@camping-eden.net

alanrogers.com/FR73060

L'Eden is open almost all year round (it is closed for three weeks in May). Beside the Iser river and set in beautiful woodland glades, it is perfect for winter skiing and summer walking and cycling. The site is set in a valley with the Alpine peaks as a backdrop. The 132 good, spacious pitches all have 10A electrical hook-ups and individual water supplies (available when no frost is likely). The pristine, modern sanitary blocks are heated in colder weather and include a large drying room. There is a pool for summer lounging, a bar and a welcoming communal area with bar, TV and internet access.

Facilities

Two heated toilet blocks include drying rooms, good facilities for disabled visitors and for babies. Launderette. Communal area with bar, TV and internet. Snack bar and takeaway (July/Aug). Swimming pool (13.5x5 m; June-Sept). Games room. Play area. Fishing. Ski passes for sale on-site. Off site: Shops and restaurants in village. Many leisure pursuits including rafting, paragliding, cycle and cross country ski tracks. Riding 10 km. Golf 15 km.

Open: All year excl. 1-23 May.

Directions

From the RN90 take D87 towards Landry. Site is on left after 250 m. and is well signed from the RN90. GPS: 45.57652, 6.73457

Charges guide

Per unit incl. 2 persons	€ 10,70 - € 21,40
extra person	€ 2,90 - € 5,70
child (0-7 yrs)	€ 2,30 - € 4,50
electricity (10A)	€ 2,00 - € 6,00

Largentière

Kawan Village les Ranchisses

Route de Rocher, F-07110 Largentière (Ardèche) T: 04 75 88 31 97. E: reception@lesranchisses.fr

alanrogers.com/FR07070

This is a very well equipped, modern campsite in a lesser known area of the Ardèche. There are 93 good-sized, level, grassy pitches, 38 for touring units with electricity including 55 which are fully serviced, both shaded and part shaded. There is traffic noise in some areas. A small river pool provides opportunities for bathing, fishing or canoeing (free life jackets) with one part of the bathing area quite safe for youngsters. Well run and with the emphasis on personal attention, this is a highly recommended site.

Facilities

Comprehensive toilet buildings include facilities for babies and disabled visitors. Laundry facilities. Motorcaravan services. Shop. Bar. Restaurant (regional specialities), takeaway/pizzeria and terrace. Two large pools, paddling pool (heated). Wellness centre with sauna, jacuzzi and hammam, and semi-covered pool. Adventure style playground. Organised amusements for children (from 1/7). Skate park. Tennis. Minigolf. Boules. Canoeing. Internet access. Off site: Canoe, kayaking arranged (mid June-end Aug). Medieval village, Largentière (1.5 km) with Tuesday market. Riding 8 km. Bicycle hire 10 km. Take to the back roads to see the real Ardèche.

Open: 16 April - 25 September.

Directions

Largentière is southwest of Aubenas best approached using D104. Just beyond Uzer, 16 km. From Aubenas, turn northwest on D5. After 5 km. at far end of Largentière, fork left downhill signed Rocher and Valgorge. Site on left in about 1.8 km. just beyond rocky gorge. The approach from Valgorge is not recommended. GPS: 44.56071, 4.28463

Charges guide

Per unit incl. 2 persons and electricity (10A)	€ 19,00 - € 42,00
extra person (over 1 yr)	€ 5,00 - € 9,00
dog	€ 3,30

Camping Cheques accepted.

Larnas

La Domaine d'Imbours

F-07220 Larnas (Ardèche) T: 04 75 54 39 50. E: info@domaine-imbours.com
alanrogers.com/FR07290

This large site is part of a holiday complex with many mobile homes (99), chalets (41), hotel and 200 camping pitches. These are on scrub grass, not marked, with some shade from mature trees and 6A electricity (long leads may be helpful). For those looking for more or less everything organised for them in high season, this complex may suit. Out of season it is different, with not much happening. The complex is dominated by the hotel which is about 1 km. from the camping area along a descending site road. Around the hotel is a large and well designed pool complex. In high season there are evening shows and dancing, again at the hotel.

Facilities

Good sanitary blocks with well designed showers and hot and cold water for washing (in cubicles). Facilities for children and disabled visitors. Laundry. Small but well stocked supermarket (the site is quite remote). ATM. Bar and restaurant. Takeaway (1/6-31/8). Swimming pool complex (outdoor pools heated 1/4-30/9, indoor pool all season). Play area on sand. Tennis. Bicycle and quad bike hire. Archery. Riding. Activity clubs for all ages and entertainment (high season). Barbecues are not permitted.

Open: 24 March - 6 October.

Directions

From the N86 Bagnols - Aubanas road, exit onto the D4 at Bourg St Andeo to Remeze (a good road). Turn right at entrance to village on the D362 towards Larnas and site is on the right in Imbours. Do not attempt other routes with a caravan.
GPS: 44.43681, 4.57754

Charges guide

Per person	€ 4,20 - € 7,00
pitch (low season)	€ 4,20
pitch incl. 3 persons (high season)	€ 26,00 - € 29,00

Lathuile

Camping l'Idéal

715 route de Chaparon, F-74210 Lathuile (Haute-Savoie) T: 04 50 44 32 97. E: camping-ideal@wanadoo.fr
alanrogers.com/FR74200

For panoramic views of mountains and the lake, this family run site is excellent. Trim and neat, the site is well cared for and the welcome is warm. The 300 pitches are generally large and well drained, some with small hedges but mostly open and with 6A electricity. These pitches share the site with chalets which are located at the top of the site well away from the tourers. L'Idéal is far enough from the lake to avoid the noise and crowds but close enough to take advantage of the facilities there. From the site you can cycle downhill to the Annecy cycle route.

Facilities

Three very well designed toilet blocks include excellent facilities for babies and disabled visitors. A further new block is planned. Laundry facilities. Shop (June-Sept). Bar. Restaurant, snack bar and takeaway (June-mid Aug). Two swimming pools. Tennis. Paragliding lessons. Bicycle hire. Play area. Children's club. Activities and excursions in high season. Off site: Lake 900 m. Golf and riding 5 km.

Open: 8 May - 5 September.

Directions

Lathüile is 18 km. southeast of Annecy and site is well signed in the village. GPS: 45.79514, 6.20564

Charges guide

Per unit incl. 2 persons and electricity	€ 18,70 - € 25,20
extra person	€ 3,50 - € 5,00
child (2-7 yrs)	€ 2,50 - € 4,20
dog	€ 2,50

Laurac en Vivarais

Flower Camping Saint-Amand

Route des Défilés de Ruoms, quartier Saint Amand, F-07110 Laurac en Vivarais (Ardèche)
T: 04 75 36 84 45. E: st-amand@wanadoo.fr alanrogers.com/FR07640

Saint Amand is a member of the Flower group and can be found around 15 km. west of Vallon Pont d'Arc, close to the appropriately named village of Bellevue. There are 100 pitches, most with electrical connections and good shade. A number of pitches are occupied by mobile homes and fully equipped tents (available for rent). From the site's pool, there are some fine views across the surrounding scrubland and vineyards. Other amenities include a small restaurant, specialising in home-made pizzas and a new playing area for children. The closest shops are in the village of Laurac (2.5 km).

Facilities

Small shop. Pizzeria and snack bar. Takeaway. Swimming pool. Children's pool. Play area. Activity and entertainment programme. Mobile homes for rent. New sanitary building with family shower. Off site: Laurac 2.5 km. Vallon Pont d'Arc 15 km. Cycle and walking tracks.

Open: 2 April - 18 September.

Directions

Approaching from the north (Privas), head southwest on the D104 to Aubenas and then continue to Bellevue. Site is clearly signed from here.
GPS: 44.49964, 4.30619

Charges 2011

Per unit incl. 2 persons and electricity	€ 15,50 - € 23,90
extra person	€ 3,00 - € 4,50
child (2-7 yrs)	€ 2,00 - € 4,00
dog	€ 2,00 - € 2,50

Le Bourget-du-Lac

Camping International l'île aux Cygnes

501 boulevard Ernest Coudurier, F-73370 Le Bourget-du-Lac (Savoie) T: 04 79 25 01 76
E: camping@lebourgetdulac.fr alanrogers.com/FR73130

This is a large municipal site in a fantastic location with wonderful views on the shores of Lake Bourget, the largest natural lake in France. The surrounding mountains create a scenic backdrop. The 235 pitches are level and a few have dividing hedges. Mature trees give some shade, but the site is mostly open. Many pitches border the lake or rivers which run along two sides of the site. Caution must be taken as there are some unfenced stretches. All pitches have easy access to electricity (6/10A) and there are adequate water points around the site. The lake offers many watersports.

Facilities

Four sanitary blocks with some basins in cubicles, preset showers, baby room, children's washbasins, en-suite facilities for disabled visitors. Washing machines and dryer. Motorcaravan service point. Well stocked shop. Bar, restaurant with terrace, takeaway and pizzas. Play area. TV room. Internet access. Fishing, swimming, canoes. Bicycle hire. Off site: Minigolf, archery, tennis, boat launching, sailing all within 500 m. Golf 10 km.

Open: Last week of April - last week of September.

Directions

From motorway junction of A43 Lyon - Chambéry with A41 Annecy - Grenoble (exit 14 at Chambéry), head north on N201/N504 for 8 km. to Lac-du-Bourget. Then follow signs for 'Plage Municipal' and yacht club. Site is 300 m. after the yacht club. GPS: 45.6553, 5.8613

Charges guide

Per unit incl. 2 persons and electricity	€ 15,95 - € 19,50
extra person	€ 3,00 - € 4,30

Le Grand-Bornand

Camping Caravaning l'Escale

Route de la Patinoire, F-74450 Le Grand-Bornand (Haute-Savoie) T: 04 50 02 20 69
E: contact@campinglescale.com alanrogers.com/FR74070

You are assured a good welcome in English from the Baur family at this beautifully maintained and picturesque site, situated at the foot of the Aravis mountain range. There are 149 pitches with 122 for touring. Of average size, part grass, part gravel they are separated by trees and shrubs that give a little shade. All pitches have electricity (2-10A) and 86 are fully serviced. Rock pegs are essential. A 200-year-old building houses a bar/restaurant decorated in traditional style and offering regional dishes in a delightful, warm ambience. The village is 200 m. and has all the facilities of a resort with activities for summer or winter holidays. An excellent choice for an outdoor holiday, in summer a variety of well signed footpaths and cycle tracks provide forest or mountain excursions. In winter the area provides superb facilities for downhill and cross-country skiing. This very popular campsite, beside the picture postcard ski resort of Le Grand-Bornand, has wonderful views and is surrounded by fields of flowers in summer.

Facilities

Good toilet blocks (heated in winter) have all the necessary facilities. Drying room. Superb pool complex with interconnected indoor (all season) and outdoor pools and paddling pools (15/6-29/8), jacuzzi and water jets. Cosy bar/restaurant and takeaway (all season). Play area. Tennis. WiFi. Activities for adults and children. Video games. Discounts on walks and visits to Chamonix-Mont Blanc. Off site: Village (5 minutes walk), shops, bars, restaurants, archery, paragliding, golf, minigolf. 150 km. of signed walks. Bicycle hire 200 m. Riding and golf 3 km. Free bus for cable car (500 m) for skiing.

Open: 15 December - 25 April, 1 June - 25 September.

Directions

From Annecy follow D16 and D909 towards La Clusaz. At St Jean-de-Sixt, turn left at roundabout D4 signed Grand-Bornand. Just before village fork right signed Vallée de Bouchet and camping. Site entrance is on right at roundabout in 1.2 km. GPS: 45.94036, 6.42842

Charges guide

Per unit incl. 2 persons and electricity	€ 19,80 - € 29,40
extra person (over 2 yrs)	€ 4,90 - € 5,70
dog	€ 2,30

Camping Caravaneige L'Escale

74450 Le Grand Bornand - France - Tel: +33 (0)4 50 02 20 69 - Fax: +33 (0)4 50 02 36 04
Email: contact@campinglescale.com - www.rentlescale.com

For latest campsite news, availability and prices visit

alanrogers.com

Les Abrets

Kawan Village le Coin Tranquille

6 chemin des Vignes, F-38490 Les Abrets (Isère) T: 04 76 32 13 48. E: contact@coin-tranquille.com
alanrogers.com/FR38010

alan rogers Winner 2010 Awards

Les Abrets is well placed for visits to the Savoie regions and the Alps. It is an attractive, well maintained site of 192 grass pitches (178 for tourers), all with electricity. They are separated by neat hedges of hydrangea, flowering shrubs and a range of trees to make a lovely environment doubly enhanced by the rural aspect and marvellous views across to the mountains. This is a popular, family run site with friendly staff that makes a wonderful base for exploring the area. Set in the Dauphiny countryside north of Grenoble, Le Coin Tranquille is truly a 'quiet corner', especially outside school holiday times, although it is still popular with families in high season.

Facilities

The central well appointed sanitary block is well kept, heated in low season. Facilities for children and disabled visitors. Two smaller blocks provide facilities in high season. Busy shop. Excellent restaurant. Swimming pool (heated from 2011) and paddling pool (15/5-30/9; no Bermuda style shorts) with sunbathing areas. Play area. TV and games in bar. Quiet reading room. Weekly entertainment for children and adults (July/Aug) including live music (not discos). Bicycle hire (limited). WiFi.
Off site: Riding 6 km. Fishing 8 km. Les Abrets 2 km.

Open: 1 April - 31 October.

Directions

Les Abrets is 70 km. southeast of Lyon at junction of N6 and N75. From roundabout in town take N6 towards Chambéry, turning left in just under 2 km. (signed Restaurant and Camping). Follow signs along country lane for just over 1 km. and entrance is on right. GPS: 45.54115, 5.60778

Charges 2011

Per unit incl. 2 persons	€ 18,00 - € 32,00
extra person	€ 4,00 - € 7,50

Camping Cheques accepted.

Les Ollières-sur-Eyrieux

Camping le Domaine des Plantas

F-07360 Les Ollières-sur-Eyrieux (Ardèche) T: 04 75 66 21 53. E: plantas.ardeche@wanadoo.fr
alanrogers.com/FR07090

Under new ownership, this is a good quality site in a spectacular setting on the steep banks of the Eyrieux river. Old, original buildings house the reception, restaurant and bar. The terrace provides a stunning viewpoint. The 169 pitches (100 for touring) are steeply terraced and shaded with electricity (10A, long leads may be needed). Much up and down walking is required making this site unsuitable for those with walking difficulties. There is a sandy beach beside the quite fast-flowing, but fairly shallow river (used for bathing). The 3 km. approach road is a twisting, single track and may present a problem to those with larger outfits.

Facilities

Two excellent well equipped toilet blocks (one heated). Washing machine. Motorcaravan services. Small shop, bar, restaurant, disco. Heated, covered and outdoor swimming pools, paddling pool and toboggans. Adventure play area. High season children's activities, discos for 14-18 year olds (strictly no alcohol). Many activities and excursions. Only gas and electric barbecues. Off site: Riding 15 km. Mountain biking, canoeing, canyoning, riding and walking.

Open: 21 April - 5 October.

Directions

Leave A7 exit 15 (Valence Sud). Turn right to Valence centre, follow signs to Montélimar via N7 for 7 km. Turn right towards Charmes sur Rhône to Beauchastel. Take D120 to Ollières-sur-Eyrieux. Cross river, turn left and follow site signs (3 km) along narrow track. GPS: 44.80917, 4.63581

Charges guide

Per unit incl. 2 persons and electricity	€ 19,00 - € 31,00
extra person over 4 yrs	€ 4,00 - € 7,50

Les Ollières-sur-Eyrieux

Kawan Village Mas de Champel

Quartier Champel, F-07360 Les Ollières-sur-Eyrieux (Ardèche) T: 04 75 66 23 23
E: masdechampel@wanadoo.fr alanrogers.com/FR07440

This is a simple campsite with easy access and within walking distance of a small village. It has a lively entertainment programme plus many organised activities in the high season. There are 95 unmarked, level grassy pitches, 51 for touring (electricity 6A, may need long leads) with almost no shade. A small sandy beach alongside the Eyrieux river offers lots of space for children to play in the shallow water. The bar and restaurant offer a range of meals including breakfast, and entertainment is provided adjacent.

Facilities

Two small old, adequate toilet blocks with all necessary facilities. Bar, restaurant/takeaway. Swimming pool, heated paddling pool and sunbathing area. Games/TV room. Small, simple play area. Fishing. Bicycle hire. Motorcaravan services. Only gas barbecues permitted. Many organised family activities in July/Aug.
Off site: Ollières-sur-Eyrieux 500 m. Riding 7 km.

Open: 11 April - 30 September.

Directions

Leave N86 south of Valence at Beauchastel. Turn west, D120, to Ollières sur Eyrieux (about 20 km). Site is on right at entrance to village and is signed. GPS: 44.80721, 4.61489

Charges guide

Per unit incl. 2 persons	€ 17,90 - € 28,80
extra person	€ 3,90 - € 6,90

Camping Cheques accepted.

For latest campsite news, availability and prices visit

alanrogers.com

Lus-la-Croix-Haute

Camping Champ la Chèvre

F-26220 Lus-la-Croix-Haute (Drôme) T: 04 92 58 50 14. E: info@campingchamplachevre.com

alanrogers.com/FR26270

This is a pleasant, unpretentious site with some really magnificent views across towards the western Alps. Formerly a farm (hence its name!) and now under new management, Champ la Chèvre is undergoing a steady process of refurbishment and is attractively located just 200 m. from the village and 500 m. from the N75. There are 100 pitches, for the most part sunny and quite spacious, and many with fine mountain views. Some pitches are sloping and most pitches have 6A electrical connections. This is a good base for exploring the mountains and the owners have many ideas for excursions in the area, including downhill mountain biking, swimming in local rivers and hundreds of kilometres of walking trails. The nearby pretty village of Lus-La-Croix Haute has a good range of shops and a small railway station.

Facilities

Centrally located toilet block with facilities for disabled visitors. Motorcaravan services. Play area. Minigolf. Mobile homes and chalets for rent. Heated swimming pool (15/6-31/8). Restaurant, bar. Off site: Village of Lus-La-Croix Haute 200 m. Railway station 300 m. Tennis. Many walking and cycle trails. Riding 100 m. Bicycle hire 500 m. Fishing 3 km.

Open: All year.

Directions

From the north, head south from Grenoble initially on the A480 and then the A51 towards Sisteron. Then join the southbound N75 for around 35 km. to Lus-La-Croix Haute. Drive through the village and site is well signed. GPS: 44.66440, 5.70742

Charges guide

Per unit incl. 2 persons and electricity	€ 18,05 - € 20,85
extra person	€ 4,10 - € 5,00
child (under 10 yrs)	€ 3,00 - € 3,90

Lussas

Ludocamping

Route de Lavilledieu, F-07170 Lussas (Ardèche) T: 04 75 94 21 22. E: info@ludocamping.com

alanrogers.com/FR07170

This is a quiet family campsite offering a really wide range of activities. From mid July to early August, only families with children under 14 years are accepted which allows the activities to be focused on this age group. The 160 grassy pitches, all for touring with 5-10A electricity, are in two areas. The upper area has large super pitches with wonderful views but little shade. The lower area, closer to the small river, has pitches set naturally amongst the trees and they have good shade. There is an attractive swimming pool (heated all season), good sized paddling pool and large sunbathing area. Ludocamping is set amongst the magnificent scenery of the Auzon valley, a delight for nature lovers particularly in early season when the many wild flowers and cherry trees are at their best.

Facilities

Clean, good quality toilet blocks offer all necessary facilities. Bar (all season), takeaway (from 1/5), terrace overlooking the valley. Play area. Recreational area next to river. Fishing. Bicycle hire. Club for over 6-7 yr olds offering a very wide range of activities. Off season club for older children. Seniors excursions in campsite coach. Only gas and electric barbecues. Off site: Lussas (few shops, restaurant, bar) 600 m. Riding 6 km. Gliding, hang-gliding, canoeing, speed boating.

Open: 1 April - 15 October.

Directions

From Montélimar take N102 west towards Aubenas, pass around Villeneuve, at traffic lights in Lavilledieu turn right onto D224 towards Lussas. Site entrance is on right just before village (about 4 km. from N102). GPS: 44.60495, 4.4712

Charges guide

Per unit incl. 2 persons	€ 11,00 - € 25,00
extra person	€ 2,00 - € 6,00
child (under 6 yrs)	€ 2,00 - € 3,00
electricity (6A)	€ 3,00

Special long stay, low season offers. No credit cards.

Massignieu-de-Rives

Kawan Village Lac du Lit du Roi

La Tuillière, F-01300 Massignieu-de-Rives (Ain) T: 04 79 42 12 03. E: info@camping-savoie.com

alanrogers.com/FR01040

This attractive and well cared for, family run site is ideal for those seeking an active holiday in a peaceful setting. This superb, picturesque area offers wonderful opportunities for exploration by foot, bicycle, car and boat. Take time to sample the wines and other local produce on offer. Of the 120 pitches (electricity 10A), 90 are available for touring, all being close to the lake and many having wonderful views over the lake and the wooded hills beyond. The slightly sloping, grassy pitches are set on low terraces and are partly separated by hedging and a variety of trees give some shade.

Facilities

Two modern toilet blocks offer all necessary facilities with provision for disabled visitors. Washing machines. Motorcaravan services. Small shop, bar, restaurant and terrace. Bread. Swimming pool, children's play area with water features. Tennis. Play area beside lake. Grassy beach, pedaloes, canoes, surf bikes for hire. Bicycle hire. Lake fishing. Winter caravan storage. Internet and free WiFi. Fridge and barbecue rental. Off site: Shops at Belley 8 km. Lac du Bourget (watersports, boat hire). Nature reserve. Marina nearby. Golf 8 km. Riding 15 km.

Open: 11 April - 4 October.

Directions

Site is about 8 km. east of Belley. Travelling south on N504 towards Aix-les Bains bypass Belley and at roundabout (Champion supermarket) turn east D992, signed Culoz and Seyssel. After 4 km. turn right over bridge, D37 signed Massignieu. Follow signs to site (2 km). GPS: 45.76883, 5.76942

Charges guide

| Per unit incl. 2 persons and electricity | € 22,50 - € 29,00 |
| extra person | € 5,00 - € 6,50 |

Camping Cheques accepted.

Matafelon-Granges

Camping des Gorges de l'Oignin

Rue du Lac, F-01580 Matafelon-Granges (Ain) T: 04 74 76 80 97. E: camping.lesgorgesdeloignin@wanadoo.fr

alanrogers.com/FR01050

This family run, terraced site (English spoken) offers lovely views across the lake to the hills beyond. There are 132 good sized pitches, 102 for touring, separated by young trees and flowering shrubs and with a choice of grass or hardstanding. About half have their own water point and all have 10A electricity. Twin-axle caravans are not accepted. The reception, bar/restaurant and the pool complex are at the top of the site with a steep road down to the terraces and the rest of the campsite. At the bottom of the site is a large grassy area next to the lake for sunbathing and activities.

Facilities

Two modern, well equipped and clean toilet blocks with all the usual facilities except those for disabled visitors. Bar/restaurant, takeaway and TV room (July/Aug). Swimming pool, paddling pool and new 'lazy river' (1/6-30/9). Playground and sports area. Swimming, fishing and boating on the lake (no motorboats). Off site: Golf 2 km. Riding 2 km. Matafelon 800 m. Thoirette 6 km. Oyonnax 10 km.

Open: 1 April - 30 September.

Directions

Matafelon is 40 km. east of Bourg-en-Bresse. Leave autoroute A404 at Oyonnax, exit 11 and head west on D13 to Matafelon (10 km). On entering village and opposite the Mairie turn left, signed camping, and descend to site (800 m). GPS: 46.25535, 5.55717

Charges guide

| Per unit incl. 2 persons | € 16,60 - € 24,00 |
| extra person | € 3,60 - € 5,20 |

Menglon

Kawan Village l'Hirondelle

Bois Saint Ferreol, F-26410 Menglon (Drôme) T: 04 75 21 82 08. E: contact@campinghirondelle.com

alanrogers.com/FR26130

This is a natural, spacious and popular, family run site; you are assured a good welcome. It lies in a beautiful valley, south of the Vercors mountains and the Vercors National Park, beside the River Bez. The 170 large to very large pitches, 122 for touring, are stony and slightly uneven (rock pegs advised). They lie in natural openings in woodland and some have views over the fields and hills beyond. For 2011 there are 53 new huge pitches, some with good views and 20 have a private bathroom. All have electricity (3/6/10A) and long leads are advised. Only electric or gas barbecues.

Facilities

Six large toilet blocks offer all the necessary facilities (20 private bathrooms). Good bar/restaurant/takeaway. Small shop, including bread. Excellent pool complex with toboggans, paddling pool/slide and jacuzzi (1/5-13/9). Play room. River bathing. Club/TV room. WiFi (charged). Fishing. Football, boules, volleyball. Multisports court. Bicycle hire. Organised events (high season). Off site: Riding 3 km. Canoeing, kayaking, climbing, mountain biking and cycling over the local passes.

Open: 28 April - 17 September.

Directions

From Die follow D93 southwards and after 6 km. at Pont de Quart, turn left on D539 signed Châtillon. After about 4 km. turn right on D140, signed Menglon. Site entrance is shortly on right just after crossing a small river. GPS: 44.68142, 5.44743

Charges guide

Per unit incl. 2 persons and electricity	€ 21,50 - € 34,10
extra person	€ 5,20 - € 8,30
child (2-10 yrs)	free - € 6,40

For latest campsite news, availability and prices visit

alanrogers.com

Mens

Camping le Pré Rolland

Rue de la Piscine, F-38710 Mens (Isère) T: 04 76 34 65 80. E: contact@camping-prerolland.fr

alanrogers.com/FR38230

Le Pré Rolland is a small, well maintained family run site on the outskirts of the little town of Mens. It is surrounded by beautiful mountain scenery making it an ideal base for nature lovers touring this little known region of the Trièves. There are 98 mainly level, good sized grass pitches, 90 for touring and all having electricity (10A). Some are delineated by flowering shrubs and mature trees and are quite shady, others are more open and sunny. The snack bar and bar, with terrace overlooking the pools is a peaceful place to unwind after a day exploring the region. There is no on-site entertainment.

Facilities

Two well maintained and clean toilet blocks includes facilities for babies and disabled visitors. Covered area with tables, small kitchen and bunk room. Bar/snack bar. Adjacent municipal swimming pool, free (1/6-31/8). Day room/TV. Playground. WiFi (free). Off site: Small town of Mens with small shops, bar and restaurant 500 m. Fishing 1.5 km. Riding 2 km. Rock climbing, bungee jumping.

Open: 1 May - 30 September.

Directions

From the A51 going south from Grenoble take the N75 towards Sisteron. After about 50 km, at Clelles, turn east D521 to Mens. On entering town turn right, signed site and 'piscine'. GPS: 44.814807, 5.7485

Charges guide

Per unit incl. 2 persons and electricity	€ 16,50 - € 19,00
extra person	€ 4,00 - € 6,00

Mirabel-et-Blacons

Gervanne Camping

Bellevue, F-26400 Mirabel-et-Blacons (Drôme) T: 04 75 40 00 20. E: info@gervanne-camping.com

alanrogers.com/FR26120

This spacious, riverside site, run by a friendly family, has 174 pitches, with 154 for touring (electricity 6A). It is in two sections either side of a road, connected by an underpass. The upper section is adjacent to the bar, restaurant and good swimming pool with mountain views. The pitches are of average size with some shade and are separated by a few small shrubs and trees. The lower section, closer to the river, is less formally laid out with mature trees offering plenty of shade. Access to and on site is easy here. Only gas and electric barbecues are permitted.

Facilities

Four well appointed, very clean toilet blocks including good facilities for campers with disabilities, and babies. Laundry. Bar/restaurant (1/6-15/9) with simple menu, takeaway service and free WiFi. Heated swimming pool (1/5-30/9). Small play area. Football pitch. Boules. Bicycle hire. Electric and gas barbecues only. Good motorcaravan service point. Off site: Supermarket next door. Canoeing and bathing in adjacent River Drôme. Riding 5 km.

Open: 1 April - 30 September.

Directions

Leave A7 autoroute, exit 16 Loriol. Take D104 then D164 bypassing Crest. After 6 km, at roundabout, turn left D164A. Cross river into Mirabel-et-Blacons, left at roundabout, site in 200m. GPS: 44.71110, 5.09015

Charges guide

Per unit incl. 2 persons and electricity	€ 17,00 - € 23,80
extra person	€ 3,70 - € 6,00

Murs-et-Gélignieux

Camping Ile de la Comtesse

Route des Abrets, F-01300 Murs-et-Gélignieux (Ain) T: 04 79 87 23 33. E: camping.comtesse@wanadoo.fr

alanrogers.com/FR01060

A very pleasant, family run, lakeside site, there are 100 medium to large, level grassy pitches here. With 58 for touring, many are separated by low hedges and tall poplar trees offer some shade. All have 6A electricity (but very long leads may be necessary) and most have views over the lake and craggy hills beyond. High season activities are aimed mainly at younger children and the family. Fishing, sailing, canoeing and bathing are possible on the lake that borders the site. There is plenty of space around the lake for leisure activities, including marked walks and cycle trails.

Facilities

Traditionally styled, modern and well appointed toilet block with facilities for disabled visitors. Motorcaravan service point. Small bar/restaurant with takeaway and small shop. Large marquee used for TV and organised activities. Heated outdoor swimming and paddling pools. Daily activities for young children and the family in high season. Bicycle hire. WiFi. Off site: Restaurant adjacent. 300 m. to beach. Aost with shops, etc. 5 km. Walaibi Theme Park 10 km. Riding 10 km. Golf 20 km.

Open: 3 April - 30 September.

Directions

From the A43 (Lyon - Chambery) autoroute, take exit 10 and go north on D592 for about 10 km. After crossing the lake turn right on the D992 and site is shortly on the right. GPS: 45.63995, 5.64900

Charges guide

Per unit incl. 2 persons and electricity	€ 14,90 - € 30,50
extra person	€ 4,90 - € 7,50
child (2-7 yrs)	€ 2,90 - € 5,40

For latest campsite news, availability and prices visit

alanrogers.com

Neydens

Camping la Colombière

Saint Julien-en-Genevois, F-74160 Neydens (Haute-Savoie) T: 04 50 35 13 14. E: la.colombiere@wanadoo.fr
alanrogers.com/FR74060

La Colombière, a family owned site, is on the edge of the small village of Neydens, a few minutes from the A40 autoroute and only a short drive from Geneva. It is an attractive site with 115 pitches (93 for touring with electricity 5-15A), all reasonably level and separated by fruit trees, flowering shrubs and hedges. Neydens makes a good base for visiting Geneva and the region around the lake. It is a very pleasant, friendly site where you may drop in for a night stop – and stay for several days! The site is open all year for motorcaravans and suitable caravans. English is spoken. There are views to the east and west of the mountain ridges. M. Bussat owns a small vineyard close to the site, has the wine made in Switzerland and sold in his restaurant. A Sites et Paysages member.

Facilities

Good sanitary blocks (one heated) include facilities for disabled visitors. Motorcaravan services. Fridge hire. Gas supplies. Good bar/restaurant (all season) and terrace overlooking the pool (1/5-15/9). New heated, indoor pool, spa pool and jacuzzi (21/3-11/11). Games room. Organised visits and activities (all season). Bicycle hire. Archery. Boules. Playground. Internet (WiFi).
Off site: Fishing, riding 1 km. Golf 7 km. Lake beach and windsurfing 12 km. Switzerland 3 km. St Julien-en-Genevois 5 km. Bus to Geneva.

Open: 20 March - 11 November
(all year for motorcaravans and suitable caravans).

Directions

From A40 south of Geneva take exit 13 and then N201 towards Annecy. After 2 km. turn left into village of Neydens and follow campsite signs to site in just over 1 km. GPS: 46.1201, 6.10552

Charges guide

Per unit incl. 2 persons and electricity	€ 21,00 - € 30,50
extra person	€ 4,00 - € 6,00
child (2-12 yrs)	€ 3,50 - € 4,50
dog (max. 1)	€ 2,00

Camping Cheques accepted.

Passy

Village Center les Iles

Villagecenter

245 route des Lacs, F-74190 Passy (Haute-Savoie) T: 04 99 57 21 21
E: resa@village-center.com **alanrogers.com/FR74210**

This Alpine site is approached by a lakeside road with mountains to the left and with unrivalled views of Mont Blanc straight ahead. Set in an area with oak trees giving shade, there are 253 very good pitches (196 for tourers, most with electricity 6A), which are all large and divided by 1.2 m. high, well trimmed beech hedges. A small, high season takeaway is located beside the play area allowing relaxed child supervision. An electric railway may cause some noise. This is an ideal site for Alpine lovers, a perfect base for walking and cycling, while the municipal water sports area in which the site is set offers a whole range of water based activities.

Facilities

Two toilet blocks, screened by attractive hedges, are not modern but are acceptable and include hot showers and a WC/shower for disabled visitors. Laundry facilities. Bar and takeaway in high season. Chalets to rent.
Off site: Site is in the centre of a large municipal water sports complex. Fishing 500 m. Riding 10 km. Golf 20 km. Excellent centre for walking and cycling. Passy has shopping, restaurants and bars, 2 km.

Open: 5 December - 13 March, 14 May - 10 December.

Directions

Site is west of Passy. From the A40 take exit 21 (Chamonix) and drive through Passy to site (well signed). GPS: 45.9239, 6.6504

Charges guide

| Per unit incl. 2 persons and electricity | € 14,00 - € 18,00 |

For latest campsite news, availability and prices visit
alanrogers.com

Peisey-Nancroix

Camping les Lanchettes

F-73210 Peisey-Nancroix (Savoie) T: 04 79 07 93 07. E: lanchettes@free.fr

alanrogers.com/FR73030

This site is close to the beautiful Vanoise National Park and at 1,470 m. is one of the highest campsites in this guide. There is a steep climb to the site but the spectacular scenery is well worth the effort. It is a natural, terraced site with 90 good size, reasonably level and well drained, grassy/stony pitches, with 70 used for touring units, all with electricity (3-10A). Outside taps are only available in summer because of the altitude and cold winters. For those who love walking and biking, the wonderful scenery, flora and fauna, this is the site for you. Underpowered units are not advised to make the climb. In winter it is ideal for the serious skier, being close to the famous resort of Les Arcs (via free bus service and cable car) and about 30 of the pitches at the bottom of the site are unused as they become part of a cross country ski run. A wide range of footpaths and mountain bike rides is available in the valley and mountains around. Some chair lifts carry bikes up to the walking/bike tracks high up in the mountains; the descent is breathtaking. In winter, there are the ski resorts of Peisey Vallandry, les Arcs and la Plagne with a variety of snow sports to try – snowshoeing, sledge dog excursions, and Nordic skiing.

Facilities

Well appointed heated toilet block. Motorcaravan services. Restaurant, takeaway (July/Aug. and winter). Playground. Club/TV room. Large tent/marquee used in bad weather. In winter a small bus (free) runs to the ski lifts every 30 minutes. Free WiFi. Off site: Walks in National Park. Riding next to site. Peisey-Nancroix, restaurants, bars and shops 3 km. Les Arcs winter sports centre 6 km. Outdoor swimming pool and bicycle hire 6 km. Golf and indoor pool 8 km. Lakeside beach 10 km.

Open: 15 December - 30 April, 1 June - 15 October.

Directions

From Albertville take N90 towards Bourg-St-Maurice, through Aime. In 9 km. turn right on D87, signed Peisey-Nancroix. Follow a winding hilly road (with hairpin bends) for 10 km. Pass through Peisey-Nancroix; site on right about 1 km. beyond Nancroix. GPS: 45.53137, 6.77560

Charges guide

Per unit incl. 2 persons	€ 12,30 - € 13,80
extra person	€ 4,10 - € 4,60
electricity (3-10A)	€ 3,10 - € 8,20

Camping Cheques accepted.

CAMPING CARAVANEIGE LES LANCHETTES ***

www.caravaneige-camping-savoie.com

Pélussin

Camping Bel'Epoque du Pilat

Route de Malleval, F-42410 Pélussin (Loire) T: 04 74 87 66 60. E: camping_belepoque@orange.fr

alanrogers.com/FR42030

This is a peaceful, family run site located within the relatively little known Pilat Regional Park overlooking the attractive town of Pélussin. There are 70 good sized, slightly uneven and sloping, grassy pitches, of which 50 are for touring (electricity 6A). They are separated by trees and some hedging with most having some shade and some having good views over the valley below. The site is well maintained with an attractive pool and small bar and snack bar with takeaways (only July and August). Large outfits are accepted but care is needed on narrow winding roads. A Sites et Paysages member.

Facilities

Well appointed toilet block with facilities for disabled visitors. Bar (1/5-30/8), snack bar, takeaway meals (1/7-31/8). Swimming pool (May-Sept). Tennis. Play area. WiFi. Bicycle hire. Entertainment for young children in peak season. Off site: Fishing, riding 500 m. Water sports 7 km. Golf 25 km. Vienne (Roman town). Safari park at Peaugres. Excursions to Côtes du Rhône vineyards. Lyon (50 km. to the north). Regional park.

Open: 1 April - 30 September.

Directions

Leave A7 autoroute, exit 10 Vienne, take N86 south to Chavanay. Turn west D7, climb to Pélussin. On entering the village bear left, site signed. Site on right in 1.5 km. Only use the recommended route. GPS: 45.4139, 4.69139

Charges guide

Per unit incl. 2 persons and electricity (6A)	€ 19,50 - € 22,50
extra person	€ 3,50 - € 5,00

For latest campsite news, availability and prices visit

alanrogers.com

Pont-de-Vaux

Camping les Ripettes

Chavannes-sur-Reyssouze, F-01190 Pont-de-Vaux (Ain) T: 03 85 30 66 58. E: info@camping-les-ripettes.com

alanrogers.com/FR01030

A friendly welcome is assured from the owners of this spacious site situated in quiet, flat countryside near the pleasant small town of Pont-de-Vaux. The 2.5 hectare (6 acre) site has 54 large (100 sq.m. to 400 sq.m) level grassy pitches, 51 of which are available to tourists. Nearly all are separated by hedges and about half are shaded by the many trees on the site. All but two have electrical connections (10A), and there are ample water points. The site is a useful stop on the way to or from the south of France, and also serves as a centre to explore the interesting surrounding area.

Facilities	Directions
Two well appointed, small sanitary blocks contain a suite for disabled visitors. Washing machine and dryer. Limited range of food stocked and wine, ice cream, meat for barbecues at reception. Two swimming pools. Areas for ball games. Board games, books. WiFi. Communal Sunday barbecues are popular. Off site: Restaurant 1 km. Riding 2 km. Pont-de-Vaux 4 km. Fishing 4 km. Golf 15 km. **Open:** 1 April - 30 September.	Leave N6 at Fleurville (14 km. south of Tournus). Go east on D933A to Pont-de-Vaux (5 km) where site is signed. Take D2 east towards St Trivier-de-Courtes. After 3 km. turn left after water tower, left again at next junction (100 m). Site is 300 m. GPS: 46.44455, 4.98067

Charges guide

Per unit incl. 2 persons	€ 15,60 - € 19,00
extra person	€ 3,15 - € 3,50

Pradons

Camping les Coudoulets

Pradons, F-07120 Ruoms (Ardèche) T: 04 75 93 94 95. E: camping@coudoulets.com

alanrogers.com/FR07130

For those who prefer a more intimate, peaceful campsite beside the river Ardèche, only a short distance away from the main centre, then this very well cared for site, run by a very friendly family, could be for you. There are 125 good sized, grassy and well shaded pitches, separated by trees and shrubs. There are 109 for touring, all with 10A electricity. Organised family activities take place in July/August such as barbecues and musical evenings (no discos). There is an area for bathing in the river and it is an ideal spot for canoeists. The family own a small vineyard and their wine is on sale in the bar.

Facilities	Directions
Good, clean, recently refurbished block has all the necessary facilities including excellent facilities for disabled visitors. Motorcaravan services. Bar, TV, terrace (May-Sept) bread, ices, drinks. Snacks (July/Aug). Butcher calls in high season. Small heated swimming pool, paddling pool. Superb new aquatic play area and pool for children (May-Sept). Fishing. WiFi. Off site: Shop 300 m. Ruoms with range of shops 4 km. **Open:** 1 May - 10 September.	Leave Montélimar westwards on N102 towards Aubenas. After passing Villeneuve-de-Berg turn left on D103 towards Vogüé for 5 km. Turn left on D579 towards Ruoms, site on right on entering Pradons (10 km). GPS: 44.47663, 4.35857

Charges guide

Per unit incl. 2 persons	€ 14,00 - € 25,00
extra person	€ 4,50 - € 6,00
electricity (6A)	€ 4,00

Privas

Kawan Village Ardèche

Boulevard de Paste, F-07000 Privas (Ardèche) T: 04 75 64 05 80. E: jcray@wanadoo.fr

alanrogers.com/FR07180

This spacious, family run site is on the southern outskirts of Privas and would be a good base for exploring the lesser known parts of the Ardèche. Bus and coach trips are available to explore these areas. The site has 166 large, grass, reasonably level pitches, of which 153 are for tourers. A wide variety of trees provide reasonable shade and electricity (6/10A) should now be available on most pitches. Two tour operators use the site. Recent additions include new heated swimming and paddling pools. There is a play area for children and a miniclub, but (deliberately) no provision for teenagers.

Facilities	Directions
Two toilet blocks, only one open in low season. Facilities for disabled visitors. Motorcaravan service point. Bar and restaurant (1/5-30/9). Boules. Play area. Miniclub. Entertainment (high season). Only gas barbecues are permitted. Tents (4) for rent. Off site: Swimming pool and tennis courts adjacent. Supermarket 100 m. Bicycle hire 2 km. Riding 5 km. **Open:** 1 April - 30 September.	At traffic lights in the centre of town take D2, signed Montélimar. Descend the winding road for about 1 km. then at roundabout (by Intermarché) turn right and then shortly left, signed Espace Ouvéze. The entrance is straight on. GPS: 44.72611, 4.59845

Charges guide

Per unit incl. 2 persons	€ 14,50 - € 19,00
extra person	€ 3,50 - € 5,00
electricity (6A)	€ 3,50
Camping Cheques accepted.	

Recoubeau-Jansac

Camping le Couriou

F-26310 Recoubeau-Jansac (Drôme) T: 04 75 21 33 23. E: camping.lecouriou@wanadoo.fr

alanrogers.com/FR26340

Le Couriou is a family run site in the beautiful Drôme countryside just south of Die. There are 131 stony/grassy, level pitches of varying sizes with 102 for touring (6A electricity). They are laid out on high terraces with views over the surrounding wooded hills; not ideal for those with walking difficulties. The pitches are separated by some shrubs and a variety of trees giving some shade. Though the site roads are quite steep, access is not difficult for large outfits. It has a large swimming pool complex, bar and restaurant, all open to the public. Only electric barbecues allowed on site.

Facilities

Three adequate toilet blocks with facilities for babies and campers with disabilities. Washing machines/dryer. Shop, bar, restaurant/takeaway (1/6-30/8). Four heated swimming pools, toboggans, paddling pool, sauna, massage (all season, open to public). Multisport area, boules. Off site: Fishing 500m. Riding 5 km. Bike hire 10 km. Recoubeau 1 km. Luc-en-Diois 5 km. Die, some shops bars/restaurants, interesting market town 14 km. Many marked walking and cycling routes and tracks.

Open: 1 May - 30 August

Directions

From Die take D93 south for 14 km. Just before Recoubeau turn right, site signed, to site. GPS: 44.658534, 5.407172

Charges guide

Per unit incl. 2 persons and electricity	€ 16,60 - € 28,70
extra person	€ 4,00 - € 7,30
child (under 12 yrs)	€ 2,50 - € 5,90
dog	free - € 2,00

Ruoms

Yelloh! Village la Plaine

F-07120 Ruoms (Ardèche) T: 04 75 39 65 83. E: info@yellohvillage-la-plaine.com

alanrogers.com/FR07250

One of the 'all singing, all dancing' type of campsite, La Plaine is quiet in low season, but in high season with all-day and evening activities for both teenagers and adults, and a miniclub each day, there is no reason to feel bored! There are 212 pitches of moderate size (77 used for their air-conditioned mobile homes), of which 160 have electricity. They are protected from the sun and marked by many trees. Stage and sound equipment are in use most nights and might cause some noise problems. This is a young family site for people with lots of energy, perhaps not for a quiet holiday in high season!

Facilities

Three sanitary blocks, clean and modern with all facilities under cover. Good facilities for disabled visitors. Excellent laundry room. Fridge hire. Shop, restaurant, bar and takeaway. Heated swimming pool complex (all season). Gym. Games room and TV. Boules. Small football field. Play area (unfenced). Fitness room. Activity and entertainment programme day and evening. Miniclub (5-12 yrs). Fishing. River beach. New multisport area. Bicycle hire. Off site: Town facilities 3 km. Riding 2 km.

Open: 16 April - 17 September.

Directions

Exit Ruoms south on the D579 and at junction 2 km, south, take D111 signed St Ambroix. Site is on the left. GPS: 44.427067, 4.335617

Charges 2011

Per unit incl. 2 persons and electricity (6A)	€ 15,00 - € 42,00
extra person	€ 5,00 - € 8,00
child (3-7 yrs)	free - € 7,00
dog	€ 4,00

Ruoms

Camping le Petit Bois

87 rue du Petit Bois, F-07120 Ruoms (Ardèche) T: 04 75 39 60 72. E: vacances@campinglepetitbois.fr

alanrogers.com/FR07360

Situated only 800 metres from the ancient town centre of Ruoms, and yet within an area of trees and rocky outcrops, this site offers a centre for those wishing to explore this part of the Ardèche valley. The 118 pitches are of irregular shape and size and are a mix of stone and grass (76 are used for mobile homes). There is some shade. The site is now thirty years old and is needing some restoration, which is now underway. Some standpipes have coils of tubing attached. Perhaps these should not be used for domestic water purposes. A Sites et Paysages member.

Facilities

Three toilet blocks (only one open in low season) were in need of some maintenance when we visited. Cleaning appeared somewhat erratic. Motorcaravan service point. Bar (all season). Restaurant and takeaway (1/7-31/8). New heated swimming pool (1/4-30/6) and solarium. Playground. Games and TV rooms in season. Fishing. Entertainment organised in high season. Off site: Town with shops, etc. 300 m. Riding and bicycle hire 1 km.

Open: 1 April - 30 September.

Directions

Approaching Ruoms on the D579 from Vallon-Pont-d'Arc go straight on at first (Super U) and second roundabouts. At third roundabout turn left (southwest) signed Largentier (site is signed). GPS: 44.46063, 4.3373

Charges guide

Per unit incl. 2 persons	€ 15,00 - € 28,00
with electricity (10A)	€ 19,00 - € 28,00
extra person	€ 4,80 - € 5,80
child (1-7 yrs)	€ 2,80 - € 3,80

Sahune

Flower Camping les Ramières

Curnier, F-26510 Sahune (Drôme) T: 04 75 27 40 45. E: contact@lesramieres.com

alanrogers.com/FR26310

This rugged area of La Drôme Provençale is in contrast with the gentler landscape in the northern parts of the département. The new owners are completely rebuilding this site from scratch. The very large level, stony pitches are on terraces with wonderful views over the surrounding hills. The 75 fully serviced pitches (electricity 10A), 65 for touring, have little shade at present though over 3,000 shrubs and trees have been planted. It also has access to the shallow River Eygues, ideal for young children in hot weather. Not suitable for large outfits or those with walking difficulties. Only gas and electric barbecues. The site has a swimming pool, bar and snack bar with takeaway meals. A small number of wooden chalets and mobile homes are available for rent.

Facilities

New well appointed toilet block with another planned, including family showers and facilities for campers with disabilities. Washing machine. Small swimming pool (all season). Direct access to river. Play area. Volleyball. Picnic area. Bar/snack bar/takeaway (all season). Free WiFi by bar. Tourist information. Chalets for rent. Off site: Sahune 2 km. Nyons 15 km. Walking and cycle tracks. Riding. Rock climbing. Canoeing.

Open: 3 April - 26 September.

Directions

Take D94 east from Nyons 15 km. to Sahune. Turn right D205, signed Montréal and les Ramières. Cross river, turn right and follow narrow lane for just over 2 km. to site. GPS: 44.402254, 5.253589

Charges guide

Per unit incl. 2 persons and electricity	€ 15,50 - € 23,30
extra person	€ 3,50 - € 5,00
child (2-7 yrs)	€ 2,50 - € 4,00

Saint Alban-Auriolles

Sunêlia le Ranc Davaine

Saint Alban-Auriolles, F-07120 Ruoms (Ardèche) T: 04 75 39 60 55. E: camping.ranc.davaine@wanadoo.fr

alanrogers.com/FR07050

Le Ranc Davaine is a large, busy, family oriented site with direct access to the River Chassezac. There are 435 pitches with 87 for touring, all with electricity (10/16A) for which very long leads are required (some may cross roads). Most pitches are scattered between static caravan and tour operator pitches on fairly flat, stony ground under a variety of trees, some of which are quite low giving much needed shade. Rock pegs are advised. The site can get very busy for much of the season. A lively entertainment programme is aimed at young children and teenagers with an enclosed disco four nights a week (until 03.00). Sunbathing areas surround the pool complex, overlooked by the terrace of the restaurant, providing very pleasant surroundings, especially attractive with evening floodlighting.

Facilities

Fully equipped, very clean and modern toilet blocks include facilities for disabled visitors. Washing machines, dryers. Large shop. Internet. Bar/restaurant, pizzeria, takeaway. Swimming pool, covered pool (heated), two small square pools, slide (all facilities, all season; no shorts allowed). Large play area. Tennis. Minigolf. Fishing. Extensive activity and entertainment programme (July/Aug). Discos. Fitness hall (charged). Off site: Canoe hire nearby for excursions down the River Ardèche. Canyoning. Bicycle and quadbike hire 2 km. Riding 5 km.

Open: 4 April - 13 September.

Directions

From Ruoms go south on the D111. Just before Grospierres turn right onto D246, cross the river bridge (2.5 m. width restriction) and then left on D208 towards Chandolas and site. GPS: 44.4141, 4.2729

Charges guide

Per unit incl. 2 persons	€ 20,60 - € 36,00
incl. electricity	€ 25,75 - € 40,20
extra person	€ 6,40 - € 9,60
child (2-13 yrs)	€ 3,75 - € 9,60

Saint Alban-de-Montbel
Camping le Sougey

Lac Rive Ouest, F-73610 Saint Alban-de-Montbel (Savoie) T: 04 79 36 01 44. E: info@camping-sougey.com

alanrogers.com/FR73120

In scenic surroundings, this site is only 200 m. from Lake Aiguebelette, the third largest natural lake in France. The 165 pitches (140 for touring units) all have 6/10A electricity and are set amongst many mature trees and well-manicured hedges, giving a tropical feel and plenty of shade and privacy. Most pitches are flat, but some are on a steep hillside and therefore sloping. There are adequate water points around the site and 30 serviced pitches are available. This is a very peaceful quality site with good views of the surrounding countryside and mountains. The owner, Philippe Kremer, is very friendly and speaks excellent English. The restaurant and shop are in a converted barn just outside the main entrance and the patio has terrific views across the lake. A traditional wood oven is used for pancakes and pizzas or there is a good choice of speciality Savoyard dishes. The lake offers many types of water sports, but to keep the purity of the water, motorboats are not allowed. The beach is free for campsite users, and lifeguards are present in July and August (dogs are not permitted). Walks with llamas and paragliding are organised from reception.

Facilities

Two identical sanitary blocks provide excellent facilities, washbasins in cabins, controllable showers, baby bath, 2 shower units with en-suite washbasin. Good facilities for disabled visitors. Separate laundry. Freezer. Shop (1/7-21/8). Bar and restaurant (open to public, just outside main gate). Well maintained play area. Miniclub. TV room. Chalets to rent. Off site: Fishing, boating, swimming, rafting at lake 200 m. Bicycle hire 3 km. Walks with llamas and paragliding.

Open: 1 May - 16 September.

Directions

From A43 Chambéry - Lyon motorway, take exit 12 and D921 south towards Lac d'Aiguebelette. Follow signs to Plage du Sougey. Site is on the left just before the Plage. GPS: 45.55582, 5.79081

Charges guide

Per unit incl. 2 persons	
incl. electricity (6A)	€ 16,50 - € 20,70
with full services	€ 18,00 - € 25,10
extra person (over 5 yrs)	€ 3,80
dog	€ 1,80

CAMPING LE SOUGEY****

Campsite du Sougey is nestled in the heart of a site naturally rich in exceptional panoramas, located at a height of 380 meters at the foot of the 'Massif de l'Epine'. You are looking for quality services and service, for a complete and diversified atmosphere of tourism then do not hesitate: **you found your place for holidays!**

Lac Rive Ouest - 73610 Saint Alban de Montbel
Tel : 0033 479 36 01 44 - Fax : 0033 479 44 19 01
E-mail : info@camping-sougey.com - Internet : www.camping-sougey.com

Saint Avit
Domaine la Garenne

156 chemin de Chablezin, F-26330 Saint Avit (Drôme) T: 04 75 68 62 26. E: garenne.drome@wanadoo.fr

alanrogers.com/FR26160

This very spacious, partly terraced rural site lies in pleasant countryside to the east of the Rhône valley. Most of the very large pitches are spread out naturally under pine trees but a grassy lower area is more open and young trees give little shade at present. Although all the pitches have electricity (3/6A) very long leads are necessary. Of the 74 touring pitches, 25 are taken up by long stay units. The facilities are old but very clean and could entail a long walk. The small pool and its sunbathing area are next to the reception but there are few other amenities. Torches and rock pegs are essential.

Facilities

Four small basic toilet blocks with washbasins in cabins. Some facilities for disabled visitors but rough paths and terracing could be a problem. Washing machine. Motorcaravan services. Baker calls July/Aug. Small bar plus takeaway food (July/Aug). Small swimming pool. Large sports area. Play area. Communal barbecue (not allowed on the pitches). Family activities (July/Aug). WiFi at reception. Off site: Fishing 1 km. Riding 2 km. Golf 15 km. Village shops at Châteauneuf 3 km.

Open: 1 May - 15 September.

Directions

Leave the N7 16 km. north of Tournon. Turn east on D51, signed Châteauneuf. After about 15 km. at Mureils, turn right on D363, signed St Avit. After 2 km. turn left on D53 (site signed) and site entrance is shortly on the right. GPS: 45.20205, 4.95719

Charges guide

Per unit incl. 2 persons	
and electricity	€ 14,00 - € 24,00
extra person	€ 5,50

For latest campsite news, availability and prices visit

alanrogers.com

Saint Donat-sur-Herbasse

Domaine des Ulèzes

Route de Romans, F-26260 Saint Donat-sur-Herbasse (Drôme) T: 04 75 47 83 20
E: contact@domaine-des-ulezes.com **alanrogers.com/FR26330**

A neat and tidy family run site with a long season only five minutes' walk from St Donat and only 16 km. from the A7 and A49 autoroutes. There are 85 level, grassy pitches with 77 for touring; all are fully serviced with 10A electricity and close to one of the nine toilet blocks. Those in the older section are separated by hedging and a variety of mature trees giving good shade to most pitches. The hedges and trees in the newer section offer little shade at the moment. No twin-axle caravans and only gas and electric barbecues.

Facilities

Nine small toilet blocks with all necessary facilities, some new and others to be refurbished soon. Facilities for children and campers with disabilities. Washing machines. Basic shop, bar, restaurant with simple menus and takeaways (all season). Small swimming pool (8/5-15/9). Children's play area, mini-golf, boules. Games/TV room. Off site: St Donat with a few shops, bars, restaurants five minutes on foot, 1.1 km. by car. River bathing close by. Riding 3 km. Fishing 10 km. Golf 15 km.

Open: 1 April - 31 October.

Directions

Leave A7 Autoroute (exit 13), take D532 east for 5 km. to Curson. Take D67 north 10 km. through St Donat. At a roundabout turn south, D53 and follow signs to site (1 km). GPS: 45.1192, 4.9927

Charges guide

Per unit incl. 2 persons	€ 14,00 - € 18,50
extra person	€ 4,00
child (over 2 yrs)	€ 3,00
electricity	€ 4,50

Saint Galmier

Campéole Val de Coise

Campéole

Route de la Thiéry, F-42330 Saint Galmier (Loire) T: 04 77 54 14 82. E: val-de-coise@campeole.com
alanrogers.com/FR42040

Val de Coise is a member of the Campéole group and has an attractive location in the Massif Central, north of St Etienne. This is rugged, dramatic country – ideal for walking and mountain biking. The nearby spa town of St Galmier is home to the Badoit water plant (guided tours possible), as well as a number of art galleries. Val de Coise is an attractive site located between the River Coise and a dense forest. The 94 pitches (52 for touring units) are grassy and of a good size, mostly with electricity (16A). Mobile homes, chalets and fully equipped tents are available for rent (short term hire possible). There is a swimming pool on site and other on-site amenities include minigolf and giant chess. There is plenty of activity here in high season with a children's club and regular discos and karaoke evenings. Off site, guided walks are organized by the local tourist office in the surrounding forests, and the Monts du Forez and Monts du Lyonnais are within easy access. Given its location, close to France's geographical centre, this site may be a good option for an en route overnight stop.

Facilities

Swimming pool (July/Aug). Multisports terrain. Volleyball. Badminton. TV room. Shop. Play area. Giant chess. Bouncy castle. Activities and entertainment programme. Tourist information. Mobile homes, chalets and equipped tents for rent. Off site: St Galmier 2 km. Tennis 2 km. Fishing (in River Coise). Hiking and cycling tracks. Riding. Golf. St Etienne 22 km.

Open: 15 April - 15 October.

Directions

From St Etienne, head north on the A72 and leave at the Andrezieux Bouthéon St Galmier exit. The site is well indicated from here. GPS: 45.59272, 4.33542

Charges guide

Per unit incl. 2 persons and electricity	€ 15,50 - € 19,50

For latest campsite news, availability and prices visit
alanrogers.com

Saint Gervais-les-Bains

Camping les Dômes de Miage

197 route des Contamines, F-74170 Saint Gervais-les-Bains (Haute-Savoie) T: 04 50 93 45 96
E: info@camping-mont-blanc.com alanrogers.com/FR74140

Saint Gervais is a pretty spa town in the picturesque Val-Monjoie valley and this site is 2 km. from its centre. It is 22 km. west of Chamonix and centrally located for discovering this marvellous mountain region. Nestled among the mountains, this sheltered, well equipped site provides 150 flat grassy pitches. Of a good size, about half have shade and 100 have electricity points (3-10A). The remainder on terraced ground are used for tents. Third generation hosts, Stéphane and Sophie, will welcome you to the site and their passion for this area at the foot of Mont Blanc is infectious. A number of Savoyard style chalets to let are planned for the future. This is a good site for large motorcaravans. There is no on-site entertainment programme, but a wealth of information about the area and activities available nearby is provided at reception where they will help you plan your itinerary. The region is good for walking and there is a bus service into Saint Gervais, from where there is a frequent shuttle bus to its spa and a tramway to the Mont Blanc range. There is good public transport between the town and Chamonix.

Facilities

Two sanitary blocks, one heated, with a suite for disabled visitors and baby room. Washing machines, dryer. Motorcaravan services. Small basic shop. Bar/restaurant. TV room, library, ironing board. Excellent playground. Playing field. Off site: Fishing 100 m. Bicycle hire 1 km. Riding 7 km. Shops, etc. and outdoor swimming pool in St Gervais.

Open: 1 May - 12 September.

Directions

From St Gervais take D902 towards Les Contamines and site is on left after 2 km.
GPS: 45.87389, 6.7199

Charges guide

Per unit incl. 2 persons	
and electricity	€ 19,40 - € 25,10
extra person	€ 3,00 - € 4,10
child (2-10 yrs)	€ 2,50 - € 3,50
dog	€ 2,00

Camping Cheques accepted.

Les Dômes de Miage
CAMPING

A new way to discover the mountains...
A campsite in the middle of untouched nature, in a quiet location at the foot of Mont-Blanc, in the center of many hiking paths. A wide choice of activitities and services, sports centre with swimming pool, tennis etc... at 800 yards.

Aiguille du Midi, Mer de glace & Chamonicix 15 miles, St-Gervais 1,2 miles, Megève 7 miles.

197 ROUTE DES CONTAMINES
F-74170 SAINT-GERVAIS-LES-BAINS
TÉL. 33(0)4 50 93 45 96
FAX 33(0)4 50 78 10 75
WWW.CAMPING-MONT-BLANC.COM
CAMPING.ST-GERVAIS@WANADOO.FR

Saint Jean-de-Chevelu

Camping Lacs de Chevelu

F-73170 Saint Jean-de-Chevelu (Savoie) T: 04 79 36 72 21. E: camping-des-lacs@wanadoo.fr
alanrogers.com/FR73080

This is a small, family orientated campsite which is run by a friendly family and surrounded by delightful scenery, not far from Lac du Bourget. Beside the site is a small lake which is fed by springs and has a sandy beach ideal for swimming and playing around in small boats. The site has 120 average to large size, grass pitches with 110 for touring. There are 50 with 10A electricity (long leads advised). They are numbered and marked by very small trees with a few having some shade. This site ideal for families who are happy to make their own entertainment.

Facilities

Excellent newly refurbished toilet block with all necessary facilities including those for babies and campers with disabilities. Motorcaravan services. Shop. Bar (1/6-30/8). Takeaway snacks (1/6-30/8). Fishing. Lake bathing (lifeguard in high season). Organised walks and bike rides. Covered games area. Boules. TV room. Play area. Some family entertainment in high season. Off site: Riding, bicycle hire, canoeing, hang-gliding 5 km. Boat ramp, tennis 7 km. Golf 10 km. Yenne 5 km. Chambéry 13 km.

Open: 1 May - 15 September.

Directions

Leave A43 at exit 13 (Chambéry) and take N504 north towards Belley. After the 'Tunnel du Chat', in Saint-Jean-de-Chevelu, turn right (site signed). Site is just over 1 km. GPS: 45.69378, 5.82491

Charges guide

Per unit incl. 2 persons	
and electricity	€ 16,50 - € 25,50
extra person	€ 3,40 - € 4,90
child (2-7 yrs)	€ 2,40 - € 3,90

Saint Jorioz

Village Camping Europa

1444 route Albertville, F-74410 Saint Jorioz (Haute-Savoie) T: 04 50 68 51 01. E: info@camping-europa.com
alanrogers.com/FR74100

You will receive a friendly welcome at this quality, family run site. The flowers, shrubs and trees are lovely and everything is kept neat and tidy. There are 210 medium to large size pitches (110 for touring) on level stony grass. Rock pegs are advised. All pitches have electricity (6A) close by and 18 have water and drainage. The static units are separated from the touring section by high hedges giving the impression that you are on a small site. There may be some noise from the adjacent main road. This is a good base from which to tour the Lake Annecy area.

Facilities

Two very good toilet blocks, recently modernised to a high standard, have all the necessary facilities including some large cubicles with both showers and washbasins. Motorcaravan service point. Good bar and restaurant (1/6-31/8). Swimming pool complex (entry bracelet € 2 each). Bicycle hire. Internet access. Miniclub. Some musical evenings. Off site: Fishing 300 m. Boat launching 500 m. Lakeside beach 2 km. Riding 3 km. Golf 8 km. Lakeside bike ride (40 km). St Joriz. Canyoning and hang-gliding nearby. Boat trips.

Open: 30 April - 20 September.

Directions

From Annecy take N508 signed Albertville. Site is well signed on the right on leaving Saint Jorioz. GPS: 45.8246, 6.1758

Charges guide

Per unit incl. 2 persons	
and electricity	€ 14,50 - € 29,10
serviced pitch	€ 22,70 - € 37,30
extra person	€ 4,20 - € 6,20
child (2-6 yrs)	free - € 5,50
dog	€ 3,00

Saint-Jorioz

Camping International du Lac d'Annecy

1184 route d'Albertville, F-74410 Saint-Jorioz (Haute-Savoie) T: 04 50 68 67 93
E: contact@camping-laclannecy.com alanrogers.com/FR74270

International du Lac d'Annecy is a good quality, family run campsite within 500 m. of the crystal clear water of Lac d'Annecy which in high season offers a very wide range of watersports and other leisure activities. Passing close to the site is an excellent cycle route alongside the full length of the lake. The site has 163 level, grass pitches of a good size. There are 140 for touring units, all with electricity (6/10A). The pitches are arranged in pairs separated by a few flowering shrubs with mature trees giving some shade. Access is easy for large outfits. A new swimming pool complex was planned for 2010.

Facilities

Very good toilet block with all necessary facilities including those for campers with disabilities. Bar/restaurant and takeaway. Heated swimming pool (8/5-18/9). Play areas. Multisport pitch. Boules. Bicycle hire. Children's club and family entertainment (July/Aug). WiFi (charged). Off site: Fishing and bathing in lake 500 m. Beach, boat ramp, windsurfing 1 km. Golf 10 km. Riding 15 km. St Jorioz with bar/restaurants, shops 1 km. Annecy 10 km. Cycle track (30 km) alongside lake.

Open: 8 May - 18 September.

Directions

From Annecy take D1580 south, signed Albertville, for 10 km. to Jorioz. Site is on the right 1 km. after traffic lights. GPS: 45.83084, 6.17842

Charges guide

Per unit incl. 2 persons	
incl. electricity	€ 16,00 - € 24,00
extra person (over 2 yrs)	€ 25,00 - € 31,00
	€ 3,90 - € 4,60

Saint Laurent-du-Pape

Camping la Garenne

Chemin de la Garenne, F-07800 Saint Laurent-du-Pape (Ardèche) T: 04 75 62 24 62. E: info@lagarenne.org
alanrogers.com/FR07100

This spacious, family orientated site has a long season and is within easy reach of the A7/N7 south of Valence. It is only a short stroll from the village which has a range of small shops. Guests are mainly Dutch but all are made welcome and English is widely spoken. The 120 hard pitches (rock pegs advised), some terraced and some sloping, have varying degrees of shade. Some are separated by hedges and all have electricity, but only 4A (some need long leads). Visitors' pursuits have been carefully considered resulting in a variety of family activities from mid May to mid September.

Facilities

Excellent and very clean, modern toilet blocks provide all necessary facilities including those for children and disabled visitors. Small shop for basics. Bar, restaurant and takeaway (all 15/5-15/9). Swimming pool and sunbathing terrace (20/5-30/9). Paddling pool. Boules. Games room. Barbecues are not permitted.
Off site: Village. Fishing 1 km. Riding 2 km. Bicycle hire 3 km. Walking, biking, canoeing, canyoning and exploring.

Open: 1 March - 1 November.

Directions

Leave the N86 at Beauchastel, 20 km. south of Valence and follow the D21 to Saint Laurent-du-Pape. In the village, turn right just before the post office and the site is at the end of this road, beyond the tennis court. GPS: 44.82663, 4.76171

Charges guide

Per unit incl. 2 persons	€ 18,50 - € 30,50
extra person	€ 5,50

Saint Laurent-en-Beaumont

Camping Belvédère de l'Obiou

Les Egats, F-38350 Saint Laurent-en-Beaumont (Isère) T: 04 76 30 40 80. E: info@camping-obiou.com
alanrogers.com/FR38130

This very good, small Alpine site with just 45 pitches is in the centre of the Ecrins National Park. It is therefore ideal for walkers and cyclists looking to take advantage of the well marked trails. It has most things a good site should have, with its restaurant (high season), heated pool and sitting room with TV and library. The welcoming owners will even supply you with breakfast. The views from the terraced pitches are spectacular and there is a wealth of activities in the area ranging from bungee jumping to beaver watching by the Lac du Vallon. Bicycles are available to hire.

Facilities

Two modern toilet blocks, one part of the main building, the other Portacabin style, are immaculate and can be heated. High standard facilities for disabled visitors. Excellent laundry. Motorcaravan services. Restaurant (May-Sept) with Savoyard menu, high quality takeaway and breakfast. Small family run shop with ice cream and soft drinks. Heated swimming pool (May-Sept). Bicycle hire. Good play area. Off site: Fishing 5 km. Walking, cycling and mountain activities.

Open: 15 April - 15 October.

Directions

From Grenoble take exit 8 onto the RN85. After 9 km. left onto D529 towards La Motte d'Aveillans and back onto the RN85 at La Mure. 7 km. south of La Mure site is clearly signed on the left. GPS: 44.87593, 5.83741

Charges guide

Per unit incl. 2 persons	€ 13,00 - € 18,00
extra person	€ 3,00 - € 5,00
electricity (4-10A)	€ 3,00 - € 5,50
Camping Cheques accepted.	

Saint Pierre-de-Chartreuse

Camping de Martinière

Route du Col de Porte, F-38380 Saint Pierre-de-Chartreuse (Isère) T: 04 76 88 60 36
E: camping-de-martiniere@orange.fr alanrogers.com/FR38160

Chamechaude, the 2,082 m. Eiger-like peak, presides benevolently over the 90 touring pitches at this beautiful, high alpine site open from May to September for the summer season. The large touring pitches, all with electricity (2-10A), have some shade and are slightly sloping. The site has a heated pool in the open air so that not a moment of the views is lost. This well run, family owned enterprise, set around a traditional Savoyard farmhouse, is a peaceful centre for walking, climbing, cycling or just soaking up the air. It is in the centre of the Chartreuse National Forest. A Sites et Paysages member.

Facilities

Two heated toilet blocks provide excellent, clean facilities. Facilities for babies but not for disabled visitors. Laundry facilities. Shop (1/6-11/9). Bar (10/6-5/9) with snacks (1/7-31/8). Heated swimming and paddling pools (1/6-5/9; heated in July/Aug). Play area. Indoor sitting area for poor weather. Extensive paperback library.
Off site: Restaurant 50 m. from entrance. Fishing 500 m. Bicycle hire 3 km. Skiing 6 km. Walking, cycling and mountain activities. Riding 15 km. Golf 40 km.

Open: 30 April - 11 September.

Directions

From St Laurent-du-Pont (north from Voiron or south from Chambery), take D512 signed St Pierre-de-Chartreuse. Site is well signed in the village (the road south from St Pierre-d'Entremont is not recommended for towing). GPS: 45.3258, 5.7972

Charges guide

Per unit incl. 2 persons and electricity	€ 17,00 - € 26,20
extra person	€ 4,90 - € 5,60
Camping Cheques accepted.	

For latest campsite news, availability and prices visit

alanrogers.com

Saint Romans

Flower Camping Lac du Marandan

F-38160 Saint Romans (Isère) T: 04 76 64 41 77. E: contact@camping-lac-marandan.com
alanrogers.com/FR38250

Lac du Marandan is ideally situated at the foot of the regional park of the Vercors. It has direct access to an inviting lake which has a temperature of 28 degrees and is surrounded by a fine sandy beach. Christelle and Yannick will make sure you enjoy your stay. The site has 100 pitches from 80-100 sq.m. in size and located in a wooded area where old oaks will provide shade. Many activities are possible around the lake but the area itself also offers also a rich variety of sporting activities and sightseeing. The village of Saint Romans boast a fine heritage with a chapel, a castle and a farm from the 18th century. Hiking can be enjoyed in the Martin Pêcheur bird reserve which has varied and colourful flora.

Facilities

Sanitary buildings with showers. Facilities for disabled visitors. Washing machine. Snack bar. Tennis courts. Table tennis. Boules pitch. Playground. Canoe hire. Accommodation to rent.

Open: 12 June - 29 September.

Directions

Leave the A49 at exit 9 and follow the D518 towards Saint Romans. Then take the D1532, to Base de Loisirs du Marandan (signed). GPS: 45.103198, 5.292631

Charges guide

Per unit incl. 2 persons	
and electricity	€ 14,90 - € 22,50
extra person	€ 3,40 - € 4,50
child (2-7 yrs)	€ 2,40 - € 3,50

Saint Sauveur-de-Montagut

Camping Caravaning l'Ardéchois

Le Chambon, Gluiras, F-07190 Saint Sauveur-de-Montagut (Ardèche) T: 04 75 66 61 87
E: ardechois.camping@wanadoo.fr alanrogers.com/FR07020

This attractive site is quite a way off the beaten track and the approach road is winding and narrow in places. However, it is worth the effort to find it in such a spectacular setting. This site has 106 pitches (83 for touring with 10A electricity) laid out on steep terraces and many separated by trees and plants. Some are alongside the small, fast-flowing stream, while the rest (60%) are on higher, sloping ground nearer the restaurant/bar and pool. The main site access roads are tarmac but are quite steep and larger units may find access to some terraces difficult. On arrival park outside reception.

Facilities

Two very good sanitary blocks include facilities for families and disabled visitors. Laundry facilities. Motorcaravan services. Shop. Cosy restaurant. Swimming and paddling pools (heated), adjacent bar, snack bar, terrace. TV. Bicycle hire, archery, fishing. Good entertainment programme. Only gas/electric barbecues. Off site: Canyoning, climbing, river walking and canoeing trips organised.

Open: 27 April - 30 September.

Directions

From Valence take N86 south for 12 km. At La Voulte-sur-Rhône turn right onto D120 to St Sauveur-de-Montagut (site well signed), in centre turn left onto D102 towards Mézilhac for 8 km. to site. GPS: 44.82842, 4.52332

Charges guide

Per unit incl. 2 persons	
and electricity	€ 28,30 - € 47,50
extra person	€ 5,50 - € 8,50
child (2-13 yrs)	€ 4,00 - € 6,70
Camping Cheques accepted.	

Saint Théoffrey

Camping Ser Sirant

Lac de Laffrey, Petichet, F-38119 Saint Théoffrey (Isère) T: 04 76 83 91 97. E: info@campingsersirant.com
alanrogers.com/FR38020

This small lakeside site, a few kilometres from La Route Napoléon, has 87 touring pitches (6A reverse polarity) and six chalets, set on a level, partly terraced, grassed area. There is a pleasant lakeside terrace just outside the bar and reception, whilst about 70 metres up the lakeside there is a sailing school for you to improve (or start) your sailboarding skills. On site there are kayaks for hire and fishing on the lake. This is a picturesque site with the minimum of extras which will appeal especially to water lovers.

Facilities

A single toilet block is at one end of the site. Equipped to basic standards it could be under pressure at peak times. Half the WCs are Turkish style. No facilities for children. Launderette. Small bar with shop for basic supplies. Takeaway at weekends in July/Aug. Kayak hire. Fishing. Chalets to rent. Off site: Shops and restaurants within 1 km. Riding and bicycle hire 5 km.

Open: 1 May - 30 September.

Directions

Petichet is on the Route Napoléon between Grenoble and La Mure. Site is well signed and easy to find by the lake. GPS: 45.00817, 5.79267

Charges guide

Per unit incl. 2 persons	
and electricity	€ 19,50 - € 21,00
extra person	€ 3,90 - € 4,90
child (2-10 yrs)	€ 2,50 - € 3,50
No credit cards.	

Saint Martin-d'Ardèche

Camping Indigo le Moulin

F-07700 Saint Martin-d'Ardèche (Ardèche) T: 04 75 04 66 20. E: moulin@camping-indigo.com

alanrogers.com/FR07650

Le Moulin is a member of the Indigo group and is situated just 300 m. from the centre of St Martin-d'Ardèche. The site has its own river beach and is very well placed for canoe trips on the Ardèche. There are 200 pitches here, extending over the site's seven hectares. The pitches are well shaded and most have electrical connections. Rental accommodation includes innovative 'wood and canvas' tents and Romany style caravans. Amenities include a pleasant snack bar and a small shop. A children's club (recré-enfants) operates in peak season, focusing on craft activities and games.

Facilities

Snack bar. Small shop. Play area. Children's activity programme. Tourist information. Heated outdoor swimming pool (all season). Direct river access. Canoeing. Football. Tents and caravans for rent. Max. 1 dog. Off site: Bicycle hire 100 m. St Martin 300 m. (shops, cafes and restaurants). Cycle and walking tracks. Aiguèze (pretty craft village). Riding 3 km.

Open: 22 April - 2 October.

Directions

From Pont St Esprit, take northbound D6086, becoming D86 after crossing the river, and then D290 to St Martin-d'Ardèche. The site is clearly signed. GPS: 44.300272, 4.571171

Charges guide

Per unit incl. 2 persons	
and electricity	€ 18,50 - € 45,60
extra person	€ 3,60 - € 5,20
child (2-7 yrs)	€ 2,10 - € 3,70

Camping Cheques accepted.

Samoëns

Camping Caravaneige le Giffre

La Glière, F-74340 Samoëns (Haute-Savoie) T: 04 50 34 41 92. E: camping.samoens@wanadoo.fr

alanrogers.com/FR74230

Surrounded by magnificent mountains in this lesser known Alpine area, yet accessible to major ski resorts, le Giffre could be the perfect spot for those seeking an active, yet relaxing holiday. There are 300 firm, level pitches on stony grass (rock pegs advised) with 288 for touring units. Most have electricity (6/10A) but long leads may be needed. They are spaced out amongst mature trees which give varying amounts of shade and some overlook the attractive lake and leisure park. The small winter/summer resort of Samoëns is only a 15 minutes level stroll away. M. Dominach loves gardening and the site is bedecked with flowers. Make sure you do not miss the small vegetable and herb garden at the entrance. There is little in the way of on-site entertainment but there are many activities available in Samoëns and the surrounding area.

Facilities

Three adequate toilet blocks, heated in winter with facilities for campers with disabilities. Games room. Play area. Boules. Fishing. Accommodation for hire. Off site: Leisure park next to site – pool (entry free summer), ice skating (entry free winter), tennis (summer), archery, adventure park. Paragliding. Rafting, many walks and bike rides (summer) and ski runs (winter). Snack bar and baker (high season) 100 m. Samoëns with a good range of shops, bars, restaurants 1 km. Grand Massif Express cable car 150 m. Bicycle hire 200 m. Riding 2 km.

Open: All year.

Directions

Leave A40 autoroute at Cluses (exit 18 or 19). Go north on D902 towards Taninges. Just before Taninges turn east on D4 to Samoëns. After crossing river, at roundabout, turn left and site is immediately on the left. Park outside the entrance. GPS: 46.07731, 6.71851

Charges guide

Per unit incl. 2 persons	
and electricity	€ 14,60 - € 25,50
extra person	€ 3,80
child (4-12 yrs)	€ 2,50

Camping Cheques accepted.

For latest campsite news, availability and prices visit

alanrogers.com

Sampzon

Yelloh! Village Soleil Vivarais

F-07120 Sampzon (Ardèche) T: 04 75 39 67 56. E: info@yellohvillage-soleil-vivarais.com
alanrogers.com/FR07030

A large, lively, high quality site bordering the River Ardèche, complete with beach, Soleil Vivarais offers much to visitors, particularly families with children. Of the 350 pitches, 110 generously sized, shady and level pitches are for tourers, all with 10A electricity. Rock pegs are advised. During the day the proximity of the swimming pools to the terraces of the bar and restaurant make it a pleasantly social area. A new section beyond the beach has a very attractive new pool complex. In the evening the purpose built stage, with professional lighting and sound system, provides an ideal platform for a regular family entertainment programme, mostly mimed musical shows.

Facilities

Modern, clean, well equipped toilet blocks, facilities for disabled visitors. Washing machines, dryers. Motorcaravan services. Supermarket. Bar/restaurant, takeaways and pizzas. Heated pool (refurbishment planned for 2010), paddling pool. Water polo. Aquarobics. Fishing. Boules. Archery. Bicycle hire. River bathing. Entertainment programme (June-Aug). Massage and beauty parlour. Off site: Riding 800 m. Mountain biking, walking, canoeing, rafting, climbing, caving.

Open: 1 April - 12 September.

Directions

On D579, 2 km. south of Ruoms, turn left at roundabout, signed Vallon-Pont-d'Arc. Shortly turn right over river bridge, site on right. GPS: 44.42917, 4.35531

Charges guide

Per unit incl. 2 persons and electricity	€ 15,00 - € 43,00
extra person	€ 5,00 - € 7,00
dog	free - € 4,00

Sampzon

RCN la Bastide en Ardèche

Route d'Alès (D111), Sampzon, F-07120 Ruoms (Ardèche) T: 04 75 39 64 72
E: info@rcn-labastideenardeche.fr **alanrogers.com/FR07080**

You can be assured of a good welcome at this recently upgraded site. There are 300 good sized, level, grassy pitches marked out by trees which give plenty of shade of which 260 are touring pitches. All have electricity 6A, and 86 are fully serviced. On driving down to your pitch, it seems that there are many mobile homes, actually there are only 30 plus another 20 pitches used by a tour operator. Canoe trips are arranged down the Gorge d'Ardèche and in late June each year a large section of the river bank next to the site is cleared of boulders and sand put down. Security patrols ensure quiet nights.

Facilities

Two well equipped toilet blocks, one new and one refurbished, with baby room and facilities for disabled visitors. Shop, attractive restaurant, pizzeria and bar (1/4-1/10). Heated swimming pool (1/4-1/10) and sunbathing area. Play area. Tennis. Fishing. Organised activities. Recreation room. Only gas barbecues are permitted. Bicycle hire. Off site: Riding 3 km. Watersports on River Ardèche, quad riding, adventure camp. Ruoms 3 km. Vallon-Pont-d'Arc 7 km.

Open: 19 March - 8 October.

Directions

Going south from Ruoms on the D579, after 2.5 km. at roundabout, turn right on D111 signed Alès. After 1 km. cross river bridge and site is 200 m. on the left. GPS: 44.42292, 4.32162

Charges guide

Per unit incl. 2 persons, electricity and water	€ 19,90 - € 43,90
extra person	€ 2,50 - € 4,90
dog (max. 1)	€ 6,00

Sampzon

Flower Camping le Riviera

F-07120 Sampzon (Ardèche) T: 04 75 39 67 57. E: leriviera@wanadoo.fr
alanrogers.com/FR07400

This large, well organised, family run site is situated beside the River Ardèche not far from Vallon-Pont-d'Arc. There are 180 pitches in total with 144 of average size on grass and stone for touring (rock pegs are advised). Separated by hedges and trees, pitches have varying degrees of shade and 10A electricity connections are available. In July and August daily and evening activities are organised for all the family. The site's facilities are of a high standard and disabled visitors are well provided for. Access to some of the pitches is not ideal in some parts and may prove to be difficult for larger units.

Facilities

Two toilet blocks, one new, providing cubicles with washbasins, showers, baby room and excellent facilities for disabled visitors. Washing machines and dryer. Swimming and paddling pools (all season, heated). Bar, restaurant with covered terrace (6/8-8/9 and weekends). Shop (July/Aug). Bicycle and canoe hire (July/Aug). Fishing. Stony river beach. Disco or karaoke every evening until midnight. Off site: Riding 1 km. Bicycle hire 3 km.

Open: 1 April - 30 September.

Directions

On D579 2 km. south of Ruoms, turn left at roundabout signed Vallon-Pont-d'Arc. Shortly turn right over river bridge. Site on left. GPS: 44.42838, 4.35527

Charges guide

Per unit incl. 2 persons	€ 16,00 - € 38,00
extra person	€ 4,50 - € 8,40
child (under 7 yrs)	free - € 7,40

For latest campsite news, availability and prices visit
alanrogers.com

Séez

Camping le Reclus

F-73700 Séez (Savoie) T: 04 79 41 01 05. E: contact@campinglereclus.com

alanrogers.com/FR73100

Bordering a fast flowing but well-fenced stream, this small mountain campsite, set in the hills above Bourg-St-Maurice in the National Park de la Vanoise, is enthusiastically run by Mélanie Bonato. The 90 sunny pitches, most with electricity (4-10A), are on terraces. The village of Séez is a few minutes' walk away. Winter sports enthusiats are well catered for here, with a drying room and ski shoe heating, plus discounts on ski passes and other activities. There is a free shuttle to Les Arcs and La Rosière and it is centrally situated for the Tarentaise ski lifts. This site is not recommended for larger units. If you are looking for somewhere unusual to stay, try the Mongolian yurt, a round marquee-like structure, with a beautifully painted wooden frame. It comes complete with a four poster bed! This is proving to be very popular and advanced booking is well advised. This is the first of many unusual ideas the Bonato sisters have to make sure their campsite is different from the rest. Tree houses is another idea, and the local Mairie seems to be supporting them. We can't wait to return and see what they achieve.

Facilities

Two sanitary blocks have been renovated, the central one more modern, have small shower cubicles with preset hot water; and open style basins. Laundry room with washer/dryer and indoor drying area. Restaurant and takeaway (1/7-5/9). Small play area. Bread, drinks and ice cream for sale. Bicycle hire. TV room. Off site: Shops and bars in the village of Séez. Access to the ski resort of Les Arcs via the funicular railway in Bourg-St-Maurice 2 km. Riding 1 km. Swimming pools 2 km. Golf 15 km.

Open: All year.

Directions

From A43 Lyon - Chambéry - Grenoble motorway take A430 to Albertville and RN90 to Moutiers and Bourg-St-Maurice. Drive through town, at third roundabout follow signs for Tignes and Val d'Isère. Site is 2 km. up the hill on the right on entering village of Séez. GPS: 45.62592, 6.79371

Charges 2011

Per unit incl. 2 persons and electricity	€ 16,40 - € 20,00
extra person	€ 4,00 - € 4,40
child (4-13 yrs)	€ 2,50 - € 3,80
dog	€ 1,00

Thoissey

Hortus, La Route des Vins – Thoissey

Allée du Port, F-01140 Thoissey (Ain) T: 04 74 04 02 97. E: info@camping-hortus.com

alanrogers.com/FR01130

Camping Hortus is a large level site alongside the River Saône close to the small town of Thoissey. There are around 330 large, level, grassy pitches many under mature trees giving good shade, most have 6A electricity but long leads may be needed. The pitches are undelineated with many unmarked access roads and this could result in a very disorganised site in the high season. A few have views over the river and more have views over the surrounding farmland. Access to and on-site is easy so there are no problems with large outfits. The site is within 1.5 km. of the small town of Thoissey and only 3 km. from St Didier-sur-Chalaronne. The level area alongside the Saône is ideal for leisurely bicycle rides. Just across the river are hills covered in vines producing the famous Beaujolais wine. The site has a large swimming pool area with a toboggan and sunbathing area adjacent to the restaurant, a good spot to relax and watch the boats drift by. Close to the site are two further restaurants with views over the river.

Facilities

Four newly refurbished toilet blocks with all necessary facilities including those for campers with disabilities. Swimming pool, paddling pool and togoggan, sunbathing area. Bar/restaurant. Large children's play areas. Multisports area, volleyball, boules, fishing. Off site: Shops, restaurants etc in nearby Thoissey and Saint Didier-sur-Chalaronne.

Open: 15 April - 30 September.

Directions

Leave Autoroute A6, exit 29 (head south) or 30 (head north), take N6 to D9, signed Thoissey. Cross river Saône and leaving bridge turn sharp right to site. GPS: 46.16503, 4.79248

Charges guide

Per unit incl. 2 persons and electricity	€ 15,00 - € 20,00
dog	€ 4,00

Thonon-les-Bains

Camping Saint-Disdille

117 avenue de Saint Disdille, F-74200 Thonon-les-Bains (Haute-Savoie) T: 04 50 71 14 11
E: camping@disdille.com **alanrogers.com/FR74220**

Saint Disdille is situated close to the beautiful Lake Geneva and the famous spa town of Thonon-les-Bains, which can be reached on a bus that passes the site. There are 600 large, level pitches on stone and rough grass (rock pegs are essential). Large trees give some shade. The 300 pitches reserved for touring (200 with 6-10A electricity) are scattered amongst mobile homes and permanent weekender caravans and can be some distance from the facilities. The site is ideally situated for the large range of watersports in the area and Switzerland is easily accessible by car, bus, train or boat. This site will be lively in the high season due to the large number of long stay units and the on-site and adjacent discos finish after midnight. Although there are no problems with large units on the site, access is not easy due to the urban location. A new bypass around Thonon makes access easier.

Facilities

Five adequate toilet blocks, 4 recently refurbished inside. Shop. Bar with TV, restaurant with takeaways (all season). Diving and rafting clubs. Play area with bouncy castle. Multisports court. Boules. Games room with pool table. WiFi (free) and internet point (fee). Twin-axle vans are not accepted. Bicycle hire. Off site: Small lakeside public beach and disco 300 m. Fishing 500 m. Large open air pool 1 km. Boat ramp, windsurfing, bicycle hire 2 km. Many other water sports in the area. Golf 5 km. Thonon-les-Bains 2 km.

Open: 1 April - 30 September.

Directions

From Annemasse take N5 to Thonon-les-Bains. In Thonon follow signs for Evian to Intermarché supermarket. At next roundabout follow signs to campsite and Parc de la Chataigneraie. GPS: 46.39765, 6.50335

Charges guide

Per unit incl. 2 persons and electricity	€ 17,20 - € 23,70
extra person	€ 3,40 - € 4,80
child (3-10 yrs)	€ 2,20 - € 3,40
dog	€ 1,00 - € 2,00

Trept

Domaine les Trois Lacs du Soleil

La Plaine, F-38460 Trept (Isère) T: 04 74 92 92 06. E: les3lacsdusoleil@hotmail.fr

alanrogers.com/FR38060

Les Trois Lacs is situated on the edge of three lakes in flat, open country in the north of Dauphine. The camping area is on one side of the largest lake with tall trees on one edge and views of distant mountains. The 200 good sized pitches, with 180 for tourists, are well spaced and separated by trees and hedges. All have 6A electricity. There is plenty of activity on offer for the whole family including fishing in one lake, swimming in the other two and, for the more energetic, rollerblading. There is plenty of space around the lake for children to play. The land around the lakes has been landscaped with grassy banks and a variety of shrubs and trees. This is a good base from which to enjoy either the countryside, the historic places of the region or the programme of leisure activities provided by the site (in July/Aug).

Facilities	Directions
Two fully equipped toilet blocks are in the centre of the camping area. Toilets for children. Baby room. Laundry facilities. Small shop (July/Aug). Bar/restaurant. Snack bars. Outdoor pool (all June-Sept). Lakeside beach and water slide. Discos and entertainment in high season. TV and sports hall. Roller blade hire. Walking. Fishing. Gas barbecues only. Off site: Riding 500 m. Trept 2 km. Mountain bike hire 10 km.	From A43 take exit 7 on to D522 north. Turn left after 7 km. on to D65 then after 5 km. turn right on the D517. Site is 2 km. east of Trept with signs in village. GPS: 45.68699, 5.35191

Open: 1 May - 27 September.

Charges guide

Per unit incl. 2 persons and electricity	€ 18,50 - € 31,00
extra person	€ 3,00 - € 7,00
child (0-10 yrs)	free - € 3,50

Vallières

Camping les Charmilles

D14, 625 route du val de fier, F-74150 Vallières (Haute-Savoie) T: 04 50 62 10 60

E: les.charmilles.camping@wanadoo.fr alanrogers.com/FR74290

Les Charmilles is a friendly site in the village of Vallières, to the west of Annecy. There are 67 pitches, most with electricity (6/8A). A number of pitches are occupied by chalets and caravans (for rent). The site restaurant, Le Marilyn, is open to the public and specialises in Savoyard cuisine. Takeaway meals are also possible. On-site leisure amenities include a swimming pool, paddling pool and volleyball. During peak season, various activities are organized including themed evenings, as well as a children's club specialising in craft activities and games. The village centre is around 500 m. away with a number of shops including a post office and a specialist cheese shop. Rumilly is a larger village, around 5 km. to the south, and has two supermarkets and a wider selection of shops, cafés and restaurants. It also has a popular market every Thursday. Annecy is, of course, a delightful town and its old quarters and lakeside promenades are highly recommended.

Facilities	Directions
Bar, restaurant, takeaway service and swimming pool (all 1/4-31/10). Paddling pool. Play area. Facilities for disabled visitors. Tourist information. Entertainment and activity programme. Chalets and caravans for rent. Washing machine and motorcaravan service point. Barbecues are allowed. Off site: Village centre 500 m Rumilly 5 km. Vineyards. Mountain biking. Fishing and horse riding 5 km. Bicycle hire 6 km.	Approaching from then north, leave A40 autoroute at exit 11 and head south on D1508 and D1504 to Frangy. Then continue south on D910 to Vallières and then follow signs to the site. GPS: 45.90194, 5.92766

Open: 1 April - 31 October.

Charges year

Per unit incl. 2 persons and electricity	€ 15,50 - € 19,00
extra person	€ 3,50
child (2-7 yrs)	€ 2,00

Vernioz

Kawan Village le Bontemps

5 impasse du Bontemps, F-38150 Vernioz (Isère) T: 04 74 57 83 52. E: info@campinglebontemps.com
alanrogers.com/FR38120

This spacious, attractive and well cared for site is enhanced by a variety of trees planted by the original owner nearly 30 years ago. The 175 large, level and grassy pitches are arranged in groups, partly separated by neat hedges, all with water and electricity. Fifteen pitches are used for mobile homes and chalets and a group at the back is used by weekenders. The shop, bar/restaurant and leisure facilities are conveniently placed near the entrance and there is a large sports area and activity hall to one side. This is an excellent site for both short and long stays.

Facilities

Two toilet blocks. Motorcaravan service points. Shop, Bar (15/4-15/9). Restaurant and takeaway (15/4-15/9). Swimming pool (1/5-15/9). Several play areas. Minigolf. Tennis. Badminton. Electronic games. Fitness equipment. Extensive list of activities for all the family (high season). Small fishing lake. Max 1 dog. Off site: Small river for fishing. Vernioz 2 km. Bicycle hire 20 km. Vienne 20 km. Golf 20 km. Pilat Regional Park 15 km.

Open: 26 March - 1 October.

Directions

Exit A7 south of Lyons at junction 9. Continue south for about 7 km. on N7. Just north of Auberives turn left on D37. Follow campsite signs for 7 km. Entrance is on right 4 km. beyond Vernioz. GPS: 45.4283, 4.928233

Charges guide

Per unit incl. 2 persons	€ 22,00 - € 30,00
extra person	€ 6,00 - € 7,00

Camping Cheques accepted.

Villeneuve-de-Berg

Domaine le Pommier

RN102, F-07170 Villeneuve-de-Berg (Ardèche) T: 04 75 94 82 81. E: info@campinglepommier.com
alanrogers.com/FR07110

Domaine Le Pommier is an extremely spacious Dutch owned site of ten hectares in 32 hectares of wooded grounds. The site is steeply terraced (a tractor is available to assist) and has wonderful views over the Ardèche mountains and beyond. There are 423 pitches with 275 for touring. They are grassy/stony, of good size and well spaced. Separated by young trees and hedges, some have little or no shade. All have access to electricity and water is nearby. The site is not recommended for large units. Amenities include a mini-farm, including llamas, goats and ponies, and an unusual pancake restaurant.

Facilities

Four excellent toilet blocks, one with underfloor heating, provide all the necessary facilities. Comprehensive shop. Bar/restaurant. Swimming pool complex with slides (two new), paddling pools, etc. Everything opens all season. Boules. Minigolf. Activities including games in the woods, archery, water polo and tug-of-war. Bridge and watercolour classes. Tennis. Soundproof disco. Very extensive programme of events on and off site. Low season excursions. Off site: Villeneuve-de-Berg 1.5 km. River Ardèche 12 km. Potholing, rock climbing, canoeing, canyoning, mountain biking, walking or riding.

Open: 15 April - 17 September.

Directions

Site is west of Montélimar on the N102. The entrance is adjacent to the roundabout at the eastern end of the Villeneuve-de-Berg bypass. GPS: 44.57250, 4.51115

Charges 2011

Per unit incl. 2 persons and electricity	€ 23,50 - € 43,50
extra person	€ 5,50 - € 9,50
child (4-12 yrs)	€ 3,50 - € 6,50
dog	free - € 4,50

Max. 6 persons per pitch.
Special offers for longer stays in low season.

Vallon-Pont-d'Arc

Castel Camping Nature Parc l'Ardéchois

Route touristique des Gorges, F-07150 Vallon-Pont-d'Arc (Ardèche) T: 04 75 88 06 63
E: ardecamp@bigfoot.com alanrogers.com/FR07120

This very high quality, family run site is within walking distance of Vallon-Pont-d'Arc. It borders the River Ardèche and canoe trips are run, professionally, direct from the site. This campsite is ideal for families with younger children seeking an active holiday. The facilities are comprehensive and of an extremely high standard, particularly the central toilet block. Of the 244 pitches, there are 225 for tourers, separated by trees and individual shrubs. All have electrical connections (6/10A) and 125 have full services. Forming a focal point are the bar and restaurant (good menus), with a terrace and stage overlooking the attractive heated pool. There is also a large paddling pool and sunbathing terrace. For children, there is a well thought out play area plus plenty of other space for youngsters to play, both on the site and along the river. Activities are organised throughout the season; these are family based – no discos. Patrols at night ensure a good night's sleep. Access to the site is easy and suitable for large outfits. Member of Leading Campings Group.

Facilities

Two well equipped toilet blocks, one superb with everything working automatically. Facilities are of the highest standard, very clean and include good facilities for babies, those with disabilities, washing up and laundry. Four private bathrooms to hire. Washing machines. Well stocked shop. Swimming pool and paddling pool (no Bermuda shorts). Tennis. Very good play area. Internet access. Organised activities, canoe trips. Only gas barbecues are permitted. Communal barbecue area. Off site: Canoeing, rafting, walking, riding, mountain biking, golf, rock climbing. Vallon-Pont-d'Arc 800 m.

Open: 15 April - 30 September.

Directions

From Vallon-Pont-d'Arc (western end of the Ardèche Gorge) at a roundabout go east on the D290. Site entrance is shortly on the right.
GPS: 44.39804, 4.39878

Charges 2011

Per unit incl. 2 persons and electricity	€ 30,00 - € 47,00
extra person	€ 5,90 - € 9,80
child (0-13 yrs)	free - € 7,60
dog	€ 3,50 - € 7,50

Villars-les-Dombes

Indigo Parc des Oiseaux

Avenue des Nations, F-01330 Villars-les-Dombes (Ain) T: 04 74 98 00 21
E: parc-des-oiseaux@camping-indigo.com alanrogers.com/FR01110

The Parc des Oiseaux is one of Europe's largest and most popular ornithological parks, and can be found at Villars-les-Dombes, northeast of Lyon. This campsite is a new member of the Indigo group, reopening in 2011 (it was formerly a municipal site). The 199 pitches here are large and grassy, and are mostly supplied with electricity. A range of wooden chalets and specially made tents is available for rent. On-site amenities include a swimming pool and a small bar/restaurant. The river Chalaronne runs alongside the site and fishing is popular. A children's activity programme is run in high season, focusing on nature and the countryside. A great diversity of birds from around the world are on display at the nearby parc, and the emphasis there is very firmly on replicating the birds' natural habitat and conservation. The park has won several major awards for this reason.

Facilities

Bar/restaurant. Shop. Takeaway food. Swimming pool. Fishing. Playground. Children's activity programme. Tourist information. Chalets and tents for rent. Off site: Parc des Oiseaux. Cycle tracks and footpaths. Golf 1 km. Riding 10 km. Villars-les-Dombes. Lyon 33 km.

Open: 8 April - 28 October.

Directions

From A46, northeast of Lyons take exit 3 Bourg-en-Bresse. Take N83 to Villars-les-Dombes, about 20 km. On entering town turn right to site (D904) which is well signed. GPS: 45.99723, 5.03047

Charges 2011

Contact the site for details.

For latest campsite news, availability and prices visit

alanrogers.com

CAMPING NATURE PARC
L'ARDÉCHOIS *****

Waterpark and heated balneo (*high season*)

Heated and comfortable toilet facilities - Direct access to the river and canoes for rent
Mobile homes for rent - Chalets for rent (*Domaine de Sevenier*)
Open from April 15 to September 30

CAMPING NATURE PARC L'ARDÉCHOIS *****
Route du Pont d'Arc - 07150 VALLON PONT D'ARC
tel 0033 475 880 663 - fax 0033 475 371 497
E-mail: ardecamp@bigfoot.com - www.ardechois-camping.com

From the endless shimmering beaches and dunes and the fragrant pine forests of the Atlantic coast to the historical and beautiful Dordogne with its gastronomic delights, it's easy to see the attraction of this popular holiday region.

DÉPARTEMENTS: 24 DORDOGNE, 33 GIRONDE, 40 LANDES, 47 LOT-ET-GARONNE, 64 PYRÉNÉES-ATLANTIQUES

MAJOR CITY: BORDEAUX

The history of Aquitaine goes back many thousands of years to when man lived in the caves of the Périgord and left cave paintings at sites such as Les Eyzies and Lascaux. The ancient dukedom of Aquitaine was ruled by the English for 300 years following the marriage of Eleanor of Aquitaine to Henry Plantagenet, the future king, in 1154. The fortified villages and castles of the area bear evidence of the resulting conflict between the French and the English for control of Aquitaine, and today add character to the countryside.

This is a diverse region of mountains and vineyards, vast beaches, fertile river valleys, rolling grasslands and dense forests. Within its boundaries are the beautiful valleys of the Dordogne and Vézère, the forests of the Landes and the beaches of the Atlantic which stretch from the Gironde estuary to the Basque Country and the rocky Pyrénées mountains on the Spanish border.

Some of the world's most famous vineyards are around Bordeaux, the capital of the region. These are especially famous for their Médoc, Sauternes and St Emilion wines and most châteaux allow visits to their cellars and wine tastings.

L'Aquitaine
SOUTH WEST FRANCE-IT'S ALL YOURS

www.**tourisme-aquitaine.fr/en**
tourisme@tourisme-aquitaine.fr

Outdoor activities

Surf

The Atlantic Coast is renowned for its many superb surfing spots. Practised for the first time at Biarritz in the fifties, today numerous schools are available to teach you the pleasures of surfing the waves.

www.**tourisme-aquitaine.fr/en**

Golf

The oldest golf course in France was created in 1856 in Pau and now more than 40 courses exist in Aquitaine, offering a great variety of breathtaking landscapes: along the Atlantic near Biarritz or in the centre of the vineyards in the Médoc.

www.**golf-in-aquitaine.co.uk**

Wines

Wine Country

The Aquitaine region boasts many wine châteaux, where you can taste wines with famous names such as Saint Emilion, Médoc, Bergerac, Jurançon… and where you can also discover the secrets of the wine-maker's art.

www.**oenoland.com**

Marathon du Médoc

Each year in September, the marathon of the Médoc is a running event about fun, food, festivities, friendship and, above all, Médoc wine. The marathon takes place against a beautiful backdrop of more than 50 châteaux and vineyards, with Médoc wine tasting at every food and drink outlet.

www.**marathondumedoc.com**

Cultural Urban Heritage

From Bordeaux to Pau

Discover the cultural and historic heritage of the Aquitaine cities. From Bordeaux and its 18th-century architecture, recently classified as a world heritage site by UNESCO, to Périgueux and its sites dating from the Gallo-Roman period, or Bayonne and its typically Basque buildings and houses and Pau, traditionally linked to Great Britain.

www.**week-end-aquitaine.fr**

Images © (left to right, top to bottom): OT St-Emilion. And © CRTA; J J Brochard;
Laurent Reiz; Alain Béguerie; Laurent Reiz; J J Brochard

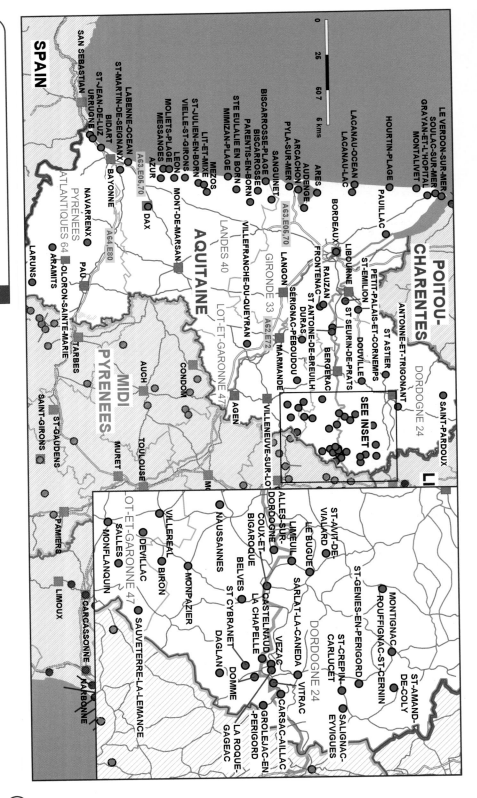

For latest campsite news, availability and prices visit

alanrogers.com

Allés-sur-Dordogne
Camping le Port de Limeuil

F-24480 Allés-sur-Dordogne (Dordogne) T: 05 53 63 29 76. E: didierbonvallet@aol.com
alanrogers.com/FR24170

At the confluence of Dordogne and Vézère rivers, opposite the picturesque village of Limeuil, this delightful family site exudes a peaceful and relaxed ambience. There are 75 marked touring pitches on grass, some spacious and all with electricity (5/10A). The buildings are in traditional Périgourdine style and surrounded by flowers and shrubs. A sports area on a large open grassy space between the river bank and the main camping area adds to the feeling of space and provides an additional recreation and picnic area (there are additional unmarked pitches for tents and camper vans along the bank here).

Facilities

Two clean, modern toilet blocks provide excellent facilities. Bar/restaurant with snacks and takeaway (all 20/5-5/9). Small shop. Swimming pool with jacuzzi, paddling pool and children's slide (1/5-30/9). Badminton, football and boules. Trampoline. Mountain bike hire. Canoe hire, launched from the site's own pebble beach. WiFi in bar area (free). Off site: The pretty medieval village of Limeuil 200 m. Riding 1 km. Golf 10 km.

Open: 1 May - 30 September.

Directions

Site is 7 km. south of Le Bugue. From D51/D31E Le Buisson to Le Bugue road turn west towards Limeuil. Just before bridge into Limeuil, turn left (site signed), across another bridge. Site shortly on the right. GPS: 44.87977, 0.88587

Charges guide

Per unit incl. 2 persons and electricity	€ 16,50 - € 25,40
extra person	€ 4,50 - € 6,50

Antonne-et-Trigonant
Camping Caravaning le Bois du Coderc

Route des Gaunies, F-24420 Antonne-et-Trigonant (Dordogne) T: 05 53 05 99 83
E: coderc-camping@wanadoo.fr alanrogers.com/FR24410

Located in the scenic Perigord region, 10 km. from Périgueux, Les Bois du Coderc, under new ownership, has been completely renovated. It is a calm, picturesque, part wooded, riverside site, ideally situated for visiting many interesting places. The touring pitches (there are no individual marked-out pitches) and mobile homes are spaced out over a field and woodland, with 10A electricity hook-ups and water points. This campsite has a calm and relaxing atmosphere. However, it is well placed near the historical town of Périgueux which is rich in history and culture and full of charm and character, with cobbled streets, various squares with restaurants, bars and a large selection of shops.

Facilities

One male and female sanitary block with preset showers (no charge) clean and well maintained (only one toilet and a shower are open in winter). Baby changing area. Laundry facilities. Small shop and bar (all year). Snacks and takeaway (July/Aug). Bar/games room. Small play area. The river Isle runs through the campsite and is suitable for paddling. WiFi. Heated (15/5-15/9) outdoor swimming pool.

Open: 10 January - 20 December.

Directions

Heading north on the N21 Limoges - Périgueux road, 2.5 km. north of Antonne et Trigonant turn right at Routier Restaurant (near km. marker 49). Continue along this country road following signs. Travelling south from Limoges direction turn is on left 3 km. south of Sarliac sur L'Isle. GPS: 45.2194, 0.8636

Charges guide

Per unit incl. 2 persons and electricity	€ 15,00 - € 18,00
per person	€ 3,50 - € 4,00
child (3-10 yrs)	€ 2,00 - € 2,50

Aramits
Camping Barétous-Pyrénées

Quartier Ripaude, F-64570 Aramits (Pyrénées-Atlantiques) T: 05 59 34 12 21. E: atso64@hotmail.com
alanrogers.com/FR64020

Located on the edge of the Pyrénées, this quiet site is well away from the tourist bustle, particularly in early or late season. It has a rural location, yet is close to the town. This is a wonderful location for exploring the region and offers a peaceful haven for those wishing to stay in quiet surroundings. The shady, grass pitches are attractive and of a good size with hedges. They offer both water and electricity (10A). The welcoming reception (English spoken) sells local produce and organic food. The heated swimming and paddling pool area is overlooked by a small sun terrace with a café/bar.

Facilities

Two sanitary blocks, one old, one modern, offer clean facilities with unisex toilets and showers. Facilities for disabled visitors. Café/bar with hot and cold meals (July/Aug). Heated swimming and paddling pools (May-Sept). Communal room with TV, games, library and drinks. Small shop selling organic food. Boules. Small play area with sandpit. Off site: Town with supermarket 250 m. Fishing 50 m. Riding 3 km. Snow skiing 25 km.

Open: 1 March - 31 October.

Directions

From Oloron-Sainte-Marie, head southwest on D919 to Aramits. Through village bear right on D918. Cross river and immediately turn right at campsite sign. GPS: 43.1214, -0.732317

Charges guide

Per unit incl. 2 persons and electricity	€ 18,30 - € 24,80
Camping Cheques accepted.	

For latest campsite news, availability and prices visit

alanrogers.com

Arcachon

Camping Club Arcachon

5 allée Galaxie, B.P. 46, F-33312 Arcachon Cedex (Gironde) T: 05 56 83 24 15. E: info@camping-arcachon.com

alanrogers.com/FR33030

This campsite enjoys a position well back from the hustle and bustle, where nights are quiet and facilities are of a high standard. The 176 touring pitches are divided into areas for caravans, motorcaravans and tents and are on neatly formed terraces beneath tall pine trees. Most have electricity (6/10A). The site is quite hilly and the narrow roads that wind around it could possibly make it difficult for larger motorcaravans to manoeuvre and find suitable pitches. At night, wardens ensure that security and noise levels are controlled. A one kilometre walk takes you to the town of Arcachon where there are plenty of shops, bars and restaurants. However, the campsite bar, restaurant and takeaway are open at weekends from April to September (daily in July and August) if you prefer to stay on site. Watersports, paragliding, sailing, tennis tournaments, climbing the biggest sand dune in Europe, and not forgetting such gastronomic delights as oysters and mussels, are readily available.

Facilities

Three sanitary blocks with the usual facilities. Washing machine and dryers. Motorcaravan services. Fridge hire. Shop (15/6-15/9). Bar, restaurant, snack bar, takeaway (April-Sept). Swimming pool (1/5-30/9). Bicycle hire. Play area. Games room. Children's club and entertainment for all age groups (1/7-31/8). Barbecues are only permitted in communal areas. Internet access and WiFi. Off site: Beach 1 km. on foot. Arcachon 2-3 km. Riding 1 km. Golf 2 km.

Open: All year (excl. 12 November - 12 December).

Directions

Approaching Arcachon from Bordeaux on the N250 take exit for Hôpital Jean Hameau (D217). Cross over bypass following signs for hospital, then signs for Abatilles. At next roundabout follow signs for camping. Take care as the route travels through suburban housing. Follow campsite signs, not satnav. GPS: 44.6513, -1.174083

Charges guide

Per unit incl. 2 persons	€ 13,00 - € 31,00
extra person	€ 4,00 - € 8,00
child (4-10 yrs)	€ 1,00
electricity	€ 3,00 - € 4,00
animal	€ 2,00 - € 4,00

Camping Cheques accepted.

Camping Club Arcachon ★★★

Atlantic Ocean

Bassin d'Arcachon

Discover nature

Water Slides

Special offer April, May, June and September :
1 week 7days/7nights
for the price of 4 days in mobil-home
4 persons 220 €* or
1 week-end 2days/2nights in mobil-home
4 persons 80 €*
*Prices without tourist tax
limited offer (subject to availability)

Online booking

5, ALLÉE DE LA GALAXIE
LES ABATILLES - BP 46
33312 ARCACHON CEDEX
Tel. +33 (0)5 56 83 24 15
Fax. +33 (0)5 57 52 28 51
Internet :
www.camping-arcachon.com
Email :
info@camping-arcachon.com

For latest campsite news, availability and prices visit

alanrogers.com

Arès

Camping la Cigale

53 rue du Général de Gaulle, F-33740 Arès (Gironde) T: 05 56 60 22 59
E: contact.lacigale@gmail.com alanrogers.com/FR33120

La Cigale is an attractive little site with charm and ambience where the owners extend a very warm welcome. Small and beautifully maintained, it is set amid a variety of trees tjat give some dappled shade. M. Pallet's floral displays add colour to the 41 neatly hedged, grassy touring pitches (100 sq.m. and most with 6A electricity, 10 also with water and a drain). There is a small unheated swimming pool and a paddling pool. The bar has a terrace where drinks, meals and snacks are served under the shade of large plane trees. Six delightful chalets for rent are spacious, modern and very well presented.

Facilities

Well equipped toilet block includes a family room with two showers and facilities for disabled visitors. Washing machine and dryer. Motorcaravan services. Simple shop. Bar, terrace, meals, snacks. Pizza takeaway (all 17/6-10/9). Swimming and paddling pools (25/5-12/9). Small play area. Entertainers for children and adults in July/Aug. Free donkey cart rides every Sunday in season. Off site: Site is convenient for a wide choice of beaches. Village centre 800 m. Fishing or riding 1 km.

Open: 23 April - 26 September.

Directions

Leave Bordeaux ring road at exit 10 (D213) or exit 11 (D106) and continue direct to Arès. Turn into Arès following road to church square. Turn right following signs for Lège - Cap Ferret. Site is 800 m. on left. GPS: 44.77287, -1.14147

Charges 2011

Per unit incl. 2 persons and electricity	€ 27,50 - € 35,50
extra person	€ 6,00

Arès

Flower Camping la Canadienne

Route de Lège, 82 rue General de Gaulle, F-33740 Arès (Gironde) T: 05 56 60 24 91
E: info@lacanadienne.com alanrogers.com/FR33420

La Canadienne is situated between Arcachon and Legé-Cap Ferret, just 7 km. from the beach and 1 km. from the centre of Arés, a pleasant little resort. There is direct access to 150 km. of cycle tracks. The campsite has 60 mobile homes for rent and 20 touring pitches, most with 15A electricity. Good shade is provided by tall oak trees. Swimming and paddling pools are centrally located, along with a shop, bar, restaurant and snack bar. In July and August dancing, musical and paella evenings are organised, together with children's clubs (3-10 yrs) and sports tournaments. Large units may have difficulty manoeuvring onto some pitches.

Facilities

Sanitary facilities are clean but in need of some updating (a new block has been added in 2010). Shop. Bar, restaurant, snack bar and takeaway (1/7-31/8). Swimming pool (1/6-15/9). Play area. Bicycle hire. TV room. Activity and entertainment programme. Mobile homes and equipped tents for rent. Solarium. Off site: Village centre 1 km. Riding 5 km. Fishing 7 km. Golf 15 km.

Open: 1 February - 29 November.

Directions

Leave the Bordeaux ring road at exit 10 (D213) and drive to Arès. Continue to the village centre and then follow signs for Lège and Cap Ferret. Site is on this road after a further 1 km. GPS: 44.77792, -1.1428

Charges guide

Per unit incl. 2 persons	€ 20,00 - € 34,00
extra person	€ 4,00 - € 6,00
child (2-7 yrs)	€ 3,00 - € 4,00

Audenge

Camping le Braou

Route de Bordeaux, F-33980 Audenge (Gironde) T: 05 56 26 90 03
E: info@camping-audenge.com alanrogers.com/FR33260

The present owners, M. and Mme. Gharbi, were the wardens of this simple, former municipal site and now lease it from the town. They have funded several developments since they took over in 2003 including a swimming pool, a snack bar, play area and new electrical hook-ups. The site is flat with easy access, and the large pitches are in avenues, separated by newly-planted small shrubs. There is little natural shade. The new electric hook-ups (on 116 of the 148 pitches) are 6A. Outside high season this is a pleasant, reasonably priced place to stay while exploring the Bassin d'Arcachon with its bird reserve, oyster-beds, way-marked walks and cycle tracks.

Facilities

The two toilet blocks have been recently refurbished and are very adequate. Washbasins are in cubicles, showers are controllable for temperature, pushbutton operated. Bar and snack bar (July/Aug). Swimming pool (1/4-31/8). Play area. Internet access. Motorcaravan service point and overnight pitches outside site. Mobile homes to rent. Off site: Town facilities 800 m. Beach and fishing 15 km. Riding 2 km. Golf 5 km.

Open: 1 April - 30 September.

Directions

From A63 take exit 22 onto A660 towards Arcachon. From A660 take exit 2 towards Facture, then D3 through Biganos to Audenge. Site is signed Camping Municipal at lights in town. GPS: 44.6841, -1.00433

Charges guide

Per unit incl. 2 persons and electricity	€ 22,00 - € 33,00
extra person	€ 3,00 - € 5,00
child (4-13 yrs)	€ 3,00 - € 4,50

For latest campsite news, availability and prices visit
alanrogers.com

Azur

Camping Village la Paillotte

66 route des Campings, F-40140 Azur (Landes) T: 05 58 48 12 12. E: info@paillotte.com

alanrogers.com/FR40040

La Paillotte, in the Landes area of southwest France, is a site with a character of its own. It lies beside the Soustons Lake only 1.5 km. from Azur village, with its own sandy beach. This is suitable for young children because the lake is shallow and slopes gradually. All 310 pitches at La Paillotte are mostly shady with shrubs and trees. The 132 pitches for touring vary in price according to size, position and whether they are serviced. La Paillotte is an unusual site with its own atmosphere which appeals to many regular clients. The campsite buildings (reception, shop, restaurant, even sanitary blocks) are all Tahitian in style. Circular in shape and constructed from local woods with the typical straw roof (and a layer of waterproof material underneath), some are now being replaced but still in character. For boating the site has a small private harbour where you can keep your own non-powered boat (of shallow draught).

Facilities

Well equipped toilet blocks. Washing machines and dryers. Motorcaravan services. Shop (1/6-1/9). Good restaurant with terrace overlooking lake, bar, takeaway (all 22/4-24/9). Swimming pool complex (22/4-24/9). Sports, games and organised activities. Miniclub. TV room, library. Fishing. Bicycle hire. Sailing, rowing boats and pedaloes for hire. Torches useful. Dogs are not accepted. Off site: Riding 5 km. Golf 10 km. Atlantic beaches 10 km.

Open: 24 April - 20 September.

Directions

Coming from the north along N10, turn west on D150 at Magescq. From south go via Soustons. In Azur turn left before church (site signed). GPS: 43.78696, -1.3093

Charges guide

Per unit incl. 2 persons and 10A electricity	€ 15,50 - € 38,00
incl. electricity and water	€ 17,50 - € 40,00
pitch by the lake with electricity	€ 20,00 - € 46,00
extra person (over 4 yrs)	€ 3,00 - € 7,50

Belvès

RCN le Moulin de la Pique

F-24170 Belvès (Dordogne) T: 05 53 29 01 15. E: info@rcn-lemoulindelapique.fr

alanrogers.com/FR24350

This high quality campsite set in the heart of the Dordogne has fine views looking up to the fortified town of Belvès. It is a splendid rural estate where there is plenty of space and a good mixture of trees and shrubs. Set in the grounds of a former mill, the superb traditional buildings date back to the 18th century. There are 200 level pitches with 154 for touring units, all with 6A electricity, a water point and drainage. The remainder are used for mobile homes to rent. The site is ideally suited for families with young and teenage children as there is so much to do, both on site and in the surrounding area.

Facilities

Three modern sanitary blocks include facilities for disabled visitors. Laundry. Shop, bar, restaurant, snack bar and takeaway (all open all season). Swimming pools (2 heated). Recreational lake. Playgrounds. Library. Fossil field. Sports field. Tennis. Minigolf. Boules. Satellite TV. Games room. Bicycle hire. Internet access. WiFi. Off site: Bars, restaurants and shops in the village of Belvès 2 km. Canoeing 2 km. Riding 5 km. Golf 7 km.

Open: 9 April - 1 October.

Directions

Site is 35 km. southwest of Sarlat on the D710, about 7 km. south of Siorac-en-Périgord. GPS: 44.76228, 1.01412

Charges guide

Per unit incl. 2 persons, electricity and water	€ 19,90 - € 43,90
extra person (over 3 yrs)	€ 2,50 - € 4,90
dog	€ 6,00

Camping Cheques accepted.

For latest campsite news, availability and prices visit

alanrogers.com

Belvès

Flower Camping les Nauves

Le Bos Rouge, F-24170 Belvès (Dordogne) T: 05 53 29 12 64. E: campinglesnauves@hotmail.com
alanrogers.com/FR24470

Les Nauves is a pretty and well maintained site, 4 km. from the beautiful medieval village of Belvès in the Périgord Noir region of the Dordogne. The site consists of 100 pitches, 60 for touring (on a slight slope, long leads necessary) and 40 dedicated to mobile homes, chalets and bungalow tents. There are some pitches that are separated and shaded by mature trees, while others are open with good views of the surrounding countryside. The ground on most of the pitches is soft, sandy soil and may cause some difficulty for large vehicles in wet weather. The owners are very dedicated to providing a quality site.

Facilities

The single sanitary block is clean and well maintained. Facilities for disabled visitors. Baby room (with adult shower). Laundry area with one washing machine. Good shop. Bar/restaurant with patio, and takeaway on request. Swimming pool and paddling pool. Good play area. Boules. Library (FR, NL). Games room. Riding. WiFi and internet access. Off site: Fishing 2 km. Small supermarket in Belves 4 km. Bicycle and mountain bike hire 4 km. Golf 10 km.

Open: 23 April - 24 September.

Directions

From Belvès take D53 southwest towards Monpazier. Site is 4 km. from Belvès on the left hand side. Follow signs and site is 800 m. off the main road. GPS: 44.75275, 0.98445

Charges guide

Per unit incl. 2 persons	
and electricity	€ 13,95 - € 24,50
extra person	€ 2,50 - € 4,90
child (2-7 yrs)	€ 2,00 - € 3,20
dog	free - € 3,00

Bidart

Camping le Pavillon Royal

Avenue du Prince de Galles, F-64210 Bidart (Pyrénées-Atlantiques) T: 05 59 23 00 54
E: info@pavillon-royal.com **alanrogers.com/FR64060**

Le Pavillon Royal has an excellent situation on raised ground overlooking the sea, with good views along the coast to the south and to the north coast of Spain beyond. There is a large heated swimming pool and sunbathing area in the centre of the site. The camping area is divided up into 303 marked, level pitches, many of a good size. About 50 are reserved for tents and are only accessible on foot. The remainder are connected by asphalt roads. All have electricity and most are fully serviced. Much of the campsite is in full sun, although the area for tents is shaded. Beneath the site – and only a very short walk down – stretches a wide sandy beach where the Atlantic rollers provide ideal conditions for surfing. A central, marked-out section of the beach is supervised by lifeguards (from mid June). There is also a section with rocks and pools. Reservation in high season is advisable.

Facilities

Good quality toilet blocks with baby baths and unit for disabled visitors. Washing facilities are closed at night except for two single night units. Washing machines and dryers. Motorcaravan services. Shop (including gas). Restaurant and takeaway (from 1/6). Bar (all season). Heated swimming and paddling pools. Playground. General room, TV room, games room, films. WiFi. Fishing. Surf school. Dogs are not accepted. Fitness room. Off site: Golf 500 m. Bicycle hire 2 km. Riding 3 km. Sailing 5 km.

Open: 14 May - 30 September.

Directions

From A63 exit 4, take the N10 south towards Bidart. At roundabout after the 'Intermarché' supermarket turn right (signed for Biarritz). After 600 m. turn left at site sign. GPS: 43.45458, -1.57649

Charges guide

Per unit incl. 2 persons, electricity	
and water	€ 30,00 - € 51,00
tent pitch incl. 1 or 2 persons	€ 24,00 - € 41,00
extra person (over 4 yrs)	€ 8,00 - € 11,00

Bidart

Castel Camping le Ruisseau des Pyrénées

Route d'Arbonne, F-64210 Bidart (Pyrénées-Atlantiques) T: 05 59 41 94 50. E: francoise.dumont3@wanadoo.fr

alanrogers.com/FR64070

This busy site, with a large play area filled with equipment is ideal for young families. It is about 2 km. from Bidart and 2.5 km. from a sandy beach. There are two swimming pools with slides on the main site and across the road, an indoor heated pool and new spa complex (charged in July/August) with outdoor fitness equipment. Pitches on the main campsite are individual, marked and of a good size, either on flat terraces or around the lake. The terrain is wooded so the great majority of them have some shade. Electrical connections are available throughout. The site has a number of steep slopes to negotiate.

Facilities

Two main blocks and some extra smaller units. Laundry facilities. Motorcaravan service point. Shop. Large self-service restaurant with takeaway and bar with terraces, and TV. Outdoor swimming pools, indoor pool and spa complex (all season). Sauna. Large play area. Two tennis courts (free outside July/Aug). Fitness track. TV and games rooms. Minigolf. Bicycle hire. Fishing. Internet access. Off site: Riding and golf 3 km.

Open: 22 May - 19 September.

Directions

Site is east of Bidart on a minor road towards Arbonne. From A63 autoroute take Biarritz exit (4), turn towards St Jean-de-Luz and Bidart on N10. After Intermarche turn left at roundabout and follow signs to site. GPS: 43.4367, -1.5677

Charges guide

Per unit incl. 2 persons and electricity	€ 19,00 - € 39,00
extra person	€ 5,00 - € 7,00

Bidart

Sunêlia Berrua

Rue Berrua, F-64210 Bidart (Pyrénées-Atlantiques) T: 05 59 54 96 66. E: contact@berrua.com

alanrogers.com/FR64140

Berrua is in a useful situation on the Basque coast, 10 km. from the Pyrenees, 20 km. from Spain and a five minute drive from Biarritz. Just 1 km. from the sea, it is an ideal location for visiting the beaches in southwest France. A neat and tidy site, it has 270 level pitches (120 for touring units) set amongst trees. Most have electricity (6A) and some are fully serviced. The focal point of the site is an excellent swimming pool complex with several pools, slides and paddling pools which is surrounded by sun beds for sunbathing. Organised activities and entertainment for both adults and children in high season, guided walks, dances, sporting competitions, bingo and karaoke. A member of the Sunêlia group.

Facilities

Toilet facilities are good (unisex) consisting of two blocks with washbasins in cabins, baby rooms, facilities for disabled visitors, washing machines and dishwashing sinks (cold water only). Motorcaravan services. Shop (July/Aug). Bar/restaurant and takeaway (15/4-15/9). New pool complex. Games room. Play area (3-10 yrs only). Bicycle hire. Archery. Boules. Off site: Fishing 1 km. Golf and riding 3 km. Beach 1 km.

Open: 6 April - 5 October.

Directions

From A63 exit 4, take N10 south towards Bidart. At roundabout after the 'Intermarché' supermarket, turn left. Bear right then take next right (site signed). GPS: 43.43822, -1.58237

Charges guide

Per unit incl. 2 persons	€ 16,10 - € 30,20
extra person	€ 3,20 - € 6,15
electricity (6A)	€ 2,90 - € 4,90

Camping Cheques accepted.

Bidart

Yelloh! Village Ilbarritz

Avenue de Biarritz, F-64210 Bidart (Pyrénées-Atlantiques) T: 04 66 73 97 39. E: info@yellohvillage-ilbarritz.com

alanrogers.com/FR64150

This is a very pleasant, reasonably priced site which will appeal greatly to couples and young families. Set on a fairly gentle hillside, the top level has reception and bar. Slightly lower are the paddling and swimming pools in a sunny location with sunbeds. Next comes the well stocked shop, tennis courts and the rest of the pitches. Some pitches are behind reception and others, lower down, some slightly sloping, are under trees and separated by hydrangea hedges. Some have electricity (10A, long leads required). There is a varied entertainment programme in July and August. The site is not suitable for American motorhomes.

Facilities

The two toilet blocks have some washbasins and showers together and facilities for disabled visitors. Laundry facilities. Motorcaravan services. Shop and bar open all season. Restaurant (1/6-10/9) and takeaway (1/7-31/8). Pool open all season. Games room. Table tennis. Tennis (charged in July/Aug). Play area (3-8 yrs). Bicycle hire. Off site: Lake 600 m. with fishing (no licence required). Golf 1 km. Riding 1 km. Beach with lifeguard 600 m.

Open: 8 May - 20 September.

Directions

Heading south on the A63 towards Spain, take exit J4 onto the N10 towards Bidart. At the roundabout straight after Intermarche turn right towards Biarritz. The site is on the right after 1 km. GPS: 43.4531, -1.5737

Charges guide

Per unit incl. 2 persons	€ 15,90 - € 24,50
extra person (over 2 yrs)	€ 3,30 - € 5,80
electricity	€ 3,30 - € 5,10

For latest campsite news, availability and prices visit

alanrogers.com

Biron

Camping le Moulinal

F-24540 Biron (Dordogne) T: 05 53 40 84 60. E: lemoulinal@franceloc.fr

alanrogers.com/FR24100

A rural, lakeside site in woodland, now owned and run by the FranceLoc company, Le Moulinal offers activities for everyone of all ages. Of the 300 grassy pitches, only around 72 are available for touring units and these are spread amongst the site's own mobile homes, chalets and a small number of Dutch tour operator tents. All pitches are flat, grassy and have 6A electricity, but vary considerably in size (75-100 sq.m). The five acre lake has a sandy beach and is suitable for boating (canoe hire available), swimming and fishing. Ambitious, well organised animation is run throughout the season including craft activities and a children's club.

Facilities

Toilet facilities, built to harmonise with the surroundings, include facilities for disabled visitors and babies. Laundry facilities. Motorcaravan services. Excellent restaurant. Bar. Snack bar/takeaway. Large, heated swimming pool with jacuzzi and paddling pool. Rustic play area. Children's club. Multisport court. Boules. Tennis. Archery. Roller skating. Mountain bike hire. Canoeing. Fishing and swimming in lake. WiFi. Evening entertainment (July/Aug). All facilities are open all season. Max. 1 dog.
Off site: Riding and climbing 5 km. Potholing 10 km. Shops and supermarket in Villeréal 12 km.

Open: 1 April - 16 September.

Directions

Site is 53 km. southeast of Bergerac. From D104 Villeréal - Monpazier road take the D53/D150 south. Just before Lacapelle Biron turn right onto D255 towards Dévillac, (site signed). Site is 1.5 km. on the left. GPS: 44.5998, 0.8708

Charges guide

Per unit incl. 2 persons and electricity	€ 19,00 - € 37,00
extra person	€ 5,00 - € 7,00

Biscarrosse

Campéole Navarrosse

Campéole

712 chemin de Navarrosse, F-40600 Biscarrosse (Landes) T: 05 58 09 84 32. E: navarrosse@campeole.com

alanrogers.com/FR40230

Navarrosse is a member of the Campéole group and is located on the very large Lac de Sanguinet, just 7 km. from the Atlantic beaches. The location of this atraditional campsite is attractive, with a long sandy beach and a small harbour (ideal for mooring small boats) on one side, and to the other, a small canal. Pitches are of a good size, mostly on fairly level, sandy soil with good shade. Most have 10A electricity. Many water-based activities take place on the lake, including sailing jet skiing and windsurfing. For cyclists there are many tracks to various places. Mobile homes, chalets and fully equipped tents are available for rent. Some units are specially adapted for disabled visitors. The lake, which is one of the largest in western Europe and the Dune de Pyla, Europe's highest sand dune is close by, as well as the Arcachon basin, the great city of Bordeaux and the world renowned Médoc vineyards.

Facilities

Two sanitary units are made up of separate blocks of toilets and showers. One modern block has all facilities under one roof including those for disabled visitors. Laundry facilities. Motorcaravan services. Bar, snack bar and takeaway (1/7-31/8). Tennis. Multisports pitch. Archery. Bicycle hire. Play area. Bouncy castle. Activity and entertainment programme (1/7-31/8). Tourist information. WiFi. Mobile homes, equipped tents and chalets for rent. Off site: Riding. Water sports. Biscarosse 3 km. Nearest beach 7 km. Golf, fishing 5 km.

Open: 22 April - 18 September.

Directions

From the north on the D652 turn right onto the D305. After about 1.5 km. turn right at campsite sign and towards lake. GPS: 44.43192, -1.16885

Charges guide

Per unit incl. 2 persons and electricity	€ 17,90 - € 31,70
extra person	€ 4,60 - € 8,90
child (2-6 yrs)	€ 2,50 - € 5,40
dog	€ 2,50 - € 3,50

Biscarrosse

Camping du Domaine de la Rive

Route de Bordeaux, F-40600 Biscarrosse (Landes) T: 05 58 78 12 33
E: info@camping-de-la-rive.fr   alanrogers.com/FR40100

Surrounded by pine woods, La Rive has a superb beach-side location on Lac de Sanguinet. It provides mostly level, numbered and clearly defined pitches of 100 sq.m. all with electricity connections (6A). The swimming pool complex is wonderful with pools linked by water channels and bridges. There is also a jacuzzi, paddling pool and two large swimming pools all surrounded by sunbathing areas and decorated with palm trees. An indoor pool is heated and open all season. There may be some aircraft noise from a nearby army base. This is a friendly site with a good mix of nationalities. The latest addition is a super children's aquapark with various games. The beach is excellent, shelving gently to provide safe bathing for all ages. There are windsurfers and small craft can be launched from the site's slipway.

Facilities

Five good clean toilet blocks have washbasins in cabins and mainly British style toilets. Facilities for disabled visitors. Baby baths. Motorcaravan service point. Shop with gas. Restaurant. Bar serving snacks and takeaway. Swimming pool complex (supervised July/Aug). Games room. Play area. Tennis. Bicycle hire. Boules. Archery. Fishing. Waterskiing. Watersports equipment hire. Tournaments (June-Aug). Skateboard park. Trampolines. Miniclub. No charcoal barbecues on pitches. Off site: Golf 8 km. Riding 5 km.

Open: 3 April - 5 September.

Directions

Take the D652 from Sanguinet to Biscarrosse and site is signed on the right in about 6 km. Turn right and follow tarmac road for 2 km.
GPS: 44.46052, -1.13065

Charges guide

Per unit incl. 2 persons	
and electricity	€ 21,50 - € 46,00
extra person	€ 3,60 - € 7,80
child (3-7 yrs)	€ 2,40 - € 6,30
dog	€ 2,10 - € 5,00

Camping Cheques accepted.

Biscarrosse-Plage

Campé●le

Campéole Plage Sud

230 rue des Bécasses, F-40600 Biscarrosse-Plage (Landes) T: 05 58 78 21 24. E: plage-sud@campeole.com
alanrogers.com/FR40420

Biscarosse Plage is a lively holiday resort with a fabulous beach. La Plage Sud is a member of the Campéole group and is located around 800 m. from the beach. This is a massive site with 911 touring pitches and a further 472 pitches occupied by mobile homes, chalets or fully equipped tents (available for rent). The site is lively in peak season with a varied programme of activities and entertainment (N.B. numbers are limited for some activities). On-site amenities include a swimming pool and paddling pool. Pitches are sandy and generally well shaded. Most are equipped with electricity. Surfing is very popular here but there are many other sports on offer. There are miles of cycle tracks through the forest (bicycle hire available on site). Alternatively, there is a multisports pitch on the site. The Marquèze ecomuseum is fascinating, tracing life in this heavily forested region over many years. To the north, the massive Dune de Pyla is recommended with fantastic views over the Arcachon basin and Landes forest.

Facilities

Bar/snack bar. Shop. Swimming pool. Paddling pool. Multisport terrain. Play area. Bicycle hire. Activity and entertainment programme. Tourist information. Mobile homes, chalets and tents for rent. Off site: Nearest beach 800 m. Surfing. Cycle and walking tracks. Dune de Pyla. Minigolf.

Open: 25 April - 20 September.

Directions

From the A63 motorway, take the A66 towards Bassin d'Arcachon, Dune du Pyla and Biscarrosse. Take the Biscarrosse exit and then D216 towards Sanguinet and Biscarrosse. In Biscarrosse, take the right turning off the second roundabout, towards la Plage. The campsite can be found before reaching Biscarrosse Plage. GPS: 44.4419, -1.2455

Charges 2011

Contact the site for details.

For latest campsite news, availability and prices visit
alanrogers.com

Domaine de la Rive

★★★★★ Village Club – Spa

Leisure pool - Slides - Jacuzzi - Rapid river - Massage jet.
1000 m² covered and heated aquatic park.
Chalets and mobile homes to rent - Attractively situated at the lakeside in the heart of the Les Landes forest.
Kids club - Animation.

NEW
2011
BAR - RESTAURANT
THEATRE

Les Landes, LE NATUREL

Route de Bordeaux - 40600 Biscarosse
Tél : + 33 5 58 78 12 33
Fax : + 33 5 58 78 12 92

www.larive.fr

info@larive.fr
www.campingaquitaine.com

Biscarrosse

Camping Mayotte Vacances

368 chemin des Roseaux, F-40600 Biscarrosse (Landes) T: 05 58 78 00 00

E: camping@mayottevacances.com **alanrogers.com/FR40240**

This appealing site is set amongst pine trees on the edge of Lac de Biscarrosse. Drive down a tree and flower lined avenue and proceed toward the lake to shady, good sized pitches which blend well with the many tidy mobile homes that share the area. Divided by hedges, all the pitches have 10A electricity and water taps. There may be some aircraft noise at times from a nearby army base. The pool complex is impressive, with various pools, slides, chutes, jacuzzi and sauna, all surrounded by paved sunbathing areas. The excellent lakeside beach provides safe bathing for all ages with plenty of watersports available. A comfortable restaurant and bar overlook the pool. A new, fully equipped gym is available free of charge. Children of all ages are catered for with organised clubs, play and sports areas and a games room. This well managed, clean and friendly site with helpful multilingual staff in reception should appeal to all and the facilities are open all season.

Facilities

Four good quality, clean toilet blocks (one open early season). Good facilities for visitors with disabilities. Unusual baby/toddler bathroom. Motorcaravan services. Laundry. Supermarket. Boutique. Comprehensive rental shop (July/Aug). Restaurant. Swimming pools (one heated; supervised July/Aug. and weekends). Play area. Further children's area (extra cost) with trampolines, inflatables and a small train. Bicycle hire. Fishing. Watersports. Organised activities and entertainment (July/Aug). Clubs for toddlers and teenagers (July/Aug). Charcoal barbecues not permitted. Hairdressers (seasonal). ATM. Internet access. Off site: Golf 4 km. Riding 100 m. Beach 10 km. Town 2 km. with restaurants, shops and bars.

Open: 30 April - 24 September.

Directions

From the north on D652 turn right on D333 (Chemin de Goubern). Pass through Goubern and Mayotte Village. Take next right (signed to site) into Chemin des Roseaux. GPS: 44.43495, -1.15505

Charges guide

Per unit incl. 2 persons	€ 17,00 - € 39,00
extra person	€ 3,50 - € 7,50
child (3-7 yrs)	free - € 3,50
dog	€ 3,00 - € 5,00

Just like a tropical island holiday

A 5th star for an exceptional campsite!

★★★★★
CAMPING VILLAGE

Mayotte Vacances
BISCARROSSE - FRANCE

This magical site in the heart of the Landes Forest, in an unspoiled setting on the banks of Lake Biscarrosse, not far from the Atlantic Ocean, has recently been awarded a 5th Star. Get ready for an unforgettable holiday: an endless choice of activities with a vast Water Park, sporting activities for all and memorable shows and concerts for the long summer evenings. And, of course, top quality accommodation with every comfort. Maybe this is what they mean by happiness?

368, chemin des Roseaux - 40600 Biscarrosse
Tél : 00 33(0)5 58 78 00 00 - Fax 00 33(0)5 58 78 83 91 · camping@mayottevacances.com · www.mayottevacances.com

Biscarrosse-Plage

Campéole le Vivier

Campé•le

681 rue du Tit, F-40600 Biscarrosse-Plage (Landes) T: 05 58 78 25 76. E: vivier@campeole.com

alanrogers.com/FR40430

Le Vivier is a member of the Campéole group and can be found 2 km. from the seaside resort of Biscarrosse-Plage. The nearest beach is 800 m. away and the crashing Atlantic breakers can be heard on site. Pitches are located amongst the towering pine trees and mostly have electrical connections. Mobile homes, chalets are available for rent (including specially adapted units for wheelchair users). Although close to the beach, there is a large swimming pool on site, and other sports amenities include volleyball, basketball and tennis. This is a lively site in high season with plenty going on, including discos and karaoke evenings, as well as sports tournaments. The Arcachon Basin and is easily accessible to the north, as well as the Dune de Pyla, Europe's highest sand dune and the Aqualand water theme park. Another popular day trip could be the great city of Bordeaux, accessible within an hour's drive. Closer to the site, there are miles of cycle trails through the forest and bikes can be hired on site. Riding is also popular – there are stables close to Biscarosse.

Facilities

Bar/snack bar. Takeaway food. Swimming pool. Tennis. Bicycle hire. Bouncy castle. Children's play area. Activities and entertainment programme. Tourist information. Mobile homes, chalets and equipped tents for rent. Off site: Nearest beach 800 m. Lake beach 5 km. Hiking and cycle tracks. Riding 8 km. Treetop adventure park 2 km. Golf 10 km

Open: 26 April - 21 September.

Directions

Head south from Arcachon on D218 passing the Dune de Pyla and continue to Biscarosse Plage. The site is well signed from here. GPS: 44.45804, -1.23968

Charges 2011

Contact the site for details.

Campé•le

CAMPSITES AND RENTALS

Le Vivier ★★★

Three star site with swimming pool at 800 meter of a sandy beach. Quality facilities, touring pitches and accomodations for rent.

AQUITAINE

40600 Biscarrosse-Plage - Tel.: +33-558-7825-76 - www.campeole.co.uk / vivier@campeole.com

Bordeaux

Camping Bordeaux Lac

Chemin de Bretous, boulevard Jacques Chaban Delmas, F-33000 Bordeaux Lac (Gironde) T: 05 57 87 70 60 E: contact@camping-bordeaux.com **alanrogers.com/FR33410**

Bordeaux is undeniably one of France's 'must see' cities and now it has a superior campsite. Adjacent to the exhibition centre and beside Bordeaux Lac, the site opened in 2009 and is open all year. The facilities and accommodation are of top quality. There are 119 touring pitches, some on well kept grass, others, primarily for motorcaravans, have hardstanding. All have electricity, 40 have water and drainage and 70 also have sewerage disposal. Within the 14 hectacre campsite there are also 93 well equipped chalets and mobile homes (3 specifically for disabled visitors) for rent. The site is arranged around five attractive, man-made lakes and set amongst tall trees.

Facilities

Modern, heated sanitary block. Laundry. Restaurant, bar and supermarket. Swimming pool. Play area. Mobile homes and chalets for rent. WiFi. Off site: Golf and fishing (Bordeaux Lac complex). Large shopping centre. Cycle and walking tracks. Bordeaux centre 5 km.

Open: All year.

Directions

At Bordeaux, take the A630 ring road and exit 4A. Follow signs for Parc des Expositions and signs for campsite. At roundabout take second exit (right) and site is 700 m. on the right. GPS: 44.89805, -0.58194

Charges guide

Per unit incl. 2 persons	
and electricity	€ 20,00 - € 29,00
extra person	€ 5,00 - € 8,00
child (5-12 yrs)	€ 3,00 - € 5,00
dog	€ 4,00 - € 6,00

For latest campsite news, availability and prices visit

alanrogers.com

Carsac-Aillac

Village Center Aqua Viva

Route Sarlat-Souillac, Carsac-Aillac, F-24200 Sarlat-la-Canéda (Dordogne) T: 08 25 00 20 30

E: contact@village-center.com alanrogers.com/FR24110

This shaded woodland site is ideally situated for visits to Rocamadour and Padirac, as well as exploring the Dordogne region, including the medieval town of Sarlat, only 7 km. away. The site is divided into two sections, separated by a small access road. The 179 pitches are flat, mainly on grass, divided by shrubs and they vary in size (80-150 sq.m). Many have shade from the numerous trees and all have electricity (6/10A). A wide range of organised activities, children's clubs and entertainments run throughout the season, making this site popular with families, especially those with pre-teen and younger teenage children. Mobile homes and chalets occupy 75 of the pitches and are available to rent.

Facilities

Each part of the site has a modern toilet block, with facilities for disabled visitors and babies. Bar, restaurant and takeaway with terrace. Good shop. Heated swimming pool (pool open all season, heated 1/6-13/9) plus children's pool. Small fishing lake. Minigolf. Half tennis. Good play park for under 7s. Floodlit boules pitch and multisport court. Bicycle hire. Off site: Aerial woodland assault course 500 m. Riding and golf 5 km.

Open: 3 April - 12 September.

Directions

Site is 6 km. from Sarlat south of the D704A road from Sarlat to Souillac. From Souillac, the access road to the site is just around a left hand bend, not easy to see. GPS: 44.8677581, 1.2794936

Charges guide

| Per unit incl. 2 persons and electricity | € 16,00 - € 29,00 |
| extra person | € 3,00 - € 5,00 |

Castelnaud-la-Chapelle

Camping Maisonneuve

Vallée du Céou, F-24250 Castelnaud-la-Chapelle (Dordogne) T: 05 53 29 51 29

E: contact@campingmaisonneuve.com alanrogers.com/FR24450

This family run site is beautifully situated in the Céou Valley, in the Perigord. There are 130 spacious touring pitches, all with 6/10A electricity. Some are well separated whilst others are on an open field. Most pitches have shade. The site's facilities are grouped around the old farmhouse. Swimming, diving, fishing and canoeing are all possible in the Céou river which borders the site and can be accessed directly. There are also swimming and paddling pools on site and in high season entertainment is organised several evenings each week. This is an excellent location from which to explore the beautiful region of the Périgord.

Facilities

Three sanitary blocks, one has been totally refurbished, are kept clean and tidy. Facilities for babies and disabled visitors. Laundry. Shop with bread. Snack bar. Bar. Swimming and paddling pools. Minigolf. Play areas. TV room. Games room. Dance evenings. Karaoke. Sport tournaments. Bicycle hire. Canoe trips. Tourist information. WiFi in rception and courtyard (free). Off site: Fishing 1 km. Riding 3 km. Golf 5 km. Canoeing. Walking and cycle routes.

Open: 28 March - 10 October.

Directions

From A20 take exit 55 on the D703 towards Sarlat and Beynac. Follow signs for D57 (Castelnaud la Chappelle). Site is well signed on edge of village. Caravans and large units over 5 m. are advised to continue on D57 for approximately 2 km. then turn left. Site is signed here at the junction with D50. GPS: 44.80367, 1.15533

Charges guide

| Per unit incl 2 persons and electricity (6A) | € 16,50 - € 23,70 |
| extra person | € 4,10 - € 5,90 |

Domme

Le Village de la Combe

Le Pradal, F-24250 Domme (Dordogne) T: 05 53 29 77 42. E: lacombe24@wanadoo.fr

alanrogers.com/FR24890

The pitches at this campsite are used exclusively for mobile home accommodation. For full details please see our PRL section starting on page 538.

For latest campsite news, availability and prices visit

alanrogers.com

Coux-et-Bigaroque

Camping les Valades

D703, F-24220 Coux-et-Bigaroque (Dordogne) T: 05 53 29 14 27. E: info@lesvalades.com

alanrogers.com/FR24420

Sometimes we come across small but beautifully kept campsites which seem to have been a well kept secret, and Les Valades certainly fits the bill. Set on a hillside overlooking countryside between the Dordogne and Vezère rivers, each pitch is surrounded by variety of flowers, shrubs and trees. There are 75 pitches are flat and grassy, mostly on terraces, all with 10A electricity and most with individual water and drainage as well. Ten very large pitches for weekly hire have their own sanitary unit, dishwashing, fridge and barbecue. At the bottom of the hill, away from the main area, is a swimming pool and a good sized lake for carp fishing, swimming or canoeing (free canoes). Rustic chalets for rent occupy 50 of the largest pitches. From the moment you arrive you can see that the owners, M. and Mme. Berger, take enormous pride in the appearance of their site and there is an abundance of well tended flowers and shrubs everywhere you look. A convivial and family atmosphere is very much in evidence and the site is therefore ideal for families with young children. Couples both young and mature will also enjoy this site.

Facilities

Two clean modern toilet blocks, one with family shower rooms. Facilities for disabled visitors. Washing machine. Main reception building houses a bar, restaurant (both July/Aug) and a terrace overlooking valley. Heated swimming pool, sun terrace, paddling pool (all season). Play area near the lake and pool. Off site: Small shop, bar, restaurant in Coux-et-Bigaroque 5 km. Supermarket at Le Bugue 10 km. Riding and bicycle hire 5 km. Golf 6 km.

Open: 1 April - 15 October.

Directions

Site is signed down a turning on west side of D703 Le Bugue - Siorac-en-Perigord road, about 3.5 km. north of village of Coux-et-Bigaroque. Turn off D703 and site is 1.5 km. along on right.
GPS: 44.86056, 0.96385

Charges 2011

Per unit incl. 2 persons and electricity	€ 25,00
extra person	€ 6,00
child (under 7 yrs)	€ 4,20
dog	€ 3,15
No credit cards.	

Les Valades ★★★ A quiet piece of nature in the Périgord Noir

Pitches and wooden chalets • Heated swimming pool • Fishing & Canoeing • Perfect for children
24220 - Coux et Bigaroque • www.lesvalades.com • +33 (0) 5.53.29.14.27

Daglan

Camping le Moulin de Paulhiac

F-24520 Daglan (Dordogne) T: 05 53 28 20 88. E: Francis.Armagnac@wanadoo.fr

alanrogers.com/FR24230

You will be guaranteed a friendly welcome from the Armagnac family, who are justifiably proud of their well-kept and attractive site, built in the grounds surrounding an old mill. The facilities have been continually updated and improved over the years. The 150 shady pitches (93 for touring) are separated by hedges and shrubs, all fully serviced. Many pitches are next to a small river that runs through the site and joins the River Ceou along the far edge. A tent field slopes gently down to the river, which is quite shallow and used for swimming. This site will appeal especially to families with younger children.

Facilities

Two clean toilet blocks provide modern facilities, including those for disabled visitors. Good shop, restaurant, takeaway. Main pool, heated and covered by a sliding roof in low season, children's pool, a further small pool and a toboggan and slide. Boules. Bicycle hire. Small river with beach. Fishing. Canoe trips organised on the Dordogne. Organised evening activities. Children's club in high season. Off site: Riding 5 km. Golf 10 km.

Open: 15 May - 15 September.

Directions

Site is 17 km. south of Sarlat and is on the east side of the D57, about 5 km. north of the village of Daglan. GPS: 44.76762, 1.17635

Charges guide

Per person	€ 7,15
child (0-10 yrs)	€ 2,70 - € 5,20
pitch	€ 9,90 - € 11,00
dog	€ 1,90
Special offers in low season.	

Dax

Camping les Chênes

Bois de Boulogne, F-40100 Dax (Landes) T: 05 58 90 05 53. E: camping-chenes@wanadoo.fr

alanrogers.com/FR40020

Les Chênes is a well established site, popular with the French themselves and situated on the edge of town amongst parkland (also near the river) and close to the spa for the thermal treatments. The 176 touring pitches are of two types, some large and traditional with hedges, 109 with electricity, water and drainage, and others more informal, set amongst tall pines with electricity if required. This is a reliable, well run site, with a little of something for everyone, but probably most popular for adults taking the 'treatments'. Dax is not a place that springs at once to mind as a holiday town but, as well as being a spa, it promotes a comprehensive programme of events and shows during the summer season.

Facilities

Two toilet blocks, one new and modern with heating, washbasins in cubicles, facilities for disabled visitors, babies and young children. The older block has been refurbished. Laundry facilities. Shop also providing takeaway food (3/4-30/10). Swimming and paddling pools (1/5-18/9). Play area. Field for ball games. Boules. Bicycle hire. Miniclub for children (July/Aug). Occasional special evenings for adults. Charcoal barbecues are not permitted. Off site: Restaurant opposite. Riding, fishing and golf all within 200 m. Beaches 28 km.

Open: 20 March - 6 November.

Directions

Site is west of town on south side of river, signed after main river bridge and at many junctions in town to Bois de Boulogne (1.5 km). In very wet weather the access road to the site may be flooded (but not the site). GPS: 43.71182, -1.07329

Charges guide

Per unit incl. 2 persons and electricity (5A)	€ 12,80 - € 17,20
incl. water and drainage	€ 16,60 - € 19,40
extra person	€ 6,00
child (2-10 yrs)	€ 4,00
animal	€ 1,50

Camping Les Chênes ★★★★

Hôtel de plein air
du Bois de Boulogne
4 0 1 0 0   D A X
Tel. 0033 558 90 05 53
Fax 0033 558 90 42 43

Devillac

Camping Fontaine du Roc

Dévillac, F-47210 Villeréal (Lot-et-Garonne) T: 05 53 36 08 16. E: fontaine.du.roc@wanadoo.fr

alanrogers.com/FR47070

Situated on the border between the lovely region of Perigord (Dordogne) and the Lot-et-Garonne, in the heart of the Pays des Bastides, is Camping Fontaine du Roc. It is a natural environment on a wooded hillside and quite isolated. The three acre site has panoramic views of the nearby Château Biron. Each medium sized pitch has access to electricity; some are in the sun and others in the shade to suit your needs. A long-established site now run by Dutch owners, the site blends well with the natural surroundings. The approach road is single track and narrow, and may cause difficulties for large units.

Facilities

One centally located sanitary block is kept spotlessly clean and includes good facilies for babies, children and disabled visitors. Washing machine. Small shop with daily deliveries of bread and milk. Bar and snack bar serving pizzas. Large swimming pool, children's pool, whirlpool. New wooden chalet with sauna, massage, whirlpool and bunkhouse. Two small play areas. Library with TV. Boules. Two purpose built stone barbecues (wood provided). Animation for children (high season). Internet access. Off site: Fishing 200 m. Riding 2 km. Golf 30 km. Town of Monflanquin 9 km. for supermarkets and local market. Château Biron 10 km.

Open: 28 March - 1 October.

Directions

From Monflanquin, take D272 heading north towards Monpazier. Fontaine du Roc is 10 km. along the road on the left hand side. GPS: 44.61405, 0.81885

Charges guide

Per unit incl. 2 persons and electricity	€ 18,50 - € 23,50
extra adult	€ 4,50 - € 5,50
child (under 6 yrs)	€ 3,00 - € 3,50
Less 10% outside 12/6-11/9.	
No credit cards.	

For latest campsite news, availability and prices visit

alanrogers.com

Domme

Camping le Bosquet

La Riviere, F-24250 Domme (Dordogne) T: 05 53 28 37 39. E: info@lebosquet.com

alanrogers.com/FR24760

Located between Sarlat and Bergerac, this great little campsite is set in lovely countryside and is beautifully landscaped with flowers and shrubs with trees to offer some shade. The site is maintained to a good standard and is kept very clean. The natural environment gives a sense of tranquillity and calm – here you can relax. M. and Mme. Vrand will do everything they can to ensure you have a great holiday. There are 60 level pitches with 10A electricity, with 40 for touring units. The remainder are used for mobile homes to rent. The Dordogne river is 300 metres away and the canoeing here is good and convenient. There are many attractions and places to visit in the area and none are very far away.

Facilities

The toilet block includes facilities for disabled visitors. Washing machine and iron. Restaurant. Takeaway. Small shop. Swimming pool. Library. Entertainment (July/Aug). Play area. Pétanque. Fishing. TV. WIFI free in reception area. Off site: Golf 2 km. Riding 4 km. Bicycle hire 1 km. Tennis 2 km. Canoeing 1 km.

Open: 1 April - 30 September.

Directions

Take the D46 from Sarlat to Vitrac. Cross the river bridge in Vitrac and the site is on the right hand side 1 km. further on. Well signed.
GPS: 44.82241, 1.225319

Charges guide

Per person	€ 3,00 - € 4,00
child (under 7 yrs)	€ 2,10 - € 2,20
pitch	€ 3,30 - € 3,80
electricity	€ 2,50
dog	free - € 2,00

Douville

Camping d'Orpheo Negro

Les trois Frères, (RN 21), F-24140 Douville (Dordogne) T: 05 53 82 96 58. E: camping@orpheonegro.com

alanrogers.com/FR24880

Orpheo Negro can be found mid-way between Perigueux and Bergerac. There are 100 grassy pitches in a park which extends over 13 hectares. Pitches are large and generally well-shaded. Most have electrical connections (6A). A number of chalets and mobile homes are available for rent. The site has been developed on the banks of a 3 hectare lake which is well stocked with carp, so this is a popular site with anglers. Rowing boats and pedaloes are available for rent too. Other amenities include a swimming pool (with water slide), tennis, an open-air bowling alley and minigolf. The nearest village is Vergt (8 km) and a good range of shops is on offer here, as well as a Friday market. Bergerac, Le Bugue and the region's capital Perigueux are all about 25 km. distant. There are some excellent walks in the area and the site's friendly owners will be pleased to recommend possible routes. The Polynesian themed bar/snack bar is the focal point of this site, and hosts evening entertainment in peak season.

Facilities

Bar/snack bar. Swimming pool. Water slide. Tennis. Minigolf. Open air bowling alley. Games room. Playground. Activity programme. Mobile homes to rent. Off site: Cycle and walking tracks. Vergt 8 km. Perigueux and Bergerac 25 km.

Open: All year.

Directions

The site is at Douville, north of Bergerac. From Bergerac, take the northbound N21 towards Perigueux and follow signs to Douville (D36). Then, follow signs to the site. GPS: 45.024654, 0.615967

Charges guide

Per unit incl. 2 persons and electricity	€ 17,00 - € 20,00
extra person (over 4 yrs)	€ 4,50 - € 5,50
dog	free

Duras

Le Cabri Holiday Village

Route de Savignac, F-47120 Duras (Lot-et-Garonne) T: 05 53 83 81 03. E: holidays@lecabri.eu.com

alanrogers.com/FR47110

This is a good quality site set in 14 acres of beautiful countryside, on the border of the Dordogne and the Lot-et-Garonne, between the two rivers of the same name. The views are superb. Le Cabri Holiday Village is an English owned and run, small holiday complex. The new owners, Peter and Eileen Marston who are keen caravanners themselves, have developed 24 new spacious pitches (generally 150 sq.m), all with electricity (4/16A) and water. The open, level pitches are all on hardstandings surrounded by grass and separated by shrubs. Access for large motorhomes causes no problems whatsoever as they were considered when the site was planned. Open all year round, the site has excellent facilities including a swimming pool, a fishing pond and other leisure facilities. Le Cabri also benefits from its own high quality restaurant which specialises in local cuisine. Open all year, it draws clientele from the local area as well as those staying on the site. Although situated in a very rural and peaceful area, the historic village of Duras is only a ten minute walk, with its good selection of shops, restaurants, bars and the famous fortified château standing guard at the head of the village square.

Facilities

Recently refurbished sanitary block is centrally located, heated in low season and includes three new private cabins. Separate cabin for disabled visitors. Laundry facilities. Shop selling basics including bread. Restaurant with occasional entertainment year round and internet access. Swimming pool. Large play area. Boules. Well stocked fishing pond. Off site: Riding 1 km. Golf (international course) 10 km. Tennis 1 km. Watersports 7 km. Canoeing 8 km. Aquatic park 45 minutes drive.

Open: All year.

Directions

In Duras, look for the D203 and follow signs for site. It is less than 1 km. away. GPS: 44.68296, 0.18615

Charges guide

Per person	€ 4,00 - € 5,00
child (under 11 yrs)	€ 2,00 - € 3,00
pitch	€ 5,00 - € 7,00
electricity (4/10A)	€ 3,00 - € 5,00

Le Cabri Holiday Village
Route de Savignac - 47120 Duras
Tel-fax: 0033 (0) 553 838 103
Mobile: 0033 (0) 685 449 711
E-mail: holidays@lecabri.eu.com - www.lecabri.eu.com

Groléjac-en-Perigord

Camping Caravaning les Granges

F-24250 Groléjac-en-Perigord (Dordogne) T: 05 53 28 11 15. E: contact@lesgranges-fr.com

alanrogers.com/FR24020

Situated only 500 metres from the village of Groléjac, Les Granges is a lively and well maintained campsite set on sloping ground in woodland. There are 188 pitches, of which 100 are available for touring units. The pitches are marked and numbered on level terraces, some shaded by mature trees and shrubs whilst others are sunny. You can choose your preference when checking in at reception. All pitches have electricity (6A) and water either on the pitch or close by. The site has a good sized swimming pool and a large shallow pool for children.

Facilities

The toilet blocks are of a very high standard with good facilities for disabled visitors. Bar/restaurant, snack bar and takeaway (16/5-11/9). No shop, but bread and milk can be ordered. Play area. Minigolf. Canoe and bicycle hire. New outdoor gym equipment. Paintball. Quad bikes. Climbing wall. Canoe trips. Entertainment, sporting tournaments and children's club all in high season. WiFi in the bar area (free). Off site: Shops in Groléjac 550 m. Golf and riding 6 km. Hypermarkets nearby.

Open: 24 April - 11 September.

Directions

In centre of village of Groléjac on main D704 road. Site signed through a gravel parking area on west side of road. Drive through this area and follow road around to T-junction. Turn right, under railway bridge, and immediately left (site signed). Site is just along this road on left. GPS: 44.81593, 1.29086

Charges guide

Per unit incl. 2 persons and electricity	€ 17,55 - € 27,85
extra person (over 5 yrs)	€ 5,50 - € 7,40

For latest campsite news, availability and prices visit

alanrogers.com

Labenne-Océan

Yelloh! Village le Sylvamar

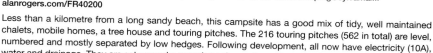

Avenue de l'Océan, F-40530 Labenne-Océan (Landes) T: 05 59 45 75 16. E: camping@sylvamar.fr
alanrogers.com/FR40200

Less than a kilometre from a long sandy beach, this campsite has a good mix of tidy, well maintained chalets, mobile homes, a tree house and touring pitches. The 216 touring pitches (562 in total) are level, numbered and mostly separated by low hedges. Following development, all now have electricity (10A), water and drainage. They are set around a superb pool complex with pools of various sizes (one heated, one not) with a large one for paddling, a wild water river, toboggans and slides. In a sunny setting, all are surrounded by ample sunbathing terraces and overlooked by the excellent bar/restaurant.

Facilities

Four modern toilet blocks have washbasins in cabins. Excellent facilities for babies and disabled visitors. Laundry. Fridge hire. Shop, bar/restaurant and takeaway (all season). Play area. Games room. Cinema, TV and video room. Fitness centre. Tennis. Football pitch. Bicycle hire. Library. Extensive entertainment programme for all ages. Internet access. No charcoal barbecues.
Off site: Beach 900 m. Fishing, riding 1 km. Golf 7 km.

Open: 1 April - 20 September.

Directions

Labenne is on the N10. In Labenne, head west on D126 signed Labenne-Océan and site is on right in 4 km. GPS: 43.59570, -1.45638

Charges guide

Per unit incl. 2 persons and electricity	€ 15,00 - € 43,00
extra person	€ 5,00 - € 8,00
child (3-7 yrs)	free - € 5,00
dog	€ 4,00

Lacanau-Lac

Camping le Tedey

Par le Moutchic, route de Longarisse, F-33680 Lacanau-Lac (Gironde) T: 05 56 03 00 15
E: camping@le-tedey.com alanrogers.com/FR33290

With direct access to a large lake and beach, this site enjoys a beautiful tranquil position set in an area of 14 hectares amidst mature pine trees. There are 700 pitches of which 670 are for touring units with just 30 mobile homes and chalets available for rent. The pitches are generally level and grassy although the site is on a slope. Dappled sunlight is available through the trees. Electricity is available to all pitches and 223 also have water and waste water drainage. The bar is close to the lake with a large indoor and outdoor seating area. The owners and staff are friendly and helpful and English is spoken. There is an open air cinema on Saturdays and Wednesdays as well as other entertainment in July and August. A children's club is also organised. The takeaway sells a variety of food and the shop next door is well stocked. This is an attractive well maintained site where you get a feeling of space and calm. There are many places of interest nearby and a short drive from Bordeaux.

Facilities

Four modern sanitary blocks with facilities for disabled visitors and babies. Laundry facilities. Bar with terrace. Crêperie. Takeaway. Bicycle hire. Boating on the lake. Pétanque. Playground. Gas barbecues only on pitches. Dogs are not accepted in July/Aug. Internet access.
Off site: Surfing. Riding. Golf. Cycling.

Open: 28 April - 19 September.

Directions

From Lacanau take the D6 to Lacanau-Océan. Take Route de Longarisse and camping is well signed. GPS: 44.98620, -1.13410

Charges 2011

Per unit incl. 2 persons and electricity	€ 20,50 - € 26,00

Le Tedey
CAMPING CARAVANING ★ ★ ★

ROUTE DE LONGARISSE
33680 LACANAU
TEL: 0033(0) 5 56 03 00 15
FAX: 0033(0) 5 56 03 01 90

LACANAU - COTE ATLANTIQUE

E-MAIL: CAMPING@LE-TEDEY.COM - INTERNET: WWW.LE-TEDEY.COM

For latest campsite news, availability and prices visit
alanrogers.com

Hourtin-Plage

Airotel Camping de la Côte d'Argent

F-33990 Hourtin-Plage (Gironde) T: 05 56 09 10 25. E: info@cca33.com

alanrogers.com/FR33110

Côte d'Argent is a large, well equipped site for leisurely family holidays. It makes an ideal base for walkers and cyclists with over 100 km. of cycle lanes in the area. Hourtin-Plage is a pleasant invigorating resort on the Atlantic coast and a popular location for watersports enthusiasts. The site's top attraction is its pool complex where wooden bridges connect the pools and islands and there are sunbathing and play areas plus an indoor heated pool. The site has 588 touring pitches (all with 10A electricity), not clearly defined, arranged under trees with some on soft sand. Entertainment takes place at the bar near the entrance (until 00.30). Spread over 20 hectares of undulating sand-based terrain and in the midst of a pine forest. The site is well organised and ideal for children.

Facilities

Very clean sanitary blocks include provision for disabled visitors. Washing machines. Motorcaravan service points. Large supermarket, restaurant, takeaway, pizzeria bar (all open 1/6-15/9). Four outdoor pools with slides and flumes (1/6-19/9). Indoor pool (all season). Fitness room. Massage (Institut de Beauté). Tennis. Play areas. Miniclub, organised entertainment in season. Bicycle hire. Internet. ATM. Charcoal barbecues are not permitted. Hotel (12 rooms). Off site: Path to the beach 300 m. Fishing and riding. Golf 30 km.

Open: 14 May - 18 September.

Directions

Turn off D101 Hourtin-Soulac road 3 km. north of Hourtin. Then join D101E signed Hourtin-Plage. Site is 300 m. from the beach. GPS: 45.22297, -1.16465

Charges guide

Per unit incl. 2 persons and electricity	€ 26,00 - € 48,00
extra person	€ 4,00 - € 8,00
child (3-9 yrs)	€ 3,00 - € 7,00
dog	€ 2,00 - € 6,00

Camping Cheques accepted.

La Roque Gageac

Camping Beau Rivage

Gaillardou, F-24250 La Roque Gageac (Dordogne) T: 05 53 28 32 05. E: camping.beau.rivage@wanadoo.fr

alanrogers.com/FR24800

Beau Rivage has an undeniably fine location, just 7 km. from Sarlat, close to La Roque Gageac, with its ancient, honey-coloured houses, sheer rock face and Dordogne river frontage. There are 290 pitches of which 242 are for touring units, the remainder used for mobile homes to rent. The pitches are level, well shaded and some are on the banks of the Dordogne. They are of a good size and 6A electricity is available. The site has a good range of amenities including a swimming pool, a restaurant, a well stocked shop and a bar overlooking the pool. Canoeing is understandably very popular in the Dordogne and there is direct access to the river from this site. Beau Rivage is popular with families and couples as it has something for everyone.

Facilities

Two toilet blocks include facilities for disabled visitors. Washing machines. Shop. Bar. Restaurant and takeaway. Swimming and paddling pools. Play area. Petanque. Tennis. Canoeing. WIFI in bar area. Electric barbecues are not permitted. Max. 2 dogs. Off site: Golf 3 km. Rding 5 km. Bicycle hire 2 km.

Open: 4 April - 10 September.

Directions

From Sarlat, take the D46 to Vitrac and then the D703 towards La Roque Gageac. Site is on the left, well signed. GPS: 44.81621, 1.21488

Charges guide

Per unit incl. 2 persons	€ 12,00 - € 22,00
extra person	€ 3,00 - € 4,00
electricity	€ 2,00 - € 4,00

For latest campsite news, availability and prices visit

alanrogers.com

A 3500 m² aquatic complex with slides and jacuzzis, covered and heated swimming pool

Club Airotel · Hourtin Plage

★★★★ Camping Caravaning

de la côte d'argent

www.cca33.com

Camping Special offer (except July and August)
14 = 11 and 7 = 6

Campsite La Cote d'Argent is a very attractive 20 acre park, situated in the heart of the pine forest and on only 300m distance from the Atlantic Ocean Beach.

This characteristic park is protected for the ocean wind by the dunes and the forest. The Village Club Cote d'Argent is the perfect destination for your calm holiday in nature.

FI - hotel - shops - restaurant bar - food - sportive animations - tennis archery - mini-club - games room - sailing (4 km) - surf (300m)

33990 Hourtin Plage
Tél : +33 (0)5.56.09.10.25   Fax : +33 (0)5.56.09.24.96
www.campingcotedargent.com   www.campingcoteouest.com
www.campingaquitaine.com

Lacanau-Océan

Yelloh! Village les Grands Pins

Plage Nord, F-33680 Lacanau-Océan (Gironde) T: 05 56 03 20 77. E: reception@lesgrandspins.com

alanrogers.com/FR33130

This Atlantic coast holiday site with direct access to a fine sandy beach, is on undulating terrain amongst tall pine trees. A large site with 576 pitches, there are 370 of varying sizes for touring units all with electricity (12A). One half of the site is a traffic free zone (except for arrival or departure day, caravans are placed on the pitch, with separate areas outside for parking). There is a good number of tent pitches, those in the centre of the site having some of the best views. This popular site has an excellent range of facilities available for the whole season.

Facilities

Four well equipped toilet blocks, one heated, including baby room and facilities for disabled visitors. Launderette. Motorcaravan services. Supermarket. Bar, restaurant and takeaway plus heated swimming pool complex (800 sq.m; lifeguard in July/Aug) with sunbathing surround and Jacuzzi (all season). Fitness activities (charged) and fitness suite. Games room. Tennis. Two playgrounds. Adventure playground. Bicycle hire. Organised activities. WiFi in the bar (on payment). Only gas barbecues are permitted. Off site: Fishing, golf, riding and bicycle hire 5 km.

Open: 16 April - 24 September.

Directions

From Bordeaux take N125/D6 west to Lacanau-Océan. At second roundabout, take second exit: Plage Nord, follow signs to 'campings'. Les Grand Pins signed to right at the far end of road.
GPS: 45.01107, -1.19337

Charges 2011

Per unit incl. 2 persons	
and electricity	€ 15,00 - € 47,00
extra person	€ 5,00 - € 9,00
child (3-12 yrs)	free - € 5,00

Laruns

Camping des Gaves

Quartier Pon, F-64440 Laruns (Pyrénées-Atlantiques) T: 05 59 05 32 37. E: campingdesgaves@wanadoo.fr

alanrogers.com/FR64040

Set in a secluded valley, Camping des Gaves is a clean, small and well managed site, open all year, with very friendly owners and staff. It is set high in Pyrennean walking country on one of the routes to Spain and is only 30 km. from the Spanish border. There are 99 pitches including 43 level grassed touring pitches of which 38 are fully serviced, numbered and separated (the remainder are used for seasonal units). Mature trees provide plenty of shade. The river runs alongside the site (well fenced) and fishing is possible. The busy little tourist town of Laruns is only a short walk.

Facilities

The very clean toilet block can be heated in cool weather. Washbasins for ladies in curtained cubicles and one shower in ladies' suitable for showering children. Laundry room. No shop but baker calls daily (July/Aug). Small bar with large screen TV, pool and video games (July/Aug). Larger bar with table tennis. Small play area. Boules. Fishing. Motorcaravan service point. Off site: Bicycle hire 500 m. Shops, restaurant and bars 1 km.

Open: All year.

Directions

Take N134 from Pau towards Olorons and branch left on D934 at Gan. Follow to Laruns and just after town, turn left following signs to site.
GPS: 42.98241, -0.41591

Charges guide

Per unit incl. 2 persons	
and electricity	€ 16,90 - € 24,40
extra person	€ 3,20 - € 4,80
child (4-10 yrs)	€ 2,10 - € 3,20

Le Bugue

Camping Caravaning la Linotte

F-24260 Le Bugue (Dordogne) T: 05 53 07 17 61. E: lalinotte@vagues-oceanes.com

alanrogers.com/FR24260

This is a really pleasant, good quality site which has plenty of space and fantastic views. It is located in the heart of the Perigord Noir and is conveniently placed to be able to visit many of the attractions in the area. The amenities are superb and include a heated swimming pool, a children's pool, a Jacuzzi and two toboggans. There are 120 pitches, of which 80 are for mobile homes and chalets (all to rent). They are on large pitches that offer a degree of privacy. There are also 40 pitches for touring uits. These are again of a good size, level and divided by shrubs and trees. Electricity is 5A.

Facilities

A smart sanitary unit provides a mix of British and Turkish style WCs, showers and washbasins in cubicles. Facilities for babies and disabled visitors. Dishwashing and laundry sinks. Bar/restaurant also providing takeaway and breakfast (1/7-30/8). Small shop with bread to order (1/7-30/8). Pool complex (15/5-15/9) main pool (unheated), water slides and splash pool, paddling pool (both heated), and jacuzzi. Small playground with trampolines. Boules. WiFi. Off site: Riding 8 km. Canoes.

Open: 4 April - 27 September.

Directions

From Le Bugue follow signs for Perigueux along the D710. On outskirts of Le Bugue turn right onto the D32E for Rouffignac and site. After about 1.5 km. turn right on to minor road for a further 1 km. to site entrance on right. GPS: 44.934117, 0.9371

Charges guide

Per unit incl. 2 persons	
and electricity	€ 19,00 - € 27,00

For latest campsite news, availability and prices visit

alanrogers.com

Le Bugue

Camping Brin d'Amour

Saint Cirq, F-24260 le Bugue (Dordogne) T: 05 53 07 23 73. E: campingbrindamour@orange.fr

alanrogers.com/FR24660

This attractive Dordogne site is situated in the Périgord Noir with wonderful views across the undulating hills and the Vezère valley. Here there is a feeling of tranquillity, spaciousness and calm. The owners offer a welcome and outstanding customer service. Of the 80 pitches, 60 are for touring units and the remaining 20 are for chalets and mobile homes which are all available to rent. All are level, easily accessible and mostly shaded. There is also a pond at the far end of the site. The main building is of fine traditional Périgordine quality and houses a very attractive restaurant and bar. This is a small site where you can relax in a family atmosphere. This is an ideal place from which you can explore the countryside by foot or by bicycle, take an excursion, visit the caves or canoe down the river. With a romantic history, the site's name translates as 'a piece of love'. Definitely a site not to be missed.

Facilities

Modern sanitary block with facilities for disabled visitors and two large rooms for mother and child, with shower, baby bath, washbasin and toilet. Washing machine. Shop (15/5-20/10). Bar (1/4-15/9). Restaurant and takeaway (1/6-15/9). Swimming and paddling pools (1/4-30/9, heated from 1/5). Tennis. Fishing. Pétanque. Play area. Children's club (July/Aug). Bicycle hire. Fridge hire. WiFi. Charcoal barbecues are not permitted. Max. 1 dog per pitch. Off site: Riding 2 km. Canoeing 5 km. Sailing, golf 10 km. Prehistoric Park. Caves.

Open: 1 April - 30 October.

Directions

Take D710 from Périgueux to Le Bugue and 500 m. after Le Bugue entry sign turn sharp left on D32e to St Cirq. Site is signed from here. GPS: 44.944837, 0.960145

Charges 2011

Per unit incl. 2 persons and electricity	€ 13,00 - € 22,50
extra person	€ 3,00 - € 6,00
child (1-10 yrs)	€ 2,50 - € 4,00
dog (max. 1)	€ 2,00

*Camping Brin d'Amour*** - 24260 Saint Cirq/Le Bugue*
Tél/Fax: 0033 553 07 23 73
campingbrindamour@orange.fr
www.brindamourcamping.com

Le Verdon-sur-Mer

Sunêlia la Pointe du Medoc

Route de la Pointe de Grave, F-33123 Le Verdon-sur-Mer (Gironde) T: 05 56 73 39 99
E: info@camping-lapointedumedoc.com **alanrogers.com/FR33210**

Situated roughly equidistant between a sandy Atlantic beach (accessed by a pleasant walk through the forest opposite the site) and the Gironde estuary, this site has 260 pitches. There are 112 for touring units with 10A electricity, 70 with water and drainage. Heavier units will need to use those pitches with plastic runners to ensure easy access on and off the sandy ground. The pitches are generally large and most are in full sun but some smaller ones towards the rear of the site offer much more shade. Out of season this is a quiet site, but in July and August it becomes busy with familes enjoying the excellent facilities.

Facilities

Good clean sanitary facilities. Shop (July/Aug). Bar, restaurant and takeaway. Outdoor swimming pool (heated) with water jets, jacuzzi and paddling pool. Indoor pool. Massage. Minigolf. Multisport terrain. Bicycle hire. Communal barbecues. Organised entertainment and children's club (4-11 yrs) all season. Small farm and children's garden. Activities for teenagers in July/Aug. Internet access and WiFi. Max. 1 dog. Off site: Sea fishing 1 km. Riding 5 km.

Open: 26 April - 12 September.

Directions

Site is on the N215 (D1215) just south of Le Verdon. Approaching Le Verdon it is important to follow the signs for Royan and Point de Medoc. Site is on the right. It is possible to take the ferry from Royan, but this can be expensive. GPS: 45.54540, -1.07950

Charges guide

Per unit incl. 2 persons and electricity	€ 18,00 - € 26,00
incl. water and drainage	€ 20,00 - € 30,00
extra person (over 4 yrs)	€ 3,00 - € 6,00
dog	€ 6,00

Léon

Yelloh! Village Punta Lago

Avenue du Lac, F-40550 Léon (Landes) T: 05 58 49 24 40. E: info@yellohvillage-punta-lago.com

alanrogers.com/FR40290

Five hundred metres from the charming village of Léon, this site offers above average size, level, grass pitches (some sandy). Most have electricity, water and drainage and they are separated by hedges. Shade is welcome from the tall oak trees. Whilst the pitches would be considered typical for the region, the buildings are a mix of old and new, the old being the sanitary block, in good order, clean and with all the usual facilities including a lovely new children's bathroom and facilities for disabled visitors. The new encompasses an indoor heated pool, a recreation room serving as a gym and a TV room.

Facilities

The single toilet block is old, but kept clean and well maintained. Facilities for children and disabled visitors. Laundry facilities. Large shop. Restaurant and takeaway. Bar. Heated indoor and outdoor pools. Bicycle hire. Play area. Fridge hire. Entertainment and activities (July/Aug). Barbecues are not permitted. Off site: Lake 300 m. with sailing, windsurfing, kayak, swimming and fishing. Léon 500 m. with market at every day (June/Sept). Beach 7 km. Golf 8 km. Riding 5 km.

Open: 20 March - 26 September.

Directions

From N10 take exit 12 towards Castets. Take D142 to Léon and at island take first exit to 'Centre Ville'. At T-junction turn left on D652 and after 300 m. turn left at sign for site and lake. After 500 m. site is on the left. GPS: 43.8842, -1.313

Charges guide

Per unit incl. 2 persons and electricity	€ 15,00 - € 40,00
extra person	€ 3,00 - € 6,00
child (3-7 yrs)	free - € 6,00
dog	€ 4,00

Léon

Gîtes et Soleil

1105 route du Puntaou, F-40550 Léon (Landes) T: 05 58 48 74 78. E: gitesetsoleil@orange.fr

alanrogers.com/FR40370

The pitches at this campsite are used exclusively for mobile home accommodation. For full details please see our PRL section starting on page 538.

Limeuil

Camping la Ferme de Perdigat

F-24510 Limeuil (Dordogne) T: 05 53 63 31 54. E: accueil@perdigat.com

alanrogers.com/FR24750

The delightful French owners, Michel and Noelle Paille, make this a happy place to stay and everyone we spoke to praised it highly. The site nestles beautifully in a very natural environment at the base of tree-lined hills which provide a wonderful scenic background. Flowers, bushes and trees give a superb sense of well being and much care and attention is given to the environment. A superb lake is 100 m. from the site where visitors staying at the farm may fish without charge. The river is also the same distance away in a different direction. There are only 49 touring pitches (all with electricity 10A), and 15 mobile homes to rent.

Facilities

The completely refurbished shower block is bright and airy. Laundry facilities. Motorcaravan services. Shop (1/5-15/9). Bar (1/5-30/9) and restaurant with terrace (newly refurbished, 1/5-15/9). Swimming and paddling pools. Games room. WiFi in the bar area. Play area. Private fishing lake and the Vezere river. Canoes and kayaks. Max. 2 dogs. Off site: Limeuil listed as one of the most beautiful villages in France. Supermarkets in Le Bugue 3 km. Riding 2 km. Golf 14 km.

Open: 1 March - 30 October.

Directions

From Le Bugue, take the D703 to La Borie and turn left to Limeuil. Campsite is well signed. GPS: 44.894765, 0.912509

Charges guide

Per unit incl. 2 persons and electricity	€ 12,00 - € 17,50
extra person	€ 3,00 - € 4,50
child (under 8 yrs)	€ 2,00 - € 3,00
dog	free - € 2,00

For latest campsite news, availability and prices visit

alanrogers.com

Messanges

Camping le Vieux Port

Plage Sud, F-40660 Messanges (Landes) T: 01 76 76 70 00. E: contact@levieuxport.com

alanrogers.com/FR40180

A well established destination appealing particularly to families with teenage children, this lively site has 1,546 pitches of mixed size, most with electricity (6A) and some fully serviced. The camping area is well shaded by pines and pitches are generally of a good size, attractively grouped around the toilet blocks. There are many tour operators here and well over a third of the site is taken up with mobile homes and another 400 pitches are used for tents. An enormous 7,000 sq.m. Aquatic Parc is now open. The heated pool complex is exceptional, boasting five outdoor pools, three large water slides plus waves and heated spa. There is also a heated indoor pool. The area to the north of Bayonne is heavily forested and a number of very large campsites are attractively located close to the superb Atlantic beaches. Le Vieux Port is probably the largest, and certainly one of the most impressive, of these. At the back of the site a path leads across the dunes to a good beach (400 m). A little train also trundles to the beach on a fairly regular basis in high season (small charge). All in all, this is a lively site with a great deal to offer an active family.

Facilities

Nine well appointed, recently renovated toilet blocks with facilities for disabled visitors. Motorcaravan services. Good supermarket and various smaller shops in high season. Several restaurants, takeaway and three bars (all open all season). Large pool complex (no Bermuda shorts; open all season) including new covered pool and Polynesian themed bar. Tennis. Multisport pitch. Minigolf. Bicycle hire. Riding centre. Organised activities in high season including frequent discos and karaoke evenings. Only communal barbecues are allowed. Off site: Fishing 1 km. Golf 8 km.

Open: 2 April - 25 September.

Directions

Leave RN10 at Magescq exit heading for Soustons. Pass through Soustons following signs for Vieux-Boucau. Bypass this town and site is clearly signed to the left at second roundabout.
GPS: 43.79778, -1.40111

Charges 2011

Per unit incl. 2 persons and electricity	€ 20,10 - € 57,00
extra person	€ 4,60 - € 8,60
child (under 13 yrs)	€ 3,60 - € 5,90
dog	€ 3,00 - € 5,50

Camping Cheques accepted.

Lit-et-Mixe

Village Center les Vignes

Route de la Plage du Cap de L'Homy, F-40170 Lit-et-Mixe (Landes) T: 05 58 42 85 60
E: contact@village-center.com **alanrogers.com/FR40160**

Village Center Les Vignes is a large holiday site close to the Atlantic coast with 450 pitches, of which 427 are occupied by a mix of mobile homes, bungalows and tents, most of which are for rent. The 15 touring pitches are relatively level on a sandy base, all serviced with electricity (10A) and water, some with waste water drains. The site's amenities, including a supermarket, restaurant and bar, are located at the entrance to the site. The rather stylish swimming pool complex includes a six lane water slide. A wide range of activities is provided and during July and August a great variety of entertainment options for both adults and children, some of which take place in the new entertainment 'Big Top'.

Facilities

Four modern sanitary units. Facilities for babies and disabled visitors. Washing machines and dryers. Large supermarket, restaurant, bar and takeaway (all 5/6-10/9). Swimming pool complex (all season), water complex (1/6-15/9). Tennis. Minigolf. Pétanque. Riding. Kids club and playground. Bicycle hire. Internet access and WiFi. Barrier closed 23.00-07.00 hrs. Off site: Golf course, canoeing, kayaking, surfing, riding. Many cycle tracks.

Open: 8 April - 2 October.

Directions

Lit-et-Mixe is on the D652 20 km. south of Mimizan. Turn west on D88 1 km. south of town towards Cap de l'Homy for 1.5 km. where site entrance is on left. GPS: 44.02292, -1.27978

Charges guide

Per unit incl. 2 persons, electricity and water	€ 14,00 - € 40,00
extra person	€ 3,00 - € 6,00

Mézos

Le Village Tropical Sen-Yan

Le Village Tropical, F-40170 Mézos (Landes) T: 05 58 42 60 05. E: reception@sen-yan.com
alanrogers.com/FR40110

This exotic family site is about 12 km. from the Atlantic coast in the Landes forest area, just outside the village. There are 140 touring pitches set around a similar number of mobile homes. Pitches are marked with hedges and have electricity (6A). The reception, bar and pool area is almost tropical with the luxuriant greenery of its banana trees, palm trees, tropical flowers and its straw sunshades. The covered, heated pool, new water slide, gym with sauna and jacuzzi all add to the attractiveness. A new covered animation area provides entertainment and discos during high season. An astonishing open swimming area (1/7-31/8), surrounded by white sand, with sun loungers, was added in 2010.

Facilities

Three well maintained and clean toilet blocks with good quality fittings and showers, washbasins in cabins and British style WCs. The newest block is especially suitable for low season visitors with a special section for babies, plus excellent facilities for disabled visitors. Shop (from 15/6). Bar, restaurant and snacks (1/7-31/8). Outdoor swimming pools (1/7-15/9). Heated indoor pool (1/5-15/9). Archery. Practise golf. Bicycle hire. No charcoal barbecues. Off site: Fishing 500 m. Riding 6 km. Beach 12 km.

Open: 1 May - 15 September.

Directions

From N10 take exit 14 (Onesse-Laharie), then D38 Bias/Mimizan road. After 13 km. turn south to Mézos from where site is signed. GPS: 44.07208, -1.15671

Charges guide

Per unit incl. 2 persons and electricity	€ 24,00 - € 38,00
extra person	€ 5,00 - € 7,00
dog	free - € 5,00
child (under 7 yrs)	free - € 6,00

For latest campsite news, availability and prices visit
alanrogers.com

Mimizan-Plage

Airotel Club Marina-Landes

Rue Marina, F-40200 Mimizan (Landes) T: 05 58 09 12 66. E: contact@clubmarina.com
alanrogers.com/FR40080

Well maintained and clean, with helpful staff, Club Marina-Landes would be a very good choice for a family holiday. Activities include discos, play groups for children, specially trained staff to entertain teenagers and concerts for more mature campers. There are numerous sports opportunities and a superb sandy beach nearby. A nightly curfew ensures that all have a good night's sleep. The site has 443 touring pitches (333 with 10A electricity) and 128 mobile homes and chalets for rent. The pitches are on firm grass, most with hedges and they are large (mostly 100 sq.m. or larger). If ever a campsite could be said to have two separate identities, then Club Marina-Landes is surely the one. In early and late season it is quiet, with the pace of life in low gear – come July and until 1 September, all the facilities are open and there is fun for all the family with the chance that family members will only meet together at meal times.

Facilities

Five toilet blocks (opened as required), well maintained with showers and many washbasins in cabins. Facilities for babies, children and disabled visitors. Laundry facilities. Motorcaravan services. Fridge hire. Shop (freshly baked bread) and bar (30/4-10/9). Restaurant, snack bar, pizzas and takeaway (1/5-10/9). Covered pool and outdoor pools (30/4-13/9). Minigolf. Tennis. Bicycle hire. Play area. Internet access. Entertainment and activities (high season). Gas or electric barbecues only.
Off site: Beach and fishing 500 m. Bus service 1 km. Riding 1 km. Golf 8 km. Mimizan 8 km.

Open: 30 April - 13 September.

Directions

Heading west from Mimizan centre, take the D626 passing Abbey Museum. Straight on at lights (crossing D87/D67). Next lights turn left. After 2 km. at T-junction turn left. Follow signs to site.
GPS: 44.20447, -1.29099

Charges guide

Per unit incl. 3 persons and electricity	€ 18,00 - € 49,00
extra person	€ 3,00 - € 8,00
child (3-13 yrs)	€ 3,00 - € 6,00
dog	€ 2,00 - € 5,00

For latest campsite news, availability and prices visit
alanrogers.com

Mimizan-Plage

Camping de la Plage

Boulevard de l'Atlantique, F-40200 Mimizan-Plage (Landes) T: 05 58 09 00 32
E: contact@mimizan-camping.com alanrogers.com/FR40380

This municipal site is located 800 m. from the Atlantic beach at Mimizan Plage. This is a large site with 787 pitches of which around 460 are available for touring units. The rest are occupied by mobile homes and chalets (available for rent; one adapted for campers with disabilities). Pitches are well shaded beneath pines and many are equipped with 10A electricity. A separate area (without electricity) is reserved for tents. Leisure amenities include a multisport terrain, two beach volley courts and a climbing wall. An entertainment and activity programme is organised in peak season, including a programme for children. The site operates to very strict environmental guidelines. Economy lighting, for example, is used throughout and a water economizer system is also in place. Guests of the site are required to wear a special bracelet which aids security and ensures access to all site amenities.

Facilities

Seven toilet blocks. Baby rooms and facilities for disabled visitors. Washing machine and drier. Shop (bread available). Bar/snack bar. Fridge hire. No swimming pool, but beach nearby. Motorcaravan service point. Games room. Boules. Multisport terrain. Climbing wall. Play area. WiFi (charged). Safe deposit boxes. Bicycle hire. Picnic tables. Security barrier. Small train passes entrance in high season. Off site: Watersports adjacent. Beach 800 m. Golf 4 km. Riding 5 km. Surfing. Fishing.

Open: 8 April - 26 September.

Directions

Approaching from the north, leave the N10 at Labouheyre and follow signs to Mimizan on D626. Drive though the town and follow signs for Mimizan Plage. Site is clearly signed and is to the north of the river. GPS: 44.216482, -1.285653

Charges guide

Per unit incl. 2 persons	
and electricity	€ 16,20 - € 21,50
extra person	€ 6,40 - € 8,50
child (3-12 yrs)	€ 4,20 - € 6,40

800 meters away from the ocean, Camping de la Plage greets you from April 8th till September 25th.

- Mobil homes and chalets for rent
- Pitches for tents and caravans
- A special area for campers
- Playground for children, activities in July and August, theme evenings, sport facilities, climbing wall.
- An air-conditionned grocer's, fastfood

Bld de l'Atlantique - 40200 MIMIZAN-PLAGE
Tél. (0)033 05 58 09 00 32
Fax (0)033 05 58 09 44 94
www.mimizan-camping.com

Moliets-Plage

529

Le Saint-Martin Camping

Avenue de l'Océan, F-40660 Moliets-Plage (Landes) T: 05 58 48 52 30. E: contact@camping-saint-martin.fr
alanrogers.com/FR40190

A family site aimed mainly at couples and young families, St-Martin is a welcome change from most of the sites in this area in that it has only a small number of chalets (85) compared to the number of touring pitches (575). First impressions are of a neat, tidy, well cared for site and the direct access to a fine sandy beach is an added bonus. The pitches are mainly typically French in style with low hedges separating them, and with some shade. Electricity hook ups are 10-15A and a number of pitches also have water and drainage. Entertainment in high season is low key (with the emphasis on quiet nights) – daytime competitions and a miniclub, plus the occasional evening entertainment, well away from the pitches and with no discos or karaoke. With chalets and mobile homes to rent, and an 18-hole golf course 700 m. away (special rates negotiated), this would be an ideal destination for a golfing weekend or longer stay.

Facilities

Seven toilet blocks of a high standard and very well maintained, have washbasins in cabins, large showers, baby rooms and facilities for disabled visitors. Motorcaravan service point. Washing machines and dryers. Fridge rental. Supermarket. Bars, restaurants and takeaways. Indoor pool, jacuzzi and sauna (charged July/Aug). Outdoor pool (15/6-15/9). Multisport pitch. Play area. Beach access. Internet access. Electric barbecues only. Off site: Bicycle hire 500 m. Golf and tennis 700 m.

Open: 19 March - 11 November.

Directions

From the N10 take D142 to Lèon, then D652 to Moliets-et-Mar. Follow signs to Moliets-Plage, site is well signed. GPS: 43.85242, -1.38732

Charges guide

Per unit incl. 2 persons	
and electricity	€ 22,00 - € 44,50
extra person	€ 6,00 - € 7,00
child (under 10 yrs)	€ 4,00 - € 5,00
Prices are for reserved pitches.	

Montignac

Camping le Paradis

Saint Léon-sur-Vézère, F-24290 Montignac (Dordogne) T: 05 53 50 72 64. E: le-paradis@perigord.com

alanrogers.com/FR24060

Le Paradis is a well maintained riverside site, halfway between Les Eyzies and Montignac. The site is very well kept and landscaped with a variety of mature shrubs and trees. The gardens are beautifully maintained which gives a wonderful sense of tranquillity. It is very easy to relax on this ecologically friendly, site. Systems of reed based filters enhance efficient natural drainage. This is a family run site and you are guaranteed a warm and friendly welcome. There are 200 good sized pitches, with 27 for mobile homes to rent. The pitches are level and with easy access, all with 10A electricity, water and drainage. There are some special pitches for motorcaravans. An excellent restaurant offers a good menu, reasonably priced and using fresh local produce where appropriate. The terraced area outside, makes for a convivial and family atmosphere. There are many sport and leisure activities. Direct access to the Vézère river is possible at one end of the site for canoeing and swimming. Organised games, competitions and evening events are aimed at maintaining a true French flavour. English is spoken. This is a site of real quality, which we thoroughly recommend.

Facilities

High quality, well equipped, heated toilet blocks are kept very clean. Well stocked shop (with gas). Good restaurant, takeaway. Good pool complex heated in low season, paddling pool. Play area. Tennis. BMX track. Multisport court. Canoe hire. Fishing. Bicycle hire. Quad bike and horse riding excursions. WiFi throughout. Large units accepted by arrangement. Mobile homes to rent (no smoking) including one for visitors with disabilities (no dogs permitted). Off site: Riding 3 km.

Open: 1 April - 19 October.

Directions

Site is 12 km. north of Les Eyzies and 3 km. south of St Léon-sur-Vézère, on the east side of the D706. GPS: 45.00207, 1.0711

Charges guide

Per unit incl. 2 persons and electricity	€ 21,60 - € 30,50
extra person	€ 5,40 - € 7,40
child (3-12 yrs)	€ 4,40 - € 6,40
dog	€ 2,00

Camping Le Paradis - 24290 St. Leon sur Vézère
tel.: 05 53 50 72 64 - fax: 05 53 50 75 90 - le-paradis@perigord.com - www.le-paradis.com

For latest campsite news, availability and prices visit

alanrogers.com

Monpazier

Village Center Moulin de David

Gaugeac, F-24540 Monpazier (Dordogne) T: 04 99 57 21 21. E: contact@village-center.com

alanrogers.com/FR24080

Village center

Set in a 14 hectare wooded valley, it has 160 pitches split into two sections, 102 are available for touring units – 33 below the central reception complex in a shaded situation, and 69 above on partly terraced ground with varying degrees of shade. All pitches have electricity (3-16A). Spacing is good and there is no crowding. The site has been planted with a variety of shrubs and trees and combined with the small stream that runs through the centre they create a beautiful and tranquil setting. Purchased in 2006 by Village Centre Group, this pleasant and attractive site is one for those who enjoy peace, away from the hustle and bustle of the main Dordogne attractions, yet sufficiently close to them to be accessible.

Facilities

Three good toilet blocks, including facilities for disabled visitors and babies. Laundry room. Good shop. Bar/restaurant with shaded patio, takeaway. Swimming pool and paddling pool, freshwater pool with waterslide. Play area. Boules. Half-court tennis. Trampoline. Library. Events, games and canoe trips. Barbecues for hire. Mobile homes for rent. Internet access and WiFi in reception area (charged). Off site: Small supermarket in Monpazier 2.5 km. Riding 3 km. Fishing 8 km.

Open: 30 April - 12 September.

Directions

From Monpazier take the D2 Villeréal road. Take third turning left (after about 2 km), signed to Moulin de David and Gaugeac Mairie. Site is about 500 m. along this road on the left. GPS: 44.65949, 0.87898

Charges guide

Per unit incl. 2 persons and electricity	€ 16,00 - € 24,00
extra person	€ 3,00 - € 4,00

Navarrenx

Camping Beau Rivage

Allée des Marronniers, F-64190 Navarrenx (Pyrénées-Atlantiques) T: 05 59 66 10 00. E: beaucamping@free.fr

alanrogers.com/FR64120

Cross the picturesque river and follow the old town walls to discover this well cared for family owned campsite (English). The site is tiered and the large, well maintained grass pitches are surrounded by mature hedges offering a peaceful and relaxed setting. The attention to well cared for detail is carried into the two sanitary blocks. Recent projects include a swimming pool, low key entertainment area (wine tasting, barbecues, etc), additional chalets, hardstandings and a baby room, adding to an already impressive campsite. Richard has now trained as a pizzaiolo and can now offer fresh pizzas.

Facilities

Two very clean sanitary blocks with good separate facilities for ladies and men include provision for disabled visitors. Laundry facilities in top block. Playground for small children has recently been renewed with improved bark finish. Play field. Max. 2 dogs. Off site: Shop at end of road. Town is five minutes walk for further shops, bars, restaurants, ATM and bicycle hire. Fishing 200 m. Riding 15 km.

Open: 25 March - 16 October.

Directions

From the north take D936 to Navarrenx. Turn left at first roundabout on D115 into Navarrenx. Turn left at T-junction, go over bridge and follow walls of town all the way around. At next island turn right on D947 and site is signed from here. GPS: 43.32001, -0.761

Charges guide

Per unit incl. 2 persons and electricity	€ 18,00 - € 24,00
extra person	€ 4,25 - € 5,25
child (0-7 yrs)	€ 2,00 - € 3,00
dog	€ 1,50

Parentis-en-Born

Camping l'Arbre d'Or

75 route du Lac, F-40160 Parentis-en-Born (Landes) T: 05 58 78 41 56. E: contact@arbre-dor.com

alanrogers.com/FR40350

L'Arbre d'Or is a friendly, family site on the outskirts of Parentis-en-Born. There are 200 pitches here, most offering electrical connections. Around 90 pitches are occupied by mobile homes and chalets. L'Arbre d'Or lies 400 m. from the large Lac de Parentis where many watersports are available. The nearest coastal beach is at Biscarosse Plage, 19 km. distant. The site boasts two swimming pools, one of which is covered in inclement weather, as well as a restaurant and an activity programme. Bicycle hire is available and there are hundreds of kilometres of cycle trails through the surrounding forest.

Facilities

Two well located toilet blocks are a good provision and are kept clean. Preset showers. Facilities for disabled visitors. Bar, restaurant and takeaway (15/5-15/9). Two heated swimming pools. Play area. Bicycle hire. Entertainment and activities in peak season. Games room. Mobile homes and chalets for rent. Off site: Shop 800 m. Golf and riding 9 km. Lac de Parentis 400 m.

Open: 1 April - 31 October.

Directions

From Bordeaux head south on the A63 and then the N10 as far as Liposthey. Then head west on the D43 to Parentis-en-Born. The site is well signed from here on the Route du Lac. GPS: 44.34622, -1.0929

Charges guide

Per unit incl. 2 persons and electricity	€ 17,20 - € 21,50

For latest campsite news, availability and prices visit

alanrogers.com

Pauillac

Camping Municipal les Gabarreys

Route de la Rivière, F-33250 Pauillac (Gironde) T: 05 56 59 10 03. E: camping.les.gabarreys@wanadoo.fr
alanrogers.com/FR33150

An attractive, small site with well tended flower beds, Les Gabarreys is surrounded by the vineyards of the Médoc region. An excellent site, it has 59 pitches, most with hardstanding for caravans or motorcaravans (so pegging out awnings could be a problem), some grass pitches for tents and six mobile homes, all with electric hook-ups (5/10A, some may require long leads). The 'Maison du Tourisme et du Vin' should be your first port of call. The surrounding area is well supplied with wine caves, and being fairly level you could perhaps cycle to some of them.

Facilities

Two immaculate toilet blocks provide open and cubicle washbasins and excellent facilities for disabled visitors. Motorcaravan services. General room with satellite TV, fridge-freezer and a small library. New play area. Minigolf (free) and volleyball. New spa and sauna. Off site: Fishing 1 km.

Open: 3 April - 9 October.

Directions

Pauillac lies NNW of Bordeaux. From Bordeaux take D1 to St Laurent, then D206 to Pauillac. At roundabout turn right to Pauillac Guais, then straight ahead at next roundabout and turn right before the Maison du Tourisme. GPS: 45.1852, -0.742397

Charges guide

Per unit incl. 2 persons and electricity	€ 17,00 - € 20,20

Petit Palais et Cornemps

Flower Camping le Pressoir

29 Queyrai, F-33570 Petit Palais et Cornemps (Gironde) T: 05 57 69 73 25
E: contact@campinglepressoir.com alanrogers.com/FR33090

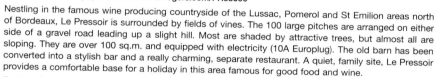

Nestling in the famous wine producing countryside of the Lussac, Pomerol and St Emilion areas north of Bordeaux, Le Pressoir is surrounded by fields of vines. The 100 large pitches are arranged on either side of a gravel road leading up a slight hill. Most are shaded by attractive trees, but almost all are sloping. They are over 100 sq.m. and equipped with electricity (10A Europlug). The old barn has been converted into a stylish bar and a really charming, separate restaurant. A quiet, family site, Le Pressoir provides a comfortable base for a holiday in this area famous for good food and wine.

Facilities

Fully equipped toilet block with excellent facilities for disabled visitors, and washing machine. Bar and pleasant restaurant with indoor and outdoor seating (open all year). Heated swimming pool (15/5-15/9, no Bermuda shorts). Playground with timber equipment. Pétanque. Mountain bike hire. Free WiFi. Mobile homes and bungalow tents to rent. Bicycle hire. No barbecues, but communal area provided. Off site: Tennis nearby. Fishing 1 km. Riding 5 km. Large aquatic centre 7 km. St Emilion 11 km.

Open: All year.

Directions

From A89 Bordeaux - Périgueux take exit 11 to Saint Médard de Guizières where you turn south towards Lussac on the D21 (site signed from Saint Médard). From Castillon-la-Bataille on D936 Libourne-Bergerac road, south of site, take D17 north towards St Médard then D21 through Petit Palais. Site signed. GPS: 44.9971, -0.06326

Charges guide

Per unit incl. 2 persons and electricity	€ 16,50 - € 28,00
extra person	€ 4,00 - € 7,50

Pyla-sur-Mer

Village Center la Forêt

Route de Biscarrosse, F-33115 Pyla-sur-Mer (Gironde) T: 04 99 57 21 21. E: resa@village-center.com
alanrogers.com/FR33280

Village Center la Forêt is one of a number of sites in this area that is dominated by the massive Dune du Pyla. The dune has to be negotiated in order to get to the beach (either over it or around, which is about 3 km), and the virtual wall of bright sand is all you have by way of a view to the east. This is a very well kept site with good facilities, easy access for all types of unit, and plenty of attractions. Set on a gentle slope, mixed pine and oak trees give shade on most pitches. There are 24 pitches on hardstanding for motorcaravans, and all of the remaining grass touring pitches have good access to water and electricity. A large area nearest to the dune has unserviced pitches for tents.

Facilities

Six unisex toilet blocks (not all open in low season) have good facilities. Facilities for disabled visitors (key from reception). Washing machines and dryers. Motorcaravan service area. Well stocked shop. Bar, takeaway and restaurant (1/5-30/9). Swimming and paddling pools. Two tennis courts (free except in July/Aug). Minigolf. Boules. Bicycle hire. Large play area. Children's club (with clowns) in July/Aug. Off site: Bus from outside site to Biscarrosse and on to Bordeaux. Golf, riding and sailing within 5 km.

Open: 8 April - 2 October.

Directions

From A63 (north or south) take A660 towards Arcachon. At La Teste turn off towards Dune du Pyla and at Dune car park roundabout take left turn towards Biscarrosse. Site is about 2 km. on the right. GPS: 44.5951, -1.1966

Charges 2011

Per unit incl. 2 persons	€ 16,00 - € 32,00

Pyla-sur-Mer

Yelloh! Village Panorama du Pyla

Grande Dune du Pyla, route de Biscarrosse, F-33260 Pyla-sur-Mer (Gironde) T: 04 66 73 97 39
E: info@yellohvillage-panorama.com alanrogers.com/FR33310

Many campsites set amongst pine trees have a rather untidy look, but Panorama is different. Here the entrance is inviting with well tended flower beds and a pleasant, airy reception. There is a steep climb up to the first of the touring pitches, passing the swimming pool and play area. Some pitches are suitable for caravans and motorcaravans and others suitable for tents. The touring pitches are on terraces amongst the tall pines and most have electricity (3-10A). The sea views from almost all pitches are stunning. Access to the toilet blocks may involve a steep climb (the site is probably not suitable for those with disabilities).

Facilities

Seven toilet blocks (only two open in low season) are clean and well maintained with baby rooms and facilities for disabled visitors. Fridge hire. Laundry facilities. Motorcaravan services. Restaurant with panoramic view of the ocean. Three heated swimming pools and jacuzzi. Adjacent play area. Tennis. Minigolf. Paragliding. Sub-aqua diving. Entertainment in high season. Library. Internet access in reception. Off site: Riding and golf 10 km.

Open: 18 April - 29 September.

Directions

From N250, just before La Teste, take D259 signed Biscarrosse and Dune du Pyla. At roundabout at end of road turn left (south) on D218 coast road signed Biscarrosse and Dune du Pyla. Site is 4 km. on right. GPS: 44.57265, -1.22053

Charges guide

Per unit incl. 2 persons and electricity	€ 17,00 - € 40,00
extra person	€ 4,00 - € 7,00

Rouffignac-Saint Cernin

Camping BleuSoleil

Domaine Touvent, F-24580 Rouffignac-Saint Cernin (Dordogne) T: 05 53 05 48 30
E: infos@camping-bleusoleil.com alanrogers.com/FR24380

Camping BleuSoleil is delightfully and quietly located in the countryside and has magnificent views from all areas of the site. It comprises 70 acres and, at present, has 110 pitches, 90 for touring and 20 used for wooden chalets. Electricity (10A) is now available on every pitch. Set in an open, woody, and hilly area, some of the pitches have partial shade from well sited trees and hedges. There is some terracing. You will receive a warm welcome at BleuSoleil from Jack and Tonny, the new Dutch owners, and a comfortable stay. The village of Rouffignac-St Cernin-de-Reilhac, is 1 km. away and is within walking distance. There you will find bars, restaurants and other amenities. The site is divided by a very quiet minor road. The wooden chalets on the site are available for rent from the owner. Noisy entertainment is actively discouraged and a peaceful and tranquil environment is promoted. A good sized supermarket is less than 5 km. The site is well placed for sightseeing and the famous caves of Lascaux, Font de Gaume, and the fossil depository are nearby. There is also the troglodyte village at La Madeleine.

Facilities

Three modern unisex sanitary blocks are clean, well maintained and adequate for the number of pitches. En-suite toilet for disabled visitors. Baby room with bath. Enclosed laundry area with two washing machines and dryer. Shop (1/6-31/8). Small bar with TV, and restaurant (1/5-30/9) Large 200 sq.m. swimming pool and paddling pool (1/5-15/9). New multisport area. Boules. Small play area and a pen with donkeys and goats. Off site: Supermarket in village 1 km. Fishing 2 km. Riding 4 km. Bicycle hire 15 km. Sunday market on Rouffignac.

Open: 1 April - 30 September.

Directions

From Périgueux take N89 east for 17 km. to Thenon, then D31 south signed Balou. Continue from Balou for 3 km. to the outskirts of Rouffignac-St Cernin-de-Reilhac and look for site sign on the left. Turn off main road to site (less than 1 km). GPS: 45.05497, 0.98691

Charges guide

Per unit incl. 2 persons and electricity (10A)	€ 14,50 - € 24,70
extra person	€ 3,00 - € 5,60
child (2-5 yrs)	€ 2,00 - € 3,80

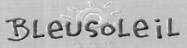

Rauzan

Camping Du Vieux Château

D123, F-33420 Rauzan (Gironde) T: 05 57 84 15 38. E: contact@camping-levieuxchateau.com

alanrogers.com/FR33440

Camping du Vieux Château is located in the heart of the Bordeaux vineyards and adjacent to the fortress town of Rauzan. It was taken over by the present owners in 2010 and is an ideal starting point for walking and cycling along small tracks through the vineyards, and for day trips. The flat, grassy site has 78 well shaded pitches, many with views of the château. 50 pitches are for touring (25 with 6/10A electricity); some are rather uneven and require long leads. Eight mobile homes are available to rent. Families with young children should be aware of the unfenced water ditch on the northern edge of the site.

Facilities

The sanitary block is kept clean and offers some washbasins and preset showers in cubicles. Facilities for babies and disabled visitors. Laundry facilities. Small shop. Bar, snack bar and takeaway. Outdoor swimming pool and children's pool (unheated). Play area and mini farm. Outdoor sports area. Boules. Bicycle hire. Electric barbecues to hire. WiFi (free). Off site: Rauzan 200 m. Tennis 2 km. Riding 5 km. Beach and fishing 6 km.

Open: 1 April - 31 October.

Directions

From Libourne, join D670 in the direction of St Emilion and Castillon-la-Bataille. At St Laurent-des-Combes turn right towards Sauveterre-de-Guyenne. At sign for Rauzan turn right onto D231. Campsite is signed from the village. GPS: 44.782472, -0.127139

Charges guide

Per unit incl. 2 persons and electricity	€ 12,00 - € 19,00
extra person	€ 3,25 - € 5,00

Saint Amand-de-Coly

Yelloh! Village Lascaux Vacances

F-24290 Saint Amand-de-Coly (Dordogne) T: 04 66 73 97 39. E: info@yellohvillage-lascaux-vacances.com

alanrogers.com/FR24690

Situated on a wooded hillside in the heart of the Périgord Noir, this site, has undergone total renovation and redevelopment. It is owned by Monsieur Cedric Rocher (also the owner of the very popular Panorama de Pyla) and managed by Phillipe and Jocelyne who are committed to ensuring that your stay is a memorable one. The swimming pool complex is impressive and incorporates a spa bath, and a terraced lounging area. The nearby village of St Armand-de-Coly is listed as one of the most beautiful in France and is a must to visit. There are 150 pitches, 40 are available for touring (20 can access the electricity supply), the remainder are occupied by chalets, mobile homes and tent bungalows, some of which are for hire. Some of the touring pitches are at the bottom of the slope and access to the bar, restaurant, pool and other facilities may be difficult. Various activities are organised in high season, including canoe trips on the Dordogne and Vézère rivers - transport to these events calls at the site. Although the area is lit, a torch might be helpful in avoiding any trips on stray tree roots. Lascaux is an essential visit and the stunning mediaeval town of Sarlat is just 20 km. away.

Facilities

The two main toilet blocks were brightly decorated and spotlessly clean when we visited. There is adequate provision, but may be stretched in high season. One block has a baby room, the other has disabled facilities. Laundry and dishwashing area. Fridge hire. Shop. Bar. Restaurant. Takeaway food. Swimming pools with spa bath. Activities and entertainment. Play area. Bicycle hire. Riding. Small library. WiFi around bar. Off site: Fishing. Walking and cycle tracks. Lascaux caves 2 km. Sarlat 20 km.

Open: 16 April - 20 September.

Directions

Leave the A89 (Bordeaux - Clermont Ferrand) at exit 17 (Peyrignac) and head south on the D6089 as far as Le Lardin - Saint Lazare. Here, join the southbound D62 to Coly and then follow signs to Saint Amand-de-Coly. Site is well signed from here. GPS: 45.05494, 1.24656

Charges guide

Per unit incl. 2 persons and electricity	€ 15,00 - € 30,00
extra person	€ 5,00 - € 6,00

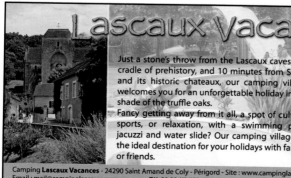

For latest campsite news, availability and prices visit

alanrogers.com

Saint Antoine-de-Breuilh

Flower Camping la Rivière Fleurie

180 rue Théophile Cart, F-24230 Saint Antoine-de-Breuilh (Dordogne) T: 05 53 24 82 80
E: info@la-riviere-fleurie.com alanrogers.com/FR24300

This quiet and pleasant campsite is close to the vineyards of Pomerol and St Emilion, and not far from the extensive shopping of St Foy la Grande and Bergerac. The 66 pitches are all spacious, divided by shrubs and maturing trees are beginning to provide shade. All pitches have electricity (4/10A). There are no tour operators, but 16 pitches are used for mobile homes to rent and there are studio apartments to let throughout the year. The site has a tranquil and peaceful ambience, suitable for anyone looking for a quiet and relaxing holiday. You will receive a warm and friendly welcome and there is a convivial, family atmosphere.

Facilities	Directions
Sanitary facilities are plentiful and modern including an excellent new block. Bar and terrace restaurant. Heated swimming pool (100 sq.m) and toddlers' pool. TV room. Weekly soirées where the owners host an evening of French food and entertainment. Canoe trips arranged. WiFi (free). Off site: Tennis court adjacent. Fishing 100 m. Riding 4 km. Bicycle hire 8 km. Golf 10 km. Supermarket 5 km.	Site is in St Aulaye, 3 km. south of D936 Bordeaux - Bergerac road. 6 km. east of Lamothe-Montravel turn south on local roads and follow signs to site 150 m. from river. GPS: 44.82905, 0.12238

Open: 1 April - 30 September.

Charges 2011

Per unit incl. 2 persons and electricity	€ 19,90 - € 25,90
extra person	€ 4,50 - € 5,90

Camping Cheques accepted.

Saint Astier

Flower Camping le Pontet

Route D41, F-24110 Saint Astier (Dordogne) T: 05 53 54 14 22
E: camping.lepontet@flowercampings.com alanrogers.com/FR24900

Le Pontet is a good choice for anglers, located on the banks of the pretty River Isle. Trout, carp, black bass and pike are all regularly caught here. The river is also popular for swimming and canoeing (canoe hire on site), but the site has its own pool too. On-site services include a bar/snack bar and a small shop. Pitches are grassy and of a good size. Most are equipped with electricity (6A). Since the opening of the A89 motorway (Bordeaux-Clermont Ferrand) access to this formerly remote region has become more straightforward and enables the site to be used as a good base for exploring.

Facilities	Directions
Bar/snack bar. Small shop. Swimming pool. Paddling pool. Minigolf. Games room. TV room. Direct river access. Off site: Cycle and walking tracks in the surrounding country. Supermarket. Perigueux.	Approaching from the north, take N21 towards Périgueux and the follow D6089 to Saint-Astier, and follow local directions to the site. GPS: 45.147353, 0.533121

Open: 1 April - 30 September.

Charges guide

Per unit incl. 2 persons and electricity	€ 11,50 - € 14,55
extra person	€ 3,00 - € 4,00
child (2-7 yrs)	€ 1,50 - € 2,00

Saint Avit-de-Vialard

Castel Camping Caravaning Saint Avit Loisirs

Le Bugue, F-24260 Saint Avit-de-Vialard (Dordogne) T: 05 53 02 64 00. E: contact@saint-avit-loisirs.com
alanrogers.com/FR24180

Although Saint Avit Loisirs is set in the middle of rolling countryside, far from the hustle and bustle of the main tourist areas of the Dordogne the facilities are first class, providing virtually everything you could possibly want without the need to leave the site. This makes it ideal for families with children of all ages. The site is in two sections. One part is dedicated to chalets and mobile homes, which are available to rent, whilst the main section of the site contains 199 flat and mainly grassy, good sized pitches, 99 for touring, with electricity (6A), arranged in cul-de-sacs off a main access road.

Facilities	Directions
Three modern unisex toilet blocks provide high quality facilities, but could become overstretched in high season. Shop, bar, restaurant, cafeteria. Outdoor swimming pool, children's pool, water slide, crazy river, heated indoor pool with jacuzzi, fitness room. Soundproofed disco. Minigolf. Boules. BMX track. Tennis. Quad bikes. Play area. Bicycle hire. Canoe trips and other sporting activities organised. Good walks and cycle routes. Off site: Boulangerie, supermarket, Tuesday market, Birdland at Le Bugue 6 km. Sarlat 20 km. Canoeing, golf, riding, fishing nearby.	Site is 6 km. north of Le Bugue. From D710 Le Bugue - Périgueux road, turn west on narrow and bumpy C201 towards St Avit-de-Vialard. Follow road through St Avit, bearing right and site is 1.5 km. GPS: 44.95161, 0.85042

Open: 30 March - 18 September.

Charges guide

Per unit incl. 2 persons and electricity	€ 19,50 - € 40,40
extra person	€ 4,00 - € 10,20
child (under 4 yrs)	free

Saint Crépin-Carlucet
Camping les Peneyrals

Le Poujol, F-24590 Saint Crépin-Carlucet (Dordogne) T: 05 53 28 85 71. E: infos@peneyrals.com

alanrogers.com/FR24320

Within easy reach of all the attractions of the Périgord region, M. and Mme. Havel have created an attractive and friendly family campsite at Les Peneyrals. There are 250 pitches, 111 of which are for touring. The pitches at the bottom of the hill tend to be quieter as they are further from the main facilities, but are all level and grassy (some on terraces), with electricity (5/10A), and most have some shade. An attractive bar and restaurant with terrace overlook the excellent pool complex and at the bottom of the site is a small fishing lake. The site is set on a wooded hillside, with flowers in abundance (thanks to the dedication of Mme. Havel's mother). Activities are organised over a long season, including archery, various sports tournaments, aquagym, discos and a children's club. On-site entertainment is provided in and around the bar and terrace area every night except Saturdays. The site is used fairly unobtrusively by a UK tour operator (76 pitches) with mobile homes and pre-erected tents. Flights from London arrive at a new airport some 30 km. away which may prove to be popular with visitors using the rented accommodation. Sarlat la Caneda is just 11 km. away with its many attractions and shops, restaurants and supermarkets. For those wishing to venture further afield there are endless opportunities and the site reception carries a comprehensive supply of information.

Facilities

Two modern, unisex toilet blocks provide good quality facilities, including provision for babies and disabled visitors. Motorcaravan services. Good value shop, excellent restaurant and takeaway (whole season). Pool complex with two large pools (one heated), paddling pool and four slides with splash pool. Indoor heated pool. Bicycle hire. Minigolf. Tennis (charged). Badminton. Play area. Games room, WiFi (charged), TV room and small library. Fishing. Off site: Supermarkets, banks, etc. in Sarlat 11 km. Châteaux of the Dordogne. Prehistoric caves of the Vezere.

Open: 12 May - 14 September.

Directions

Site is 11 km. north of Sarlat. From D704 Sarlat - Montignac road turn east on D60 towards Salignac-Eyvigues. After 4 km. turn south on D56 towards St Crépin-Carlucet. Site is about 500 m. along this road on the right. GPS: 44.95776, 1.2729

Charges guide

Per unit incl. 2 persons and electricity	€ 19,40 - € 33,10
extra person	€ 4,90 - € 8,40
child (under 7 yrs)	free - € 6,50
dog	€ 1,60 - € 2,40

Saint Cybranet
Camping Bel Ombrage
F-24250 Saint Cybranet (Dordogne) T: 05 53 28 34 14. E: belombrage@wanadoo.fr

alanrogers.com/FR24140

Bel Ombrage is a quiet, well maintained site located in a pretty location by the little River Céou, with a pebble beach that is safe and clean for bathing. The site has a good pool complex, but otherwise there are few on site facilities. The 180 well shaded, good sized and flat grass pitches are marked by trees and bushes and all with electricity. The quiet and tranquil setting makes the site particularly popular with couples. Bel Ombrage is very close to Domme and Castelnaud and would make an ideal and inexpensive base for visiting the southern Dordogne area. It is a short walk to the village of St Cybranet, with bar, restaurant and a small well stocked supermarket, and a short drive takes you to the beautifully restored village of Daglan.

Facilities

Two modern toilet blocks are kept spotlessly clean, with facilities for disabled visitors and babies. Laundry facilities. Bread van. Large swimming pool with sun terrace, children's pool. Paddling pool. Play area. Games room. Fishing. Excursions can be booked at reception. WiFi. Off site: Pizzeria next door. Tennis and canoeing close. Riding and bicycle hire 3 km. Golf 6 km. More shops at Cénac.

Open: 1 June - 5 September.

Directions

Site is about 14 km. south of Sarlat, on the east side of the D57 Castelnaud-la-Chapelle - St Cybranet road, about 1 km. north of the junction with the D50. GPS: 44.79128, 1.16214

Charges guide

Per unit incl. 2 persons and electricity	€ 21,80
extra person	€ 5,40
child (under 7 yrs)	€ 3,40
dog	free

No credit cards.

Bel Ombrage camping-caravaning

24250 St. Cybranet • Tel: 0033 (0)553 28 34 14 • Fax: 0033 (0)553 59 64 64
E-mail: belombrage@wanadoo.fr • www.belombrage.com

Saint Emilion
Yelloh! Village Saint Emilion
Route de Montagne, D122, F-33330 Saint Emilion (Gironde) T: 05 57 24 75 80. E: barbanne@wanadoo.fr

alanrogers.com/FR33080

La Barbanne is a pleasant site in the heart of the Bordeaux wine region, only 2.5 km. from the famous town of St Emilion. It became part of the Yelloh! group in 2010. With 160 pitches, most for touring, the owners have created a carefully maintained, well equipped site. The large, level and grassy pitches have dividing hedges and electricity (long leads necessary). The original parts of the site bordering the lake have mature trees, good shade and pleasant surroundings, whilst in the newer area the trees have yet to provide full shade and it can be hot in summer. Twelve pitches for motorcaravans are on tarmac surrounded by grass. La Barbanne has an attractive entrance and reception area with ample space for parking or turning. The site owners run a free minibus service twice a day to St Emilion and also organise excursions in July and August to local places of interest, including Bordeaux. The lake provides superb free fishing, pedaloes, canoes and lakeside walks.

Facilities

Two modern, fully equipped toilet blocks include facilities for children and for disabled visitors. Motorcaravan services. Well stocked shop. Bar, terrace, takeaway, restaurant (1/7-20/9). Breakfast service. Two swimming pools, one heated with water slide (16/6-26/9). Enclosed play area. Children's club (from 1/7). Tennis. Boules. Volleyball. Minigolf. Bicycle hire. Dog shower. Evening entertainment (from 1/7). WiFi (charged). Max. 1 dog. Off site: St Emilion and shops 2.5 km. Riding 8 km.

Open: 16 June - 26 September.

Directions

Site is 2.5 km. north of St Emilion. Caravans and motorhomes are forbidden in the village of St Emilion and they must approach the site from Libourne on D243 or from Castillon leave D936 and take D130/D243. GPS: 44.91679, -0.14148

Charges guide

Per unit incl. 2 persons and electricity	€ 22,00 - € 35,00
extra person	€ 6,50 - € 9,00
child (under 10 yrs)	€ 3,00 - € 8,00

For latest campsite news, availability and prices visit

alanrogers.com

Saint Geniès-en-Périgord

Camping Caravaning la Bouquerie

F-24590 Saint Geniès-en-Périgord (Dordogne) T: 05 53 28 98 22. E: labouquerie@wanadoo.fr

alanrogers.com/FR24310

La Bouquerie is situated within easy reach of the main road network in the Dordogne, but without any associated traffic noise. The main complex is based around some beautifully restored traditional Périgordin buildings. It includes a shop and a bar and restaurant overlooking the pool complex, with a large outdoor terrace for fine weather. The excellent restaurant menu is varied and reasonably priced. Of the 180 pitches, 91 are used for touring units and these are of varying size (80-120 sq.m), flat and grassy, some with shade, and all with electrical connections (10A). The rest of the pitches are taken up by site owned mobile homes and a UK tour operator. In high season the site offers a range of tournaments and sporting activities (aqua-gym, archery, canoeing, walks etc) as well as a children's club each week day morning. La Bouquerie is ideally situated for exploring the Périgord region, and has something to offer families with children of all ages. Reception has a very comprehensive supply of information leaflets and brochures so visitors can play days out.

Facilities

Three toilet blocks with facilities for disabled visitors and baby rooms. Washing machines and covered drying lines. Small shop (15/5-15/9), takeaway food. Bar, restaurant (both 15/5-15/9). Heated swimming pool complex including water slides, paddling pool and sunbathing areas with loungers. Carp fishing in lake on site. Bicycle hire. Riding. WiFi. Off site: Shops, restaurants and Sunday market in the nearby village of St Geniès. The prehistoric caves at Lascaus. Museum and animal park at Le Thot.

Open: 19 April - 19 September.

Directions

Site is signed on east side D704 Sarlat - Montignac, about 500 m. north of junction with D64 St Geniès road. Turn off D704 at campsite sign and take first left turn signed La Bouquerie - site is straight ahead. GPS: 44.99865, 1.24549

Charges guide

Per unit incl. 2 persons and electricity	€ 19,00 - € 25,50
extra person	€ 4,60 - € 6,50
child (under 7 yrs)	€ 3,20 - € 4,50
dog	€ 2,50

Since 2009 we offer you a new aquatic park with water slides and a lazy river!

CAMPING LA BOUQUERIE - F-24590 Saint Geniès en Périgord
Tel: +33 553 28 98 22 - Fax: +33 553 29 19 75
labouquerie@wanadoo.fr - www.labouquerie.com

La Bouquerie

Domaine de la Barbanne

The only camp site in Saint-Emilion!!

Route de Montagne - F-33330 Saint-Emilion - France
Tel: [33] 5 57 24 75 80 - Fax: [33] 5 57 24 69 68
barbanne@wanadoo.fr - www.camping-saint-emilion.com

For latest campsite news, availability and prices visit

alanrogers.com

Saint Jean-de-Luz

Camping Tamaris Plage

Quartier Acotz, 720 route des Plages, F-64500 Saint Jean-de-Luz (Pyrénées-Atlantiques) T: 05 59 26 55 90
E: tamaris1@wanadoo.fr alanrogers.com/FR64080

This is a popular, small and pleasant site which is well kept. It is situated outside the town and just across the road from a sandy beach. The 30 touring pitches, all with 7/10A electricity, are of good size and separated by hedges, on slightly sloping ground with some shade. The site becomes full for July and August with families on long stays, so reservation then is essential. Mobile homes for rent occupy a further 40 pitches. A leisure centre and club provide a heated pool and various other free facilities for adults and children. A gym, Turkish bath, massage and other relaxing amenities are available at an extra charge. There is no shop, but bread is available daily across the road. Opposite the site, a popular surf school offers instruction to new and experienced surfers from the sandy Mayarco beach.

Facilities	Directions
The single heated toilet block of good quality and unusual design should be an ample provision. Facilities for disabled visitors. Washing machine. Wellness health club with free facilities: swimming pool, TV and play room and club for children (4-11 yrs) and on payment: gym, Turkish bath and other spa facilities, sunbathing area, jacuzzi, adult TV lounge. Off site: Beach, fishing, surfing (with instruction) 30 m. Bicycle hire and golf 4 km. Riding 7 km.	Proceed south on N10 and 1.5 km. after Guethary take first road on right (before access to the motorway and Carrefour centre commercial) and follow site signs. GPS: 4325077, 0137429

Open: All year.

Charges guide

Per unit incl. 2 persons and electricity	€ 17,00 - € 29,00
extra person (over 2 yrs)	€ 5,00 - € 7,00
dog	€ 6,00

TAMARIS PLAGE**** CAMPSITE HOLIDAY VILLAGE

ACOTZ 64500 ST. JEAN DE LUZ | TEL. 00 33 5 59 26 55 90 | FAX 0033 5 59 47 70 15
WWW.TAMARIS-PLAGE.COM | GPS: 43.413499. - 1.607297

Saint Jean-de-Luz

Camping International Erromardie

Avenue de la Source, F-64500 Saint Jean-de-Luz (Pyrénées-Atlantiques) T: 05 59 26 07 74
E: camping-international@wanadoo.fr alanrogers.com/FR64170

There are not many sites right by the sea in this region. Erromardie is a good one, with only the access road to cross to reach a beach of fine shingle. The site is mainly flat and grassy, with several different parts separated by hedges, but not much shade. There are 210 pitches, mainly adjoining access roads and backing onto hedges, including 70 for tourers with electricity (5A), of which 20 also have water and waste water. St Jean-de-Luz is an attractive, lively seaside resort with plenty of history and character. The more select and sedate Biarritz and the Spanish border at Hendaye and Behobia are about 15 km.

Facilities	Directions
The large sanitary buildings are of good quality, with individual cabins, free hot water, facilities for disabled visitors and laundry room. Open air swimming pool. Shop, bar, restaurant and takeaway. Motorcaravan service point. Boules. Fishing. Mobile homes for hire. Off site: Golf 5 km. Biarritz and Spain 15 km.	Take exit 3 from the A63 (E05, E70) St Jean de Luz Nord towards Saint Jean-de-Luz/Guéthary/Ascain onto Ave. de Lahanchipia, then left onto Ave. André Ithurralde (D810), first right Ave. Claude Farrère and follow site signs. GPS: 43.406247, -1.637286

Open: 3 April - 30 September.

Charges guide

Per unit incl. 2 persons and electricity	€ 17,00 - € 32,00
extra person	€ 3,00 - € 6,00
child (2-9 yrs)	€ 2,00 - € 5,00
dog	€ 5,00

For latest campsite news, availability and prices visit

alanrogers.com

Saint Jean-de-Luz

Camping Atlantica

Quartier Acotz, F-64500 Saint Jean-de-Luz (Pyrénées-Atlantiques) T: 05 59 47 72 44
E: info@campingatlantica.com **alanrogers.com/FR64250**

This is a friendly, family run site with 200 shady and well kept grass pitches set amongst many shrubs, flowers and hedges. There are 99 pitches for touring, 69 have 6A electricity and 41 have water and drainage. The excellent swimming pool area is attractively landscaped with plenty of sunbeds. With a bar, restaurant and takeaway open June to September, the beach 500 m. and the cosmopolitan town of St Jean de Luz only 3 km. away, this site is suitable for families and couples of all ages. If excessively wet, motor caravans are advised to call ahead to check availability. The three bright and very clean sanitary blocks are well maintained with large showers and piped music. A comprehensive fitness room includes a sauna and during July and August a trained attendant is available for advice.

Facilities

Three immaculate toilet blocks include facilities for babies and campers with disabilities. Excellent laundry. Swimming pool and fitness room (April-Sept). Bar, restaurant, shop, takeaway (all 15/6-15/9). Games Room. Multisport court. Motorcaravan services. Modern, fenced children's play area. Family entertainment (July/Aug). Off site: Bus to major town 400 m. Large supermarket 1 km. Golf 4 km.

Open: 1 April - 30 September.

Directions

Leave A63, exit 3, taking N10 toward Bayonne. Take the second left turn signed 'Acotz Campings Plages'. At T-junction turn right and follow signs. Campsite is on the right. GPS: 43.41569, -1.61646

Charges guide

Per unit incl. 2 persons	
and electricity	€ 17,60 - € 33,60
extra person	€ 3,20 - € 6,50
child (under 7 yrs)	€ 2,20 - € 4,00
dog	free - € 2,50

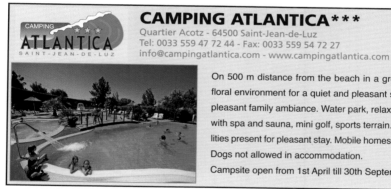

Saint Julien-en-Born

Yelloh! Village Lous Seurrots

606 avenue de l'Ocean, Contis Plage, F-40170 Saint Julien-en-Born (Landes) T: 05 58 42 85 82
E: info@yellohvillage-lous-seurrots.com **alanrogers.com/FR40070**

Lous Seurrots is only a short 400 m. walk from the beach and parts of the site have views across the estuary. There are 611 pitches, mainly in pine woods on sandy undulating ground. They are numbered but only roughly marked out, most have good shade and all 345 touring pitches have 6A electricity (adaptors required). The site's pool complex (two are heated) is in a superb setting of palm trees and flower beds and the paved sunbathing areas have wonderful views out to the estuary and the sea. For all its size, Lous Seurrots is a family site with the emphasis on peace and tranquillity (no discos).

Facilities

Three well kept, modern toilet blocks, baby rooms and facilities for disabled visitors. Washing machines. Motorcaravan services. Large shop and bar (1/5-19/9). Restaurant (19/4-19/9) plus takeaway. Swimming pool complex (1/5-19/9) and a jacuzzi with keep fit classes (July/Aug). Tennis. Archery. Minigolf. Canoeing. Bicycle hire. Fishing. Miniclub. Evening entertainment twice weekly in high season in open air auditorium. Electric barbecues are permitted. Internet. Off site: Beach 400 m. Riding 3 km.

Open: 9 April - 18 September.

Directions

Turn off D652 on D41 (15 km. south of Mimizan) to Contis-Plage and site is on left as you reach it. GPS: 44.08881, -1.31634

Charges 2011

Per unit incl. 2 persons	
and electricity	€ 15,00 - € 41,00
extra person	€ 5,00 - € 7,00
child (3-7 yrs)	free - € 6,00
animal	€ 4,00

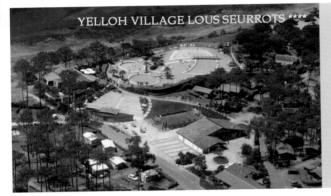

YELLOH VILLAGE LOUS SEURROTS ★★★★

40170 Saint Julien en Born
Tél: 00 33 (0)5 58 42 85 82
Fax: 00 33 (0)5 58 42 49 11
info@lous-seurrots.com
www.lous-seurrots.com
Camping Village
400 meters from the beach
Accomodations,
Chalets, mobil-homes, pitches
Swimming pool, Activities
Restaurant, grocery,
bicycle rental, Internet

Saint Martin-de-Seignanx

Camping Caravaning Lou P'tit Poun

530

110 avenue du Quartier Neuf, F-40390 Saint Martin-de-Seignanx (Landes) T: 05 59 56 55 79
E: contact@louptitpoun.com **alanrogers.com/FR40140**

The manicured grounds surrounding Lou P'tit Poun give it a well kept appearance, a theme carried out throughout this very pleasing site which celebrated its 20th anniversary in 2009. It is only after arriving at the car park that you feel confident it is not a private estate. Beyond this point an abundance of shrubs and trees is revealed. Behind a central sloping flower bed lies the open plan reception area. The avenues around the site are wide and the 168 pitches (142 for touring) are spacious. All have 10A electricity, many also have water and drainage and some are separated by low hedges. The jovial owners not only make their guests welcome, but extend their enthusiasm to organising weekly entertainment for young and old during high season. A Sites et Paysages member.

Facilities

Two unisex sanitary blocks, maintained to a high standard and kept clean, include washbasins in cabins, a baby bath and provision for disabled visitors. Laundry facilities with washing machine and dryer. Motorcaravan service point. Small shop (1/7-31/8). Café/restaurant (1/7-31/8). Swimming pool (1/6-15/9) Play area. Games room, TV. Half-court tennis. Off site: Bayonne 6 km. Fishing or riding 7 km. Golf 10 km. Sandy beaches of Basque coast ten minute drive.

Open: 2 June - 12 September.

Directions

Leave A63 at exit 6 and join D817 in the direction of Pau. Site is signed at Leclerc supermarket. Continue for 3.5 km. and site is clearly signed on right. GPS: 43.52406, -1.41196

Charges guide

Per unit incl. 2 persons	
and electricity	€ 22,00 - € 33,00
extra person	€ 7,00 - € 7,50
child (under 7 yrs)	€ 5,00 - € 5,50
dog	€ 4,00 - € 5,00

For latest campsite news, availability and prices visit

alanrogers.com

Saint Pardoux

Kawan Village Château le Verdoyer

Champs Romain, F-24470 Saint Pardoux (Dordogne) T: 05 53 56 94 64. E: chateau@verdoyer.fr
alanrogers.com/FR24010

The 26 hectare estate has three lakes, two for fishing and one with a sandy beach and safe swimming area. There are 135 good sized touring pitches, level, terraced and hedged. With a choice of wooded area or open field, all have electricity (5/10A) and most share a water supply between four pitches. There is a swimming pool complex and in high season activities are organised for children (5-13 yrs) but there is no disco. This site is well adapted for those with disabilities, with two fully adapted chalets, wheelchair access to all facilities and even a lift into the pool. Le Verdoyer has been developed in the park of a restored château and is owned by a Dutch family. We particularly like this site for its beautiful buildings and lovely surroundings. It is situated in the lesser known area of the Dordogne sometimes referred to as the Périgord Vert, with its green forests and small lakes. The courtyard area between reception and the bar is home to evening activities, and provides a pleasant place to enjoy drinks and relax. The château itself has rooms to let and its excellent lakeside restaurant is also open to the public. There are Dutch tour operators on site with pre-erected tents for hire that occupy some of the touring pitches.

Facilities

Well appointed toilet blocks include facilities for disabled visitors and baby baths. Serviced launderette. Motorcaravan services. Fridge rental. Shop with gas (1/5-30/9). Bar, snacks, takeaway and restaurant (1/5-30/9). Bistro (July/Aug). Two pools the smaller covered in low season, slide, paddling pool. Play areas. Tennis. Minigolf. Bicycle hire. Small library. Wifi(charged), Computer in reception for internet access. International newspapers daily. Off site: Riding 5 km. 'Circuit des Orchidées' (22 species of orchid). Vélo-rail at Bussière Galant. Market (Thu and Sun) at Saint Pardoux 12 km.

Open: 23 April - 6 October.

Directions

Site is 2 km. from the Limoges (N21) - Chalus (D6bis-D85) - Nontron road, 20 km. south of Chalus and is well signed from main road. Site on D96 about 4 km. north of village of Champs Romain. GPS: 45.55035, 0.7947

Charges guide

Per unit incl. 2 persons and electricity	€ 21,00 - € 32,00
extra person	€ 5,00 - € 6,50
child (6-11 yrs)	€ 4,00 - € 5,00
dog	free - € 4,00

Saint Seurin-de-Prats

Camping la Plage

F-24230 Saint Seurin-de-Prats (Dordogne) T: 05 53 58 61 07. E: info@camping-in-france.net

alanrogers.com/FR24120

This is a beautiful site where the natural environment blends in perfect harmony with nature. It is more like a park than a campsite with a differing array of trees and shrubs. Camping la Plage nestles gently beside the River Dordogne where there is a feeling of spaciousness, tranquillity and calm. The owners are friendly and helpful and are keen to ensure you enjoy your holiday. The 85 pitches are generous in size with some being open and some shaded, and 15A electricity is provided. They are separated by shrubs and hedges. Access for motorcaravans and large units does not cause a problem.

Facilities

Two traditional style sanitary blocks. No facilities for disabled visitors. Bar (all year) and restaurant (April -Oct). Takeaway. TV. Swimming pool. Petanque. Play area. Private access to the river. Fishing. Communal barbecues only. Off site: Golf 12 km. Riding 6 km.

Open: 15 May - 15 September (gites longer).

Directions

Take the D936 from Bergerac to Bordeaux. Bypass St Foy Le Grande and a few kilometres further on is a roundabout with St Seurin-de-Prats on the left. Take that road and site is on the right, well signed. GPS: 44.82205, 0.07501

Charges guide

Per unit incl. 2 persons	€ 15,00 - € 18,50
extra person	€ 4,00 - € 6,00
electricity (15A)	€ 4,00

Sainte Eulalie-en-Born

Le Camping du Lac

1590 route du Lac, F-40200 Sainte Eulalie-en-Born (Landes) T: 05 58 09 70 10
E: contact@lecampingdulac.com alanrogers.com/FR40400

Camping du Lac is a municipal site on the shores of the massive Etang de Biscarosse, one of the largest lakes in France. Cecile and Dave will be delighted to welcome you to their haven of quiet. The site has direct access to a sandy beach, as well as its own swimming pool. The nearest Atlantic beach is at Mimizan-Plage, around 15 minutes away by car. There are 120 touring pitches here. These are generally grassy and with shade. All pitches have electrical connections. A small marina with slipway is available to site users. In high season, various activities are available on the lake.

Facilities

A single toilet block provides washbasins and showers in cubicles. Facility for disabled visitors and children. Laundry. Motorcaravan service point. Shop. Snack bar. Takeaway (all July/Aug). Direct access to lake. Sandy beach. Watersports. Swimming pool/paddling pool (no Bermuda shorts). Fishing. Play area. WiFi (charged). Communal barbecue (only gas barbecues on pitches). Mobile homes and chalets for rent. Off site: Shops and restaurants in Sainte Eulalie and Mimizan.

Open: All year excl. February.

Directions

Approaching from the north (Bordeaux), take exit 17 D43 towards Parentis-en-Born. Then D652 towards Gastes, site is then signed. GPS: 44.307781, -1.181127

Charges guide

Per unit incl. 2 persons and electricity (10A)	€ 12,50 - € 18,60
extra person	€ 3,00 - € 4,20
child (under 10 yrs)	€ 1,50 - € 2,50

Salignac-Eyvigues

Flower Camping le Temps de Vivre

F-24590 Salignac-Eyvigues (Dordogne) T: 05 53 28 93 21. E: contact@temps-de-vivre.com

alanrogers.com/FR24460

Le Temps de Vivre is situated in the centre of the Périgord Noir, in the countryside and lies about 250 m. above sea level. The area of the campsite covers about 4.5 acres in total, with 1.5 acres in use at present. It is a small, friendly, family run site with 50 pitches, 30 of which are for touring and 20 for mobile homes available for rent. The pitches are wide and terraces separate some of them. All have electricity connections available (10A) and you will find a variety of trees and bushes often as a natural separation. This is a delightful and peaceful rural site.

Facilities

One modern unisex sanitary block is clean and well maintained. En-suite toilet for disabled visitors. Baby room with bath. Laundry area. Small shop in reception. Small bar, restaurant and takeaway (July/Aug). Two swimming pools (one for children). Boules. Play area. Pottery and painting workshops for young children (high season). Themed meals (high season). WiFi in reception area (free). Off site: Shops and restaurants, etc. within walking distance in the nearby village of Salignac-Eyvigues. Riding and golf 5 km. Canoe hire.

Open: 23 April - 12 September.

Directions

From Brive-La-Gaillarde heading south on the A20 continue for 30 km. to exit 55 signed Souillac. Take D62/D15 northwest for 12 km. until Salignac-Eyvigues. As you drive through the town centre look for blue sign for site. Follow the sign off the main road for about 2 km. GPS: 44.96374, 1.32813

Charges guide

Per unit incl. 2 persons and electricity (10A)	€ 15,50 - € 23,50
extra person	€ 2,50 - € 5,00

For latest campsite news, availability and prices visit

alanrogers.com

Salles

Camping des Bastides

Terre Rouge, F-47150 Salles (Lot-et-Garonne) T: 05 53 40 83 09. E: info@campingdesbastides.com
alanrogers.com/FR47130

Attractive and well maintained, this six and a half-hectare site is hilly and terraced with good views from the top of the site. The new French owners, Gaelle and Christian, are warm and welcoming. Although the terrain is hilly, most of the 90 medium sized touring pitches are fairly level and moderately shaded. Tight turns with narrow gravel paths and overhanging trees may cause some difficulties for larger units. A range of different types of accomodation including Mongolian tents are available to rent. Reception keeps information on a variety of local walking and cycling routes.

Facilities

Two modern, clean and well maintained sanitary blocks can be heated. Facilities for disabled visitors. Excellent children's facilities with baby bath and child-size facilities. Private en-suite facilities for hire. Shop for essentials (with gas). Bar/reception and snack restaurant (including takeaway). Swimming pool complex with swimming pool, pool with slides, two paddling pools and a spa. Boules. Play area with bouncy castle. Small indoor play area with TV and small library. WiFi. Entertainment (high season). Off site: Fishing 1 km. Fumel 8 km. Riding and bicycle hire 10 km. Golf 25 km.

Open: 1 May - 15 October.

Directions

From Fumel, take D710 north towards Cuzorn. Before reaching Cuzorn, turn northwest on the D162 and site is 6 km. on the right hand side (well signed). GPS: 44.5525, 0.8815

Charges guide

Per unit incl. 2 persons and electricity (6A)	€ 15,00 - € 26,50
extra person	€ 4,00 - € 5,00
child (2-12 yrs)	€ 2,25 - € 3,00
dog	free - € 2,00

Sanguinet

Campéole le Lac Sanguinet

Campéole

526 rue de Pinton, F-40460 Sanguinet (Landes) T: 05 58 82 70 80. E: lac-sanguinet@campeole.com
alanrogers.com/FR40440

Le Lac Sanguinet is a member of the Campéole group, and is located just 100 m. from the large lake of the same name. There are 400 pitches here, of which 290 have electrical connections (10/16A). Around 70 pitches are occupied by mobile homes, chalets and fully equipped bungalow tents, all available for rent, including some models specially adapted for the disabled. An attractive swimming pool was added for the 2008 season and other amenities include volleyball and two children's playgrounds. A marquee is used for activities and entertainment during the peak season. The Lac de Sanguinet is one of Europe's largest lakes (6,800 hectares!) and is renowned for the clarity of its waters. It's understandably popular for fishing but also for water sports. A sailing and windsurfing centre is adjacent to the site. This is a region for superlatives – Europe's highest sand dune, the Dune de Pyla is close, and from the top, there are wonderful views of the Arcachon basin and surrounding forest.

Facilities

Snack bar. Small shop. Swimming pool. Games room. Bicycle hire. Bouncy castle. Play areas. Activities and entertainment programme. Tourist information. Mobile homes, equipped tents and chalets for rent. Off site: Lac de Sanguinet 100 m. Sailing centre. Walking and cycle tracks through the forest. Fishing. Dune de Pyla. Bordeaux 60 km.

Open: 1 May - 20 September.

Directions

Approaching from Bordeaux, head south on the A63 and then join the A660 towards Arcachon. Leave this motorway at the first exit and follow signs to Sanguinet (D216). Upon arrival in Sanguinet follow signs to 'Le Lac' and from here the site is well signed. GPS: 44.4816, -1.0938

Charges 2011

Contact the site for details.

Sanguinet

Camping les Grands Pins

1039 avenue de Losa, F-40460 Sanguinet (Landes) T: 05 58 78 61 74. E: info@campinglesgrandspins.com

alanrogers.com/FR40250

Approached by a road alongside the lake, this Airotel group site is set amongst tall pine trees. Of the 345 pitches, the 80 sand/gravel pitches are of average size, mostly level and have little shade. Low hedges and immature trees divide those available for tourers and most are set away from the many mobile homes/chalets. There are no water taps in the pitching area. Large units may find manoeuvring difficult. There may be some aircraft noise at times from a nearby base. A central pool complex includes a covered heated indoor pool, an outdoor pool, water slide and flume, children's pool and jacuzzi. In early and late season this is a very quiet site with very few facilities open. However, there are plenty of walks, cycle rides and the lake to enjoy. The poolside bar, restaurant and shops are only open in July and August when the site becomes busy, offering watersports, minigolf, a children's club, boat trips and organised activities. Volleyball, tennis and boules are available all season. Fishing is also available. The charming small village of Sanguinet is 2 km. away with supermarket and shops, bank, bars, restaurants and an archaeological museum.

Facilities

Three toilet blocks include washbasins in cabins, showers and British style toilets (not all open in low seasons). Baby bath and provision for disabled visitors. Laundry facilities. Motorcaravan service point. Shop, bar, restaurant and takeaway (1/7-31/8). Indoor pool (all season). Outdoor pool complex with jacuzzi (1/7-31/8). Play area. Games room and TV in bar. Tennis, volleyball, boules. Sports equipment available to hire. Bicycle hire (July/Aug). Children's club. WiFi (charged). Dogs are not accepted in July/Aug. Barbecues are not allowed (dedicated areas provided). Off site: Beach 30 m. Boat launching 1 km. Fishing 2 km. Golf and riding 15 km. Windsurfing 30 km.

Open: 1 April - 31 October.

Directions

Enter Sanguinet from the north on the D46. At one way system turn right. Do not continue on one way system but go straight ahead toward lake (signed) on Rue de Lac. Site is 2 km. on left. GPS: 44.48396, -1.089716

Charges guide

Per unit incl. 2 persons and electricity	€ 18,00 - € 40,00
extra person	€ 5,50 - € 8,00
child (3-7 yrs)	€ 4,50 - € 5,50
dog	€ 3,00

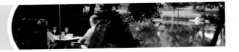

Sarlat-la-Canéda

Castel Camping le Moulin du Roch

Route des Eyzies-Le Roch (D47), F-24200 Sarlat-la-Canéda (Dordogne) T: 05 53 59 20 27
E: moulin.du.roch@wanadoo.fr alanrogers.com/FR24040

The site has 195 pitches, of which 124 are for touring units. They are mostly flat (some slope slightly) and grassy and all have electricity (6A). Pitches on the upper levels have plenty of shade, whilst those on the lower level near the amenities and the fishing lake are more open. Entertainment and activities are organised from June to September, with something for everyone from quizzes and sports tournaments to canoeing and riding for the more adventurous. An excellent multi-lingual children's club runs in July and August. Walking and mountain biking routes lead from the site through surrounding woodland. Le Moulin du Roch is set on natural sloping woodland in the grounds of a former water mill and the Dutreux family have worked hard to ensure that it is an attractive and well run family campsite, fully deserving of its place in the Castels and Camping chain. Only 10 km. from the charming medieval town of Sarlat and 52 km. from Pèrigueux – the capital town of the Périgord region – this campsite is well situated for exploring the natural, historical, cultural and gastronomic riches of the Dordogne.

Facilities

Modern, well maintained, clean toilet blocks. Washing machines, dryers. Good shop. Bar with WiFi and terrace. Takeaway. Superb restaurant, Attractive swimming pool, paddling pool, sun terrace, (all open all season). Fishing lake. Tennis. Boules. Playground. Evening entertainment throughout the high season. Pets are not accepted. Off site: Supermarkets, banks, etc. at Sarlat 10 km. Bicycle hire and riding 10 km. Golf 15 km.

Open: 9 May - 16 September.

Directions

Site is 10 km. west of Sarlat-la-Canéda, on south side of D47 Sarlat - Les Eyzies road. GPS: 44.90867, 1.1148

Charges guide

Per unit incl. 2 persons and electricity	€ 19,00 - € 35,00
incl. full services	€ 23,00 - € 39,00
extra person	€ 5,00 - € 9,50
child (3-7 yrs)	free - € 4,50

Camping Cheques accepted.

Les Grands Pins
CAMPING CARAVANING ★★★★

Club Airotel

Sanguinet

Lac de Biscarrosse

Chalets and mobile homes for rent

Camping Caravaning les Grands Pins
Avenue de Losa (route du lac) 40460 SANGUINET
Tél : 00 33 (0)5 58 78 61 74 - Fax : 00 33 (0)5 58 78 69 15
info@campinglesgrandspins.com www.campingaquitaine.com

Situated
at the lakeside
Aquatic Parc
The best place to enjoy t
the Les Landes Sun!

www.campinglesgrandspins.com

Sarlat-la-Canéda

Camping Domaine des Mathevies

Les Mathevies, Sainte Nathalène, F-24200 Sarlat (Dordogne) T: 05 53 59 20 86. E: mathevies@mac.com

alanrogers.com/FR24740

This site is a rustic treasure, situated in the rural heart of the Perigord. Family run, the delightful owners, Patrick and Natalie McAlpine, will give you a warm and friendly welcome. The rural location gives a wonderful feeling of a tranquillity. The 26 pitches are large and generous at 150-280 sq.m. and all have 10A electricity, 5 also with water and drainage. In addition, there are 6 wooden chalets, 3 mobile homes and a traditional stone gite to rent. A shaded terrace is next to the beautiful, original Perigordine building and the barn has been lovingly converted into the restaurant. The restaurant offers superb home cooked food with local produce. Entertainment includes a barbecue soirée and themed activities. Pony riding and a campfire for children go down really well and children can enjoy themselves in a safe environment. The facilities are well maintained and the site is beautifully landscaped with flowers and shrubs There are some wonderful views over the rolling countryside. This site is ideal for couples and families with young children and all will enjoy what it has to offer.

Facilities

Sanitary facilities include provision for disabled visitors. Washing machine and dryer. Bar. Restaurant. Swimming and paddling pools. Tennis court. Library. Selection of games. Satellite TV. Free WiFi. Playground. Petanque. Special interest groups catered for. Crèche (under 5 yrs). Badminton court. Basketball. Off site: Riding 2 km. Fishing and canoeing 5 km. Golf 8 km.

Open: 24 April - 26 September.

Directions

From the A20 exit 55 for Souillac follow road to Roufillac and Carlux. Continue to Sainte Nathalene and site is signed from there.
GPS: 44.918056, 1.277778

Charges 2011

Per unit incl. 2 persons	
and electricity	€ 18,50 - € 25,50
extra person	€ 4,50 - € 7,00
child (under 7 yrs)	€ 3,50 - € 4,50
dog	€ 1,00 - € 1,50

T: +33 (0)5 53 59 20 86   E: mathevies@mac.com   www.mathevies.com

Sarlat-la-Canéda

Camping les Tailladis

Marcillac-Saint Quentin, F-24200 Sarlat-la-Canéda (Dordogne) T: 05 53 59 10 95. E: tailladis@wanadoo.fr

alanrogers.com/FR24480

Les Tailladis is a well situated, mature campsite of some 17 hectares of woodland, owned by the same Dutch/French family for over 47 years. It is about 12 kilometres from Sarlat, Eyzies and Montignac-Lascauax, and 35 km. from Souillac. Four hectares of the total provides 78 medium to large pitches which are grassy, terraced and partially shaded, with electricity (6A), and water points close by. There is also a small stream and pond. The access road and campsite roads/tracks are narrow and winding, which may cause difficulties for some larger units. The hosts are welcoming and enthusiastic and you will be greeted with a drink and warm, friendly service.

Facilities

One heated sanitary block is well sited for all pitches. En-suite toilet for disabled visitors. Baby bath and changing area. Laundry room. Large shop (fresh bread and milk to order). Restaurant, bar. Swimming pool and paddling pool. Play area with trampoline. Library. Activities organised during high season. Internet access (charged). Fishing. Off site: Riding 3 km. Bicycle hire 12 km. Golf 25 km. Boat launching 25 km. Sarlat with supermarkets, shops, restaurants and markets (Wed and Sat) 12 km.

Open: 1 March - 30 November.

Directions

From Sarlat-la-Canéda, take D704 heading north. After 10 km, look for signs on the left for Marcillac-St Quentin. Take this road heading northwest, and site is less than 3 km. after Marcillac-St Quentin on the left hand side. Access and site roads are narrow for large units. GPS: 44.97450, 1.18832

Charges guide

Per unit incl. 2 persons	
and electricity (6A)	€ 16,83 - € 21,25
extra person	€ 4,01 - € 5,35

For latest campsite news, availability and prices visit

alanrogers.com

Sarlat-la-Canéda

Camping les Grottes de Roffy

Sainte Nathalène, F-24200 Sarlat-la-Canéda (Dordogne) T: 05 53 59 15 61. E: contact@roffy.fr

alanrogers.com/FR24130

531

About 5 km. east of Sarlat, Les Grottes de Roffy is a pleasantly laid out, family site. There are 162 clearly marked pitches, some very large, set on very well kept grass terraces. They have easy access and good views across an attractive valley. Some have plentiful shade, although others are more open, and all have electricity (6A). The reception, bar, restaurant and shop are located within converted farm buildings surrounding a semi-courtyard. The site shop is well stocked with a variety of goods and a tempting epicerie. Those with very large units are advised to check availability in advance. In season there is something for all the family, with evening entertainment (including jazz and Latin evenings) and daily activities for children. A variety of activities and excursions for all ages includes quad biking, pottery, massage and yoga. Conveniently located for Sarlat (a bus calls at the site on a Saturday to take visitors to and from the market) and all other Dordogne attractions, this is a good site for families. The site is used by tour operators and there are a small number of mobile homes and chalets available for rent.

Facilities

Two toilet blocks with modern facilities are more than adequate. Well stocked shop. Bar and gastronomique restaurant with imaginative and sensibly priced menu. Takeaway. Good swimming pool complex comprising two deep pools (one heated), a fountain, paddling pool and heated jacuzzi. Tennis. Games room. Room for teenagers. Play area. Entertainment and activities for all ages. Internet access. Free WiFi in courtyard area. Off site: Fishing 2 km. Bicycle hire 7 km. Riding 10 km. Golf 15 km.

Open: 18 April - 21 September.

Directions

Take D47 east from Sarlat to Ste Nathalène. Just before Ste Nathalène the site is signed on the right hand side of the road. Turn here, and the site is about 800 m. along the lane. GPS: 44.90404, 1.2821

Charges guide

Per pitch incl. 2 persons	€ 21,70 - € 29,00
with full services	€ 23,70 - € 31,00
extra person	€ 5,70 - € 7,60
child (2-7 yrs)	€ 4,20 - € 5,70

les Grottes de Roffy camping caravaning

★ ★ ★ ★

Sainte-Nathalèle • 24200 Sarlat • France

E-mail contact@roffy.fr Tél. +33 (0)5 53 59 15 61 • Fax +33 (0)5 53 31 09 11

Sarlat-la-Canéda

Camping la Palombière

Sainte Nathalène, F-24200 Sarlat-la-Canéda (Dordogne) T: 05 53 59 42 34. E: la.palombiere@wanadoo.fr

alanrogers.com/FR24570

This site is set in a gorgeous, rural part of France amongst the beauty of the Perigord countryside with its rolling green hills and ancient buildings. The restored and preserved buildings at la Palombière add to the pleasure of this delightful site. It is evident that much investment has gone into making this holiday destination a place to remember. There are 177 pitches of which 88 are for touring caravans and tents. All have electricity (10A) and some are fully serviced. Most are level and shaded from the sun, with some terracing because of the different levels. There are 89 mobile homes with 45 to rent.

Facilities

Two modern sanitary blocks include facilities for babies and disabled visitors. Washing machines and dryers. Well stocked shop. Bar. Restaurant, snack bar and takeaway (1/5-10/9) Heated swimming pool complex with slide and toboggan (all season). Gymnasium. Playgrounds. Library. Sports field. Tennis. Minigolf. Boules. Satellite TV. Games room. Bicycle hire. Internet facilities. WiFi. Off site: Riding 3 km. Canoeing 3 km. Golf 10 km.

Open: 23 April - 11 September.

Directions

Take the D47 east from Sarlat to Ste Nathalène. Site is signed from village and is reached by taking a left turn just beyond it. GPS: 44.90819, 1.29252

Charges 2011

Per unit incl. 2 persons and electricity	€ 14,50 - € 29,70
extra person	€ 4,50 - € 7,80
child (1-7 yrs)	€ 4,50 - € 5,50
dog	€ 2,00

Sarlat-la-Canéda

Camping le Montant

Saint André-d'Allas, F-24200 Sarlat-la-Canéda (Dordogne) T: 05 53 59 18 50. E: lemontant@wanadoo.fr
alanrogers.com/FR24610

Camping le Montant is a family run site and is located on a hillside overlooking beautiful countryside only 2 km. away from Sarlat. The 100 large touring pitches, all with electricity (up to 10A) are divided into two areas, each with its own sanitary block. A main central building, surrounded by flowers, houses the reception, bar with terrace and takeaway. One part of the site is shaded with hedges, the other area is more open with flat terraced pitches looking out over the wooded hills. The site has an excellent heated pool area on three levels with a covered jacuzzi, pool and children's pool.

Facilities

Both toilet blocks are very well equipped especially the new one with its baby room and large laundry (washing machines, dryers etc). Restaurant, takeaway and bar (1/5-20/9). Pool table, table football and some electronic games. Minigolf. Boules. Activities organised for children, teenagers and adults both during the day and evenings (July/Aug). Off site: Historic Sarlat 2 km. Riding 3 km. Fishing and golf 5 km.

Open: 1 May - 20 September.

Directions

Site is 2 km. south of Sarlat off the D57 Sarlat - Baynac road. If approaching from Sarlat, site is signed to the right. Follow this road for about 1 km. GPS: 44.865344, 1.187704

Charges guide

Per unit incl. 2 persons	
and electricity	€ 13,90 - € 26,10
extra person	€ 3,50 - € 6,50
child (2-7 yrs)	€ 2,10 - € 4,50
dog	free - € 1,00

ONLY 4 KM FROM THE HISTORICAL VILLAGE OF SARLAT

Sarlat-la-Canéda

Camping les Terrasses du Périgord

Pech-d'Orance, F-24200 Sarlat-la-Canéda (Dordogne) T: 05 53 59 02 25
E: terrasses-du-perigord@wanadoo.fr alanrogers.com/FR24670

Set on a hill top on the edge of Sarlat, this site has panoramic views across the Perigord. There are 90 pitches, of which 75 are for touring units, with the remaining 15 being for chalets and mobile homes for rent. The site is sloping on different levels but the pitches are generally level. All are shady, marked and separated by trees. Electricity is 6, 10 or 16A. For those with larger units, it is essential to phone in advance for pitch availability, as not all are suitable. A warm and friendly welcome is given by the French owners. An old, fully restored farmhouse fitted out as a bar and a wine cave offers you tasting together with a bistro. A well stocked shop is next to the games room which doubles up for evening entertainment. This includes Perigordine dancing and shows. The swimming pool and children's pool have only recently been added and a large playground has a cable slide.

Facilities

One modern sanitary block divided into two provides all facilities including those for disabled visitors and babies. Washing machine and dryer. Motorcaravan services. Shop. Bar with snack bar and takeaway. Wine tastings. Swimming pool and toddler's pool. Play area with cable slide. Minigolf. Bicycle hire. Gas and electric barbecues only. Evening entertainment. Off site: Caves. Châteaux. Fishing 2 km. Canoeing 2 km. Riding 8 km.

Open: 25 April - 7 September.

Directions

From Sarlat, take D47 to Proissans. Continue on D56 to Proissans and site is 500 m. on the left. In Sarlat, follow the signs for hospital as it is nearby. GPS: 44.9058, 1.23598

Charges guide

Per unit incl. 2 persons	
and electricity	€ 15,60 - € 19,70
extra person	€ 3,90 - € 5,00
child (under 7 yrs)	€ 2,20 - € 2,90

No credit cards.

Sauveterre-la-Lemance

Flower Camping Moulin du Périé

F-47500 Sauveterre-la-Lemance (Lot-et-Garonne) T: 05 53 40 67 26. E: moulinduperie@wanadoo.fr
alanrogers.com/FR47010

Set in a quiet area and surrounded by woodlands this peaceful little site is well away from much of the tourist bustle. It has 95 reasonably sized, grassy touring pitches, all with 6A electricity, divided by mixed trees and bushes with most having good shade. All are extremely well kept, as indeed is the entire site. The attractive front courtyard is complemented by an equally pleasant terrace at the rear. Two small, clean swimming pools overlook a shallow, spring water lake, ideal for inflatable boats and paddling and bordering the lake, a large grass field is popular for games.

Facilities

Two clean, modern and well maintained toilet blocks include facilities for disabled visitors. Motorcaravan services. Basic shop. Bar/reception, restaurant and takeaway. Two small swimming pools (no Bermuda-style shorts). Boules. Outdoor chess. Playground. Small indoor play area. Bicycle hire. Organised activities in high season include canoeing, riding, wine tasting visits and sightseeing trips. Off site: Fishing 1 km. Riding 7 km. Small shop in village. Supermarket in Fumel.

Open: 12 May - 18 September.

Directions

From D710, Fumel - Périgueux, turn southeast into Sauveterre-la-Lemance. Turn left (northeast) at far end on C201 signed Château Sauveterre and Loubejec (site also signed). Site is 3 km. on right. GPS: 44.59016, 1.04761

Charges guide

Per unit incl. 2 persons and electricity	€ 18,15 - € 27,65
extra person	€ 4,50 - € 7,00
child (2-7 yrs)	€ 1,90 - € 3,70

Sérignac-Péboudou

Camping la Vallée de Gardeleau

F-47410 Sérignac-Péboudou (Lot-et-Garonne) T: 05 53 36 96 96. E: valleegardeleau@Wanadoo.fr
alanrogers.com/FR47120

Camping La Vallée is a delightful, small, family run site established over 12 years ago. It is well hidden and private, some 9 km. from civilization and deep in the countryside of Lot-et-Garonne, very close to the border of the Dordogne and 150 km. from the Atlantic coast. It has a total of 33 pitches, 26 for touring, 7 mobile homes, and 4 bungalow tents. The medium sized pitches are well laid out, all with hedges and some shade, some with views. The owners, Virginie and Laurent Faivre, are very conscientious and work extremely hard to keep the site clean and well maintained.

Facilities

Two heated sanitary blocks are well sited and clean. Facilities for disabled visitors. Baby room. Washing machine. Shop with daily deliveries of fresh bread. Bar with snack bar and TV. Restaurant (high season). Swimming pool. Boules area (need to bring own boules). Small play area. Communal barbecue. Library. Animation for children (high season). Minigolf. Off site: Fishing and riding 2 km. Bicycle hire 9 km. Golf 20 km.

Open: 2 March - 31 October.

Directions

From Castillones on the N21 find the D254 to Sérignac-Péboudou and follow this. Some 10 km. along this road, look for signs to site which is on the left hand side. GPS: 44.61606, 0.51821

Charges guide

Per unit incl. 2 persons and electricity	€ 12,30 - € 20,20
extra person	€ 2,60 - € 4,00

Soulac-sur-Mer

Yelloh! Village le Lilhan

8 allée Michel Montaigne, F-33780 Soulac-sur-Mer (Gironde) T: 05 56 09 77 63. E: contact@lelilhan.com
alanrogers.com/FR33330

This is a well established woodland site, popular with families. Now part of the Yelloh! Village group, Le Lilhan has benefited from an extensive programme of investment and development. There are around 58 large touring pitches (all with 10A electricity), the remainder used for mobile homes and chalets to rent. Most pitches are heavily shaded and on natural woodland floor terrain. A special area is kept for younger campers away from the quieter family areas. There is an attractive and well laid out pool complex, together with a small shop selling bread and basic provisions, a bar and a restaurant.

Facilities

Two new unisex toilet blocks and an older refurbished unit provide a family bathroom with double shower, facilities for babies, washbasins in cubicles, and a suite for disabled visitors. Laundry facilities. Swimming pool complex, new balnéo, sauna and jacuzzi (15/6-15/9). Shop, bar, restaurant and pizzeria, takeaway (15/6-15/9). Minigolf. Playground. Tennis. Archery. Riding. Bicycle hire. Entertainment and children's club (high season). Internet access. American RVs or units over 8 m. are not accepted. Off site: Town and beach 3 km.

Open: 1 April - 15 September.

Directions

Soulac-sur-Mer is on the Atlantic coast just south of the tip of the Gironde peninsula. Site is signed off the D101 – turn east on a minor road about 3 km. south of Soulac town, and site is on the left after a short distance. GPS: 45.48576, -1.1179

Charges guide

Per unit incl. 2 persons and electricity	€ 19,90 - € 26,95
extra person	€ 3,00 - € 5,00
No credit cards.	

We can book this site for you! Call 01580 214000

alan rogers travel

We can book this site for you! Call 01580 214000

alan rogers travel

For latest campsite news, availability and prices visit

alanrogers.com

Soulac-sur-Mer

Camping Club Les Lacs

126 route des Lacs, F-33780 Soulac-sur-Mer (Gironde) T: 05 56 09 76 63. E: info@camping-les-lacs.com

alanrogers.com/FR33400

Given its proximity to the Gironde ferry terminal at Le Verdon, many campers head south through Soulac. It is, however, a smart resort with a fine sandy beach. Camping Club Les Lacs is one of the best sites here and has 228 pitches on offer, of which 114 are available to touring units. All pitches have electrical connnections (5A). Site amenities are impressive with a large, modern complex at the entrance housing a large bar, restaurant, shop and stage for evening entertainment (high season). There is a large outdoor pool and covered pool adjacent (open for the full season). The site has recently been extended and 40 new pitches, although large are currently lacking shade. The nearest beach is 3 km. away and Soulac has many attractive shops and restaurants. The northern Médoc vineyards are also within easy access. A Sites et Paysages member.

Facilities	Directions
Good quality, modern toilet blocks. with showers and washbasins in cubicles. Facilities for disabled visitors. Washing machines and dryers. Shop. Bar, restaurant and takeaway (1/6-15/9). Swimming and paddling pools (1/6-15/9). Indoor pool all season. Water slide. Minigolf. Games room. Playground. Entertainment and children's club in peak season. Off site: Nearest beach 2.5 km. Bicycle hire 2 km. Riding 12 km. Fishing 4 km.	Site is 1 km. south of Soulac on the D101 (Routes des Lacs) and is well signed. GPS: 45.48355, -1.11952

Charges guide

Per unit incl. 2 persons	€ 16,00 - € 26,00
extra person	€ 4,00 - € 5,00
child (3-10 yrs)	€ 2,00 - € 4,00
electricity (5A)	€ 5,00

Open: 5 April - 8 November.

Vézac

Camping les Deux Vallées

La Gare, F-24220 Vézac (Dordogne) T: 05 53 29 53 55. E: contact@campingles2vallees.com

alanrogers.com/FR24150

This site is enviably situated almost under the shadow of Beynac castle in the heart of the Dordogne. There are 92 flat marked touring pitches, most of a good size, some large, and with electricity (6/10A). There is plenty of shade and the general feel is of unspoilt but well managed woodland. There is a small fishing lake on site and it is only a short distance to the Dordogne river for bathing or canoeing. The site is being steadily upgraded by its Dutch owners who provide a warm and friendly welcome. English is spoken. A small train passes close to the site but it is unobtrusive. Nearby Beynac is a short walk through the woods and Roque-Gageac, with its troglodyte fort and ancient church, is just 3 km. away.

Facilities	Directions
The modern unisex, clean toilet blocks (one heated) have facilities for disabled visitors and babies. Shop, bar/restaurant with takeaway (24/4-30/10). Refurbished pool complex (24/4-30/10). Minigolf. Boules. Play area. Games room. Fishing. Entertainment including quiz nights and barbecues (July/Aug). Internet access and WiFi in bar area (free). Off site: Bicycle hire 200 m. Riding 2 km. Golf 8 km. Lake beach 450 m. Canoeing can be booked on site (bus picks up and returns). Beynac 1 km. Roque-Gageac 3 km. Sarlat with Saturday market 8 km.	Leave A20 at exit 55 and follow D804/D703 to Sarlat. From Sarlat continue onto the D57 towards Beynac-et-Cazenac and directly after village sign for Vézac take first right turn to site, about 1 km. (cross railway line and turn left). GPS: 44.83560, 1.15873

Charges guide

Per unit incl. 2 persons and electricity	€ 16,90 - € 25,60
extra person	€ 4,20 - € 6,30
child	free - € 3,80

Open: All year.

Urrugne

Sunêlia Col d'Ibardin

F-64122 Urrugne (Pyrénées-Atlantiques) T: 05 59 54 31 21. E: info@col-ibardin.com

alanrogers.com/FR64110

This family owned site at the foot of the Basque Pyrénées is highly recommended and deserves praise. It is well run with emphasis on personal attention, the friendly family and their staff ensuring that all are made welcome, and is attractively set in the middle of an oak wood with a mountain stream cascading through it. Behind the forecourt, with its brightly coloured shrubs and modern reception area, various roadways lead to the 191 pitches. These are individual, spacious and enjoy the benefit of the shade (if preferred a more open aspect can be found). There are electricity hook-ups (4/10A) and adequate water points. A very attractive chalet village has recently been added. From this site you can enjoy the mountain scenery, be on the beach in 7-10 km. or cross the border into Spain in about 14 km.

Facilities

Two toilet blocks, one rebuilt to a high specification, are kept very clean. WC for disabled visitors. Dishwashing and laundry facilities. Motorcaravan service point. Shop for basics and bread orders (15/6-15/9). Restaurant, takeaway service and bar (15/6-15/9). Heated swimming pool and paddling pool. Playground and club (adult supervision). Tennis. Boules. Video games. Bicycle hire. Multisport area. Not suitable for American motorhomes. Off site: Supermarket and shopping centre 5 km. Fishing and golf 7 km. Riding 20 km.

Open: 1 April - 30 September.

Directions

Leave A63 at St Jean-de-Luz sud, exit no. 2 and join RN10 in direction of Urrugne. Turn left at roundabout (Col d'Ibardin) on D4. Site on right after 5 km. Do not turn off to the Col itself, carry on towards Ascain. GPS: 43.33376, -1.68458

Charges guide

Per unit incl. 2 persons	
and electricity	€ 16,50 - € 34,00
extra person	€ 3,00 - € 6,00
child (2-7 yrs)	€ 2,00 - € 3,50
pet	€ 2,50

For latest campsite news, availability and prices visit

alanrogers.com

Vielle-Saint-Girons

Campéole les Tourterelles

F-40560 Vielle-Saint-Girons (Landes) T: 05 58 47 93 12. E: tourterelles@campeole.com

alanrogers.com/FR40450

Les Tourterelles is a large site extending over 20 hectares of forest and is a member of the Campéole group. The site has direct access to the beach, using 2 footpaths, one of which is decked. The beach is vast and is very popular with surfers. A lifeguard is in attendance during the high season. There are 660 pitches at Les Tourterelles, of which around 160 are occupied by mobile homes, chalets and fully equipped bungalow tents, all available for rent, and including some units specially adapted for disabled visitors. Pitches are well shaded by pines and most have electrical connections. Leisure facilities here include a multi sport terrain, cycle hire and several children's play areas. There are many appealing tracks through the surrounding forests and the site organises occasional accompanied walks (high season). Various other activities are on offer including beach volleyball and surfing lessons. A daily children's club is in operation as well as regular evening entertainment, including concerts and discos.

Facilities

Bar. Snack bar. Takeaway meals. Shop. Direct beach access. Volleyball. Beach volleyball. Bicycle hire. Bouncy castle. Play areas. Games room. Activity and entertainment programme. Tourist information. Mobile homes, chalets and equipped tents for rent. Off site: St Girons Plage (attractive resort with all services) 200 m. Fishing. Walking and cycle tracks through the forest. Basque country.

Open: 1 May - 30 September.

Directions

Approaching from Bordeaux, take the A63 towards Bayonne. Leave at the Castets - Vielle-St -Girons exit and continue to Vielle St Girons. At the traffic lights follow signs to St Girons Plage (and the site). When you reach St Girons Plage turn right at the roundabout and the site can be found after a further 50m. GPS: 43.9397, -1.3258

Charges 2011

Contact the site for details.

Vielle-Saint-Girons

Sunêlia le Col-Vert

Lac de Léon, F-40560 Vielle-Saint-Girons (Landes) T: 0890 710 001. E: contact@colvert.com

alanrogers.com/FR40050

This large, well maintained campsite is well laid out on the shores of Lac de Léon and offers 185 mobile homes for rent and 380 touring pitches. The pitches range from simple ones to those with water and a drain, and there are 8 with private, well designed, modern sanitary facilities. In low season it is a quiet site and those pitches beside the lake offer a wonderful backdrop to relaxing pastimes. During the main season it is a lively place for children of all ages. A pool complex offers a standard pool for swimming, a pool for children with water canon and fountains, plenty of sunbeds and a heated indoor pool.

Facilities

Four toilet blocks, one heated. One block with fun facilities for children based on Disney characters. Facilities for disabled visitors. Laundry facilities. Motorcaravan services. Shops, bar/restaurant, takeaway (1/4-5/9). Swimming pool complex with three pools. Spa, fitness centre and sauna. Play area. Games room. Sports areas. Boules. Tennis. Bicycle hire. Minigolf. Fishing. Riding. Sailing school (15/6-15/9). Communal barbecues. Internet access and WiFi. Off site: Walking and cycle ways in the forest. Atlantic beaches 5 km. Golf 10 km.

Open: 1 April - 19 September.

Directions

Site is off D652 Mimizan - Léon road, 4 km. south of crossroads with D42 at St Girons. The road to the lake and the site is signed at Vielle. GPS: 43.90285, -1.3125

Charges guide

Per unit incl. 2 persons	
and electricity	€ 14,20 - € 53,80
extra person	€ 2,00 - € 6,50
child (3-13 yrs)	€ 1,50 - € 5,50
dog	€ 1,00 - € 4,30

For latest campsite news, availability and prices visit

alanrogers.com

Vielle-Saint-Girons

Camping Club International Eurosol

Route de la Plage, F-40560 Vielle-Saint-Girons (Landes) T: 05 58 47 90 14. E: contact@camping-eurosol.com
alanrogers.com/FR40060

Eurosol is an attractive and well maintained site extending over 15 hectares of undulating ground amongst mature pine trees giving good shade. 209 of the 356 pitches have electricity (10A) with 120 fully serviced. A wide range of mobile homes and chalets are available for rent too. This is very much a family site with multilingual entertainers. Many games and tournaments are organised and a beach volleyball competition is held each evening in front of the bar. The adjacent boules terrain is also floodlit. An excellent sandy beach 700 metres from the site has supervised bathing in high season, and is ideal for surfing. The landscaped swimming pool complex is impressive with three large pools, one of which is covered and heated, and a large children's paddling pool. There is a convivial restaurant and takeaway food service. A large supermarket is well stocked with fresh bread daily and international newspapers. A number of cycle trails lead from the site through the vast forests of Les Landes, and a riding centre is located just 100 m. from Eurosol. To the south, the Basque country and Biarritz are within easy access.

Facilities

Four main toilet blocks and two smaller blocks are comfortable and clean with facilities for babies and disabled visitors. Motorcaravan services. Fridge rental. Well stocked shop and bar (all season). Restaurant, takeaway (9/6-4/9). Stage for live shows arranged in July/Aug. Outdoor swimming pool, paddling pool and heated covered pool (all season). Tennis. Multisport court. Bicycle hire. Internet and WiFi. Charcoal barbecues are not permitted. Off site: Riding school opposite. Surf school 500 m. Fishing 700 m. Golf 18 km.

Open: 14 May - 10 September.

Directions

Turn off D652 at St Girons on D42 towards St Girons-Plage. Site is on left before coming to beach (4.5 km). GPS: 43.95166, -1.35212

Charges guide

Per unit incl. 2 persons	
and electricity	€ 18,00 - € 35,00
extra person (over 4 yrs)	€ 5,00
dog	€ 4,00

Villefranche-de-Queyran

Camping Moulin de Campech

F-47160 Villefranche-de-Queyran (Lot-et-Garonne) T: 05 53 88 72 43. E: camping@moulindecampech.co.uk
alanrogers.com/FR47050

This well shaded, pretty site is run by Sue and George Thomas along with Sue's parents, Dot and Bob Dunn. At the entrance to the site, a trout lake with graceful weeping willows feeds under the restored mill house which is home to the owners as well as housing the bar and restaurant. Children will need supervision around the lake and at the pool which is on an elevated area above the mill house. The 60 large-sized pitches are mostly divided by hedges, with electricity (6A, long leads may be necessary in places, but can be borrowed free of charge).

Facilities

The single, rather ordinary toilet block has modern fittings. Washing machine and tumble dryer. Shop and bar (1/4-30/9). Restaurant (25/4-20/9). Terraced heated swimming pool (1/5-30/9). Open grassy games area. Board games and English library. Boules. Barbecue and quiz nights in high season. Fishing (discounted rate for campers, no permit required). Torch useful. Off site: Watersports, bicycle hire, golf or riding 10 km. Numerous wine caves and armagnac products.

Open: 1 April - 14 October.

Directions

Take A10 south to Bordeaux. Join A62 for Toulouse and take exit 6 for Damazan. Follow D8 to Mont de Marsan, at Cap du Bosc turn right onto D11 for Casteljaloux. Site is signed, 5 km. on right. GPS: 44.27179, 0.19093

Charges guide

Per unit incl. 2 persons	
and electricity	€ 20,00 - € 27,00
extra person	€ 4,10 - € 5,95
child (under 7 yrs)	€ 2,90 - € 4,10

Villeréal

Camping le Château de Fonrives

Rives, F-47210 Villeréal (Lot-et-Garonne) T: 05 53 36 63 38. E: chateau.de.fonrives@wanadoo.fr

alanrogers.com/FR47030

Le Château de Fonrives is situated in Lot-en-Garonne. The site is set in pretty part-farmed, part-wooded countryside. It is a mixture of hazelnut woodland with lake and château (mostly 16th century). An attractive tree-lined avenue leads to the barns adjacent to the château which have been converted to house the site's amenities. There are 251 pitches, 101 of which are for touring units, with electricity. They are of a generous size and are well defined by neatly trimmed hedges and small shrubs. Pitches near the woodland receive moderate shade, but elsewhere there is light shade from hedges and young trees. There are also a large number of mobile homes here but they do not detract from the general feeling of spaciousness and due to the position of the touring pitches they appear well separated.

Facilities

Three well positioned, modern sanitary blocks with facilities for disabled visitors. Laundry facilities. Shop (20/5-15/9). Restaurant, snacks and takeaway (May-Sept). Bar with disco area and terrace (1/6-5/9). Covered swimming pool (April-Oct), outdoor pool, water slides, paddling pool. Jacuzzi. Gym. Sauna. Trim trail. Small play area. Small field for volleyball and football. Library. Minigolf, tennis, bicycle hire (all charged). Activities organised for children and adults in season, including excursions and walks. Caravan storage. Hairdresser (July/Aug). WiFi in bar area (charged). Off site: Riding 8 km. Golf, walking and cycling.

Open: 4 April - 3 October.

Directions

Site is about 2 km. northwest of Villeréal, on west side of the D14/D207 Bergerac - Villaréal road. Pass through Rives and site is signed on the left. GPS: 44.65723, 0.72847

Charges guide

Per unit incl. 2 persons	
and electricity	€ 15,00 - € 34,50
extra person	€ 4,00 - € 4,90
child (under 6 yrs)	€ 2,00 - € 2,80
dog	€ 3,00

Villeréal

Camping de Bergougne

D250, Rives, F-47210 Villeréal (Lot-et-Garonne) T: 05 53 36 01 30. E: info@camping-de-bergougne.com

alanrogers.com/FR47160

Camping de Bergougne is a small site located close to the 13th-century bastide of Villeréal in the Haut-Agenais. This restful site is a good choice for either relaxing at the poolside or exploring the surrounding country. There are 60 pitches, 48 for touring, with the remainder for mobile homes and tent-bungalows which are available for hire. The touring pitches are mainly in the shade and all have electricity. One toilet block is situated near the reception area and is converted from original farm building – be careful, head room is limited! The site is very well located for exploring the region.

Facilities

Two toilet blocks, one close to reception has limited head room. The second is newly built and of a high standard with facilities for babies and visitors with disabilities. Laundry and dishwashing area. Bar, restaurant, snack bar and takeaway (1/6-15/9). New swimming and paddling pools. Play area. Games room. Library. Pony riding. Fishing. WiFi in bar area. Tourist information. Off site: Shops and bicycle hire in Villareal 2 km. Golf 15 km. Within 30 minutes of the Lot Valley and the Valley of the Dordogne.

Open: 1 May - 30 September.

Directions

Site is northwest of Villeréal. From Villeréal take the northbound D207 and at Rives, follow local signs to site. GPS: 44.652503, 0.723488

Charges guide

Per unit incl. 2 persons	
and electricity (6A)	€ 12,10 - € 18,60
extra person	€ 2,50 - € 3,80

Vitrac

Domaine de Soleil Plage

Caudon par Montfort, Vitrac, F-24200 Sarlat-la-Canéda (Dordogne) T: 05 53 28 33 33. E: info@soleilplage.fr

alanrogers.com/FR24090

531

This site is in one of the most attractive sections of the Dordogne valley, with a riverside location. There are 199 pitches, in three sections, with 104 for touring units. The smallest section surrounds the main reception and other facilities. There are 40 mobile homes, 20 chalets and 17 bungalow tents. The site offers river bathing from a sizeable pebble or sand bank or there is a very impressive heated pool complex. All pitches are bounded by hedges and are of adequate size. Most pitches have some shade and have electricity and many have water and a drain. If you like a holiday with lots going on, you will like this one. Various activities are organised during high season including walks and sports tournaments, and daily canoe hire is available from the site. Once a week in July and August there is a soirée'(charged for) usually involving a barbecue or paella, with band and lots of free wine – worth catching! The site is busy and reservation is advisable. English is spoken. The site is quite expensive in high season and you also pay more for a riverside pitch, but these have fine river views. There is some tour operator presence.

Facilities

Toilet facilities are in three modern unisex blocks. You will need to borrow a plug for the baby bath (€ 5 deposit). Washing machines and dryer. Motorcaravan service point. Well stocked shop, pleasant bar with TV and attractive, newly refurbished restaurant with terrace (all open from May 1st). Picnics are available to order. Very impressive heated main pool, paddling pool, spa pool and two water slides. Tennis. Minigolf. Playground. Fishing. Canoe and kayak hire. Bicycle hire. Currency exchange. Small library. WiFi in bar/reception area (charged). Tourist information. Activities and social events are organised in high season. Off site: Golf 1 km. Riding 5 km. Many attractions of the Dordogne are within easy reach.

Open: 3 April - 27 September.

Directions

Site is 6 km. south of Sarlat. From A20 take exit 55 (Souillac) towards Sarlat. Follow the D703 to Carsac and on to Montfort. At Montfort castle site is signed on left. Continue for 2 km. down to the river and site. GPS: 44.825, 1.25388

Charges guide

Per unit incl. 2 persons	
and electricity	€ 21,00 - € 34,50
incl. full services	€ 24,50 - € 49,00
extra person	€ 5,00 - € 7,50
child (2-8 yrs)	€ 3,00 - € 4,50

For latest campsite news, availability and prices visit

alanrogers.com

Rolling fields of yellow sunflowers, the Armagnac vineyards and crumbling, ancient stone buildings amidst the sleepy villages make this colourful region popular with those who enjoy good food, good wine and a taste of the good life.

DÉPARTEMENTS: 09 ARIÈGE, 12 AVEYRON, 31 HAUTE-GARONNE, 32 GERS, 46 LOT, 65 HAUTES-PYRÉNÉES, 81 TARN, 82 TARN-ET-GARONNE.

MAJOR CITY: TOULOUSE

The Midi-Pyrénées is the largest region of France, extending from the Dordogne in the north to the Spanish border. The charming and historic villages of Marciac, Cordes du Ciel and Saint-Cirq-Lapopie will attract you in the same way as they attracted the many painters, sculptors and jazz musicians who live and work there. The welcoming cities of Toulouse, Albi (15th-century cathedral), Cahors and Auch (statue of d'Artagnan) are ideal for for a leisurely stroll while visiting their historic sites.

Breathe some wonderful fresh air in the Pyrénées national park and enjoy the pine forests, waterfalls, high plains and lakes between the Cirque de Gavarnie and the Cauterets-Pont d'Espagne.

Experience the vertiginous Pic du Midi and the Viaduc de Millau. The first is almost 3,000 metres high, whilst the latter soars 343 metres above the river Tarn. Conques and Moissac hold other records: for over 1,000 years, pilgrims have passed through these cities on their way to Saint Jacques de Compostella. Other destinations for pilgrims in the region are Lourdes and Rocamadour, towns renowned for their spiritual and cosmopolitan atmosphere.

www.tourism-midi-pyrenees.co.uk

www.**tourism-midi-pyrenees.co.uk**
greatsites-midipyrenees.co.uk

Outdoor activities

Hiking

Midi-Pyrénées abounds in hiking trails, including the famous GR10 and its emerald lakes in the Pyrénées; the spiritual paths of St Jacques de Compostella; or back to the Middle Ages on the trail of the Cathars and the Knights Templar: there is a route for everyone.

www.**tourism-midi-pyrenees.co.uk**

Cycling

The opportunities for cycling during your holiday in the Midi-Pyrénées are numerous: 'voies vertes' (green roads) and 'véloroutes' alongside the Canal du Midi or in the Lot for those who like to take it gently, sporting itineraries following the routes of the Tour de France for athletes, or the mountain bike tracks for those who want to go wild.

www.**tourism-midi-pyrenees.co.uk**

Regional specialities

The region is proud to have some 15 AOC products, such as Roquefort cheese and the tasty golden grape Chasselas de Moissac and many famous specialities such as cassoulet, aligot, foie gras, truffle and melons of Quercy. Treat yourself!

www.**tourism-midi-pyrenees.co.uk**

Wines

Wine Country

Strong or light, tannic or fruity, the wines of the Midi-Pyrénées are just as varied as those in more well-known wine regions. The aperitives Hypocras in Ariège, Pousse-Rapière and Floc de Gascogne of the Gers. Cahors, Gaillac, Fronton and Madiran are the most prestigious AOC wines, and don't forget Côtes de St-Mont, Coteaux du Quercy and all 'vins de pays'. And of course Armagnac, the oldest 'eau de vie' of France.

www.**tourism-midi-pyrenees.co.uk**

Images CRT Midi Pyrénées - Dominique VIET

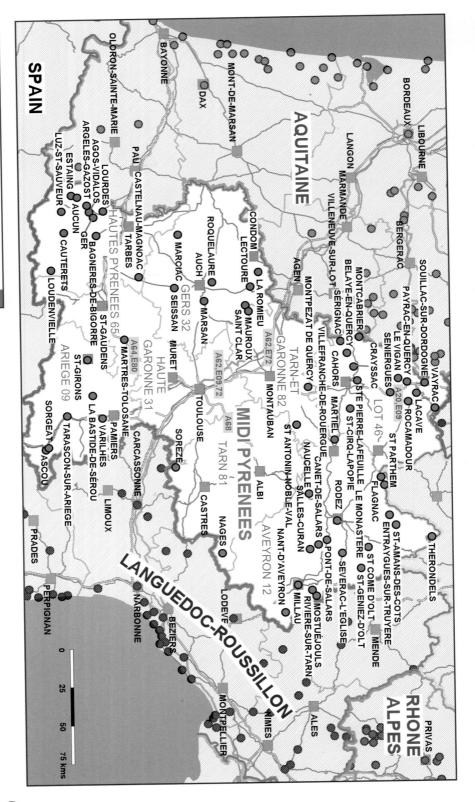

For latest campsite news, availability and prices visit
alanrogers.com

Agos-Vidalos

Camping Soleil du Pibeste

16 avenue du Lavedan, F-65400 Agos-Vidalos (Hautes-Pyrénées) T: 05 62 97 53 23
E: info@campingpibeste.com alanrogers.com/FR65090

The Dusserm family, owners, are very proud of their regional culture and heritage and will ensure you are a made welcome. The reception is friendly, with an area for local foods, maps and good tourist information. This site is special because of the range and type of activities which it offers. These include tai chi, qi gong, massage, archery, walking, climbing and canoeing. Choral and creative activities are offered. There are 38 touring pitches all with 3-15A electricity. Mobile homes and chalets are available to rent. The mountain view from the terrace is magnificent.

Facilities

Two heated toilet blocks. Baby room. Facilities for disabled visitors (key). Cleaning can be variable. Washing machine, dryer. Motorcaravan services. Bar, snacks, piano, internet. Room for playing cards or reading. Swimming, paddling pools. Small play area. Boules, archery, basketball, volleyball. Table tennis. Bicycle hire. Tai chi and other classes. Off site: Fishing 800 m. Rafting 2 km. Golf 10 km. Riding 15 km. Skiing 20 km.

Open: 1 May - 30 September.

Directions

Agos Vidalos is on the N21, which becomes the D821, 5 km. south of Lourdes. Leave express-way at second exit, signed Agos Vidalos and continue on D921B to site, a short distance on the right. GPS: 43.03557, -0.07093

Charges guide

Per unit incl. 2 persons and electricity	€ 25,00 - € 34,00
extra person	€ 8,00

Argelès-Gazost

Sunêlia les Trois Vallées

Avenue des Pyrénées, F-65400 Argelès-Gazost (Hautes-Pyrénées) T: 05 62 90 35 47. E: 3-valles@wanadoo.fr
alanrogers.com/FR65020

The attractive outdoor pools, jacuzzi, water chutes and heated indoor pool with opening roof are features of this large and lively site. It has 200 level grassy touring pitches, with some mountain views, and 283 mobile homes. All have electricity (3-6A). The two sanitary blocks are dated. Reception staff are helpful and friendly. Visitors can gather in the new, imaginatively designed centre to eat, drink, chat, use the WiFi, watch events on the overhead TVs, and in season enjoy the daily programme of professional entertainers. All visitors can enjoy an impressive programme of activities. The pilgrimage town of Lourdes is nearby.

Facilities

The toilet blocks are a little dated and could be busy at peak times. Facilities for disabled visitors. Bar/disco. Café, takeaway, restaurant (15/6-15/9). Bread. Swimming pool complex (from 15/5), heated indoor pool (all year), paddling pool, spa bath, large jacuzzi and two water slides. TV room. Good playground. Volleyball, football, boules, archery. Entertainment and activities in high season. WiFi (charged in high season). Off site: Bicycle hire 50 m. Fishing 500 m. Riding 3 km.

Open: 1 April - 2 November.

Directions

Argelès-Gazost is 13 km. south of Lourdes. Take D821 towards Argelés-Gazost, then onto 'La Voie Rapide' and turn right at the first roundabout, after 300 m. right at the new roundabout and you are at the site. GPS: 43.01216, -0.09711

Charges guide

Per unit incl. 2 persons	€ 13,50 - € 34,00
extra person	€ 5,00 - € 10,00
child (2-13 yrs)	€ 3,50 - € 9,00

Argelès-Gazost

Kawan Village du Lavedan

Lau-Balagnas, 44 Route des Vallees, F-65400 Argelès-Gazost (Hautes-Pyrénées) T: 05 62 97 18 84
E: contact@lavedan.com alanrogers.com/FR65080

Camping du Lavedan is an old established, family owned site set in the Argelès-Gazost valley south of Lourdes, where a warm welcome and an impressive mountain view await you. There are 60 level touring pitches, all with electricity (2-10A) and most have shade from trees. They are set away from the 48 mobile homes, of which 12 are to rent. Landscaping has been carefully considered. The large well-designed restaurant and bar area is the scene of some lively evening entertainment in the summer. There is some noise from the road.

Facilities

Recent well maintained toilet block. Baby room. Facilities for disabled visitors. Washing machines and dryer in separate block heated in winter. Restaurant with terrace, pizzeria and snacks (1/5-15/9). Bar, TV (all year). No shop, bread delivery (1/5-15/9). Swimming pool (with cover), paddling pool. Play area. WiFi (charged). Boules, table tennis. Off site: Trout fishing, bicycle hire 1 km. Supermarket 2 km. Riding 5 km. Golf 15 km.

Open: All year.

Directions

From Lourdes take the N21 (Voie rapide) south. This becomes the N821/N821A. Take exit 3 (Argeles-Gazost). Take D921 then D921B to Lau-Balagnas. Site is on the right, at southern edge of town. GPS: 42.98822, -0.089

Charges guide

Per unit incl. 2 persons	€ 15,00 - € 24,00

For latest campsite news, availability and prices visit
alanrogers.com

Ascou

Camping Ascou la Forge

F-09110 Ascou (Ariège) T: 05 61 64 60 03. E: info@ascou-la-forge.fr

alanrogers.com/FR09120

The Dutch owners of Ascou La Forge will give you a warm, friendly welcome at their oasis in the mountains of the Pyrenees, close to the borders of Andorra and Spain. The site is 3,500 feet above sea level but is easily accessible for motorhomes and caravans. Lying alongside the Lauze river, there are 50 pitches. In low season 44 mainly level, grass touring pitches with electricity are available, but this number reduces to 20 in July and August to allow more room for the large influx of campers with tents. There are also two chalets and one apartment available to rent. The site is quite open but a few trees scattered around provide some shade.

Facilities

Modern, bright, sanitary block is fully equipped including facilities for disabled visitors which double as a family shower room with a baby bath. Shop. Bar with large screen for major sports events and films about the local flora/fauna. Play area. Maps and walking routes are available from reception. Free WiFi. Off site: Restaurant next door to site (all year). Restaurants, bars and shops in Ax-les-Thermes 7 km.

Open: All year.

Directions

From Ax-Les-Thermes take D613 signed Quérigat, Quillan and Ascou-Pailhéres. After 3.6 km. turn right on D25 to site on right after 3.4 km. GPS: 42.72444, 1.89274

Charges guide

Per unit incl. 2 persons and electricity	€ 15,00 - € 23,00
extra person	€ 3,50 - € 5,00
child (0-7 yrs)	€ 2,50 - € 3,50

Aucun

Camping Azun Nature

1 route des Poueyes, F-65400 Aucun (Hautes-Pyrénées) T: 05 62 97 45 05. E: azun.nature@wanadoo.fr

alanrogers.com/FR65190

This site is attractively located on the edge of the National Park of the High Pyrenees with superb walking, mountain biking and paragliding opportunities. The 25 open and grassy touring pitches, most with electricity (3/6A), have fine views of the surrounding mountains. There are 12 rental chalets. The owner is friendly and enthusiastic. A small shop is provided and drinks can be served on the terrace in summer, though there is no bar. The site prides itself on its relative simplicity and its environmental ethos. The owners are delighted to recommend walking or cycling itineraries and to help organise excursions. There are also many kilometres of marked tracks.

Facilities

Good quality sanitary block with facilities for babies and visitors with disabilities. No restaurant/snack bar but drinks and coffee served on the terrace in high season. Bread delivery (1/7-31/8). Simple shop. Play area. Activities room. Maps and tourist information. Internet and WiFi. Large field area for sports and games. Off site: Walking. Mountain biking. Skiing. Paragliding schools. Arrens-Marsous 2 km.

Open: 15 May - 30 September.

Directions

From Argeles-Gazost take the 921B then the D918 following signs for Aucun. At sign for Aucun village turn left for 'Las Poueyes' and drive for 100 m. Azun Nature's entrance is on the right between the barns. GPS: 42.97344, -0.18501

Charges guide

Per unit incl. 2 persons and electricity (6A)	€ 16,10
extra person	€ 4,20
child (under 7 yrs)	€ 2,50

Bagnères-de-Bigorre

Camping le Monlôo

Chemin du Monlôo (RD8), F-65200 Bagnères-de-Bigorre (Hautes-Pyrénées) T: 05 62 95 19 65
E: campingmonloo@yahoo.com alanrogers.com/FR65160

A relatively small site of 120 touring pitches, le Monlôo is set in a wide valley in the Pyrenees. The immediate surroundings of farmland, with crops growing and cows at pasture, give way to some magnificent views of the mountains towering away from the front of the site, whilst the back is right at the foot of some smaller foothills. This area is a paradise for walkers and cyclists and just traveling a short distance opens up new horizons with some large waterfalls not far away. The friendly family take their job seriously and will show you a selection of available pitches from the comfort of their electric car.

Facilities

Ample toilet facilities are provided in three blocks. Facilities for disabled visitors. Washing machines. Motorcaravan services. Bread to order. Open air heated pool with slide. Simple play area. Gas or electric barbecues are permitted. Off site: Spa town of Bagnères-de-Bigorre 2 km.

Open: All year.

Directions

From the A64 take exit 14 signed Bagnères-de-Bigorre. Enter town and take D8 road to the right for Ordizan. Site is just a few hundred metres along this road, well signed. GPS: 43.08180, 0.15139

Charges guide

Per unit incl. 2 persons	€ 11,00 - € 16,50
extra person	€ 3,50 - € 4,00
child (2-8 yrs)	€ 1,50 - € 2,80
electricity (2-6A)	€ 2,00 - € 5,50

Bélaye-en-Quercy

Camping la Tuque

F-46140 Bélaye (Lot) T: 05 65 21 34 34. E: camping@la-tuque.info
alanrogers.com/FR46130

The Quercy region of southwest France is renowned for its sunny climate and attractive terrain, ranging from the dry 'Causse' landscape to the lusher Lot valley and vineyards of Cahors. La Tuque extends over 22 acres, close to the pretty village of Bélaye. The 90 pitches are large (some to 120 sq.m) and well shaded. Unusually, except for loading and unloading, cars are not allowed in the camping area, and large parking areas are provided at the entrance. This is a good centre for an active holiday – walking, mountain biking, canoeing and rock climbing are all possible and the site also has a large swimming pool and three water slides, as well as a separate children's pool.

Facilities

Small shop with daily delivery of fresh bread. Bar and snack bar with freshly baked pizzas. Swimming pool with water slides and paddling pool. Floodlit tennis court. Minigolf. Library. Playground. Games room. Laundry carried out by site staff. Fridge hire. Mobile homes for rent. WiFi in bar area (charged). Off site: Walking and cycle routes. Fishing 5 km. Bélaye with shops and cafés 5 km.

Open: 30 April - 10 September.

Directions

Leave the A20 autoroute at exit 57 (Cahors) and take the D811 (D911) towards Puy l'Evêque. In Prayssac, take the D67 towards Bélaye/Boulvé. From Belaye take the D6, following signs to La Tuque. Site is well signed from here. GPS: 44.44407, 1.17244

Charges guide

Per unit incl. 2 persons and electricity	€ 19,50 - € 25,50
extra person	€ 5,00 - € 6,00
child (under 7 yrs)	€ 3,50 - € 4,50

No credit cards.

Canet-de-Salars

Castel Camping le Caussanel

Lac de Pareloup, F-12290 Canet-de-Salars (Aveyron) T: 05 65 46 85 19. E: info@lecaussanel.com
alanrogers.com/FR12170

The site has 235 large, fairly level, grassy pitches, 105 for touring. Most have 6A electricity but very long leads may be necessary, and 37 are fully serviced. The pitches are defined by a tree or boulder in each corner and offer little privacy but many have wonderful views over the lake. Most pitches have little shade, a few having good shade. The site has swimming pools with toboggan and slides and a large paddling pool for children with small slides. The adjacent lake offers a large area, 1 km. long, for swimming and all the usual watersports. This large, extremely spacious site on the banks of Lac de Pareloup is greatly improved. It is ideal, in low season, for those seeking a tranquil holiday in a beautiful region of France or in high season, for those seeking an active holiday.

Facilities

Modern toilet blocks have all the necessary facilities. Motorcaravan services. Shop. Bar. Restaurant, takeaway (5/6-4/9). Swimming pool complex (10/5-4/9). Large play area. Boules. Tennis. Football. Organised activities (July/Aug). Fishing. Bicycle hire (July/Aug). Motor boat launching. Water sports (July/Aug). Swimming in lake. Internet access. Max. 1 dog. Off site: Paths around lake (24 km). Other marked walks and cycle rides. Shops, banks, restaurants 8 km. Riding 10 km. Golf 30 km. Canoeing, rafting, paragliding caving, windsurfing.

Open: 23 May - 17 September.

Directions

From D911 Rodez - Millau road, just east of Pont de Salars, turn south on D993 signed Salles-Curan. In 6 km. at crossroads turn right on D538 signed Le Caussanel. Very shortly turn left and continue to site. GPS: 44.21462, 2.76658

Charges guide

Per unit incl. 2 persons and electricity	€ 17,90 - € 44,20

For latest campsite news, availability and prices visit

alanrogers.com

Cauterets

Camping Cabaliros

Pont de Secours, F-65110 Cauterets (Hautes-Pyrénées) T: 05 62 92 55 36. E: info@camping-cabaliros.com

alanrogers.com/FR65110

This is a delightful site, with friendly family owners who provide a warm welcome to this magnificent mountain area. The open, grassy site has stupendous panoramic views. A separate field has 36 pitches for small tents and another 60 touring pitches with electricity (6A Europlug). These are large and grassy and some shade is provided by mature trees. A communal room is used by visitors to make music, play games, watch television, read the English books and enjoy themselves. The site is within walking distance of Cauteret, with its shops and restaurants, and Argelès-Gazost and the major pilgrimage town of Lourdes are suitable for day visits.

Facilities

Sanitary block near site entrance with WCs, hot showers and washbasins in cubicles. Facilities for disabled campers. Dishwashing and laundry sinks with cold water only. Washing machine and dryer. Motorcaravan service point. Large library (some English) and excellent meeting room with television. Play area for over 7s. Fishing. Off site: Restaurant (July/Aug) 50 m. Supermarket 1 km. Shops, restaurants and bars 2 km. Indoor and outdoor swimming pools 2 km. Walking. Pont d'Espagne 9 km. Route des Cascades (waterfalls) 4 km. Riding 10 km.

Open: 1 June - 30 September.

Directions

From Argelès-Gazost take D921B followed by the D920A to Cauterets. Site is on right 1 km. after 'SHOPI' supermarket just before Cauterets.
GPS: 42.90347, -0.10714

Charges guide

Per unit incl. 2 persons and electricity (6A)	€ 15,80 - € 17,60
tent incl. 2 persons and car	€ 12,70 - € 14,10
extra person	€ 4,40 - € 4,90
child (under 7 yrs)	€ 2,30 - € 2,55

Crayssac

Campé**o**le

Campéole les Reflets du Quercy

Mas de Bastide, F-46150 Crayssac (Lot) T: 05 65 30 00 27. E: reflets-du-quercy@campeole.com

alanrogers.com/FR46170

Set in the west of the Lot department, about 16 km. from the large town of Cahors, this site is owned by the Campéole group and is classed as a holiday village. Located on a hill with good views of the surrounding countryside, the 150 pitches (75 touring, 30 with 6A electricity) are hilly and terraced. Most are partially shaded with Quercy oak trees and some are set apart by small Crayssac stone walls. Almost half of the touring pitches are located on good, level hardstanding. At the rear of the site is a large area of independently owned mobile homes and residents here also have access to the campsite facilities. The site has a good 25 m. swimming pool overlooked by the terrace of the bar and snack bar. The site is managed by a very friendly French couple and a welcoming Campéole team.

Facilities

Three clean and well maintained sanitary blocks (not all open outside high season). Facilities for disabled visitors. Baby room with bath. Laundry facilities. Motorcaravan service point. Shop (July/Aug). Bar and snacks (July/Aug). Swimming and paddling pools (July/Aug). TV and games room. Boules. Tennis court. Play area with large bouncy castle. Entertainment in high season. Off site: Fishing and riding 7 km. Bicycle hire 15 km. Good shops 16 km.

Open: 9 April - 25 September.

Directions

From Cahors on the RN20, follow D911 northwest towards Puy-l'Évêque, Mercuès and Prayssac. Several kilometres after Labarthe, take D23, on the left near Crayssac. Site is well signed from Crayssac.
GPS: 44.50690, 1.32410

Charges guide

Per unit incl. 2 persons and electricity	€ 15,10 - € 24,50

Entraygues-sur-Truyère

Camping du Val de Saures

Village de Gîtes le Bastie, F-12140 Entraygues-sur-Truyère (Aveyron) T: 05 65 44 56 92
E: info@camping-valdesaures.com alanrogers.com/FR12260

Camping Le Val de Saures is a well presented, value for money site only five minutes across a river bridge from the interesting old town of Entraygues. Situated at the confluence of the rivers Lot and Truyère, it is a good base for relaxing and exploring this beautiful area of Aveyron. There are 110 good sized level grassy pitches (6A electricity) separated by small shrubs and trees with varying amount of shade. Many overlook the river Lot. Although the site has no shop, bar or restaurant these are all available in the town. In the area there are many wonderful medieval villages, with their narrow streets and Tudor houses with the famous grey Lauze tiles. Canoeing or rafting are possible and there are marked paths to explore on foot, on horseback or by bike.

Facilities

Three very clean and well appointed toilet blocks with all the necessary facilities including those for disabled visitors. Motorcaravan service point. TV/games room. WiFi. Playground. River fishing but no bathing. Off site: Fortified town of Entraygues (400 m. by footbridge) with a good range of shops, banks, bars and restaurants. Swimming pool (free) and tennis courts and large playground close by. Watersports excursion 400 m. Riding 10 km.

Open: 1 May - 24 September.

Directions

Entraygues-sur-Truyère is 42 km. southeast of Aurillac on the D920. At southern end of Entraygues on the D920 turn right (site signed), over river bridge onto the D904 and immediately right again. Just past the tennis courts fork right and follow lane down to site. GPS: 44.64243, 2.56414

Charges guide

Per unit incl. 2 persons	€ 10,00 - € 17,00
extra person	€ 2,50 - € 4,00
child (3-13 yrs)	€ 2,50 - € 3,00
electricity	€ 3,50

Estaing

Camping Pyrénées Natura

Route du Lac, F-65400 Estaing (Hautes-Pyrénées) T: 05 62 97 45 44. E: info@camping-pyrenees-natura.com
alanrogers.com/FR65060

Pyrénées Natura, at an altitude of 1,000 m. on the edge of the National Park is the perfect site for lovers of nature. The 60 pitches (47 for tourers), all with electricity (3-10A), are in a landscaped area with 75 varieties of trees and shrubs – but they do not spoil the fantastic views. A traditional style building houses the reception, bar and indoor games/reading room. There is a small, well-stocked shop in the former water mill. Prices are very reasonable and homemade bread can be purchased. Children will love the animals, including the unusual hens, the guinea pigs, goat and donkey. On the river there is a small beach belonging to the site for supervised water play.

Facilities

First class toilet blocks. Facilities for disabled visitors and babies. Washing machine and airers (no lines allowed). Motorcaravan services. Small shop, takeaway (15/5-15/9). Bar (15/5-15/9). Lounge, library, TV. Games/reading room. Bird watching is a speciality of the site and equipment is available. Sauna, solarium (free between 12.00-17.00). Music room. Play area for the very young. Small beach beside river. Boules. Giant chess. Weekly evening meal in May, June and Sept. Internet. Walks organised. Off site: Village with two restaurants. Bicycle hire 4 km. Riding 4 km. Walking and hiking.

Open: 1 May - 20 September.

Directions

At Argelès-Gazost, take D918 towards Aucun. After 8 km. turn left on D13 to Bun, cross the river, then right on D103 to site (5.5 km). Narrow road, few passing places. GPS: 42.94152, -0.17726

Charges guide

Per unit incl. 2 persons and electricity (3A)	€ 16,50 - € 40,00
extra person	€ 5,50
child (under 8 yrs)	€ 3,50
dog	€ 2,00

Flagnac
Flower Camping le Port de Lacombe

F-12300 Flagnac (Aveyron) T: 05 65 64 10 08. E: accueil@campingleportdelacombe.com
alanrogers.com/FR12290

The new managers, Patrick and Marie-Claude Comtat, have plans to improve this leased municipal site. It is well kept and is situated on the banks of the Lot river, a location ideal for walking, cycling, fishing and canoeing. The 91 grass touring pitches are level and range in size from 100-130 sq.m. A large natural swimming pool is fed by the river and provides a separate paddling area and a large slide. Using the D42, one can wind through the valley and climb to over 2,000 feet to the Plateau de la Viadene. The scenery is panoramic and picturesque.

Facilities
Two separate sanitary blocks, each with the usual facilities including provision for disabled visitors. Washing machine. Bar (all season) with restaurant and takeaway (both 15/6-15/9). TV in function room. Play area. Swimming pool fed from the river and paddling pool (1/7-31/8). Bicycle hire. Fishing in river. Entertainment (July/Aug).

Open: 1 April - 30 September.

Directions
Driving south from Brive-la-Gaillarde, take N140 to Decazeville, turning north on D963 to Flagnac. Site is well signed on the left. From Rodez take N140 to Decazeville, then as above. GPS: 44.60915, 2.23597

Charges guide
Per unit incl. 2 persons	€ 8,00 - € 22,00
incl. electricity (6A)	€ 11,00 - € 20,00
extra person	€ 2,00 - € 4,00

Ger
Aire Naturelle de Camping l'Arrayade

Arrayade, 18 impasse de l'arremissant, F-65100 Ger (Hautes-Pyrénées) T: 05 62 94 17 73
E: contact@arrayade.com alanrogers.com/FR65170

This unique little campsite, situated quite high up in the Pyrenees with some amazing views down the valley, could well be near perfect for anyone seeking a relaxing, informal and friendly atmosphere. On a very small site of just 16 large pitches, all with electricitry (6-10A), Mme. Piqué is a gracious host who will do her utmost to ensure your stay is as pleasant as possible. She has prepared plenty of information on the local area, the best walks to go on and the cycle pathway that runs past the site that takes you into Lourdes centre in just three kilometres. You can taste the freshness of the air up here and outdoor lovers will feel really at one with nature.

Facilities
One very modern toilet block situated in the reception area. Provision is adequate. All fittings are very new and the arrangement makes this area feel almost like a private bathroom. Washing machine and dryer. Small bar where breakfast and evening meals are served. Peaceful lounge. Sauna, jacuzzi and small gym. Internet access. Fishing. Bicycle hire. Off site: Walking, climbing cycling and fishing all on the door step. M. Piqué, a qualified pilot, offers flights over the Pyrénées for the ultimate sightseeing experience. Golf and riding 5 km.

Open: 15 May - 15 September.

Directions
From Lourdes head south on the D921 signed Lugagnan. After 3 km. bear right on D13 for Ger. As you approach a few houses on your left the site entrance is on the right, set back a little in a lay-by. GPS: 43.05771, -0.04151

Charges 2011
Per unit incl. 2 persons and electricity	€ 14,50 - € 17,00
extra person	€ 3,00
child (under 7 yrs)	€ 1,50

La Bastide-de-Sérou
Camping l'Arize

532

Lieu-dit Bourtol, F-09240 La Bastide-de-Sérou (Ariège) T: 05 61 65 81 51. E: camparize@aol.com
alanrogers.com/FR09020

The site sits in a delightful, tranquil valley among the foothills of the Pyrenees and is just east of the interesting village of La Bastide-de-Sérou beside the River Arize (good trout fishing). The river is fenced for the safety of children on the site, but may be accessed just outside the gate. The 70 large pitches are neatly laid out on level grass within the spacious site. All have 3/6A electricity and are separated into bays by hedges and young trees. An extension to the site gives 24 large, fully serviced pitches (10A) and a small toilet block.

Facilities
Toilet block includes facilities for babies and disabled visitors. Laundry room. Motorcaravan services. New shop and restaurant planned for 2011. Small swimming pool and sunbathing area. Entertainment in high season. Weekly barbecues and welcome drinks on Sundays. Fishing, riding and bicycle hire. WiFi. Off site: Several restaurants and shops within a few minutes drive. The nearest restaurant is at the national stud for the famous Merens horses away and will deliver takeaway meals

Open: 12 March - 10 November.

Directions
Site is southeast of the village La Bastide-de-Sérou. Take the D15 towards Nescus and site is on right after about 1 km. GPS: 43.00182, 1.44538

Charges guide
Per unit incl. 2 persons and electricity	€ 16,40 - € 24,70
extra person	€ 4,00 - € 5,40
child (0-7 yrs)	€ 3,00 - € 3,60
dog	€ 1,00 - € 1,80
Discounts for longer stays in mid and low season.	

For latest campsite news, availability and prices visit
alanrogers.com

La Romieu

Kawan Village le Camp de Florence

Route Astaffort, F-32480 La Romieu (Gers) T: 05 62 28 15 58. E: info@lecampdeflorence.com

alanrogers.com/FR32010

532

Camp de Florence is an attractive site on the edge of an historic village in pleasantly undulating Gers countryside. The 183 large, part terraced pitches (100 for tourers) all have electricity (10A), 14 with hardstanding and eight fully serviced. They are arranged around a large field (full of sunflowers when we visited) with rural views, giving a feeling of spaciousness. The 13th-century village of La Romieu is on the Santiago de Compostela pilgrim route. The Pyrenees are a two hour drive, the Atlantic coast a similar distance. The site has been developed by the friendly Mynsbergen family who are Dutch (although Susan is English). They have sympathetically converted the old farmhouse buildings to provide facilities for the site. The collegiate church, visible from the site, is well worth a visit (the views are magnificent from the top of the tower), as is the local arboretum, the biggest collection of trees in the Midi-Pyrénées.

Facilities

Three toilet blocks (one completely rebuilt for 2009), provide all the necessary facilities. Washing machines and dryers. Motorcaravan services. Restaurant (1/5-30/9, also open to the public). Takeaway. Bread. Swimming pool area with water slide. Jacuzzi, protected children's pool (open to public in afternoons). Adventure playground, games and pets areas. Bouncy castle, trampoline. Outdoor fitness machines. Games room. Tennis. Pétanque. Bicycle hire. Video shows, discos, picnics, musical evenings. Excursions. Internet and WiFi. Off site: Shop 500 m. Fishing 5 km. Riding 10 km. Walking tours, excursions and wine tasting arranged.

Open: 1 April - 10 October.

Directions

Site signed from D931 Agen - Condom road. Small units turn left at Ligardes (signed), follow D36 for 1 km, turn right turn La Romieu (signed). Otherwise continue until outskirts of Condom and take D41 left to La Romieu, through village to site. GPS: 43.98299, 0.50183

Charges guide

Per unit incl. 2 persons and electricity	€ 17,50 - € 34,90
extra person	€ 3,60 - € 7,20
child (4-9 yrs)	€ 2,60 - € 5,20
dog (max. 2)	€ 1,50 - € 2,25

Camping Cheques accepted.

Le Camp de Florence - 32480 La Romieu

Sun * Comfort * Nature * Water

The Gers - A region waiting to be discovered, an unspoilt landscape of rolling hills, sunflowers and historic fortified villages and castles. Peace, tranquillity, the home of Armagnac, Fois Gras and Magret de Canard. A 4* site with spacious pitches, panoramic views and luxury mobile homes for hire.

Tel: 0033 562 28 15 58 - Fax: 0033 562 28 20 04
E-mail: info@lecampdeflorence.com - www.lecampdeflorence.com

Le Monastère

Campéole Domaine de Combelles

F-12000 Le Monastère (Aveyron) T: 05 65 78 29 53. E: combelles@campeole.com

alanrogers.com/FR12400

Campéole

The pitches at this campsite are used exclusively for mobile home and chalet accommodation. For full details please see our PRL section starting on page 538.

Lacave

Camping la Rivière

Le Bougayrou, F-46200 Lacave (Lot) T: 05 65 37 02 04. E: camping.la.riviere@wanadoo.fr

alanrogers.com/FR46370

Camping La Riviere is situated on the banks of the Dordogne with direct access to the river and a sand and pebble beach. It is a natural rural site and in a pleasant location. The A20 motorway and the town of Souillac are just 15 km. away. The welcome from the owners is warm and friendly and they place much importance on customer service and a family atmosphere is of conviviality. There are 110 pitches of which 15 are for mobile homes (all for rent). The remaining 95 pitches are for touring units. Of average size, all are level and on grass and divided by trees and shrubs which provide a good amount of shade. All have electricity (4/10A). There is a lagoon shaped swimming pool together with a paddling pool. Thoughtfully, there are two separate games areas, one for the toddlers and one for the rest. There is a children's club for 5-11 year olds and teen evenings for 11-15 year olds. The site has its own snack bar but within 4 km. there is a choice of numerous gastronomic restaurants. The closest one, which has an excellent reputation, is just 300 m. away. Many interesting places to visit are within a short distance.

Facilities

Three toilet blocks include facilities for disabled visitors and babies. Laundry. Shop. Bar. Snack bar. Takeaway. Two swimming pools including a children's pool. Two games areas. Minigolf. Barbecue and picnic areas. Organised excursions. Disco and Karaoke evenings. Off site: The Caves of Padirac. Rocamadour. Sarlat and numerous theme parks. Museums. Off road cycling. Canoeing. Kayaking. Climbing. Riding. Golf. Lacave 3 km. St Sozy 4 km.

Open: 2 April - 24 September.

Directions

From Souillac take the D43 and site is very well signed. GPS: 44.86171, 1.559372

Charges guide

Per unit incl. 2 persons and electricity	€ 16,00 - € 20,20
extra person	€ 4,20 - € 5,20
child (under 10 yrs)	€ 2,50 - € 3,10
dog	free - € 1,50

Le Vigan

Camping le Rêve

F-46300 Le Vigan (Lot) T: 05 65 41 25 20. E: info@campinglereve.com

alanrogers.com/FR46050

Le Rêve is a peaceful site situated in the heart of rolling countryside where the Perigord runs into Quercy. You are assured of a warm reception from the van Iersels, a Dutch couple who have been providing a friendly and hospitable welcome to their clients since 1987. The 56 flat and grassy touring pitches are all of good size, with access to electricity (6A) and divided by shrubs and trees. A few of the pitches are situated at the edge of the forest and provide plenty of shade.

Facilities

The toilet block includes an enclosed area for cooler weather. Washbasins in cabins, special cubicles for disabled visitors and a baby room. New laundry facilities. Small shop for basics (bread, milk etc), pleasant bar, restaurant and takeaway (all open all season). Heated swimming pool (all season) and large paddling pool with 'mushroom' fountain. Play area. Boules. Internet access and WiFi (charged). Off site: Fishing 5 km. Riding 8 km.

Open: 1 May - 21 September.

Directions

From D820 Souillac - Cahors road turn west onto D673 3 km. south of Payrac. After 2 km. site signed down lane on west side of road. Turn here, follow signs, site in 2.5 km. GPS: 44.77304, 1.44097

Charges guide

Per person	€ 5,30
child (under 7 yrs)	€ 3,20
pitch incl. electricity (6A)	€ 10,15
Credit cards accepted July/Aug only.	

Lectoure

Yelloh! Village le Lac des Trois Vallées

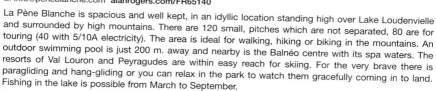

F-32700 Lectoure (Gers) T: 04 66 73 97 39. E: info@yellohvillage-lac-des-3-vallees.com
alanrogers.com/FR32060

This is a large 140 hectare site with many facilities. It is a large holiday complex and good for families with young children or teenagers. The large lake provides the opportunity for canoeing, swimming, diving and there are four water slides. There is a large safe paddling area and a separate fishing lake. The impressive heated pool complex complete with gymnasium and jacuzzi also has paved areas for sunbathing and a large paddling pool. Of the 500 pitches, over 200 are well situated for touring on shaded or open ground, all with electricity (10A). Used by tour operators (100 pitches).

Facilities

Eight modern sanitary blocks each with baby bathing facilities. Provision for disabled visitors. Laundry facilities. Motorcaravan services. Shop. Restaurants and bars. Lakeside snack bar and drinks kiosk. Heated swimming pool complex. Lake complex. Multisports pitch. BMX/skateboard area. Fishing. Tennis. Minigolf. Video games room. Disco. Cinema. Children's club. Internet access (charged). Off site: Golf 10 km. Walking and mountain bike trails. Quad bikes. Hot air balloon rides.

Open: 1 June - 11 September (with all facilities).

Directions

Take N21 south from Lectoure for 2 km. Site is well signed and is a further 2 km. after turning left off the N21. GPS: 43.91250, 0.64852

Charges 2011

Per unit incl. 2 persons	
and electricity	€ 19,00 - € 44,00
extra person	€ 5,00 - € 8,00
child (3-7 yrs)	free - € 8,00
dog	€ 4,00

Loudenvielle

Flower Camping Pène Blanche

9 chemin de la Mainette, F-65510 Loudenvielle (Hautes-Pyrénées) T: 05 62 99 68 85
E: info@peneblanche.com alanrogers.com/FR65140

La Pène Blanche is spacious and well kept, in an idyllic location standing high over Lake Loudenvielle and surrounded by high mountains. There are 120 small, pitches which are not separated, 80 are for touring (40 with 5/10A electricity). The area is ideal for walking, hiking or biking in the mountains. An outdoor swimming pool is just 200 m. away and nearby is the Balnéo centre with its spa waters. The resorts of Val Louron and Peyragudes are within easy reach for skiing. For the very brave there is paragliding and hang-gliding or you can relax in the park to watch them gracefully coming in to land. Fishing in the lake is possible from March to September.

Facilities

Two toilet blocks, one traditional, one modern and heated including facilities for campers with disabilities. Indoor dishwashing and laundry room. Play area. Off site: Restaurant, snack bar, bar and local shops all within 100 m. Cinema 200 m. Motorcaravan services 300 m. Balnéo Centre with spa water baths and adjacent swimming pool with waterslide. Tennis. Minigolf. Hiking. Mountain biking. Paragliding. Hang-gliding. Skiing.

Open: 20 December - 31 October.

Directions

From the A64 Tarbes to Toulouse, take exit 16, on D929 follow signs to Arreau, then D618 to D25 signed Loudenvielle. GPS: 42.796107, 0.406679

Charges guide

Per unit incl. 2 persons	
and electricity	€ 16,00 - € 23,70
extra person	€ 3,90 - € 5,50
child (2-7 yrs)	€ 2,90 - € 4,30
dog	€ 1,90 - € 2,20

Lourdes

Camping le Moulin du Monge

Avenue Jean Moulin no 28, F-65100 Lourdes (Hautes-Pyrénées) T: 05 62 94 28 15
E: camping.moulin.monge@wanadoo.fr alanrogers.com/FR65100

A well organised, family run site with a friendly welcome, Moulin du Monge is in an ideal location for visiting Lourdes, only 3 km. away. There will be some traffic noise from the nearby N21 and railway line. This attractive garden-like site has 57 pitches, all with electricity (2-6A) in three grassy areas, mostly shaded by trees and easy to access. The swimming pool is slightly apart from most of the pitches. There is a separate adjacent pool for children. There are ten mobile homes available to rent.

Facilities

The heated toilet blocks have all necessary facilities, including washing machine and dryer. Facilities for disabled campers. Baby room. Motorcaravan services. Well-stocked shop (15/6-20/9). Heated swimming pool, sliding cover (20/5-20/9), paddling pool. Sauna. Games/TV room. WiFi. Barbecue, terrace. Boules. Playground, trampolines. Off site: Good transport links to the city centre with its famous grotto and all shops and services. Bicycle hire 500 m. Fishing 3 km. Golf 4 km. Riding 15 km.

Open: 1 April - 10 October.

Directions

Site is just off the N21 on northern outskirts of Lourdes. From north, on N21 (2 km. south of Adé) be prepared to take slip lane in centre of road. Turn left into Ave Jean Moulin. Site shortly on left. GPS: 43.115516, -0.031583

Charges guide

Per unit incl. 2 persons	
and electricity	€ 17,30 - € 19,30
extra person	€ 5,10
child (0-7 yrs)	€ 3,30
dog	free

Luz-Saint-Sauveur

Camping Pyrenevasion

Route de Luz-Ardiden, Sazos, F-65120 Luz-Saint-Sauveur (Hautes-Pyrénées) T: 05 62 92 91 54
E: camping-pyrenevasion@wanadoo.fr alanrogers.com/FR65130

In the heart of the Pyrénées, Camping Pyrenevasion has panoramic views of the mountains and the town of Luz-St-Sauveur in the valley below. This welcoming, family run site has 60 well laid out touring pitches, all with electricity (3-10A), on level, grassy hillside terraces partially shaded by young trees. There are 12 modern chalets for rent (all year), ideal for the nearby skiing, and in summer guided walks are arranged, with one free weekly walk. The heated outdoor poor has a separate paddling pool and jacuzzi. In July and August, activities are organised for 4-12 year olds and weekly entertainment for adults. A member of Sites et Paysages.

Facilities

Heated sanitary block with showers, WCs, washbasins (cubicles and open area). Facilities for disabled visitors, steep access. Baby bath. Washing machine and dryer. Motorcaravan services. Bread can be ordered at reception for next morning delivery. Bar (all year). Takeaway (1/6-20/9). Heated swimming and paddling pools (15/5-1/10). Small play area. Sports area. WiFi (charged). Off site: Shops, restaurant and bar 2 km. Fishing 200 m. Riding 10 km. Skiing 10 km. Golf 30 km.

Open: All year excl. 21 October - 19 November.

Directions

From the north take the D921 to Luz-St-Sauveur. Follow signs from Luz-St-Sauveur to Luz-Ardiden (D12). Site is on right as you enter the village of Sazos. GPS: 42.88283, -0.02241

Charges guide

Per unit incl. 2 persons	€ 10,00 - € 20,50
extra person	€ 5,50
child (2-6 yrs)	€ 3,50
electricity (3-10A)	€ 3,50 - € 11,50

Marciac

Camping du Lac

F-32230 Marciac (Gers) T: 05 62 08 21 19. E: camping.marciac@wanadoo.fr
alanrogers.com/FR32020

Summer wine and cheese tastings from local producers are a feature of this site, set in the beautiful Gers region, and close to the ancient fortified town of Marciac. Rob and Louise Robinson, the English owners since 2002, offer a quiet, relaxing stay. The well shaded site has 95 pitches, including 15 used for mobile homes and chalets for rent. 60 spacious touring pitches have electrical connections (6/10A, Europlug). There are five with hardstanding for motorcaravans, and an attractive natural terrace has 20 pitches without electricity for tents. A major jazz festival is held in early August in the town.

Facilities

The centrally situated sanitary block uses solar energy to help to heat water. Washbasins in cubicles. Facilities for disabled visitors (two separate bathrooms with shower, WC and washbasin). Washing machine. Motorcaravan service point. Shop. Bar. Snacks. Bread daily (order at reception). Swimming pool (15/4-30/9). Play area. WiFi (charged). Off site: Fishing, watersports, sailing and riding 300 m. Shops, restaurant and bars 1 km. Golf 7 km.

Open: 20 March - 17 October.

Directions

The site is 800 m. from Marciac. From the town square take the D3 towards Plaisance. With the lake on your left, turn right and site is 300 m. on the left. GPS: 43.5323, 0.1667

Charges guide

Per unit incl. 2 persons and electricity (6A)	€ 13,00 - € 22,50
extra person	€ 2,50 - € 5,00
child (4-16 yrs)	€ 1,50 - € 3,50

Marsan

Flower Camping Aramis

Quartier Gaubette, F-32270 Marsan (Gers) T: 05 62 65 60 11. E: piraux.sylvie@wanadoo.fr
alanrogers.com/FR32170

Aramis is a family campsite located 10 km. east of Auch, former capital of Gascony when it was the land of Musketeers! There are 65 large pitches here, mostly well shaded and with electrical connections. A number of mobile homes and chalets are available for rent. Leisure facilities include a swimming pool and tennis court. Several activities take place around the site's convivial bar, particularly during peak season. These include Gascon evenings, evening markets and large scale barbecues. Other activities include visits to local farms, guided walks through the rolling countryside and a daily children's club.

Facilities

Snack bar/bar. Swimming pool. Children's pool. Tennis. Play area. Tourist information. Entertainment and activity programme. Mobile homes for rent. Off site: Auch 10 km. Walking and cycle tracks. Jazz festival at Marciac. Riding. Golf.

Open: 1 April - 30 September.

Directions

Camping Aramis can be found around 10 km. east of Auch. From there, head east on N124 to Marsan and then follow signs to the site. GPS: 43.658577, 0.733429

Charges guide

Per unit incl. 2 persons and electricity	€ 15,50 - € 23,00

Martiel

Flower Camping du Lac de Bannac

Moulin de Bannac, F-12200 Martiel (Aveyron) T: 05 65 29 44 52. E: info@camping-lac-aveyron.com
alanrogers.com/FR12450

This site is a member of the Flower group and enjoys a pleasant rural setting, just a stone's throw from the 22 hectare Lac de Bannac. Leisure activities here include a tree-top activity park (charge applicable), with a zip wire across the lake! There are 50 standard pitches and a further 16 luxury pitches (with electricity, water and drainage). Additionally, there are a number of mobile homes available for rent. Other on-site amenities include a swimming pool (with separate padding pool) and a woodland minigolf course. The site's cosy restaurant specialises in local cuisine. Lac de Bannac can be found to the west of Villefranche-de-Rouergue and is very well located for exploring the region. A number of long distance footpaths run close to the site, and an attractive path leads around the lake (about 90 minutes). Mountain biking is also very popular. Further afield, popular visits include the 13th-century fortress at Najac, or the delightful medieval villages of Cordes-sur-Ciel, Saint Cirq Lapopie and Cajarc.

Facilities

Bar. Restaurant. Takeaway food. Shop. Aerial adventure course. Swimming pool. Paddling pool. Pedalo hire. Fishing. Play area. TV room. Minigolf. Motorcaravan services. Entertainment and activity programme. Mobile homes to rent. Off site: Riding. Cycle and walking tracks. Aveyron gorges (35 km).

Open: 1 May - 30 September.

Directions

Take exit 58 from A20 motorway, and head towards Villefranche de Rouergue. Pass through Martiel towards Limogne. Continue for 2 km and you will see the campsite on the left just after the village. GPS: 44.384214, 1.88768

Charges guide

Per unit incl. 2 persons	€ 9,00 - € 20,50
extra person	€ 3,00 - € 5,00

Camping Flower du Lac de Bannac**

Moulin de Bannac - F-12200 Martiel - France
Tel. 0033 565 29 44 52 - info@camping-lac-aveyron.com
www.camping-lac-aveyron.com - www.flowercampings.com

le camping c'est humain.

Martres-Tolosane

Camping le Moulin

Lieu-dit le Moulin, F-31220 Martres-Tolosane (Haute-Garonne) T: 05 61 98 86 40
E: info@campinglemoulin.com alanrogers.com/FR31000

With attractive shaded pitches and many activities, this family-run campsite has 12 hectares of woods and fields beside the River Garonne. It is close to Martres-Tolosane, an interesting medieval village. Some of the 60 level and grassy pitches are 'supersize' and all have electricity (6/10A). There are 24 chalets to rent. Summer brings opportunities for guided canoeing, archery and walking. A large sports field is available all season, with tennis, volleyball, basketball, boules and birdwatching on site. Facilities for visitors with disabilities are very good, although the sanitary block is a little dated. Some road noise. Large grounds for dog walking. A member of Sites et Paysages.

Facilities

Large sanitary block with separate ladies' and gents WCs. Communal area with showers and washbasins in cubicles. Separate heated area for disabled visitors with shower, WC and basin. Baby bath. Laundry facilities. Motorcaravan services. Outdoor bar with WiFi. Snack bar and takeaway (1/6-15/9). Daily baker's van (except Mon). Heated swimming and paddling pools (1/6-15/9). Fishing. Tennis. Canoeing. Archery. BMX track. Playground. Games room. Entertainment programme and children's club (high season). Off site: Martres-Tolosane 1.5 km. Walking trails and cycle routes. Riding 4 km. Golf 12 km.

Open: 1 April - 30 September.

Directions

From the A64 motorway (Toulouse-Tarbes) take exit 21 (Boussens) or exit 22 (Martres-Tolosane) and follow signs to Martres-Tolosane. Site is well signed from village. GPS: 43.19048, 1.01788

Charges guide

Per unit incl. 2 persons and electricity	€ 20,00 - € 36,00
extra person	€ 4,50 - € 6,50
child (under 7 yrs)	€ 2,50 - € 3,50
dog	€ 1,50 - € 2,30

Less 20% outside July/Aug.

Millau

Camping Le Millau Plage

Route de Millau-Plage, F-12100 Millau (Aveyron) T: 05 65 60 10 97. E: info@campingmillauplage.com

alanrogers.com/FR12390

This slightly old site is situated on the banks of the Tarn river 1.5 km. outside Millau. This is an historical town in its own right and a very popular place for hang-gliding and watersports, as well as for people wishing to get a view of the Millau suspension bridge further down the valley. Plenty of trees provide ample shade and the site could be a little dark on cloudy or dull days. The river will attract older children who will love to climb the trees and jump or dive into the water, but as the site is open onto the river younger children would need supervision. Everyone will enjoy the large pool that is next to the restaurant and bar area.

Facilities

Four toilet blocks along the middle of the site provide easy access from most pitches. The blocks are old and due some modernisation. Motorcaravan services. Small shop, bar with TV and snack type restaurant, takeaway (all 1/7-31/8). Large irregular shaped pool filled with river water (1/5-31/8). Limited children's club in high season along with video and non-professional entertainment for adults in the evening in high season. Off site: Bicycle hire 800 m. Riding 2 km. Beach 25 km. Historic town of Millau. Hang-gliding, fishing and canoeing and walking in the impressive Massif Central.

Open: 1 April - 30 September.

Directions

Millau is best accessed from the A75 motorway. From either north or south take the N9, following it round the town until roundabout signed for Millau Plage. Cross the river and take third exit at next roundabout. Site is on left 1.5 km. after the final roundabout and after passing two other sites. GPS: 44.11552, 3.08692

Charges 2011

Per unit incl. 2 persons	
and electricity	€ 16,00 - € 28,00
extra person	€ 3,50 - € 6,50
child (2-4 yrs)	€ 2,00 - € 4,00
dog	€ 2,00 - € 4,00

Camping ★★★★ Le Millau Plage

Route de Millau Plage • F-12100 Millau • Tél.: 0033 (0)5 65 60 10 97
Mail: info@campingmillauplage.com • www.campingmillauplage.com

Millau

Camping Caravaning les Rivages

860 avenue de l'Aigoual, F-12100 Millau (Aveyron) T: 05 65 61 01 07. E: campinglesrivages@orange.fr

alanrogers.com/FR12020

Les Rivages is a large, well established site on the outskirts of the town. It is well situated, being close to the high limestone Causses and the dramatic gorges of the Tarn and Dourbie. Smaller pitches, used for small units, abut a pleasant riverside space suitable for sunbathing, fishing or picnics. Most of the 314 pitches are large, and well shaded. A newer part of the site has less shade but larger pitches. All pitches have electricity (6A), and 282 have water and drainage. The site offers a very wide range of sporting activities, close to 30 in all.

Facilities

Four well kept modern toilet blocks have all necessary facilities. Special block for children. Small shop (1/6-15/9). Terrace, restaurant and bar overlooking swimming pool, children's pool (from 10/5). Play area. Entertainment, largely for children, child-minding, miniclub. Impressive sports centre with tennis (indoor and outdoor), squash and badminton. Boules. River activities, walking, bird watching, fishing. WiFi by reception. Off site: Rafting and canoeing arranged. Bicycle hire 1 km. Riding 10 km. Abseiling, paragliding, caving, canyoning and white-water activities all nearby. Hypermarket in Millau.

Open: 15 April - 30 September.

Directions

From Millau, cross the Tarn bridge and take D991 road east towards Nant. Site is about 400 m. from the roundabout on the right, on the banks of the Dourbie river. GPS: 44.10079, 3.09605

Charges guide

Per unit incl. 2 persons	
and electricity	€ 18,00 - € 30,00
extra person	€ 3,50 - € 6,50
child (2-7 yrs)	€ 2,00 - € 5,00
dog	€ 1,50 - € 3,50

For latest campsite news, availability and prices visit

alanrogers.com

Millau

Camping du Viaduc

121 avenue de Millau Plage, F-12100 Millau (Aveyron) T: 05 65 60 15 75. E: info@camping-du-viaduc.com
alanrogers.com/FR12280

Run by a French couple, this site is situated on the banks of the Tarn, across the river from Millau. Of medium size, the site has 237 pitches of which 199 are for touring units and the remainder for chalets. Being close to the town it has access to its services but there is also easy access for discovering the beauty and nature of the gorges. The pitches are flat, of average size, shaded under tall trees and have adequate water and electricity points. The site is on the banks of the shallow Tarn, where a sandy beach has been created.

Facilities

One large, centrally situated sanitary block with the usual facilities. Bar with restaurant and takeaway. Swimming pool and children's pool. Shop (1/6-31/8). Laundry area. Entertainment in July/Aug. Children's club (high season). Play area. Fishing and river bathing. WiFi by reception (charged). Off site: Bicycle hire and canoe hire 200 m. Hypermarket, shops and restaurants in Millau.

Open: 22 April - 26 September.

Directions

Follow signs for 'campings' from Millau centre across the Tarn to the east side. At roundabout take last exit signed Paulhe (D187) to second campsite on the left in a short distance. GPS: 44.10508, 3.08826

Charges guide

Per unit incl. 2 persons	
and electricity	€ 19,00 - € 31,00
extra person	€ 3,00 - € 6,50
child (under 7 yrs)	free - € 4,00
dog	€ 2,00 - € 3,00

We can book this site for you! Call 01580 214000

Montcabrier

Camping Moulin de Laborde

F-46700 Montcabrier (Lot) T: 05 65 24 62 06. E: moulindelaborde@wanadoo.fr
alanrogers.com/FR46040

Based around a converted 17th-century watermill, Moulin de Laborde has been created by the van Bommel family to provide a tranquil and uncommercialised campsite for the whole family to enjoy. Bordered by woods, hills and a small river, there are 90 flat and grassy pitches, all of at least 100 sq.m. with electricity (6A). A variety of pretty shrubs and trees divide the pitches and provide a moderate amount of shade. A gate at the back of the site leads walkers onto a Grande Randonée footpath which passes through the village of Montcabrier, 1 km. away.

Facilities

Well designed, clean toilet block, unit for disabled visitors. Washing machine, dryer. Basic shop (all season). Small bar, restaurant, takeaway. Swimming pool, sunbathing area, paddling pool (all season). Play area. Small lake, free rafts and rowing boats. Fishing. Volleyball. Badminton. Boules. Covered recreation area. Mountain bike hire. Rock climbing. Archery. WiFi (free). Dogs are not accepted. Off site: Riding 5 km. Golf 8 km. Tennis nearby and canoeing on the Lot. Fumel 12 km.

Open: 25 April - 8 September.

Directions

Site is on the north side of the D673 Fumel - Gourdon road about 1 km. northeast of the turn to village of Montcabrier. GPS: 44.5475, 1.08388

Charges guide

Per unit incl. 2 persons	
and electricity	€ 19,68 - € 24,60
extra person	€ 5,20 - € 6,50
child (under 7 yrs)	€ 2,80 - € 3,50
No credit cards.	

Mostuéjouls

Camping Saint-Pal

Route du Gorges du Tarn, F-12720 Mostuéjouls (Aveyron) T: 05 65 62 64 46. E: saintpal@wanadoo.fr
alanrogers.com/FR12240

Saint-Pal is ideally situated on the approach road to the Gorges du Tarn, so access to the site is easy. This small, very neat site is run by a very friendly family and is aimed at those who prefer peace and quiet and less in the way of organised activity. Beside the Tarn river, the site is arranged in the open valley and is fairly flat. There are 74 large, level, grassy pitches, with 58 for touring. Separated by hedging, most are shaded by mature trees and 6/10A electricity is available. Some pitches are by the attractive river.

Facilities

One very clean, modern toilet block with good facilities includes a room for babies and campers with disabilities. Motorcaravan service point. Small shop (1/6-15/9). Bar/restaurant and takeaway (1/7-31/8). Small swimming pool (all season). Play area, TV/games room. River bathing, boating and fishing. Organised walks and low key entertainment (July/Aug) but no musical events. WiFi in bar area. Off site: Bicycle hire 500 m. Riding 5 km. Le Rozier 1 km. Millau 20 km.

Open: 1 May - 30 September.

Directions

Leave A75 at exit 44, north of Millau. Take N9 south for 14 km. to Aquessac. Turn left on D907 and site is on right in 14 km. just before village of Le Rosier. GPS: 44.19585, 3.199717

Charges guide

Per unit incl. 2 persons	
and electricity	€ 16,00 - € 25,70
extra person	€ 3,50 - € 5,20
child (under 5 yrs)	€ 2,50 - € 4,00
dog	€ 1,20 - € 2,00

For latest campsite news, availability and prices visit

alanrogers.com

Montpezat de Quercy

Camping le Faillal

F-82270 Montpezat de Quercy (Tarn-et-Garonne) T: 05 63 02 07 08. E: contact@revea-vacances.com

alanrogers.com/FR82050

Le Faillal is located at Montpézat de Quercy, around 35 km. north of Montauban. There are 69 pitches here, all of a good size and each has its own electricity (4/6A), water and light. The surrounding trees and hedges give shade and some privacy. The site forms a part of the Parc de Loisirs de Faillal and includes a swimming pool, tennis court and minigolf, all of which are free for campers. There is no bar, restaurant or snack provision. These amenities are available in the town, a short walk away. Le Faillal provides some activities for children in high season and some entertainment for families, including barbecues and karaoke evenings. There are many excellent cycle tracks through the rolling countryside of the Quercy and the site managers will be pleased to recommend routes. Cahors and its world renowned vineyards are just 25 km. distant and the Aveyron gorges are around 30 km. away. Le Faillal is open for a long season and is a tranquil spot for a holiday, particularly outside the peak holiday period.

Facilities

One sanitary block with no facilities for disabled campers. Washing machines and irons. Municipal swimming pool, tennis court, basketball and mini-golf (all open to public). Very small play area. Tourist information and limited WiFi in reception. Service for motorcaravans. Gîtes for rent. Communal barbecue area, no others allowed. Max. 1 dog. Torch useful. Off site: Village centre 800 m. Riding 18 km. Golf 25 km.

Open: 4 April - 10 October.

Directions

Approaching from the north, leave A20 autoroute at exit 58 and head west on D19 and then south on D820 as far as La Baraque. Then head southwest on D20 to Montpézat de Quercy and follow signs to the site. GPS: 44.243139, 1.47764

Charges guide

Per unit incl. 2 persons	
and electricity	€ 15,60 - € 18,10
extra person	€ 3,00 - € 3,60
child (2-7 yrs)	free - € 1,60
dog	€ 1,50

Nages

Village Center Rieu Montagné

Lac du Laouzas, F-81320 Nages (Tarn) T: 05 63 37 24 71. E: contact@village-center.com

alanrogers.com/FR81070

Villagecenter

Rieu Montagné is a delightful site in the heart of the Haut Languedoc Regional park and at the corner of the départements of the Tarn, Aveyron and Hérault. There are 123 touring pitches, mostly on broad terraces with reasonable shade, all with electrical connections (10A) and 56 fully serviced. A heated swimming pool overlooks the lake and is used for occasional aquagym. In high season there is a varied entertainment programme, and a number of guided walks. Most leisure facilities are available at the lakeside complex.

Facilities

The two toilet blocks provide mostly British style toilets, washbasins in cubicles and facilities for disabled visitors and babies. Laundry. Shop with basic provisions, bar, restaurant and takeaway, swimming pool (all open all season). Entertainment programme (high season). Chalets, tents and mobile homes to let (53). Off site: Lakeside leisure complex.

Open: 13 June - 13 September.

Directions

Nages about 80 km. southeast of Albi. From Albi, D999 east towards St Affrique. 11 km. after Albon right, D607, to Lacaune. At T-junction left, D622, for 6.5 km. Right, D62, 2 km. South of town left over bridge, D162. First left uphill to site. GPS: 43.64795, 2.78147

Charges guide

Per unit incl. 2 persons	
and electricity	€ 14,00 - € 24,00
extra person	€ 3,00 - € 5,00
dog	€ 3,00

For latest campsite news, availability and prices visit

alanrogers.com

Nant-d'Aveyron

RCN Val de Cantobre

F-12230 Nant-d'Aveyron (Aveyron) T: 05 65 58 43 00. E: info@rcn-valdecantobre.fr
alanrogers.com/FR12010

Imaginatively and tastefully developed by the Dupond family over the past 30 years, this very pleasant terraced site is now owned by the RCN group. Most of the 200 touring pitches (all with electricity and water) are peaceful, generous in size and blessed with views of the valley. The terrace design provides some peace and privacy, especially on the upper levels. Rock pegs are advised. An activity programme is supervised by qualified instructors (July/August) and a new pool has been added. The magnificent carved features in the bar create a delightful ambience, complemented by a recently-built terrace.

Facilities

The fully equipped toilet blocks are well appointed. Fridge hire. Small shop including many regional specialities, attractive bar, restaurant, pizzeria and takeaway (all season). There is some fairly steep up and down walking from furthest pitches to some facilities. Swimming pools (all season). Minigolf. Play area. Activity programme. All-weather multisports pitch. Torch useful. Internet (charged). Off site: Fishing 4 km. Riding 15 km. Bicycle hire 25 km.

Open: 9 April - 1 October.

Directions

Site is 4 km. north of Nant, on D991 road to Millau. From Millau direction take D991 signed Gorge du Dourbie. Site is on left, just past turn to Cantobre. GPS: 44.04467, 3.30228

Charges guide

Per unit incl. 2 persons, electricity and water	€ 19,90 - € 43,90
extra person (4 yrs and over)	€ 2,50 - € 4,90

Naucelle

Flower Camping du Lac de Bonnefon

L'Etang de Bonnefon, F-12800 Naucelle (Aveyron) T: 05 65 69 33 20
E: camping-du-lac-de-bonnefon@wanadoo.fr alanrogers.com/FR12250

This small family run site, popular with French campers, lies in a picturesque region waiting to be discovered, with rolling hills, deep river valleys, lakes and many old fortified villages. This site is more suitable for those seeking a quieter holiday with less in the way of entertainment. There are 112 good sized, grassy, slightly sloping pitches with 74 for touring (50 with 10A electricity). Some are separated by laurel hedging with others more open and maturing trees give a little shade. The new enthusiastic and friendly owners have recently extended the site and refurbished the facilities to a high standard.

Facilities

Two toilet blocks include some washbasins in cabins and good facilities for disabled visitors. No shop but bread to order. Bar with TV (all season). Snack bar (July/Aug, other times on demand). Swimming and paddling pools (1/6-30/9). Playground. Archery. Good lake fishing but no bathing. Activities for all the family in July/Aug. Off site: Riding 500 m. Small village of Naucelle with a few shops and large heated pool complex 1 km.

Open: 1 April - 15 October.

Directions

Site is just off the N88 about halfway between Rodez and Albi. From Naucelle Gare take D997 towards Naucelle. In just over 1 km. turn left on D58 and follow signs to site in just under 1 km. GPS: 44.18805, 2.34827

Charges guide

Per unit incl. 2 persons	€ 15,50 - € 23,90
extra person	€ 3,50 - € 5,00
child (2-10 yrs)	€ 2,00 - € 3,00

Payrac-en-Quercy

Flower Camping les Pins

F-46350 Payrac-en-Quercy (Lot) T: 05 65 37 96 32. E: info@les-pins-camping.com
alanrogers.com/FR46030

Set amongst four hectares of beautiful pine forest, Camping Les Pins is well situated for exploring the historical and natural splendours of the Dordogne region, as well as being a convenient overnight stop when heading north or south. There are 125 clearly marked, level pitches (100 sq.m), of which 50 are for touring units. The pitches are well marked and separated by small shrubs or hedges. Many have shade from the abundant pine trees and all have 10A electricity connections. There is a bar and a good value restaurant with a terrace overlooking the pool area.

Facilities

Three toilet blocks (heated Apr/May) are well maintained and include washbasins in cabins and good baby bath facilities. Laundry facilities (with plenty of drying lines). Motorcaravan service point. Shop with basics (1/6-12/9). Bar with TV. Restaurant and takeaway. Heated swimming pool (1/5-12/9), three slides and smaller paddling pool. Tennis. Small library. WiFi in bar area. Some entertainment in season, including weekly family discos. Walking routes starting from site. English and Dutch are spoken. Off site: Fishing 7 km. Riding 10 km.

Open: 17 April - 12 September.

Directions

Site entrance is 16 km. from Souillac on western side of the N20 just south of the village of Payrac-en-Quercy. GPS: 44.78946, 1.47204

Charges guide

Per unit incl. 2 persons and electricity	€ 17,50 - € 28,50
extra person	€ 4,50 - € 6,60
child (under 7 yrs)	€ 2,00 - € 4,50
dog	€ 2,00 - € 2,50
Special low season prices.	

For latest campsite news, availability and prices visit

alanrogers.com

Pont-de-Salars

Flower Camping les Terrasses du Lac

Route du Vibal, F-12290 Pont-de-Salars (Aveyron) T: 05 65 46 88 18
E: campinglesterrasses@orange.fr alanrogers.com/FR12050

A terraced site, it provides 180 good sized, level pitches, 110 for touring, with or without shade, all with electricity. Some pitches have good views over the lake which has direct access from the site at two places – one for pedestrians and swimmers, the other for cars and trailers for launching small boats. This site is well placed for excursions into the Gorges du Tarn, Caves du Roquefort and nearby historic towns and villages. Although there are good facilities for disabled visitors, the terracing on the site may prove difficult. At an altitude of some 700 m. on the plateau of Le Lévézou, this outlying site enjoys attractive views over Lac de Pont-de-Salars.

Facilities

Four toilet blocks with adequate facilities. Fridge hire. Shop. Bar/restaurant with a lively French ambience serving full meals (high season) snacks (other times), takeaway (all 1/7-31/8). Heated swimming pool, children's pool (1/6-30/9). Solarium. Playground. Pétanque. Billiards. Games/TV rooms. Activities high season. Barbecue area. Off site: Tennis, bicycle hire 3 km. Riding 5 km. Golf 20 km.

Open: 29 March - 29 September.

Directions

Using D911 Millau - Rodez road, turn north at Pont-de-Salars towards lake on D523. Follow site signs. Ignore first site and continue, following lake until Les Terrasses du Lac on right (about 5 km). GPS: 44.30498, 2.73556

Charges guide

Per unit incl. 2 persons	
and electricity	€ 16,50 - € 26,50
extra person	€ 3,50 - € 5,00
child (2-7 yrs)	€ 2,50 - € 4,00
dog	€ 1,50 - € 2,00

Rivière-sur-Tarn

Flower Camping Caravaning de Peyrelade

Route des Gorges du Tarn, F-12640 Rivière-sur-Tarn (Aveyron) T: 05 65 62 62 54
E: campingpeyrelade@orange.fr alanrogers.com/FR12000

The 145 touring pitches (100-150 sq.m) are terraced, level and shady with 6A electricity hook-ups (long leads may be required for the riverside pitches). There are also 43 mobile homes. The site is ideally placed for visiting the Tarn, Jonte and Dourbie gorges, and centres for rafting and canoeing are a short drive up the river. Other nearby attractions include the Caves of Aven Armand, the Chaos de Montpellier, Roquefort (of cheese fame) and the pleasant town of Millau. Many of the roads along and between the Gorges are breathtaking for passengers, but worrying for drivers who may not like looking down!

Facilities

Two well equipped toilet blocks. Young children are catered for, also people with disabilities. Washing machines, dryer. Bar, restaurant, pizzeria, takeaway (all from 1/6). Paddling pool, attractive heated swimming pool (proper swimming trunks, no shorts). A new pool complex is planned for 2011. Good playground. Games room. Miniclub. Fishing. WiFi in bar area. Off site: Bicycle hire 100 m. Riding 3 km. Nearby leisure centre can be booked at reception at reduced charges. Millau, hypermarket, shops, night markets.

Open: 15 May - 15 September.

Directions

Take autoroute A75 to exit 44-1 Aguessac then onto D907 (follow Gorges du Tarn signs). Site is 2 km. past Rivière-sur-Tarn, on the right - the access road is quite steep. GPS: 44.19047, 3.15638

Charges guide

Per unit incl. 2 persons	
and electricity	€ 19,00 - € 31,00
extra person	€ 3,50 - € 7,00
child (under 7 yrs)	€ 2,00 - € 5,00
dog	€ 2,00

Rivière-sur-Tarn

Kawan Village les Peupliers

Route des Gorges du Tarn, F-12640 Rivière-sur-Tarn (Aveyron) T: 05 65 59 85 17
E: lespeupliers12640@orange.fr alanrogers.com/FR12160

Les Peupliers is a friendly, family site on the banks of the Tarn river. Most of the good-sized pitches have shade, all have electricity, water and a waste water point and are divided by low hedges. It is possible to swim in the river and there is a landing place for canoes. The site has its own canoes (to rent). In a lovely, sunny situation on the site is a swimming pool with a paddling pool, sunbeds and a new slide, all protected by a beautifully clipped hedge and with a super view to the surrounding hills and the Château du Peyrelade perched above the village. A treat for us at dusk was to watch beavers playing and swimming on the far river bank. We were told this happens nearly every day. The site is near the village of Rivière-sur-Tarn and the mouth of the Gorges du Tarn. It is 10 km. from the town of Millau, now famous for its spectacular bridge designed by Norman Foster that carries the A75 over the Tarn valley. Some English is spoken.

Facilities

Large, light and airy toilet facilities, baby facilities with baths, showers and WCs, facilities for disabled visitors. Washing machines. Shop (1/6-30/9). Bar, TV. Internet. Snack bar, takeaway (1/5-30/9). Swimming pool (from 1/5). Games, competitions (July/Aug). Fishing. Play area. Weekly dances (July/Aug). Canoe hire. WiFi in bar area. Off site: Village with shops and restaurant 300 m. Riding 500 m. Bicycle hire 2 km. Golf 25 km. Rock climbing, canyoning, cycling and walking.

Open: 1 May - 30 September.

Directions

Heading south from Clermont Ferrand to Millau on the A75 autoroute take exit 44-1 signed Aguessac/Gorges du Tarn. In Aguessac turn left and follow signs to Riviere-sur-Tarn (5 km). Site is clearly signed down a short road to the right.
GPS: 44.18577, 3.13068

Charges guide

Per unit incl. 2 persons and electricity	€ 20,00 - € 32,00
extra person	€ 5,00 - € 7,00
child (2-7 yrs)	€ 2,00 - € 4,00
dog	€ 2,50

For latest campsite news, availability and prices visit

alanrogers.com

Rocamadour

Camping les Cigales

L'Hospitalet, F-46500 Rocamadour (Lot) T: 05 65 33 64 44. E: camping.cigales@wanadoo.fr

alanrogers.com/FR46380

Les Cigales has 100 pitches of which 47 are for mobile homes and bungalows which are all available to rent. The remaining 53 are used for touring caravans, motorcaravans and tents. Most are level with some shade and range in size from 80-120 sq.m; 53 have 10A electricity. The site is quite spacious with a large area for activities and, with the emphasis on conviviality in a family atmosphere, it is ideally suited to families with children of all ages. There is entertainment in high season day and evening, the latter including discos, karaoke, bingo and cinema evenings. There are also themed nights as well as bowls tournaments.

Facilities

Sanitary facilities include washbasins in cabins. Facilities for disabled visitors. Swimming and paddling pools. Play area. Boules. Minigolf. Giant screen for films and TV. Motorcaravan service point. Day and evening entertainment. Off site: Golf 20 km. Riding 5 km. Bicycle hire 20 km. Monkey Park. Caves of Merveilles.

Open: 4 April - 24 October.

Directions

From the A20 take exit 55 for Souillac and take the road to Gramat. Site is signed in Rocamadour centre. GPS: 44.804981, 1.632242

Charges guide

Per unit incl. 2 persons	€ 17,00
extra person	€ 6,00
electricity	€ 3,00

Roquelaure

Kawan Village le Talouch

F-32810 Roquelaure (Gers) T: 05 62 65 52 43. E: info@camping-talouch.com

alanrogers.com/FR32080

Although enjoying a quiet and rural location, this neat and tidy site is only a short drive from the town of Auch with its famous legendary son, d'Artagnan. The entrance is fronted by a parking area with reception to the right and the bar and restaurant facing. Beyond this point lies the top half of the touring area with generous pitches of at least 120 sq.m. located between mature trees and divided by hedges, some with chalets. There are 100 pitches for touring, with electricity (6A). The rear half of the site has unshaded pitches in a more open aspect.

Facilities

Two toilet blocks with open style washbasins and controllable showers. Baby unit. One toilet for disabled visitors. Coin operated washing machine and laundry sinks. Small shop (1/4-30/9). Bar, restaurant and takeaway. Two excellent swimming pools, one heated and covered. Sauna and spa. Bicycle hire. GPS hire with pre-programmed walking routes and special activities for children. Play areas. Tennis and hard surface sports area. Organised entertainment in high season. Small library. Internet and WiFi in reception. Off site: Walking routes. Fishing and riding within 8 km.

Open: 1 April - 24 September.

Directions

Situated some 11 km. north of Auch on the D149, and 64 km. east of Toulouse the site is well signed. From the north approach via the A62 motorway, leaving at Layrac and heading towards Auch on the N21. GPS: 43.71283, 0.5645

Charges 2011

Per unit incl. 2 persons and electricity	€ 18,00 - € 33,50
extra person	€ 4,65 - € 7,60
child (2-7 yrs)	€ 3,75 - € 6,30
Camping Cheques accepted.	

Saint Amans-des-Cots

Village Center les Tours

Villagecenter

F-12460 Saint Amans-des-Cots (Aveyron) T: 04 99 57 21 21. E: resa@village-center.com

alanrogers.com/FR12040

This impressive campsite is set in beautiful countryside close to the Truyère Gorges, Upper Lot valley and the Aubrac Plateau. Efficiently run, it is situated on the shores of the Lac de la Selves. There are 275 average sized pitches (108 for touring) with 6A electricity, some bordering the lake, the rest terraced and hedged with views of the lake. About 100 pitches also have water points. The site has a spacious feel, enhanced by the thoughtfully planned terraced layout and it is well kept and very clean. There is some up and down walking to the facilities, especially from the upper terraces.

Facilities

Four very well equipped toilet blocks. Attractive central complex housing the amenities. Shop (with gas). Restaurant, bar. Takeaway (high season). Swimming pools (May-Sept). Play area. Tennis. Varied programme of daytime and evening activities, with miniclub and tree climbing (all supervised). Lake activities include fishing, canoeing, pedaloes, windsurfing, water skiing and provision for launching small boats. Internet. Max. 1 dog.

Open: 30 April - 5 September.

Directions

Take D34 from Entraygues-sur-Truyère to St Amans-des-Cots (14 km). In St Amans take D97 to Colombez and then D599 to Lac de la Selves (site signed, 5 km. from St Amans). GPS: 44.66668, 2.68001

Charges guide

Per unit incl. 2 persons and electricity	€ 16,00 - € 34,00
extra person	€ 3,00 - € 5,00

For latest campsite news, availability and prices visit

alanrogers.com

Saint Antonin-Noble-Val

Flower Camping les Gorges de l'Aveyron

Marsac bas, F-82140 Saint Antonin-Noble-Val (Tarn-et-Garonne) T: 05 63 30 69 76
E: info@camping-gorges-aveyron.com alanrogers.com/FR82040

This is a friendly, family site which is undergoing a process of renovation by its new owners, Stephane and Johanna Batlo. The site has an attractive wooded location, sloping down to the River Aveyron and facing the Roc d'Anglars. Reception and the two toilet blocks are housed in traditional, converted farm buildings. There are 80 pitches of which 50 are for touring units and these all have electrical connections (3-10A). The pitches are grassy and well shaded and may become very soft in times of poor weather. Some pitches are available close to the river but we would suggest that these are unsuitable for younger children as the river is unfenced. The owners have ambitious plans for the future and are planning to add a swimming pool and third toilet block. This is a very quiet site in low season and some amenities, notably the snack bar and shop are only available in the peak season. The nearby town of St Antonin-Noble-Val dates back to the eighth century and is just 1.5 km. from the site. The town is well worth a visit and has a good range of shops and restaurants.

Facilities

Two toilet blocks with washing machines and dryers. Small shop, bar, snack bar and takeaway (June-Sept). Direct access to river. Fishing. Canoeing. Play area. Entertainment and activities in high season. Mobile homes for rent. Off site: St Antonin-Noble-Val with a wide choice of shops, restaurants and bars 1.5 km. Bicycle hire 1.5 km. Riding 2 km. Cordes-sur-Ciel 35 km. Many walking paths and cycle trails.

Open: 10 April - 26 September.

Directions

From the north, take exit 59 from the A20 autoroute joining the D926 and follow signs to St Antonin. Site can be found on the D115, 1.5 km. east of the town. GPS: 44.1519, 1.7715

Charges guide

Per unit incl. 2 persons and electricity	€ 9,40 - € 16,30
extra person	€ 2,90 - € 5,00
child (under 7 yrs)	€ 1,60 - € 2,50

Camping Cheques accepted.

Les Gorges de l'Aveyron***

Nature, sport and culture!

82140 St. Antonin Noble Val - Tel: 0033 (0)563 306 976 - Fax: 0033 (0)563 306 761
E-mail: info@camping-gorges-aveyron.com - www.camping-gorges-aveyron.com

Saint Cirq-Lapopie

Camping la Truffière

F-46330 Saint Cirq-Lapopie (Lot) T: 05 65 30 20 22. E: contact@camping-truffiere.com
alanrogers.com/FR46150

Set in four hectares of mature oak woodland, only 2.5 km. from the cliff top village of St Cirq-Lapopie, La Truffière is well suited to those seeking a peaceful countryside holiday amongst the stunning natural scenery of the 'Parc naturel régional des Causses de Quercy'. The 90 terraced touring pitches are of varying sizes and on a mixture of grass and gravel (larger units should reserve pitches in advance). All pitches have electricity (6A) and most have shade from the abundant trees. There are various walks and mountain bike trails in the area and you can hire bikes on site.

Facilities

Two well appointed, clean, modern toilet blocks (one heated) include facilities for disabled visitors. Motorcaravan services. Fridge hire. Small shop (open all season). Bar/restaurant (1/6-31/8), terrace overlooking pool and playing field. Snack bar (1/6-31/8). Swimming pool, paddling pool, sun terrace (1/5-15/9). Playing field, volleyball, basketball, football. Adventure style play area. Trampolines. Boules. English spoken. Off site: Small shop in village. Supermarkets in Cahors 25 km. Riding 3 km. Fishing (in the River Lot) 3 km.

Open: 3 April - 15 September.

Directions

From D911 Cahors - Rodez road, turn north on D42 at Concots (signed St Cirq-Lapopie). Site about 5 km. on right. Approaching from north on D42 via St Cirq-Lapopie not recommended due to extremely tight left turn in village. GPS: 44.44855, 1.67455

Charges guide

Per unit incl. 2 persons and electricity	€ 19,00 - € 23,00
extra person	€ 5,00 - € 5,50

Camping Cheques accepted.

For latest campsite news, availability and prices visit
alanrogers.com

Saint Come d'Olt

Camping Belle Rive

Rue du Terral, F-12500 Saint Come d'Olt (Aveyron) T: 05 65 44 05 85. E: bellerive12@voila.fr

alanrogers.com/FR12380

Small and simple, this family run campsite beside the River Lot is on the edge of a delightful medieval village. The region has many historic towns and villages with châteaux and ancient churches and is close to the Pilgrim route. The local produce, for example Roquefort cheese, is well worth sampling. The site is good for those seeking a tranquil spot with little in the way of on-site activities. There are 71 good sized grassy pitches delineated by a variety of tall trees that give good shade on most of the pitches (6A electricity). Access to the site is not suitable for large outfits due to the many small twisting roads.

Facilities

Adequate but very clean old style central block with combined shower and washbasin cubicles. Washing machine. Facilities for disabled campers. Takeaway (all season). Play area. Some family activities (high season). River bathing and fishing. Off site: Village, small shops, bank, bar/restaurants 400 m. Espalion with larger shops and market 4 km. Swimming pool 4 km. Riding 12 km. Canoeing. Ancient villages, châteaux, churches. Many walking and cycling routes.

Open: 1 April - 30 September.

Directions

Leave A75 at exit 42, signed Sévérac le Château. Take N88 west, then D28 to Espalion. Cross river on D987 to St Côme d'Olt (4 km). On entering village bear left, following signs to site. Do not drive through the village. GPS: 44.51376, 2.81847

Charges 2011

Per unit incl. 2 persons and electricity	€ 13,70
extra person	€ 3,20
child (under 7 yrs)	€ 1,80
dog	€ 0,70

No credit cards.

Saint Geniez-d'Olt

Campé●le

Campéole la Boissière

Route de la Cascade, F-12130 Saint Geniez-d'Olt (Aveyron) T: 05 65 70 40 43. E: boissiere@campeole.com

alanrogers.com/FR12090

With trout in the river and carp in the lakes, La Boissière is a fisherman's paradise. The site is a member of the Campéole group and is situated on the banks of the River Lot, surrounded by wooded hills. Walking, swimming, canoeing or cycling are alternative pursuits here. Mature trees provide plenty of shade on the generous, partly hedged, grassy pitches, all of which have electricity connections (6A) and frequently placed water points. Reception is housed in an old, converted farmhouse. The nearby old town of St Geniez d'Olt should satisfy all shopping needs and day or longer fishing licences can be obtained there (the helpful site staff will advise). There is direct access through the site to the river, which is suitable for swimming and canoeing. La Boissière has 150 pitches, of which around 70 are used for mobile homes, chalets or fully equipped tents (available for rent) There is much of interest in the area and the Tarn gorges and Grandes Causses are both within easy access.

Facilities

Two modern, clean toilet blocks with washbasins in cubicles and preset showers. Baby changing facilities in female area. Basic facilities for visitors with disabilities (no rails). Shop with basic provisions (milk and bread in high season only). Bar with terrace. Large, heated swimming pool and paddling pool. Multisports terrain. Bouncy castle and playground. Entertainment is organised in July/Aug. Mobile homes, chalets and tents for rent. Internet (first 15 mins. free). Off site: St Geniez d'Olt (500 m). Bicycle and canoe hire.

Open: 20 April - 30 September.

Directions

From Saint Geniez d'Olt follow the D988 eastwards towards Banassac. After 500 m. follow signs on right to La Boissière campsite. GPS: 44.4686, 2.9825

Charges guide

Per unit incl. 2 persons	
and electricity	€ 15,10 - € 24,50
extra person	€ 4,00 - € 6,10
child (2-6 yrs)	€ 3,60 - € 4,00
dog	€ 2,00 - € 2,60

For latest campsite news, availability and prices visit

alanrogers.com

Saint Geniez-d'Olt

Kawan Village Marmotel

F-12130 Saint Geniez-d'Olt (Aveyron) T: 05 65 70 46 51. E: info@marmotel.com
alanrogers.com/FR12150

The road into Marmotel passes various industrial buildings and is a little off-putting – persevere, as they are soon left behind. The campsite itself is a mixture of old and new. The old part provides many pitches with lots of shade and separated by hedges. The new area is sunny until the trees grow. These pitches each have a private sanitary unit, with shower, WC, washbasin and dishwashing. New and very well designed, they are reasonably priced for such luxury. All the pitches have electricity (10A). A lovely restaurant has a wide terrace with views of the hills and overlooking the heated swimming and paddling pools. These have fountains, a toboggan and sun beds either on grass or the tiled surrounds. The Lot river runs alongside the site where you can fish or canoe.

Facilities	Directions
Good sanitary facilities include baby baths and facilities for disabled visitors. Washing machines. Bar/restaurant, takeaway. Swimming pools. Small play area. Multisports area. Entertainment July/Aug. including disco below bar, cinema, karaoke, dances, miniclub for 4-12 yr olds. Bicycle hire. Fishing. Canoeing. Off site: Large supermarket 500 m. Riding 10 km. Bicycle tours and canoe trips on the Lot and rafting on the Tarn.	Heading south on autoroute 75 (free) take exit 41 and follow signs for St Geniez-d'Olt. Site is at western end of village. Site is signed onto D19 to Prades d'Aubrac, then 500 m. on left. GPS: 44.46165, 2.96318

Open: 10 May - 11 September.

Charges guide

Per unit incl. 1 or 2 persons and electricity	€ 18,00 - € 27,00

Camping Cheques accepted.

Saint Girons

Parc d'Audinac les Bains

Montjoie-Audinac, F-09200 Saint Girons (Ariège) T: 05 61 66 44 50. E: accueil@audinac.com
alanrogers.com/FR09100

Remnants of an old thermal springs can be found on the site at Parc d'Audinac les Bains, a tranquil haven with wonderful views of the surrounding mountains. Owned by a charming French couple, Olivia and Jérôme Barbry, you are guaranteed a friendly welcome on this site which has 60 touring pitches and 40 chalets for rent. The terraced touring pitches are mostly level, although some do have a slight slope. They are on well drained grass and each has 10A electricity supplied (the older part of the site via French sockets). Water supplies are conveniently located for all of the pitches, as are the modern sanitary facilities. The site swimming pool is popular and although it is not heated, it reaches good temperatures in the height of summer. In July and August a children's club (4-12 yrs) provides organised games and other activities, while adults and older children are well catered for with sports facilities.

Facilities	Directions
Two small bright and modern toilet blocks (one unisex) with hot and cold water to showers and washbasins. British and Turkish style WC's. Washing machines. Motorcaravan service point. Good sized outdoor swimming pool and paddling pool with WCs, showers and changing facilities. Small shop for drinks and ice creams (July/Aug). Children's club (July/Aug). Tennis. Boules. Sports area. Off site: Shops, bars, restaurants and supermarket at St Girons 3 km. Many outdoor activities available in the surrounding area (the owners will advise and have arranged discounts at some).	From St Girons take D117 towards Foix. Turn left on D627 signed St Croix and Merigon. Site is on the right just after Audinac-les-Bains. GPS: 43.0074, 1.1826

Open: 1 May - 30 September.

Charges guide

Per unit incl. 2 persons	€ 11,50 - € 16,00
extra person	€ 4,00 - € 6,00
child (0-6 yrs)	€ 3,00 - € 5,00
electricity (10A)	€ 3,50

Saint Parthem

Camping la Plaine

F-12300 Saint Parthem (Aveyron) T: 05 65 64 05 24. E: infos@camping-laplaine.fr

alanrogers.com/FR12360

Strung out along the bank of the Lot river, this small, spacious, delightful site is family run. The enthusiastic and very friendly Dutch owners are making many improvements here including the addition of a new swimming pool. There are 65 grassy, fairly level pitches with 61 for touring (6A electricity, long leads advised). The pitches are separated by maturing trees and some hedging with views over the river and the wooded gorge. Some pitches have little shade. Swimming and canoeing are possible from the small pebbly beach. The site makes a good base for exploring this interesting and beautiful region.

Facilities

Old style but very clean central block and small satellite block with all necessary facilities. Facilities for disabled visitors. Washing machine, ironing board. Small bar/restaurant with takeaway (all season). Bread to order. Swimming pool with patio. River fishing and bathing from pebble beach. Tennis. Boules. Off site: Small village, small shop, 500 m. Riding 8 km. Canoeing 15 km. Picturesque medieval towns and villages, e.g. Conques 14 km.

Open: 5 April - 14 September.

Directions

Site is northeast of Decazeville. Leave Decazeville on the D963 signed Aurillac. After 6 km. cross river and turn east onto D42 to St Parthem (6 km). Site is well signed. GPS: 44.6292, 2.32059

Charges guide

Per unit incl. 2 persons	€ 12,50
extra person	€ 3,50
electricity (6A)	€ 3,00
No credit cards.	

Sainte Pierre-Lafeuille

Camping Quercy Vacances

Mas de la Combe, F-46090 Sainte Pierre-Lafeuille (Lot) T: 05 65 36 87 15. E: quercy-vacances@wanadoo.fr

alanrogers.com/FR46240

This clean and well run site is owned by a young, English speaking, French couple who are determined to improve the facilities and ambiance. It is only 4.5 km. from the A20 and is an ideal stopover site for holidaymakers travelling to and from Spain. However, it is better than just a stopover site and is worth staying a few extra days. It has 70 large unmarked touring pitches most of which have 6/10A hook-ups. The site facilities include a rustic bar and restaurant which has hand painted murals on the walls. The toilets and laundry are also housed in this single split-level building with the toilets located to the rear of the building on a lower level.

Facilities

Clean, modern toilet block, recently refurbished. Facilities for campers with disabilities are located in a separate building adjacent to the camping area. Small basic shop. Bar and takeaway. Restaurant serving specials like couscous and paella once a week. Large round swimming pool (20/6-15/9), children's pool. Live music, dancing (July/Aug). Small play area. Off site: Riding 5 km. Bicycle hire, fishing 10 km.

Open: 1 April - 30 September.

Directions

Leave A20 exit 57 (Cahors). Shortly turn left on N20 and then turn right on small un-named road (site signed) before reaching St Pierre-Lafeuille (about 4.5 km. from the A20). Site on right in about 600 m. GPS: 44.53136, 1.45926

Charges guide

Per unit incl. 2 persons and electricity	€ 17,50 - € 24,10
extra person	€ 3,80 - € 5,00

---

alan rogers ◉ travel

Salles-Curan

Kawan Village les Genêts

Lac de Pareloup, F-12410 Salles-Curan (Aveyron) T: 05 65 46 35 34. E: contact@camping-les-genets.fr

alanrogers.com/FR12080

This family run site is on the shores of Lac de Pareloup and offers both family holiday and watersports facilities. The 163 pitches include 80 grassy, mostly individual pitches for touring units. These are in two areas, one on each side of the entrance lane, and are divided by hedges, shrubs and trees. Most have electricity (6A) and many also have water and waste water drain. The site slopes gently down to the beach and lake with facilities for all watersports including water skiing. A full animation and activities programme is organised in high season, and there is much to see and do in this very attractive corner of Aveyron. The site is not suitable for American style motorhomes.

Facilities

Two sanitary units with suite for disabled visitors. The older unit has been refurbished. Baby room. Laundry. Well stocked shop (from 1/6). Bar, restaurant, snacks (14/6-5/9). Swimming pool, spa pool (from 1/6; unsupervised). Playground. Minigolf. Boules. Bicycle hire. Pedaloes, windsurfers, kayaks. Fishing licences available. WiFi in bar.

Open: 21 May - 11 September.

Directions

From Salles-Curan take D577 for about 4 km. and turn right into a narrow lane immediately after a sharp right hand bend. Site is signed at junction. GPS: 44.18933, 2.76693

Charges 2011

Per unit incl. 2 persons and electricity	€ 18,00 - € 40,00
extra person	€ 4,00 - € 8,00
Camping Cheques accepted.	

For latest campsite news, availability and prices visit

alanrogers.com

Seissan

Domaine Lacs de Gascogne

Rue du Lac, F-32260 Seissan (Gers) T: 05 62 66 27 94. E: info@domainelacsdegascogne.eu
alanrogers.com/FR32180

This is a spacious site located at Seissan in the Pyrenees foothills. Its impressive drive sweeps around the largest of the three lakes into the spacious and relaxing Domaine. The 25 large grassy touring pitches mostly have shade and lake views. Electricity is 16A (long leads). Comfortable chalets (25) can be rented. The attractive swimming and saltwater pools are on a creamy stone terrace, close to the sauna, gym, and new sanitary block. The bar and restaurant are open all season and the food is very good. The lakes are perfect for fishing, kayaking, and evening beach campfires. Across the lakes is ideal for 'wilder' camping, this area also has five tepees.

Facilities

Excellent sanitary facilities in a new block were clean, tidy and well maintained. Baby changing mats and facilities for disabled visitors. Restaurant with lunch and à la carte menus. Breakfast service. Lounge. TV room. Swimming pool. Health pool. Sauna. Gym. Fishing. Kayaks. Rope raft across lake. Play area. Children's play room. Tennis court. Bicycle hire. Entertainment and activity programme. Mobile home and B&B accommodation. Off site: Riding 5 km. Golf 6 km. Supermarket 7 km. Auch 19 km.

Open: 15 February - 15 December.

Directions

Head south from Auch on N21 and, at Beaulieu, join the southbound D929. Continue on this road as far as Seissan and then follow signs to the site. GPS: 43.49535, 0.57826

Charges guide

Per unit incl. 2 persons	€ 9,00 - € 30,00
extra person	€ 6,00

Séniergues

Domaine de la Faurie

F-46240 Séniergues (Lot) T: 05 65 21 14 36. E: contact@camping-lafaurie.com
alanrogers.com/FR46190

A stunning array of tended shrubs and thoughtful flower plantings is spread throughout this very pretty 27-hectare site which is located on a hilltop with wide open views of the surrounding hills and valleys. Although hidden away, it is an excellent base for exploring the Lot and Dordogne regions. The site is separated into two distinct areas, an open, lightly shaded front section and a much more densely shaded area with tall pine trees all around the pitches. The pitches are large and most are at least 100 sq.m. The friendly French owners will tell you that they consider the site their personal garden.

Facilities

The two sanitary blocks are clean and well maintained. Facilities for disabled visitors. Washing machine. Motorcaravan service point. Excellent gift shop selling regional and local produce (bread available). Bar, restaurant and takeaway. Swimming pool and paddling pool. TV and games rooms. Boules. Bicycle hire. Play area. Small library. Weekly soirées in high season. Max. 1 dog. Off site: Fishing 3 km. Golf 8 km. Riding 15 km.

Open: 7 April - 30 September.

Directions

From the A20 exit on N56 and turn right towards St Germain du Bel Air. Continue for 5 km. and the site is on the right. GPS: 44.69197, 1.53461

Charges guide

Per person	€ 4,50 - € 6,70
child (1-7 yrs)	€ 3,50 - € 4,70
pitch	€ 6,00 - € 9,50
electricity (6A)	€ 4,50

Sévérac-l'Eglise

Flower Camping la Grange de Monteillac

F-12310 Sévérac-l'Eglise (Aveyron) T: 05 65 70 21 00. E: info@la-grange-de-monteillac.com
alanrogers.com/FR12070

La Grange de Monteillac is a modern, well equipped site in the beautiful, well preserved small village of Sévérac-l'Eglise. A spacious site, it provides 105 individual pitches, 70 for touring, on gently sloping grass, separated by flowering shrubs and mostly young trees offering little shade. All pitches have electricity (6A, long leads may be required), and 24 have water and waste water connections. There are 35 chalets, mobile homes and tents for rent in separate areas. The friendly owner will advise about the many interesting activities in the region. An evening stroll around this delightful village is a must.

Facilities

Modern toilet block with facilities for babies and disabled campers. Washing machine, dryer. Shop (1/7-31/8). Poolside restaurant/snack bar serving pizzas, grills etc, takeaway (15/5-15/9). Music or groups feature in the bar (July/Aug). Two swimming pools (15/5-15/9). Spacious, well equipped playground. Bicycle hire. Archery. Floodlit boules court. Organised activities. Off site: Fishing 1 km. Shops in village 3 km. Riding 9 km. Canoeing, rafting, canyoning, rock climbing and hang gliding.

Open: 1 May - 15 September.

Directions

Site is on the edge of Sévérac-l'Église village, just off N88 Rodez - Sévérac Le Château road. From A75 use exit 42. At Sévérac-l'Église turn south onto D28, site is signed. Site entrance is very shortly on left. GPS: 44.3652, 2.85142

Charges guide

Per unit incl. 2 persons and electricity	€ 16,50 - € 26,90
extra person	€ 3,00 - € 6,00
child (2-7 yrs)	€ 2,00 - € 3,80

For latest campsite news, availability and prices visit

alanrogers.com

Sorèze

Camping Saint Martin

F-81540 Sorèze (Tarn) T: 05 63 50 20 19. E: campings.occitanie@orange.fr

alanrogers.com/FR81110

There are 48 individual touring pitches with 10A electricity and six wooden chalets for rent at this site. The pitches are all on grass, some divided by newly planted hedging and there are some mature trees for shade. Six pitches are reserved for motorcaravans, although these are rather compact. A small swimming pool is well fenced and gated. Reception has a small bar and snack bar and can also provide basic supplies including drinks, sweets, speciality foods and snacks. However, you are only 100 metres from the town centre shops.

Facilities

Sanitary unit is well built. Facilities for disabled visitors. Covered dishwashing and laundry sinks plus a washing machine. Small shop. Bar with TV. Snack bar. Swimming pool. WiFi (free). All amenities open 15/6-15/9. Boules. Communal barbecue. Small playground. Entertainment in high season. Off site: Municipal leisure and sports facilities including tennis courts adjacent.

Open: 15 June - 15 September.

Directions

Sorèze is on the D85 about 25 km. southwest of Castres, 5 km. east of Revel. The site is well signed within the town. GPS: 43.454517, 2.069583

Charges guide

Per unit incl. 2 persons and electricity	€ 15,05 - € 18,50
extra person	€ 3,40 - € 4,50
child (0-7 yrs)	€ 2,00 - € 2,70

Sorgeat

Camping Municipal la Prade

F-09110 Sorgeat (Ariège) T: 05 61 64 36 34. E: sorgeat.mainie@wanadoo.fr

alanrogers.com/FR09050

Superbly situated high on the mountainside overlooking a valley, this site has magnificent views, with a river 300 m. and a lake 2 km. A small site, it provides just 40 pitches on terraces, some of which are occupied by long stay units, (electricity 5/10A). Well supervised, with the warden present at varying times, the site is kept very clean. A small stream tinkles through the edge of the site and the attractive hills towering above it reverberate with the sound of goat bells. A separate area has permanent brick barbecues for use by campers. A most reasonably priced campsite.

Facilities

The original, rather small sanitary block has only two showers and two WCs in each half. However, a second block has now been added and standards are very high. Facilities for disabled visitors are also very good with special washbasin and a very large shower suite. Washing machine. Small play area. Off site: Shop and cafêé in village. Fishing 500 m. Riding and bicycle hire 5 km.

Open: All year.

Directions

From Ax-les-Thermes take D613 towards Quillan 4 km. Turn onto D52 and continue for 1 km. Follow site signs. Bear left at first junction up through Sorgeat village to site. Mountain roads may be difficult for large units. GPS: 42.7329, 1.8539

Charges guide

Per unit incl. 2 persons and electricity	€ 13,60
extra person	€ 3,30
child (0-10 yrs)	€ 1,60
No credit cards.	

Souillac

Flower Camping les Ondines

Rue des Ondines, F-46200 Souillac (Lot) T: 05 65 37 86 44. E: info@camping-lesondines.com

alanrogers.com/FR46390

Souillac is a picturesque town lying between the Dordogne and Lot. It is just a five minute walk from Les Ondines to the town's attractive pedestrianised centre where there are many cafés, restaurants and shops, as well as an abbey and, unusually, a robotic toy museum! There are 242 pitches here. These are grassy and well-sized (mostly with electricity). A number of mobile homes and fully equipped tents are available for rent. In peak season, various activities are organized, including a children's club. The site lies on the banks of the Dordogne and canoe rental is available in the town.

Facilities

Two traditional toilet blocks with basic but clean facilities, including those for visitors with disabilities. Washing machine. Access to municipal swimming pool (free July/Aug). Pétanque. Volleyball. Play area. Tourist information. Activity and entertainment programme. Mobile homes and tents for rent. Off site: Swimming pool 300 m. Souillac (cafés, shops, restaurants and takeaway). Walking and cycle tracks. Riding. Canoeing. Supermarket Quercyland water park.

Open: 1 May - 30 September.

Directions

Approaching from the north, leave the A20 motorway at exit 55 and head for Souillac. Drive through the town and, around 500 m. beyond the traffic lights, turn right following signs to Les Ondines and Quercyland. Continue to follow signs to the site. GPS: 44.888871, 1.474196

Charges guide

Per unit incl. 2 persons and electricity	€ 11,00 - € 16,00
extra person	€ 3,00 - € 4,90
child (2-7 yrs)	€ 1,60 - € 2,20

Souillac-sur-Dordogne
Castel Camping le Domaine de la Paille Basse
F-46200 Souillac-sur-Dordogne (Lot) T: 05 65 37 85 48. E: info@lapaillebasse.com
alanrogers.com/FR46010

Set in a rural location some 8 km. from Souillac, this family owned site is easily accessible from the N20 and well placed to take advantage of excursions into the Dordogne. It is part of a large domain of 80 hectares, all available to campers for walks and recreation. The site is quite high up and there are excellent views over the surrounding countryside. The 262 pitches are in two main areas – one is level in cleared woodland with good shade, and the other on grass with limited shade. Numbered and marked, the pitches are a minimum 100 sq.m. and often considerably more. All have electricity (3/6A) with 80 fully serviced. The site is well placed for excursions into the Dordogne. A wide range of activities and entertainment are organised in high season. The site can get very busy in high season and is popular with three tour operators. If you like a livelier type of site, you will enjoy La Paille Basse.

Facilities

Three main toilet blocks all have modern equipment and are kept very clean. Laundry. Small shop with a large selection of wine. Restaurant, bar (open until 02.00 in high season), terrace, pizza takeaway. Crêperie. Main swimming pool, a smaller one, paddling pool (unheated), water slides. Sun terrace. Soundproofed disco (three times weekly in season). TV (with satellite). Cinema below the pool area. Tennis. Play area. Library. WiFi in office/bar area (charged). Off site: Golf 4 km.

Open: 15 May - 15 September.

Directions

From Souillac take D15 and then D62 roads leading northwest towards Salignac-Eyvignes and after 6 km. turn right at site sign and follow steep and narrow approach road for 2 km. GPS: 44.94728, 1.43924

Charges guide

Per person	€ 5,40 - € 7,50
child (under 7 yrs)	€ 3,80 - € 5,50
pitch	€ 7,80 - € 10,80
incl. water and drainage	€ 9,80 - € 13,00
dog	€ 4,00

Less 20% outside 15/6-1/9.

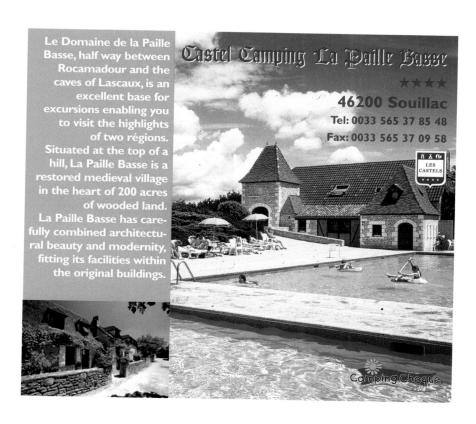

Le Domaine de la Paille Basse, half way between Rocamadour and the caves of Lascaux, is an excellent base for excursions enabling you to visit the highlights of two régions. Situated at the top of a hill, La Paille Basse is a restored medieval village in the heart of 200 acres of wooded land. La Paille Basse has carefully combined architectural beauty and modernity, fitting its facilities within the original buildings.

Castel Camping La Paille Basse
★★★★
46200 Souillac
Tel: 0033 565 37 85 48
Fax: 0033 565 37 09 58
LES CASTELS
Camping Cheque

Tarascon-sur-Ariège

Yelloh! Village le Pré Lombard

F-09400 Tarascon-sur-Ariège (Ariège) T: 05 61 05 61 94. E: leprelombard@wanadoo.fr

alanrogers.com/FR09060

This busy, good value site is located beside the attractive river Ariège near the town. There are 180 level, grassy, pitches with shade provided by a variety of trees (electricity 10A). At the rear of the site are 70 site-owned chalets and mobile homes. A gate in the fence provides access to the river bank for fishing. Open for a long season, it is an excellent choice for early or late breaks, or as a stopover en-route to the winter sun destinations in Spain. This region of Ariège is in the foothills of the Pyrenees and 85 km. from Andorra. Didier Mioni, the manager here follows the town motto S'y passos, y demoros – 'if you wish to come here, you will stay here' in his aim to ensure your satisfaction on his site. At Tarascon itself you can visit the Parc Pyrénéen de l'Art Préhistorique to view prehistoric rock paintings, or the really adventurous can take to the air for paragliding, hang-gliding, or micro lighting.

Facilities

Five toilet blocks of varying ages, facilities for disabled campers. Laundry. Motorcaravan services. Bar and takeaway. Shop. Restaurant, entertainment, dancing (15/5-30/9). Heated swimming pool (15/5-30/9). Playgrounds for toddlers and older children. Video games machines. Boules. Multisports court. Fishing. Internet and WiFi (charged). Satellite TV. Entertainment (high season), nightclub, children's club, sports tournaments. Activity programmes for small groups. Off site: Supermarket 300 m. Town 600 m. Archery, kayaking and fishing nearby. Riding 5 km. Golf 30 km. Skiing 20 km.

Open: 15 March - 15 October.

Directions

Site is 600 m. south of town, adjacent to the river. From north, turn off main N20 into the town, site well signed. From south (Andorra) site signed at roundabout on town approach.
GPS: 42.83985, 1.612

Charges guide

Per unit incl. 2 persons and 10A electricity	€ 15,00 - € 32,00
extra person	€ 4,00 - € 8,00
child (2-7 yrs)	free - € 6,50
dog	free - € 2,50

Camping Cheques accepted.

★★★★ Camping Village

Le Pré Lombard

Tarascon sur Ariège

In a natural environment totally protected, lined with the Ariege river, the "Pré Lombard", with its 110 camping places, its 70 rents spreading over 3.5 hectares, offers you exceptional conditions of life and comfort ! Heated swimming pool, restaurant, shop, personalized supervision, cultural stays, organisation of guided visits to local famous attractions... A whole range of services at your disposal on site. Here, you will enjoy a peaceful rhythmic existence, according to the seasons. Rest and sweet life are proposed to you in spring and in autumn. During the summer, this is the party in the "Pré Lombard" with quality entertainments. In a club atmosphere, every day from morning until night, the "Pré Lombard" invites children, teenagers, adults to practise a mass of activities.

Open from 15/03 until 15/10 - Located at 600 m from Tarascon sur Ariège
Altitude: 478 meters -Train station 1 KM – Bus stop 600 M
110 km from Toulouse – 320 km from Barcelone
leprelombard@wanadoo.fr - www.prelombard.com

yelloh! VILLAGE

For latest campsite news, availability and prices visit

alanrogers.com

Therondels

Flower Camping la Source

Presqu'île de Laussac, F-12600 Therondels (Aveyron) T: 05 65 66 27 10
E: info@camping-la-source.com alanrogers.com/FR12210

This extremely spacious, steeply terraced site borders the long and narrow Lac de Sarrans with its steep wooded sides. The site is run by a very friendly family and is better suited for the younger family wanting to 'get away from it all'. All the facilities are first class, although the layout of the site means that pitches may be some distance and a steep climb away. The owners prefer to provide tractor assistance for caravans. There are 108 medium to large, slightly sloping, grassy pitches with 63 for touring, all with 6/10A electricity, water and drainage. They are separated by mostly silver birch trees offering some shade and have views through the trees over the lake. Rock pegs are essential. The site is not suitable for very large units and those with walking difficulties.

Facilities

Two large, well appointed and clean toilet blocks with all the necessary facilities including those for babies and campers with disabilities. Bar with TV (all season). Shop, restaurant and takeaway. Heated swimming pool with toboggan and paddling pool (all season). Play area. TV room. Activities in high season for all the family. Lake fishing. Off site: Boat ramp 500 m. Golf 6 km. Riding and bicycle hire 15 km.

Open: 13 May - 6 September.

Directions

Leave the A75 at exit 28 or 29 (St Flour). Go through town and take D921 towards Rodez. After 12 km. turn right on D990 to Pierrefort and 3 km. after village turn left on D34, signed Laussac. Follow narrow twisting lanes down to site (about 9 km). GPS: 44.853716, 2.77105

Charges guide

Per unit incl. 2 persons	
and electricity	€ 15,50 - € 27,50
extra person	€ 3,70 - € 4,90
child (0-7 yrs)	€ 2,70 - € 3,90

Vayrac

Camping les Granges

F-46110 Vayrac (Lot) T: 05 65 32 46 58. E: info@les-granges.com
alanrogers.com/FR46310

Situated just over 3 km. outside Vayrac in a very rural position, this site nestles quietly beside the river in a tranquil and peaceful area. Pitches along the river frontage are popular and this should be remembered when reserving a space if that area is preferred. There is direct access to the river at one end of the site which can be useful for setting off in a canoe and enjoying the pleasures of the Dordogne river. There are 150 pitches with 116 of average size for touring units and the remaining 34 for mobile homes, the latter all available for rent. The pitches are level, mostly shaded and have 10A electricity. Entertainment is organised in high season. The owners are friendly and helpful and are keen to ensure you enjoy your holiday whilst on their family orientated site.

Facilities

Two modern sanitary blocks include facilities for disabled visitors. Washing machine and ironing board. Snack bar and takeaway Swimming pool and fun pool for small children. Play area. Organised entertainment (12/7-16/8). Fishing. Max. 1 dog. Off site: Bicycle hire 1 km. Golf and riding 10 km.

Open: 1 May - 18 September.

Directions

From Brive, take the D20 towards Figeac. In Vayrac turn right just before the church at sign for 'Campings' and 'Stade'. Site is signed from here. GPS: 44.93462, 1.67981

Charges guide

Per unit incl. 2 persons	
and electricity	€ 16,48 - € 19,60
extra person	€ 5,00
child (2-10 yrs)	€ 2,80
dog (max. 1)	€ 1,60

For latest campsite news, availability and prices visit

alanrogers.com

-10%

on pitch fee in low season
for Alan Rogers' readers

Yelloh! Village: N° 1 in top-class camping villages.

Take advantage of this exceptional reduction, and enjoy unforgettable holidays in one of our 46 camping villages.

Booking is really simple: go online on **www.yellohvillage.co.uk** and type in the promotion code ALANYV11

When you get to the campsite reception, don't forget to bring with you this guide, or the voucher which you can obtain from Signature magazine or the 'Special Offers' page on the www.alanrogers.com website.

Yelloh! Color holidays

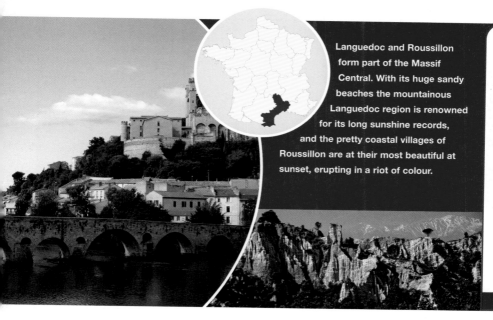

Languedoc and Roussillon form part of the Massif Central. With its huge sandy beaches the mountainous Languedoc region is renowned for its long sunshine records, and the pretty coastal villages of Roussillon are at their most beautiful at sunset, erupting in a riot of colour.

DÉPARTEMENTS: 11 AUDE, 30 GARD, 34 HÉRAULT, 48 LOZÈRE, 66 PYRÉNÉES-ORIENTALES

MAJOR CITIES: MONTPELLIER, PERPIGNAN, CARCASSONNE

Once an independent duchy, the ancient land of Languedoc combines two distinct regions: the vineyards of the Corbières and Minervois and the coastal plain stretching from the Rhône to the Spanish border. Much of the region is rugged and unspoilt, offering opportunities for walking and climbing.

There is ample evidence of the dramatic past. Ruins of the former Cathar castles can be seen throughout the region. The walled city of Carcassonne with its towers, dungeons, moats and drawbridges is one of the most impressive examples of medieval France.

Today, Languedoc and Roussillon are wine and agricultural regions. Languedoc, with considerable success, is now a producer of much of the nation's better value wines. But above all, vast hot sandy beaches and long hours of sunshine make this a paradise for beach enthusiasts. La Grande Motte, Cap d'Agde and Canet, are all being promoted as an alternative to the more famous Mediterranean stretches of the Côte d'Azur.

Places of interest

Aigues-Mortes: medieval city.

Béziers: wine capital of the region, St Nazaire cathedral, Canal du Midi.

Carcassonne: largest medieval walled city in Europe.

Limoux: medieval town, Notre Dame de Marseilla Basilica, St Martin church.

Montpellier: universities, Roman sites; Gothic cathedral.

Nîmes: Roman remains, Pont du Gard.

Perpignan: King's Palace; Catalan characteristics, old fortress.

Villeneuve-lés-Avignon: Royal City and residence of popes in 14th century.

Cuisine of the region

Cooking is characterised by garlic and olive oil with sausages and smoked hams. Fish is popular along the coast. Wines include Corbières, Minervois, Banyuls and Muscat.

Aïgo Bouido: garlic soup.

Boles de picoulat: small balls of chopped-up beef and pork, garlic and eggs.

Bouillinade: a type of *bouillabaisse* with potatoes, oil, garlic and onions.

Boutifare: a sausage-shaped pudding of bacon and herbs.

Cargolade: snails, stewed in wine.

Ouillade: heavy soup of *boutifare* leeks, carrots, and potatoes..

Touron: a pastry of almonds, pistachio nuts and fruit.

www.sunfrance.com
contact.crtlr@sunfrance.com
(0) 4 67 20 02 20

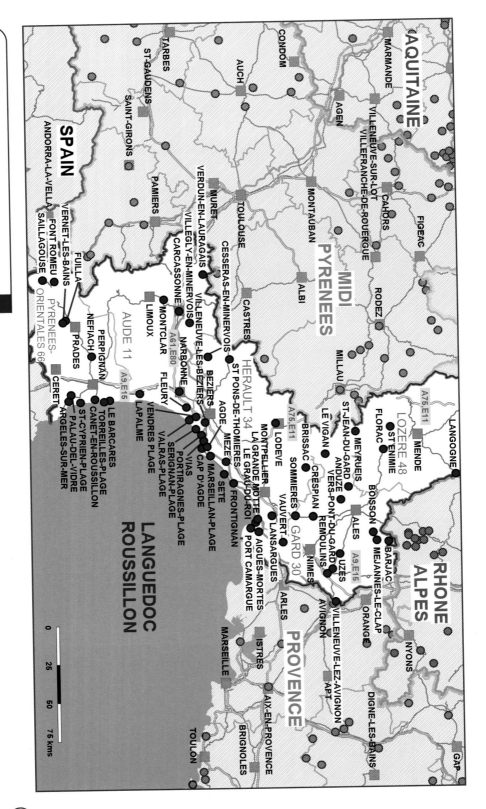

Agde

Camping le Neptune

46 boulevard du St Christ, F-34300 Agde (Hérault) T: 04 67 94 23 94. E: info@campingleneptune.com
alanrogers.com/FR34130

Camping le Neptune is a rare find in this area. This small, family run site with only 165 pitches makes a delightful change. The pitches are mostly separated by flowering bushes, with some shade, most with 6/10A electricity. There is also a good number of mobile homes to rent. The Fray family are welcoming and even though this is a busy area, this site is an oasis of calm, suited to couples and young families. Situated alongside the splendid Herault river, one can cycle or walk into the village of le Gau d'Agde or on into the historic centre of Agde itself.

Facilities

Two toilet blocks provide roomy preset showers, washbasins in cabins, three cold showers for hot weather. Facilities for disabled visitors. Laundry. Small shop, bar and snack bar (all 15/5-30/9). Heated swimming pool (15/4-30/9, bracelets required). Field for sports. WiFi. Boat mooring facility on the River Hérault across the road. Barbecues not permitted. Max. 1 dog. Off site: Beach 2 km. Riding 2 km. Golf 5 km. Fishing in Herault. Canal du Midi and round lock 2 km.

Open: 1 April - 30 September.

Directions

From A9 exit 34 follow signs for (Agde, Bessau, Vias), then Cap d'Agde. Exit for Grau d'Agde. At roundabout (with statue) left following signs for Grau d'Agde, and again at 2nd roundabout (left). Straight on to 5th roundabout where left and under bridge. Site is 600 m. on left. GPS: 43.29803, 3.45628

Charges guide

Per unit incl. 2 persons	€ 17,90 - € 27,20
extra person	€ 6,00 - € 7,20

Camping Cheques accepted.

Agde

Kawan Village les Champs Blancs

Route de Rochelongue, F-34300 Agde (Hérault) T: 04 67 94 23 42. E: champs.blancs@wanadoo.fr
alanrogers.com/FR34190

Les Champs Blancs is set amongst tall trees, 2 km. from Agde and 2 km. from the sea at Rochelongue in a shady environment. There are over 300 pitches, with 117 level, sandy pitches for touring units. Bordered with bushes and plenty of trees, all pitches have 10A electricity and unusually 60 have private sanitary cabins. Mobile homes occupy separate areas. The area nearest the road is bordered by trees to deaden possible road noise. The pool area has been augmented by a super irregular pool, with slides, a cascade, jacuzzi, bridges and palms but retaining the original pool and paddling pool. There are tennis courts and other leisure facilities. Games, shows and competitions are arranged in July and August. Champs Blancs is set in the centre of the three areas of Agde. There is the old town of Agde with a history going back to Greek and Roman times and known as the 'black pearl of the Mediterranean'. Its striking cathedral is made of black volcanic rock. Grau d'Agde is the port with a fish quay on the Herault river and from where white sandy beaches stretch past Rochlongue to Cap d'Agde.

Facilities

Modern, fully equipped toilet blocks include 60 en-suite private cabins containing WC, shower and washbasin. Unit for disabled visitors. Washing machines and dryers. Motorcaravan services. Well stocked shop (high season, bread only in low season). Bar (from 1/6). Restaurant (20/6-15/9). Swimming complex (from 8/4 depending on weather; bracelet required € 5). Good play area. Minigolf. Tennis. Multisport court. Off site: Riding 1 km. Golf and bicycle hire 2 km. Beach 2 km.

Open: 8 April - 30 September.

Directions

From A9 exit 34, follow N312 for Agde, joins N112 Béziers - Sète road. Cross bridge over river, take first turn signed Rochelongue, turn right at roundabout, next left, then next left (signed Agde). Site on left before another bridge back over N112. GPS: 43.29702, 3.47547

Charges guide

Per unit incl. 2 persons	€ 22,00 - € 43,00
incl. individual sanitary facilities	€ 25,00 - € 50,00
extra person	€ 10,00

Camping Cheques accepted.

Agde

Camping Le Rochelongue

Route de Rochelongue, F-34300 Agde (Hérault) T: 04 67 21 25 51. E: le.rochelongue@wanadoo.fr

alanrogers.com/FR34610

Situated between le Grau d'Agde and Cap d'Agde, close to a long sandy beach, this small family site is worth consideration. A total of 106 pitches provide 48 for touring units (most with 10A electricity and water), 23 mobile homes to rent and 30 privately-owned mobile homes. Pitches are of reasonable size on sandy soil with shade from tall trees. A large, fully equipped toilet block is centrally situated and the rest of the amenities are by the entrance. There is a pleasant pool area near the snack bar, and a shop and laundrette beside reception, just outside the entrance. The modern resort of Cap d'Agde, has a huge marina, shops and restaurants, a superb water park and long, sandy beaches. The town of Agde itself with its black basalt cathedral overlooking the Hérault river is worth exploring, while the large fishing boats moor up at the mouth of the river at le Grau d'Agde to sell their catch. In the last couple of years, Ryanair has opened up a service to Béziers/Cap d'Agde Airport and we understand free transport can be arranged to and from the airport.

Facilities

One fully equipped toilet block includes facilities for children. Washing machine. Shop (1/4-30/10). Bar, snack bar and takeaway (10/06-10/09). Heated pool (1/4-30/10). Children's entertainment (July/Aug). Aquagym and themed evenings in the bar for adults. WiFi. Gas or electric barbecues only. Off site: Beach 500 m. Bicycle 500 m. Riding 1 km. Golf 2 km. Fishing 2 km. Sailing 1.5 km. New sports pool 2 km.

Open: 2 April - 30 October.

Directions

From A9 exit 34 follow N312 for Agde and follow as it joins N112 Béziers-Sète road. Cross bridge over Hérault river and turn right for Rochelonge. Turn left at roundabout and right at next one and site is on left before roundabout. GPS: 43.279167, 3.481389

Charges guide

Per unit incl. 2 persons and electricity	€ 14,00 - € 43,00
extra person	€ 3,00 - € 7,00
child (3-10 yrs)	free - € 4,00

Camping Club Le Rochelongue***

Route de Rochelongue | F-34300 Agde | Tel: +33 467 21 25 51 | le.rochelongue@wanadoo.fr
www.camping-le-rochelongue.fr

Agde

Camping les Romarins

Route du Grau, F-34300 Agde (Hérault) T: 04 67 94 18 59. E: contact@romarins.com

alanrogers.com/FR34420

A small family campsite beside the River Hérault, Les Romarins is only 1 km. from a wide sandy beach and 800 metres from the village. With 120 level pitches separated by shrubs, 50 are available for touring units, the rest are taken by mobile homes and chalets (80 to let). Electricity (6A) is available on all pitches, some of which have more shade than others. The site was bought by the Schwartz family seven years ago and is gradually being improved. A pleasant walk beside the river and past the fish quay, takes you to the shops, restaurants and beach of Le Grau.

Facilities

Two modern toilet blocks are fully equipped. Good facilities for babies and disabled visitors. Bar with snacks (from 1/5). Bread can be ordered. Heated pool. Large playing field and play area at the back of the site (closed at night). Archery. Bicycle hire. Sports activities and evening entertainment in season. Off site: Beach 900 m. Shops and restaurants 700 m. Boat launching 50 m. Riding 2 km. Golf 2 km. Cap d'Agde and Aqualand 3 km.

Open: 15 April - 25 September.

Directions

From A9 exit 34, follow N112 towards Agde picking up the N112. Take exit for Grau d'Agde. Left at roundabout, left at next roundabout by Hyper U, and straight over next two roundabouts towards river. Left at roundabout beside river following sign along riverside (one way). Site is third on left opposite fish quay. GPS: 43.29446, 3.45005

Charges guide

Per unit incl. 2 persons	€ 12,00 - € 21,05
extra person	€ 4,00 - € 6,45
electricity	€ 4,15

For latest campsite news, availability and prices visit

alanrogers.com

Agde

Camping les 7 Fonts

Route de Sète, F-34300 Agde (Hérault) T: 04 99 57 21 21. E: contact@village-center.com
alanrogers.com/FR34590

If you are seeking a less hectic option, 7 Fonts has a rural feel to it, albeit that it is situated on the edge of the town of Agde, close to the Canal du Midi. A long time ago it was a vineyard but the traditional three storied house with its courtyard (now reception) is the only evidence remaining. The site is now owned by the Village Center Group. It is split into two parts separated by a small road. There are around 300 grass pitches, partially separated by shrubs and with good shade from tall trees. At least half are taken by mobile homes some of which are for rent.

Facilities

Two traditional style toilet blocks. Facilities for disabled visitors. Small shop. Bar, simple restaurant and takeaway. Swimming pool complex with water slides and spa bath (1/5-15/9). Hairdressing and beauty salon (1/7-31/8). Bicycle hire. Activity and entertainment programme (1/7-31/8). Mobile homes and equipped tents to rent. Free shuttle bus for beach (high season). WiFi around reception (charged). Off site: Riding, golf and fishing 4 km. Beach 4 km.

Open: 27 May - 18 September.

Directions

From the autoroute take exit 34 towards Agde and Bessan. Follow the N312 (Agde, Vias) then pick up the N112 (Agde, Sète). Pass turnings for Agde until road divides. Right is for Sète but take left for Agde and Centre commercial. Site is signed some 250 m. up this road. Turn right immediately after small garden centre. Follow carefully across junction to site (narrow entrance). GPS: 43.31157, 3.49844

Charges guide

Per unit incl. 2 persons	€ 14,00 - € 34,00
extra person	€ 3,00 - € 8,00

Aigues-Mortes

Yelloh! Village la Petite Camargue

B.P. 21, D62, F-30220 Aigues-Mortes (Gard) T: 04 66 53 98 98. E: info@yellohvillage-petite-camargue.com
alanrogers.com/FR30020

This is a large, impressive site (553 pitches) with a huge swimming pool complex and other amenities to match, conveniently situated beside one of the main routes across the famous Camargue. The busy road is an advantage for access but could perhaps be a drawback in terms of traffic, although when we stayed overnight in season it was virtually silent. It offers a variety of good sized pitches, regularly laid out and with varying amounts of shade. There are 144 touring pitches (with 6/10A electricity) interspersed amongst more than 300 mobile homes and 145 tour operator pitches.

Facilities

Three toilet blocks provide modern facilities including combined showers and washbasins. Laundry facilities. Motorcaravan service point. Shops, bar/restaurant with pizzeria and takeaway. Hairdresser and beauty centre. Swimming pool complex with jacuzzi. Play area, and children's club. Tennis. Jogging circuit. Bicycle hire. Quad bikes. Disco. Diving school. Nightclub (over 16 years). Off site: Riding at adjoining stables. Fishing 3 km. Beach 3.5 km. with free bus service July/Aug. Golf 8 km.

Open: 23 April - 19 September (with all services).

Directions

From A9, exit 26 (Gallargues), towards Le Grau-du-Roi, site 18 km. Continue past Aigues-Mortes on D62, site is 2 km. on the right, just before large roundabout for La Grand-Motte and Le Grau-du-Roi junction. GPS: 43.56307, 4.15888

Charges guide

Per unit incl. 2 persons and electricity	€ 15,00 - € 43,00
extra person	€ 4,00 - € 8,00

Anduze

Domaine de Gaujac

Boisset-et-Gaujac, F-30140 Anduze (Gard) T: 04 66 61 67 57. E: contact@domaine-de-gaujac.com
alanrogers.com/FR30000

The 275 level, well shaded pitches include 175 for touring, with electricity (4-10A), and 22 are fully serviced. Access to some areas can be difficult for larger units due to narrow winding access roads, trees and hedges. Larger units should ask for lower numbered pitches (1-148) where access is a little easier. In high season this region is dry and hot, thus grass quickly wears off many pitches leaving just a sandy base. There are 12 special hardstanding pitches for motorcaravans near the entrance. The site has a new covered entertainment area and courtyard terrace. Only gas and electric barbecues.

Facilities

Toilet blocks (one heated) include facilities for disabled visitors. Washing machines and dryer. Motorcaravan services. Shop (2/6-27/8). Newsagent. Bar, restaurant (15/4-15/9). Takeaway/crêperie. New heated swimming pool (all season with lifeguard 5/7-15/8) and jacuzzi. Playground. Tennis. Minigolf. WiFi in bar area. Off site: Fishing 100 m. Bicycle hire 10 km. Riding, golf 8 km. Mining museum at Alès.

Open: 1 April - 30 September.

Directions

From Alès take N110 towards Montpellier. At St Christol-les-Alès fork right on D910 towards Anduze and in Bagard, at roundabout, turn left on D246 to Boisset et Gaujac. Follow signs to site in 5 km. GPS: 44.03580, 4.02425

Charges guide

Per unit incl. 2 persons	€ 20,50 - € 31,50
extra person	€ 5,00 - € 6,00

Credit cards accepted in high season only.

Argelès-sur-Mer

Camping le Soleil

Route du Littoral, F-66702 Argelès-sur-Mer (Pyrénées-Orientales) T: 04 68 81 14 48
E: camping.lesoleil@wanadoo.fr alanrogers.com/FR66040

Le Soleil is an attractive site with direct access to a sandy beach. It is a busy, popular, family owned site which over the years has developed into a small village. It has over 800 pitches of ample size, of which around 550 are used for touring units, on sandy/grassy ground and with a mixture of trees and shrubs providing plenty of shade, all with electricity (6A). Around 20 fully serviced pitches are to be added. Caravans sometimes need care on the narrow access roads. The site has a wide range of amenities, including an impressive pool complex with activities and entertainment for all the family. All facilities are open when the site is open. Spain and the Pyrénées are near enough for excursions. There are over 200 pitches used by tour operators and 70 occupied by mobile homes. English is spoken and there is a comprehensive reservation system (advised for most of July/Aug). Le Soleil also works with the group Les Pieds dans l'Eau (sites with direct access to water such as the sea, river or lake).

Facilities

Seven toilet blocks of the type with external access to individual units. Some family cabins with washbasins, showers. Washing machines. Supermarket, general shop, press, tabac. Restaurant. Takeaway. Bar with disco (July/Aug), beach bar. Heated California type swimming pool complex and entertainment area. Adventure playground. TV room. Internet. WiFi. Tennis. Diving and riding in high season (charged). No dogs. Off site: Fishing and mooring boats on the adjacent river. Golf 5 km.

Open: 14 May - 17 September.

Directions

Site is at north end of the beach, about 1 km. from Argelès-Plage village. GPS: 42.57552, 3.04232

Charges 2011

| Per unit incl. 2 persons and electricity | € 25,97 - € 40,10 |
| extra person (over 5 yrs) | € 6,83 - € 10,50 |

Less 30% in May, June and August.

Anduze

Camping Cévennes-Provence

Corbès-Thoiras, F-30140 Anduze (Gard) T: 04 66 61 73 10. E: marais@camping-cevennes-provence.com
alanrogers.com/FR30200

You are sure of a very warm welcome at this spacious, family owned site. New arrivals are taken on a tour so that they can select a good pitch. There are 250 pitches on various levels, 200 with electricity (3-10A). Some are on the level land close to the river and others are scattered on high terraces having privacy and fine views across the Cévennes countryside. The river is very popular for swimming. There are few on-site activities, however, the family is happy to advise visitors who wish to explore off site, perhaps negotiating a discount on their behalf. There is a special area, away from the main site, where teenagers can safely 'let off steam'. This is easily accomplished in the 30 hectares of this natural and unusual site. The site lighting is turned off at 22.30, to encourage early nights. Young children can enjoy one of the best play areas we have seen. Cleanliness of the whole site including the toilet blocks is paramount (there are ten blocks so that nobody has to walk too far up and down hill).

Facilities

Ten excellent, modern, clean toilet blocks (one heated). Good facilities for disabled visitors. Well stocked shop (1/4-30/9). Restaurant, takeaway, bar (1/5-31/8). Good play area. Minigolf. Volleyball. River bathing and fishing. Many off site activities arranged. Internet point. Free WiFi near reception. Off site: Bicycle hire 2 km. Riding 4 km. Golf 10 km. Adventure park on opposite bank of river.

Open: 20 March - 2 October.

Directions

Only viable access. From D907 Anduze, take D284 alongside the river. Site signed on right about 3 km. from town. Take care on the approach – narrow lane for 100 m., then a narrow bridge, visibility good. GPS: 44.07763, 3.96484

Charges 2011

| Per unit incl. 2 persons | € 17,90 - € 26,90 |
| extra person | € 3,50 - € 7,00 |

For latest campsite news, availability and prices visit

alanrogers.com

Argelès-sur-Mer

Camping la Sirène

Route de Taxo á la Mer, F-66702 Argelès-sur-Mer (Pyrénées-Orientales) T: 04 68 81 04 61
E: contact@camping-lasirene.fr alanrogers.com/FR66560

From the moment you step into the hotel-like reception area you realise that this large site offers the holiday maker everything they could want in a well managed and convenient location close to Argelès -sur-Mer and the beaches. The 740 mobile homes and chalets vary in standard but all are less than five years old, very clean, comfortable and located on neat tidy pitches. There are also some touring pitches. In the summer there are 170 staff on duty to ensure your stay is as enjoyable as they can make it. All the shops and amenities are near reception making the accommodation areas quite peaceful and relaxing. There are many things to do and summer visitors have the option of using the free bus service to the beach where the site has its own club where you can even go windsurfing at no charge.

Facilities

Restaurant, bar and takeaway. Large shop (all season). Large aqua park, paddling pools, slides, jacuzzi. Games room. Multisports field, tennis, archery, minigolf, football. Theatre, evening entertainment, discos, show time spectacular. Riding. Bicycle hire. Off site: Resort of Argelès-sur-Mer and its beaches 2 km, as is karting, 10-pin bowling, amusement park and the sites private beach club Emeraude. Interesting old town of Collioure close by. Fishing 4 km. Golf 7 km.

Open: 17 April - 26 September.

Directions

Leave A9 motorway, junction 42, take D114, towards Argelès. Leave D114, junction 10 and follow signs for Plage Nord. Site signed after first roundabout. Site on right 2 km. after last roundabout. GPS: 42.57093, 3.02906

Charges guide

Per unit incl. 1-3 persons and electricity	€ 26,00 - € 43,00
extra person	€ 6,00 - € 9,00
child (under 5 yrs)	€ 4,00 - € 6,00
dog	free

Argelès-sur-Mer

Camping l'Hippocampe

Route de Taxo á la Mer, F-66702 Argelès-sur-Mer (Pyrénées-Orientales) T: 04 68 81 04 61
E: contact@camping-lasirene.fr alanrogers.com/FR66570

A sister site to La Sirène just opposite, this site has some touring pitches along with 170 mobile home and chalet pitches and is aimed at families with young children and adults looking for a quieter site. The mobile homes and chalets are all modern, well maintained and have space around them to provide privacy. The pool on site is dedicated to the smaller children and is a great place for them to gain confidence in the water whilst still being able to play. Entertainment, shops, bars and the full range of activities offered by La Sirène are just across the road. Visitors here also have free access to the beach club Emeraude which offers free transport to Plage Nord where the club is situated complete with bar and snacks.

Facilities

Pool and laundry. Shop, small bar (all season). All other facilities are at La Sirène just across the road. Riding. Bicycle hire. Off site: Beach, Argelès-sur-Mer within 2 km. Karting, 10-pin bowling, amusement park within 1 km. Fishing 4 km. Golf 7 km.

Open: 17 April - 26 September.

Directions

Leave A9 junction 42. Take D114, Argelès road. Leave D114 junction 10, follow signs for Plage Nord. Site signed after the first roundabout, on left 2 km. after last roundabout. GPS: 42.5705, 3.03065

Charges guide

Per unit incl. 1-3 persons and electricity	€ 26,00 - € 43,00
extra person	€ 6,00 - € 9,00
child (under 5 yrs)	€ 4,00 - € 6,00
dog	free

Argelès-sur-Mer

Camping le Bois du Valmarie

F-66702 Argelès-sur-Mer (Pyrénées-Orientales) T: 04 68 81 09 92. E: contact@camping-lasirene.fr
alanrogers.com/FR66590

Pitches here are exclusively for mobile home and chalet accommodation.

For latest campsite news, availability and prices visit

alanrogers.com

CAMPINGS
CLUBS ★★★★
ARGELÈS/MER
MÉDITERRANÉE

LA SIRÈNE • LE BOIS DE VALMARIE • L'HIPPOCAMPE

Quick and easy,
**your reservation
in just one
click on:**

route de Taxo
66702 Argelès-sur-Mer
Tél. : +33 (0)4 68 81 04 61
Fax : +33 (0)4 68 81 69 74
e-mail : contact@camping-lasirene.fr

www.camping-lasirene.fr

Argelès-sur-Mer

Castel Camping les Criques de Porteils

RD114, Corniche de Collioure, F-66701 Argelès-sur-Mer (Pyrénées-Orientales) T: 04 68 81 12 73
E: contactcdp@lescriques.com alanrogers.com/FR66150

This is an amazing site situated on the cliff top with views across the sea to Argelès, set against a backdrop of mountains and close to Collioure, the artist's paradise. What more could you ask? A lot of work has been carried out to improve the facilities here and pitches have been redesigned for easier access. There are around 250 of varying sizes and shapes due to the nature of the terrain, level in places, up and down in others. All have 5A electricity available and either a sea view or views towards the mountains. There are three small coves accessed by steep steps (gated). There is a new bar and restaurant and some unusual artistic workshops for children. Classical music sessions and guided walks are also available. A 30 minute walk will take you to Collioure, or the sandy beach at Le Racou. A small, heated swimming pool has been built by reception at the entrance close to a duck pond and a small animal area. A few special level concreted places have also been designed for motorcaravans and 49 mobile homes and Bengali tents are available to hire. On the down side, the entrance off the main road needs care and there could be some road and train noise. The inaccessible parts of the cliffs are home to cormorants.

Facilities

Two renovated toilet blocks, fully equipped with super children's room (all small equipment and colourful). Laundry room with internet point and WiFi. Motorcaravan service point. Shop. New bar and restaurant with takeaway. Swimming pool. Play area. Golf practise. Tennis. Volleyball. Boules. Fishing. Duck pond and small animal area. Off site: Collioure and sandy beach at Le Racou (both a 30 minute walk). Riding, bicycle hire, boat launching within 6 km.

Open: 2 April - 22 October.

Directions

Exit A9 at Perpignan Sud or Le Boulou. Head for Argelès to pick up signs for 'Collioure par la Corniche'. Watch for site signs coming into a bend as you come down a hill by hotel.
GPS: 42.53508, 3.06854

Charges 2011

Per unit incl. 2 persons	
and electricity	€ 26,00 - € 46,00
extra person	€ 6,00 - € 10,50
child (under 5 yrs)	€ 4,00 - € 6,50
dog	free - € 4,00

Argelès-sur-Mer

Camping le Littoral

Route du Littoral, F-66700 Argelès-sur-Mer (Pyrénées-Orientales) T: 04 68 81 17 74
E: infos@camping-le-littoral.fr alanrogers.com/FR66060

Sites with access to the beach are difficult to find and, even though le Littoral is not directly beside the beach, it is only 800 metres away by footpath. It offers much accommodation in mobile homes as well as 20 good sized, level touring pitches with shade and 6A electricity. An attractive pool area is open from May to September. Argelès is a very popular holiday resort with good sandy beaches. The border with Spain is only 30 km. The site is on the north side of Argelès between the coast road and the beach, so access is good, although there could be some road noise in high season. The site has been taken over by a new group, Camp'Atlantic and is looking smart with a new reception and tarmac roadways. However, there are now fewer touring pitches and the emphasis is on mobile homes with over 127 to let and 105 privately owned. The site is well looked after and the pool area is particularly welcoming.

Facilities

Large modern toilet block, fully equipped and with some washbasins in cabins. Baby bath. Some facilities for disabled visitors. Washing machines. Shop. Bar, restaurant and takeaway (15/6-15/9). Heated swimming pool (May-Sept). Entertainment in high season. Play area. Bicycle hire. Internet. Path to beach. Communal barbecues only. Off site: Tourist train in high season. Within walking distance aquatic park, adventure park, karting, riding and minigolf.

Open: 2 April - 24 September.

Directions

From A9 take exit 42 (Perpignan-Sud) and follow N114 for Argelès. At exit 10 follow directions for Taxo d'Avall then Plage Nord. Site is clearly signed off coast road in the St Cyprien direction.
GPS: 42.58, 3.031667

Charges guide

Per unit incl. 2 persons	
and electricity	€ 32,00 - € 44,00
extra person	€ 6,00 - € 9,00
child (4-10 yrs)	€ 4,00 - € 7,00
dog	€ 5,00

Credit cards accepted.

MarEstang ★★★

Route de St Cyprien
66140 Canet Plage
www.marestang.com
contactme@marestang.com
TEL: 04 68 80 35 53
FAX: 04 68 73 32 94

LES CRIQUES DE PORTEILS ★★★★

RD 114 - Corniche de Collioure
66701 Argelès-sur-Mer
www.lescriques.com
contactcdp@lescriques.com
TEL: 04 68 81 12 73
FAX: 04 68 95 85 76

LES
CASTELS ★★★★
Hôtellerie de Plein Air

Argelès-sur-Mer

Camping le Dauphin

Route de Taxo á la Mer, F-66700 Argelès-sur-Mer (Pyrénées-Orientales) T: 04 68 81 17 54
E: info@campingledauphin.com **alanrogers.com/FR66110**

Near Taxo in the quieter, northern part of Argelès (a somewhat frenzied resort in season), this family owned site on flat, grassy parkland with plenty of tall trees enjoys good views of the Pyrénées from the terrace area surrounding its excellent complex of swimming pools. There are 346 level, grassy, well shaded pitches, all with 10A electricity and some with individual sanitary units. Located some 1.5 km. from the town and beach, there is a regular connecting 'road train' service to and fro throughout the day and evening until midnight.

Facilities

Good central sanitary block with all modern facilities including washbasins en-suite and facilities for disabled visitors and children. One third of the pitches have their own fully equipped individual sanitary unit. Shops, bar/restaurant, pizzeria with takeaway (all 15/5-4/9). Two large swimming pools and padding pool (all season). Two play areas. Tennis. Multisport courts. Minigolf. Games room. Entertainment programme in high season. Torches useful in some areas. WiFi in restaurant. Off site: Beach 1.5 km. Riding 1 km. Fishing 2 km. Bicycle hire 3 km.

Open: 15 May - 17 September.

Directions

Site is on north side of Argelès. From autoroute take exit Perpignan-Nord for Argelès and follow directions for Plage-Nord and Taxo-d'Avall (similarly from the N114). GPS: 42.57229, 3.02167

Charges guide

Per unit incl. 2 persons	
and electricity	€ 18,00 - € 32,20
extra person	€ 4,00 - € 6,90
child (under 5 yrs)	free - € 4,30
dog	€ 2,50 - € 3,50

Argelès-sur-Mer

Camping la Massane

25 avenue Molière, F-66702 Argelès-sur-Mer (Pyrénées-Orientales) T: 04 68 81 06 85
E: info@camping-massane.com **alanrogers.com/FR66260**

Set a little bit back from the seafront, La Massane is one of the traditional older sites with good views of the Canigou and a heated pool open for a longer season. With 184 pitches and only 30 taken by mobile homes, it could make a good, quiet and relaxing choice. In July and August it will be a little more hectic (as is the whole resort) with a bar and family entertainment. Other amenities are within walking distance. Pitches are divided, level and semi-grassed with a mixture of shade from tall trees or shrubs. Electricity is available. The site has recently installed an outside adult exercise area with various equipment.

Facilities

Two toilet blocks, one large and modernized with a baby room and facilities for disabled visitors. A smaller, traditional block is used early in the season. Laundry room. Swimming pool (heated 15/4-30/9) with paddling pool. Shop, bar, takeaway and entertainment July/Aug only. Play area. Minigolf. No charcoal barbecues. WiFi around reception (free). Adult exercise and games area. Off site: Village of Argelès. Beach 1 km. Bicycle hire 1 km.

Open: 15 March - 15 October.

Directions

From the A9 take exit 42 (Perpignan Sud) and follow N114 for Argelès to exit 10 for Pujols. At first roundabout take 'Centre Plage'. Pass school on left and site is almost immediately on left. GPS: 42.550717, 3.031267

Charges guide

Per unit incl. 2 persons	
and electricity (6/10A)	€ 11,50 - € 31,00
extra person	€ 2,50 - € 5,50

Boisson

Castel Camping le Château de Boisson

Boisson, F-30500 Allègre-les-Fumades (Gard) T: 04 66 24 85 61. E: reception@chateaudeboisson.com
alanrogers.com/FR30070

Château de Boisson is a quiet family site within easy reach of the Cévennes, Ardèche or Provence. The site is hilly and the 178 pitches, with 102 for touring, are on two levels. They are separated by neat hedges and a variety of trees providing some shade. All have 5 or 10A electricity, 40 are fully serviced and five have personal bathrooms. Rock pegs are essential. The large attractive swimming pools, one indoor (heated all season) with paddling pool and toboggan are near the château in a sunny location at the top of the site. Gas and electric barbecues only. Dogs are not accepted in July/Aug.

Facilities

Two excellent, very clean toilet blocks with all necessary facilities including those for disabled visitors. Small shop (10/4-10/9). Good restaurant, bar, snacks (all season). Play area. Pools - indoor (all season), outdoor (1/5-25/9). Bridge tournaments in low season. Painting classes. Tennis. Boules. WiFi (charged). Off site: Fishing 2 km. Riding 4 km. Golf 30 km. Allègre les Fumades (thermal baths and Casino) 5 km. Alès 16 km. Vallon Pont d'Arc and the Ardèche gorges 30 km.

Open: 10 April - 24 September.

Directions

From Alès take D16 northeast through Salindres and Auzon. After Auzon turn right across river, immediately left, signed Barjac and site. Shortly turn right to site entrance. Only route for trailers and motorcaravans. Do not drive through the village of Boissons. GPS: 44.20967, 4.25625

Charges guide

Per unit incl. 2 persons	
and electricity	€ 19,00 - € 47,00
extra person	€ 3,00 - € 7,50

For latest campsite news, availability and prices visit

alanrogers.com

Canet-en-Roussillon

Kawan Village Caravaning Ma Prairie

1 avenue des Coteaux, F-66140 Canet-en-Roussillon (Pyrénées-Orientales) T: 04 68 73 26 17
E: ma.prairie@wanadoo.fr alanrogers.com/FR66020

Ma Prairie is an excellent site and its place in this guide goes back over 30 years. Then it was simply a field surrounded by vineyards. The trees planted then have now matured and more continue to be planted, along with colourful shrubs providing a comfortable, park-like setting with some 200 touring pitches, all with electricity and 15 with water and drainage. There are also 50 mobile homes available to rent and 10 privately owned. It is a peaceful haven some 3 km. back from the sea but within walking distance of Canet village itself. The Gil family still provide a warm welcome and reception boasts an impressive international collection of hats, helmets and uniform caps. The restaurant and bar is across the road and overlooks a modern, attractive pool complex and wonderful old palm tree. Today there is internet access, some mobile homes and modern housing has crept up but there are still vineyards close and the wine sold in reception is from the family vineyard.

Facilities

Fully equipped toilet blocks, baby bath. Washing machines and dryers. No shop but bread can be ordered. Covered snack bar and takeaway. Air-conditioned bar and restaurant. Large adult pool, splendid children's pool. Multisport court. TV. Amusement machines. Busy daily activity and entertainment programme in season including dancing and live music once a week. WiFi available over most of the site and internet access is available in reception. Off site: Sandy beach 3 km. Supermarket 400 m. Riding 600 m. Golf 6 km. Canet Village within walking distance with all amenities. Bus/tram services to the busy modern resort of Canet Plage.

Open: 5 May - 25 September.

Directions

Leave autoroute A9 at Perpignan North towards Barcarès. Site access is from the D11 Perpignan road (exit 5), close to the junction with D617 in Canet-Village. Go under bridge, right at roundabout then left to site. GPS: 42.70135, 2.99968

Charges guide

Per unit incl. 2 persons	
and electricity	€ 21,50 - € 38,50
extra person	€ 4,00 - € 7,50
child (4-9 yrs)	free - € 6,00
dog	free - € 3,00

ma prairie ★★★★

Camping-Club Ma Prairie
1, avenue des Coteaux
66140 Canet-en-Roussillon

Tel. +33 (0)4 68 73 26 17 - ma.prairie@wanadoo.fr - www.maprairie.com

Brissac

Domaine d'Anglas

F-34190 Brissac (Hérault) T: 04 67 73 70 18. E: contact@camping-anglas.com
alanrogers.com/FR34600

In the upper Hérault valley to the south of the Cévennes mountains, Camping d'Anglas is a delightful small site. The top part of the site is on quite stony ground with pitches divided by vines and mixed trees that provide a degree of shade. The lower part is more open with some mature trees and pitches are not clearly divided but it makes a wonderful spot to camp. With 100 pitches in total, there are 91 for touring units. A stream runs through the site, dry when we visited, but it is quite possibly a torrent in winter time. Wooden bridges allow access to the toilet blocks on the other side.

Facilities

Two toilet blocks provide all necessary facilities. Baby bath. Facilities for disabled visitors with up and down walking on site. Washing machine. Shop for bread and simple needs. Communal barbecue. Playing field. Wine evening. Off site: Register at reception for canoeing, climbing, karting, mountain biking, walks and adventure tours through the woods and on Saturday evenings tour through the owners' vineyard.

Open: 30 April - 5 September.

Directions

From Montpellier follow the D986 north towards Ganges. After about 40 km, just before entering the village of St Bauzille de Putois turn right signed Brissac. Cross the Hérault river over a narrow bridge and pick up site signs. GPS: 43.876056, 3.716083

Charges guide

Per unit incl. 2 persons	
and electricity	€ 12,00 - € 21,50
extra person	€ 3,50 - € 5,50

For latest campsite news, availability and prices visit

alanrogers.com

Cap d'Agde

Yelloh! Village Mer et Soleil

Chemin de Notre Dame à Saint Martin, Rochelongue, F-34300 Cap d'Agde (Hérault) T: 04 67 94 21 14

E: contact@camping-mer-soleil.com alanrogers.com/FR34290

Close to Cap d'Agde, this is a popular, well equipped site with many facilities. The pool area is particularly attractive with large palm trees, a whirlpool and slides as well as a gym and wellness centre. An upstairs restaurant overlooks this area and the entertainment stage next to it. All ages are catered for and evening entertainment in July and August includes live shows. There are 477 pitches, around half taken by mobile homes and chalets (some to let, some privately owned). The touring pitches are hedged and have good shade from tall trees, all with 6A electricity. From the back of the site, a 1 km. long path leads to the wide sandy beach at Rochelongue. A smart new reception has been built and a state-of-the-art balnéo can be found at the front of the site offering a wide range of treatments. It is open for public use with a 10% reduction offered to campers. The design inside is very impressive with a central grass area and fountain. The hydro pools are under a church-like roof and the massage rooms, sauna and turkish bath are off to the sides providing a very calm and relaxed atmosphere.

Facilities

One large toilet block plus three smaller ones are fully equipped. Attractive units for children with small toilets, etc. Units for disabled visitors. Motorcaravan service point. Washing machine. Shop. Bar and restaurant. Heated swimming pools. Gym. State-of-the-art balnéo with hydro pools, massage rooms, sauna and turkish bath. Hairdresser. Play area. Tennis. Archery. Sporting activities and evening entertainment. Miniclub. WiFi. Off site: Beach 1 km. Riding 1 km. Beziers airport within easy reach.

Open: 3 April - 9 October.

Directions

From A9 exit 34, follow N312 for Agde. It joins the N112 Béziers - Sète road. Cross bridge over Hérault river and turn right for Rochelongue. Turn left at next roundabout and site is a little further on the right. GPS: 43.286183, 3.478

Charges 2011

Per unit incl. 2 persons and electricity	€ 15,00 - € 44,00
extra person	€ 4,00 - € 8,00
child (3-7 yrs)	free - € 7,00

Canet-en-Roussillon

Camping Mar Estang

Route de Saint-Cyprien, F-66140 Canet-en-Roussillon (Pyrénées-Orientales) T: 04 68 80 35 53

E: contactme@marestang.com alanrogers.com/FR66090

Le Mar Estang is a large, 'all singing, all dancing' site with something for everyone. Situated on the edge of Canet, between the Etang (part of the Réserve Naturelle de Canet/St Nazaire) and the sea, there is access to the beach from the site by a tunnel under the road. If you don't fancy the beach, the site has a water park (renovated in 2011) with a new slide and heated pool. There are 600 pitches, some 200 used for mobile homes and Bengali tents, with 6A electricity, some degree of shade and on sandy ground. A very wide range of activities and entertainment is organised all season, with children's clubs in high season and a beach club for watersports.

Facilities

Nine well equipped sanitary blocks are well placed around the site. Facilities for babies. Laundry. Motorcaravan service point. Shop, bars, restaurant and takeaway all open when site is open. Swimming pools, Jacuzzi and solarium. Fitness club. Entertainment. Disco. Communal barbecue. Sailing club. Tennis. Bicycle hire. Play areas. Direct access to beach. Off site: Riding nearby. Canet 500 m. with tourist train in high season. Perpignan 10 km.

Open: 23 April - 17 September.

Directions

Take exit 41 from A9 autoroute and follow signs for Canet. On outskirts of town follow signs for St Cyprien/Plage Sud. Site is very clearly signed on southern edge of Canet Plage. GPS: 42.6757, 3.03135

Charges 2011

| Per unit incl. 2 persons and electricity | € 20,00 - € 44,00 |
| extra person | € 7,00 - € 13,00 |

See advertisement on page 423.

For latest campsite news, availability and prices visit

alanrogers.com

Canet-en-Roussillon

Yelloh! Village le Brasilia

B.P. 204, F-66141 Canet-en-Roussillon (Pyrénées-Orientales) T: 04 68 80 23 82
E: info@yellohvillage-brasilia.com alanrogers.com/FR66070

Situated across the yacht harbour from the upmarket resort of Canet-Plage, le Brasilia is an impressive, well managed family site directly beside the beach. It is pretty, neat and well kept with an amazingly wide range of facilities – indeed, it is camping at its best. There are 473 neatly hedged touring pitches, all with electricity and many with water and drainage. They vary in size from 80 to 120 sq.m. and some of the longer pitches are suitable for two families together. With a range of shade from pines and flowering shrubs, less on pitches near the beach, there are neat access roads (sometimes narrow for large units). There are also 130 pitches with mobile homes or chalets to rent (the new ones have their own gardens). The sandy beach here is busy, with a beach club (you can hire windsurfing boards) and a naturist section is on the beach to the west of the site. A completely new pool complex is planned with pools catering for all ages and hydrotherapy facilities for adults and all overlooked by its own snack bar and restaurant. The village area of the site offers a range of shops, a busy restaurant and bar, entertainment (including a night club) and clubs for children of all ages. In fact you do not need to stir from the site which is almost a resort in itself. It does have a nice, lively atmosphere but is orderly and well run. If you would like to visit Canet-Plage, a free tourist train runs in summer and a small ferry crosses the harbour. A member of Yelloh! Village and Leading Campings Group.

Facilities

Ten modern sanitary blocks are very well equipped and maintained, with British style WCs (some Turkish) and washbasins in cabins. Good facilities for children and for disabled visitors. Laundry room. Motorcaravan services. Range of shops. Gas supplies. Bars and restaurant. New pool complex (heated). Play areas. Sports field. Tennis. Sporting activities. Library, games and video room. Hairdresser. Internet café and WiFi. Daily entertainment programme. Bicycle hire. Fishing. ATM. Exchange facilities. Post office. Weather forecasts. Only gas or electric barbecues are allowed. Off site: Boat launchng and sailing 500 m. Riding 5 km. Golf 12 km.

Open: 26 April - 27 September.

Directions

From A9 exit 41 (Perpignan Centre, Rivesaltes) follow signs for Le Barcarès and Canet on D83 for 10 km. then for Canet (D81). At first Canet roundabout, turn fully back on yourself (Sainte-Marie) and watch for Brasilia sign almost immediately on right.
GPS: 42.70467, 3.03483

Charges guide

Per unit incl. 2 persons and electricity (6A)	€ 19,00 - € 47,50
extra person	€ 6,00 - € 8,50
child (3-6 yrs)	free - € 8,50
dog (max. 2)	€ 4,00

Carcassonne

Campéole la Cité

Route de Saint-Hilaire, F-11000 Carcassonne (Aude) T: 04 68 25 11 77. E: cite@campeole.com

alanrogers.com/FR11100

A visit to the medieval cité of Carcassonne is a must and Campéole la Cité is within walking distance along a shaded footpath beside a stream. The majority of pitches are very large, separated by bushes and with good shade. There are also some undefined places under trees for small tents. In total there are 200, with 143 for touring, 95 having 10A electricity and the rest used for mobile homes or chalets to hire. Because of its situation it is very popular and you need to arrive early in the high season. A swimming pool, snack bar and small shop make this a very comfortable and useful site. It is a neat and tidy site that is very well organised. A shuttle bus (charge) runs to the town centre during the high season. There are also good facilities for children with activities and sports organized in July and August. The Black mountain is to the north, the Corbières to the east, the Pyrénées to the south and the beaches of the Mediterranean only 70 km. away. If you are there for Bastille Day (14 July), there is a magnificent fireworks display covering the citadel.

Facilities

Shop, bar and snack bar. Takeaway meals. TV and games room. Bread delivery. Motorcaravan service point. Fridge hire. Multisport pitch. Swimming and paddling pools. Play area. Communal barbecue (only gas or electric permitted on pitches). Chalets and mobile homes to rent.
Off site: Golf 2 km. Bicycle hire 2 km. Riding 3 km. Lake with beaches 6 km. Mediterranean beaches 70 km.

Open: 15 March - 15 October.

Directions

From A61 autoroute take exit 24 onto the N113 following signs for city centre. Site is well signed (look carefully) from all roads into the city. GPS: 43.200315, 2.353767

Charges guide

Per unit incl. 2 persons and electricity	€ 21,10 - € 29,50

Crespian

Kawan Village le Mas de Reilhe

Chemin du Mas de Reilhe, F-30260 Crespian (Gard) T: 04 66 77 82 12. E: info@camping-mas-de-reilhe.fr
alanrogers.com/FR30080

This is a pleasant family site in the heart of the Gard region with a favourable climate. There are 95 pitches, 73 for tourers, 64 have electricity (6/10A), 22 also have water and waste water and some of the upper ones may require long leads. The large lower pitches are separated by tall poplar trees and hedges, close to the main facilities but may experience some road noise. The large terraced pitches on the hillside are scattered under mature pine trees, some with good views, more suited to tents and trailer tents but with their own modern sanitary facilities. The heated swimming pool is in a sunny position and overlooked by the attractive bar/restaurant. There are no shops in the village, the nearest being in the city of Sommières 10 km. away. From here you can explore the Cévennes gorges, enjoy the Mediterranean beaches, visit the Petite Camargue or Nîmes with its Roman remains. The entertainment in July and August is mainly for children with occasional competitions and musical evenings for adults.

Facilities

Excellent, very clean toilet facilities with facilities for campers with disabilities. Laundry facilities. Reception. Limited shop (bread to order). Bar (30/4-18/9). Takeaway. Restaurant (1/6-11/9). Small grass play area. Pétanque. Heated swimming pool (30/4-18/9). Internet access. WiFi (charged). Motorcaravan services. Off site: Tennis 500 m. Fishing 3 km. Riding 5 km. Bicycle hire 10 km. Golf 25 km. Sea and gorges about 30 km. and Nîmes 25 km.

Open: 2 April - 18 September.

Directions

From the A9 take exit 25, Nimes-ouest signed Alès, then D999 towards Le Vigan (about 23 km). Turn north on the D6110, site shortly on right at southern edge of Crespian. GPS: 43.87931, 4.09637

Charges 2011

Per unit incl. 2 persons and electricity	€ 20,00 - € 26,00
extra person	€ 5,00 - € 6,00

LE MAS DE REILHE ★★★★

Camping Caravaning

"Situated between the Cevennes Mountains and the Mediterranean sea, a small charming & shaded camp site in the sun". Mobil-homes, chalets and bungalows A. Trigano to rent.

- Heated swimming-pool 140 m² (30/4 - 19/9)
- Restaurant, pizzeria & takeaway (1/6 - 12/9)
- Animations for children (July - August)
- New heated sanitary blocks

Tél : 0033 466 77 82 12 - Fax : 0033 466 80 26 50
E-mail : info@camping-mas-de-reilhe.fr
Website : www.camping-mas-de-reilhe.fr

Font-Romeu

Huttopia Font-Romeu

Route de Mont-Louis, F-66120 Font-Romeu (Pyrénées-Orientales) T: 04 68 30 09 32
E: font-romeu@huttopia.com alanrogers.com/FR66250

This is a large, open site of some seven hectares, nestling on the side of the mountain at the entrance to Font-Romeu. This part of the Pyrénées offers some staggering views and the famous Mont Louis is close by. An ideal base for climbing, hiking or cycling, it would also provide a good stopover for a night or so whilst traveling between Spain and France or to or from Andorra into France. The terraced pitches are easily accessed, with those dedicated to caravans and motorcaravans at the top of the site, whilst tents go on the lower slopes. Trees provide shade from the sun, which can be quite hot at this altitude. Facilities on site are limited to very good toilet blocks and a very large games room and assembly hall which is used by those in tents when it rains.

Facilities

Two traditional style toilet blocks are bright and clean with modern fittings. Toilet for children and excellent facilities for disabled visitors. Shop (27/5-11/9). Bar, restaurant and takeaway service (all July/Aug). Outdoor heated swimming pool (27/5-11/9). Laundry facilities at each block. Large games hall. Gas barbecues only. Max. 1 dog. Off site: Opportunities for walking and climbing are close by as are golf, riding, fishing, cycling and tennis. The small town of Font-Romeu is very near with all the usual shops and banking facilities. Beach 8 km.

Open: 27 May - 11 September, 4 December - 4 April.

Directions

Font-Romeu is on the D118, some 12 km. after it branches off the N116 heading west, just after Mont Louis. This is an interesting road with magnificent views and well worth the climb. The site is just before the town, on the left and accessed off the car park. GPS: 42.51511, 2.05183

Charges guide

Per unit with 2 persons and electricity	€ 20,15 - € 28,55
extra person	€ 5,00 - € 6,30
child (2-7 yrs)	€ 3,00 - € 4,30

For latest campsite news, availability and prices visit
alanrogers.com

Florac

Camping le Pont du Tarn

Route de Pont de Montvert (RN106), F-48400 Florac (Lozère) T: 04 66 45 18 26
E: contact@camping-florac.com alanrogers.com/FR48100

Le Pont du Tarn, just outside Florac and close to the River Tarn, is an excellent base for touring this beautiful Cévennes region of France. There are 181 pitches with 28 pitches occupied by mobile homes and chalets (available for rent). The pitches are large, level, grassy and well shaded. All have electricity (10A) and 36 are fully serviced. Access to this site and on-site is good for large outfits. Leisure amenities include a swimming pool, a paddling pool, minigolf and a sports area. A children's club is also operated in peak season. Only gas and electric barbecues allowed on site.

Facilities	Directions
The clean toilet facilities are in an older-style, heated building, with a second similar block, and include preset showers. Facilities for disabled visitors and babies. Laundry facilities. Shop. Bar/restaurant/takeaway (10/5-30/8). Swimming pool, paddling pool (8/5-30/9). Sports area. Minigolf. Play area. Motorcaravan services. River beach. Tourist information. Entertainment and activities (high season). Off site: Florac with shops, bars and restaurants 2.5 km. Bicycle hire 3 km. Riding 12 km.	Florac is 56 km northwest of Alès on N106. Bypass Florac and at roundabout turn right onto D998, signed Pont de Montvert, site shortly on left. GPS: 44.33569, 3.589729

Open: 1 April - 1 October.

Charges guide

Per unit incl. 2 persons	€ 11,50 - € 18,00
extra person	€ 3,20 - € 4,00
child (under 13 yrs)	€ 2,50 - € 3,00
electricity (10A)	€ 3,50

Frontignan

Camping les Tamaris

140 avenue d'Ingril, F-34110 Frontignan-Plage (Hérault) T: 04 67 43 44 77. E: les-tamaris@wanadoo.fr
alanrogers.com/FR34440

This is a super site, unusually situated on a strip of land that separates the sea from the étang or inland lake, and therefore Frontignan Ville from Frontignan-Plage. The design of the site is unusual which adds to its attractiveness. The pitches are laid out in hexagons divided by tall hedging and colourful shrubs. In total, there are 250 pitches with 100 taken by mobile homes which are let by the site. All are 'grand confort' with 10A electricity, water and waste water and on level sandy grass. Direct access to the sandy beach is possible via three gates.

Facilities	Directions
Three modern toilet blocks with some en-suite showers and washbasins. Excellent facilities for children. Unit for disabled visitors. Motorcaravan service point. Shop. Bar, restaurant and takeaway. Swimming pool. Hairdresser. Gym. Play area. Miniclub. Archery. Bicycle hire. Internet access in reception and free WiFi around bar/restaurant area. Entertainment for all ages. Off site: Riding 150 m. Sailing 1 km. Boat launching 2.5 km. Golf 15 km.	From the north on A9 take exit 32 and follow N112 towards Sète and Frontignan. After 16 km. ignore sign for Frontignan town, on to Frontignan-Plage, follow site signs between the sea and étang. From the south, exit 33, follow N300 to roundabout beside port of Sète (11 km). Turn left on N112, take second exit (Frontignan-Plage). GPS: 43.44970, 3.80603

Open: 1 April - 22 September.

Charges guide

Per unit incl. 2 persons	€ 25,00 - € 43,00
extra person	€ 5,00 - € 9,00
No credit cards.	

Fuilla

Camping le Rotja

F-66820 Fuilla (Pyrénées-Orientales) T: 04 68 96 52 75. E: campinglerotja.ellenetwim@wanadoo.fr
alanrogers.com/FR66310

La Rotja is a pretty, Dutch-owned site, set up a little valley above the fortified old town of Villefranche-de-Conflent and watched over by the impressive, snow-capped Pic d'Canigou. The older part of the site is semi-wooded with wonderful silver birches, whilst the newer part further up the hill is more open and terraced. There is room for 100 fairly level pitches of which 80 have 6/10A electricity and one can chose a shaded place or not. A small pool at the top of the site is very welcome in high season. Trips are organised into the mountains, along with barbecue evenings.

Facilities	Directions
Two toilet blocks, both fully equipped. The older one beside the bar area can be heated, a larger, more modern one is in the new area. Facilities for disabled visitors and babies. Bar, outside restaurant (15/5-30/9). Swimming and paddling pools (1/5-30/9). Gas barbecues only. Bicycle hire. Off site: Tennis 100 m. Fishing 300 m. Riding 7 km. Beach 55 km. Rafting, canyoning, hydro-speed and 'parc-aventure' possible with trained guides. Walking, VTT.	Follow the N116 from Perpignan (route to Andorra). After about 50 km. bypass Prades and continue to Villefranche-de-Conflent. Follow around and past it to take left turn (Fuilla and Sahorre). After 2 km. turn right at village to site. GPS: 42.56241, 2.35942

Open: 1 April - 31 October.

Charges guide

Per unit incl. 2 persons	€ 13,25 - € 18,25
incl. electricity	€ 15,50 - € 20,50
extra person	€ 2,75 - € 3,75

For latest campsite news, availability and prices visit

alanrogers.com

La Grande Motte

Camping le Garden

44 place des Tamaris, F-34280 La Grande Motte (Hérault) T: 04 67 56 50 09. E: campinglegarden@orange.fr
alanrogers.com/FR34020

Le Garden is a well cared for and pretty site, situated amongst tall pines and flowering shrubs, some 400 m. back from a fine sandy beach. The pitches are of a good size (100 sq.m.) on sandy grass. There are 116 mobile homes to rent and 86 touring places, most with 10A electricity, water and waste water drain. An attractive pool is overlooked by the restaurant. The site also has a small 'centre commercial' with a range of shops and a bar which is next door and open to the public. Le Garden is a very comfortable and quiet site (possible road noise during the day) within pleasant walking distance of the town centre and port. La Grande Motte is a product of the sixties tourist boom when much building went on and, at the time the apartment blocks seemed very futuristic. It has now matured into a smart, upmarket seaside resort with plenty of green space. There is much to see in the area, being on the edge of the Petite Camargue and only a few kilometres from the old walled town of Aigues Mortes. A regular bus service (half hourly) runs from outside the site to Montpellier and other places.

Facilities

Three well situated toilet blocks, smartly refurbished in Mediterranean colours, include washbasins in cabins and baby bath. Laundry facilities. Unit for disabled visitors. Shops to one side of the site with groceries, cigarettes, newspapers, boutique and bar (1/3-31/10). Restaurant and takeaway on site (from 15/5). Swimming pool and paddling pool (15/5-30/9). Play area. TV room. Internet access and WiFi. Off site: Beach 400 m. Tennis, riding, bicycle hire and boat launching 500 m. Golf and fishing 2 km. Watersports centre, casino and nightclub nearby.

Open: 1 April - 15 October.

Directions

Entering La Grande Motte from D62 dual-carriageway, keep right following signs for 'campings' and petite Motte. Turn right at traffic lights by the Office de Tourisme and right again by the Bar Le Garden and site almost immediately on right. GPS: 43.56322, 4.07278

Charges guide

Per unit incl. 1-3 persons	€ 29,50
incl. electricity, water and drainage	€ 39,50
extra person	€ 9,50
Bracelet required for the pool € 10.	

Langogne

Camping les Terrasses du Lac de Naussac

Lac de Naussac, F-48300 Langogne (Lozère) T: 04 66 69 29 62. E: info@naussac.com
alanrogers.com/FR48060

With friendly, family owners, this very spacious campsite and hotel complex is on the side of a steep hill at nearly 1,000 m. altitude (nights can be cold). There are 180 good sized, grassy, sloping pitches, often with part hardstanding (165 for touring). All have 6/10A electricity and many have panoramic views over the lake and surrounding hills. There are small trees on site offering a little shade. The lake offers a wide range of water based activities, notably sailing and fishing. The Lac de Naussac is the largest in the Lozère and this site has direct access to the it.

Facilities

Three modern and well maintained, newly refurbished toilet blocks. Motorcaravan service point. Small shop (1/5-30/9). Restaurant/takeaway in hotel. Small swimming pool (1/6-30/9). Lively animation programme in peak season including children's club but no discos. Play area. Communal barbecue area. Gas and electric barbecues only. Internet point and WiFi. Off site: Disco 300 m. Water sports with equipment for hire on lake. Cycle ride around lake of 30 km. Langogne with shops and restaurants 2 km. 9-hole golf 3 km. Riding and bicycle hire 3 km.

Open: 15 April - 30 September.

Directions

Leave N88 (Le Puy - Mende) just southwest of Langogne. Turn north on D26 towards Lac de Naussac and follow signs to site (2.5 km). Park beside lake and just before hotel. Reception inside hotel. GPS: 44.73472, 3.83527

Charges guide

Per unit incl. 2 persons	€ 12,50 - € 13,50
extra person	€ 3,50
electricity	€ 2,50
Camping Cheques accepted.	

For latest campsite news, availability and prices visit

alanrogers.com

Lansargues

Camping le Fou du Roi

Chemin des Codoniers, F-34130 Lansargues (Hérault) T: 08 74 56 00 27. E: campinglefouduroi@free.fr

alanrogers.com/FR34470

Beside the mellow stone village of Lansargues on the edge of the Camargue, le Fou du Roi was taken over by the Brunel family two years ago. They have done much to update it with a new reception/bar area complete with an attractive Tahitian style construction which can be left open or closed depending on the weather. Altogether this is a lovely little site. There are 82 pitches with 30 for touring units with 10A electricity, arranged in light shade amongst the vineyards. A small pool and play area for children make it a very comfortable site with a nice long season.

Facilities

Two toilet blocks, the first modern and fully equipped, the second not open when we visited. Facilities for disabled visitors. Washing machine and dryer. Motorcaravan service point. Small shop (July/Aug). Bar, simple snacks and takeaway (fully open July/Aug). Swimming pool (1/5-15/9). Play area. Only gas barbecues are permitted (communal area provided). Off site: Fishing and riding 3 km. Golf 4 km. Tennis in village. Village within easy walking distance with restaurants and shops.

Open: 30 March - 14 October.

Directions

From A9 exit 27 follow signs for Lunel and from there pick up D24 going south. Lansargues is 7 km. Do not take 'village centre' sign but continue past and pick up site sign just past village on right. GPS: 43.65181, 4.06635

Charges guide

Per unit incl. 2 persons	€ 13,50 - € 18,60
extra person	€ 3,00 - € 6,00
child (under 7 yrs)	free - € 3,00
electricity	€ 4,00

Le Barcarès

Camping Club le Floride et l'Embouchure

Route de Saint-Laurent, F-66423 Le Barcarès (Pyrénées-Orientales) T: 04 68 86 11 75

E: campingfloride@aol.com   alanrogers.com/FR66290

Essentially a family run enterprise, le Floride et l'Embouchure is really two sites in one – l'Embouchure the smaller one with direct access to the beach and le Floride on the opposite side of the road into le Barcarès village. There are a number of pitches with their own individual sanitary facility and in total the site offers 632 reasonably sized pitches, all with 10A electricity. A good range of chalets and mobile homes are available for rent. This is a very friendly family-centred site, very popular with Dutch visitors. It is relatively inexpensive, especially outside the July/August peak period. There is an excellent aquapark at le Floride with a number of water slides and a covered pool. The busy town of Le Barcarès is within easy walking distance. The 'Voie Verte' cycleway runs alongside the river Agly which borders L'Embouchure (the river has high banks so it is not seen from the site). This is a purpose-built cycleway from Le Barcarès to Rivesaltes.

Facilities

Four fully equipped toilet blocks on le Floride and two on l'Embouchure where 50 pitches near the beach have individual facilities. Facilities for disabled visitors and babies. Motorcaravan service point. Shop, bar, restaurant and takeaway (all 15/6-5/9). Pool complex (indoor pool is heated outside July/Aug). Excellent play area. Multisport court. Gym. Tennis. Entertainment and sports programmes (mid June-mid Sept). Bicycle hire. Charcoal barbecues are not permitted. Max. 1 dog. Off site: Beach 100 m. Fishing 1 km. Riding 1.5 km.

Open: 1 April - 30 September.

Directions

From A9 take exit 41 (Perpignan Nord) and follow signs for Canet and le Barcarès via D83. At exit 9 follow D81 (Canet) then next left into le Barcarès Village. Site is 1 km. on the left and right sides of the road. GPS: 42.77855, 3.0301

Charges guide

Per unit incl. 2 persons	
and electricity	€ 12,50 - € 34,00
incl. individual sanitary facility	€ 16,00 - € 42,00
extra person	€ 2,60 - € 6,20
child (1-4 yrs)	free - € 3,60

For latest campsite news, availability and prices visit

alanrogers.com

Le Barcarès

Yelloh! Village le Pré Catalan

Route de Saint-Laurent, F-66420 Le Barcarès (Pyrénées-Orientales) T: 04 68 86 12 60
E: info@yellohvillage-pre-catalan.com alanrogers.com/FR66300

The green foliage from the mixed trees and the flowering shrubs makes the site very attractive and an avenue of palms is particularly spectacular. There has been a camping site on the spot since 1960 but the present owners, the Galidie family, took over in 1982 and the site is now run to a very high standard by their son Francois and his English wife Jenny. With 250 pitches in total, there are 140 taken by mobile homes and chalets either to let or privately owned and some are used by tour operators. These are mixed amongst the 80 touring pitches which are on level, sandy ground, clearly divided by hedging and all with 10A electricity. The newer part has been planted in the same way as the original areas. It has less shade but enjoys views across to the mountains. The facilities are opened all season but hours are adapted according to the number of visitors on site. An upstairs bar has a long terrace which overlooks the pool complex. A footpath of just less than 1 km. leads to the sandy beach. All in all, this a pleasant and comfortable place to stay.

Facilities

Good modern facilities include small showers for children. Laundry. Small shop. Bar, restaurant and takeaway (all season). Heated swimming pool complex including fun pools, whirlpool and paddling pool. Excellent play area. Tennis. Archery. Internet access. Library. Activities for children with miniclub and evening entertainment (July/Aug). No charcoal barbecues. Off site: Beach 900 m. River fishing 1 km. Riding 1.5 km. Boat launching 3 km. Nearby La Réserve Africaine de Sigean and Le Château de Salses.

Open: 14 May - 19 September.

Directions

From A9 exit 41 (Perpignan Nord), follow signs for Le Barcarès and Canet (D83). At exit 9 take D81 (Canet), then first left to le Barcarès (D90). Site is on left after 500 m. next to le California. Follow narrow lane to site entrance. GPS: 42.78106, 3.02282

Charges guide

Per unit incl. 2 persons and electricity	€ 15,00 - € 38,00
extra person	€ 4,00 - € 7,00

Le Barcarès

Camping Club las Bousigues

Avenue des Corbières, F-66423 Le Barcarès (Pyrénées-Orientales) T: 04 68 86 16 19
E: info@camping-barcares.com alanrogers.com/FR66480

Under new ownership, las Bousigues enjoys a quiet situation set well back from le Barcarès amongst the vineyards. A mature site with lots of greenery, it provides a mix of mobile homes or chalets to rent and pitches for touring, some of which have individual sanitary blocks. The area in front of the pool, bar and restaurant with its plane trees is like a village square. Indeed, the site has a distinctly French ambience unlike some of the 'all singing, all dancing' sites nearer the beach. With around 200 pitches, most with 10A electricity, the site is of a comfortable size and would suit families with younger children.

Facilities

Two fully equipped toilet blocks, one with access for disabled visitors. Small shower and toilet for children. Individual en-suite units on some pitches. Dog shower. Laundry. Shop. Bar, restaurant and takeaway (holiday weekends and main season). Swimming pool (heated in low season) with small toboggan. Good sized play area beside communal barbecue. Internet access.

Open: 31 March - 30 September.

Directions

From the A9 take exit 40 signed Leucate. Follow D627 towards Port Leucate, then D83 towards le Barcarès. Take exit 10 for le Barcarès village. At first roundabout follow campsite sign to right. Site short distance on left. GPS: 42.78583, 3.01927

Charges guide

Per unit incl. 2 persons	€ 9,00 - € 25,00
incl. electricity (10A)	€ 11,00 - € 34,00
extra person	€ 4,60 - € 7,00
child (under 10 yrs)	free - € 4,50

Le Barcarès

Camping Club Village l'Europe

Route de Saint Laurent, F-66420 Le Barcarès (Pyrénées-Orientales) T: 04 68 86 15 36
E: reception@europe-camping.com alanrogers.com/FR66670

Le Barcarès is a popular resort with a busy market and a fishing port. It has a good number of campsites but l'Europe is a little different in that it is open all year and each pitch has its own private sanitary facilities. There is a gate at the back of the site for the sandy beach which is a walk of some 600 m. However, the site has its own pool complex overlooked by the bar/restaurant and stage where nightly shows are performed in high season. In total, there are 339 pitches of a good size (100 for touring units) and with some shade from mixed trees and shrubs. The partly hedged pitches are level on sandy grass. The fact that the site is open all year round and that Perpignan airport is nearby has proved popular with visitors looking to buy their own mobile home. There are 75 mobile homes and chalets to rent and 145 privately owned. A new concept financed by the local authority has resulted in a tarmac path, the 'voie verte de l'Agly' which follows the Agly river running past the site. It is 15 km. long from le Barcarès to Rivesaltes and is used for cycling, jogging, walking or roller skating (but no cars). It is popular with those who wish to keep fit.

Facilities

Individual sanitary facilities on every pitch including dishwashing sink. Laundry. Shop (15/4–30/9). Bar/restaurant and takeaway (high season, on demand at other times). Outdoor pool (15/4-30/9). Play area. Tennis. Evening shows and children's club (high season). WiFi at reception. Off site: Nearest beach 600 m. Supermarket. Fishing. Watersports. Le Barcarès resort with many shops, cafes, restaurants and market.

Open: All year.

Directions

From A9 take exit 41 (Perpignan Nord) and follow signs for Canet and Le Barcarès via the D83. At exit 9 follow the D81 (Canet), then next left for Le Barcarès. Site is almost immeadiately on the right. GPS: 42.774931, 3.021004

Charges guide

Per unit incl. 2 persons and electricity	€ 23,50 - € 47,50
extra person	€ 4,00 - € 8,00
child (3-6 yrs)	free - € 5,50

www.europe-camping.com   66420 LE BARCARÈS Tél. 04 68 86 15 36

Le Grau-du-Roi

Camping Caravaning le Boucanet

B.P. 206, F-30240 Le Grau-du-Roi (Gard) T: 04 66 51 41 48. E: contact@campingboucanet.fr
alanrogers.com/FR30160

Le Boucanet has a superb situation beside the beach between La Grande Motte and Le Grau-du-Roi. Many trees have been planted and are growing but as yet most are not tall enough to give much shade. As to be expected, the 458 pitches are sandy. They are on the small side, but are level and most have 6A electricity (long leads and adaptors useful). The 250 for touring are mixed amongst the mobile home and chalet pitches and are separated by small bushes. Plenty of flowers decorate the site and the pleasant restaurant (open lunchtimes and evenings) overlooks the pool area.

Facilities

The fully equipped toilet blocks include facilities for disabled visitors. Baby rooms. Laundry facilities. Fridge hire. Motorcaravan services. Shops. Restaurant, bar and snacks (16/5-15/9). Takeaway (1/7-31/8). Large swimming pool, smaller covered pool, toboggans and paddling pool. Play area on sand. Miniclub (July/Aug). Tennis. Bicycle hire. Windsurfing board hire (July/Aug). Internet access and WiFi. No dogs. Off site: Riding 1 km. Golf 2 km. Shops, restaurants and bars within 3 km.

Open: 11 April - 4 October.

Directions

Site is between La Grande Motte and Le Grau-du-Roi on the D255 coastal road, on the seaward side of the road. GPS: 43.5543, 4.10706

Charges guide

Per unit incl. 2 persons and electricity	€ 22,00 - € 39,00
pitch on first row of beach, plus	€ 5,00 - € 6,00
extra person	€ 6,00 - € 9,00
child (under 7 yrs)	€ 4,50 - € 7,90

For latest campsite news, availability and prices visit

alanrogers.com

Le Grau-du-Roi

Yelloh! Village Secrets de Camargue

Route de l'Espiguette, F-30240 Le Grau-du-Roi (Gard) T: 04 66 80 08 00
E: info@yellohvillage-secrets-de-camargue.com alanrogers.com/FR30380

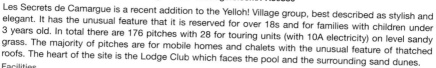

Les Secrets de Camargue is a recent addition to the Yelloh! Village group, best described as stylish and elegant. It has the unusual feature that it is reserved for over 18s and for families with children under 3 years old. In total there are 176 pitches with 28 for touring units (with 10A electricity) on level sandy grass. The majority of pitches are for mobile homes and chalets with the unusual feature of thatched roofs. The heart of the site is the Lodge Club which faces the pool and the surrounding sand dunes.

Facilities

Fully equipped sanitary block includes facilities for disabled visitors. Small shop (2/4-19/9). Restaurant, bar (all season). Swimming pool. Aquagym. Activities and entertainment. Mobile homes and chalets for rent. Off site: Free use of facilities at the nearby Camping les Petits Camarguais. Nearest beach 1.5 km. Riding 0.8 km. Fishing 5 km. Golf 16 km. Watersports 4 km. Village of Le Grau-du-Roi 3 km. Walled town of Aigues Mortes 12 km.

Open: 26 March - 3 October.

Directions

Leave the A9 at exit for Gallargues and head for Aigues Mortes on the D979. Continue to Le Grau-du-Roi and then follow signs to Port Camargue on the D62, continuing to join the D255. Site is well signed from this point. GPS: 43.48736, 4.14202

Charges guide

Per unit incl. 2 persons	€ 15,00 - € 44,00
extra person	€ 4,00 - € 8,00
pet	€ 4,00

Le Grau-du-Roi

Yelloh! Village les Petits Camarguais

Route de l'Espiguette, F-30240 Le Grau-du-Roi (Gard) T: 04 66 51 16 16
E: info@yellohvillage-petits-camarguais.com alanrogers.com/FR30390

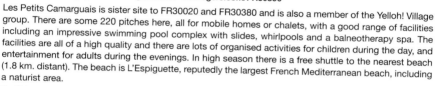

Les Petits Camarguais is sister site to FR30020 and FR30380 and is also a member of the Yelloh! Village group. There are some 220 pitches here, all for mobile homes or chalets, with a good range of facilities including an impressive swimming pool complex with slides, whirlpools and a balneotherapy spa. The facilities are all of a high quality and there are lots of organised activities for children during the day, and entertainment for adults during the evenings. In high season there is a free shuttle to the nearest beach (1.8 km. distant). The beach is L'Espiguette, reputedly the largest French Mediterranean beach, including a naturist area.

Facilities

Shop. Bar. Restaurant. Takeaway food. Swimming pool complex with slides, paddling pools, counter current swimming, water games and a balneotherapy spa. Aquagym in high season. Volleyball. Mini football. Activity and entertainment programme. Dogs are not accepted. Mobile homes and chalets for rent. Off site: Nearest beach 1.8 km. (free shuttle in peak season). Riding. Sea fishing. Golf. Casino. Lunapark fairground. Seaquarium park.

Open: 2 April - 19 September.

Directions

Leave the A9 autoroute at the Gallargues exit and head for Aigues Mortes on the D979. Continue to Le Grau-du-Roi and then follow signs to Port Camargue on the D62, continuing to join the D255b. The site is well signed from this point. GPS: 43.50847, 4.14554

Charges guide

Contact the site for details.

Lodève

Camping Municipal les Vailhés

B.P. 62, F-34702 Lodève (Hérault) T: 04 67 44 25 98
alanrogers.com/FR34550

Les Vailhés is a popular municipal site with a wonderful situation on the shores of the Lac du Salagou which is a haven for watersports. The views across the lake are good, and the red rocks are most unusual. In total there are 200 pitches, most with electricity; some are for mobile homes on ground sloping towards the lakeside beach. The majority are hedged and there is a fair amount of shade from various types of trees. The site is fenced off from the lake but the gates are open during the day. A sailing school is next door to the site offering a range of watersports.

Facilities

Two toilet blocks, fully equipped if a little Spartan include washing machines. Play area with small climbing wall. Lake amenities (lifeguards July/Aug) and beach café (July/Aug). Windsurfing, sailing, canoes and pedalos. Archery. Off site: Ancient town of Lodève 6 km. Beaches of the Mediterranean one hour's drive.

Open: 1 April - 30 September.

Directions

From the A75 take exit 54 or 55, and follow directions to Lac du Salagou. Then follow site signs to left. GPS: 43.67026, 3.35572

Charges guide

Per person	€ 3,11
child (under 7 yrs)	€ 1,84
pitch	€ 3,44 - € 4,26
electricity	€ 2,50

For latest campsite news, availability and prices visit

alanrogers.com

Le Vigan

Camping le Val de l'Arre

Route du Pont de la Croix, F-30120 Le Vigan (Gard) T: 04 67 81 02 77. E: valdelarre@wanadoo.fr

alanrogers.com/FR30230

Camping Val de l'Arre is situated along the Arre river, a tributary of the Hérault river and in the centre of the Cévennes National Park. The site is well managed by the very friendly Triaire family, who speak English, Dutch, Spanish and French. There are 180 grassy, level pitches, 145 for touring, many have some shade and most have electricity (10A). There is a pleasant swimming pool with an outdoor bar. A pebble beach at the river bank provides opportunities for play and fishing enthusiasts will also certainly appreciate the river. Only gas and electric barbecues on site. There are numerous possibilities for outdoor activities such as white water rafting, canoeing and mountain biking. Qualified guides can take you on mountain expeditions on foot or by bicycle. The nearby Les Grottes des Demoiselles are some of France's foremost caves. There is also the opportunity to taste the great wines of the Hérault region.

Facilities

Three clean and well-appointed toilet blocks are well spaced around the site with controllable showers. Facilities for babies and visitors with disabilities. Washing machines. Shop, open air bar with snacks and restaurant (all 1/6-31/8). Swimming and paddling pools (1/6-15/9). Boules. Play area. Motorcaravan services. Guided walks organised. Off site: Bicycle hire 2.5 km. Riding 8 km. Many opportunites for walkers, cyclists and mountain bikers.

Open: 1 April - 30 September.

Directions

Leave A75 at exit 48 and follow the D7 and then D999 east to Le Vigan (43 km). Drive through town, signed Nîmes, at roundabout turn right D110B, site signed. Cross river, turn left, site in 800m. GPS: 43.992067, 3.6374

Charges guide

Per unit incl. 2 persons and electricity	€ 17,00 - € 21,50
extra person	€ 4,00 - € 5,00
child (2-6 yrs)	€ 3,00 - € 3,50

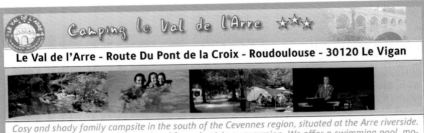

Camping le Val de l'Arre ★★★

Le Val de l'Arre - Route Du Pont de la Croix - Roudoulouse - 30120 Le Vigan

Cosy and shady family campsite in the south of the Cevennes region, situated at the Arre riverside. Many walking paths are close at hand for a day trip or excursion. We offer a swimming pool, modern sanitary facilities, a playground, WIFI, shop and a snack bar/restaurant with terrace. Mobile homes for rent. All ready to give you a relaxing and comfortable holiday.

Tel: 0033 467 810 277 - Fax: 0033 467 817 123 E-mail: valdelarre@wanadoo.fr - www.valdelarre.com

Marseillan-Plage

Yelloh! Village les Méditerranées

262 avenue des campings, F-34340 Marseillan-Plage (Hérault) T: 04 67 27 94 49
E: info@yellohvillage-mediterranees.com alanrogers.com/FR34150

Marseillan-Plage is a small, busy resort east of Cap d'Agde and it enjoys a super position immediately beside a long, gently shelving sandy beach. Les Méditerranées is made up of two sites – Nouvelle Floride beside the beach and Charlemagne across the road, both with super pool complexes. Both are good quality sites set under tall trees with neat hedges separating around 500 pitches. There are about 200 for touring units on sandy soil, all with water and 6A electricity. The pitches nearer the sea have less shade. Amenities and facilities are generally of excellent quality and include a smart bar area overlooking the beach with a raised stage for entertainment.

Facilities

Very impressive toilet blocks include some en-suite showers and washbasins, facilities for disabled visitors, dog shower. Motorcaravan services. Shops. Bars, restaurants. Two swimming pool complexes, slides, jacuzzi, paddling pools (all season). Play area. Fitness centre. Multisport court. Watersports. Weekly films, variety of organised games, competitions, dances, discos. WiFi. Miniclub in school holidays. Bicycle hire. Off site: Riding, bicycle hire 500 m. Boat launching and watersports 1 km. Golf 5 km.

Open: 15 April - 1 October.

Directions

From A9 autoroute exit 34, follow N312 to Agde then take N112 towards Sète. Watch for signs to Marseillan-Plage from where site is well signed. GPS: 43.3087, 3.54168

Charges 2011

Per unit incl. 2 persons and electricity	€ 15,00 - € 50,00
extra person	€ 6,00 - € 8,50
child (3-7 yrs)	free - € 8,50
dog	€ 4,00

Marseillan-Plage
Camping la Creole

74 avenue des campings, F-34340 Marseillan-Plage (Hérault) T: 04 67 21 92 69
E: campinglacreole@wanadoo.fr alanrogers.com/FR34220

This is a surprisingly tranquil, well cared for small campsite in the middle of this bustling resort that will appeal to those seeking a rather less frenetic ambience typical of many sites in this area. Essentially a family orientated site, it offers around 110 good-sized, level sandy pitches, all with 6A electricity and mostly with shade from trees and shrubs. There are also 15 mobile homes available to rent. It benefits from direct access to an extensive sandy beach (gated access) and the fact that there is no swimming pool or bar actually contributes to the tranquillity. It may even be seen as an advantage for families with younger children. The beach will be the main attraction here no doubt, and the town's extensive range of bars, restaurants and shops are all within a couple of minutes walk. It is well situated for visiting Sète, a miniature Venice, or Pézenas with an interesting history and lots of art and craft shops. Cap d'Agde, a modern resort with its large marina and super water park for children is popular. If you take a trip on the famous Canal du Midi you may get to see the oyster beds in the Etang de Thau, the inland saltwater lake. There are also many vineyards to visit and it is the home area of sweet Muscat wine.

Facilities
Toilet facilities are housed in a traditional building, modernised inside to provide perfectly adequate, if not particularly luxurious facilities including some washbasins in private cabins, a baby room and dog shower. Motorcaravan service point. Small play area. In high season beach games, dances, sangria evenings etc, are organised, all aimed particularly towards families. Communal barbecues only. WiFi. Off site: Local market day Tuesday. Bicycle hire outside site. Riding 1 km. Boat launching 1.5 km. Aqua park at Agde 5 km.

Open: 1 April - 15 October.

Directions
From A9 exit 34 take N312 towards Agde, then N112 towards Sète keeping a look-out for signs to Marseillan-Plage off this road. Site is well signed in Marseillan-Plage. GPS: 43.3206, 3.5501

Charges guide

Per unit incl. 2 persons and electricity	€ 16,30 - € 30,50
extra person (over 2 yrs)	€ 3,00 - € 5,50
dog	€ 2,00 - € 3,00

Meyrueis
Camping Caravaning le Champ d'Ayres

Route de la Brèze, F-48150 Meyrueis (Lozère) T: 04 66 45 60 51. E: campinglechampdayres@wanadoo.fr
alanrogers.com/FR48000

You can be sure of a warm welcome at this traditional, family run site, set in the heart of the Cevennes and its magnificent gorges. Champ d'Ayres is neat, tidy and well kept and is run with young families in mind. The 85 slightly sloping grass pitches, 62 for touring, are mostly hedged with well trimmed bushes and many have some shade. All have electricity (6/10A) but some may require long leads. The area is surrounded by mountains and gorges and some of the narrow and winding roads are not for the faint-hearted or those with large and under-powered units.

Facilities
The toilet block is kept very clean and has all the necessary facilities. A new block is planned for 2011. Baby room. Facilities for disabled visitors. Laundry facilities. Shop, small bar and takeaway (all 1/5-15/9). New heated swimming and paddling pools (8/5-15/9). Play area. Games room. Boules. Activities arranged (July/Aug). WiFi (free). Off site: Meyrueis with good shops and restaurants 500 m. Fishing 100 m. Riding and bicycle hire within 1 km. Maison du Vautours 18 km.

Open: 3 April - 18 September.

Directions
Leave A75 at exit 44-1, east on D29 through Aquessac, D907 to le Rozier then D996 to Meyrueis. In Meyrueis (narrow roads) cross river and follow signs for Ayres. Site is 500 m. east of the town. GPS: 44.18077, 3.43507

Charges guide

Per unit incl. 2 persons	€ 10,00 - € 21,50
extra person	€ 3,00 - € 5,00
electricity	€ 3,00

Meyrueis

Kawan Village de Capelan

F-48150 Meyrueis (Lozère) T: 04 66 45 60 50. E: camping.le.capelan@wanadoo.fr

alanrogers.com/FR48020

The Lozère is one of France's least populated regions but offers some truly spectacular, rugged scenery, wonderful flora and fauna and old towns and villages. Le Capelan, which is only 1 km. from the attractive market town of Meyrueis, has 116 level, grassy pitches strung out alongside the unfenced River Jonte. Of these, 72 are for touring, most with some shade and all with electrical connections (6/10A). There is direct river access from the site with a 3 km. stretch available for trout fishing. Although there are special facilities, the site is not ideal for disabled visitors. English and Dutch spoken.

Facilities

Well maintained toilet blocks, facilities for disabled visitors (but not ideal for those with walking difficulties). Three bathrooms for rent. Small shop. Bar (both from 1/6). Takeaway (from 1/7). Swimming and paddling pools (from 1/6), access via 60 steps. Multisports terrain. Satellite TV. Play area. Supervised rock climbing. Fishing. Internet access. Free WiFi. Communal barbecue area, only gas and electric barbecues. Off site: Town centre 1 km. Bicycle hire 1 km. Riding 3 km. Canoeing.

Open: 1 May - 15 September.

Directions

Exit A75 at 44-1, take D29 to Aguessac, D907 to le Rozier, then D996 towards Meyrueis. The site is on the right 1 km. before town. It is well signed. GPS: 44.18583, 3.41988

Charges guide

Per unit incl. 2 persons and electricity	€ 17,00 - € 25,00

Mèze

Kawan Village Beau Rivage

RD613, F-34140 Mèze (Hérault) T: 04 67 43 81 48. E: reception@camping-beaurivage.fr

alanrogers.com/FR34260

Beau Rivage is situated on the inland shore of the 4.5 km. by 19.5 km. Etang du Thau. This inland salt lake, lying parallel to the Mediterranean and separated by a very narrow strip of land, is well known for its oyster beds. It is also popular for fishing, diving and watersports. The campsite, on the edge of the town, is within easy walking distance of the harbour and the shops. The site has 150 level, sandy grass pitches all with 6A electricity available for touring units and 134 mobile homes to rent. The main features of the site are a pleasant pool and paddling pool with a bar and snack restaurant for the high season.

Facilities

One fully equipped small toilet block is open all season and a larger block for the main season. Baby bath. Facilities for disabled visitors. Washing machine. Motorcaravan service point. Bar providing snacks and simple takeaway food (July/Aug). Swimming and paddling pools. Play area. Activities in July/Aug. Communal barbecues. Off site: Restaurant 300 m. Supermarket 200 m. Beach 500 m. All facilities of the town within easy walking distance. Tennis and bicycle hire 1 km. WiFi (free).

Open: 8 April - 17 September.

Directions

From the A9 take exit 33 for Sète. Follow RN113 for Poussan, Bouzigues and Mèze. Continue for 5 km. to outskirts of Mèze and site entrance is on left between the petrol station and a pottery (not too easy to see). GPS: 43.43051, 3.61038

Charges 2011

Per unit incl. 2 persons and electricity	€ 19,00 - € 38,00
extra person	€ 4,00 - € 7,00

Camping Cheques accepted.

Montclar

Yelloh! Village Domaine d'Arnauteille

F-11250 Montclar (Aude) T: 04 68 26 84 53. E: info@arnauteille.com

alanrogers.com/FR11060

Enjoying some beautiful and varied views, this site is ideal for exploring the little known Aude Département and for visiting the walled city of Carcassonne. The site is set in farmland on hilly ground with the original pitches on gently sloping, lightly wooded land. Newer ones are on open ground, of good size, with water, drainage and electricity (5/10A), semi-terraced and partly hedged. Of the 198 pitches, 138 are for touring. The facilities are quite spread out with the swimming pool complex, in the style of a Roman amphitheatre, set in a hollow basin surrounded by fine views. Access, although much improved, could be difficult for large, twin-axle vans.

Facilities

Toilet blocks, one with a Roman theme. Laundry, facilities for disabled visitors and a baby bath. Motorcaravan services. Small shop, bar, restaurant and takeaway (all open 15/5-15/9). Swimming pool (25 m. open 1/5-30/9), paddling pool, river with water massage and sunbathing terrace. Games court. Boules. Play area. Games room. TV. Riding (1/7-31/8). Library. Internet. Off site: Fishing 3 km. Bicycle hire 8 km. Golf 10 km. Rafting and canoeing.

Open: 1 April - 26 September.

Directions

D118 from Carcassonne, pass Rouffiac d'Aude. Before the end of dual carriageway, turn right to Montclar up narrow road (passing places) for 2.5 km. Site signed very sharp left up hill before village. GPS: 43.12714, 2.25953

Charges guide

Per unit incl. 2 persons and electricity	€ 15,00 - € 36,00
extra person	€ 6,00 - € 8,00

For latest campsite news, availability and prices visit

alanrogers.com

Narbonne

Kawan Village les Mimosas

Chaussée de Mandirac, F-11100 Narbonne (Aude) T: 04 68 49 03 72. E: info@lesmimosas.com
alanrogers.com/FR11070

533

Six kilometres inland from the beaches of Narbonne and Gruissan, this site benefits from a less hectic situation than others by the sea. The site is lively with plenty to amuse and entertain the younger generation whilst offering facilities for the whole family. A free club card is available in July/August to use the children's club, gym, sauna, tennis, minigolf, billiards etc. There are 250 pitches, 150 for touring, many in a circular layout of very good size, most with electricity (6A). There are a few 'grand confort', with reasonable shade, mostly from 2 m. high hedges. There is also a number of mobile homes and chalets to rent. This could be a very useful site offering many possibilities to meet a variety of needs, on-site entertainment (including an evening on Cathar history), and easy access to popular beaches. Nearby Gruissan is a fascinating village with its wooden houses on stilts, beaches, ruined castle, port and salt beds. Narbonne has Roman remains and inland Cathar castles are perched on rugged hill tops.

Facilities

Sanitary buildings refurbished to a high standard include a baby room. Washing machines. Shop and Auberge restaurant (open all season). Takeaway. Bar. Small lounge, amusements (July/Aug). Landscaped heated pool with slides and islands (open 1/5), plus the original pool and children's pool (high season). New play area. Minigolf. Mountain bike hire. Tennis. Sauna. gym. Children's activities, sports, entertainment (high season). Bicycle hire. Multisports ground. WiFi. Off site: Riding. Windsurfing/sailing school 300 m. Gruissan's beach 10 minutes. Lagoon, boating fishing via footpath (200 m).

Open: 28 March - 1 November.

Directions

From A9 exit 38 (Narbonne Sud) take last exit on roundabout, back over the autoroute (site signed from here). Follow signs La Nautique and then Mandirac and site (6 km. from autoroute). Also signed from Narbonne centre.
GPS: 43.13662, 3.02562

Charges guide

Per unit incl. 2 persons and electricity	€ 17,50 - € 33,00
incl. water and waste water	€ 21,70 - € 38,00
extra person	€ 4,10 - € 10,00

Camping Cheques accepted.

Narbonne

Camping la Nautique

La Nautique, F-11100 Narbonne (Aude) T: 04 68 90 48 19. E: info@campinglanautique.com

alanrogers.com/FR11080

Owned and run by a very welcoming Dutch family, this well established site has pitches each with individual sanitary units. It is an extremely spacious site situated on the Etang de Bages, where flat water combined with strong winds make it one of the best windsurfing areas in France. La Nautique has 390 huge, level pitches, 270 for touring, all with 10A electricity and water. Six or seven overnight pitches with electricity are in a separate area. The flowering shrubs and trees give a pleasant feel. Each pitch is separated by hedges making some quite private and providing shade. Entertainment is organised for adults and children from Easter to September (increasing in high season), plus a sports club for supervised surfing, sailing, rafting, walking and canoeing (some activities are charged for). The unspoilt surrounding countryside is excellent for walking or cycling and locally there is horse riding and fishing. This site caters for families with children including teenagers and is fenced off from the water for the protection of children. Windsurfers can have a key for the gate (with deposit) that leads to launching points on the lake. English is spoken in reception by the very welcoming Schutjes family.

Facilities

Each pitch has its own fully equipped sanitary unit. Specially equipped facilities for disabled visitors. Laundry. Shop. Bar/restaurant, terrace, TV. Takeaway (all 1/5-30/9). Snack bar (1/7-31/8). Swimming pools, water slide, paddling pool. Play areas. Tennis. Minigolf. Petanque. Miniclub (high season). Games room. Internet. Only electric barbecues are permitted. Torch useful. Off site: Large sandy beaches at Gruissan (12 km) and Narbonne Plage (20 km). Narbonne is only 4 km. Walking and cycling. Canoeing, sailing and windsurfing.

Open: 15 February - 15 November.

Directions

From A9 take exit 38 (Narbonne Sud). Go round roundabout to last exit and follow signs for La Nautique and site, then further site signs to site on right in 2.5 km. GPS: 43.14696, 3.00439

Charges 2011

Per unit incl. 2 persons, electricity, water and sanitary unit	€ 19,50 - € 42,00
extra person	€ 5,00 - € 8,00
child (2-7 yrs)	€ 3,00 - € 6,00
dog	€ 2,50 - € 4,00

Enjoy a luxury holiday!

Private sanitary facilities

LA NAUTIQUE ★★★★
CAMPING - CARAVANING NARBONNE

(+33) 04 68 90 48 19
www.campinglanautique.com

Néfiach

Flower Camping la Garenne

RD916, F-66170 Néfiach (Pyrénées-Orientales) T: 04 68 57 15 76
E: camping.lagarenne.nefiach@wanadoo.fr alanrogers.com/FR66490

Situated just off the N116 which runs through the foothills of the Pyrénées from Perpignan to Andorra, this site is ideally situated for hiking, climbing, cycling and canoeing. The pitches are all level with very easy access and have a degree of privacy to them, and all are close to the swimming pool and children's play area. A few mobile homes are on the site and some of these are attractively designed to look like chalets found high up in the mountains. Great views of the surrounding hills and mountains are enjoyable from all areas of the site whilst at the back there are vineyards with black grapes in abundance.

Facilities

Single toilet block in the centre of the site provides modern facilities. Baby area and facilities for disabled visitors. Washing machine. Cosy bar area and snack type restaurant with covered area for singing and dancing. Weekly paella evening. Swimming pool with sunbathing terrace and small pool for young children. Play area. Outdoor fitness machines for adults. Max. 1 dog. Off site: Ile-sur-Têt 3 km.

Open: All year.

Directions

From the N116 (Perpignan - Andorra), take exit for Néfiach and head up the old road to Ile-sur-Têt and the site is on the right. GPS: 42.69067, 2.65785

Charges guide

Per unit incl. 2 persons and electricity	€ 17,50 - € 23,50
extra person	€ 4,00 - € 6,00
child (2-7 yrs)	€ 3,00 - € 4,00

For latest campsite news, availability and prices visit

alanrogers.com

Palau-del-Vidre

Kawan Village le Haras

Domaine Saint Galdric, F-66690 Palau-del-Vidre (Pyrénées-Orientales) T: 04 68 22 14 50
E: haras8@wanadoo.fr alanrogers.com/FR66050

Situated in the mature grounds of an old hunting lodge, later developed into an arborteum, le Haras is a rather special site. The 131 pitches are in bays of four arranged amidst an amazing variety of trees and shrubs that provide colour and shade for 97 touring units and some 34 mobile homes (18 to rent). All the touring pitches have 6A electricity, 29 are fully serviced. Some of the access roads are narrow. Under the same family management as Ma Prairie at Canet Village (FR66020), this is a comfortable site popular with British visitors. Rail noise is possible, although the line is screened by large trees. A restaurant and its courtyard area (developed from the old stable block) and a pleasant pool complex reflect the Mediterranean atmosphere.

Facilities

Fully equipped toilet blocks. Facilities for disabled visitors. Washing machines. Motorcaravan service point. Fridge hire. Bar, restaurant and takeaway (all 15/4-30/9). Swimming and paddling pools (1/5-15/9). Play area. Archery (10/7-25/8). Only gas or electric barbecues are allowed. Internet access (charged) and WiFi (free). Max. 1 dog. Off site: Three bakers in the village, two butchers and a general store. Beaches 10 minutes drive. Fishing 500 m. Riding 2 km. Bicycle hire 6 km. Golf 7 km.

Open: 1 April - 30 September.

Directions

From A9, exit 43 (Le Boulou) follow D618 towards Argelès for 13 km. From the bypass at St André, turn left for Palau-del-Vidre (D11). Bear right through village, on D11 towards Elne. Site on right at end of village, before railway bridge.
GPS: 42.57639, 2.96444

Charges 2011

Per unit incl. 2 persons and electricity (5A)	€ 19,00 - € 31,50
extra person	€ 3,60 - € 5,80
child (under 7 yrs)	free - € 3,80

Camping Cheques accepted.

Port Camargue

Camping Abri de Camargue

320 route du Phare de l'Espiguette, Port Camargue, F-30240 Le Grau-du-Roi (Gard) T: 04 66 51 54 83
E: contact@abridecamargue.fr alanrogers.com/FR30030

Situated 1 km. from the Mediterranean and 1.5 km. from the town of Le Grau-du-Roi, this pleasant, family oriented site has an attractive pool area. Overlooked by the bar with its outdoor tables on a pleasant sheltered terrace, the larger outdoor pool has surrounds for sunbathing. The smaller indoor pool is heated. With 277 level pitches, there are 57 for touring units, mainly of 100 sq.m (there are also smaller ones). Electricity and water are available on most, and the pitches are well maintained and shaded, with trees and flowering shrubs, quite luxuriant in parts. Recent additions include an air-conditioned cinema and a new sports area.

Facilities

Well appointed toilet blocks and facilities for disabled visitors. Motorcaravan services. Shop. Bar with TV. Restaurant and takeaway. Heated indoor pool, outdoor pool and paddling pool. New sports area. Outdoor fitness room. Cinema (air conditioned). High quality play area. Entertainment programme and children's club (high season). Petanque. Music room for young people in high season. WiFi near restaurant (charged). Site access card (deposit € 15). Off site: Tennis 800 m. Riding, bicycle hire 1 km. Fishing 2 km. Golf 5 km. Nearest beach Port Camargue 900 m. L'Espiguette 4 km. (free bus passes the gate in July/Aug). Boat, surfboard hire nearby.

Open: 1 April - 30 September.

Directions

Site is 45 km. southwest of Nimes. From A9 exit 26, Gallargues to Le Grau-du-Roi. From bypass follow signs Port Camargue and Campings. Then follow Rive gauche signs towards Phare l'Espiguette. Site is on right opposite Toboggan Park.
GPS: 43.5225, 4.1491

Charges guide

Per unit incl. 2 persons and electricity	€ 27,00 - € 56,00
with 3-5 persons	€ 32,00 - € 61,00
pet	€ 7,00

Portiragnes-Plage

Camping les Sablons

Avenue des Muriers, F-34420 Portiragnes-Plage (Hérault) T: 04 67 90 90 55. E: contact@les-sablons.com

alanrogers.com/FR34400

Les Sablons is an impressive and popular site with lots going on, a village in itself. Most of the facilities are arranged around the entrance with shops, a restaurant, a bar and a large pool complex with no less than five slides and three heated pools. There is also direct access to the white sandy beach at the back of the site close to a small lake. There is good shade on the majority of the site, although some of the newer touring pitches have less shade but are nearer the gate to the beach. On level sandy grass, all have 6A electricity. Of the 800 pitches, around half are taken by a range of mobile homes and chalets (many for hire, and a few for use by tour operators). A new animation office enables you to book a wide wide range of sporting, cultural and musical events as well as excursions. Children's clubs and evening entertainment is organised. In fact, this is a real holiday venue aiming to keep all the family happy. Some visitors simply stay on the site for their entire holiday – it certainly has everything. This site is very convenient for Béziers airport.

Facilities

Well equipped, modernised toilet blocks include large showers, some with washbasins. Baby baths and facilities for disabled visitors. Supermarket, bakery and newsagent. Restaurant, bar and takeaway. Swimming pool complex. Entertainment and activity programme with sports, music and cultural activities. Children's club. Beach club. Tennis. Archery. Play areas. Electronic games. ATM. Internet access. WiFi throughout site. Off site: Village 100 m. Beach 200 m. Bicycle hire 100 m. Riding 200 m. Canal du Midi 1 km. Parc Adventure (high wire adventure park) 1.5 km.

Open: 1 April - 30 September.

Directions

From A9 exit 35 (Béziers Est) follow signs for Vias and Agde (N112). After large roundabout pass exit to Cers then take exit for Portiragnes (D37). Follow for about 5 km. and pass over Canal du Midi towards Portiragnes-Plage. Site is on left after roundabout. GPS: 43.28003, 3.36396

Charges guide

Per unit incl. 2 persons	
and electricity	€ 18,00 - € 48,00
extra person	€ 6,00 - € 10,00
child (5-13 yrs)	free - € 8,00
dog	€ 4,00

Portiragnes-Plage

Camping Caravaning les Mimosas

Port Cassafières, F-34420 Portiragnes-Plage (Hérault) T: 04 67 90 92 92
E: les.mimosas.portiragnes@wanadoo.fr **alanrogers.com/FR34170**

Les Mimosas is quite a large site with 400 pitches – 200 for touring units, the remainder for mobile homes – in a rural situation. The level, grassy pitches are of average size, separated and numbered, all with 6A electricity (long leads may be required), some have good shade others have less. The pool area, a real feature of the site, includes a most impressive wave pool, various toboggans, the 'Space Hole' water slide, a large swimming pool and a super paddling pool (nine pools in all) with lots of free sun beds. This is a friendly, family run site with families in mind with something new for each year. Les Mimosas has a less hectic situation than sites closer to the beach. However, it is possible to walk to a lovely sandy beach (1.2 km). There is lots going on and many day trips and excursions are arranged all season, from canoeing to visiting castles. Portiragnes-Plage is about 2 km. and it can be reached by cycle tracks. The Canal du Midi runs along the edge of the site (no access), providing another easy cycle route.

Facilities

Good, modern toilet blocks include baby rooms, children's toilets, facilities for disabled visitors (whole site wheelchair friendly). En-suite facilities on payment. Washing machines and dryers. Motorcaravan services. Fridge hire. Large well stocked shop. Bar, snacks all season, restaurant (from 1/6). Swimming pool complex (early June), lifeguards all season. Good play area. Miniclub (4-8 yrs). Boules. Gym with instructor and sauna. Multisport court. Bicycle hire. Games/TV room. Variety of evening entertainment. Internet access and WiFi (charged). Communal barbecue (not permitted on pitches). Off site: Fishing and riding 1 km. Portiragnes-Plage with beach bars and restaurants 2 km. Golf 10 km.

Open: 1 June - 4 September.

Directions

From A9 exit 35 (Béziers Est) take N112 south towards Serignan (1 km). Large roundabout follow signs for Cap d'Agde, watch carefully for D37, Portiragnes (1-2 km), follow signs for Portiragnes -Plage. Site well signed before Portiragnes-Plage (5 km). GPS: 43.29153, 3.37348

Charges 2011

Per unit incl. 2 persons	
and electricity	€ 25,00 - € 40,00
extra person	€ 5,00 - € 9,50
child (under 4 yrs)	free - € 4,00
dog	€ 2,00 - € 5,50
private sanitary unit	€ 8,50 - € 10,00

Remoulins

Camping la Soubeyranne

1110 route de Beaucaire, F-30210 Remoulins (Gard) T: 04 66 37 03 21. E: soubeyranne@franceloc.fr
alanrogers.com/FR30140

Owned by the group FranceLoc, this site is well positioned for visiting the Pont du Gard, Nîmes and Uzès, famed for their Roman connections. The 200 pitches offer extremely generous amounts of shade and keeping the 6 hectares watered involves over 5 km. of hose pipe. The touring pitches, of which there are 79, are large, level, numbered and separated, and all have 6A electricity connections. An entertainment programme (July/August) is aimed mainly at young children (teenagers may find the site rather quiet).

Facilities

One unisex toilet block is basic but clean and includes washbasins in cubicles. Motorcaravan service point. Fridges for hire. Small shop selling basics. Restaurant, bar and takeaway (all 4/4-27/9). Heated swimming pool complex (4/4-27/9) with 20x10 m. pool and smaller toddlers' pool (unsupervised). Play area including inflatable castle. Minigolf. Boules. Tennis. Bicycle hire. Off site: Fishing 1 km. Remoulins 1.5 km.

Open: 4 April - 27 September.

Directions

From Uzès take D981 to Remoulins, turn right at lights over river bridge, left at roundabout, then left (signed D986 Beaucaire). Site is 1.5 km. further on left. GPS: 43.942282, 4.559669

Charges guide

Per unit incl. 2 persons	
and electricity	€ 19,70 - € 31,20
extra person	€ 4,70 - € 7,00

Saillagouse

PRL Le Vedrignans

Route de Vedrignans, F-66800 Saillagouse (Pyrénées-Orientales) T: 04 68 04 04 79
E: contact@levedrignans.com alanrogers.com/FR66700

The pitches at this campsite are used exclusively for mobile home and chalet accommodation. For full details please see our PRL section starting on page 538.

Saint Cyprien-Plage

Camping Cala Gogo

Avenue Armand Lanoux, les Capellans, F-66750 Saint Cyprien-Plage (Pyrénées-Orientales) T: 04 68 21 07 12
E: camping.calagogo@wanadoo.fr alanrogers.com/FR66030

This is an excellent, well organised site and it is agreeably situated by a superb sandy beach with a beach bar and boat launching. There are 654 pitches in total with 450 average sized, level, pitches for touring, electrical connections (6A) everywhere and some shade. Around 20 fully serviced pitches are to be added. The site has a most impressive pool complex carefully laid out with palm trees in ample sunbathing areas. The large bar complex becomes very busy in season and dancing or entertainment is arranged on some evenings on a large stage recently built alongside the bar. A feature of the site is the provision of special beach buggies for visitors with disabilities. The site is now part of the Les Pieds dans l'Eau group (having direct access to water – either sea, river or lake).

Facilities

Fully equipped toilet blocks are of a high standard. Good supermarket and small shopping mall. Sophisticated restaurant with excellent cuisine. Self-service restaurant with simple menu. Takeaway. Bar. Small beach bar (high season). Disco. TV. Three swimming pools (heated) plus one for children, water jets, jacuzzi, waterfall. Play area. Tennis. Fishing. Diving club. Internet access and WiFi. Bicycle hire. Events, sports and entertainment organised in season. Torches useful. Off site: Golf, riding and boat launching 3 km. Boat excursions and courses in skin-diving, windsurfing or sailing nearby.

Open: 14 May - 17 September.

Directions

Using D81 (southward) avoid St Cyprien-Plage and continue towards Argelès. Turn right at roundabout signed Le Port and Aquapark and pick up site signs. Site is just past the Aquapark.
GPS: 42.59939, 3.03761

Charges 2011

Per unit incl. 2 persons	
and electricity	€ 25,40 - € 39,10
extra person	€ 10,30
child (under 5 yrs)	free
dog	€ 4,00

See advertisement on page 419.

Saint Enimie

Camping Couderc

Route de Millau, F-48210 Saint Enimie (Lozère) T: 04 66 48 50 53. E: contact@campingcouderc.fr
alanrogers.com/FR48080

A spacious rural site, Couderc is strung out along 1 km. of the clear shallow River Tarn, although access to the river is not easy. The beautiful Gorges du Tarn and the high plateaux are well worth exploring. Come in May and June to see the wonderful flowers and butterflies with vultures soaring overhead. There are 130 good sized, level grassy/stony pitches here, separated by vines and mature trees. With 123 for touring units, most have welcome shade and 10A electricity (long leads may be needed). Rock pegs are advised. Although the local roads are winding and narrow, access on the site is good.

Facilities

Several toilet blocks with adequate facilities including those for children. Facilities for disabled visitors (but the terrain is not ideal for those with walking difficulties). Bar/TV room. Breakfast (all season). Basic shop, bread to order. Swimming and paddling pools (a steep climb from pitches). Play area. Canoe hire and trips run from site. Boules. River fishing. Electric barbecues only – communal barbecues provided. Off site: Ste Enimie 1.5 km. with shops, restaurants and bars. Grottes, canyoning, rock climbing, caving.

Open: 19 April - 20 September.

Directions

Leave A75 at exit 40 for La Canourgue. Take the D998 to Ste Enimie (28 km) following signs for Millau, Gorges du Tarn. Take the D907 to site on left in 1.5 km. Approach from south not recommended for large outfits. GPS: 44.353606, 3.401347

Charges guide

Per unit incl. 2 persons	
and electricity	€ 14,00 - € 22,00
extra person	€ 3,00 - € 4,00
child (under 7 yrs)	€ 1,30 - € 1,60

Saint Jean-du-Gard

Camping les Sources

Route de Mialet, F-30270 Saint Jean-du-Gard (Gard) T: 04 66 85 38 03
E: camping-des-sources@orange.fr alanrogers.com/FR30150

This is a small, family run site situated in the foothills of the beautiful Cévennes. There are 92 average to good sized, slightly sloping pitches on small terraces with 72 for touring units, all with electricity (6/10A). A number of attractive mobile homes and chalets are also available for rent. They are separated by a variety of flowering shrubs and trees offering good shade. Near the entrance is the attractive reception, bar, restaurant and terrace overlooking the swimming pools and children's play area. The emphasis here is on a quiet family holiday with little organised activity.

Facilities

Two well appointed, modern toilet blocks with washbasins in cabins. Facilities for babies and visitors with disabilities. Washing machine. Motorcaravan service point. Small shop. Bar/restaurant with takeaway. Small swimming and paddling pools (from late May). Games/TV room. Play area. Gas and electric barbecues. Occasional children's activities and family evening meals. WiFi (charged). Off site: St Jean-du-Gard 1.5 km. Fishing and bathing 1.5 km. Riding 12 km. Bicycle hire 14 km. Golf 20 km.

Open: 1 April - 30 September.

Directions

From Alès take D910A to Anduze, then D907 to St Jean-du-Gard. Take ring road (autre directions) towards Florac. Turn right at traffic lights on D98. Right onto D50 (site signed). Very shortly, on sharp right-hand bend, fork right to site. Access impossible from the north. GPS: 44.11322, 3.89052

Charges guide

Per unit incl. 2 persons	€ 14,50 - € 21,00
incl. electricity	€ 16,50 - € 24,00
extra person	€ 3,50 - € 4,50

Saint Jean-du-Gard

Camping Mas de la Cam

Route de Saint André-de-Valborgne, F-30270 Saint Jean-du-Gard (Gard) T: 04 66 85 12 02
E: camping@masdelacam.fr alanrogers.com/FR30180

Camping Mas de la Cam is a superb, high quality family run touring site; you are assured of a warm welcome here (English and Dutch spoken). It is a very pleasant and spacious site with well trimmed grass and hedges and a profusion of flowers and shrubs. Lying alongside the small Gardon river, the banks have been left free of pitches giving neat grass for sunbathing and some trees for shade, whilst children can amuse themselves in the water (no good for canoes). The 200 medium to large pitches, all for touring, are on low level terraces, with varying amounts of shade, and electricity (6/10A). In the low season bridge drives, painting courses and boules are organised. In the high season there is some family entertainment and a musical evening once a week. Nearby one can walk in the footsteps of Robert Louis Stevenson (Travels with a Donkey), ride on a steam train, explore the deep underground caverns and visit a giant bamboo forest. Entrance is via a narrow unfenced bridge, so not ideal for large outfits. Nine gîtes for rent in a beautiful old farmhouse. Only gas and electric barbecues allowed on site.

Facilities

Three high quality, very clean toilet blocks with baby bath and facilities for visitors with disabilities. Washing machines. Bar/restaurant, terrace. Small shop. Large swimming (heated) and paddling pools. Excellent play and sports areas, multisports court for football, volleyball and basketball. Boules. Fishing. WiFi. Off site: St Jean-du-Gard (3 km) with shops, Tues market. Bus twice a day. Riding 5 km. Bicycle hire 15 km. Narrow lanes, old towns and villages to explore. Steam train fron St Jean-du-Gard to Anduze. Bamboo forest.

Open: 26 April - 20 September.

Directions

Site is 3 km. northwest of St Jean-du-Gard in direction of St André-de-Valborgne on D907, site signed, fork left, descend across a narrow unfenced bridge to site. Site entrance not accessible from north. GPS: 44.11235, 3.8541

Charges guide

Per unit incl. 2 persons	€ 15,00 - € 27,00
extra person	€ 3,60 - € 6,90
child (under 7 yrs)	€ 2,70 - € 4,50
electricity (6A)	€ 3,00 - € 5,50

camping mas de la cam ★★★
F-30270 St Jean du Gard
Cévennes
www.masdelacam.fr

For latest campsite news, availability and prices visit

alanrogers.com

Sérignan-Plage

Yelloh! Village le Sérignan-Plage

Le Sérignan Plage, F-34410 Sérignan-Plage (Hérault) T: 04 67 32 35 33. E: info@leserignanplage.com

alanrogers.com/FR34070

With direct access onto a superb 600 m. sandy beach (including a naturist section) and with three swimming pools and another planned for next year, this is a must for a Mediterranean holiday. It is a friendly, family orientated site with perhaps the most comprehensive range of amenities we have come across. The enthusiastic owners, Jean-Guy and Catherine, continually surprise us with their unique style and new developments. A collection of spa pools (balnéo) built in Romanesque style with colourful terracing and columns, overlooked by a very smart restaurant, Le Villa, is the 'pièce de résistance'. The balnéo spa is shared with the adjoining naturist site (under the same ownership). Having recently acquired an adjacent site, there are now over 1,000 pitches with 350 available for touring units and this is now a pretty large campsite. The touring pitches vary in size and in terms of shade. They are mainly on sandy soil and all have electricity. There are over 300 mobile homes and chalets to let, plus some 400 privately owned units. The heart of the site developed in the local Catalonian style is some distance from reception and is a busy and informal area with shops, another good restaurant, the Au Pas d'Oc, an indoor pool and a super roof-top bar. There is a range of entertainment for all in the evenings.

Facilities

Several modern blocks of individual design with good facilities including showers with washbasin and WC. Facilities for disabled visitors. Baby bathroom. Launderette. Motorcaravan services. Supermarket, bakery and newsagent (all season). Other shops (21/4-2/10). ATM. Restaurants, bar and takeaway. Hairdresser. Balnéo spa. Gym. Heated indoor pool. Outdoor pools (21/4-2/10). Children's clubs. Evening entertainment. Sporting activities. Bicycle hire. Bus to Sérignan village July/Aug. Beach (lifeguards 1/6-15/9). Off site: Riding 2 km. Golf 10 km. Sailing and windsurfing school on beach (lifeguard in high season). Local markets.

Open: 21 April - 2 October.

Directions

From A9 exit 35 (Béziers Est) follow signs for Sérignan, D64 (9 km). Before Sérignan, turn left, Sérignan-Plage (4 km). At small sign (blue) turn right. At T-junction turn left over small road bridge and after left hand bend. Site is 100 m.
GPS: 43.26308, 3.31976

Charges 2011

Per unit incl. 2 persons and electricity	€ 15,00 - € 52,00
extra person	€ 5,00 - € 8,50
child (3-7 yrs)	free - € 8,50
dog	€ 4,00

Low season offers.

Saint Pons-de-Thomières

Camping la Borio de Roque

Route de la Salvetat, F-34220 Saint Pons-de-Thomières (Hérault) T: 04 67 97 10 97. E: info@borioderoque.com

alanrogers.com/FR34180

La Borio de Roque is a peaceful site in a very rural location hidden in a wooded valley 4 km. from Saint Pons. It lies at the end of a 1.5 km. rough track but it is well worth the effort and it is set around a lovely restored farmhouse with the outbuildings made into four very attractive gites. The 25 large, individually shaped, terraced pitches have 10A electricity and some shade. Some are private to which the owners will escort you. When the site was developed, many different varieties of trees were planted which has created a very attractive environment. Children are encouraged to help with feeding the chickens and grooming the ponies and horses. There are numerous walks and tracks for mountain bikes from the site and your Dutch hosts will be only too happy to advise on routes. Saint Pons (4 km) is an attractive small town with bars, restaurants and a museum. La Borio is especially suited to couples and young families – not a site for teenagers who like lots of entertainment.

Facilities

Toilet block, baby bath. Use of large freezer. Bread all season. Local wine, coffee and tea. Swimming pool (from 1/6). Small fishing lake. Small grassy play area. Barbecue areas. Not suitable for American motorhomes. Off site: Bicycle hire 5 km. Golf and riding 20 km. Beach 50 km.

Open: 15 May - 15 September.

Directions

St Pons-de-Thomières is on the N112 northwest of Béziers. Site is 4.5 km. north of the town on the D907 signed Salvetat, on the right on a bend, then 1.5 km. on a rough track (signed).
GPS: 43.51093, 2.74648

Charges guide

Per person	€ 3,50 - € 4,50
child (under 7 yrs)	€ 2,50 - € 3,50
pitch	€ 7,75 - € 9,00
electricity	€ 3,00
vehicle	€ 2,00 - € 2,25

No credit cards.

For latest campsite news, availability and prices visit

alanrogers.com

Imagine – hot sunshine, blue sea, vineyards, olive and eucalyptus trees, alongside a sandy beach – what a setting for a campsite – not just any campsite either! With three pool areas, one with four toboggans surrounded by sun bathing areas, an indoor pool for baby swimmers plus a magnificent landscaped, Romanesque spa-complex with half Olympic size pool and a superb range of hydromassage baths to let you unwind and re-charge after the stresses of work. And that's not all – two attractive restaurants, including the atmospheric "Villa" in its romantic Roman setting beside the spa, three bars, a mini-club and entertainment for all ages, all add up to a fantastic opportunity to enjoy a genuinely unique holiday experience.

Le Sérignan Plage

The Mediterranean
The place for your holidays

34410 Sérignan Tél : +33 (0)4 67 32 35 33 Fax : +33 (0)4 67 32 68 39
info@leserignanplage.com www.leserignanplage.com

yelloh! VILLAGE

Sérignan-Plage

Yelloh! Village Aloha

F-34410 Sérignan-Plage (Hérault) T: 04 67 39 71 30. E: info@alohacamping.com

alanrogers.com/FR34390

An impressive and well run site beside the beach at Sérignan-Plage, Aloha offers a wide range of good quality facilities all open when the site is open. There are 465 pitches with 170 mobile homes for hire in attractively landscaped settings. The 295 pitches for touring units are of a good size, regularly laid out on level, sandy grass. Easily accessed from tarmac roads, all have 10A electricity. Half are on one side of the small beach road with the swimming pools and other facilities, the other half are somewhat quieter with more grass but less shade across the road.

Facilities

Seven toilet blocks, including three large ones, offer all modern facilities and are well equipped for children. Laundry. Motorcaravan service point. Supermarket including fresh produce market. Bakery. Newsagent. Bazaar. Hairdresser. Bar, restaurant, snack bar, pizzeria and takeaway. Large heated pool and fun pools. Paddling pool. Playground. Tennis. Multisports facility. Bicycle hire. Miniclub. Activities and evening entertainment. Internet access and WiFi. ATM. Off site: Minigolf and trampolines 500 m. Riding 800 m. Boat launching 8 km. Golf 20 km.

Open: 25 April - 13 September.

Directions

From A9 exit 35 (Béziers Est) follow signs for Sérignan then Sérignan-Plage (D37, about 10 km). Once at Sérignan-Plage continue straight. Follow the sign for Aloha to right after the pink building. GPS: 43.273333, 3.348333

Charges guide

Per unit incl. 2 persons	
and electricity	€ 15,00 - € 46,00
extra person	€ 5,00 - € 8,00
child (3-7 yrs)	free - € 8,00

Sérignan-Plage

Camping le Paradis

Route de Valras, F-34410 Sérignan (Hérault) T: 04 67 32 24 03. E: paradiscamping34@aol.com

alanrogers.com/FR34560

Family owned and run, le Paradis is a little haven of tranquillity set some 3 km. back from the sea. With only 129 average sized, grassy pitches, of which 22 are taken by mobile homes to rent, it is comfortable and peaceful. Even the pool is hidden behind fencing so it does not intrude. A mix of trees and shrubs give shade and all the pitches are level with 6A electricity. There is a pleasant shaded area to one corner of the pool near the bar. Entertainment is arranged on simple lines – music evenings two nights a week in July and August with darts and tennis tournaments for children.

Facilities

Fully equipped central toilet facilities. Provision for disabled visitors and a baby bath. Laundry facilities. Small shop for essentials (15/5-30/9). Bar/restaurant (meals need to be pre-booked), takeaway (all 15/5-20/9). Reasonably sized pool. Play area. Gas and electric barbecues only. Dogs are not accepted. Off site: Supermarket 200 m. Beach 2.5 km. Fishing and boat launching 2 km. Bicycle hire 1 km. Riding 3 km. Golf 15 km.

Open: 1 April - 30 September.

Directions

From A9 exit 35 (Béziers Ouest), follow signs for Valras Plage. At second roundabout beside McDonalds and Hyper U take left turn to site on right, clearly signed. GPS: 43.26926, 3.28727

Charges guide

Per unit incl. 2 persons	
and electricity	€ 15,50 - € 31,50
extra person	€ 3,00 - € 5,00

Sète

Village Center le Castellas

RN112, F-34200 Sète (Hérault) T: 04 99 57 21 21. E: contact@village-center.com

alanrogers.com/FR34240

One would expect a campsite beside a beachside main road and a railway to be noisy, whereas once within the confines of this site it is surprisingly peaceful offering everything one could want. It is situated across the road from 14 km. of superb sandy beach, with the Etang du Thau behind, yet within a short drive of Sète, Marseillan-Plage or Agde. It is a very large site with over 800 mobile homes and chalets to rent. There are also 200 sandy and hedged pitches for touring units, most with 6A electricity and some have been purpose-built for motorcaravans. Pitches are accessed by hard roads with a variety of shade – the sorts of shrubs that will grow by the sea.

Facilities

The toilet facilities include en-suite showers and basins. Laundry. Provision for disabled visitors. Supermarket, shops and café open to the public. Bars, snack bars and restaurant. Swimming pool with lifeguards (heated April-June). Toboggans. Games room. Multisport court. Sports field. Archery. Play area, bouncy castles. Outdoor fitness area. WiFi (charged). ATM. Entertainment. Miniclub and teenage club (July/Aug). Sea fishing. Watersports. Off site: Bus for Sète (July/Aug). Riding 3 km. Golf 10 km.

Open: 3 April - 26 September.

Directions

Site is beside the RN112 which links Marseillan-Plage and Sète (nearer Marseillan-Plage). This road can get very busy indeed in main season but it is being re-routed behind the site. GPS: 43.34192, 3.58449

Charges guide

Per unit incl. 2 persons	
and electricity (6A)	€ 18,00 - € 40,00
extra person (over 5 yrs)	€ 4,00 - € 8,00
dog	€ 3,00

Sommieres

Castel Camping Domaine de Massereau

Les Hauteurs de Sommieres, route d'Aubais, F-30250 Sommieres (Gard) T: 04 66 53 11 20
E: info@massereau.fr alanrogers.com/FR30290

A member of the Castels group, de Massereau was opened in August 2006 and is set within a 50-hectare vineyard dating back to 1804. There are now 120 pitches, with 75 available for touring units. Pitch sizes range from 150-250 sq.m. but the positioning of trees on some of the pitches severely limits the useable space. The large modern sanitary block is thoughtfully designed with superb facilities for disabled visitors and children. There is an attractive pool complex and a wide range of leisure facilities for all ages. The restaurant offers a reasonable range of good value cuisine and there is a well stocked shop including the vineyard's wines. Good English is spoken.

Facilities

The modern toilet block incorporates excellent facilities for children and disabled visitors. Laundry area. Motorcaravan service point. Well stocked shop and newspapers. Restaurant. Bar. Pizzeria and outdoor grill. Takeaway. Heated swimming pool with slide. New sauna, steam bath and jacuzzi. Play area. Trampoline. Minigolf. Bicycle hire. Fitness trail. Petanque. Short tennis. TV room. Barbecue hire. Fridge hire. Gas. WiFi. Charcoal barbecues are not allowed. Off site: Fishing 3 km. Riding 3 km. Golf 30 km.

Open: 27 March - 15 November.

Directions

From the south on A9 take exit 27 and D12 towards Sommieres. Site is 5 km. on right. From the north, there is a width and weight restriction in Sommieres. To avoid this remain on the N110 and then take the N2110 into Sommieres, crossing the river and turn right onto the D12. Site is on left in 1 km. GPS: 43.76717, 4.09849

Charges guide

Per unit incl. 2 persons	€ 19,40 - € 38,40
extra person	€ 3,00 - € 9,30

Torreilles-Plage

Village Camping Spa Marisol

Boulevard de la Plage, F-66440 Torreilles-Plage (Pyrénées-Orientales) T: 04 68 28 04 07
E: marisol@camping-marisol.com alanrogers.com/FR66170

Good quality sites with direct access to the beach are hard to find and Marisol is a useful option. It is a fairly large site with 377 pitches with a significant number of mobile homes, but with 170 available for touring. These are sandy grass pitches of a good size with some shade. All have electricity. There is a beauty centre where you can enjoy a sauna, Turkish or spa bath. This is essentially a holiday site with all the popular facilities and an extensive entertainment programme, fitness courses and children's club throughout the main season. The owners have renovated the pool area and continue with improvements.

Facilities

Fully equipped toilet blocks, baby bath. Washing machine. Small supermarket. Bar. TV. Restaurant. Takeaway. Heated swimming pool, water slide, children's pool. Beauty centre. Fitness room. Play area. Tennis. Archery. Path access to sandy beach. Watersports activities. Max. 1 dog. Off site: Sea fishing, watersports on beach. Riding 500 m. Minigolf 500 m. Bicycle hire 2 km. Golf 10 km.

Open: 9 April - 24 September.

Directions

From A9 take exit 41 (Perpignan Nord) towards Le Barcarès for 9 km. Then south on D81 towards Canet for 3 km. before turning to Torreilles-Plage. Site is signed. GPS: 42.78432, 3.0329

Charges 2011

Per unit incl. 2 persons and electricity (10A)	€ 15,00 - € 54,00
extra person	€ 5,90 - € 9,90

Torreilles-Plage

Sunêlia les Tropiques

Boulevard de la plage, F-66440 Torreilles-Plage (Pyrénées-Orientales) T: 04 68 28 05 09
E: contact@campinglestropiques.com alanrogers.com/FR66190

Les Tropiques makes a pleasant holiday destination, only 400 metres from a sandy beach and also boasting two pools. It will provide families with children of all ages with an ideal seaside holiday. There are 450 pitches with 200 given over to mobile homes and chalets. Pleasant pine and palm trees with other Mediterranean vegetation give shade and provide an attractive environment. Activities are provided for all including a large range of sports, activities, caberets and shows. An identity bracelet for entry to the site is obligatory in high season (a small payment is required).

Facilities

Modern, fully equipped sanitary facilities, provision for disabled visitors. Launderette. Shop (9/4-30/9). Bar (15/4-15/9). Restaurant (15/5-15/9). Takeaway and pizzeria (1/6-15/9). Heated pool and water slides. Paddling pool. Tennis (floodlit). Multisport area. Pétanque. Archery (1/7-31/8). TV, billiards room. Play area. Disco (every evening). Miniclub (July/Aug). Bicycle hire (15/6-15/9). WiFi. Off site: Minigolf 300 m. Windsurf board hire, sea fishing 400 m. Riding 400 m. Golf 15 km.

Open: 9 April - 1 October.

Directions

From A9 exit Perpignan Nord, follow D83 towards Le Barcarès for 9 km. Take D81 south towards Canet for 3 km. turn left at roundabout for Torreilles-Plage. Site is the last but one on left. GPS: 42.7675, 3.02972

Charges guide

Per unit incl. 2 persons and electricity	€ 17,50 - € 44,00
extra person	€ 3,85 - € 8,75

Uzès

Camping du Mas de Rey

Arpaillargues, F-30700 Uzès (Gard) T: 04 66 22 18 27. E: info@campingmasderey.com

alanrogers.com/FR30110

A warm welcome from the English speaking Maire family is guaranteed at this small, attractive, 70 pitch site. Most of the 64 large (150 sq.m) touring pitches are separated by bushes, many are shaded and all have 10A electricity. A good site for couples and families with young children. Due to the wonderful climate, grass can at times be hard to find. The reception, bar, restaurant and shop are in the same large airy building. The owners are always willing to give advice on the numerous things to see and do in the area. The owners have made the site 'green' with ecologically aware measures such as solar heating.

Facilities

Two well maintained excellent, very clean toilet blocks, both quite new with solar heating, facilities for disabled visitors, baby room and en-suite family cubicles. Laundry facilities. Shop (Jul/Aug), bread to order (all season). Takeaway (1/5-30/9). Terrace restaurant with French meals (1/7-31/8). New heated swimming pool and paddling pool (1/5-15/10, closed lunchtimes). Gas and electric barbecues only. New chalets. Off site: Golf 4 km. River bathing 12 km. Canoeing 10 km.

Open: 10 April - 15 October.

Directions

Leave A9 Autoroute, junction 23, signed Pont du Gard. Take N86 then D981 to Uzès (approx 18 km). Take D982 west, signed Arpaillargues, Moussac. Site signed on left, 3 km. GPS: 43.99843, 4.38424

Charges guide

Per unit incl. 2 persons	€ 16,80 - € 21,00
extra person	€ 5,60 - € 7,00
electricity (10A)	€ 3,20 - € 4,00

Credit cards accepted in July/August only.

Valras-Plage

Camping Blue Bayou

Vendres Plage Ouest, F-34350 Valras-Plage (Hérault) T: 04 67 37 41 97. E: infobluebayou@orange.fr

alanrogers.com/FR34370

A pleasant site, Blue Bayou is situated at the far end of Vendres Plage near Le Grau Vendres (the port of Vendres). It is therefore in a much quieter location than many other sites, away from the more hectic, built-up areas of Vendres and Valras-Plage. The beach is 300 m. across sand dunes and there are open views from the site creating a feeling of spaciousness. There are 256 pitches, all with 10A electricity, with 74 privately owned mobile homes and 92 to let, including some chalets. The touring pitches are large, some with their own sanitary arrangements. Light shade is provided by a mixture of trees. The restaurant and bar area is very attractive, overlooking two swimming pools, one with a toboggan, joined by a bridge where lifeguards station themselves. The owners and their family are very proud of their site and you are made to feel very welcome. The site would make a good choice for couples and families, perhaps best visited outside the height of the season when it becomes very busy. In July and August a tourist train runs to link Valras and Vendres.

Facilities

Individual toilet units for about half the touring pitches. Two separate blocks are fully equipped and are to be renovated. Baby bath and facilities for children. Facilities for disabled visitors. Laundry. Bar, restaurant and takeaway (open on demand in early season). Swimming pool (heated all season). Multisport court. Play area. Miniclub and entertainment in high season. WiFi throughout (charged). Off site: Fishing, boat launching and riding 1 km. Bicycle hire 3 km. Golf 25 km.

Open: 2 April - 24 September.

Directions

From A9 exit 36 (Béziers Ouest) follow directions for Valras-Plage and Vendres Plage over four roundabouts. At fifth roundabout (Port Conchylicole) follow sign for Vendres Plage Ouest and site is 500 m. on the left past the Ranch and tourist office. The entrance is quite tight. GPS: 43.227408, 3.243536

Charges guide

Per unit incl. 2 persons and electricity	€ 21,00 - € 39,00
incl. private sanitary facility	€ 25,00 - € 51,00
extra person	€ 5,00 - € 9,00

Valras-Plage

Camping Caravaning Domaine de la Yole

B.P. 23, F-34350 Valras-Plage (Hérault) T: 04 67 37 33 87. E: info@campinglayole.com
alanrogers.com/FR34090

A busy happy holiday village with over 1,100 pitches could seem a little daunting. There are 590 pitches for touring with the remainder occupied by a range of mobile homes available to rent. Pitches are of a good size, all are level, hedged and have electricity (5A), water and waste water points and, very importantly for this area, they all have shade. The extensive pool area is impressive, more like an aqua park with its six pools and water slides. The central shopping and entertainment area form the heart of the site and provide everything you need. The beach, a long stretch of beautiful sand, is 500 m. and there is trampolining, paragliding and jet-skis to enjoy.

Facilities

Well maintained toilet blocks include baby rooms. Facilities for families and disabled visitors. Laundry facilities. Motorcaravan service points. Shops. Good restaurant, terrace, amphitheatre for entertainment (in season). Large pool complex with six pools and water slides (all season). Tennis. Multisport court. Play areas. High wire adventure park. Bicycle hire. Miniclub. Youthclub. Boules. Internet access and WiFi. Site-owned farm, vineyard and winery. Off site: Fishing or riding 2 km. Beach 500 m.

Open: 25 April - 19 September.

Directions

From A9 autoroute take Béziers Ouest exit for Valras-Plage (13-14 km) and follow Casino signs. Site is on left, just after sign for Vendres-Plage. GPS: 43.23708, 3.26234

Charges guide

Per unit incl. 2 persons	
and all services	€ 20,00 - € 57,40
extra person	€ 5,90 - € 8,50
child (3-16 yrs)	free - € 5,50

Vauvert

Flower Camping Mas de Mourgues

Gallician, F-30600 Vauvert (Gard) T: 04 66 73 30 88. E: info@masdemourgues.com
alanrogers.com/FR30040

John and Lynn Foster are proud of their campsite on the edge of the Petite Camargue region, a unique area of France. It can be hot here, the Mistral can blow and you may have some road noise, but having said all that, the present owners, who moved from England over ten years ago and live in the old Mas, have created quite a rural idyll and fit in well with the local community. There are 71 pitches with 46 for touring units (10A electricity), nine mobile homes to rent and four apartments. Originally a vineyard on stony ground (strong pegs needed), some of the vines are now used to mark the pitches.

Facilities

Two small toilet blocks provide for all needs. Facilities for disabled visitors. Washing machine. Motorcaravan service point. Chips and panini to takeaway (high season). Reception keeps essentials. Bread to order (evening before). Play area. Games for children (July/Aug). Internet access and WiFi (charged). Communal barbecue, but gas or electric ones are allowed. Apartments, mobile homes and tents to rent. Off site: Fishing 2 km. Riding 8 km. Bicycle hire 1 km. Golf 20 km. Boat launching 25 km. Beach 26 km. Nîmes and Arles within 30 minutes drive.

Open: 1 April - 30 September.

Directions

Leave A9 autoroute at exit 26 (Gallargues) and follow signs for Vauvert. At Vauvert take N572 towards Arles and St Gilles. Site is on left after 4 km. at crossroads for Gallician. GPS: 43.6575, 4.2943

Charges guide

Per unit incl. 2 persons	
and electricity	€ 13,50 - € 20,40
extra person	€ 3,00 - € 4,40
child (2-10 yrs)	€ 1,50 - € 2,20
dog	€ 1,90 - € 2,50

Vendres Plage

Campéole les Mûriers

Campéole

37E route départemental, F-34350 Vendres Plage (Hérault) T: 04 67 32 67 22. E: muriers@campeole.com
alanrogers.com/FR34620

Les Mûriers is a member of the Campéole group and is located among a group of sites situated on the route to le Grau de Vendres, the port of Vendre at the mouth of the River Aude. A marina has been developed there recently and there is also access to a sandy beach. You need to look carefully for the Campéole reception as there is a large reception for a separate mobile home site under the same name. There are 105 bungalow tents available to rent, quite distinctive and fully equipped. They are arranged in a circular layout on grass pitches with hedging served by two toilet blocks.

Facilities

Two fully equipped toilet blocks. Washing machine. Bar/restaurant (28/6-30/8), takeaway, shop, heated swimming pool (all 15/6-15/9). Entertainment and miniclub for 5-12 yrs (28/6-28/8). Play area. Volleyball/basketball court. WiFi. No barbecues allowed. Off site: Beach 800 m. Sailing 800 m. Fishing 1 km. Boat launching 1 km. Morning market in peak season in Vendres Plage.

Open: 12 June - 11 September.

Directions

From A9 take exit 36 (Béziers Ouest), towards Valras Plage and Vendres Plage. Continue over four roundabouts. At 5th roundabout (Port Conchylicole) follow signs for Vendres Plage Ouest. Continue for 800 m. and site is on right signed Les Mûriers. GPS: 43.223433, 3.23945

Charges 2011

Contact the site for details.

Verdun-en-Lauragais

Yelloh! Village le Bout du Monde

Ferme de Rhodes, Verdun-en-Lauragais, F-11400 Castelnaudary (Aude) T: 04 68 94 95 96
E: info@yellohvillage-leboutdumonde.com alanrogers.com/FR11230

Le Bout du Monde is a really special place at the heart of the Montagne Noire, on the edge of the Haut Languedoc regional park. Here you can experience life as it used to be. Children help with the animals on the farm, roam the woods, swim in the natural pool, learn to make bread and pottery. Grown ups have a chance to unwind in wonderful natural surroundings. This small site is a member of the Yelloh! Village group and at present there are 26 large grass pitches with water and 8A electricity, most hedged.

Facilities

Two fully equipped toilet bocks. Washing machine. Small shop, wine bar for simple food. Auberge (specialising in local cuisine, open all year). Takeaway food. Swimming pool and natural swimming pool. Entertainment and activity programme. Archery. Sports field. Fishing lake. Children's farm. Electric barbecues only. WiFi. Mobile homes for rent. Off site: Riding 7 km. GR7 long distance footpath. Haut Languedoc Regional Park. Sailing. Canoeing. Accrobranche aerial assault course.

Open: 30 April - 11 September.

Directions

From the A61 take Castelnaudary exit and proceed to Castelnaudary. Here, take the D103 towards Saissac. After passing through St Papoul, turn left to join the D803 to Verdun-en-Lauragais. Join the northbound D903 (narrow uphill road) and site is well signed with distinctive goat logo.
GPS: 43.37671, 2.07463

Charges guide

Per unit incl. 2 persons	€ 15,00 - € 30,00
extra person	€ 4,00 - € 5,00

Vernet-les-Bains

Hotel de Plein Air l'Eau Vive

Chemin de Saint-Saturnin, F-66820 Vernet-les-Bains (Pyrénées-Orientales) T: 04 68 05 54 14
E: contact@leauvive-camping.com alanrogers.com/FR66130

Enjoying dramatic views of the Pic du Canigou (3,000 m), this small site is 1.5 km. from the centre of Vernet-les-Bains in the Pyrénées. It is approached via a twisting road through a residential area. The 70 tourist pitches, with electricity (4/10A) and 45 fully serviced, are on a slight slope, part hedged and some terraced, with a separate tent field. Most pitches have some shade. Although there is no swimming pool, the site has a very attractive, natural pool with water pumped from the nearby stream, with a small beach. There is a central floating safety line across the pool but parents should keep an eye on children around the pool as there is no supervision or safety fence.

Facilities

First class toilet facilities and provision for disabled visitors. Washing machine. Bread, main season. Bar/reception, pool table, library. Snack bar, takeaway (15/6-31/8). A 'meal of the day' can be ordered. Play area. Natural pool for children. Sports field. WiFi (free) on the terrace. Off site: Fishing 200 m. Swimming pool, thermal centre in village 1 km. Organised rafting, canoeing, hydrospeed trips. Bicycle hire 2 km.

Open: 16 December - 25 October.

Directions

Following N116 towards Andorra. At Ville Franche, turn south, D116, for Vernet-les-Bains. After 5 km. keep right avoiding town. Turn right over bridge towards Sahorre. Immediately turn right (ave de Saturnin) for about 1 km. beyond houses, site signed. GPS: 42.55506, 2.37779

Charges guide

Per unit incl. 2 persons and electricity	€ 15,00 - € 22,00
extra person (over 4 yrs)	€ 2,50 - € 3,50
car on pitch	€ 3,00

Vers-Pont-du-Gard

Camping des Gorges du Gardon

762 Chemin de la Barque Vieille, F-30210 Vers-Pont-du-Gard (Gard) T: 04 66 22 81 81
E: gorges-gardon@franceloc.fr alanrogers.com/FR30190

Probably the main attraction in the Gardon area of France is the Pont-du-Gard, an amazing Roman aqueduct built around 50AD. The site, run by France Loc, has 180 level, mostly good-sized pitches, 119 for touring (electricity 6A). Many are on stony terraces in a woodland setting offering good to heavy shade. Others are more open with some having good views across the river. Rock pegs are essential. There is direct access to the river where swimming is permitted, although in summer the water level may be a little low. Attractive, heated swimming and paddling pools and separate toboggan.

Facilities

Two toilet blocks with facilities for disabled visitors. Baby room. Laundry facilities. Bar (all season), good restaurant and takeaway (27/3-19/9). Heated swimming, paddling pools (27/3-19/9). Play areas. Games room and TV. Organised entertainment during Jul/Aug. Canoeing arranged. Fishing. Bicycle hire (high season). Electric barbecues only. WiFi on terrace. Off site: Riding 1 km. Golf 6km. Many old towns and villages with markets.

Open: 27 March - 19 September.

Directions

Leave A9 Autoroute, exit 23, Remoulins, take D981 towards Uzès. Approx 4 km. beyond Remoulins, just after the junction for the Pont-du-Gard, turn left, site signed. Site in 600 m. GPS: 43.95744, 4.51503

Charges guide

Per unit incl. 2 persons	€ 16,00 - € 28,00
extra person	€ 4,70 - € 7,00
electricity (6A)	€ 6,00

Vias

Yelloh! Village le Club Farret

F-34450 Vias-Plage (Hérault) T: 04 67 21 64 45. E: info@yellohvillage-club-farret.com

alanrogers.com/FR34110

Well maintained and with welcoming, helpful staff, everywhere is neat and tidy. It is a large, busy site but the atmosphere is very relaxed. There are 710 good sized, level, grassy pitches, with 340 for touring with 6A electricity. And there is some shade from many trees. The large heated pool has lots of sunbathing room with a new terrace. The safe beach is alongside the site so some pitches have sea views. There is a wide range of entertainment and the activities include an extensive art programme. The restaurant is high above the pool with views of the sea, everything is open all season. This superb site of excellent quality has been developed by the Giner family with love and care over the last 50 years. Activities include pottery, silk painting, mosaics and water colours. A new spa and wellness centre opened for the 2010 season. The mobile home areas are very smart and have been attractively landscaped, with African and Balinese themes. A new area for mobile homes is vehicle free.

Facilities

Very clean toilet blocks, children's toilets, baby rooms, facilities for disabled visitors. Washing machines. Dog shower. Well stocked supermarket. Hairdresser. Bars with pizzas, snacks, takeaway. Restaurant. Heated swimming pool complex (now enlarged to 1,000 sq.m) with lifeguard all season. New spa and wellness centre with sauna, jacuzzi etc. Excellent play area. Miniclub (5-12 yrs). Teenagers' club (13-17 yrs). Tennis. Archery. Programme of games. Multisports court. Bicycle hire. Off site: Riding 1 km. Golf 10 km. Sailing and windsurfing on beach.

Open: 14 April - 8 October.

Directions

Site is south of Vias at Vias-Plage. From N112 (Béziers - Agde) take D137 signed Vias-Plage. Site is signed on the left. GPS: 43.29103, 3.41912

Charges guide

Per unit incl. 2 persons	
and electricity	€ 19,00 - € 47,00
extra person	€ 6,00 - € 8,00
extra tent	€ 3,00
pet	€ 4,00

For latest campsite news, availability and prices visit

alanrogers.com

Vias

Camping le Méditerranée Plage

Côte Ouest, F-34450 Vias (Hérault) T: 04 67 90 99 07. E: contact@mediterranee-plage.com

alanrogers.com/FR34410

Set beside the beach in a quiet part of the coast, this site is somewhat different from the majority of beach sites. It has a most impressive entertainment complex situated to one side of the site with very comfortable outdoor seating facing a large stage for entertainment and a very smart bar and restaurant. The colourful furnishings and modern design reflect its Mediterranean setting. The site is very well cared for, with 410 pitches (some 185 used for touring units). Either grassy with a degree of shade or, as you get nearer the beach, more sandy with less shade, all have 6A electricity.

Facilities

Two large toilet blocks are modern, one very impressive with a special smart nursery unit. Two small ones are more traditional. Facilities for disabled visitors. Laundry. Motorcaravan service point. Smart restaurant and bar. Supermarket. Snack bar. Hairdressers. TV room. Play area. Games room. Tennis. Archery. Windsurfing possible from beach. Activity programme, children's entertainment, circus school, evening shows and dancing. Internet access. Off site: Riding 2 km. Canal du Midi nearby.

Open: 22 March - 20 September.

Directions

From A9 exit 35 (Béziers Est) follow directions for Agde and Sète on N112. After 4.2 km. turn for Portiragnes. Pass village and continue for 2.5 km. over Canal du Midi then turn left and follow site signs. GPS: 43.28202, 3.37105

Charges guide

Per unit incl. 2 persons and electricity	€ 16,50 - € 36,40
extra person	€ 3,00 - € 6,20

Vias

Sunêlia Domaine de la Dragonnière

RD612, F-34450 Vias-sur-Mer (Hérault) T: 04 67 01 03 10. E: contact@dragonniere.com

alanrogers.com/FR34450

La Dragonnière is a busy family site, located between the popular resorts of Vias and Portiragnes. There are no fewer than nine swimming pools here and a lively entertainment programme in high season. Many of the pitches are occupied by mobile homes and chalets but there are 70 reasonably sized touring pitches, all offering some shade. The pitches all have electrical connections (6A) as well as water and drainage. La Dragonnière lies 5 km. from the nearest beach and a free shuttle operates in peak season. This is an ideal site for families with teenagers searching for a wide range of activities.

Facilities

Well maintained toilet blocks include facilities for babies and disabled visitors. Laundry. Supermarket. Two swimming pool complexes with children's pools. Bar and restaurant complex (9/4-18/9), takeaway (18/6-11/9). Play area. Sauna and gym (9/4-18/9). Multisport pitch. Sports competitions, children's club and evening entertainment in high season. Animation program in the low season. Mobile homes and chalets for rent. Gas barbecues only. Bicycle hire. Off site: Beach and boat launching 5 km. Fishing 4 km. Golf 12 km.

Open: 9 April - 18 September.

Directions

Take the Béziers Est exit from the A9 autoroute. Follow directions to Villeneuve, Serignan and Valras-Plage. After 800 m. at the large roundabout, follow signs to Vias aéroport on the N112. After a further 7 km. the campsite can be found on the right. GPS: 43.313, 3.36517

Charges guide

Per unit incl. 3 persons, water, waste water and electricity	€ 20,00 - € 51,00
extra person	€ 7,00 - € 9,00
Camping Cheques accepted.	

Vias

Camping les Salisses

Route de la Mer, F-34450 Vias-Plage (Hérault) T: 04 67 21 64 07. E: info@salisses.com

alanrogers.com/FR34520

A traditional style French campsite, les Salisses is well run and managed with an impressive range of swimming pools and other facilities. The 400 plus level pitches of average size are separated by flowering shrubs and trees that provide shade – all rather pretty. There are just over 100 places for touring units with 8A electricity, the rest being taken by a range of mobile homes, some to let. Vias-Plage is a busy, somewhat hectic resort and les Salisses has its own section of beach with a bar. However, the site's own pools are also very welcoming, the indoor one reserved for naturists in the high season.

Facilities

Four fully equipped toilet blocks. Facilities for disabled visitors. Laundry. Shop. Bar and restaurant. Takeaway pizzeria (1/7-31/8). One indoor pool heated for low season, used for naturists in high season. Two other pool complexes, one for swimming plus a long slide and one with cascades and islands. Play area. Sports field. Multisport court. Tennis. Minigolf. Bicycle hire. Watersports at beach (800 m). Entertainment and activities. Off site: Riding 1 km. Golf 5 km. Bus stop for Vias town.

Open: 5 April - 13 September.

Directions

From the A9 take exit 34, then the N312 towards Vias and Agde. Join the N112 to avoid Vias town to pick up sign for Vias-Plage. Site is first on the right. GPS: 43.29657, 3.4164

Charges guide

Per unit incl. 2 persons and electricity	€ 24,00 - € 36,00
extra person	€ 6,50 - € 8,50
Camping Cheques accepted.	

Vias

Camping International le Napoléon

1171 ave. de la Méditérranée, F-34450 Vias-Plage (Hérault) T: 04 67 01 07 80
E: reception@camping-napoleon.fr alanrogers.com/FR34030

Le Napoléon is a smaller, family run site situated in the village of Vias-Plage bordering the Mediterranean. The Graziani family celebrated their 40th anniversary at Napoléon in 2009. Vias-Plage is hectic to say the least in season, but once through the security barrier and entrance to le Napoléon, the contrast is marked – tranquillity, yet still only 150 m. from the beach and other attractions. It has a Californian style pool, amphitheatre for entertainment and other new facilities, but thoughtful planning and design ensure that the camping area is quiet. With good shade from many tall trees, there are 239 fairly small, hedged and level pitches, 92 for touring units, all with 10A electricity. They are mixed in with a range of mobile homes for rent.

Facilities

Fully equipped sanitary blocks are of a reasonable standard. Baby bath. Facilities for disabled visitors. Laundry. Motorcaravan services. Fridge hire. Supermarket and bakery. Bar. Restaurant/pizzeria. Swimming pool complex with lively piped music (heated in early and late season) includes a jacuzzi, hammam and solarium. Gym/fitness room with new equipment. Bicycle hire. Tennis, archery, boules. TV. Children's club. Amphitheatre, wide range of free entertainment until midnight. Disco outside site (Easter-Sept). Internet access and WiFi (charged). Off site: Beach 150 m. Shops, restaurants, and laundry immediately adjacent. Bus service in Vias village. Fishing 500 m. Riding 800 m. Golf 6 km.

Open: 8 April - 30 September.

Directions

From autoroute A9 take exit Agde-Pezenas, direction Béziers. Continue for 5 km. direction Vias-Vias -Plage. Site is on the right near the beach; watch carefully for turning between restaurant and shops. GPS: 43.29197, 3.41535

Charges 2011

Per unit incl. 2 persons and electricity	€ 20,00 - € 45,00
extra person (over 4 yrs)	€ 6,00 - € 9,00
dog	€ 4,00

Villegly-en-Minervois

Camping le Moulin de Sainte Anne

Chemin de Sainte Anne, F-11600 Villegly-en-Minervois (Aude) T: 04 68 72 20 80
E: campingstanne@wanadoo.fr alanrogers.com/FR11210

Just a few years ago le Moulin Sainte Anne was a vineyard but, with much hard work by Antoine and Magali Laclive and the backing of the Mairie, there is now a flourishing campsite on the edge of the town. There are 45 level grass pitches of a good size and hedged. All have water and electricity and are terraced where necessary and landscaped with growing trees and shrubs. The facilities are modern, well kept and in keeping with the area. They include a heated pool and a very attractive entertainment area. There is close co-operation with the village and villagers are welcome to the evening entertainment. A Sites et Paysages member.

Facilities

A modern toilet block is very well equipped. Shared facilities for disabled visitors and babies. Washing machine. Motorcaravan service point. Bar, snack bar with takeaway (15/6-25/8). Heated swimming and paddling pools (1/5-30/9). Games room. Play area. Communal barbecue (no barbecues on pitches). Chalets to rent (15). Off site: Fishing (licence from garage). Shops. Carcassonne 12 km. Golf 18 km. Bicycle hire 12 km.

Open: 1 March - 15 November.

Directions

Driving north from Carcassonne on D118 turn on D620 signed Villalier and Villegly for 7 km. Site is at entrance to village. Turn right over bridge just before the cemetery. GPS: 43.28308, 2.44152

Charges guide

Per person	€ 3,00 - € 4,40
child (under 13 yrs)	€ 1,90 - € 3,20
pitch incl. electricity	€ 6,20 - € 7,80
dog	€ 1,50 - € 2,00

Villeneuve-lez-Avignon

Campéole Ile des Papes

Barrage de Villeneuve, F-30400 Villeneuve-lez-Avignon (Gard) T: 04 90 15 15 90
E: ile-des-papes@campeole.com alanrogers.com/FR30120

Camping Ile des Papes is a large, open and very well equipped site. Avignon and its Palace and museums are 8 km. away. The site has an extensive swimming pool area and a fishing lake with beautiful mature gardens. The railway is quite near but noise is not too intrusive. The 450 pitches, 246 for touring (all with 6A electricity), are of a good size on level grass, but with little shade. Games and competitions for all ages are organised in high season. This site is very popular with groups and is especially busy at weekends and in high season. In July and August a minibus is available for transport to Avignon, the airport and the railway station; the local bus can also take you directly to Avignon. A good base to explore the famous Routes des Vins and the old villages and ancient towns of the Provençal region. There are many walks and cycle routes close by.

Facilities

Good quality toilet blocks (may be stretched when busy) include baby rooms and facilities for visitors with disabilities. Washing machines. Motorcaravan services. Well stocked shop. Bar and restaurant (1/4-20/10 limited hours in low season). Large swimming pool complex and pool for children, all unheated, (15/4-31/10). Play area. Lake for fishing. Archery, tennis, minigolf and basketball (all free). Bicycle hire. Only gas and electric barbecues allowed. Off site: Riding 3 km. Golf 6 km. Boat launching 5 km. Parachuting, paintball, jetski. Villeneuve-lez-Avignon with shops, bars, restaurants. Avignon 6 km.

Open: 25 March - 20 October.

Directions

Leave the A9 at exit 22 (Roquemaure) and take D976 to Roquemaure, turn south D980 towards Villeneuve. Near railway bridge turn hard left, D780 (site signed). Cross river, immediately turn right to site. GPS: 43.97660, 4.79440

Charges guide

Per unit incl. 2 persons and electricity	€ 19,10 - € 29,00
extra person	€ 4,50 - € 4,90
child (under 7 years)	free - € 3,90
dog	€ 2,00 - € 2,90

LANGUEDOC-ROUSSILLON

Campéole
CAMPSITES AND RENTALS
Île des Papes ★★★★
Four star site close to Avignon, famous for it's architectural highlights and theatre festival. 2 swimming pools, touring pitches and quality accommodations for rent.

30400 Villeneuve-lez-Avignon - Tel.: +33-490-1515-90 - www.campeole.co.uk / ile-des-papes@campeole.com

Villeneuve-les-Béziers

Camping les Berges du Canal

Promenade les Vernets, F-34420 Villeneuve-les-Béziers (Hérault) T: 04 67 39 36 09
E: contact@lesbergesducanal.com alanrogers.com/FR34210

There are surprisingly few campsites which provide an opportunity to enjoy the rather special ambience for which the Canal du Midi is renowned, but this pleasant little site is right alongside the canal at Villeneuve-les-Béziers. The campsite is in a peaceful and shady situation, separated from the canal by an unmade access road with a total of 75 level pitches on sandy grass. Some are large with 10A electricity, others are smaller and more suitable for tents. Of these, 20 are occupied by privately owned mobile homes and a further 25 are available to rent. There is a pleasant pool complex, one of the two pools being fitted with a jacuzzi-style facility.

Facilities

Fully equipped toilet block with some washbasins in cabins. Facilities for disabled visitors (with key) and children. Beauty therapist visits weekly. Laundry facilities. Motorcaravan service point. Bar/snack bar (serving breakfast too). Small restaurant attached to site. Two swimming pools. Multisport court. Play area. Fishing. Evening entertainment during high season. Off site: Attractive old village centre of Villeneuve-les-Béziers. Beach at Portiragnes-Plage. Bicycle hire 100 m. Riding 5 km. Canal du Midi. Beach 7 km.

Open: 15 April - 15 September.

Directions

From A9 exit 35, follow signs for Agde, at first roundabout take N112 (Béziers). First left onto D37 signed Villeneve-les-Béziers and Valras-Plage. Pass traffic lights, left at roundabout and follow site signs (take care at junction beside bridge). GPS: 43.31673, 3.28433

Charges guide

Per unit incl. 2 persons and electricity	€ 17,00 - € 24,00
extra person	€ 3,00 - € 5,00

This is a corner of France that evokes dreamy images of lazy afternoons amongst sleepy village squares, sunny vineyards and beautiful lavender fields basking under the dazzling blue of the sky.

DÉPARTEMENTS: 04 ALPES-DE-HAUTE-PROVENCE, 05 HAUTES-ALPES, 13 BOUCHES-DU-RHÔNE, 83 VAR, 84 VAUCLUSE

MAJOR CITY: MARSEILLES

Provence is a region of magical light, bleached landscapes, olive groves, herb-scented garrigue, vineyards and Roman and medieval antiquities. The river valleys provide natural routes through the mountain barrier. Roman monuments can be seen at Orange, and Vaison-la-Romaine, where a 2,000-year-old bridge is still in use. Avignon was the site of the papal court and the Palais des Papes at Avignon is a spectacular construction.

The Hautes-Alpes will reward with stunning vistas, peace and quiet. Briançon is the highest town in Europe and many of the high passes are not for the faint-hearted. The Vaucluse, where in the late spring the southern slopes of the Montagne du Luberon are a mass of colour with wild flowers. The extinct volcanic cone of Mont Ventoux provides dramatic views. The scents, colours and an amazing intensity of light have encouraged artists and writers to settle amidst the sleepy villages, with narrow streets and ancient dwellings topped with sun-baked terracotta tiles, where the air is fragrant with the perfume of wild herbs and lavender.

Places of interest

Avignon: ramparts, old city, Papal Palace, old palace, Calvet museum.

Mont Ventoux: near Carpentras, one of the best known stages of the classic Tour de France annual cycle race.

Orange: Roman city, gateway to the Midi, Colline St Europe.

St Vaison la Romaine: Roman city, the French Pompei.

Cuisine of the region

Influenced by the Savoie area to the north and the Côte d'Azur to the south, with emphasis on herbs and garlic, and fish. The wine region is mainly known for its dry, fruity rosé wines: Bandol, Bellet, Palette, Cassis. Red wines include Côtes du Rhône and Châteauneuf-du-Pape.

Aigo Bouido: garlic and sage soup with bread (or eggs and cheese).

Aïoli (ailloli): a mayonnaise sauce with garlic and olive oil.

Bouillabaisse: fish soup served with rouille sauce, saffron and aioli.

Bourride: a creamy fish soup (usually made with large white fish), thickened with aïoli and flavoured with crawfish.

Pissaladière: Provençal bread dough with onions, anchovies, olives.

Pollo pépitora: Provençal chicken fricassee thickened with lemon-flavoured mayonnaise.

Ratatouille: aubergines, courgettes, onions, garlic, red peppers and tomatoes in olive oil.

www.discover-southoffrance.com
information@cft-paca.fr
(0)4 91 56 47 00

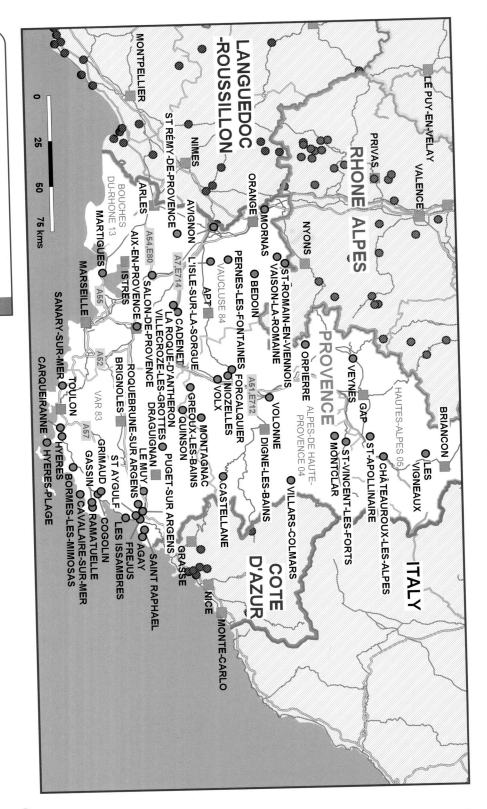

For latest campsite news, availability and prices visit

alanrogers.com

Agay-St Raphaël

Campéole du Dramont

Campéole

986 bld 36ème Division Texas, F-83530 Agay-St Raphaël (Var) T: 04 94 82 07 68. E: dramont@campeole.com
alanrogers.com/FR83700

Le Dramont stretches over a shady hillside, sloping gently down to a pebble beach (direct access), close to the attractive resort of Agay. This site is popular with scuba divers, and is an ideal base for exploring the turquoise waters. There is an international diving school on site and other amenities here include a beauty salon (July and August) and a sports field. Le Dramont has 212 pitches, of which over 180 are occupied by mobile homes, chalets and fully equipped tents, for rent. Pitches are well shaded and generally of a good size.

Facilities

Snack bar. Shop. Beauty salon. Takeaway food. Games room. Playground. Diving school. Boat launching (charged). Sports field. Activity and entertainment programme. Tourist information. Direct beach access. Mobile homes, chalets and tents for rent. Off site: Fishing. Golf. Rock climbing. Walking and mountain biking in the Esterel hills. St Raphaël and Fréjus.

Open: 15 March - 11 October.

Directions

From Saint Raphaël, take the RN98 towards Cannes. The site is 7 km beyond Saint Raphaël (between Boulouris and Agay).
GPS: 43.417864, 6.848195

Charges 2011

Contact site for details.

Aix-en-Provence

Camping Chantecler

41 avenue du Val Saint André, F-13100 Aix-en-Provence (Bouches du Rhône) T: 04 42 26 12 98
E: info@campingchantecler.com alanrogers.com/FR13120

Cézanne is amongst Aix's most famous former residents, but many just see the town as a stop on the journey south. This good, quiet campsite might change that image; on the southeast edge of the town, close to the motorway it is only minutes by the good bus service from the city centre. The site provides 240 pitches (160 for tourers) in mature woodland with good facilities. Under the new leadership of Serge Carcolse, the site is destined to change for the good whilst retaining the best that already exists. Cézanne's studio is amongst the numerous places to visit in Aix. The town has something to offer everyone, from modern pedestrian shopping to numerous museums and cultural sites and endless restaurants and bars. The Office du Tourisme also arranges a variety of excursions on a weekly basis to the surrounding area, ranging from bird sanctuaries in the Camargue to Marseille and the Luberon.

Facilities

Four sanitary blocks provide ample WCs, washbasins and hot showers around the site. Facilities for disabled campers. Motorcaravan service point. Bar and restaurant (1/5-15/9). Swimming pool (1/5-15/9). Tennis. Boules. Internet access and WiFi. Barbecues are not permitted. Twin axle units are not accepted. Mobile homes to rent. Off site: Bus service 200 m. Aix-en-Provence 2 km. Riding 2 km. Golf 5 km.

Open: All year.

Directions

Leave the A8 at exit 31 (Aix-Sud) and at roundabout turn right. At second set of lights turn left and within 300 m. at roundabout turn right to the site in 200 m.
GPS: 43.51636, 5.47495

Charges guide

Per unit incl. 2 persons and electricity	€ 22,90 - € 24,20
extra person	€ 6,10 - € 6,50
child (under 7 yrs)	€ 3,60 - € 3,70
dog	€ 3,40 - € 3,50

For latest campsite news, availability and prices visit
alanrogers.com

Agay

Camping Caravaning Esterel

Avenue des Golf, Agay, F-83530 Saint Raphaël (Var) T: 04 94 82 03 28. E: contact@esterel-caravaning.fr

alanrogers.com/FR83020

Esterel is a quality, award-winning caravan site east of St Raphaël, set among the hills at the back of Agay. The site is 3.5 km. from the sandy beach at Agay where parking is perhaps a little easier than at most places on this coast. It has 230 pitches for tourers, for caravans but not tents, all have electricity and water tap, 18 special ones have their own en-suite washroom adjoining. Pitches are on shallow terraces, attractively landscaped with good shade and a variety of flowers, giving a feeling of spaciousness. Some 'maxi-pitches' from 110 to 160 sq.m. are available; all pitches have 10A electricity. Developed by the Laroche family for over 30 years, the site has an attractive, quiet situation with good views of the Esterel mountains. This is a very good site, well run and organised in a popular area. A pleasant courtyard area contains the shop and bar, with a terrace overlooking the attractively landscaped (floodlit at night) pool complex. Great efforts have been made over the last year to improve the site's 'green credentials' and they are looking at all possible ways to do so.

Facilities

Excellent refurbished, heated toilet blocks. Individual toilet units on 18 pitches. Facilities for disabled visistors. Laundry room. Motorcaravan services. Shop. Gift shop. Takeaway. Bar/restaurant. Five circular swimming pools (two heated), one for adults, one for children (covered and heated), three arranged as a waterfall (all season). Spa with sauna etc. Disco. Archery. Minigolf. Tennis. Pony rides. Pétanque. Squash. Playground. Nursery. Bicycle hire. Internet access. Organised events in season. No barbecues. Off site: Golf nearby. Trekking by foot, bicycle or by pony in L'Esterel forest park. Fishing, beach 3 km.

Open: 27 March - 2 October.

Directions

From A8, exit Fréjus, follow signs for Valescure, then for Agay, site on left. The road from Agay is the easiest to follow but it is possible to approach from St Raphaël via Valescure. Look carefully for site sign, which is difficult to see. GPS: 43.453775, 6.832817

Charges guide

Per unit incl. 2 persons and electricity	€ 18,00 - € 83,00
extra person	€ 9,00
child (1-7 yrs)	€ 7,00
dog	€ 2,00

Avignon

Camping du Pont d'Avignon

10 chemin de la Barthelasse, Ile de la Barthelasse, F-84000 Avignon (Vaucluse) T: 04 90 80 63 50

E: info@camping-avignon.com alanrogers.com/FR84090

This is a city site, yet it is in a quiet location and only a short walk or free ferry ride from the town. The well shaded and neat layout of the pitches and the very good access will ensure a pleasant stay. There are 300 level pitches, some on grass and some with hardstanding, 120 with 10A electricity. A good play area, tennis courts and volleyball pitch are in the centre of the site separating the tent pitches on one side and the electric pitches on the other. Many pitches are separated by hedges. The restaurant, bar and terrace overlook the attractive pool. With its island situation, a few pitches have views of the Pope's Palace, which is floodlit at night. The site, although close to the historic centre of Avignon, has a very rural feel, due no doubt to the many flowering trees and shrubs and the fact it is on an island. English is spoken at reception.

Facilities

Well maintained and clean toilet blocks, facilities for disabled visitors. Washing machines, dryer. Motorcaravan services. Well stocked shop (4/4-3/10). Bar/restaurant, takeaway (4/4-20/9). Swimming pool, paddling pool (2/5-20/9). Play area with climbing frame. Tennis (free). Bicycle hire (July/Aug). Internet access and WiFi (charged). Off site: Avignon with famous bridge and Pope's Palace. Ferry to town centre. Bicycle hire 2 km. Riding 3 km. Golf 10 km.

Open: 16 March - 1 November.

Directions

Site is on an island in River Rhône. Well signed from roads into Avignon, ring road has complex junctions. Accessed from Pont Daladier towards Villeneuve les Avignon. Just after crossing first section of river fork right, site signed, site about 1 km. GPS: 43.95153, 4.80193

Charges guide

Per unit incl. 2 persons and electricity	€ 16,82 - € 26,72
extra person	€ 3,41 - € 4,86
child (3-12 yrs)	free - € 4,30
dog	€ 0,90 - € 2,20
Camping Cheques accepted.	

★★★★

ESTEREL
CARAVANING
SAINT-RAPHAËL . FRENCH-RIVIERA

Avenue des Golfs - 83530 Agay/Saint-Raphaël - France
Tel : +33 4.94.82.03.28   Fax : +33 4.94.82.87.37

Welcome to our luxurious camping caravanning site.

Situated in the Côte d'Azur, between Cannes and Saint-Tropez. In the heart of the Esterel mountains, yet only 3 km from the sandy beaches at Agay.

w w w . e s t e r e l - c a r a v a n i n g . f r

Wellness centre, indoor heated childrens' pool, Baby Club. Private Jacuzzi, new luxurious mobile homes for up to 8 people…

Easter Special : 07/04 - 30/04/2011
from 18 € per night for 2 persons in Standard pitch
for caravan/camper van.

20% discount : 01/05 - 29/05/2011
on a stay of minimum 7 nights in High Tech, Luxe,
Royal Maxi and Palace de Luxe pitches.

www.blog-esterel-caravaning.com
Join us on Facebook !

Bormes-les-Mimosas

Camp du Domaine

B.P. 207 La Favière, F-83230 Bormes-les-Mimosas (Var) T: 04 94 71 03 12
E: mail@campdudomaine.com alanrogers.com/FR83120

Camp du Domaine, 3 km. south of Le Lavandou, is a large, attractive beach-side site with 1,200 pitches set in 45 hectares of pinewood, although surprisingly it does not give the impression of being so big. The pitches are large (up to 200 sq.m) and most are reasonably level, 800 with 10A electricity. The most popular pitches are beside the beach, but the ones furthest away are generally larger and have more shade. Amongst the trees, many are more suitable for tents. The price for all the pitches is the same – smaller but near the beach or larger with shade. The beach is the attraction and everyone tries to get close. American motorhomes are not accepted. Despite its size, the site does not feel too busy, except perhaps around the supermarket. This is mainly because many pitches are hidden in the trees, the access roads are quite wide and it all covers quite a large area (some of the beach pitches are 600 m. from the entrance). Its popularity makes early reservation necessary over a long season (about mid June to mid Sept) as regular clients book from season to season. A good range of languages is spoken.

Facilities

Ten modern, well used but clean toilet blocks. Mostly Turkish WCs. Facilities for disabled visitors (but steep steps). Baby room. Washing machines. Fridge hire. Well stocked supermarket, bars, pizzeria (all open all season). No swimming pool. Excellent play area. Boats, pedaloes for hire. Wide range of watersports. Games, competitions (July/Aug). Children's club. Tennis. Multisport courts. Barbecues are strictly forbidden. Dogs are not accepted 10/7-21/8. Off site: Bicycle hire 500 m. Riding and golf 15 km.

Open: 9 April - 5 November.

Directions

From Bormes-les-Mimosas, head east on D559 to Le Lavandou. At roundabout, turn off D559 towards the sea on road signed Favière. After 2 km. turn left at site signs. GPS: 43.11779, 6.35176

Charges guide

Per unit incl. 2 persons and electricity	€ 27,00 - € 39,00
extra person	€ 5,60 - € 8,50
child (under 7 yrs)	free - € 4,50

Cadenet

Camping Val de Durance

F-84160 Cadenet (Vaucluse) T: 04 90 68 37 75. E: info@homair.com
alanrogers.com/FR84170

Homair
vacances

Val de Durance is an ideal holiday site for a family or for a couple wishing to discover Provence or the Luberon National Park. Cadenet, a small paradise between Pertuis and Lourmarin, is one of the most beautiful villages in France. Leaning against a rocky headland overlooking the Durance it has panoramic views over the Luberon and the Alpilles. This green, 27 acre campsite has its own ten-acre spring water lake and private sandy beach. There are 232 pitches with 92 for touring, all fully serviced with electricity.

Facilities

Three well equipped toilet blocks, conveniently situated at various parts of the site. Children's WC and facilities for campers with disabilities. Small shop, bar/snack bar, takeaway (all season). Swimming and paddling pools (all season). Lake fishing, beach. Off site: River Fishing 500 m. Hiking trails. Golf 10 km. Riding 12 km. Avignon and Orange.

Open: 1 April - 30 September.

Directions

A7 Autoroute, exit 26 (Senas), take N7 southeast towards Lambesc. At Pont Royal turn east onto D561. Beyond La Roque d'Antheron (14 km), turn north across river, onto D943 to Cadenet. GPS: 43.71971, 5.35499

Charges guide

Per person	€ 3,00 - € 8,00
child (under 10 yrs)	€ 2,00 - € 5,50
pitch	€ 6,00 - € 14,00
electricity (10A)	€ 5,00

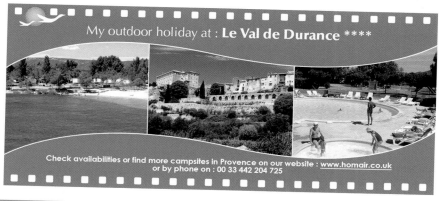

My outdoor holiday at : **Le Val de Durance** ★★★★

Check availabilities or find more campsites in Provence on our website : www.homair.co.uk
or by phone on : 00 33 442 204 725

Carqueiranne

Camping le Beau Vezé

Route de la Moutonne, F-83320 Carqueiranne (Var) T: 04 94 57 65 30. E: info@camping-beauveze.com
alanrogers.com/FR83130

Le Beau Vezé is a quiet site, inland from the busy resort of Hyères. The owner tries to keep it as a family site with its quiet position, although the superb beaches and hectic coastal areas are within easy reach. On a steep hillside it has terraced pitches and a plateau with more pitches on the top. The 150 pitches are well shaded and some will be rather difficult to manoeuvre onto due to overhanging trees and could be difficult for motorcaravans. There is some road noise on the lower pitches. The young staff are friendly and helpful, adding to the ambiance of what is already a relaxed and informal site. It is suitable for all who seek clean, fresh air and peaceful surroundings, yet only a few minutes drive to all that Hyères has to offer. Famed for its breathtaking palm trees, the town is positively packed with both ancient and modern history. For those interested in French markets, these can be found almost every day close by. Beaches are a short drive away, however, with the comfortable sun loungers beside the pool, you may just want to stay where you are.

Facilities

Reasonable standard sanitary blocks, two heated, although maintenance may be variable. Some showers with washbasin. Baby room. Washing machines. Bar/restaurant, takeaway. Bread. Medium sized pool, paddling pool. Play area. Minigolf, boules and tennis. Jet-ski hire. Walking tours, visits to vineyard. Evening entertainment in restaurant. Off site: Golf 2 km. Fishing 3 km. Riding 5 km. The old town of Hyères is only 8 km.

Open: 15 May - 15 September.

Directions

From A57 take exit for Toulon Est and follow D559 between Carqueiranne and Le Pradet. Take D76 northwards signed La Moutonne and site is signed on right of D76. GPS: 43.11413, 6.0564

Charges guide

Per unit incl. 2 persons and electricity	€ 20,00 - € 33,00
extra person	€ 4,50 - € 6,50
child (under 7 yrs)	€ 3,00 - € 4,50

No credit cards.
Camping Cheques accepted.

For latest campsite news, availability and prices visit
alanrogers.com

Carqueiranne

Campéole les Arbousiers

Campé⊙le

Chemin du Canebas, F-83220 Carqueiranne (Var) T: 04 94 58 56 56. E: arbousiers@campeole.com

alanrogers.com/FR83670

Les Arbousiers is a small site located on a hilltop overlooking the beautiful Gulf of Giens. There are 77 pitches occupied by mobile homes, chalets and fully-equipped bungalow tents; a further 23 pitches are for small tents only. Access to pitches by car is authorised for arrivals and departures only, and vehicles are parked in a large car park close to reception. With all the activities taking place at the bar/restaurant area, this ensures a tranquil ambiance within the site. The pool area has plenty of relaxation space and will attract people looking for a peaceful vacation. The site is well shaded by pines and pitches are attractively divided by oleanders. It becomes livelier in high season with a busy entertainment and activity programme, including children's clubs for different ages.

Facilities

Two modern, clean sanitary blocks. Laundry facilities. Bar/restaurant with takeaway. Swimming pool and children's pool with 'beach' area. Boules pitch. Volleyball. Play area. Activity and entertainment programme. Tourist information. Mobile homes, chalets and tents for rent. Off site: Nearest beach and sailing 3 km. Sub aqua diving 5 km. Hyères old town 10 km. Close proximity to parc naturel for bird watching and walks.

Open: 1 April - 30 September.

Directions

From the A57 motorway (Aix-en-Provence - Toulon), take exit 2 and follow signs for Carqueiranne and Le Pradet. Upon reaching Carqueiranne, follow signs to Le Canebas and Fort de la Bayarde and the campsite. GPS: 43.093081, 6.058429

Charges guide

Per unit incl. 2 persons and electricity	€ 17,90 - € 27,60
extra person	€ 7,60

Castellane

RCN les Collines de Castellane

RCN

Route de Grasse, F-04120 Castellane (Alpes-de-Haute-Provence) T: 04 92 83 68 96

E: info@rcn-lescollinesdecastellane.fr alanrogers.com/FR04040

RCN, a Dutch company, runs a chain of nine good campsites in the Netherlands. They also operate seven sites in France, all with Dutch managers who speak good French and English. Les Collines de Castellane is pleasantly situated in the mountainous landscape of the Alpes-de-Haute-Provence. There are 160 touring pitches spread over a series of flat terraces under umbrella pines with electric tricycles provided for transport up and down the quite steep pathways. At the top of the site, near the entrance, is a combined reception and small restaurant area. The adjoining swimming pool is quite large and offers a water slide and a paddling pool for small children. The unspoiled nature of the surrounding mountains provides attractive views and many opportunities for hiking, cycling, rafting, abseiling or canoeing.

Facilities

Tiled, modern toilet facilities include individual cabins and facilities for disabled visitors and babies. Washing machines, dryers and ironing area. Shop. Library. Small restaurant (including takeaway) with terrace. Heated swimming pool with slides and paddling pool. Tennis court. Boules. Three play areas. Organised activities (May-Sept). Off site: Distance to horse riding 6 km. Beach and golf 10 km.

Open: 16 April - 23 September.

Directions

Take the N85 (Route Napoléon) from Digné-les-Bains towards Castellane and Grasse. Site is 6 km. south of Castellane, on the right hand side of the road. GPS: 43.82423, 6.57296

Charges guide

Per unit incl. 2 persons, electricity and water	€ 18,90 - € 39,90
incl. up to 4 persons	€ 23,90 - € 49,70
dog	€ 4,00

For latest campsite news, availability and prices visit

alanrogers.com

Castellane

Castel Camping le Domaine du Verdon

Camp du Verdon, F-04120 Castellane (Alpes-de-Haute-Provence) T: 04 92 83 61 29
E: contact@camp-du-verdon.com **alanrogers.com/FR04020**

534

Close to the Route des Alpes and the Gorges du Verdon. Two heated swimming pools and numerous on-site activities during high season help to keep non-canoeists here. Du Verdon is a large level site, part meadow, part wooded, with 500 partly shaded, rather stony pitches (390 for tourists). Numbered and separated by bushes, they vary in size, have 6A electricity, and 125 also have water and waste water. They are mostly separate from the mobile homes (60) and pitches used by tour operators (110). Some overlook the unfenced river Verdon, so watch the children. This is a very popular holiday area, the gorge, canoeing and rafting being the main attractions, ideal for active families. One can walk to Castellane without using the main road. Dances and discos in July and August suit all age groups. The latest finishing time is around 23.00, after which time patrols make sure that the site is quiet. The site is popular and very busy in July and August.

Facilities

Refurbished toilet blocks include facilities for disabled visitors. Washing machines. Motorcaravan services. Restaurant, terrace, log fire for cooler evenings. New supermarket. Pizzeria/crêperie. Takeaway. Heated swimming pools, paddling pool with 'mushroom' fountain (all open all season). Organised entertainment (July/Aug). Play areas. Minigolf. Archery. Organised walks. Bicycle hire. Riding. Small fishing lake. ATM. Room for games and TV. Internet access and WiFi. Off site: Castellane and the Verdon Gorge 1 km. Riding 2 km. Boat launching 4.5 km. Golf 20 km. Water sports.

Open: 15 May - 15 September.

Directions

From Castellane take D952 westwards towards Gorges du Verdon and Moustiers. Site is 1 km. on left. GPS: 43.83921, 6.49396

Charges guide

Per unit incl. 2-3 persons and electricity	€ 25,00 - € 41,00
extra person (over 4 yrs)	€ 8,00 - € 13,00
dog	€ 3,00

Camping Cheques accepted.

For latest campsite news, availability and prices visit
alanrogers.com

Cavalaire-sur-Mer

Kawan Village Cros de Mouton

B.P. 116, F-83240 Cavalaire-sur-Mer (Var) T: 04 94 64 10 87. E: campingcrosdemouton@wanadoo.fr

alanrogers.com/FR83220

Cros de Mouton is a reasonably priced campsite in a popular area. High on a steep hillside, about 2 km. from Cavalaire and its popular beaches, the site is a calm oasis away from the coast. There are stunning views of the bay but, due to the nature of the terrain, some of the site roads are very steep – the higher pitches with the best views are especially so. There are 199 large, terraced pitches (electricity 10A) under cork trees with 73 suitable only for tents with parking close by, and 80 for touring caravans. A range of languages is spoken by the welcoming and helpful owners. The terrace of the restaurant and the pool area share the wonderful view of Cavalaire and the bay. Olivier and Andre are happy to take your caravan up with their 4x4 Jeep if you are worried, and they will help you set up if necessary.

Facilities

Clean, well maintained toilet blocks have all the usual facilities including those for disabled customers (although site is perhaps a little steep in places for wheelchairs). Washing machine. Shop. Bar/restaurant with reasonably priced meals and takeaway. Swimming and paddling pools with many sun beds on the terrace and small bar for snacks and cold drinks. Small play area. Games room. Off site: Beach 1.5 km. Bicycle hire 1.5 km. Riding 3 km. Golf 15 km.

Open: 15 March - 9 November.

Directions

Take the D559 to Cavalaire (not Cavalière 4 km. away). Site is about 1.5 km. north of Cavalière-sur-Mer, very well signed from the approach to the town. GPS: 43.18247, 6.5161

Charges guide

Per unit incl. 2 persons	
and electricity	€ 24,00 - € 29,10
extra person	€ 6,50 - € 8,20
child (under 7 yrs)	€ 4,10 - € 4,50
dog	free - € 2,00

Camping Cheques accepted.

Châteauroux-les-Alpes

Camping les Cariamas

Fontmolines, F-05380 Châteauroux-les-Alpes (Hautes-Alpes) T: 04 92 43 22 63. E: p.tim@free.fr

alanrogers.com/FR05070

Set 1,000 metres up in the stunning scenery of the Alps, les Cariamas is at the gateway to Ecrin National Park and within easy reach of the Serre-Ponçon lake and the Rabioux-Durance river. Of the 150 pitches, 120 are for touring and all have electrical connections (6-10A). They are pleasantly shaded and many offer beautiful views of the surrounding countryside. There are some mobile homes and chalets to rent. Amenities on the site include an outdoor heated swimming pool.

Facilities

Sanitary facilities include washbasins in cabins and hot showers. No facilities for disabled visitors. Laundry. Small shop and takeaway (from 1/5). Communal barbecue area. Swimming pool (1/5-30/9). Play area. Mountain bike hire. Fishing. Off site: Riding 15 km. Canoeing, climbing, hiking, mountain biking and rafting. Tennis.

Open: 1 April - 31 October.

Directions

From Gap follow signs to Embrun Briançon. Take turning for Châteauroux-les-Alpes at first roundabout after Embrun. Shortly (800 m.) before the village turn right and follow signs to site. GPS: 44.58981, 6.511294

Charges 2011

Per unit incl. 2 persons and electricity	€ 20,75
extra person	€ 5,50
child (under 6 yrs)	€ 2,75
dog	€ 3,75

Cavalaire-sur-Mer

Camping Bonporteau

B.P. 18 (RD559), F-83240 Cavalaire-sur-Mer (Var) T: 04 94 64 03 24. E: contact@bonporteau.fr

alanrogers.com/FR83340

This terraced site is situated northeast of and above the pleasant and popular holiday resort of Cavalaire where there is a harbour, restaurants and shops. A long, sandy beach runs right round the bay and there are plenty of watersport activities nearby. The site is only 200 metres from the beach, very well positioned for a family holiday, and only a short walk from a very good hypermarket. The 170 individual touring pitches are on sloping, sandy ground with terracing and good access roads, and all have electricity hook-ups (10A). The remaining 70 pitches are used for mobile homes and chalets. There is a special entrance gate to bring larger units in and the site has a strong 4x4 available for towing heavy units. Trees have grown well to give plenty of shade and there is a very attractive swimming pool. English is spoken by the young and enthusiastic management team.

Facilities

Three main toilet blocks are modern and include washbasins in cabins, Toilets are mainly British style. Launderette. Small shop. Small but attractive, restaurant (1/4-30/9). Bar. Takeaway. Entertainment with dance evenings. Swimming pool with terrace (15/3-30/9) and small paddling pool. Playground. Table tennis. TV and games room. Off site: Beach 200 m. Bicycle hire 800 m. Riding 2 km. Golf 20 km.

Open: 15 March - 15 October.

Directions

Take D559 to Cavalaire-sur-Mer (not Cavalière, some 4 km. away). Site is signed by yellow signs from the main road before entering the town. GPS: 43.16681, 6.51953

Charges 2011

Per unit incl. 2 persons and electricity	€ 19,00 - € 45,00

Weekly bookings only 28/6-22/8.

For latest campsite news, availability and prices visit

alanrogers.com

Cogolin

Camping l'Argentière

Chemin de l'Argentière (D48), F-83310 Cogolin (Var) T: 04 94 54 63 63. E: campinglargentiere@wanadoo.fr

alanrogers.com/FR83310

This little jewel of a site is in a pleasant setting and the intervening wooded area seems to give it sufficient screening to make the campsite itself quite peaceful. It is only 5 km. from the beach at Cogolin or St Tropez, so its position is handy for one of the showplaces of the Riviera, but away from the hustle and bustle of the beach resorts. There are 150 good sized touring pitches (out of 238 with the others used for mobile homes to rent). All have electricity although long leads may be necessary. The site is very well maintained.

Facilities

Two of three toilet blocks are near the touring pitches and are well kept and clean. Washbasins have warm water (some in cabins). Washing machines (near site entrance). Water has to be taken from the sanitary block. Fridge hire. Shop (1/6-30/9). Bar (1/6-30/9). Restaurant (15/6-15/9) and takeaway (15/6-31/8). Large swimming pool (15/5-30/9). Play equipment. Bicycle hire. Barbecues are only permitted in a communal area. Off site: Shops close. Riding 2 km. Fishing 4 km. Golf 6 km. Beach 5 km.

Open: 1 April - 30 September.

Directions

From the A8 (Aix-en-Provence - Cannes) take exit 36 (Le Muy), then, D25 to Ste Maxime and the coast road N98 towards St Tropez. After Grimaud keep following signs for Cogolin. When near that village follow D48 towards St Maur-en-Collobrière, then signs to site in the suburb of l'Argentière. GPS: 43.256083, 6.5124

Charges guide

Per unit incl. 2 persons and electricity	€ 16,00 - € 35,00
extra person	€ 3,00 - € 4,00

Forcalquier

Camping Indigo Forcalquier

Route de Sigonce, F-04300 Forcalquier (Alpes-de-Haute-Provence) T: 04 92 75 27 94

E: forcalquier@camping-indigo.com **alanrogers.com/FR04120**

Although Camping Indigo is an urban site, there are extensive views over the surrounding countryside where there are some excellent walks. The pitches are on grass and are of a good size, all with electricity, six fully serviced. The site is secure, with an electronic barrier (card deposit required) and there is no entry between 22.30 and 07.00. Local guides lead tours of the historic town and areas. This is an excellent base for visiting Forcalquier, a 15th-century fortified hill town. Since new owners acquired this site, an extensive modernisation programme has been put into effect.

Facilities

Two refurbished toilet blocks with washbasins in cubicles and excellent facilities for disabled visitors. Shop (all season). Bar, snack bar and takeaway (July and August). Play area. Heated swimming and paddling pools. Max. 1 dog. Off site: All shops, banks etc. in town centre 200 m. Horse riding 5 km. Fishing 15 km and golf 20 km.

Open: 22 April - 2 October.

Directions

From town centre, follow signs for Digne, Sisteron for 400 m, turning sharp left onto Sigonce road after Esso petrol station, then first right and site is 200 m. on the right. Well signed from town. GPS: 43.96206, 5.78743

Charges guide

Per unit incl. 2 persons	€ 19,05 - € 24,35
extra person	€ 4,80 - € 5,90

Fréjus

Yelloh! Village Domaine du Colombier

Route de Bagnols-en-Forêt, 1052 rue des Combattants d'AFN, F-83600 Fréjus (Var) T: 04 66 73 97 39

E: info@domaine-du-colombier.com **alanrogers.com/FR83230**

Domaine du Colombier is located between Cannes and St Tropez, alongside a main road 2 km. from the centre of Fréjus and 4 km. from the sandy beaches of Fréjus and Saint-Raphaël. There are 52 touring pitches, ranging in size from 80-150 sq.m. and all with 16A electricity. Over recent years there has been much ongoing investment in high quality facilities. An attractive pool complex includes a heated pool (600 sq.m), a large paddling pool, water slides and jacuzzis and is surrounded by sunloungers, a fitness area and a grill restaurant. Plenty of activities and excursions are arranged all season and the site caters principally for families.

Facilities

Three well maintained, fully equipped toilet blocks (two heated and with baby rooms). Facilities for disabled visitors. Laundry. Well stocked shop. Bar/restaurant, takeaway. Soundproofed nightclub. Large heated swimming pool with paddling pool, slides and jacuzzis (all season). Fitness facilities. Three play areas and four sports areas. Internet access and WiFi over site. Fridge, safe and barbecue hire. Off site: Bus stop 50 m.

Open: 28 March - 12 October.

Directions

From A8 exit 37, follow signs for Fréjus, turning left at second lights (D4) and site is 1 km. on the right. From A8 exit 38 east (Nice) straight on at three roundabouts, then right at fourth and fifth. Site is 300 m. on right. GPS: 43.44583, 6.72727

Charges guide

Per unit incl. 2 persons	€ 15,00 - € 49,00
extra person	€ 5,00 - € 9,00

Fréjus

Camping Caravaning les Pins Parasols

3360 rue des Combattants d'Afrique du Nord, F-83600 Fréjus (Var) T: 04 94 40 88 43
E: lespinsparasols@wanadoo.fr alanrogers.com/FR83010

Les Pins Parasols with its 189 pitches is a comfortably sized site, which is quite easy to walk around. It is family owned and run. Although on very slightly undulating ground, virtually all the pitches (all have electricity) are levelled or terraced and separated by hedges or bushes with pine trees for shade. There are 48 pitches equipped with their own fully enclosed, sanitary unit, with WC, washbasin, hot shower and dishwashing sink. These pitches naturally cost more but may well be of interest to those seeking a little bit of extra comfort. The nearest beach is Fréjus-Plage with its new marina, adjoining St Raphaël. The site is used by tour operators (10%).

Facilities

Good quality toilet blocks (one heated) providing facilities for disabled visitors. Small shop with reasonable stock, restaurant, takeaway (both 15/4-20/9). Heated swimming pool with attractive rock backdrop, separate long slide with landing pool and small paddling pool. Half-court tennis. General room, TV. Volleyball. Basketball court. Children's play area. Internet in reception (charged). Off site: Bicycle hire and riding 2 km. Fishing 6 km. Golf 10 km. Bus from the gate into Fréjus 5 km. Beach 6 km.

Open: 4 April - 24 September.

Directions

From A8 take exit 38 for Fréjus Est. Turn right immediately on leaving pay booths on a small road which leads across to D4, then right again and under 1 km. to site. GPS: 43.46290, 6.72570

Charges guide

Per unit incl. 2 persons	
and electricity	€ 18,00 - € 27,30
pitch with sanitary unit	€ 22,70 - € 34,00
extra person	€ 4,50 - € 6,35
child (under 7 yrs)	€ 3,00 - € 3,85
dog	€ 1,85 - € 2,80

Fréjus

Camping Holiday Green

Rue des Combattants d'Afrique du Nord, F-83600 Fréjus (Var) T: 04 94 19 88 30. E: info@holidaygreen.com
alanrogers.com/FR83600

Holiday Green is seven kilometres inland from Fréjus. It is a large, modern campsite with a fantastic view of the red massif of Esterel – very impressive as you arrive. The site has been developed on a hillside; by reception at the top of the hill is a large Californian style outside swimming pool as well as a new covered and heated swimming pool and waterslide. The rest of the site is terraced into the hillside and almost completely hidden in the 15 hectares of pine woods which absorbs about 500 mobile homes and some 43 touring pitches. Sloping in parts, there is plenty of shade and electricity (6/13A) available. The pool complex on the site is the centre of all the fun and there are activities and entertainment from morning until closing. Please note that a € 30 a week charge is levied on sunloungers and parasols.

Facilities

Modern toilet facilities include good hot showers. Laundry. Shopping centre. Bar, restaurant, fast food. Soundproofed disco. Swimming pool. Three tennis courts. Archery. Pétanque. All open all season. Excursions on foot, on horseback and on mountain bikes (to hire) to explore the countryside. Entertainment programme of dances, concerts and festivals. Playground. Children's club (July/Aug). No charcoal barbecues. Off site: Bus route outside entrance. Beach 8 km. Golf 8 km.

Open: 1 April - 30 September.

Directions

From A8 autoroute exit 38 follow signs for Bagnols -en-Forêt. Site is along this road, past a military base. Entrance is clearly marked at roundabout. GPS: 43.48563, 6.71745

Charges guide

Per unit incl. 2 persons	
and electricity	€ 27,00 - € 47,00
extra person	€ 6,00 - € 9,00
dog	€ 3,00 - € 5,00

For latest campsite news, availability and prices visit
alanrogers.com

Fréjus

Camping Resort la Baume – la Palmeraie

3775 rue des Combattants d'Afrique du Nord, F-83618 Fréjus (Var) T: 04 94 19 88 88
E: reception@labaume-lapalmeraie.com alanrogers.com/FR83060

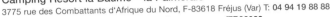

La Baume is a large, busy site about 5.5 km. from the long sandy beach of Fréjus-Plage, although with its fine and varied selection of swimming pools many people do not bother to make the trip. The pools with their palm trees are remarkable for their size and variety (water slides, etc) – the very large 'feature' pool is a highlight. Aquatic play area and two indoor pools with a slide and a spa area. The site has nearly 250 adequately sized, fully serviced pitches, with some separators and most have shade. Although tents are accepted, the site concentrates mainly on caravanning. It becomes full in season. Adjoining la Baume is its sister site la Palmeraie, providing self-catering accommodation, its own landscaped pool and offering some entertainment to supplement that at la Baume. There are 500 large pitches with mains sewerage for mobile homes. La Baume's convenient location has its downside as there is traffic noise on some pitches from the nearby autoroute – somewhat obtrusive at first but we soon failed to notice it. It is a popular site with tour operators.

Facilities

Seven toilet blocks. Supermarket, several shops. Two bars, terrace overlooking pools, TV. Restaurant, takeaway. Six swimming pools (heated all season, two covered, plus steam room and jacuzzi). Fitness centre. Tennis. Archery (July/Aug). Skateboard park. Organised events, daytime and evening entertainment, some English. Amphitheatre. Discos all season. Children's club (all season). 2 play areas renewed. Off site: Bus to Fréjus passes gate. Riding 2 km. Fishing 3 km. Golf 5 km. Beach 5 km.

Open: 27 March - 25 September (with full services).

Directions

From west, A8, exit Fréjus, take N7 southwest (Fréjus). After 4 km, turn left on D4 and site is 3 km. From east, A8, exit 38 Fréjus and follow signs for Cais. Site is signed. GPS: 43.45998, 6.72048

Charges guide

Per unit incl. 2 persons, electricity, water and drainage	€ 19,00 - € 45,00
extra person	€ 5,00 - € 13,00
child (under 7 yrs)	free - € 7,00
dog	€ 4,00 - € 5,00

Min. stay for motorhomes 2 nights.
Large units should book.

Gassin

Camping Parc Saint James-Gassin

Route de Bourrian, F-83580 Gassin (Var) T: 04 94 55 20 20. E: gassin@camping-parcsaintjames.com
alanrogers.com/FR83620

A member of the Parc Saint James group, this attractive campsite was formerly known as Parc Montana and is very well positioned close to St Tropez. The majority of the pitches are occupied by individually owned mobile homes and chalets but there are also 50 touring pitches on the lower part of the site. The 30 hectare estate clings to the hillside with fragrant woodland providing good shade to the mainly terraced pitches. There is a good range of activities here, many concentrated around the large swimming pool complex. In high season, the activity and entertainment programme is popular and includes soirées on the site's attractive bar terrace. The site lies close to many places of interest – St Tropez is close at hand, as well as Ramatuelle with its famous beach of Pampelone. The site is also well located for Port Grimaud, Ste Maxime and Gassin itself with a range of restaurants offering superb views over the gulf.

Facilities

Five toilet blocks provide adequate facilities although rather dated. Facility for disabled visitors in one block. Laundry. Small supermarket. Swimming pools and separate children's pool. Bar and restaurant. Takeaway. Play area. Tennis. Multisports area. Games room. Children's club. Evening entertainment. Disco. Mobile homes and chalets for rent. Off site: St Tropez, Port Grimaud and Cogolin. Nearest beaches 5 km. Riding. Fishing. Walking trails.

Open: 8 January - 19 November.

Directions

From A8 autoroute take Le Muy exit and follow signs to St Tropez and La Croix-Valmer. Pass Sainte Maxime and continue on the N98. At large roundabout take signs to Gassin. Cross first roundabout and turn left at next traffic lights. Site is also signed as Parc Montana in places. GPS: 43.24035, 6.57345

Charges 2011

Per unit incl. 2 persons and electricity	€ 19,00 - € 40,00
extra person	€ 3,00 - € 6,00
child (4-10 yrs)	€ 2,00 - € 5,00
dog	€ 5,00

For latest campsite news, availability and prices visit

alanrogers.com

Fréjus

La Pierre Verte Camping Village

Route de Bagnols-en-Forêt, F-83600 Fréjus (Var) T: 04 94 40 88 30. E: info@campinglapierreverte.com
alanrogers.com/FR83360

This attractive, terraced site, set on a hillside under umbrella pines, has been gradually and thoughtfully developed. The genuine, friendly welcome means many families return year upon year, bringing in turn new generations. The site is divided into terraces, each with its own toilet block. The 130 generously sized pitches for touring units enjoy good shade from trees and have either 6A or 10A electricity. There are 300 mobile homes in separate areas. For those seeking to 'get away from it all' in an area of outstanding natural beauty, there can be few more tranquil sites, but the many beaches, watersports and excursions the Gulf of St Tropez has to offer can also be enjoyed. Height restrictions could be an issue for larger units. For those staying on site, there are two large, (one heated) swimming pools with large sunbathing areas and exciting water slides. Not far away, some exhilarating hang-gliding and parascending can be enjoyed.

Facilities

Five toilet blocks with WCs and washbasins in cubicles are extremely clean and accessible from all levels. Baby bath. Laundry facilities. Supermarket. Bar with reasonably priced takeaway service. One heated (15 x 15 m) and one unheated swimming pool (25 x 15 m) and paddling pool. Play area. Boules. Games room. Fridge and bicycle hire. Entertainment and activities in high season. WiFi in pool/bar area (charged). Off site: Riding 1 km. A few shops 2 km. Fréjus 8 km. Fishing 8 km. Golf 12 km.

Open: 2 April - 30 September.

Directions

From the A8 (Aix-en-Provence - Nice) take exit 38 onto D4 towards Bagnols-en-Forêt. Site lies along this road past a military camp, clearly marked at the roundabout. GPS: 43.48389, 6.72058

Charges guide

Per unit incl. 2 persons and electricity	€ 24,00 - € 40,00
extra person	€ 6,00 - € 8,00
child (2-6 yrs)	€ 4,00 - € 6,00

La Pierre Verte Camping Village ★★★★
8 km from the sandy beaches of Fréjus
www.campinglapierreverte.com
E-mail : info@campinglapierreverte.com
Rte de Bagnols en Forêt
83600 FREJUS
FRANCE
Tél : 00 33 4 94 40 88 30
Fax : 00 33 4 94 40 75 41

Gréoux-les-Bains

Yelloh! Village Verdon Parc

Domaine de la Paludette, F-04800 Gréoux-les-Bains (Alpes-de-Haute-Provence) T: 04 66 73 97 39
E: info@yellohvillage-verdon-parc.com alanrogers.com/FR04110

Friendly and family run, this very spacious site borders the River Ardèche and is close to the attractive spa town of Gréoux-les-Bains. The 280 medium to very large, stony or gravel pitches (150 for tourists) are in two sections. The main part of the campsite has large pitches laid out in rows separated by poplar trees. Along the river bank the larger, more natural pitches are scattered amongst the trees and are of irregular shape and size. These have very pleasant views across the river to the town beyond. Electrical connections (10A) and water taps are reasonably close to most pitches. Unfortunately river swimming is forbidden, but there is a large swimming pool on site.

Facilities

Several toilet blocks (one heated in low season) are clean and to a high standard, with all the necessary facilities including those for disabled visitors. Laundry room. Motorcaravan service point. Small shop. Bar and courtyard terrace. Restaurant and takeaway (Apr-Sept). TV. Internet point. Large play area. Miniclub for younger children (high season). Evening entertainment. Dogs are not accepted 30/6-25/8. Gas and electric barbeques only. Off site: Gréoux-les-Bains 1 km. Bicycle hire 1 km.

Open: 21 March - 29 October.

Directions

Leave A51 at Manosque and take D907 southeast towards Gréoux-les-Bains. Turn right on D4, then left on D82 to Gréoux-les-Bains. Follow road through town to roundabout. Take second right, signed D8 St Pierre and descend for 1 km. Cross river and immediately turn left to site GPS: 43.7602, 5.8825

Charges guide

Per unit incl. 2 persons and electricity	€ 15,00 - € 33,00
extra person	€ 4,00 - € 5,00

For latest campsite news, availability and prices visit

alanrogers.com

Grimaud

Domaine des Naïades

Quartier Cros d'Entassi, Saint Pons-les-Mûres, F-83310 Grimaud (Var) T: 04 94 55 67 80
E: info@lesnaiades.com alanrogers.com/FR83640

Les Naïades is a well equipped site with an enviable setting close to the modern resort of Port Grimaud and the Gulf of St Tropez. The 454 pitches (219 are mobile homes for rent) are of a good size and well shaded, most have electricity (10A). The site boasts an Olympic sized pool and two water slides, as well as a separate children's pool. The restaurant specialises in Mediterranean cuisine and local wines. Les Naïades becomes lively in high season with a full activity and entertainment programme, as well as a miniclub for children. Port Grimaud is a stylish resort, built in the 1960s in the marshy delta of the Giscle. It is modelled on Venice and is a car-free environment. Most property owners are able to moor their boats on the many canals which criss-cross the resort. Grimaud, in contrast, is a hilltop village dominated by its partially restored 11th-century castle. St Tropez needs little introduction and, although very busy in the summer months, it resumes a rather more sedate character in the low season.

Facilities

Four basic but adequate toilet blocks. Facilities for disabled visitors, but access can be difficult. Laundry facilities. Covered dishwashing area. New supermarket for 2011. Bar. Restaurant. Swimming pool with water slides. Play area. Tourist information. Motorcaravan services. Mobile homes for rent. Off site: Port Grimaud. St Tropez. Fishing. Watersports. Walking and cycle routes in the Massif des Maures.

Open: 9 April - 5 November.

Directions

The site is located slightly to the north of Port Grimaud. From D98 head north to N98, Pons-les-Mûres and site is clearly signed. GPS: 43.285278, 6.579722

Charges guide

Per unit incl. 3 persons and electricity	€ 29,00 - € 50,00
extra person (over 7 yrs)	€ 5,00 - € 8,00
dog	€ 5,00

OPEN from 09th April until 05th November 2011.

Holiday home rental and camping pitches.

Heated olympic-sized swimming pool.

900 m from the beach

Saint-Pons-les-Mûres
+33(0)4 94 556 780
info@lesnaiades.com
www.lesnaiades.com

Grimaud

Club Holiday Marina

Le Ginestrel (RN98), F-83310 Grimaud (Var) T: 04 94 56 08 43. E: info@holiday-marina.com
alanrogers.com/FR83400

Owned and operated by an English family this site is an established favourite with British families. It is located in the busy holiday area of the Gulf of St Tropez. The site has a large and well kept pool area and its own adjacent moorings for small boats. Smaller than many sites in this area, there are 230 good sized pitches of which 49 are for touring units. Each of these has its own spacious bathroom with a good shower, washbasin and WC and outdoor sink. The Grand Luxe plus pitches have a small mobile home instead of the sanitary unit, with kitchen, bathroom, bedroom and terrace and are suitable for extra large motorhomes. On level, rather sandy ground, with variable shade, all have 16A electricity. Cars are parked separately to reduce noise.

Facilities

Private toilet blocks include washbasin, shower and WC, heated in low seasons. Dishwashing sinks. Laundry. Two restaurants with varied and full menu (15/6-31/8). Snacks and takeaway. Separate building houses a bar and games room. TV room. Heated swimming and paddling pools (1/4-31/9). Miniclub for children and evening entertainment in season. Fishing in adjacent canal. Mobile homes for hire. Off site: Beach 850 m. Golf 4 km.

Open: 1 April - 31 October.

Directions

From the A8 (Aix-en-Provence - Cannes) take exit 36 (Le Muy) and D25 to Ste Maxime. Follow N98 coast road towards St Tropez and site is 10 km. after very busy roundabout at Grimaud. GPS: 43.2728, 6.5215

Charges 2011

Per unit incl. 2 persons and electricity	€ 21,00 - € 79,00
family rate (2 adults, up to 3 chilpen)	€ 21,00 - € 95,00
extra person	€ 5,00 - € 16,00

Hyères

Campéole

Campéole Eurosurf

Plage de La Captel, F-83400 Hyères (Var) T: 04 94 58 00 20. E: eurosurf@campeole.com

alanrogers.com/FR83690

Facing towards the shimmering island of Porquerolles, Campéole Eurosurf, has an enviable setting, with direct access to a fine sandy beach. The site extends over 10 hectares of dunes and is bordered to the west by a road leading to the Giens peninsula. Eurosurf becomes lively in peak season with frequent evening entertainment and activities for children. This is a large site with 600 pitches, of which around 450 are available for touring units. The remainder are occupied by mobile homes, chalets and fully equipped tents, available for rent. Pitches are of a good size and are well shaded beneath parasol pines.

Facilities

Bar/restaurant. Snack bar. Shop. Takeaway food. Games room. Playground. Diving school. Boat launching (charged). All terrain sports area. Activity and entertainment programme. Tourist information. Direct beach access. Mobile homes, chalets and tents for rent. Off site: Sentier des Douaniers coastal walk. Fishing. Etang des Pesquiers (bird sanctuary)

Open: 14 March - 4 November.

Directions

Take the A57 motorway as far as Hyères. Then follow signs to Giens/Les Iles. The site is on the left hand side of the road, 1 km. after the village of La Capte. GPS: 43.0561, 6.1475

Charges 2011

Contact site for details.

Hyères-Plage

Camping la Presqu'île de Giens

153 route de la Madraque-Giens, F-83400 Hyères (Var) T: 04 94 58 22 86. E: info@camping-giens.com

alanrogers.com/FR83190

La Presqu'île de Giens is a well run, family campsite at the southern end of the Giens peninsula. The site is well maintained and extends over 17 acres of undulating terrain. Of the site's 460 pitches, 170 are reserved for touring. These are generally of a good size and well shaded – there is a separate area of smaller pitches reserved for tents. Electrical connections (16A) are available on all pitches. In high season this becomes a lively site with a well run children's club (small charge) and an evening entertainment programme including discos, singers and dancers.

Facilities

Five toilet blocks, three very good new ones (heated in low season), and two refurbished. All was clean and well maintained. Facilities for disabled visitors. Washing machines and dryers. Shop. Bar, restaurant and takeaway (all season). Play area. Children's club. Evening entertainment. Sports pitch. Diving classes. Sports tournaments. Excursion programme. Only electric barbecues are permitted. Off site: Beach 800 m. Fishing 1 km. Bicycle hire 1 km. Riding 5 km. Golf 20 km. 'Golden islands' excursions.

Open: 2 April - 9 October.

Directions

From the west, leave A57 at Hyères and continue to Hyères on the A570. At Hyères follow signs to Giens - Les Iles (D97). At end of this road, after 11 km. turn right towards Madraque. Site is on the left. GPS: 43.04071, 6.1435

Charges guide

Per unit incl. 2 persons and electricity	€ 19,70 - € 27,90
extra person	€ 4,50 - € 7,20

Camping Cheques accepted.

Isle-sur-la Sorgue

Camping Caravaning la Sorguette

Route d'Apt, F-84800 Isle-sur-la Sorgue (Vaucluse) T: 04 90 38 05 71. E: sorguette@wanadoo.fr

alanrogers.com/FR84050

This popular, well organised site is well placed, 1.5 km. from Isle-sur-la Sorgue. Arranged in groups of four, the 164 medium sized level pitches (124 for touring) all have electricity (6-10A). Each group is separated by tall hedges and most have a little shade during the day. In high season a few competitions are organised (boules or volleyball), plus some children's entertainment, but this is quite low key. Running alongside the site, the River Sorgue is only 6 km. from its source in the mountains. It is still very clear and used for canoeing, swimming and fishing.

Facilities

Well maintained toilet blocks, washing machines. Units for disabled visitors. Baby room. Motorcaravan services. Fridge hire. Shop, bar, snacks (1/7-25/8). Entertainment in July/Aug. Play area, volleyball, half-court tennis, basketball. Canoe, bicycle hire. Internet point. Indian tepees, yurts; Mongolian and Inuit style tents. 40 mobile homes (1 equipped for disabled campers). WiFi. Off site: Indoor/outdoor swimming pools (preferential rates) 2 km. Fishing and riding 5 km. Walking and cycling circuits. Canoeing on River Sorgue.

Open: 15 March - 15 October.

Directions

Site is 1.5 km. east of Isle-sur-la Sorgue on the D901 towards Apt. It is well signed from the town. GPS: 43.91488, 5.07758

Charges guide

Per unit incl. 2 persons and electricity	€ 19,80 - € 25,60
extra person	€ 5,80 - € 7,30
child (1-11 yrs)	€ 3,00 - € 3,70
dog	€ 2,40 - € 3,00

For latest campsite news, availability and prices visit

alanrogers.com

La Roque d'Anthéron

Village Center le Domaine des Iscles

B.P. 47, route du Plan d'Eau, F-13640 La Roque d''nthéron (Bouches du Rhône) T: 04 99 57 21 21
E: resa@village-center.com **alanrogers.com/FR13070**

Villagecenter

Village Center le Domaine des Iscles is probably the best of the three sites in this area. There are over 400 pitches, including 234 mobile homes for rent. The remaining pitches for touring units are well laid out with shared electricity and water points. There is shade for some. An attractive feature is a lake with a pebble beach, used for swimming and with a high slide into the water. Fishing is also permitted here in the low seasons. There are 150 km. of footpaths around La Roque d'Anthéron and the Luberon hills are only 10 km. with good opportunities for excursions in this very pleasant landscape.

Facilities

Three basic toilet blocks (only one open in low season) have only two British WCs, the remainder are Turkish style. Small shower cubicles. One washing machine at each block. Shop and bar. Restaurant and snack bar. Circular swimming pool. Lake for swimming with slide. Some entertainment and activities for children (July/Aug). Bicycle hire. Off site: Fishing nearby. Riding 3 km.

Open: 8 April - 2 October.

Directions

From the A7 (Avignon - Marseille) take exit 26 (Senas) and N7 towards Pertuis. Turn left at Pont Royal on D561 towards Peyrolles. Pass town of La Roque d'Antheron and site is signed where the access road passes under the Canal de Marseille. GPS: 43.729683, 5.318283

Charges guide

Per unit incl. 2 persons and electricity	€ 16,00 - € 28,00

Le Muy

RCN Domaine de la Noguière

Route de Fréjus, F-83490 Le Muy (Var) T: 04 94 45 13 78. E: info@rcn-domainedelanoguiere.fr
alanrogers.com/FR83090

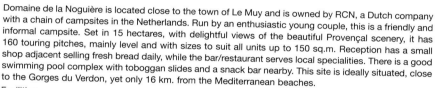

Domaine de la Noguière is located close to the town of Le Muy and is owned by RCN, a Dutch company with a chain of campsites in the Netherlands. Run by an enthusiastic young couple, this is a friendly and informal campsite. Set in 15 hectares, with delightful views of the beautiful Provençal scenery, it has 160 touring pitches, mainly level and with sizes to suit all units up to 150 sq.m. Reception has a small shop adjacent selling fresh bread daily, while the bar/restaurant serves local specialities. There is a good swimming pool complex with toboggan slides and a snack bar nearby. This site is ideally situated, close to the Gorges du Verdon, yet only 16 km. from the Mediterranean beaches.

Facilities

Two modern sanitary buildings have been added with family showers and children's rooms. Toilets are fully tiled with individual cubicles and access for disabled visitors. Laundry facilities. Shop (1/4-29/10). Bar/restaurant with terrace (12/4-29/10) plus takeaway service (12/4-1/11). Swimming pool complex with slides and snack bar. Small room with library and large TV. Tennis. Boules. Games field. Children's play area. WiFi. Off site: Bicycle hire nearby. Rafting and canyoning 1.5 km. Golf nearby. Riding 15 km. Boat launching and sailing 18 km.

Open: 19 March - 29 October.

Directions

From A8 Autoroute exit 36 Le Muy, take DN7 Le Muy. At roundabout in town, take direction Route de Fréjus. Site is approx. 2 km. from centre of village. GPS: 43.46832, 6.59202

Charges guide

Per unit incl. 2 persons, electricity and water	€ 19,90 - € 43,90
incl. up to 4 persons	€ 24,90 - € 53,90
dog	€ 6,00

Camping Cheques accepted.

Les Issambres

Au Paradis des Campeurs

La Gaillarde-Plage, F-83380 Les Issambres (Var) T: 04 94 96 93 55
alanrogers.com/FR83080

Family owned and run, this popular site has 180 pitches, all with 6A electricity and 132 with water and drainage. The original pitches vary in size and shape but all are satisfactory and most have some shade. The newer pitches are all large and have rather less shade although trees and bushes are maturing nicely. There is no entertainment which gives peaceful nights. The gates are surveyed by CCTV (especially the beach gate) and a security man patrols all day. With direct access to a sandy beach (via an underpass) and being so well maintained, the site has become deservedly popular so it is essential to book for June, July and August.

Facilities

Excellent, refurbished, well maintained toilet blocks. Facilities for babies and children with shower at suitable height. En-suite for disabled visitors. Washing machines and dryer. Motorcaravan services. Shop, restaurant and takeaway service (all season). TV room. Internet and WiFi. Excellent play areas catering for the under and over 5s. Off site: Bicycle hire 2.5 km. Riding 3 km. Golf 6 km.

Open: 28 March - 16 October.

Directions

Site is signed from N98 coast road at La Gaillarde, 2 km. south of St Aygulf. GPS: 43.36593, 6.71230

Charges guide

Per unit incl. 2 persons	€ 18,00 - € 27,00
incl. water and drainage	€ 20,00 - € 31,00
extra person	€ 6,00
child (under 5 yrs)	€ 3,00

For latest campsite news, availability and prices visit
alanrogers.com

Les Vigneaux

Campéole le Courounba

D994, F-05120 Les Vigneaux (Hautes-Alpes) T: 04 92 23 02 09. E: courounba@campeole.com

alanrogers.com/FR05140

Campéole

Le Courounba is a member of the Campéole group, located at the entrance to the magnificent Parc National des Ecrins. Pitches are shady and spacious, dispersed around 12 hectares of woodland. Many of the 250 pitches have superb views of the surrounding mountain scenery. There are 50 mobile homes for rent (including specially adapted units for disabled campers). There is also a good sized swimming pool with a water slide and other on-site amenities include two tennis courts and a volleyball pitch. Most facilities are free of charge (including tennis). The site has a friendly bar/restaurant and also a well stocked shop (high season only). There is dramatic mountain scenery all around. The Mont Brison is the highest limestone rockface in France and the Mont Pelvoux, at 3,943 metres has an all year snow cap. Le Courounba is on the banks of the River Gyronde, popular for fishing. A little further afield, Briançon is a superb town, fortified by Vauban and well worth a visit.

Facilities	Directions
Shop, bar/snack bar, swimming pool and water slide (all July/Aug). Volleyball. Tennis. Bouncy castle. Shop. Play area. Activity and entertainment programme. Tourist information. Mobile homes for rent. Off site: Fishing 100 m. Hiking and cycle tracks. Riding, bicycle hire 5 km. Briançon 17 km. **Open:** 22 May - 26 September.	The site is close to the village of Les Vigneaux, south of Briançon. From Briançon, head south on N94 as far as Prelles and then join the D4 to Les Vigneaux. The site is well indicated from here. GPS: 44.82483, 6.52566

Charges guide

Per unit incl. 2 persons and electricity	€ 17,10 - € 24,70

Campéole

CAMPSITES AND RENTALS

Le Courounba***

In the middle of nature, at the foot of the mountains, beautiful site with swimming pool and restaurant. Pitches and accommodations of high quality.

RHÔNE-ALPES

05120 Les Vigneaux - Tel.: +33-492-2302-09 - www.campeole.co.uk / courounba@campeole.com

---

Martigues

Flower Camping Marius

Route de la Saulce, la Couronne, F-13500 Martigues (Bouches du Rhône) T: 04 42 80 70 29

E: contact@camping-marius.com alanrogers.com/FR13140

East of the Camargue, past the oil tankers anchored in the Gulf de Fos and south of the Etang de Berre is Martigues. Camping Marius is 7 km. further south, tucked away beside a 'calanque' (or inlet) on this rocky coast. There are steps up and then down to the beach across the rocky cliffs. The site is a colourful oasis, regularly laid out with shade from shrubs and mixed trees. It provides 113 pitches, of which 53 are occupied by mobile homes for rent and 35 are seasonal pitches, leaving 25 for touring units. The pitches are rather small but each has its own sink and water supply.

Facilities	Directions
A good modern toilet block is well equipped and is supplemented by a smaller one. Baby bath. Facilities for disabled visitors. Very small shop. Bar and takeaway (all season). Play area. Bicycle hire. Canoe hire. Activity and entertainment programme. Direct access via steep steps and some rough walking to beach 200 m. Mobile homes for rent. Off site: Nearest village is La Couronne (good range of shops and restaurants and railway station). Fishing village of Carro (3 km) with daily fish market. Riding 5 km. Snack bar 200 m. **Open:** 1 April - 6 November.	Approach Martigues from the north on the D5 and cross the Canal de Caronte, continuing south on the D5, then D49 to La Couronne (7 km). At roundabout on outskirts of La Couronne, turn left for Sausset-les-Pins and Saint Croix. Site is signed from there. Using the A55 take left turn immediately on crossing the bridge signed Fos (exit 12) and follow road back under bridge until right sign for La Couronne. GPS: 43.335, 5.0673

Charges 2011

Per unit incl. 2 persons and electricity	€ 20,00 - € 28,90
extra person	€ 4,00 - € 6,50
child (2-7 yrs)	€ 2,00 - € 3,50

Les Vigneaux

Camping les Vaudois

Campéole

F-05120 Les Vigneaux (Hautes-Alpes) T: 04 92 23 02 09. E: campeolelesvigneaux@orange.fr
alanrogers.com/FR05150

Les Vaudois is located at the edge of the Parc National des Ecrins. The site stands on the banks of the River Gyronde and at the foot of Mont Brison, France's highest limestone rock face. There are very few amenities on site but guests are able to use the facilities at the sister site, le Couraunba, around 1 km. distant. Amenities there include a swimming pool (with water slide) and a bar/restaurant. There are 141 touring pitches at les Vaudois, and a further 9 pitches reserved for mobile homes. Most pitches are equipped with electricity. This is, of course, excellent country for adventure sports and les Vaudois is well located for a wide range of activities, including white water rafting, rock climbing and mountain biking. The Parc National des Ecrins is a vast area, one of only nine French national parks, established back in 1913 as the Parc National Bérarde. There are over 700 km. of marked footpaths in the park and a great wealth of wildlife.

Facilities

Play area. Tourist information. Mobile homes for rent. Off site: Swimming pool. Bar/restaurant. Cycle and walking tracks. Tennis. Canoeing. White water sports on the Gyronde.

Open: 26 June - 28 August.

Directions

From Briançon, take N94 towards Prelles and St Martin de Queyrières, and then follow signs for l'Argentière. Take the D104A to La Batie des Vigneaux and then continue to Les Vigneaux and the campsite. GPS: 44.8213, 6.5355

Charges guide

Per unit incl. 2 persons
and electricity   € 15,10 - € 18,30

Montagnac-Montpezat

Village Center Côteau de la Marine

Villagecenter

Vauvert, F-04500 Montagnac-Montpezat (Alpes-de-Haute-Provence) T: 04 99 57 21 21
E: resa@village-center.com alanrogers.com/FR04200

Located to the west of the Lac de Sainte Croix and the Gorges de Verdon, Côteau de la Marine is a well equipped site with a fine setting. The site is a member of the Village Center group and has direct access to the River Verdon and its own small harbour. There are 116 touring pitches (60-120 sq.m.), mostly with electrical connections (10A). There is plenty of activity in high season, with a club for children and various competitions and tournaments. There is a large swimming pool and a separate children's pool. Other on-site amenities include a sports field, bar and restaurant. The adjacent watersports centre has canoe and electric boat hire. The Gorges du Verdon are, of course, an essential day trip but there is much of picture postcard Provence in the area, including the lavender fields of the Valensole plateau and the valley of the Durance. A number of cycle and walking tracks run very close to the site.

Facilities

Shop. Restaurant/snack bar and takeaway. Bar. Swimming and paddling pools. Play area. Activity and entertainment programme. Direct river access. Mobile homes for rent. Off site: Montagnac-Montpezat 5 km. Bicycle and walking tracks. Gorges du Verdon. Lac de Sainte Croix (watersports).

Open: 10 April - 19 September.

Directions

Approaching from the north (Gap), leave the A51 at exit 19 (La Brillane) and follow signs to Oraison. From here, head south on D4 and then D15 to Valensole. Then head southeast on D6 to Riez and then follow signs to Montagnac-Montpezat. Site is clearly signed from here. GPS: 43.74768, 6.09845

Charges guide

Per unit incl. 2 persons
and electricity   € 16,00 - € 29,00

For latest campsite news, availability and prices visit
alanrogers.com

Montclar

Yelloh! Village l'Etoile des Neiges

F-04140 Montclar (Alpes-de-Haute-Provence) T: 04 66 73 97 39. E: info@yellohvillage-etoile-des-neiges.com

alanrogers.com/FR04080

This attractive, family run site near the mountain village and ski resort of St Jean Montclar is open most of the year. Being at an altitude of 1,300 m. the nights can get quite cold in summer. The 130 shady terraced pitches, with 70 for touring, are separated by small shrubs and alpine trees. All pitches are close to electricity and water points. An attractive bar and restaurant overlooks the two swimming pools, with the shallow pool having a water slide ideal for children. The site has no shop but local shops are only a few minutes walk away. Although situated in the southern high Alps, the site can be reached without climbing any stiff gradients. This beautiful alpine region offers all the usual alpine activities.

Facilities

Central toilet block (heated in winter) and facilities for disabled visitors. Two washing machines. Motorcaravan services. Bar/restaurant. Swimming pool (all amenities open 15/5-9/9). Tennis. Boules. Two play areas. Rafting, walking (July/Aug). Off site: Shops in village a few minutes walk. Bicycle hire and riding in village. Fishing 1.5 km. Watersports and beach at Lac Serre Ponçon 7 km.

Open: All year excl. 26/3-29/4 and 16/9-19/12.

Directions

Site is 35 km. south of Gap via D900B. Beyond Serre Ponçon, turn right, D900 signed Selonnet, St Jean Montclar. Entering St Jean Montclar turn left, pass chalets, shops, fork right to campsite. Approach roads are steep and icy in winter. GPS: 44.39367, 6.34400

Charges guide

Per unit incl. 2 persons	€ 17,00 - € 31,00
extra person	€ 4,00 - € 5,00
electricity (6A)	€ 3,00 - € 4,00

Mornas

Camping Beauregard

Route d'Uchaux, F-84550 Mornas (Vaucluse) T: 04 90 37 02 08. E: beauregard@wanadoo.fr

alanrogers.com/FR84140

Just a kilometre off the D7 and near an A7 exit, this site may appeal to those needing a night stop when travelling to or from the Mediterranean coast. Although there are many mobile homes, there are 89 pitches available for touring units. The pitches are under large pine trees and are rather sandy and firm pegging might be difficult. They are of various shapes and sizes, mainly about 90 sq.m. Efforts are being made to upgrade what was an old fashioned campsite. There is a new and attractive pool complex including a covered pool (heated from April) – the pools are used by some local people. Entertainment is organised for high season evenings. A good sized shop sells the essentials.

Facilities

Two toilet blocks, one of which is heated when necessary, with washbasins in cabins. Facilities for disabled visitors (access by key). Laundry facilities. Shop (April-Oct). Bar, restaurant and takeaway (April-Sept). Swimming pools, one covered. Tennis. Play area. Boules. Quad bike hire. Fitness trail. Entertainment (high season). Barbecues are not permitted. Off site: Fishing and riding 5 km. Golf 12 km.

Open: 25 March - 4 November.

Directions

From the A7 take exit for Bollene, then the N7 towards Orange. At north end of Mornas village, turn left on D74 signed Uchaux. Site is on left after 1.7 km. GPS: 44.21540, 4.74530

Charges guide

Per unit incl. 2 persons	€ 21,00 - € 24,00
extra person	€ 4,60 - € 7,00
child (under 7 yrs)	€ 2,50 - € 4,20
electricity	€ 4,70

Pernes les Fontaines

Camping les Fontaines

125 chemin de la Chapelette, route de Sudre, F-84210 Pernes-les-Fontaines (Vaucluse) T: 04 90 46 82 55
E: pascalbourrat@gmail.com **alanrogers.com/FR84190**

Camping les Fontaines is a small family run site set in two hectares, with magnificent views of Mont Ventoux and the maintains of the Vaucluse. There are 90 pitches in total, with 65 for touring units. Good shade on most of the level pitches is provided by mature trees and shrubs, electricity (6A) and water are nearby. On-site amenities include a 200 m² lagoon-style pool, an excellent restaurant and cocktail bar with a wide choice of smoothies. The whole site enjoys WiFi coverage at no extra charge. A warm welcome awaits the holidaymaker from the owners, Pierine and Pascal.

Facilities

Modern, clean sanitary block. Small nursery for babies and children and good facilities for disabled visitors. Laundry. Motorcaravan service point. Bar, restaurant with decked terrace overlooking the pool, takeaway food (all May-Sept). Lagoon-style pool with large 'beach' area. Small shop in reception selling basics and fresh bread daily. Children's play area. Off site: Bicycle hire, riding 2 km. Golf, fishing 10 km.

Open: 1 April - 31 October.

Directions

From Autoroute A7 take exit 23 Avignon Nord, direction Carpentras. Then D16 Entraigues. Follow signs for Pernes-les-Fontaines. Site is signed from roundabout in town. GPS: 44.006351, 5.038771

Charges guide

Per unit incl. 2 persons and electricity	€ 18,90 - € 28,50
extra person	€ 5,50 - € 7,00
Camping Cheques accepted.	

For latest campsite news, availability and prices visit

alanrogers.com

Niozelles

Camping le Moulin de Ventre

Niozelles, F-04300 Forcalquier (Alpes-de-Haute-Provence) T: 04 92 78 63 31. E: moulindeventre@aol.com

alanrogers.com/FR04030

This is a friendly, family run site in the heart of Haute-Provence, near Forcalquier, a bustling small French market town. Attractively located beside a small lake and 28 acres of wooded, hilly land, which is available for walking. Herbs of Provence can be found growing wild and flowers, birds and butterflies abound – a nature lovers' delight. The 124 level, grassy pitches for tourists are separated by a variety of trees and small shrubs, 114 of them having electricity (6A; long leads may be necessary). Some pitches are particularly attractive, bordering a small stream. English is spoken. The site is well situated to visit Mont Ventoux, the Luberon National Park, the Gorges du Verdon and a wide range of ancient hill villages with their markets and museums etc. A Sites et Paysages member.

Facilities

Refurbished toilet block. Facilities for disabled visitors. Baby bath. Washing, drying machines. Fridge hire. Bread. Bar/restaurant, takeaway (all season), themed evenings (high season). Pizzeria. Swimming pools (15/5-15/9). New playground. Bouncy castle. Fishing, boules. Some activities organised in high season. No discos. Only electric or gas barbecues are permitted. Internet access. Off site: Shops, local market, doctor, tennis 2 km. Supermarket, chemist, riding, bicycle hire 5 km. Golf 20 km. Walking, cycling.

Open: 9 April - 30 September.

Directions

From A51 motorway take exit 19 (Brillanne). Turn right on N96 then turn left on N100 westwards (signed Forcalquier) for about 3 km. Site is signed on left, just after a bridge 3 km. southeast of Niozelles. GPS: 43.93364, 5.86815

Charges 2011

Per unit incl. 2 persons	
and electricity	€ 20,00 - € 29,00
extra person (over 4 yrs)	€ 4,20 - € 6,00
child (2-4 yrs)	€ 2,50 - € 4,00
dog	€ 3,00

No credit cards.

Haute-Provence
Camping
Moulin de Ventre
04300 Niozelles
Tel: 0033 492 78 63 31
Fax: 0033 492 79 86 92
www.moulin-de-ventre.com
Situated between Verdon and Luberon

For latest campsite news, availability and prices visit

alanrogers.com

Orpierre

Camping des Princes d'Orange

F-05700 Orpierre (Hautes-Alpes) T: 04 92 66 22 53. E: campingorpierre@wanadoo.fr

alanrogers.com/FR05000

This attractive, terraced site, set on a hillside above the village has been thoughtfully developed. The genuine, friendly welcome means many families return year upon year, bringing in turn new generations. Divided into five terraces, each with its own toilet block, all its 100 generously sized pitches (96 for tourists) enjoy good shade from trees and wicker canopies and have electricity connections (10A). In high season one terrace is reserved as a 1-star camping area for young people. Orpierre also has an enchanting maze of medieval streets and houses, almost like a trip back through the centuries. Whether you choose to drive, climb, walk or cycle there is plenty of wonderful scenery to discover in the immediate vicinity, whilst not far away, some exhilarating hang-gliding and parascending can be enjoyed. It is renowned as a serious rock climbing venue. For those seeking to 'get away from it all' in an area of outstanding natural beauty, there can be few more tranquil sites. There can be no doubt that you will be made most welcome and will enjoy the quiet splendours the region has to offer.

Facilities

Six well equipped toilet blocks. Baby bath. Laundry facilities. Bread. Bar (1/4-31/10). Heated swimming pool, paddling pool (15/6-15/9). Play area with small trampoline with safety net. Boules. Games room. Fridge hire. Only gas barbecues are permitted. Off site: Orpierre with a few shops and bicycle hire 500 m. Fishing 7 km. Nearest shopping centre Laragne 12 km. Riding 19 km. Hang-gliding, parascending. Gorges de Guil.

Open: 1 April - 31 October.

Directions

Turn off N75 road at Eyguians onto D30 - site is signed on left at crossroads in the centre of Orpierre village. GPS: 44.31121, 5.69677

Charges guide

Per unit incl. 2 persons and electricity	€ 26,30
extra person	€ 7,00
child (under 7 yrs)	€ 3,50
dog	€ 1,50

Less 25% in low season. No credit cards.

Camping des Princes d'Orange

05700 Orpierre
Tel: 0033 492 662 253
Fax: 0033 492 663 108
campingorpierre@wanadoo.fr
www.camping-orpierre.com

Puget-sur-Argens

Camping Club la Bastiane

1056 chemin de Suvières, F-83480 Puget-sur-Argens (Var) T: 04 94 55 55 94. E: info@labastiane.com

alanrogers.com/FR83040

La Bastiane is an attractive, established site with good amenities, well located for exploring the Côte d'Azur and with easy access to nearby beaches. There are 180 pitches here of which 47 are reserved for touring. They are generally of a good size and are all supplied with 6A electrical connections. The terrain is somewhat undulating but most of the pitches are on level terraces. There is a good swimming pool and a range of amenities including a shop, bar and restaurant with a well priced menu. The site becomes lively in peak season with a range of activities. The access road is limited, and therefore unsuitable for larger units.

Facilities

Three toilet blocks, clean and immaculately maintained. Facilities for disabled visitors. Washing machines, dryers. Shop, bar and takeaway (8/4-20/10). Restaurant (17/4-12/10). Heated swimming pool (8/4-20/10). Tennis. Multisport terrain. Children's club. Play area. Games/TV room. Bicycle hire. Evening entertainment in peak season. Excursion programme. Only electric barbecues. WiFi (charged). Max. 1 dog. Off site: Beach 7 km. Lake beach 8 km. Riding 500 m. Fishing 3 km. Golf 9 km.

Open: 9 April - 23 October.

Directions

Leave A8 at exit 37 (Puget), take right turn at first roundabout (signed Roquebrune), join N7. Turn right, first traffic lights (200 m), then left at roundabout. Site signed from here, on the right 2.5 km. from the motorway. GPS: 43.46966, 6.67845

Charges guide

Per unit incl. 2 persons and electricity	€ 19,90 - € 39,90

For latest campsite news, availability and prices visit

alanrogers.com

Quinson

Village Center les Prés du Verdon

Villagecenter

F-04500 Quinson (Alpes-de-Haute-Provence) T: 04 99 57 21 21. E: contact@village-center.com
alanrogers.com/FR04230

This family site is attractively located close to the River Verdon, and it is a good base for exploring the famous gorges. The site boasts a fine pool complex with a large main pool and separate paddling pool. Other on-site amenities include a small shop and a children's play area. There are 119 touring pitches here (from 70 to 110 sq.m), some well shaded and others rather sunnier. Most are equipped with electrical connections. A further 81 pitches are used for mobile homes, most of which are available for rent. This is a great region for an active holiday. Popular activities include rafting and canoeing on the Verdon river, and canyoning. The picturesque town of Quinson is close at hand.

Facilities

Bar. Shop. Takeaway. Swimming pool with paddling pool. Animation: sports and evening entertainment. Volleyball, table tennis, children's play area, lounge and TV room, miniclub. Off site: Walking and cycling routes. River 100 m. Fishing 100 m. Lake 100 m. Canoeing 100 m. Climbing 500 m. Supermarket 200 m. Tennis 500 m.

Open: 10 April - 13 September.

Directions

Approaching on A51 motorway, head for Digne les Bains and leave at exit 17 (St Paul-les-Durance and Gréoux Les Bains). After Gréoux, follow signs to Quinson and Musée de la Préhistoire. The site is then clearly signed. GPS: 43.69713, 6.04162

Charges guide

Per unit incl. 2 persons and electricity	€ 14,50 - € 18,50

Ramatuelle

Yelloh! Village les Tournels

yelloh! VILLAGE

Route de Camarat, F-83350 Ramatuelle (Var) T: 04 94 55 90 90. E: info@yellohvillage-les-tournels.com
alanrogers.com/FR83210

Les Tournels is a large site set on a hillside and pitches have panoramic views of the Gulf of St Tropez and Pampelonne beach. The hillside is covered in parasol pines and old olive trees. The pitches are reasonably level, shady, of variable size, and most have electricity. The swimming pool, play area, shop and bar may be some distance away. The site has a superb new spa centre with gym, sauna and jacuzzi, with an excellent pool alongside, all reserved for over 18s, and a new restaurant with a large terrace. Competitions and shows are organised for adults and children in July and August. The beaches are a big draw, but who can resist a visit to St Tropez where the floating 'gin palaces' are a sight to behold.

Facilities

Well equipped toilet blocks, some heated, baby baths, children's WCs, facilities for disabled visitors. Laundry facilities. Fridge hire. Bar and restaurant (1/4-30/10). Takeaway. Bar and disco well away from most pitches. Large heated swimming pool (1/4-30/10). Fitness centre and pool. Good quality play area. Boules. Archery. Miniclub (over 5 yrs). Safety deposit boxes. Electric and gas barbecues permitted. Off site: Shopping centre 500 m, shuttle bus service. Golf 6 km. Beach 1.5 km.

Open: 1 April - 7 January.

Directions

From A8 exit 36 take D25 to Ste Maxime, then D98 towards St Tropez. Take D93 to Ramatuelle. Site is clearly marked after approx. 9 km.
GPS: 43.20596, 6.65083

Charges guide

Per unit incl. 2 persons and electricity and water	€ 18,00 - € 52,00
extra person	€ 6,00 - € 7,00
child (3-6 yrs)	free - € 7,00

Ramatuelle

Campéole la Croix du Sud

Campéole

Route des Plages, CD93, F-83350 Ramatuelle (Var) T: 04 94 55 51 23. E: croix-du-sud@campeole.com
alanrogers.com/FR83710

La Croix du Sud is perched on a little hill and pleasantly shaded by parasol pines and eucalyptus trees. The nearby fine sandy beach of Pampelonne is maybe the most celebrated in France, and famed for its association with St Tropez (although it is actually closer to Ramatuelle!). There are 120 pitches here, of which around half are available for touring units. Pitches are well shaded and are mostly equipped with electricity. Other pitches are occupied by mobile homes, chalets and tents, available for rent. The nearest beach (Pampelonne) is 1.6 km. away and can be accessed by a cycle track with just one road to cross. There is a small swimming pool and a separate children's pool.

Facilities

Restaurant. Bar/snack bar. Shop. Takeaway food. Swimming pool. Children's pool. Games room. Playground. Sports field. Activity and entertainment programme. Tourist information. Mobile homes, chalets and tents for rent. Off site: Nearest beach 1.6 km. Fishing. Golf. Walking and mountain biking. St Tropez. Ramatuelle.

Open: 1 April - 11 October.

Directions

From the A8 (La Provençale) motorway take the exit to Le Luc. Take the D558 towards La Garde-Freinet and Saint Tropez, and then the D93 towards Ramatuelle. In Ramatuelle, follow signs to les Plages and Pampelonne, at the second roundabout go straight on for 1.5 km and then turn left to the site GPS: 43.2422, 6.6491

Charges 2011

Contact the site for details.

Roquebrune-sur-Argens

Camping Caravaning Leï Suves

Quartier du Blavet, F-83520 Roquebrune-sur-Argens (Var) T: 04 94 45 43 95. E: camping.lei.suves@wanadoo.fr

alanrogers.com/FR83030

This quiet, pretty site is a few kilometres inland from the coast, 2 km. north of the N7. Close to the unusual Roquebrune rock, it is within easy reach of St Tropez, Ste Maxime, St Raphaël and Cannes. The site entrance is appealing – wide and spacious, with a large bank of well tended flowers. Mainly on a gently sloping hillside, the 310 pitches are terraced with shade provided by the many cork trees which give the site its name. All pitches have electricity and access to water. A pleasant pool area is beside the bar/restaurant and entertainment area. Please note that reception is closed on Sundays. It is possible to walk in the surrounding woods. There are 150 mobile homes available to rent.

Facilities

Modern, well kept toilet blocks include facilities for disabled visitors, washing machines and dryers. Shop. Good sized swimming pool, paddling pool. Bar, terrace, snack bar, takeaway (all 2/4-30/9). Outdoor stage near the bar for evening entertainment in high season. Excellent play area. Table tennis, tennis, sports area. WiFi over whole site. Only gas barbecues are permitted.
Off site: Bus stop at site entrance. Riding 1 km. Fishing 3 km. Bicycle hire 5 km. Golf 7 km. Beach at St Aygulf 15 km.

Open: 2 April - 15 October.

Directions

Leave autoroute at Le Muy and take the N7 towards St Raphaël. Turn left at roundabout onto D7 heading north signed La Boverie (site also signed). Site on right in 2 km. GPS: 43.47793, 6.63881

Charges guide

Per unit incl. 2 persons and electricity	€ 25,50 - € 43,00
incl. 3 persons	€ 27,50 - € 45,50
extra person	€ 5,00 - € 9,00
child (under 7 yrs)	€ 3,10 - € 6,20
dog	€ 2,00 - € 3,50

Roquebrune-sur-Argens

Camping Domaine de la Bergerie

Vallée du Fournel, route du Col-du-Bougnon, F-83520 Roquebrune-sur-Argens (Var) T: 04 98 11 45 45
E: info@domainelabergerie.com alanrogers.com/FR83170

This excellent site near the Côte d'Azur will take you away from all the bustle of the Mediterranean to total relaxation amongst the cork, oak, pine and mimosa in its woodland setting. The 60 hectare site is quite spread out with semi-landscaped areas for mobile homes and grassy avenues of 200 separated pitches for touring caravans and tents. All pitches average over 80 sq.m. and have electricity, with those in one area also having water and drainage. The restaurant/bar, a converted farm building, is surrounded by shady patios, whilst inside it oozes character with high beams and archways leading to intimate corners. Activities are organised daily and, in the evening, shows, cabarets, discos, cinema, karaoke and dancing at the amphitheatre prove popular (possibly until midnight). A superb new pool complex supplements the original pool adding more outdoor pools with slides and a river feature, an indoor pool and a fitness centre with jacuzzi, sauna, turkish bath, massage, reflexology and gym.

Facilities

Four toilet blocks are kept clean and include washbasins in cubicles, facilities for disabled visitors and babies. Supermarket. Bar/restaurant. Takeaway. Pool complex (all season) with indoor pool and fitness centre (body building, sauna, gym, etc). Tennis courts. Archery. Roller skating. Minigolf. English speaking children's club. Mini-farm for children. Fishing. Internet access and WiFi. Only gas barbecues are permitted. Off site: Riding and golf 2 km. Bicycle hire 7 km. Beaches at St Aygulf and Ste Maxime 7 km. Water skiing and rock climbing nearby.

Open: 24 April - 30 September
(mobile homes 15 February - 15 November).

Directions

Leave A8 at Le Muy exit on N7 towards Fréjus. Proceed for 9 km. then right onto the D7 signed St Aygulf. Continue for 8 km. and then right at the roundabout on D8; site is on the right. GPS: 43.4091, 6.6747

Charges guide

Per unit incl. 2 persons and electricity (6A)	€ 19,00 - € 36,50
incl. water and drainage	€ 24,50 - € 46,50
extra person	€ 5,00 - € 9,30
child (under 7 yrs)	€ 3,70 - € 6,70
dog	free - € 5,00

Roquebrune-sur-Argens

F 536

Camping les Pêcheurs

F-83520 Roquebrune-sur-Argens (Var) T: 04 94 45 71 25. E: info@camping-les-pecheurs.com

alanrogers.com/FR83200

Les Pêcheurs will appeal to families who appreciate natural surroundings together with many activities, cultural and sporting. Interspersed with mobile homes, the 150 good sized touring pitches (6/10A electricity) are separated by trees or flowering bushes. The Provençal style buildings are delightful, especially the bar, restaurant and games room, with its terrace down to the river and the site's own canoe station (locked gate). Across the road is a lake used exclusively for water skiing with a sandy beach and restaurant. Enlarged spa facilities include swimming pool, large jacuzzi, massage, steam pool and sauna. Developed over three generations by the Simoncini family, this peaceful, friendly site is set in more than four hectares of mature, well shaded countryside at the foot of the Roquebrune Rock. Activities include climbing the Rock with a guide. We became more and more intrigued with stories about the Rock, and the Holy Hole, the Three Crosses and the Hermit all call for further exploration which reception staff are happy to arrange; likewise trips to Monte Carlo, Ventimigua (Italy) and the Gorges du Verdon, etc. The medieval village of Roquebrune is within walking distance.

Facilities

Modern, refurbished, well designed toilet blocks, baby baths, facilities for disabled visitors. Washing machines. Shop. Bar and restaurant (all open all season). Heated outdoor swimming pool (all season), separate paddling pool (lifeguard in high season), ice cream bar. Games room. Spa facilities. Playing field. Fishing. Canoeing. Waterskiing. Rafting and diving schools. Activities for children and adults (high season), visits to local wine caves. Only gas or electric barbecues. WiFi in reception, bar/restaurant and pool area. Off site: Bicycle hire 1 km. Riding 5 km. Golf 5 km. (reduced fees).

Open: 1 April - 30 September.

Directions

From A8 take Le Muy exit, follow N7 towards Fréjus for 13 km. bypassing Le Muy. After crossing A8, turn right at roundabout towards Roquebrune-sur-Argens. Site is on left after 1 km. just before bridge over river. GPS: 43.450783, 6.6335

Charges guide

Per unit incl. 2 persons and electricity	€ 23,00 - € 43,00
extra person	€ 4,00 - € 7,80
child (5-10 yrs)	€ 3,20 - € 6,20
dog (max. 1)	€ 3,20

Camping Cheques accepted.

For latest campsite news, availability and prices visit

alanrogers.com

Roquebrune-sur-Argens

Camping Caravaning Moulin des Iscles

Chemin du Moulin des Iscles, F-83520 Roquebrune-sur-Argens (Var) T: 04 94 45 70 74
E: moulin.iscles@wanadoo.fr alanrogers.com/FR83240

Moulin des Iscles is a small, pretty site beside the River Argens with access to the river in places for fishing, canoeing and swimming, with some sought after pitches overlooking the river. The 90 grassy, level pitches have water and electricity (6A). A nice mixture of deciduous trees provides natural shade and colour and the old mill house is near the entrance, which has a security barrier closed at night. This is a quiet site with little on-site entertainment, but with a pleasant restaurant. Visitors with disabilities are made very welcome. It is a real campsite, not a 'camping village'.

Facilities

Fully equipped toilet block, plus small block near entrance, ramped access for disabled visitors. Some Turkish style toilets. Washbasins have cold water. Baby bath and changing facilities. Washing machine. Restaurant, home cooked dish-of-the-day. Well stocked shop. Library with some English books. TV, pool table, table tennis. Play area, minigolf, boules all outside the barrier. Internet terminal. Canoeing. Off site: Bicycle hire 1 km. (cycle way to St Aygulf). Riding and golf 4 km. Beach 9 km.

Open: 1 April - 30 September.

Directions

From A8, exit Le Muy, follow N7 towards Fréjus for 13 km. Cross over A8 and turn right at roundabout through Roquebrune-sur-Argens towards St Aygulf for 1 km. Site signed on left. Follow private unmade road for 500 m. GPS: 43.44513, 6.65783

Charges guide

Per unit incl. 2 persons and electricity	€ 20,10 - € 23,40
extra person	€ 2,60 - € 3,30

Camping Cheques accepted.

Saint Apollinaire

Campéole le Clos du Lac

Campé●le

Route des Lacs, F-05160 Saint Apollinaire (Hautes-Alpes) T: 04 92 44 27 43. E: clos-du-lac@campeole.com
alanrogers.com/FR05130

Le Clos du Lac is a member of the Campéole group and can be found close to the little mountain village of St Apollinaire on the southern fringe of the immense Ecrins National Park. The site is at an altitude of 1450 m. and has 68 pitches including 50 for tourers (most with electricity 7A), and 18 mobile homes for hire. Many of the pitches have fine views of the Lac de Serre Ponçon below and the mountain scenery all around. There is a smaller lake nearby, popular for its 'no kill' fly fishing, and also for swimming. This is also a great place to watch the night sky with a special astronomy week in August. The nearby Boscodon forest has been officially acknowledged as the least polluted place in France. On-site amenities include a small shop and communal barbecue area. The Lac de Serre Ponçon is popular for many watersports and the site is well located for exploring this wonderful mountain landscape. The popular Montagne aux Marmottes animal park is close at hand, along with the Cathedral of Notre Dame du Réal at Embrun. Le Clos du Lac is a good base for walking and mountain biking and the site's friendly managers will be pleased to recommend possible itineraries.

Facilities

Shop. Play area. Tourist information. Mobile homes for rent. Off site: St Apollinaire (shops and restaurants). Canoe hire. Fishing. Minigolf. Water sports. Hiking and mountain biking. Bicycle hire. National park of Les Ecrins.

Open: 21 May - 24 September.

Directions

St Apollinaire is on the north side of Lac de Serre Ponçon. From Gap head west on N94 towards Embrun. At Chorges join the D9 to St Apollinaire from where the site is well indicated.
GPS: 44.5647, 6.3652

Charges guide

Per unit incl. 2 persons and electricity	€ 15,10 - € 18,30

For latest campsite news, availability and prices visit

alanrogers.com

Saint Aygulf

Caravaning l'Etoile d'Argens

F-83370 Saint Aygulf (Var) T: 04 94 81 01 41. E: info@etoiledargens.com

alanrogers.com/FR83070

First impressions of l'Etoile d'Argens are of space, cleanliness and calm. This is a site run with families in mind and many of the activities are free, making it an excellent choice for a good value holiday. There are 450 level, fully serviced grass pitches (all with 10/16A electricity). Separated by hedges, they range in size from 100-250 sq.m. and mainly have good shade. The pool and bar area is attractively landscaped with olive and palm trees on beautifully kept grass. There are two heated pools (one for adults, one for children) both of which are designed very much with families in mind. Reception staff are very friendly and English is spoken. The exceptionally large pitches could easily take two caravans and cars or one family could have a very spacious plot with a garden like atmosphere. The river runs alongside the site with a free boat service to the beach (15/6-15/9). This is a good family site for the summer but also good in low season for a quiet stay in a superb location with excellent pitches. There are 88 mobile homes for rent. For a large site, it is unusually calm and peaceful, even in July.

Facilities	Directions
Over 20, well kept, small toilet blocks. Supermarket and gas supplies. Bar, restaurant, pizzeria, takeaway. Two adult pools (heated 1/4-30/6), paddling pool, Jacuzzi, solarium. Floodlit tennis with coaching. Minigolf. Aerobics. Archery (July/Aug). Football and swimming lessons. Boules. Good play area. Children's entertainment (July/Aug). Activity programme with games, dances and escorted walking trips to the surrounding hills within 3 km. Off site: Golf and riding 2 km. Beach 3.5 km. **Open:** 1 April - 30 September (with all services).	From A8 exit 36, take the N7 towards Le Muy, Fréjus. After 8 km. at roundabout take D7 signed Roquebrune, St Aygulf. In 9.5 km. (after roundabout) turn left signed Fréjus. Site is signed. Ignore width and height limit signs as site is before the limit (500 m). GPS: 43.41581, 6.70545

Charges guide

Per tent pitch (100 sq.m) incl. electricity and 2 persons	€ 14,00 - € 38,00
comfort pitch (130 sq.m) incl. 3 persons	€ 29,00 - € 62,00
incl. 4 persons (180 sq.m)	€ 33,00 - € 72,00
extra person	€ 6,00 - € 9,00
child (under 7 yrs)	€ 5,00 - € 7,00

Saint Raphaël

Castel Camping Douce Quiétude

3435 boulevard Jacques Baudino, F-83700 Saint Raphaël (Var) T: 04 94 44 30 00

E: info@douce-quietude.com alanrogers.com/FR83250

Douce Quiétude is 5 km. from the beaches at Saint Raphaël and Agay but is quietly situated at the foot of the Estérel massif. There are 400 pitches, only 70 of these are for touring. Set in pleasant pine woodland or shaded, green areas, the pitches are of a comfortable size, separated by bushes and trees with electricity (10A), water, drainage and telephone/TV points provided. This mature site offers a wide range of services and facilities complete with a pool complex. It can be busy in the main season yet is relaxed and spacious. Security is good, with the wearing of identity bracelets mandatory throughout your stay. This area is a real golfers' paradise, with many beautiful courses close by.

Facilities	Directions
Fully equipped modern toilet blocks, facilities for babies and disabled visitors. Launderette. Bar, restaurant, takeaway, pizzeria (3/4-3/9). Shop. Three swimming pools (two heated), water slide, jacuzzi. Play area. Children's club, activities for teenagers (all July/Aug). Sports area. Games room. Tennis. Minigolf. Archery. Fitness centre, sauna. Evening entertainment, shows, karaoke, discos (July/Aug). Mountain bike hire. Only gas barbecues. Off site: Bus route 1 km. Golf and riding 2 km. Windsurf hire and sea fishing 5 km. **Open:** 3 April - 2 October.	From A8 exit 38 (Fréjus/St Raphaël) take the D100, signed Valescure then Agay. Follow site signs. Access via N98 coast road turning north at Agay on D100. Pass Esterel Camping, then site signed. GPS: 43.44727, 6.80600

Charges guide

Per unit incl. 2 persons and electricity	€ 19,00 - € 52,50
extra person	€ 6,00 - € 10,00
child (3-13 yrs)	€ 5,00 - € 8,00
pet	€ 5,00

Camping Cheques accepted.

For latest campsite news, availability and prices visit

alanrogers.com

L'Étoile d'Argens

✦✦✦✦✦

2011

Camping-Caravaning

www.etoiledargens.com

E-mail : info@etoiledargens.com

83370 Saint Aygulf - Tel : +33 4 94 81 01 41

Saint Aygulf

Camping Résidence du Campeur

B.P. 12, D7, F-83371 Saint Aygulf (Var) T: 04 94 81 01 59. E: info@residence-campeur.com

alanrogers.com/FR83050

This excellent site near the Côte d'Azur will take you away from all the bustle of the Mediterranean coast. Spread out over ten hectares, there are separate areas for mobile homes and touring caravans and tents, with pitches arranged along avenues. The 67 touring pitches average 100 sq.m. in size and all have electricity connections and private sanitary facilities (although washbasins double as dishwashing sinks). The bar/restaurant is surrounded by a shady terrace, whilst friendly staff provide an excellent service. A pleasant pool complex is available for those who wish to stay on site instead of going swimming in the nearby lake or from the Mediterranean beaches. Activities are organised daily during the summer season and the site has its own open air cinema.

Facilities

Private toilet blocks are cleaned at regular intervals and include a washbasin, shower and WC. Laundry area with washing machines. Well stocked supermarket. Bar/restaurant. Takeaway (all open all season). New swimming pool complex with four water slides (high season). Two tennis courts. Minigolf. Boules. Fishing. Bicycle hire. Play area. Games/TV room. Only gas or electric barbecues are permitted. Off site: Riding 1.5 km. Golf 2 km. Beach and St Aygulf 2.5 km. Water skiing nearby.

Open: 27 March - 30 September.

Directions

Leave A8 at Le Muy exit (no. 36) on N555 towards Draguignan then onto the N7 towards Fréjus. Turn right on D7 signed St Aygulf and site is on the right about 2.5 km. before the town.
GPS: 43.40905, 6.70893

Charges guide

Per unit incl. 3 persons and electricity	€ 30,10 - € 50,15
extra person	€ 5,19 - € 8,65
child (under 7 yrs)	€ 3,54 - € 5,90
dog	€ 4,00

La Résidence du Campeur
Camping Club ★★★★
Provence - Côte d'Azur

2,5 km away from the fine sandy beaches, discover the charm of this shady campsite where one can enjoy well being and comfort: small supermarket, bar, restaurant, open air cinema. Disco, playing room, mini golf, multi sports terrain, petanque, archery. Animations and Kids Club in July and August.

B.P 12   Les grands châteaux de Villepey-D7 83371 Saint-Aygulf cedex
Tél : +33(0)4.94.81.01.59   Fax : +33(0)4.94.81.01.64
www.residence-campeur.com   Email : info@residence-campeur.com

Saint Rémy-de-Provence

Camping Mas de Nicolas

Avenue Plaisance du Touch, F-13210 Saint Rémy-de-Provence (Bouches du Rhône) T: 04 90 92 27 05
E: camping-masdenicolas@nerim.fr alanrogers.com/FR13050

The site has a very spacious feel to it, due mainly to the central area of gently sloping grass dotted with shrubs, that is kept clear of pitches and used for leisure and sunbathing. The 140 pitches are separated by hedges and flowering shrubs, 34 for mobile homes, the remainder for touring units. The pitches all have electricity, water and drainage, and access roads are wide. Some pitches are an irregular shape and some are sloping, but many have views and they are mostly organised into groups of two and four. There is an attractive pool area with 'Balneotherapie', or as we would call it a spa and gym.

Facilities

Good, modern toilet blocks including baby bathroom. Plans to refurbish one block. Dishwashing and laundry sinks, washing machines. Small bar (w/ends only until high season), occasional paella evenings. Swimming pool (15/5-15/9). Sauna, steam room, spa bath, gym. Play area. Bicycle hire. Internet access. Off site: Adjacent municipal gym, tennis, volleyball courts. Bicycle hire, riding 1 km. Fishing 2 km. Golf 15 km. St Rémy has a wide selection of restaurants, Wednesday market.

Open: 1 March - 31 October.

Directions

St Rémy-de-Provence is located where the D571 from Avignon connects with the D99 Tarascon - Cavaillon road. Site is signed from the village centre on the north side. Leave the A7 at Cavaillon or Avignon-Sud. GPS: 43.79622, 4.83879

Charges guide

Per unit incl. 2 persons and electricity	€ 18,00 - € 24,00
extra person	€ 5,50 - € 7,00
child (under 10 yrs)	€ 2,50 - € 5,50

For latest campsite news, availability and prices visit

alanrogers.com

Saint Rémy-de-Provence

Camping Monplaisir

Chemin de Monplaisir, F-13210 Saint Rémy-de-Provence (Bouches du Rhône) T: 04 90 92 22 70
E: reception@camping-monplaisir.fr alanrogers.com/FR13040

Only a kilometre from the centre of St Rémy, in the foothills of the Alpilles mountains, this is one of the most pleasant and well run sites we have come across. St Rémy is a very popular town and the site was full when we visited in mid June. Everything about it is of a high standard and quality. The good impression created by the reception and shop continues through the rest of the site. In all there are 130 level grass pitches with 9 taken by smart mobile homes, with 10A electricity everywhere. Flowering shrubs and greenery abounds, roads are tarmac and all is neat and tidy. There are six toilet blocks strategically placed for all areas. All are heated and one is larger, but all are unisex. The recreation area with a swimming pool (18 x 10 m), jacuzzi and paddling pool is overlooked by the bar. Open in July and August, it provides light meals and snacks and some entertainment.

Facilities

Six good quality, unisex toilet blocks are all heated in low season and have some washbasins in cabins. Two have family rooms, and en-suite facilities for disabled visitors. Washing machines. Two motorcaravan service points. Shop with essentials (good cheese and cold meat counter), also takeaway pizzas. Bar with snacks (July/Aug). Swimming pool. Play area. Boules. Only gas and electric barbecues are permitted. Mobile homes and chalets for hire. Off site: St Rémy 1 km. Les Baux 5 km. Bicycle hire 1 km. Fishing 2 km. Riding 5 km. Golf 10 km.

Open: 6 March - 31 October.

Directions

From St Rémy town centre follow signs for Arles and Nîmes. At roundabout on western side of town take D5 signed Maillane and immediately left by a supermarket. Site is signed and is 500 m. on the left. GPS: 43.79695, 4.82372

Charges guide

Per unit incl. 2 persons and electricity (6A)	€ 18,60 - € 28,00
extra person	€ 5,00 - € 8,00
child (2-7 yrs)	€ 3,00 - € 6,00
dog	€ 1,80 - € 2,00

Saint Romain-en-Viennois

Camping le Soleil de Provence

Route de Nyons, F-84110 Saint Romain-en-Viennois (Vaucluse) T: 04 90 46 46 00
E: info@camping-soleil-de-provence.fr alanrogers.com/FR84100

This site has been developed to a high standard. The 162 average sized pitches, 150 for touring, are separated by hedges and a variety of young trees offering only a little shade (10A electricity). The excellent pool, surrounded by a sunbathing terrace, and overlooked by the bar, is an unusual shape with an island in the centre. Although there is no paddling pool one end of the pool is very shallow. There is some organised entertainment in July and August but the emphasis is on a quiet and peaceful environment and is an ideal site for relaxing and unwinding.

Facilities

Modern well appointed, heated toilet blocks, facilities for disabled visitors, baby room. Washing machine, dryer. Motorcaravan services. Small shop for bread, open on demand. Bar, snack bar (all season). New aqua park with waterslides and paddling pool. Small play area. Volleyball, table tennis, boules. Off site: Tennis 1 km. Vaison-la -Romaine 4 km. Rafting, hiking, cycling, mountain biking 4 km. (Mont Ventoux is a real challenge). Bicycle hire 5 km. Fishing 15 km. Medieval villages, market towns. vineyards, wine tasting.

Open: 15 March - 31 October.

Directions

Site is 4 km. north of Vaison-la-Romaine on the D938 road to Nyons. Turn right, signed St Romain -en-Viennois (site signed) and take first left to site. GPS: 44.26902, 5.10597

Charges guide

Per person	€ 3,50 - € 7,50
child (0-7 yrs)	€ 2,50 - € 5,00
pitch	€ 3,00 - € 6,00
car	€ 3,00 - € 6,00
electricity (10A)	€ 4,00
No credit cards.	

Saint Vincent-les-Forts

Campé•le

Campéole le Lac

Le Fein, F-04340 Saint Vincent-les-Forts (Alpes-de-Haute-Provence) T: 04 92 85 51 57. E: lac@campeole.com

alanrogers.com/FR04210

Le Lac is a member of the Campéole group and enjoys a fine location in the mountains of Haute Provence. The site can be found at an altitude of 800m on the banks of the large Lac de Serre Ponçon and many of the site's 300 pitches (200 for tourers) have fine views of the lake and the surrounding mountains. The waters of the lake have an alluring blue-green hue and shelve gradually from the site's beach. There is also an ecological swimming pool, using natural water, consistent with this stunning natural setting. Other on-site amenities include a shop, restaurant and various sports facilities, notably volleyball and tennis. A number of pitches have lakeside locations and are particularly popular with fishermen. Water sports are popular and a hire service is offered, including canoes, electric boats and wakeboards. This is understandably a great area for hiking and mountain biking, with a number of excellent routes passing very close to the campsite. Reception staff have full details and will be pleased to make recommendations.

Facilities

Bar and restaurant (1/6-15/9). Shop and takeaway (1/7-31/8). Eco swimming pool. Fishing. Volleyball. Tennis. Play area. Canoes and boat hire. Activity and entertainment programme. Tourist information. Mobile homes, chalets and equipped tents for rent. Off site: Hiking and cycle tracks. Montagne aux Marmottes (animal park). Riding 10 km. Serre Ponçon dam.

Open: 1 May - 30 September.

Directions

From Gap, head south on N85 and then join the D900b following signs to Barcelonnette. Continue on this road along the valley of the Durance passing the massive Barrage (dam) de Serre Ponçon and continue towards St Vincent-les-Forts. The site is well indicated from here. GPS: 44.45682, 6.36529

Charges guide

Per unit incl. 2 persons and electricity	€ 17,10 - € 26,60

RHÔNE-ALPES

Campé•le

CAMPSITES AND RENTALS

Le Lac*

Direct access to the Lac de Serre Ponçon, natural swimming pool; amenities, pitches and accommodations of high quality.

04340 St Vincent Les Forts - Tel.: +33-492-8551-57 - www.campeole.co.uk / lac@campeole.com

Salon-de-Provence

Camping le Nostradamus

Route d'Eyguières, F-13300 Salon-de-Provence (Bouches du Rhône) T: 04 90 56 08 36

E: gilles.nostra@wanadoo.fr alanrogers.com/FR13030

Only some 5 km. from Salon-de-Provence, near the village of Eyguières, this is a very pleasant campsite with grassy shaded pitches thanks to the many trees which have been preserved here as a result of the imaginative irrigation scheme developed by the owners in the 18th century. The campsite edging the canal was first opened 42 years ago as a farm site but has now been developed to offer 83 hedged pitches including 10 used for mobile homes. There are 20 with full services, the rest having electricity connections (4/6/10A). This is a family site but having said that the canal is unfenced.

Facilities

One large block with showers and toilets upstairs, and one small toilet block both provide all modern facilities including an en-suite unit for babies and children and another for disabled visitors (key). Washing machine (key). Motorcaravan service point. Shop (basic essentials) and bar. Takeaway/restaurant (15/5-30/9). Swimming and paddling pools (15/5-30/9). Play area outside entrance. Petanque. Fishing. WiFi (charged). Off site: Regular bus service on the main road, timetables in reception. Riding 5 km. Golf 12 km.

Open: 1 March - end October.

Directions

From A7 exit 26 (Senas) follow N538 south for 5 km. Then take D175 west and pick up the D17 going south to Salon. Site is at junction of the D17 and CD72 with the entrance off the CD72. From A54 exit 13 go north towards Eyguières and take first right on CD72 (site signed). Entrance is just before the T-junction with the D17. GPS: 43.67772, 5.06476

Charges guide

Per unit incl. 2 persons and electricity	€ 18,95 - € 25,00
extra person	€ 4,50 - € 5,60
Camping Cheques accepted.	

For latest campsite news, availability and prices visit

alanrogers.com

Sanary-sur-Mer

Campasun Parc Mogador

167 chemin de Beaucours, F-83110 Sanary-sur-Mer (Var) T: 04 94 74 53 16
E: mogador@campasun.com alanrogers.com/FR83320

This site in the Mediterranean countryside is very much geared for family holidays with children. Some 20 minutes on foot from the beach, the site has a very large and well kept pool area and a stage for entertainment. Somewhat smaller than other sites of this type, there are 180 good sized pitches (160 for touring units). The ground is mainly level, if rather stony and sandy. Variable shade is available and all pitches have 10A electricity. There are plans to enlarge some of the smaller, 80 sq.m. pitches. The attractive pool is surrounded by ample paved sunbathing areas.

Facilities

Two large, super de-luxe toilet blocks, one including washbasins and showers in cabins. The high-tech toilets are automatically cleaned and disinfected after every use. Laundry. Motorcaravan services. Restaurant with varied and full menu (1/4-5/11), also snacks, pizzas and takeaway. Swimming pool and paddling pool, solarium. Boules. TV room also used for entertainment shows, cabarets, etc. Miniclub for children and evening entertainment in season. Dogs are not accepted. Off site: Beach 800 m. Golf 6 km. Fishing 800 m.

Open: 15 March - 5 November.

Directions

Take Bandol exit 12 from A50 and head for Six Fours on the N559. Arriving at Sanary-sur-Mer turn left towards Beaucours and site is on left after 100 m. GPS: 43.1488, 5.7732

Charges guide

Per unit incl. 2 persons and electricity (10A)	€ 18,00 - € 36,00
with individual sanitary facility	€ 22,00 - € 42,00
extra person	€ 5,00 - € 7,00

Camping Cheques accepted.

Vaison-la-Romaine

Camping l'Ayguette

Faucon (CD86), F-84110 Vaison-la-Romaine (Vaucluse) T: 04 90 46 40 35. E: info@ayguette.com
alanrogers.com/FR84060

Set in the beautiful region of north Provence, surrounded by vineyards and wooded hills, the 99 slightly sloping, stony pitches, 91 for touring, are widely spaced out on terraces amongst pine and oak trees giving plenty of dappled shade, only a few suitable for large units. All have 10A electricity (long leads necessary) but some are a considerable distance from the amenities, not ideal for those with walking difficulties. Rock pegs are essential. The reception building houses a bar, snack bar, small shop and terrace. Close by is an attractive swimming pool (heated all season) and sunbathing area.

Facilities

Two well equipped toilet blocks, one heated. Room for disabled campers or families with young children. Washing machines. Heated swimming pool, terrace (all season). Internet access. Bar, snack bar, takeaway (July/Aug). Small shop, bread to order. Playground. Occasional entertainment, some activities for children. WiFi (charged). Only gas and electric barbecues. Off site: Faucon 1 km. Vaison-la-Romaine 5 km. Bicycle hire 5 km. Riding 7 km.

Open: 16 April - 1 October.

Directions

From Vaison-la-Romaine take the D938 towards Nyons. Shortly turn right on D71, signed St Romain -en-Viennois. Drive through village and then turn right on D86. Site is well signed, on the right. GPS: 44.2622, 5.129133

Charges guide

Per unit incl. 1 or 2 persons	€ 14,50 - € 23,50
extra person	€ 4,00 - € 5,30

Long stay reductions off season.

Vaison-la-Romaine

Domaine le Carpe Diem

Route de Saint-Marcellin, B.P. 68, F-84110 Vaison-la-Romaine (Vaucluse) T: 04 90 36 02 02
E: carpe-diem@franceloc.fr alanrogers.com/FR84070

Carpe Diem is attractively themed with Greek statues and an amphitheatre surround to its older pool. The situation is quite impressive with magnificent views over one of the most beautiful parts of France, yet only 1 km. from the fascinating town of Vaison-la-Romaine. There are 275 pitches with 119 small to medium sized, grassy/stony touring pitches all with electricity (6/10A); most with little or no shade. A new area has mobile homes, and a few unshaded touring pitches. This is a good site for active families seeking all day entertainment. Only gas barbecues allowed on site.

Facilities

Two modern toilet blocks with facilities for children and campers with disabilities. Washing machine. Motorcaravan services. Reception, small shop (25/3-1/11). Bar, pizzeria, restaurant/takeaway (1/5-30/9). TV. Swimming pools including slides and flumes, one new, covered and heated (all season). Play area. Minigolf, archery. Mountain bike hire. Miniclub. Extensive entertainment programme (high season). Off site: Fishing 1 km. Riding, bicycle hire 2 km. Golf 20 km. Vaison-la-Romaine 1 km.

Open: 25 March - 1 November.

Directions

Leave Vaison-la-Romaine on D938 heading south towards Carpentras. 1 km. beyond the 'Super U' roundabout turn left on D151, signed St Marcellin. Site entrance is on the left immediately after the junction. GPS: 44.23431, 5.08964

Charges guide

Per unit incl. 2 persons	€ 16,00 - € 30,00
extra person	€ 4,70 - € 7,00
electricity (6A)	€ 4,00

Veynes

Camping Solaire

F-05400 Veynes (Hautes-Alpes) T: 04 92 58 12 34. E: info@camping-solaire.com

alanrogers.com/FR05080

An attractive, well kept site surrounded by mountains and scenes of pastural beauty, the owners have developed le Solaire to offer a wide range of facilities including a large jacuzzi heated to 30ºC. The swimming pools for adults and youngsters are supervised by a lifeguard, who also gives swimming lessons. The owners are particularly proud of their grasslands and of the 167 large pitches. There are 73 for touring in a separate area, many with good shade and all having 6A electricity with water close by. You can use the site's website to view and select your pitch. The site is well placed to explore the area around Gap and the surrounding countryside.

Facilities

Modern, clean and heated toilet blocks with facilities for campers with disabilities. Bar (1/6-30/9). Shop, snacks, takeaway (1/7-30/9). Swimming pools (1/6-30/9). Jacuzzi (1/7-30/9). Large games room/TV. Football. Bicycle hire. Off site: Fishing 100 m. Lake, beach, swimming, boating, 300 m. Rafting, hang gliding, Rock climbing, many bike rides and hiking tracks. Veynes with range of shops and facilities 2 km.

Open: All year.

Directions

From Grenoble on N75, in town of Aspres-sur-Bu'ch, take D994a to join D994 travelling northeast towards Veynes. Site is signed on right 1 km. before village. After 300 m. take next right, entrance on right within 50 m. GPS: 44.52161, 5.80341

Charges guide

Per unit incl. 2 persons	€ 10,00 - € 17,00
extra person	€ 4,00 - € 6,90
electricity (5A)	€ 3,00

Villars-Colmars

Camping Caravaning le Haut-Verdon

RD908, F-04370 Villars-Colmars (Alpes-de-Haute-Provence) T: 04 92 83 40 09
E: campinglehautverdon@wanadoo.fr **alanrogers.com/FR04060**

For those seeking a quiet, family site set in most spectacular scenery, Camping le Haut-Verdon is ideal. It is on the banks of the Verdon, an excellent trout river, which flows through the spectacular gorge. Surrounded by the majestic peaks of the Alpes-de-Haute-Provence, it is on the doorstep of the Mercantour National Park. Set amongst the pines, the 109 pitches are mostly on the large size but are rather stony. With 73 for touring units, all have electricity (6/10A) but some require long leads. There is a small village nearby and the town of St André is 23 km. away.

Facilities

Refurbished, heated toilet block. Washing machines. Freezer for ice packs. Room for tenters for inclement weather. Motorcaravan services. Small shop. Bar/restaurant, takeaway. Heated swimming, paddling pools (from 1/6). Small play area. Giant chess. Boules. Skittle alley. Tennis. TV room. Organised games and competitions. Fishing. Barbecue areas (portable ones banned). Off site: Riding 1 km. Bicycle hire 3 km.

Open: 5 May - 16 September.

Directions

Follow D955 north from St André les Alpes towards Colmar. After 11 km. road number changes to D908. Site on right at southern edge of Villars-Colmars. Caravans not advised to use the D908 from Annot or Col d'Allos from Barcelonnette. GPS: 44.1601, 6.60625

Charges guide

Per unit incl. 2 persons	€ 13,00 - € 25,00
electricity (6/10A)	€ 3,00 - € 4,00

Villecroze-les-Grottes

Camping Club le Ruou

Les Esparrus, 309, RD 560, F-83690 Villecroze-les-Grottes (Var) T: 04 94 70 67 70. E: info@leruou.com

alanrogers.com/FR83410

This is a family oriented site in the Provençal countryside, very much geared for family holidays with children. Some 45 minutes by car from the coast at Fréjus, the site has a large and well kept pool area and a mobile stage for entertainment. Smaller than some other sites of this type, there are 134 good sized pitches (50 for touring units). On mainly terraced, rather stony, ground with good shade, all have 6/10A electricity. Some of the pitches for caravans are along a steep path but there is a 4x4 available to assist. The attractive heated pool complex with three slides is surrounded by a sunbathing area.

Facilities

One new super de-luxe toilet block includes washbasins in cabins. Facilities for babies and disabled visitors. Laundry facilities. Snacks and takeaway (1/7-31/8). The main building houses a bar and entertainment room with TV. Area for shows, cabarets, etc. with mobile stage. Two swimming pools. Boules. Play area. Miniclub for children and evening entertainment in season. Charcoal barbecues are not permitted. Off site: Beach 35 km. Fishing, riding and bicycle hire 5 km. Golf 25 km.

Open: 1 April - 30 October.

Directions

From the A8 (Toulon - Mandelieu-la-Napoule) take exit 13 onto the N7 towards Le Muy. At Les Arcs turn left on D555 (Draguignan), then onto D557 to Villecroze. Site is on the left side of this road. GPS: 43.55345, 6.297983

Charges guide

Per unit incl. 2 persons	€ 17,00 - € 32,40
extra person	€ 3,80 - € 5,80
Camping Cheques accepted.	

For latest campsite news, availability and prices visit

alanrogers.com

Volonne

Sunêlia Hippocampe

Route de Napoléon, F-04290 Volonne (Alpes-de-Haute-Provence) T: 04 92 33 50 00
E: camping@l-hippocampe.com alanrogers.com/FR04010

Hippocampe is a friendly, family run, 'all action' lakeside site, with families in mind, situated in a beautiful area of France. The perfumes of thyme, lavender and wild herbs are everywhere and the higher hills of Haute Provence are not too far away. There are 447 level, numbered pitches (221 for touring units), medium to very large (130 sq.m) in size. All have electricity (10A) and 243 have water and drainage, most are separated by bushes and cherry trees. Some of the best pitches border the lake. The restaurant, bar, takeaway and shop have all been completely renewed. Games, aerobics, competitions, entertainment and shows, plus a daily club for younger family members are organised in July/August. A soundproofed underground disco is set well away from the pitches and is very popular with teenage customers. Staff tour the site at night ensuring a good night's sleep. The site is, however, much quieter in low season and, with its good discounts, is the time for those who do not want or need entertaining. The Gorges du Verdon is a sight not to be missed and rafting, paragliding and canoe trips can be booked from the site's own tourist information office. Being on the lower slopes of the hills of Haute-Provence, the surrounding area is good for both walking and mountain biking. All in all, this is a very good site for an active or restful holiday and is suitable for outfits of all sizes. English is spoken.

Facilities

Toilet blocks vary from old to modern, all with good clean facilities that include washbasins in cabins. Washing machines. Motorcaravan service point. Bread available (from 7/5). Shop, bar, restaurant and pizzeria (7/5-11/9). Large, heated pool complex (23/4-30/9) with five waterslides, (second pool 1/6-30/9). Tennis. Fishing. Canoeing. Boules. Bicycle hire. Charcoal barbecues are not permitted. Off site: Village of Volonne 600 m. Riding 12 km. Various sporting opportunities.

Open: 16 April - 30 September.

Directions

Approaching from the north turn off N85 across river bridge to Volonne, then right to site. From the south right on D4, 1 km. before Château Arnoux. GPS: 44.10462, 6.01688

Charges 2011

Per unit incl. 2 persons and electricity	€ 16,00 - € 33,00
extra person (over 4 yrs)	€ 3,00 - € 7,00

Camping Cheques accepted.

Volx

Flower Camping la Vandelle

F-04130 Volx (Alpes-de-Haute-Provence) T: 04 92 79 35 85. E: camping-lavandelle@orange.fr
alanrogers.com/FR04240

La Vandelle is a member of the Flower group and is located at the heart of the Luberon national park. This is small site with just 39 pitches, and open for a short season (from 15/6). These are divided into 'Nature' (without electricity) or 'Confort' (with 6A electricity). Most pitches are well shaded. The nearest supermarket is 3 km. away but a number of basic provisions are available on site. There is a swimming pool and adjacent paddling pool. The Luberon is deservedly famous for its clear skies and wonderful sunshine record (more than 300 days of sun every year).

Facilities

Swimming pool and paddling pool. Small shop. Games room. Play area. Tourist information. Off site: Cycle and walking tracks in the Luberon national park. Supermarket 3 km.

Open: 15 June - 15 September.

Directions

Approaching from the north (Sisteron) leave the A51 motorway at La Brillane and follow the southbound D4096 towards Manosque. On arrival in the village of Volx, follow signs to the site. GPS: 43.869419, 5.831584

Charges guide

Per unit incl. 2 persons	€ 16,00 - € 20,00
extra person	€ 4,00

PARC SAINT-JAMES
VILLAGES CLUB

Parc Saint-James is a small group of 4* campsites, all located in the South of France on the Côte d'Azur.

These three 'village-club' style campsites offer a warm welcome, a decent range of facilities with a real family atmosphere and a great location for beach-based holidays.

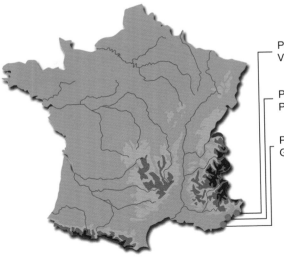

Parc Saint-James 'Le Sourire'
Villeneuve Loubet

Parc Saint-James 'Oasis Village'
Puget sur Argens

Parc Saint-James 'Gassin'
Gassin

Parc Saint-James

In Their Own Words...

Come and discover the Côte d'Azur South of France

Enjoy the pleasure of spending your holidays outdoors in village-clubs where everything has been designed for your leisure and well being.

A superb environment, a warm welcome, a friendly setting where your family can get together in a privileged world and experience true moments of happiness.

Active holidays

Parc Saint-James offers the opportunity to enjoy many activities such as volleyball, tennis, badminton and fitness. Camping Parc Saint-James Le Sourire, is a hub of sports activities. Guests can also enjoy horse riding, windsurfing, rowing, diving and climbing.

...or relaxing holidays

Parc Saint-James campsites village club is for you! You'll find a swimming pool, sun deck and shady trees. Each campsite works hard to ensure you don't need to lift a finger – just relax and we'll take care of you. Enjoy our bars and TV lounges.

Your evening

Parc Saint-James ensures you are always close to some activity and entertainment. A short distance from Fréjus and Saint-Raphaël, our location in the Gulf of St. Tropez allows you to party through the night. And the Parc Saint-James campsites organise evenings exclusively for residents, with a different daily themed programme (musical groups and/or shows) and at Oasis, from 11pm, a disco party.

Children's kingdom

At Parc Saint-James campsites, children are heroes! Children from 4 to 10 years can enjoy our mini-club and a whole range of fun activities: treasure hunts, contests, make-up, crafts and sports. They will also enjoy our playground with slides and swings or go paddling safely under the eye of a lifeguard. Older children can do battle with friends in our arcades or play ping-pong, soccer and volleyball.

www.camping-parcsaintjames.com

Bathed in sunshine from early spring to late autumn, surrounded by stunning scenery, cosmopolitan towns and superb sandy beaches, no wonder this is one of France's most sought-after destinations.

DÉPARTEMENT: 06 ALPES-MARITIME

MAJOR CITIES: NICE, CANNES, MONTE CARLO (MONACO)

The glittering Côte d'Azur, perhaps better known as the French Riviera, is a beautiful stretch of coast studded with sophisticated towns such as the famous Monte Carlo, Nice, and Cannes, not forgetting the other famous and arguably the most glamorous resort of St Tropez. With its vast expanses of golden sandy beaches and long lazy hours of sunshine, this is a paradise for sun worshippers and beach enthusiasts.

It's a spectacular coast of rugged coves, sweeping beaches and warm seas. The quaint harbours and fishing villages have become chic destinations, now full of pleasure yachts, harbour-side cafés and crowded summertime beaches. Further up in the hills are quieter tiny medieval villages with winding streets and white-walled houses with terracotta roofs, which have attracted artists for many years. In St Paul-de-Vence visitors browse through shops and galleries set on narrow winding cobblestone streets and inland Grasse is the perfume capital of the world, surrounded by the Provençal lavender fields and shady olive groves which pervade the air with a magical scent at certain times of the year.

Places of interest

Antibes: old city with 17th-century ramparts, 12th-century castle.

Cannes: popular for conventions and festivals, Cannes film festival, la Croisette, old city.

Grasse: capital of the perfume industry.

Menton: warmest of coastal cities, year round resort.

Nice: Promenade des Anglais, fine arts museum, Matisse museum.

Roquebrune: château, Ste Marguerite church.

Saint Paul-de-Vence: medieval village, Maeght Foundation.

Cuisine of the region

Aigo Bouido: garlic and sage soup.

Bouillabaisse: fish soup.

Rouille: an orange coloured sauce with peppers, garlic and saffron.

Bourride: a creamy fish soup.

Pissaladière: Provençal bread dough with onions, anchovies and olives.

Pistou (Soupe au): vegetable soup bound with *pommade*.

Pommade: a thick paste of garlic, basil, cheese and olive oil.

Ratatouille: aubergines, courgettes, onions, garlic, red peppers and tomatoes in olive oil.

www.guideriviera.com
info@guideriviera.com
(0)4 93 37 78 78

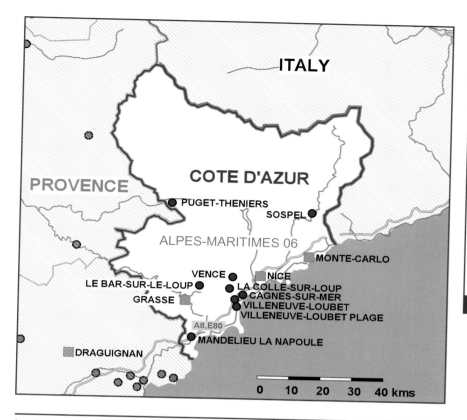

ITALY

COTE D'AZUR

PROVENCE

● PUGET-THENIERS

SOSPEL ●

ALPES-MARITIMES 06

■ MONTE-CARLO

VENCE ●   ● NICE

LE BAR-SUR-LE-LOUP ●   ● LA COLLE-SUR-LOUP
GRASSE ■   ● CAGNES-SUR-MER
        ● VILLENEUVE-LOUBET
A8,E80   VILLENEUVE-LOUBET PLAGE

● MANDELIEU LA NAPOULE

■ DRAGUIGNAN

0   10   20   30   40 kms

La Colle-sur-Loup
Camping les Pinèdes

Route du Pont de Pierre, F-06480 La Colle-sur-Loup (Alpes-Maritimes) T: 04 93 32 98 94
E: info@lespinedes.com alanrogers.com/FR06100

Les Pinèdes is 7 km. inland from the busy coast, at the centre of all the attractions of the Côte d'Azur, yet far enough away to be a peaceful retreat at the end of a busy day. Run by the third generation of family owners, the site is terraced on a wooded hillside where olives and vines used to grow. All the level pitches have electricity (6-10A), most also with water and they are separated by low bushes. Twelve new pitches at the top of the site and also a small children's pool have recently been completed. The restaurant at the site entrance has an excellent reputation. In May the evenings are alive with fireflies. A Sites et Paysages member.

Facilities

Two excellent new toilet blocks. One block has facilities for disabled visitors. Baby room. Shop, bakery. Bar, restaurant, takeaway. Swimming pool. Play area. Field for volleyball, basketball, football, archery, boules. Entertainment for young and old (July/Aug). Weekly walks in the hills (June-Sept). New mobile homes to rent. WiFi. Off site: River fishing 50 m. Village 1 km. (tennis, riding, leisure park, keep fit course, antiques quarter). St Paul-de-Vence is 15 minutes away.

Open: 15 March - 30 September.

Directions

From A8 take D2 towards Vence. At Colle-sur-Loup roundabout take D6 signed Grasse, site on right in 3 km. at large sign after the restaurant entrance. GPS: 43.6817, 7.08335

Charges guide

Per unit incl. 2 persons	
and electricity	€ 22,20 - € 35,20
extra person	€ 4,10 - € 5,50
child (under 6 yrs)	€ 2,20 - € 3,50
dog	€ 2,10 - € 3,20

Cagnes-sur-Mer

Camping Green Park

159 Vallon des Vaux, F-06800 Cagnes-sur-Mer (Alpes-Maritimes) T: 04 93 07 09 96. E: info@greenpark.fr

alanrogers.com/FR06120

Green Park has many facilities of a high standard and the family owners are justifiably proud. Situated just over 4 km. from the beaches at Cagnes-sur-Mer, Green Park is at the centre of the Côte d'Azur. The newer part of the site keeps all the family occupied with activities for children, teenagers and adults, while on the other side of the road is a quieter, traditional site, with limited facilities. There are 78 touring pitches mainly on grass with electricity and 24 are fully serviced. There are 67 mobile homes and chalets. The site has two swimming pools, one on each side of the quiet road. Green Park is situated in an area which benefits from a 'micro climate', hot during the day but pleasantly cooler at night.

Facilities

All the toilets are modern and mostly British style, with facilities for children and disabled visitors (the disabled facilities are superb). Showers and washbasins are modern and kept very clean. Dishwashing and laundry sinks and three washing machines. Bar, restaurant and takeaway (28/4-24/9). Two swimming pools (all season, one heated 5/5-24/9). Internet point. Games room. Electronic barrier (€5 card deposit) and a gate keeper on duty all night. Off site: Beach 4 km. Golf and riding 9 km.

Open: 31 March - 15 October.

Directions

From Aix, A8, exit 47 onto N7 towards Nice. Straight on at traffic lights, by racecourse, for 2 km. Turn left towards Val Fleuri, avenue du Val Fleuri. Over the roundabouts to Chemin Vallon des Vaux, site on right 2 km. Avoid the town centre.
GPS: 43.68901, 7.15598

Charges guide

Per unit incl. 2 persons	€ 13,00 - € 44,00
extra person	€ 4,60 - € 6,00
child (7-17 yrs)	€ 3,90 - € 4,50
electricity	€ 5,50 - € 6,50

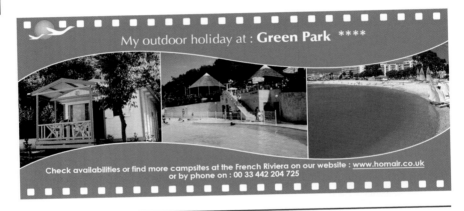

My outdoor holiday at : **Green Park** ★★★★

Check availabilities or find more campsites at the French Riviera on our website : www.homair.co.uk or by phone on : 00 33 442 204 725

Le Bar-sur-Loup

Camping Caravaning les Gorges du Loup

965 chemin des Vergers, F-06620 Le Bar-sur-Loup (Alpes-Maritimes) T: 04 93 42 45 06
E: info@lesgorgesduloup.com   alanrogers.com/FR06090

Les Gorges du Loup is situated on a steep hillside above Grasse. The one kilometre lane which leads to the site is narrow with passing places. The 70 pitches are on level terraces, all with electricity and many have stupendous views. Some pitches are only suitable for tents and the site roads are quite steep. A quiet family site, there is no organised entertainment. Grasse (9 km) is surrounded by fields of lavender, mimosa and jasmine and has been famous for the manufacture of perfume since the 16th century. The very friendly and enthusiastic owners provide 4 x 4 assistance and there is a new parking area at the entrance. The owners also speak a little English.

Facilities

Clean toilet blocks with washbasins and hot showers, dishwashing and laundry sinks have only a single hot tap. Washing machine and iron. Reception, small shop, bread. Small bar/restaurant with terrace, takeaway (all 3/6-8/9). Swimming pool, small slide, diving board, but no pool for small children. Boules. Skittles. TV room, board games, library. WiFi (charged). Children's climbing frame, slide. No charcoal barbecues. Chalets, mobile homes for hire. Off site: le Bar-sur-Loup with its few shops and restaurants is only a 500 m. walk.

Open: 3 April - 25 September.

Directions

From Grasse, D2085 Nice road. D3 briefly to Châteauneuf Pré du Lac. D2210 to Pont-de-Loup, Vence. Site signed on right. Pass village of Bar-sur-Loup on left, after sharp right turn, follow narrow access road 750 m. (passing places).
GPS: 43.7017, 6.9948

Charges guide

Per unit incl. 2 persons and electricity	€ 18,70 - € 36,50
extra person	€ 4,10 - € 5,50
child (under 6 yrs)	€ 2,20 - € 3,50
No credit cards.	

For latest campsite news, availability and prices visit

alanrogers.com

Mandelieu-la-Napoule

Camping Caravaning les Cigales

505 avenue de la Mer, F-06210 Mandelieu-la-Napoule (Alpes-Maritimes) T: 04 93 49 23 53
E: campingcigales@wanadoo.fr **alanrogers.com/FR06080**

It is hard to imagine that such a quiet, peaceful site could be in the middle of such a busy town and so near Cannes. The entrance (easily missed) has large electronic gates that ensure that the site is very secure. There are only 115 pitches (42 mobile homes) so this is quite a small, personal site. There are three pitch sizes, from small ones for tents to pitches for larger units and all have electricity (6A), some fully serviced. All are level with much needed shade in summer, although the sun will get through in winter when it is needed. The site is alongside the Canal de Siagne and for a fee, small boats can be launched at La Napoule, then moored outside the campsite's side gate. Les Cigales is open all year so it is useful for the Monte Carlo Rally, the Cannes Film Festival and the Mimosa Festival, all held out of the main season. English is spoken.

Facilities	Directions
Well appointed, clean, heated toilet blocks. Excellent facilities for babies and disabled visitors. Laundry area. Motorcaravan services. Restaurant and takeaway (May-Oct). Attractive heated swimming pool and large sunbathing area (April-Oct). New play area. Two games machines. Canal fishing. Off site: Beach 800 m. The town is an easy walk. Two golf courses within 1 km. Railway station 1 km. for trains to Cannes, Nice, Antibes, Monte Carlo. Hypermarket 2 km. Bus stop 10 minutes. **Open:** All year.	From A8, exit 40, bear right. Remain in right hand lane, continue right signed Plages-Ports, Creche -Campings. Casino supermarket on right. Continue under motorway to T-junction. Turn left, site is 60 m. on left opposite Chinese restaurant. Some other approaches have a 3.3 m. height restriction. GPS: 43.5391, 6.94275

Charges guide

Per unit incl. 2 persons	
and electricity	€ 39,00 - € 51,50
extra person	€ 8,00
child	€ 4,00

Sospel

Camping Domaine Sainte Madeleine

Route de Moulinet, F-06380 Sospel (Alpes-Maritimes) T: 04 93 04 10 48
E: camp@camping-sainte-madeleine.com **alanrogers.com/FR06010**

Domaine Sainte Madeleine is an attractive, peaceful site, with swimming pool, in spectacular mountain scenery. It is about 20 km. inland from Menton, and very near the Italian border. The approach to this site involves a 17 km. climb with hairpin bends and then a choice of going through the pass or an 800 m. long tunnel (3.5 m. high, 3 m. wide). Situated on a terraced hillside with mountain views towards Italy, manoeuvring within the site presents no problem as the pitches are on level, well drained grass. The lower ones have shade but those higher up on the hill have none. Electricity is available to 60 of the 66 pitches. English is spoken. When we visited in late July, the site was very busy with touring caravans so the climb cannot be too bad.

Facilities	Directions
Good quality toilet block with hot showers (token required). Hot water (often only warm) for dishwashing and laundry sinks drawn from single tap. Washing machines. Motorcaravan services. Gas supplies. Bread can be ordered. Swimming pool (140 sq.m. and heated in spring and autumn). Off site: The attractive small town of Sospel is 4 km. with restaurants, bars, cafés and shops. Tennis, riding and a mountain biking centre. Fishing 1 km. **Open:** 31 March - 3 October.	From A8 take Menton exit towards Sospel from where you turn onto the D2566 (route de Moulinet). Site is 4 km. north of Sospel on the left. GPS: 43.89702, 7.41685

Charges 2011

Per unit incl. 2 persons	
and electricity	€ 19,30 - € 22,90
extra person	€ 4,40
No credit cards.	

For latest campsite news, availability and prices visit

alanrogers.com

Vence

Camping Caravaning Domaine de la Bergerie

1330 chemin de la Sine, F-06140 Vence (Alpes-Maritimes) T: 04 93 58 09 36
E: info@camping-domainedelabergerie.com alanrogers.com/FR06030

La Bergerie is a quiet, family owned site, situated in the hills 3 km. from Vence and 10 km. from the sea at Cagnes-sur-Mer. With no mobile homes or chalets, this extensive, natural, lightly wooded site is in a secluded position about 300 m. above sea level. Most of the pitches are shaded and all are of a good size. There are 450 pitches, 224 with electricity (2/5A), water and drainage. Because of the nature of this site, some pitches are a little distance from the toilet blocks. With the aim of keeping this a quiet and tranquil place to stay, there are no organised activities and definitely no groups allowed. It is a large site but because it is so extensive it does not give that impression.

Facilities

Refurbished toilet blocks, excellent provision for disabled visitors (pitches near the block are reserved for disabled campers). Good shop. Small bar/restaurant, takeaway (all 1/5-30/9). Large swimming pool, paddling pool, spacious sunbathing area (1/5-30/9). Playground. Bicycle hire. Tennis. 12 shaded boules pitches (lit at night) with competitions in season. No barbecues. Off site: Riding and fishing 10 km. Golf 18 km. Hourly bus service (excl. Sundays) from site to Vence.

Open: 25 March - 15 October.

Directions

From A8 exit 47 take Cagnes-sur-Mer road towards Vence. Site is west of Vence – follow 'toutes directions' around town, join D2210 Grasse road. In 2 km. at roundabout, turn left, follow site signs, 1.5 km. GPS: 43.71174, 7.0905

Charges guide

Per unit incl. 2 persons and electricity	€ 19,50 - € 31,50
extra person	€ 5,00
Camping Cheques accepted.	

Villeneuve-Loubet

Parc Saint James le Sourire

Route de Grasse, F-06270 Villeneuve-Loubet (Alpes-Maritimes) T: 04 93 20 96 11
E: info@camping-parcsaintjames.com alanrogers.com/FR06190

Le Sourire is a member of the Parc Saint James group. There are 411 pitches here and many are occupied by mobile homes and chalets. There are however 241 touring pitches dispersed throughout the wooded terrain. The site is close to the impressive la Vanade sports complex which has a massive range of activities including no fewer than 55 tennis courts, a riding centre and a 9-hole golf course. There is a good range of activities on site too, including a large swimming pool with a regular programme of aqua gym, water polo and other activities.

Facilities

Laundry. Supermarket. Swimming pool and separate children's pool. Bar and restaurant. Takeaway. Play area. TV room. Gym. Games room. Sports competitions. Children's club. Evening entertainment. Disco. Off site: Cannes and Nice. Nearest beaches 4 km. Marineland water park. Leisure park at La Vanade.

Open: 9 April - 1 October.

Directions

Take the Villeneuve - Loubet exit from the A8 autoroute and follow signs to Grasse joining the D2085. The site can be found on the left, 2 km. from Villeneuve Loubet. GPS: 43.6603, 7.10429

Charges 2011

Per unit incl. 2 persons and electricity	€ 17,00 - € 31,00
extra person	€ 3,00 - € 5,00
child (4-10 yrs)	€ 2,00 - € 4,00

Villeneuve-Loubet-Plage

Camping la Vieille Ferme

296 boulevard des Groules, F-06270 Villeneuve-Loubet-Plage (Alpes-Maritimes) T: 04 93 33 41 44
E: info@vieilleferme.com alanrogers.com/FR06050

In a popular resort area and open all year, la Vieille Ferme is a family owned site with good facilities. It has 113 level gravel-based touring pitches, 95 fully serviced and the majority separated by hedges. Some are only small, simple pitches for little tents. There is also a fully serviced pitch on tarmac for motorhomes. There are special winter rates for long stays with quite a few long stay units on site. The entrance to the site is very colourful with well tended flower beds. English is spoken at reception and the whole place has a very friendly feel to it.

Facilities

Modern, heated, well kept toilet blocks, children's toilets, baby room, facilities for disabled campers. Motorcaravan services. Washing machines, dryer. Shop (Easter-Sept). Machine with drinks, sweets, ices in TV room. Gas, bread, milk to order. Refrigerator hire. Swimming pool, children's pool, heated and covered for winter use (closed mid Nov-mid Dec). Jacuzzi. Internet. Boules. Off site: Bus from outside site. Beach 1 km. Fishing 1 km. Golf and bicycle hire 2 km. Riding 6 km. Marineland water park.

Open: All year.

Directions

From west, A8, exit 44 Antibes, D35, 3.5 km. Left towards Nice, N7. After 3.5 km. turn left for site between Marine Land and Parc de Vaugrenier. Site is 150 m. on right. Avoid N98 Route du Bord de Mer. GPS: 43.62002, 7.12586

Charges guide

Per unit incl. 2 persons	€ 13,50 - € 31,00
extra person	€ 3,90 - € 5,00
child (under 5 yrs)	€ 2,50 - € 3,00
electricity (2-10A)	€ 2,50 - € 6,00

For latest campsite news, availability and prices visit

alanrogers.com

The island of Corsica is both dramatic and beautiful. The scenery is spectacular with bays of white sand lapped by the clear blue waters of the Mediterranean. At certain times of the year the entire island is ablaze with exotic flowers, aided by Corsica's excellent sunshine record.

DÉPARTEMENTS: 2A CORSE-SUD; 2B HAUTE-CORSE

MAJOR CITIES: AJACCIO AND BASTIA

Corsica is regarded by some as the jewel of the Mediterranean islands and is made up of two départements: Haute Corse (upper Corsica) and Corse du Sud (southern Corsica). The island has endured a bloody history, having been much disputed by the Greeks, Romans and Lombards. Five hundred years of Italian rule has influenced the look of the island with Italian-style hilltop hamlets and villages developed alongside mountain springs. Many of the villages feature rustic, unadorned churches and also a few Romanesque examples too.

The variety of scenery is spectacular. Across much of the island one can discover dramatic gorges, glacial lakes, gushing mountain torrents and magnificent pine and chestnut forests. You'll also experience the celebrated perfume of the Corsican maquis: a tangled undergrowth of fragrant herbs, flowers and bushes that fills the warm spring and summer air. The highest mountains lie to the west, while the gentler ranges, weathered to strange and often bizarre shapes, lie to the south and a continuous barrier forms the island's backbone.

Places of interest

Ajaccio: a dazzling white city full of Napoleonic memorabilia.

Bastia: historic citadel towering over the headland. The old town has preserved its streets in the form of steps connected by vaulted passages, converging on the Vieux port (the old port). The new port is the real commercial port of the island.

Cuisine of the region

Brocchui: sheeps' milk cheese is used much in cooking in both its soft form (savoury or sweet) or more mature and ripened.

Capone: local eels, cut up and grilled on a spit over a charcoal fire.

Dziminu: fish soup, like bouillabaise but much hotter. Made with peppers and pimentos.

Figatelli: a sausage made of dried and spiced pork with liver. Favourite between-meal snack.

Pibronata: a highly spiced local sauce.

Prizzutu: a peppered smoked ham; resembles the Italian prosciutto, but with chestnut flavour added.

www.visit-corsica.com
info@visit-corsica.com
(0)4 95 51 00 00

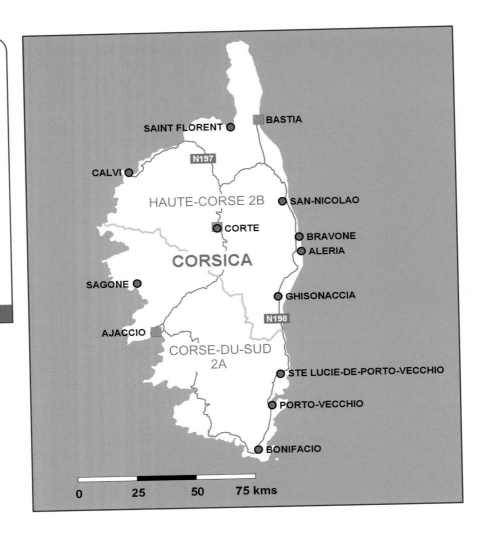

Bonifacio

Camping U-Farniente de Pertamina Village

RN198, F-20169 Bonifacio (Corse-du-Sud) T: 04 95 73 05 47. E: pertamina@wanadoo.fr

alanrogers.com/FR20000

Whether or not you are using the ferry to Sardinia, Bonifacio deserves a visit and this is a convenient site for a night stop or longer stay. The 120 pitches, many in delightful settings, have electricity (3A), are partially terraced and are hedged with trees and bushes, providing shade. They are fairly flat and vary in size, many being well over 100 sq.m. A central feature of the site is the large attractive pool, surrounded by terraces. The bar, restaurant, pizzeria/grill and crêperie are on a series of terraces above the pool and patios. This site will suit campers who like a large pool complex and do not mind a drive to the beach

Facilities

Two toilet blocks include washbasins in semi-private cubicles, British and Turkish style WCs, washing machines plus drying and ironing facilities. Motorcaravan service point at entrance (public). Shop. Takeaway. Bar, restaurant, pizzeria/grill serving set meals and á la carte menu at reasonable prices (shorter opening hours in May, June and Oct). Swimming pool. Tennis. Play area. TV room. Excellent gym. Off site: Bonifacio 4 km.

Open: Easter - 15 October.

Directions

Site is on the RN198 road, 4 km. north of Bonifacio to the east. Well signed at Pertamina Village. GPS: 41.41790, 9.17990

Charges 2011

Per unit incl. 2 persons and electricity	€ 23,00 - € 36,00

Camping Cheques accepted.

For latest campsite news, availability and prices visit

alanrogers.com

Bonifacio

Camping Rondinara

Suartone, F-20169 Bonifacio (Corse-du-Sud) T: 04 95 70 43 15. E: reception@rondinara.fr
alanrogers.com/FR20240

The views from every pitch in this site are stunning, either coastal or the rolling hills and cliffs inland. The 'great outdoors' describes this campsite which is away from the any tourist over-development and is at one with nature. The natural and informal pitches sit on the hillside above a superb bay with sheltered water, fine silver sand and safe swimming. Most pitches have shade but most tree foliage is relatively low as yet. Large boulders make natural divisions and some pitches need long leads for the 6A electricity. The beach is a 400 m. walk down a rough track through the maquis.

Facilities

Three excellent, modern toilet blocks are very clean and offer hot water throughout, hot showers and single sex British style toilets. Motorcaravan service point. Shop. Pizza restaurant. Bar. Swimming pool. Play area. Games room. Electronic games. Animation and family activities. Torches are essential here. Off site: Beach, boat launching and fishing 400 m. Golf, riding and sailing 15 km.

Open: 15 May - 30 September.

Directions

Site is mid-way between Bonifacio and Porto-Vecchio off the RN198. Take the D158 to Baie de la Rondinara for 7 km. (site is well signed). The road is rough and narrow but large units will have no trouble negotiating it. GPS: 41.47323, 9.26316

Charges guide

Per unit incl. 2 persons and electricity	€ 21,40 - € 26,80
extra person	€ 5,90 - € 7,60
child (2-7 yrs)	€ 2,90 - € 3,60

Calvi

Camping Paduella

Route de Bastia, F-20260 Calvi (Haute-Corse) T: 04 95 65 06 16. E: campingpaduella@wanadoo.fr
alanrogers.com/FR20170

Camping Paduella is a beautifully maintained, simple site which has been run by the friendly Peretti family for 40 years. As it is a popular site, it is best to book ahead for high season. There is a wide choice of pleasant pitches, some shaded under pines, others grassed and hedged with less shade. All are well maintained on level terraces with good access. The lovely white sandy beach is 300 m. away and the picturesque town of Calvi is a delightful 30 minute walk. There is a fairly busy road and light railway to cross to get to the beach but most of the walk is through the shaded beach parkland.

Facilities

Two centrally located spotless modern sanitary blocks (British style WCs). Well equipped showers. New baby bathroom. Laundry with washing machines, ironing board. Small shop with basic supplies and fresh bread. Pizzeria and bar. Internet access. Play area. Sports ground. Fridge hire can be arranged. Off site: Supermarket and ATM 200 m. Adventure activities 200 m. Riding and bicycle hire 700 m. Boat launching and marina 1 km. Scuba diving, rowing and sailing nearby.

Open: 5 May - 5 October.

Directions

From the north, site is just before the town of Calvi. It is directly off the RN197 on the left and is well signed. GPS: 42.5521, 8.7641

Charges guide

Per unit incl. 2 persons and electricity	€ 22,10 - € 26,10
extra person	€ 6,40 - € 7,90
child (0-7)	€ 3,20 - € 3,95
No credit cards.	

Calvi

Camping la Pinède

Route de la Pinède, F-20260 Calvi (Haute-Corse) T: 04 95 65 17 80. E: info@camping-calvi.com
alanrogers.com/FR20180

Camping la Pinède is a well ordered, family site of 185 touring pitches, all with 4-16A electricity. The pitches are marked and level (although the pine roots are a nuisance in places). There is access for large units in some areas. Water points are spread around the site and everything is kept tidy and clean. Under the mature pines it can be quite dark but there are plenty of alternatives in the light. The site is divided into areas of accommodation – pitches for tour operators, mobile homes and tourers. Unusually all facilities are in separate buildings.

Facilities

Three well maintained and well placed concrete sanitary buildings offer hot showers and facilities for disabled campers. Washing machines. Clean and fresh, these blocks are better than most on the west coast. Motorcaravan service point. Shop (June-Sept). Bar. Restaurant (May-Sept). Swimming pool (no lifeguard). Internet access. Play area. Tennis. Off site: Beach 200 m. Fishing 200 m. Riding 500 m. Bicycle hire 2 km.

Open: 1 April - 31 October.

Directions

Site is north of Calvi off the RN197, just south of the D251 road to the airport. Look for signs off the roundabout here and take care along a narrow road with leaning fir trees. GPS: 42.55320, 8.7686

Charges guide

Per person	€ 6,50 - € 8,50
child (under 7 yrs)	€ 3,50 - € 4,50

For latest campsite news, availability and prices visit
alanrogers.com

Corte

Camping Restonica

Faubourg Saint Antoine, F-20250 Corte (Haute-Corse) T: 04 95 46 11 59. E: vero.camp@worldonline.fr

alanrogers.com/FR20110

Tucked away alongside the pretty Restonica river and near the Pont Neuf leading into the stunning mountainside old city of Corte, Camping Restonica is ideally placed for tourists wanting to visit Corte or travel on the popular inland mountain railway (the station is only a few hundred metres from the site). This is a small, simple site catering for those who want to enjoy the many delights of Corte. The entrance is steep but manageable for all but very large units, there are flat pitches for campers and caravans in the middle of the site, and many beautiful terraced pitches for tents dotted along the river bank under shady trees. The facilities, whilst somewhat dated, were spotlessly clean.

Facilities

Single, central toilet block is unisex and somewhat dated, although very clean. Toilet for disabled visitors but site not really suitable. Washing machine. Bread to order. Bar and snack bar. River fishing. Off site: Sightseeing. Famous train journeys across Corsica. Museum. Only university in Corsica (politically significant).

Open: 15 April - 30 September.

Directions

Approaching the town, turn left at first roundabout onto Ave du 9 Septembre. Site is 300 m. on the right. It is signed from the roundabout and at the top of the steep, narrow access road.
GPS: 42.3015, 9.152

Charges guide

Per unit incl. 2 persons	€ 18,00 - € 20,50

No credit cards.

Ghisonaccia

Camping Arinella Bianca

Route de la Mer, F-20240 Ghisonaccia (Haute-Corse) T: 04 95 56 04 78. E: arinella@arinellabianca.com

alanrogers.com/FR20010

Arinella is a lively, family oriented site on Corsica's east coast. The 403 pitches are level, grassy, good sized and irregular shaped (198 for touring units) with trees and shrubs providing ample shade; 163 have 6A electricity (long leads needed). Some pitches overlook the attractive lakes which have fountains and are lit at night. The site has direct acess to a huge long beach of soft sand. The brilliantly designed resort style pools and paddling pool, overlooked by an attractive large restaurant, terraced bar and entertainment area, form the hub of Arinella Bianca. The extremely active children's club with an information point, boutique and supermarket complete the area. When we visited the area was buzzing with activity at night and appeared to delight everyone by incorporating excellent family entertainment. A huge range of sport and leisure facilities is also available. Evening entertainment starts at 21.00 and unfortunately a local disco can continue until the early hours. This site is a tribute to its owner's design and development skills as it appears to be in entirely natural glades where, in fact, these have been created from former marshland with a fresh water lake.

Facilities

Four open plan sanitary blocks provide showers, (some with dressing area), washbasins in cabins, mainly British style WCs. Laundry. Motorcaravan services. Shop, bar, terrace, restaurant, snack bar (all 10/5-15/9). Swimming pool (all season, heated 16/4-10/6). Windsurfing. Canoeing. Fishing. Tennis. Riding. Bicycle hire. Miniclub. Play area. Disco. Good entertainment programme in the main season. Communal barbecue area. WiFi. Off site: Sailing 300 m. Boat launching 2 km.

Open: Mid April - 30 September.

Directions

Site is 4 km. east of Ghisonaccia. From N198 in Ghisonaccia look for sign 'La Plage, Li Mare'. Turn east on D144 at roundabout just south of town. Continue for 3.5 km. to further roundabout where site is signed to right. Site is 500 m.
GPS: 41.9984, 9.442

Charges 2011

Per unit incl. 2 persons and electricity	€ 29,00 - € 45,00

Camping Cheques accepted.

ARINELLA Bianca

Camping Caravaning
20240 Ghisonaccia
Tel: 0033 495 56 04 78 - Fax: 0033 495 56 12 54
www.arinellabianca.com

Camping Cheque

For latest campsite news, availability and prices visit

alanrogers.com

Porto-Vecchio

Camping la Vetta

Route de Bastia, la Trinité, F-20137 Porto-Vecchio (Corse-du-Sud) T: 04 95 70 09 86
E: info@campinglavetta.com alanrogers.com/FR20060

This is a site not to be missed in Corsica, the English/French owners Nick and Marieline Long having created a very friendly and peaceful country park setting for their campsite to the north of la Trinité village. The 8.5 hectares of well maintained campsite are part sloping, part terraced with an informal pitch allocation system. It seems to stretch endlessly. The abundance of tree varieties including many cork oaks give shade to 111 pitches which all have 10A electricity. The site has a brilliant lagoon-style pool. What an enjoyable experience we had at la Vetta! Many of the delights of Corsica are only a short drive away and la Vetta is only 3 km. from Porto-Vecchio and its magnificent sandy beaches.

Facilities	Directions
Spotless, traditional style toilet facilities have plenty of hot water. Laundry facilities. Shop (July/Aug), gas supplies. Bar (July/Aug). Swimming pool, paddling pool and water play area (all season). Snooker table. Play area. TV. Entertainment in high season. Off site: Beach 1.5 km. Supermarket 2 km. Fishing, watersports and boat launching 1.5 km. Riding 4 km. Bicycle hire 5 km. Golf 7 km. Public transport 800 m.	Site is in La Trinité village, off the RN198 (east side), north of Porto-Vecchio. GPS: 41.6316, 9.2929

Charges guide

Per unit incl. 2 persons and electricity	€ 21,50 - € 26,60
extra person	€ 6,50 - € 7,80
child (under 7 yrs)	€ 3,00 - € 4,00

Open: 1 June - 1 October.

Sagone

Camping le Sagone

Route de Vico, F-20118 Sagone (Corse-du-Sud) T: 04 95 28 04 15. E: sagone.camping@wanadoo.fr
alanrogers.com/FR20230

Situated outside the bustling seaside resort of Sagone, surrounded by protective hills, this campsite, which used to be a fruit farm, is in an ideal location for exploring Corsica's wild and rocky west coast or its mountainous interior. The large site borders a pleasant river and has 300 marked, shaded pitches, 250 with electricity (6A). There are 105 bungalows offered for rent, which are generally separated. The restaurant/bar and games room overlook the pool and they are the focal point of this well managed site.

Facilities	Directions
Clean, fully equipped toilet blocks with washbasins in cubicles. Facilities for disabled campers. Baby baths. Washing machines, dryers. Motorcaravan services. Large supermarket (all year). Restaurant, pizzeria, bar, games room. Swimming pool (June-Sept). Half-court tennis. Play area. Sub-aqua experience in pool. Communal barbecues. Satellite TV. Internet. Car wash. New putting and golf practice area. Off site: Riding 500 m. Diving, windsurfing, mountain biking, fishing, bicycle hire, climbing nearby. Tours to local places of interest.	From Ajaccio take the RD81 in direction of Cergése and Calvilby (by coast road). In Sagone take RD70 in direction of Vico, Sagone can be found on left after 1.5 km. next to supermarket. GPS: 42.1304, 8.7055

Charges guide

Per unit incl. 2 persons	€ 14,50 - € 23,00
extra person	€ 4,50 - € 7,70
child (under 12 yrs)	€ 2,25 - € 3,90
electricity	€ 3,00

Camping Cheques accepted.

Open: 1 May - 30 September.

Saint Florent

Camping d'Olzo

L.D. Strutta, F-20217 Saint Florent (Haute-Corse) T: 04 95 37 03 34. E: info@campingolzo.com
alanrogers.com/FR20150

The friendly Barenghi family who own this site are delightful. They are pleased to welcome you to their compact site and Dutch, Italian and English are spoken. The site is flat and very peaceful with a wide variety of trees, including gums and olives, which offer shade to most of the informal pitches. There is ample room to manoeuvre for large units. All 60 pitches have electricity (10A) and are not far from the central sanitary block or the facilities which are grouped near reception. The site is a short walk from the beach. A swimming pool has been added.

Facilities	Directions
Single central block has unisex toilets (Turkish and British style) and single sex hot showers. Water at the sinks is cold. Everything is kept very clean and smart. Washing machines. Motorcaravan service point. Facilities for disabled campers. Small shop (July/Aug), bread to order. Restaurant/pizzeria and bar. Swimming pool planned. Internet access. Play area. Communal barbecue area. Mobile homes for hire. Off site: Town of St Florent with usual facilities. Bus from gate. Riding 500 m. Bicycle hire 2 km. Boat launching 2 km. Sailing 2 km. Fishing 500 m.	From Bastia take the D81 west to St Florent. After some 30 minutes the site is well signed as you enter the village on the right. GPS: 42.6936, 9.3265

Charges guide

Per unit incl. 2 persons and electricity	€ 22,00 - € 26,50
extra person	€ 3,30 - € 6,00
child (under 10 yrs)	€ 1,65 - € 3,00
dog	€ 1,20 - € 1,50

Open: 1 April - 30 September.

Sainte Lucie-de-Porto-Vecchio

Camping Caravaning Santa Lucia

Lieu-dit Mulindinu, F-20144 Sainte Lucie-de-Porto-Vecchio (Corse-du-Sud) T: 04 95 71 45 28
E: information@campingsantalucia.com alanrogers.com/FR20070

Camping Santa Lucia is a very small, friendly, family run site in a delightful southern Corsican setting, where little English is spoken. Behind the little reception hut is an unsophisticated restaurant and bar which have terraces overlooking the pool. It is very pleasant in the evenings when ornamental lamps light up the area. There are 160 pitches, 60 with 6A electrical connections and 18 serviced pitches. Some of the pitches are in enclosed bays created from huge boulders, making them very private. This site is only minutes by car from Porto-Vecchio and with very reasonable prices, will suit many. The entrance road encircles a huge palm tree. Chalets and bungalow tents blend unobtrusively with the setting. The site is surrounded by lovely beaches and other points of interest.

Facilities

Two clean and pleasant toilet blocks include British style toilets, some washbasins in cubicles, dishwashing and laundry sinks, and a washing machine. Facilities for disabled visitors. Bread to order. Bar (15/6-15/9). Restaurant and takeaway (1/7-31/8). Swimming and paddling pools. Play area and high season miniclub for children. Minigolf. Communal barbecues. Satellite TV. WiFi. Off site: Beach, fishing and watersports 5 km. Golf 20 km. Supermarket opposite site entrance.

Open: 15 May - 10 October.

Directions

Site is at south end of Sainte-Lucie-de-Porto-Vecchio village, off N198 and well signed. GPS: 41.69660, 9.3434

Charges guide

Per person	€ 5,00 - € 7,00
child (2-10 yrs)	free - € 3,30
pitch	€ 3,20 - € 4,75
incl. electricity	€ 5,00 - € 7,50

San-Nicolao

Camping Merendella

Moriani-Plage, F-20230 San-Nicolao (Haute-Corse) T: 04 95 38 53 47. E: merendel@club-internet.fr
alanrogers.com/FR20030

This attractive family run site has the advantage of direct access to a pleasant, long sandy beach. It is peacefully situated on level grass with many well tended trees and shrubs providing shade and colour. Level green sites such as this are unusual in Corsica and are ideal for families or those with mobility problems. There are 196 pitches, all with electricity (2/5A, long leads required) and a minimum of 100 sq.m. There is a dedicated night parking area if you arrive late. An excellent bar, restaurant/pizzeria is close to the site entrance (takeaway pizzas are available). The focus at Merendella is on 'old fashioned' camping in a natural setting. We found it delightful and relaxing but in high season there may be noise from local discos. The site is 800 m. from the village and an hour from the ferry terminal at Bastia.

Facilities

Modern blocks, two individual cabin units near the beach. Washbasins in private cubicles. British and Turkish style WCs. Facilities for disabled campers. Laundry facilities. Motorcaravan services. Shop. Bar/restaurant, pizzeria. TV room. Games room. Late arrival area. Diving centre. Play area. Torches essential. Dogs are not accepted. Off site: Restaurant outside gate. All watersports 200 m. along beach from site. Bus 800 m. from gate. Town 800 m. Bicycle hire 800 m. Tennis and riding 2 km.

Open: 15 May - 30 September.

Directions

Site is to seaward side of the RN198, 800 m. south of Moriani Plage. GPS: 42.3631, 9.5298

Charges guide

Per person	€ 6,35 - € 7,50
caravan and car	€ 6,15 - € 6,95
motorcaravan	€ 5,95 - € 7,10
electricity (2/5A)	€ 3,30 - € 4,30

Today there are many more people that enjoy naturist campsites than one would at first think.

Some are dedicated naturists who practise their way of life wherever they may be and who in the UK may well belong to clubs of like-minded people. For others, especially those who have enjoyed sunbathing on one of the many designated naturist areas on European beaches and feel comfortable with it, the logical next step is to try a holiday in a naturist village or campsite.

This growing number of 'holiday naturists' clearly enjoy the relaxed atmosphere prevailing on naturist sites. If they are not members of British Naturism they can pick up a naturist card on the first site they visit. The rules are simple: respect for the environment and for other visitors. You are encouraged to strip off but, in reality, it is up to you, except in and around the swimming pool where there is always a 'no clothes' rule. Clothes do tend to label people and without them there is a relaxed informality and sense of equality often missing in today's 'designer society'.

We feature some 23 naturist campsites in this guide and have been impressed by the friendly welcome and cultural aspects of their entertainment and range of activities – classical music beside the pool, walking trails to discover local wildlife or book-binding classes, for example. Most campsites make an effort to provide good entertainment and to make your holiday memorable; on the naturist sites in particular this is usually achieved quite elegantly without the frenzy that sometimes pervades more commercially-minded sites.

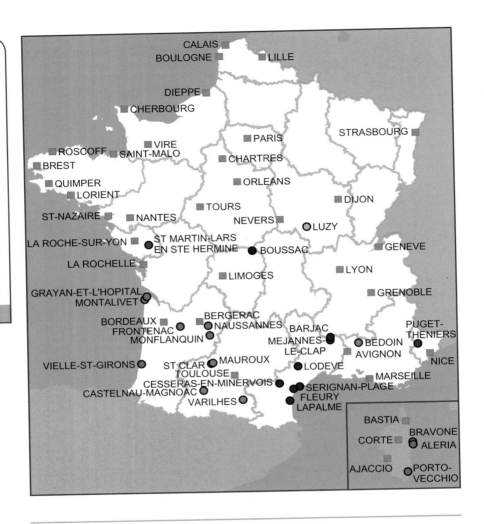

Saint Martin-Lars en Sainte Hermine

Camping Naturiste le Colombier

Le Colombier, F-85210 St Martin-Lars en Ste Hermine (Vendée) T: 02 51 27 83 84
E: lecolombier.nat@wanadoo.fr alanrogers.com/FR85140

A countryside site for naturists near La Roche sur Yon, just right for those seeking a peaceful holiday. It provides around 160 pitches in seven very natural fields on different levels linked by informal tracks. There are level, terraced areas for caravans and a feeling of spaciousness with pitches around the edges of fields, unmarked and with electricity (6/10A, some may require long leads). The bar/restaurant is in a converted barn. The site's 125 acres provide many walks throughout the attractive, wooded valley and around the lake. English is spoken by the Dutch owner and staff.

Facilities

Fully equipped toilet blocks are good, providing some showers in cubicles. Dishwashing sinks. Motorcaravan service point. Grocer/baker calls daily. Bar/restaurant with á la carte and full menu (order before 13.00), home baked bread and pizzas. Heated swimming pool. Fishing. Volleyball, boules and table tennis. Playground. Pony and trap rides and one day a week children can make their own bread. Plans for a sauna and aquagym.
Off site: Shop 1 km.

Open: 1 April - 30 October.

Directions

From N148, La Roche-sur-Yon - Niort road, at St Hermine, turn onto D8 eastward for 4 km. Turn left on D10 to St Martin-Lars. Site is signed.
GPS: 46.59795, -0.96936

Charges guide

Per unit incl. 2 persons	
and electricity	€ 18,50 - € 21,50
child (3-9 yrs)	€ 3,40 - € 3,50
child (10-16 yrs)	€ 4,70 - € 4,80

Luzy

Domaine Naturiste de la Gagère

F-58170 Luzy (Burgundy) T: 03 86 30 48 11. E: info@la-gagere.com

alanrogers.com/FR58060

At this secluded and attractive campsite, you will receive a really good welcome from the enthusiastic founders of Naturocamp. The site is spacious and well equipped with 120 good sized level grassy pitches, some shaded, some open, of which 100 are available for tourers. Many are arranged in groups around three sides of rectangles between hedges. Electricity (4-10A) is supplied to 84 pitches, six of which are fully serviced, but some require leads of up to 40 m. There are plenty of water points. In high season there are organised activities and entertainment and a children's club meets twice per week.

Facilities

Three modern unisex toilet blocks, one heated, contain British style WCs, washbasins and pre-set showers. Facilities for disabled visitors. Baby changing. Motorcaravan services. Laundry facilities. Shop (31/5-15/9). Bar (all season). Restaurant with snack bar and takeaway (1/5-15/9). Satellite TV. Two heated swimming pools (one all season, the other 15/5-15/9). Sauna and health suite. Playgrounds. Boules. Bicycle hire. Only gas barbecues permitted (available for hire). Off site: Luzy 10 km. Fishing 10 km. Riding 20 km.

Open: 1 April - 1 October.

Directions

Leave Autun, N81, southwest towards Bourbon-Lancy. In 27 km. turn left (signed Gagère) down a narrow lane. Site is approx. 3 km. GPS: 46.81692, 4.05636

Charges guide

Per unit incl. 2 persons and electricity	€ 30,75 - € 34,00
extra person	€ 6,50
child (3-12 yrs)	€ 3,75

Less 10-30% outside July/Aug.
Admin fee for stays of 3 nights or less (€ 5).

Boussac

Creuse Nature Naturisme

Route de Bétête (D15), F-23600 Boussac (Limousin) T: 05 55 65 18 01. E: creuse.nature@wanadoo.fr

alanrogers.com/FR23030

You are sure of a warm welcome by the Dutch owners of this very spacious, naturally laid out and well maintained naturist site. It is set in the beautiful but lesser known Limousin region in the centre of France. There are 100 large grassy/stony pitches, 80 of which are for touring with 10A electricity. Some are slightly sloping and there are varying degrees of shade. They are laid out in an open wooded parkland setting around the perimeter of the site and beside the small fishing lake. An attractive central feature is the swimming pool, sauna, bar and restaurant complex.

Facilities

Four modern, very clean toilet blocks with the usual facilities (open-plan, so little privacy). Facilities for disabled visitors. Dishwashing and laundry facilities. Small shop (baker calls). Indoor (heated) and outdoor pools. Paddling pool. Sauna. Bar and restaurant (all season). Archery (high season). Boules. Bicycle hire. Lake fishing. Internet access with free WiFi. Gas barbecues only on pitches. Accommodation for hire. Off site: Boussac 3 km. Lake bathing 7 km. Riding 10 km. Golf 15 km.

Open: 1 April - 31 October.

Directions

Boussac lies 35 km. west of Montluçon between the A20 and A71 autoroutes. In Boussac site is well signed. Take D15 west for about 3 km. Site is on the right. GPS: 46.34902, 2.18691

Charges guide

Per unit incl. 2 persons and electricity	€ 21,50 - € 29,50
extra person	€ 4,00 - € 7,00
child (3-11 yrs)	€ 2,50 - € 4,50

Frontenac

Domain Naturiste Château Guiton

F-33760 Frontenac (Aquitaine) T: 05 56 23 52 79. E: accueil@chateau-guiton.com

alanrogers.com/FR33450

A small naturist site situated in the park of an 18th-century castle, just 8 km. south of the Dordogne. The owners, Isabelle and Jean-Marc, offer a warm welcome and a family atmosphere. The site makes good use of the château's outbuildings, and wisteria hangs over the tiny reception area. There are 26 large pitches (electricity 6A) mainly on level grass, separated by mature hedges giving considerable privacy. The site is an excellent starting point for walking and cycling along small tracks through the vineyards.

Facilities

One small, unheated, unisex toilet block has washbasins (some in cubicles) and preset open showers. Baby bath and facilities for disabled visitors. Washing machine. Small swimming pool, but no children's pool. Small shop, fresh bread daily. Bar and snack bar. Entertainment programme (July/Aug). Play area. Boules. Badminton. Bicycle hire. Fitness room and sauna (charged). Bread oven. WiFi (free). Ice packs frozen. Off site: Frontenac with shops, restaurants, small supermarket, bank and post office. Fishing 2 km. Riding 15 km. Golf 2 km.

Open: 15 May - 15 September.

Directions

From Libourne, join D670 towards St Emilion and Castillon-la-Bataille. At St Laurent-des-Combes turn right towards Sauveterre-de-Guyenne. At sign for Rauzan turn right onto D231. Continue on this road and follow signs to Frontenac. Site is signed from outskirts of village. GPS: 44.725512, -0.150767

Charges guide

Per unit inc. 2 persons and electricity	€ 23,30 - € 27,00
extra person	€ 6,30 - € 7,00

For latest campsite news, availability and prices visit

alanrogers.com

Grayan et l'Hopital

Espace Naturiste Euronat

F-33590 Grayan et l'Hopital (Aquitaine) T: 05 56 09 33 33. E: info@euronat.fr

alanrogers.com/FR33160

Euronat is really a large naturist town with extensive facilities, direct access to 1.5 km. of sandy beach and a Thalassotherapy centre. With a total of 3,000 pitches, those for touring are in two areas separated from the chalets and mobile homes. A variety of good sized, fairly flat and sandy pitches, include some suitable for large motorhomes. All pitches have 10A electricity and some also have water and drainage. The 'town centre' is superb with two supermarkets, an organic supermarket, cash-point, butcher, fish monger, bakery where freshly squeezed orange juice is available, restaurants including fish, brasserie, pizzeria/crêperie, and a takeaway with a selection of hot and cold dishes.

Facilities

Sanitary blocks are well maintained with some heated (not all open in low season). Facilities for campers with disabilities. Launderette. Motorcaravan services. Shops, restaurants. Swimming pool, flumes, children's pool. Swimming lessons. Activities and workshops, archery, pony club, riding, tennis, petanque. Children's activities and day care. Multi-purpose hall for dances, film nights, music evenings, sports activities. Supervised beach. No barbecues (communal areas provided). Torch may be useful. Off site: Long distance cycle path passes site.

Open: 23 March - 3 November.

Directions

From Bordeaux ring road take exit 7, then D1215 to Lesparre and Vensac, then follow (large) signed route. GPS: 45.41627, -1.13178

Charges guide

Per tent incl. 2 persons	€ 16,00 - € 30,60
incl. electricity (10A)	€ 19,50 - € 38,00
caravan or motorcaravan	
incl. 2 persons and services	€ 23,00 - € 43,50
extra person	€ 4,00 - € 7,00

Camping Cheques accepted.

Monflanquin

Camping Naturiste Domaine Laborde

Paulhiac, F-47150 Monflanquin (Aquitaine) T: 05 53 63 14 88. E: domainelaborde@wanadoo.fr

alanrogers.com/FR47140

Ideally situated on the border of Lot-et-Garonne and Dordogne, Domain Laborde is a naturist site of outstanding quality, with sweeping views from many of the higher pitches. This hilly and terraced site has 120 well maintained pitches, with 95 for touring; many are shaded, some partially shaded and all are surrounded by woodland. Electricity (3/6/10A) is available (long leads may be required). There are also 30 chalets for rent. The site has something for everyone and even in low season it is very popular. If you are new to naturist sites, then this is a must. A Sites et Paysages member.

Facilities

The three sanitary blocks and a new wash block are well sited and clean. Washing machines and dryer. Shop with daily deliveries of fresh bread and milk. Bar with TV. Snack bar serving pizzas. Restaurant (15/4-15/9). Large swimming pool, whirlpool, sauna, children's pool and indoor heated pool. Massage. Play areas. Communal stone barbecue. Animation for children (high season). Internet. Excursions. Off site: Riding 2 km. Golf 13 km.

Open: 27 March - 30 September.

Directions

From Monflanquin take D272 towards Monpazier. About 10 km. along the road look for the signs to site. It is very well signed at regular intervals. GPS: 44.613889, 0.835556

Charges guide

Per unit incl. 2 persons	
and electricity	€ 23,00 - € 29,50
extra person	€ 5,00 - € 6,00
child (under 6 yrs)	€ 4,00 - € 4,50

Montalivet

Centre Naturiste Helio-Marin de Montalivet

46 avenue de l'Europe, F-33930 Montalivet (Aquitaine) T: 05 56 73 73 73. E: infos@chm-montalivet.com

alanrogers.com/FR33370

This is a large naturist village with everything that you would need without leaving the site during your holiday. It has direct access to the sea with its own beautiful golden sandy beaches with coastguard surveillance in high season. Watersports are numerous with lessons if you require. The main emphasis here is to keep the family entertained. There is a total of 2,800 pitches, of which 1,700 are for touring. Pitches are level, on grass or sand, and mature trees provide shade in some areas. A circus school, dancing classes and skate boarding are just some of the activities organised here.

Facilities

Numerous sanitary blocks with facilities for disabled visitors and children. Shops, restaurants and bars. Launderette. Motorcaravan service point. Children's clubs. Evening entertainment. Two pool complexes with slides and toboggan. Playgrounds. Sports grounds. TV rooms and cinema. Large library. Wellness centre offering numerous treatments and massage as well as saunas and jacuzzis. Off site: Golf. Riding. Cycling. Sailing and fishing.

Open: All year.

Directions

From Royan, take the ferry to Verdon-sur-Mer and continue on N215 for 34 km. Turn right on D102 to Montalivet. Nearing the sea turn left for Hourtins and site is 1 km. on the right. GPS: 45.36348, -1.14575

Charges guide

Per unit incl. 2 persons	
and electricity	€ 16,30 - € 31,50
extra person	€ 3,30 - € 7,50

For latest campsite news, availability and prices visit

alanrogers.com

Naussannes

Centre Naturiste le Couderc

Le Couderc, F-24440 Naussannes (Aquitaine) T: 05 53 22 40 40. E: info@lecouderc.com
alanrogers.com/FR24190

This is one of the most beautiful camping sites in the Dordogne and probably the best naturist site that I have seen. Set in 28 hectares of open countryside, there is a feeling of spaciousness, calm and tranquility. The family go the extra mile to ensure visitors enjoy their visit. There are 188 pitches of which 170 are for touring units and the remainder being chalets which are available for rent. One is adapted for disabled visitors. The site is on different levels with undulating slopes but the generous pitches are level and easily accessible. Generally open but mature trees all around offer some shade.

Facilities

Five very clean modern toilet blocks with facilities for children and disabled visitors. Washing machines. Dryer. Superb restaurant and bar. Takeaway. Terrace. Shop. Heated swimming pools. Jacuzzi. Sauna. Bicycle Hire. Two ponds, one for fishing the other with cable slide. Children's club with sculpture and circus lessons. Play area. Some entertainment. Off site: Caves. Châteaux. Market towns. Walking. Riding 10 km. Golf 20 km.

Open: 1 April - 1 October.

Directions

From Bergerac take N21. Turn left on the D25 to Issigeac. Continue towards Naussannes for 8 km. Turn left at signpost indicating Naussannes 2 km. Le Couderc is 350 m. on the right.
GPS: 44.75602, 0.70212

Charges guide

Per person	€ 4,20 - € 7,00
pitch	€ 8,35 - € 13,90
electricity	€ 4,50

Vielle-Saint-Girons

Domaine Naturiste Arnaoutchot

D328, F-40560 Vielle-Saint-Girons (Aquitaine) T: 05 58 49 11 11. E: contact@arna.com
alanrogers.com/FR40120

'Arna' is a large naturist site with extensive facilities and direct access to the beach. Even with 500 pitches, its layout in the form of a number of sections, each with its own character, make it quite relaxing and very natural. These sections amongst the trees and bushes of the Landes provide a variety of reasonably sized pitches, most with electricity (3/6A), although the hilly terrain means that only a limited number are flat enough for motorcaravans. The centrally located amenities are extensive and of excellent quality. We suggest that new visitors telephone before arrival as the site can require them to be proposed by a family who have stayed at the campsite for at least three years.

Facilities

Heated sanitary facilities include the usual naturist site type of blocks with communal hot showers and also a number of tiny blocks. Motorcaravan services. Supermarket, other shops. Bar/restaurant, pizzeria and tapita (fish) bar (from 1/6). Heated indoor pool with solarium, whirlpool and slide. Outdoor pool, sunbathing area. New paddling pool. Spa, sauna, steam, whirlpool, massages. Internet point. Bicycle hire. Fishing. Torches useful. Charcoal barbecues not permitted. American motorhomes not accepted. Off site: Riding and golf 5 km.

Open: 9 April - 25 September.

Directions

Site is signed off the D652 road at Vielle-Saint-Girons. Follow D328 for 3-4 km.
GPS: 43.9075, -1.361683

Charges guide

Per unit incl. 2 persons and electricity	€ 11,90 - € 36,50
extra person (over 3 yrs)	€ 2,00 - € 7,90
dog	€ 1,50 - € 3,40
Camping Cheques accepted.	

Castelnau-Magnoac

Domaine Naturiste l'Eglantière

Aries-Espenan, F-65230 Castelnau-Magnoac (Midi-Pyrénées) T: 05 62 39 88 00. E: info@leglantiere.com
alanrogers.com/FR65010

A delightful site with an air of calm and repose, l'Eglantière is set within 50 hectares of organic farmland and woodland for walking. The fast-flowing River Gers runs through the site, bringing opportunities for watersports. Pitches are large and naturally shaped, most have electricity (16A, long leads). Many are separated by wild flowers, grasses and trees, ensuring shade and privacy. There is a separate 'wild area' for tents. The clubhouse bar, restaurant and terrace have an extremely pleasing ambiance, overlooking the attractive swimming pool area where nudity is compulsory. Member of France 4 Naturisme.

Facilities

Two toilet blocks in typically naturist style, providing under cover, open plans, facilities. Small block has individual cubicles. Shop (July/Aug). Clubhouse, bar, small restaurant (June-Sept), pizzeria, takeaway (July/Aug), WiFi. Soundproofed activities/disco area, play room for younger children. Heated swimming pool (all season). Play area, children's entertainment in season. River activities. Canoe, mountain bike hire. Trekking, cross-country cycling. Torches useful. Off site: Restaurants in the nearby village.

Open: Easter - October.

Directions

From Auch take D929 south towards Lannemezan. After Castelnau-Magnoac continue past aerodrome and turn onto the D9 towards Monleon-Magnoac. Take the first left towards Ariès-Espénan and follow site signs. GPS: 43.26466, 0.52119

Charges guide

Per unit incl. 2 persons	€ 12,50 - € 35,00
extra person	€ 4,00 - € 7,20
child (3-8 yrs)	€ 2,20 - € 4,30
electricity (10A)	€ 5,40

Mauroux

Camping Naturiste les Roches

Le Néry, F-32380 Mauroux (Midi-Pyrénées) T: 05 62 66 30 18. E: campinglesroches@wanadoo.fr

alanrogers.com/FR32190

A pleasant and friendly site in beautiful wooded countryside, where visitors can relax. The 36 large, shady pitches, some are 200 sq.m., have electricity (6A). The cool, traditional reception buildings include a bar, games room and seasonal restaurant. The site is calm with woodland walks and the swimming pool (20x8 m) is away from the pitches. Nudity is expected unless the weather prevents it. Activities are easy going: boules, lake fishing, archery and volleyball. The owners can arrange trips to local wine, garlic and foie gras producers. St Clar is a lovely village 4 km. away and well worth a visit.

Facilities

All necessary facilities, including those for visitors with disabilities. Washing machine and dryer. Restaurant (1/6-15/9) and bread in high season. Bar and takeaway. Swimming pool. Sauna (€ 7,50 including drink at bar). Lake for fishing. Various indoor games. Communal barbecue only. Small playground. Saturday communal meal. Sunday boules tournament. Internet point. No motorcaravan services. Torches needed. Off site: Village of St Clar 4 km. Golf 16 km. Bicycle hire and riding 15 km.

Open: 1 May - 15 September.

Directions

From Lectoure take the D7 to St Clar. At St Clar turn left onto D13 then after 1 km. turn right onto D167 to Gaudonville. Site is then well signed along a fairly narrow bumpy road. GPS: 43.898035, 0.811234

Charges guide

Per unit incl. 2 persons and electricity (6A)	€ 9,20 - € 13,00
extra person	€ 3,10 - € 4,75
child (0-10 yrs)	free - € 3,25
No credit cards.	

Saint Clar

Centre Naturiste Deveze

Gaudonville, F-32380 Saint Clar (Midi-Pyrénées) T: 05 62 66 43 86. E: deveze@deveze-nat.com

alanrogers.com/FR32040

This is a well established and very pleasant, French owned naturist site in 50 acres of lovely Gers countryside. The 180 pitches, the majority with electricity and many terraced, are in several different areas. All are separated by mature hedges and trees, the amount of shade available varies from area to area and some pitches are flatter than others. This site would be an excellent introduction to naturist camping, being quite 'laid-back' in terms of rules and regulations (although nudity is compulsory), but offering some activities for those who wish to join in without any pressure for those who don't!

Facilities

Sanitary facilities in three blocks include hot showers (communal) and washbasins (cold water only, but hot tap nearby), all fitted out to a high standard and very well maintained. Gas available. Shop (1/7-31/8). Takeaway, pub and restaurant (1/4-1/11). Swimming pool and children's pool (1/5-30/9). Four acre lake for fishing or boating and woodland area. Adventure play area. Bicycle hire. Tennis, boules, archery, film shows and a small gym. TV rooms. Off site: Trips arranged to local attractions.

Open: All year (limited facilities Oct-May).

Directions

From Lectoure take the D7 to St Clar. At St Clar turn left onto D13 then after 1 km. turn right onto the D167 to Gaudonville. After 4 km. turn left into narrow approach road to site. Site is a further 800 m. along narrow bumpy track. GPS: 43.891011, 0.828545

Charges guide

Per unit incl. 2 persons and electricity	€ 14,20 - € 23,30
extra person	€ 3,60 - € 7,10
dog	€ 1,80

Sérignac

Camping Naturiste le Clos Barrat

Mauroux, F-46700 Sérignac (Midi-Pyrénées) T: 05 65 31 97 93. E: thierry.schmutz@orange.fr

alanrogers.com/FR46300

This site is southwest of Cahors in ten hectares of forest and pasture amongst the rich countryside of the Lot/Quercy area. This is a family run naturist site where you will receive a warm and friendly welcome which is extended throughout your stay. It offers spaciousness and tranquillity with 90 generous pitches (over 120 sq.m), all with 6/10A electricity. There are also six mobile homes, chalets and apartments to rent. The site is on a gentle rolling slope and this is reflected in some of the pitches although most are mainly level, and access for larger units is not a problem.

Facilities

Three traditional style sanitary blocks with two offering facilities for disabled visitors. Bar and restaurant. Small shop. Swimming pool and paddling pool. Play area. Trampoline. Tennis. Archery. Organised activities. Library. Barbecues are not permitted. Mobile homes, chalets and apartments for rent. Off site: Many cycle and walking trails. Fishing 6 km. Riding 6 km. Golf 20 km.

Open: 29 April - 31 December.

Directions

From Cahors take the D653 to Villesque. Join the D656 towards Tournon d'Argenais and at St Matre follow signs to Sérignac on the D4. Site is signed from there. GPS: 44.43080, 1.06850

Charges guide

Per person	€ 5,00 - € 6,50
child (3-18 yrs)	€ 1,00 - € 2,00
pitch	€ 4,80 - € 6,50
incl. electricity	€ 7,70 - € 9,50

For latest campsite news, availability and prices visit

alanrogers.com

Varilhes

Naturiste Camping Millefleurs

Le Tuilier Gudas, F-09120 Varilhes (Midi-Pyrénées) T: 05 61 60 77 56. E: simone.groot@orange.fr
alanrogers.com/FR09090

Millefleurs is a quiet site in a secluded location for naturists. It is peaceful with some 70 acres of woods and meadows providing guided naturist walks in total privacy. The site has 40 large, flat, mostly terraced pitches (34 with 6-10A electricity), long leads if pitching off the terraces. There are also very secluded pitches in wooded areas with shade, or you can pitch a tent in the meadows if you prefer. There are few of the normal camping leisure facilities here and the site is definitely aimed at the more mature naturist camper. Owned by a Dutch couple, Gert and Annie Kos provide a warm welcome and speak excellent English. Annie has found 16 different types of orchids and keeps a picture record in the 'salle de reunion'.

Facilities

An excellent toilet block with facilities for disabled campers. Bread available to order in high season. Guests dine together in the 'salle de reunion' within the farmhouse two nights a week or just meet friends for a drink. Refrigerator with drinks. Petanque. Guide book for walks and cycle rides. Torches essential. Pick ups from airports and stations. Off site: The coast is 1.5 hours.

Open: 1 April - 1 November.

Directions

From Varilhes, 8 km. south of Pamiers on the D624 (parallel to N20). Take D13 for Dalou and Gudas cross railway and N20. The site is 2 km. past Gudas, on the right. GPS: 42.9927, 1.6788

Charges guide

Per unit incl. 2 persons	€ 19,00 - € 19,50
extra person	€ 5,25

No credit cards.

Barjac

Camping Naturiste de la Sablière

Domaine de la Sablière, Saint Privat-de-Champclos, F-30430 Barjac (Languedoc-Roussillon)
T: 04 66 24 51 16. E: contact@villagesabliere.com alanrogers.com/FR30100

Spectacularly situated in the Cèze Gorges, this well-equipped, spacious naturist site, tucked away within its wild and dramatic terrain offers a wide variety of facilities, all within a really peaceful, wooded setting. There are 497 pitches, 240 for touring. Many are large and most have electricity (6/10A). Long leads and rock pegs may possibly be needed. Nudity is only obligatory around the pool complex. There are long and steep walks between many pitches and the facilities. Cars can be used in low season and there is a shuttle service in July and August. Large outfits are not advised to visit.

Facilities

Six good open-plan unisex sanitary blocks. Naturist style baths and facilities for disabled campers. Laundry. Good supermarket. Bar (1/4-22/9). Excellent open air, covered restaurant and takeaway (1/4-22/9). Small café/crêperie. Swimming pool complex. Fitness room. Disco. Tennis. Minigolf. Play areas. River bathing. Fitness trail. Archery. Entertainment. Gas and electric barbecues only. Free WiFi at reception. Off site: Bicycle hire 8 km. Riding 10 km.

Open: 2 April - 2 October.

Directions

From Alès take D16 then D979 northeast towards Barjac. 5 km. beyound St Jean-de-Maruéjols turn right D266 signed St Privat and site. Site is 5 km. along winding lane. GPS: 44.26685, 4.35202

Charges guide

Per unit incl. 2 persons and electricity (10A)	€ 19,80 - € 35,30
extra person	€ 4,40 - € 8,00
child (0-10 yrs)	free - € 3,15

Cesseras-en-Minervois

Camping Naturiste le Mas de Lignières

F-34210 Cesseras-en-Minervois (Languedoc-Roussillon) T: 04 68 91 24 86. E: lemas1@tiscali.fr
alanrogers.com/FR34050

A naturist site hidden in the hills of the Minervois, only 3 km. from the medieval town of Minerve. There are marvellous views to the Pyrénées, the Corbières and the coast at Narbonne. Jeanne continues to run the site (following the sad death of Gilles) and offers a warm welcome, and promoting an enjoyable family atmosphere. The site now has just 26 very large pitches (electricity 6/10A), and 5 caravan holiday homes. Mainly on level grass, they are separated by mature hedges which give considerable privacy. Some smaller pitches are available for tents, with cars parked elsewhere. There is natural shade and a variety of flora and fauna including four types of orchid.

Facilities

Clean toilet block has open washbasins and showers, facilities for disabled visitors. Washing machine. Simple shop. Bread (15/6-15/9). Bar (15/7-15/8). Swimming pool, sliding cover for use when cold. Paddling pool. Room for general use with TV, library, separate provision for young people. Playground. Tennis. Boules. Torch useful. Only gas barbecues are permitted. Off site: Sailing, riding and canoeing nearby – Lac de Jouarres. Canal du Midi.

Open: 1 May - 2 October.

Directions

From A61 take exit for Lézignan-Corbières, D611 to Homps, then D910 to Olonzac. Through village following signs to Minerve (D10). Continue. 4 km. Turn left to Cesseras (D168). At Cesseras follow signs Fauzan for 4 km. (site signed) on right, narrow, winding road. GPS: 43.34092, 2.70648

Charges guide

Per unit incl. 2 persons	€ 22,00 - € 25,00
extra person	€ 4,00

Fleury

Domaine Naturiste la Grande Cosse

Saint Pierre-la-Mer, F-11560 Fleury (Languedoc-Roussillon) T: 04 68 33 61 87. E: contact@grandecosse.com

alanrogers.com/FR11190

Any slight difficulty in finding this secluded naturist site is compensated for immediately when you arrive. The abundance of flowers, shrubs and the generally peaceful ambience makes this a delightful place for a relaxing naturist holiday, and the extensive facilities mean you only need to leave the site for sightseeing rather than for necessities. In total there are 480 pitches, of which about 146 are for mobile homes, and the mainly large touring pitches, all with 8A electrical connections, are informally and very attractively arranged in a variety of different areas.

Facilities

Five sanitary blocks are opened progressively throughout the season. Fully equipped modern facilities, including a choice of private or communal showers, and some washbasins in cabins. Laundry facilities. Motorcaravan service point. Gas. Well stocked shop, bar, restaurant and takeaway (all season). Three heated swimming pools, two for adults and a smaller one for children (all season). Play area. Tennis. Archery. Internet access. Communal barbecues. Off site: Boat launching 5 km. Riding 2 km.

Open: 9 April - 9 October.

Directions

From the A9 take exit 36 to Vendres. Pass through town, on to Lespignan, then Fleury. At roundabout turn left signed Cabanes-de-Fleury. Follow for 4 km. to pick up site sign to left. Continue for 2 km. and site signed to right. GPS: 43.20582, 3.21099

Charges 2011

Per unit incl. 2 persons and electricity	€ 18,00 - € 41,00
extra person	€ 5,00 - € 7,00
child (1-13 yrs)	free - € 6,00

Lapalme

Camping Naturiste le Clapotis

Lieu dit Pech-Redon, F-11480 Lapalme (Languedoc-Roussillon) T: 04 68 48 15 40. E: info@leclapotis.com

alanrogers.com/FR11090

Le Clapotis is a small and tranquil naturist site, situated between Narbonne and Perpignan in a secluded pine wood beside the Etang de Lapalme (a large sea lagoon). There is direct access to the lagoon which is popular with those in pursuit of the ideal conditions provided for windsurfing. The site comprises 173 touring pitches, all with electricity (4A) and are of a good size on stony or sandy ground. Pitches in the older part have excellent shade from the pine trees and in the newer area, shade will be provided as the hedges grow. There is a relaxed feeling of harmony and freedom about this site.

Facilities

Two large and one small sanitary block, a little basic but fully equipped. Showers are both open and in cabins. Facilities for babies and disabled campers. Washing machines. Well stocked shop (end May-mid Sept). Bar and restaurant (from 15/6) and takeaway (from midday). Swimming pool (15/6-15/9). Two half tennis courts. Petanque. Windsurfing. Fishing. Torches useful. Internet and WiFi. Communal barbecue. Off site: Sandy beach 5 km. Riding 10 km. Bicycle hire 9 km. Golf 10 km.

Open: 15 March - 15 October.

Directions

From N9 exit 40 go towards Port Leucate. At roundabout take N9 north for 3 km. to next roundabout. Turn right (Port-la-Nouvelle). Site sign in 500 m. on right. Follow narrow, poorly made up road for 2 km. up hill to site. GPS: 42.958, 2.99586

Charges guide

| Per unit incl. 2 persons and electricity | € 22,00 - € 26,00 |
| extra person | € 4,00 |

Lodève

Domaine Naturiste de Lambeyran

Hameau de Lambeyran, F-34700 Lodève (Languedoc-Roussillon) T: 04 67 44 13 99. E: lambeyran@wanadoo.fr

alanrogers.com/FR34540

A wooded valley covering 340 hectares allows Domaine de Lambeyran a place in the Guinness Book of Records for having the largest area available for naturists in the world. It is a wonderful natural area with amazing views across to Lodève. Naturists can enjoy the marked trails around the valley or the welcome pool whilst choosing from 160 huge (200 sq.m.) pitches. Where necessary the pitches have been levelled with local stone. Electricity (3/6A) is available on 110 pitches. Many pitches are quite private, hidden away amongst wild shrubs, flowers and trees so vast is the space available.

Facilities

Two large tiled toilet blocks and a smaller one are fully equipped and give good coverage for the various areas. Washing machine. Small shop. Bar and simple restaurant (in the evenings from 7/7). Swimming pool with sunbathing terrace. Some play equipment for children and indoor area for older children. Walking/hiking trails from 5-30 km. Mountain biking. Dancing, films and organised trips such as canoeing down the Orb Gorges. Communal barbecue area. Off site: Tennis and riding 4 km.

Open: 1 May - 20 September.

Directions

From A75 take exit for Lodève and follow signs for town centre. Cross town following signs for Lunas (D35) picking up site signs. Ignore right turn for les Plans and take next right and follow up hill for 3 km. to site. The road is good but is single file in parts. GPS: 43.73615, 3.26654

Charges guide

Per person	€ 4,20 - € 6,20
pitch	€ 7,60 - € 12,80
electricity (3/6A)	€ 4,20
No credit cards.	

For latest campsite news, availability and prices visit

alanrogers.com

We can book this site for you!
Call 01580 214000

alan rogers travel

Méjannes-le-Clap

Camping Naturiste la Genèse

Route de la Genèse, F-30430 Méjannes-le-Clap (Languedoc-Roussillon) T: 04 66 24 51 82
E: info@lagenese.com alanrogers.com/FR30400

La Genèse is a well equipped naturist site close to the banks of the River Cèze on the northern edge of the Cévennes national park. This is a large site with 480 well shaded pitches, 160 are for touring. These are divided into 'sauvage' (without electricity) and 'prairie' (with electricity 6A and closer to the main facilities). A wide variety of activities are on offer here, including art and craft workshops, bridge evenings and a cinema. Sports amenities include a large swimming pool with a daily aquagym session in high season, separate children's pool, tennis, archery and river bathing. Electric or communal barbecues only.

Facilities

Five clean and well-maintained toilet blocks, one refurbished. Facilities for visitors with disabilities. Shop (1/5-31/8). Bar, restaurant, takeaway (all season). Swimming pool and children's pool. Sauna. Archery. Games room. Art and craft workshops. Cinema. Canoe hire. Play area. Activity and entertainment programme. Direct access to river, fishing. Mobile homes and chalets for rent. Motorcaravan services. WiFi (charged). Off site: Bicycle hire and riding 7 km. Méjannes-le-Clap.

Open: 2 April - 30 September.

Directions

From Pont St Esprit, take D901 west to Barjac, then D979 to Rochegude. Shortly beyond Rochegude, take D167 to Méjannes-le-Clap and follow signs to site (6 km). GPS: 44.26772, 4.37013

Charges guide

Per unit incl. 2 persons	
and electricity	€ 18,50 - € 25,50
extra person	€ 3,90 - € 5,90
child (4-17 yrs)	€ 2,95 - € 3,90

Sérignan-Plage

Camping le Sérignan-Plage Nature

l'rpellière, F-34410 Sérignan-Plage (Languedoc-Roussillon) T: 04 67 32 09 61. E: info@leserignannature.com
alanrogers.com/FR34080

Sérignan-Plage Nature benefits from the same 600 m. of white, sandy beach as its sister site next door. Being a naturist site, it actually abuts the naturist section of the beach with direct access to it. It also has the use of the Sérignan-Plage balnéotherapy pool in the mornings, an excellent facility with spa and jacuzzi pools in a Romanesque style setting. The site has 286 good sized pitches on level sandy grass of which 94 are available for touring (6A electricity). There is plenty of shade except on the pitches beside the beach. Around 75 mobile homes and chalets are available to rent.

Facilities

Two toilet blocks of differing designs (one refurbished to a very modern design) offer modern facilities with some washbasins in cabins. All clean and well maintained. Washing machines. Supermarket, fruit and vegetables, newsagent/souvenir shop and ice cream kiosk. Small bar/café. Evening entertainment. Play area, miniclub and disco for children. Facilities and pools at Sérignan-Plage. WiFi throughout (charged). Off site: Bicycle hire 200 m. Fishing 500 m. Riding 800 km. Golf 2 km.

Open: 29 April - 26 September.

Directions

From A9 exit 35 (Béziers Est) towards Sérignan, D64 (9 km). Before Sérignan, take road to Sérignan-Plage. At small sign (blue) turn right for 500 m. At T-junction turn left over bridge, site is 75 m. straight after left hand bend (the second naturist site). GPS: 43.263409, 3.320148

Charges guide

Per unit incl. 2 persons	
and electricity	€ 16,00 - € 48,00
extra person	€ 6,00 - € 8,00

Bédoin

Domaine Naturiste de Bélézy

F-84410 Bédoin (Provence) T: 04 90 65 60 18. E: info@belezy.com
alanrogers.com/FR84020

537

At the foot of Mt Ventoux, surrounded by beautiful scenery, Bélézy is an excellent naturist site with many amenities and activities and the ambience is relaxed and comfortable. The 320 pitches, 248 for touring (12A electricity, long leads required) are set amongst many varieties of trees and shrubs giving space and privacy. The attractive bar/restaurant and terrace overlook the swimming pool area and have superb views over the large recreational area and hills beyond. The site has an ecological theme with a small farm, fishpond and garden area especially for the children. Pets are not accepted.

Facilities

Four toilet blocks with very good facilities for campers with disabilities – newer ones are excellent, some have hot showers in the open air. A superb children's section. Shop (3/4-19/9). Excellent restaurant/takeaway (27/3-26/9). Swimming pools. Sauna. Tennis. Adventure play area. Activities all season. Archery. Guided walks. Children's club. Hydrotherapy centre (1/4-30/9). Off site: Bédoin with shops and restaurants 1.5 km.

Open: 23 March - 2 October.

Directions

From A7 exit 22 or RN7, south of Orange, take the D950 southeast to Carpentras, then D974 northeast to Bédoin. In Bédoin turn right at roundabout, site signed, site in 2 km. GPS: 44.13352, 5.18745

Charges guide

Per unit incl. 2 persons	
and electricity	€ 22,00 - € 39,00
extra person	€ 6,00 - € 9,40
child (3-8 yrs)	free - € 9,30

Puget-Theniers

Domaine Naturiste Club Origan

F-06260 Puget-Theniers (Côte d'Azur) T: 04 93 05 06 00. E: origan@wanadoo.fr

alanrogers.com/FR06070

Origan is a naturist site set in the mountains behind Nice, at a height of 500 m. The access road is single track and winding with a few passing places, so arrival is not recommended until late afternoon. The site's terrain is fairly wild and the roads stony and it is not suitable for caravans longer than six metres due to the steep slopes, although the site will assist with a 4 x 4 vehicle if requested. The 100 touring pitches, in three areas, are of irregular size and shape with good views. Electricity connection (6A) is possible on most pitches (by long cable). A member of France 4 Naturisme.

Facilities

Sanitary facilities, are clean and of a standard and type associated with most good naturist sites – mostly open plan hot showers. Laundry facilities. Shop (1/6-30/8). Bar/restaurant. Takeaway. Heated swimming pools. Jacuzzi and sauna. Disco. Tennis. Fishing. Bicycle hire. Organised activities for all (high season). Only gas or electric barbecues are permitted. Torches advised. Off site: Puget-Theniers offers choice of bars, cafés, shops, etc. Steam train. Eco-museum of the Roudoule.

Open: 15 April - 30 September.

Directions

Heading west on the N202, just past the town of Puget-Theniers, turn right at campsite sign at level crossing; site is 1 km. GPS: 43.957633, 6.860883

Charges guide

Per unit incl. 2 persons and electricity	€ 29,50 - € 36,50
extra person	€ 4,00 - € 8,00
child (3-8 yrs)	€ 3,00 - € 6,00
dog	€ 2,00

Camping Cheques accepted.

Bravone

Camping Bagheera Naturisme

Route 198, F-20230 Bravone (Corsica) T: 04 95 38 80 30. E: bagheera@bagheera.fr

alanrogers.com/FR20080

An extremely long private road leads you to this naturist site which is alongside a 3 km. fine sand beach and has been run by the same family for 30 years. There are 190 pitches which are separated from the numerous bungalows. Well shaded under huge eucalyptus trees, all have 10A electricity (long leads may be necessary). Some beach-side pitches have sea views but most others are further back from the sea. All pitches are on sandy grass and are kept clean and neat. Large units will have no problems with access here. The restaurant and beach bar have superb panoramic views of the sea.

Facilities

Four sanitary blocks offer hot water throughout. Washing machines. Excellent restaurant (Corsican menu, children's menu). Bar. Comprehensive beach snack bar and bar. Pizzeria. Shop. All amenities 1/6-30/10. Swimming pool. New play area. Gym. Massage. Sauna. Pedaloes. Petanque. Sub-aqua diving. Beach umbrella rental. Refrigerated lockers for hire. Tennis. Bicycle hire. Fishing. Entertainment programme all season. TV. Internet. Off site: Riding. Boat launching 15 km. Town 11 km.

Open: 1 April - 30 October (bungalows all year).

Directions

Site is between Bastia and Aleria near Bravone, 7 km. north of Aleria on the N198. It is well signed off the N198. Follow site road 4 km. east to beach. GPS: 42.2194, 9.5541

Charges guide

Per unit incl. 2 persons	€ 16,00 - € 22,40
extra person	€ 3,60 - € 5,80
child (3-15 yrs)	€ 1,60 - € 3,25

For latest campsite news, availability and prices visit

alanrogers.com

Alèria

Riva Bella Nature Resort & Spa

B.P. 21, F-20270 Alèria (Corsica) T: 04 95 38 81 10. E: rivabella.corsica@gmail.com

alanrogers.com/FR20040

This is a relaxed, informal, spacious site alongside an extremely long and beautiful beach. Riva Bella Resort is naturist from 16 May to 19 September only. It offers a variety of pitches, situated in beautiful countryside and seaside. The site is divided into several areas with 200 pitches and bungalows, some alongside the sandy beach with little shade, others in a wooded glade with ample shade. The huge fish-laden lakes are a fine feature of this site. Although electricity is available in most parts, a long cable may be needed. The ground is fairly flat with terracing for tents. There is a balnéotherapy centre with the very latest beauty and relaxation treatments based on marine techniques (men and women). The owner Marie Claire Pasqual is justifiably proud of the site and the fairly unobtrusive rules are designed to ensure that everyone is able to relax, whilst preserving the natural beauty of the environment. There is, for example, a restriction on the movement of cars in certain areas (but ample free parking).

Facilities

High standard toilet facilities. Provision for disabled campers, children and babies. Laundry. Large shop (15/5-15/10). Fridge hire. Restaurant with lake views (all season) with reasonable prices. Excellent beach/snack bar. Bar. Watersports, sailing school, fishing, sub-aqua. Balnéotherapy centre. Sauna. Aerobics. Giant draughts. Archery. Fishing. Riding. Mountain bike hire. Half-court tennis. Walk with llamas. Internet. WiFi. Professional evening entertainment programme.

Open: All year (naturist 16/5-19/9).

Directions

Site is 12 km. north of Aleria on N198 (Bastia) road. Watch for large signs and unmade road to site and follow for 4 km. GPS: 42.16151, 9.55269

Charges 2011

Per unit incl. 2 persons and electricity	€ 23,30 - € 40,30
extra person	€ 5,00 - € 9,00
child (3-8 yrs)	€ 2,00 - € 6,00
dog	€ 2,00 - € 3,50

Special offers and half-board arrangements.
Camping Cheques accepted.

Porto-Vecchio

Village Naturiste la Chiappa

537

Route de Palombaggia, F-20137 Porto-Vecchio (Corsica) T: 04 95 70 00 31. E: chiappa@wanadoo.fr

alanrogers.com/FR20050

This is a large naturist campsite on the Chiappa peninsula with 200 pitches for tourers and tents, plus 250 bungalows. A few touring pitches have sea views and are taken first in high season. The pitches are informally marked and have a variety of shapes and sizes, some with difficult slopes and access, especially for large units. (75-125 sq.m). Cars are parked separately. Very long electricity leads are necessary here for most pitches (10A electricity). The beaches are between long rocky outcrops and it is generally safe to swim, or alternatively enjoy the swimming pool by the main beach.

Facilities

The sanitary facilities were tired and needing refurbishment when we visited. Washing machines. Well stocked shop. Two bars and restaurants with snacks. Swimming pool. Play area for children. Riding. Tennis. Minigolf. Fishing. Diving, windsurfing and sailing schools. Keep fit, yoga, sauna (extra cost). Bistro. Satellite TV. Internet access. Torches essential. Off site: Excursions. Car rental.

Open: 14 May - 18 October.

Directions

From Bastia, N198 heading south, take Porto-Vecchio bypass (signed Bonifacio). At southern end, take first left signed Pont de la Chiappa, unclassified road. After 8 km. site signed. Turn left and follow rough track for 2 km. to site.
GPS: 41.59387, 9.35713

Charges guide

Per unit incl. 2 persons and electricity	€ 27,00 - € 36,00

Accommodation

Over recent years many of the campsites featured in this guide have added large numbers of high quality mobile homes and chalets. Many site owners believe that some former caravanners and motorcaravanners have been enticed by the extra comfort they can now provide, and that maybe this is the ideal solution to combine the freedom of camping with all the comforts of home.

Quality is consistently high and, although the exact size and inventory may vary from site to site, if you choose any of the sites detailed here, you can be sure that you're staying in some of the best quality and best value mobile homes available.

Home comforts are provided and typically these include a fridge with freezer compartment, gas hob, proper shower – often a microwave and radio/cassette hi-fi too but do check for details. All mobile homes and chalets come fully equipped with a good range of kitchen utensils, pots and pans, crockery, cutlery and outdoor furniture. Some even have an attractive wooden sundeck or paved terrace – a perfect spot for outdoors eating or relaxing with a book and watching the world go by.

Regardless of model, colourful soft furnishings are the norm and a generally breezy décor helps to provide a real holiday feel.

Although some sites may have a large number of different accommodation types, we have restricted our choice to one or two of the most popular accommodation units (either mobile homes or chalets) for each of the sites listed.

The mobile homes here will be of modern design, and recent innovations, for example, often include pitched roofs which substantially improve their appearance.

Design will invariably include clever use of space and fittings/furniture to provide for comfortable holidays – usually light and airy, with big windows and patio-style doors, fully equipped kitchen areas, a shower room with shower, washbasin and WC, cleverly designed bedrooms and a comfortable lounge/dining area (often incorporating a sofa bed).

In general, modern campsite chalets incorporate all the best features of mobile homes in a more traditional structure, sometimes with the advantage of an upper mezzanine floor for an additional bedroom.

Our selected campsites offer a massive range of different types of mobile home and chalet, and it would be impractical to inspect every single accommodation unit. Our selection criteria, therefore, primarily takes account of the quality standards of the campsite itself.

However, there are a couple of important ground rules:

- Featured mobile homes must be no more than 5 years old

- chalets no more than 10 years old

- All listed accommodation must, of course, fully conform with all applicable local, national and European safety legislation.

For each campsite we given details of the type, or types, of accommodation available to rent, but these details are necessarily quite brief. Sometimes internal layouts can differ quite substantially, particularly with regard to sleeping arrangements, where these include the flexible provision for 'extra persons' on sofa beds located in the living area. These arrangements may vary from accommodation to accommodation, and if you're planning a holiday which includes more people than are catered for by the main bedrooms you should check exactly how the extra sleeping arrangements are to be provided!

Charges

An indication of the tariff for each type of accommodation featured is also included, indicating the variance between the low and high season tariffs. However, given that many campsites have a large and often complex range of pricing options, incorporating special deals and various discounts, the charges we mention should be taken to be just an indication. We strongly recommend therefore that you confirm the actual cost when making a booking.

We also strongly recommend that you check with the campsite, when booking, what (if anything) will be provided by way of bed linen, blankets, pillows etc. Again, in our experience, this can vary widely from site to site.

On every campsite a fully refundable deposit (usually between 150 and 300 euros) is payable on arrival. There may also be an optional cleaning service for which a further charge is made. Other options may include sheet hire (typically 30 euros per unit) or baby pack hire (cot and high chair).

Low Cost Flights

An Inexpensive Way To Arrive At Your Campsite

Many campsites are conveniently served by a wide choice of low cost airlines. Cheap flights can be very easy to find and travellers increasingly find the regional airports often used to be smaller, quieter and generally a calmer, more pleasurable experience.

Low cost flights can make campsites in more distant regions a much more attractive option: quicker to reach, inexpensive flights, and simply more convenient.

Many campsites are seeing increased visitors using the low cost flights and are adapting their services to suit this clientele. An airport shuttle service is not uncommon, meaning you can take advantage of that cheap flight knowing you will be met at the other end and whisked to your campsite. No taxi queues or multiple drop-offs.

Obviously, these low cost flights are impractical when taking all your own camping gear but they do make a holiday in campsite owned accommodation much more straightforward. The low cost airline option makes mobile home holidays especially attractive: pack a suitcase and use bed linen and towels provided (which you will generally need to pre-book).

Pricing Tips

- Low cost airlines promote cheap flights but only a small percentage of seats are priced at the cheapest price. Book early for the best prices (and of course you also get a better choice of campsite or mobile home)

- Child seats are usually the same costs as adults

- Full payment is required at the time of booking

- Changes and amendments can be costly with low cost airlines

- Peak dates can be expensive compared to other carriers

Car Hire

For maximum flexibility you will probably hire a car from a car rental agency. Car hire provides convenience but also will allow you access to off-site shops, beaches and tourist sights.

FR35000 Camping le Vieux Chêne
Baguer-Pican, F-35120 Dol-de-Bretagne

▶ see report page 38

AR1 – REVE CONFORT – Mobile home
Sleeping: 2 bedrooms, sleeps 5: 1 double, 2 singles, bunk bed, sofa bed, pillows and blankets provided

Living: living/kitchen area, heating, shower, separate WC

Eating: fitted kitchen with hobs, oven, coffee maker, fridge, freezer

Outside: table & chairs

Pets: accepted (with supplement)

AR2 – COTTAGE DE BRETAGNE – Mobile Home
Sleeping: 2 bedrooms, sleeps 4: 2 singles, sofa bed, pillows and blankets provided

Living: living/kitchen area, heating, shower, separate WC

Eating: fitted kitchen with oven, fridge, freezer

Outside: table & chairs

Pets: accepted (with supplement)

Open: 1 April - 25 September

Weekly Charge	AR1	AR2
Low Season (from)	€ 299	€ 279
High Season (from)	€ 729	€ 689

FR29180 Camping les Embruns
Rue du Philosophe Alain, le Pouldu, F-29360 Clohars-Carnoêt

▶ see report page 54

AR1 – OCEANE – Mobile home
Sleeping: 2 bedrooms, sleeps 4: 1 double, 2 singles

Living: living/kitchen area, heating, shower, WC

Eating: fitted kitchen with hobs, oven, coffee maker, fridge

Outside: table & chairs

Pets: accepted (with supplement)

AR2 – ATLANTIQUE + VERANDA – Mobile home
Sleeping: 3 bedrooms, sleeps 6: 1 double, 2 singles, bunk bed

Living: living/kitchen area, heating, shower, WC

Eating: fitted kitchen with hobs, oven, coffee maker, fridge

Outside: table & chairs

Pets: accepted (with supplement)

Other (AR1 and AR2): cot, highchair to hire

Open: 8 April - 24 September

Weekly Charge	AR1	AR2
Low Season (from)	€ 285	€ 400
High Season (from)	€ 670	€ 860

FR29010 Castel Camping le Ty-Nadan
Route d'Arzano, F-29310 Locunolé

▶ see report page 55

AR1 – IRM – Mobile home
Sleeping: 2 bedrooms, sleeps 6: 1 double, 2 singles, sofa bed, pillows and blankets provided

Living: living/kitchen area, heating, shower, WC

Eating: fitted kitchen with hobs, oven, fridge

Outside: table & chairs, parasol, 2 sun loungers

Pets: accepted

AR2 – CHALET – Chalet
Sleeping: 2 bedrooms, sleeps 6: 1 double, 2 singles, sofa bed, pillows and blankets provided

Living: living/kitchen area, heating, shower, WC

Eating: fitted kitchen with hobs, oven, fridge

Outside: table & chairs, parasol, 2 sun loungers

Pets: accepted

Other (AR1 and AR2): bed linen, cot, highchair to hire

Open: 8 April - 3 September

Weekly Charge	AR1	AR2
Low Season (from)	€ 282	€ 414
High Season (from)	€ 910	€ 1176

FR29090 Camping le Raguenès-Plage

see report page 58

19 rue des Iles, F-29920 Névez

AR1 – VARIANTE – Mobile home

Sleeping: 2 bedrooms, sleeps 5: 1 double, 2 singles, sofa bed, pillows and blankets provided

Living: living/kitchen area, heating, air conditioning, shower, separate WC

Eating: fitted kitchen with hobs, oven, microwave, coffee maker, fridge, freezer

Outside: table & chairs, parasol, 2 sun loungers, barbecue

Pets: accepted (with supplement)

AR2 – OHARA COTTAGE – Cottage

Sleeping: 2 bedrooms, sleeps 4: 1 double, 2 singles, sofa bed, pillows and blankets provided

Living: living/kitchen area, heating, air conditioning, shower, separate WC

Eating: fitted kitchen with hobs, microwave, coffee maker, fridge, freezer

Outside: table & chairs, parasol, 2 sun loungers, barbecue

Pets: accepted (with supplement)

Other (AR1 and AR2): bed linen to hire

Open: 1 April - 30 September		
Weekly Charge	**AR1**	**AR2**
Low Season *(from)*	€ 320	€ 340
High Season *(from)*	€ 699	€ 745

FR29050 Castel Camping l'Orangerie de Lanniron

see report page 65

Château de Lanniron, F-29336 Quimper

AR1 – ZEN – Mobile home

Sleeping: 3 bedrooms, sleeps 6: 1 double, 3 singles, bunk bed, pillows and blankets provided

Living: living/kitchen area, heating, air conditioning, shower, separate WC

Eating: fitted kitchen with hobs, microwave, coffee maker, fridge, freezer

Outside: table & chairs, parasol, 2 sun loungers, barbecue

Pets: not accepted

AR2 – CONFORT – Mobile home

Sleeping: 2 bedrooms, sleeps 5: 1 double, 2 singles, sofa bed, pillows and blankets provided

Living: living/kitchen area, heating, shower, separate WC

Eating: fitted kitchen with hobs, microwave, coffee maker, fridge, freezer

Outside: table & chairs, parasol, 2 sun loungers, barbecue

Pets: not accepted

Other (AR1 and AR2): bed linen, cot, highchair to hire

Open: 1 April - 31 October		
Weekly Charge	**AR1**	**AR2**
Low Season *(from)*	€ 497	€ 406
High Season *(from)*	€ 1036	€ 938

FR29080 Camping le Panoramic

see report page 72

Route de la Plage-Penker, F-29560 Telgruc-sur-Mer

AR1 – TRIGANO ELEGANTE 33 M^2 – Mobile home

Sleeping: 3 bedrooms, sleeps 6: 1 double, 4 singles, pillows and blankets provided

Living: living/kitchen area, heating, shower, WC

Eating: fitted kitchen with hobs, fridge, freezer

Outside: table & chairs, parasol, 2 sun loungers, barbecue

Pets: accepted (with supplement)

AR2 – TRIGANO ELEGANTE 25M^2 – Mobile home

Sleeping: 2 bedrooms, sleeps 4: 1 double, 2 singles, sofa bed, pillows and blankets provided

Living: living/kitchen area, heating, shower, WC

Eating: fitted kitchen with hobs, fridge

Outside: table & chairs, parasol, 2 sun loungers, barbecue

Pets: accepted (with supplement)

Open: 1 May - 15 September		
Weekly Charge	**AR1**	**AR2**
Low Season *(from)*	€ 300	€ 280
High Season *(from)*	€ 680	€ 590

FR27070 Camping de l'Ile des Trois Rois

1 rue Gilles Nicolle, F-27700 Andelys

see report page 77

AR1 – MOBILE HOME – Mobile home	AR2 – MOBILE HOME – Mobile home
Sleeping: 2 bedrooms, sleeps 4: 1 double, 2 singles	**Sleeping:** 3 bedrooms, sleeps 6: 1 double, 4 singles
Living: living/kitchen area, heating, shower, WC	**Living:** living/kitchen area, heating, shower, WC, separate WC
Eating: fitted kitchen with hobs, fridge	
Outside: table & chairs, barbecue	**Eating:** fitted kitchen with hobs, fridge
Pets: not accepted	**Outside:** table & chairs, barbecue
	Pets: not accepted

Open: 13 March - 15 November

Weekly Charge	AR1	AR2
Low Season *(from)*	€ 330	€ 390
High Season *(from)*	€ 530	€ 630

FR27060 Domaine de Marcilly

Route de Saint-Andre-de-l'Eure, F-27810 Marcilly-sur-Eure

see report page 86

AR1 – OPHEA – Mobile home	AR2 – OPHEA – Mobile home
Sleeping: 2 bedrooms, sleeps 5: 1 double, 2 singles, sofa bed, pillows and blankets provided	**Sleeping:** 3 bedrooms, sleeps 6: 1 double, 2 singles, sofa bed, pillows and blankets provided
Living: living/kitchen area, heating, shower, WC	**Living:** living/kitchen area, heating, shower, WC
Eating: fitted kitchen with hobs, oven, microwave, fridge	**Eating:** fitted kitchen with hobs, oven, microwave, fridge
Outside: table & chairs, barbecue	**Outside:** table & chairs, barbecue
Pets: accepted	**Pets:** accepted

Open: 1 April - 29 October

Weekly Charge	AR1	AR2
Low Season *(from)*	€ 300	€ 400
High Season *(from)*	€ 590	€ 660

FR80060 Camping le Val de Trie

Rue des Sources, Bouillancourt-sous-Miannay, F-80870 Moyenneville

see report page 112

AR1 – MOREVA – Mobile home	AR2 – PRIVILEGE ZEN – Mobile home
Sleeping: 2 bedrooms, sleeps 6: 1 double, 2 singles, sofa bed, pillows and blankets provided	**Sleeping:** 3 bedrooms, sleeps 6: 1 double, bunk bed, pillows and blankets provided
Living: living/kitchen area, heating, shower, separate WC	**Living:** living/kitchen area, heating, shower, separate WC
Eating: fitted kitchen with hobs, microwave, coffee maker, fridge, freezer	**Eating:** fitted kitchen with hobs, microwave, dishwasher, coffee maker, fridge, freezer
Outside: table & chairs, parasol, barbecue	**Outside:** table & chairs, parasol, barbecue
Pets: not accepted	**Pets:** not accepted

Other (AR1 and AR2): bed linen, cot, highchair to hire

Open: 1 April - 15 October

Weekly Charge	AR1	AR2
Low Season *(from)*	€ 313	€ 399
High Season *(from)*	€ 623	€ 714

FR80070 Kawan Village la Ferme des Aulnes

▶ see report page 113

1 rue du Marais, Fresne-sur-Authie, F-80120 Nampont-Saint Martin

AR1 – CONFORT – Mobile home

Sleeping: 2 bedrooms, sleeps 5: 1 double, 2 singles, sofa bed, pillows and blankets provided

Living: living/kitchen area, heating, TV, shower, separate WC

Eating: fitted kitchen with hobs, microwave, coffee maker, fridge, freezer

Outside: table & chairs, parasol, barbecue

Pets: accepted (with supplement)

AR2 – PRIVILEGE – Mobile home

Sleeping: 3 bedrooms, sleeps 6: 1 double, 2 singles, bunk bed, pillows and blankets provided

Living: living/kitchen area, heating, TV, shower, separate WC

Eating: fitted kitchen with hobs, microwave, coffee maker, fridge, freezer

Outside: table & chairs, parasol, barbecue

Pets: accepted (with supplement)

Other (AR1 and AR2): bed linen, cot, highchair to hire

Open: 1 April - 1 November

Weekly Charge	AR1	AR2
Low Season *(from)*	€ 490	€ 590
High Season *(from)*	€ 690	€ 790

FR80150 Camping Airotel Le Walric

▶ see report page 114

Route d'Eu, F-80230 Saint Valery-sur-Somme

AR1 – COTTAGE 4 COUCHAGES – Mobile home

Sleeping: 2 bedrooms, sleeps 4: 1 double, 2 singles, pillows and blankets provided

Living: living/kitchen area, heating, TV, shower, WC

Eating: fitted kitchen with hobs, microwave, coffee maker, fridge, freezer

Outside: table & chairs, parasol, barbecue

Pets: accepted

AR2 – COTTAGE 6 COUCHAGES – Mobile home

Sleeping: 3 bedrooms, sleeps 6: 1 double, 4 singles, pillows and blankets provided

Living: living/kitchen area, heating, TV, shower, WC

Eating: fitted kitchen with hobs, microwave, coffee maker, fridge, freezer

Outside: table & chairs, parasol, barbecue

Pets: accepted

Other (AR1 and AR2): cot, highchair to hire

Open: 1 April - 1 November

Weekly Charge	AR1	AR2
Low Season *(from)*	€ 300	€ 400
High Season *(from)*	€ 620	€ 710

FR57090 Parc Résidentiel de la Tensch

▶ see report page 138

F-57670 Francaltroff

AR1 – CHALET – Chalet

Sleeping: 2 bedrooms, sleeps 5: 1 double, 2 singles, sofa bed, pillows and blankets provided

Living: living/kitchen area, heating, TV, shower, separate WC

Eating: fitted kitchen with hobs, oven, microwave, coffee maker, fridge, freezer

Outside: table & chairs

Pets: not accepted

Other (AR1 and AR2): bed linen, cot to hire

Open: 6 May - 18 December

Weekly Charge	AR1
Low Season *(from)*	€ 365
High Season *(from)*	€ 465

FR41070 Kawan Village la Grande Tortue

3 route de Pontlevoy, F-41120 Candé-sur-Beuvron

► see report page 156

AR1 – IRM SUPER MERCURE – Mobile home

Sleeping: 2 bedrooms, sleeps 5: 1 double, 2 singles, bunk bed, pillows and blankets provided

Living: living/kitchen area, heating, shower, separate WC

Eating: fitted kitchen with hobs, microwave, coffee maker, fridge

Outside: table & chairs, 2 sun loungers

Pets: accepted (with supplement)

AR2 – LOUISIANE – Mobile home

Sleeping: 3 bedrooms, sleeps 6: 1 double, 4 singles, pillows and blankets provided

Living: living/kitchen area, heating, shower, separate WC

Eating: fitted kitchen with hobs, microwave, coffee maker, fridge

Outside: table & chairs, 2 sun loungers

Pets: accepted (with supplement)

Other (AR1 and AR2): bed linen, cot, highchair to hire

Open: 5 April - 20 September

Weekly Charge	AR1	AR2
Low Season *(from)*	€ 314	€ 441
High Season *(from)*	€ 700	€ 756

FR37060 Kawan Village l'Arada Parc

Rue de la Baratière, F-37360 Sonzay

► see report page 167

AR1 – SAMIBOIS – Chalet

Sleeping: 3 bedrooms, sleeps 6: 2 doubles, bunk bed, pillows and blankets provided

Living: living/kitchen area, heating, shower, separate WC

Eating: fitted kitchen with hobs, microwave, coffee maker, fridge, freezer

Outside: table & chairs, barbecue

Pets: accepted (with supplement)

AR2 – O HARA – Mobile home

Sleeping: 2 bedrooms, sleeps 5: 1 double, 2 singles, sofa bed, pillows and blankets provided

Living: living/kitchen area, heating, shower, separate WC

Eating: fitted kitchen with hobs, microwave, coffee maker, fridge

Outside: table & chairs, barbecue

Pets: accepted (with supplement)

Other (AR1 and AR2): bed linen, cot, highchair to hire

Open: 26 March - 1 November

Weekly Charge	AR1	AR2
Low Season *(from)*	€ 345	€ 295
High Season *(from)*	€ 645	€ 595

FR44220 Le Domaine de Léveno

Route de Sandun, F-44350 Guérande

► see report page 177

AR1 – COTTAGE CONFORT – Mobile home

Sleeping: 2 bedrooms, sleeps 6: 1 double, 2 singles, sofa bed, pillows and blankets provided

Living: living/kitchen area, heating, shower, separate WC

Eating: fitted kitchen with hobs, fridge

Outside: table & chairs, parasol

Pets: accepted (with supplement)

AR2 – COTTAGE CONFORT – Mobile home

Sleeping: 3 bedrooms, sleeps 6: 1 double, 4 singles, pillows and blankets provided

Living: living/kitchen area, shower, separate WC

Eating: fitted kitchen with hobs, fridge

Outside: table & chairs, parasol

Pets: accepted (with supplement)

Other (AR1 and AR2): bed linen, cot, highchair to hire

Open: 9 April - 1 October

Weekly Charge	AR1	AR2
Low Season *(from)*	€ 310	€ 340
High Season *(from)*	€ 820	€ 850

FR44210 Camping de l'Océan

▶ see report page 182

15 route de la Maison Rouge, F-44490 Le Croisic

AR1 – COTTAGE OCEAN ESPACE – Mobile home	AR2 – OCEAN GRAND CONFORT FAMILLE – Mobile home
Sleeping: 2 bedrooms, sleeps 5: 1 double, 2 singles, sofa bed, pillows and blankets provided	Sleeping: 3 bedrooms, sleeps 6: 1 double, 4 singles, pillows and blankets provided
Living: living/kitchen area, heating, shower, WC	Living: living/kitchen area, shower, WC
Eating: fitted kitchen with hobs, fridge	Eating: fitted kitchen with hobs, fridge
Outside: table & chairs, parasol	Outside: table & chairs, parasol
Pets: accepted (with supplement)	Pets: accepted (with supplement)

Other (AR1 and AR2): bed linen, cot, highchair to hire

Open: 7 April - 1 October		
Weekly Charge	AR1	AR2
Low Season (from)	€ 400	€ 450
High Season (from)	€ 915	€ 1075

FR44070 Camping Parc du Guibel

▶ see report page 186

Route de Kerdrien, F-44420 Piriac-sur-Mer

AR1 – GALION – Chalet	AR2 – CHALET TYPE 2 – Chalet
Sleeping: 2 bedrooms, sleeps 5: 1 double, 1 single, sofa bed, pillows and blankets provided	Sleeping: 3 bedrooms, sleeps 7: 1 double, 1 single, bunk bed, sofa bed, pillows and blankets provided
Living: living/kitchen area, heating, shower, separate WC	Living: living/kitchen area, heating, shower, separate WC
Eating: fitted kitchen with hobs, oven, grill, coffee maker, fridge, freezer	Eating: fitted kitchen with hobs, oven, grill, coffee maker, fridge, freezer
Outside: table & chairs, 2 sun loungers	Outside: table & chairs, 2 sun loungers
Pets: accepted (with supplement)	Pets: accepted (with supplement)

Other (AR1 and AR2): bed linen, cot, highchair to hire

Open: 1 April - 30 September		
Weekly Charge	AR1	AR2
Low Season (from)	€ 336	€ 385
High Season (from)	€ 742	€ 826

FR44180 Camping de la Boutinardière

▶ see report page 187

Rue de la Plage de la Boutinardière 23, F-44210 Pornic

AR1 – MOBILE HOME 5 PERS. – Mobile home	AR2 – MOBILE HOME 6 PERS. – Mobile home
Sleeping: 2 bedrooms, sleeps 5: 1 double, 2 singles, sofa bed, pillows and blankets provided	Sleeping: 3 bedrooms, sleeps 6: 1 double, 4 singles, pillows and blankets provided
Living: living/kitchen area, heating, shower, WC	Living: living/kitchen area, heating, shower, WC
Eating: fitted kitchen with hobs, fridge	Eating: fitted kitchen with hobs, fridge
Outside: table & chairs, parasol	Outside: table & chairs, parasol
Pets: accepted (with supplement)	Pets: accepted (with supplement)

Other (AR1 and AR2): bed linen, cot, highchair to hire

Open: 2 April - 1 October		
Weekly Charge	AR1	AR2
Low Season (from)	€ 360	€ 360
High Season (from)	€ 880	€ 960

FR44090 Kawan Village du Deffay

B.P. 18 Le Deffay, Sainte Reine-de-Bretagne, F-44160 Pontchâteau

▶ see report page 188

AR1 – MOBILE HOME 5 – Mobile home

Sleeping: 2 bedrooms, sleeps 5: 1 double, 1 single, bunk bed, pillows and blankets provided

Living: living/kitchen area, heating, shower, separate WC

Eating: fitted kitchen with hobs, microwave, coffee maker, fridge, freezer

Outside: table & chairs, parasol, 2 sun loungers, barbecue

Pets: not accepted

AR2 – CHALET 4/6 – Chalet

Sleeping: 2 bedrooms, sleeps 6: 1 double, bunk bed, sofa bed, pillows and blankets provided

Living: living/kitchen area, heating, shower, WC

Eating: fitted kitchen with hobs, microwave, grill, dishwasher, coffee maker, fridge, freezer

Outside: table & chairs, parasol, 2 sun loungers, barbecue

Pets: not accepted

Other (AR1 and AR2): bed linen, cot, highchair to hire

Open: 1 April - 31 October		
Weekly Charge	**AR1**	**AR2**
Low Season *(from)*	€ 210	€ 247
High Season *(from)*	€ 671	€ 707

FR17280 Camping la Grainetière

Route de Saint-Martin, F-17630 La Flotte-en-Rè

▶ see report page 224

AR1 – CONFORT – Mobile home

Sleeping: 2 bedrooms, sleeps 5: 1 double, 2 singles, sofa bed, pillows and blankets provided

Living: living/kitchen area, shower, separate WC

Eating: fitted kitchen with hobs, microwave, coffee maker, fridge

Outside: table & chairs, parasol

Pets: accepted (with supplement)

AR2 – LUXE – Mobile home

Sleeping: 2 bedrooms, sleeps 5: 1 double, 2 singles, sofa bed, pillows and blankets provided

Living: living/kitchen area, shower, separate WC

Eating: fitted kitchen with hobs, microwave, coffee maker, fridge

Outside: table & chairs, parasol

Pets: accepted (with supplement)

Other (AR1 and AR2): highchair to hire

Open: 4 April - 30 September		
Weekly Charge	**AR1**	**AR2**
Low Season *(from)*	€ 230	€ 255
High Season *(from)*	€ 760	€ 790

FR17010 Camping Bois Soleil

2 avenue de Suzac, F-17110 Saint Georges-de-Didonne

▶ see report page 236

AR1 – COTTAGE DE CHARME – Mobile home

Sleeping: 2 bedrooms, sleeps 4: 1 double, 2 singles, pillows and blankets provided

Living: living/kitchen area, heating, shower, WC

Eating: fitted kitchen with hobs, microwave, fridge

Outside: table & chairs, parasol

Pets: not accepted

AR2 – COTTAGE BOIS – Mobile home

Sleeping: 2 bedrooms, sleeps 4: 1 double, 2 singles, pillows and blankets provided

Living: living/kitchen area, heating, shower, WC

Eating: fitted kitchen with hobs, microwave, fridge

Outside: table & chairs, parasol

Pets: not accepted

Open: 2 April - 9 October		
Weekly Charge	**AR1**	**AR2**
Low Season *(from)*	€ 520	€ 300
High Season *(from)*	€ 1130	€ 960

FR71070 Kawan Village Château de l'Epervière

▶ see report page 246

F-71240 Gigny-sur-Saône

AR1 – LOUISIANE PACIFIQUE 3XL – Mobile Home

Sleeping: 3 bedrooms, sleeps 6: 1 double, 4 singles, pillows and blankets provided

Living: living/kitchen area, heating, TV, shower, separate WC

Eating: fitted kitchen with hobs, microwave, coffee maker, fridge, freezer

Outside: table & chairs, parasol, 2 sun loungers

Pets: not accepted

Other (AR1 and AR2): bed linen, cot, highchair to hire

Open: 2 April - 30 September	
Weekly Charge	AR1
Low Season *(from)*	€ 399
High Season *(from)*	€ 809

FR26210 Camping les Bois du Chatelas

▶ see report page 288

Route de Dieulefit, F-26460 Bourdeaux

AR1 – GOELAND – Bungalow

Sleeping: 2 bedrooms, sleeps 6: 2 doubles, 1 single, sofa bed, pillows and blankets provided

Living: living/kitchen area, heating, shower, separate WC

Eating: fitted kitchen with hobs, microwave, coffee maker, fridge, freezer

Outside: table & chairs

Pets: accepted

AR2 – TEXAS WATIPI – Bungalow

Sleeping: 3 bedrooms, sleeps 7: 1 double, 4 singles, sofa bed, pillows and blankets provided

Living: living/kitchen area, heating, shower, separate WC

Eating: fitted kitchen with hobs, microwave, coffee maker, fridge, freezer

Outside: table & chairs

Pets: accepted

Other (AR1 and AR2): bed linen, cot, highchair to hire

Open: 8 April - 18 September		
Weekly Charge	AR1	AR2
Low Season *(from)*	€ 357	€ 329
High Season *(from)*	€ 833	€ 805

FR40100 Camping du Domaine de la Rive

▶ see report page 336

Route de Bordeaux, F-40600 Biscarrosse

AR1 – SAVANNAH – Mobile home

Sleeping: 2 bedrooms, sleeps 6: 1 double, 2 singles, sofa bed, pillows and blankets provided

Living: living/kitchen area, heating, shower, WC

Eating: fitted kitchen with hobs, microwave, fridge, freezer

Outside: table & chairs, parasol, 2 sun loungers

Pets: not accepted

AR2 – COTTAGE 3 – Mobile home

Sleeping: 3 bedrooms, sleeps 6: 1 double, 4 singles, pillows and blankets provided

Living: living/kitchen area, shower, WC

Eating: fitted kitchen with hobs, microwave, fridge, freezer

Outside: table & chairs, parasol

Pets: not accepted

Other (AR1 and AR2): bed linen, cot, highchair to hire

Open: 3 April - 5 September		
Weekly Charge	AR1	AR2
Low Season *(from)*	€ 504	€ 511
High Season *(from)*	€ 1120	€ 1134

FR33110 Airotel Camping de la Cote d'Argent
F-33990 Hourtin-Plage

▶ see report page 346

AR1 – SAVANNAH – Mobile home

Sleeping: 2 bedrooms, sleeps 5: 1 double, 2 singles, sofa bed, pillows and blankets provided

Living: living/kitchen area, shower, WC

Eating: fitted kitchen with hobs, microwave, coffee maker, fridge, freezer

Outside: table & chairs, parasol

Pets: not accepted

AR2 – SUPER FAMILY – Mobile home

Sleeping: 3 bedrooms, sleeps 6: 1 double, 4 singles, pillows and blankets provided

Living: living/kitchen area, shower, WC

Eating: fitted kitchen with hobs, microwave, coffee maker, fridge, freezer

Outside: table & chairs, parasol, 2 sun loungers

Pets: not accepted

Open: 17 May - 14 September		
Weekly Charge	AR1	AR2
Low Season *(from)*	€ 240	€ 272
High Season *(from)*	€ 994	€ 1033

FR40180 Camping le Vieux Port
Plage Sud, F-40660 Messanges

▶ see report page 351

AR1 – MOBILE HOME SANS SANITAIRE – Mobile home

Sleeping: 2 bedrooms, sleeps 4: 1 double, 2 singles, pillows and blankets provided

Living: living/kitchen area, heating, shower, WC

Eating: fitted kitchen with hobs, fridge

Outside: table & chairs, parasol

Pets: not accepted

AR2 – LODGE MEZZANINE – Mobile Home

Sleeping: 3 bedrooms, sleeps 8: 1 double, 4 singles, pillows and blankets provided

Living: living/kitchen area, heating, TV, air conditioning, shower, WC, separate WC

Eating: fitted kitchen with hobs, dishwasher, fridge, freezer

Outside: table & chairs, parasol, 2 sun loungers

Pets: not accepted

Other (AR1 and AR2): cot, highchair to hire

Open: 2 April - 25 September		
Weekly Charge	AR1	AR2
Low Season *(from)*	€ 199	€ 430
High Season *(from)*	€ 770	€ 1764

FR40190 Le Saint-Martin Camping
Avenue de l'Océan, F-40660 Moliets-Plage

▶ see report page 354

AR1 – DUO – Chalet

Sleeping: 1 bedroom, sleeps 3: 2 singles, pillows and blankets provided

Living: living/kitchen area, heating, shower, separate WC

Eating: fitted kitchen with hobs, microwave, coffee maker, fridge, freezer

Outside: table & chairs

Pets: accepted (with supplement)

AR2 – ZEPHYR – Chalet

Sleeping: 2 bedrooms, sleeps 5: 1 double, 2 singles, sofa bed, pillows and blankets provided

Living: living/kitchen area, heating, shower, separate WC

Eating: fitted kitchen with hobs, microwave, coffee maker, fridge, freezer

Outside: table & chairs

Pets: accepted (with supplement)

Other (AR1 and AR2): cot to hire

Open: 8 April - All Saints (1 Nov)		
Weekly Charge	AR1	AR2
Low Season *(from)*	€ 220	€ 430
High Season *(from)*	€ 620	€ 1320

Mobile homes & chalets

FR24320 Camping les Peneyrals

see report page 361

Le Poujol, F-24590 Saint Crépin-Carlucet

AR1 – MERCURE – Mobile home	AR2 – EQUINOXE – Chalet
Sleeping: 2 bedrooms, sleeps 5: 1 double, 2 singles, sofa bed, pillows and blankets provided	**Sleeping:** 3 bedrooms, sleeps 7: 1 double, 4 singles, sofa bed, pillows and blankets provided
Living: living/kitchen area, heating, shower, separate WC	**Living:** living/kitchen area, heating, TV, shower, separate WC
Eating: fitted kitchen with hobs, microwave, coffee maker, fridge	**Eating:** fitted kitchen with hobs, microwave, coffee maker, fridge
Outside: table & chairs, parasol, 2 sun loungers, barbecue	**Outside:** table & chairs, parasol, 2 sun loungers, barbecue
Pets: accepted (with supplement)	**Pets:** accepted (with supplement)

Other (AR1 and AR2): bed linen to hire

Open: 12 May - 14 September

Weekly Charge	AR1	AR2
Low Season *(from)*	€ 300	€ 490
High Season *(from)*	€ 850	€ 1030

FR33080 Yelloh! Village Saint Emilion

see report page 362

Route de Montagne, D122, F-33330 Saint Emilion

AR1 – BORDELAISE – Mobile Home	AR2 – JEROBOAM – Mobile Home
Sleeping: 2 bedrooms, sleeps 3: 1 double, 1 single, pillows and blankets provided	**Sleeping:** 3 bedrooms, sleeps 6: 1 double, 4 singles, pillows and blankets provided
Living: living/kitchen area, heating, shower, separate WC	**Living:** living/kitchen area, heating, shower, separate WC
Eating: fitted kitchen with hobs, microwave, coffee maker, fridge	**Eating:** fitted kitchen with hobs, microwave, coffee maker, fridge
Outside: table & chairs, parasol, 2 sun loungers, barbecue	**Outside:** table & chairs, parasol, 2 sun loungers, barbecue
Pets: accepted (with supplement)	**Pets:** accepted (with supplement)

Other (AR1 and AR2): bed linen, cot, highchair to hire

Open: 16 April - 24 September

Weekly Charge	AR1	AR2
Low Season *(from)*	€ 203	€ 343
High Season *(from)*	€ 679	€ 959

FR40140 Camping Caravaning Lou P'tit Poun

see report page 366

110 avenue du Quartier Neuf, F-40390 Saint Martin-de-Seignanx

AR1 – FABRE REVE – Chalet	AR2 – IRM MERCURE – Mobile home
Sleeping: 2 bedrooms, sleeps 5: 1 double, 3 singles	**Sleeping:** sleeps 5: 1 double, 2 singles, sofa bed
Living: living/kitchen area, shower, WC	**Living:** living/kitchen area, shower, WC
Eating: fitted kitchen with fridge	**Eating:** fitted kitchen with fridge
Outside: table & chairs, 2 sun loungers	**Outside:** table & chairs, 2 sun loungers
Pets: not accepted	**Pets:** not accepted

Open: 4 June - 10 September

Weekly Charge	AR1	AR2
Low Season *(from)*	€ 465	€ 435
High Season *(from)*	€ 790	€ 760

FR40250 Camping les Grands Pins

1039 avenue de Losa, F-40460 Sanguinet

▶ see report page 370

AR1 – OHARA OCEANE – Mobile home

Sleeping: 3 bedrooms, sleeps 6: 1 double, 4 singles, pillows and blankets provided

Living: living/kitchen area, heating, shower, separate WC

Eating: fitted kitchen with hobs, microwave, coffee maker, fridge, freezer

Outside: table & chairs, 1 sun lounger

Pets: not accepted

AR2 – GITOTEL FABRE – Chalet

Sleeping: 2 bedrooms, sleeps 4: 1 double, 2 singles, pillows and blankets provided

Living: living/kitchen area, heating, shower, WC

Eating: fitted kitchen with hobs, microwave, fridge

Outside: table & chairs

Pets: not accepted

Open: 2 April - 25 September		
Weekly Charge	**AR1**	**AR2**
Low Season *(from)*	€ 448	€ 343
High Season *(from)*	€ 987	€ 864

FR24130 Camping les Grottes de Roffy

Sainte Nathalène, F-24200 Sarlat-la-Canéda

▶ see report page 373

AR1 – OHARA – Mobile home

Sleeping: 2 bedrooms, sleeps 6: 1 double, 2 singles, bunk bed, sofa bed, pillows and blankets provided

Living: living/kitchen area, shower, separate WC

Eating: fitted kitchen with hobs, microwave, coffee maker, fridge, freezer

Outside: table & chairs, parasol, 2 sun loungers, barbecue

Pets: accepted

AR2 – OHARA 3 BEDROOMS – Mobile home

Sleeping: 3 bedrooms, sleeps 6: 1 double, 4 singles, sofa bed, pillows and blankets provided

Living: living/kitchen area, heating, shower, separate WC

Eating: fitted kitchen with hobs, microwave, coffee maker, fridge, freezer

Outside: table & chairs, parasol, 2 sun loungers, barbecue

Pets: accepted

Other (AR1 and AR2): bed linen, cot to hire

Open: 16 April - 17 September		
Weekly Charge	**AR1**	**AR2**
Low Season *(from)*	€ 270	€ 280
High Season *(from)*	€ 833	€ 903

FR24090 Domaine de Soleil Plage

Caudon par Montfort, Vitrac, F-24200 Sarlat-la-Canéda

▶ see report page 381

AR1 – CHALET PRESTIGE – Chalet

Sleeping: 3 bedrooms, sleeps 7: 1 double, 4 singles, sofa bed, pillows and blankets provided

Living: living/kitchen area, heating, TV, shower, WC, separate WC

Eating: fitted kitchen with hobs, microwave, grill, coffee maker, fridge, freezer

Outside: table & chairs, parasol, 2 sun loungers, barbecue

Pets: accepted (with supplement)

AR2 – MOBILE HOME 3 CHAMBRES – Mobile home

Sleeping: 3 bedrooms, sleeps 7: 1 double, 4 singles, sofa bed, pillows and blankets provided

Living: living/kitchen area, heating, shower, separate WC

Eating: fitted kitchen with hobs, microwave, coffee maker, fridge

Outside: table & chairs, parasol, 2 sun loungers, barbecue

Pets: accepted (with supplement)

Other (AR1 and AR2): bed linen, cot, highchair to hire

Open: 15 April - 11 November		
Weekly Charge	**AR1**	**AR2**
Low Season *(from)*	€ 450	€ 380
High Season *(from)*	€ 840	€ 890

FR09020 Camping l'Arize

see report page 390

Lieu-dit Bourtol, F-09240 La Bastide-de-Sérou

AR1 – LOUISIANE FLORES CONFORT PLUS – Mobile home

Sleeping: 2 bedrooms, sleeps 7: 1 double, 2 singles, bunk bed, sofa bed, pillows and blankets provided

Living: living/kitchen area, heating, shower, separate WC

Eating: fitted kitchen with hobs, microwave, grill, fridge, freezer

Outside: table & chairs, parasol, barbecue

Pets: accepted (with supplement)

AR2 – CHALET 3 BEDROOMS – Chalet

Sleeping: 3 bedrooms, sleeps 8: 1 double, 3 singles, bunk bed, sofa bed, pillows and blankets provided

Living: living/kitchen area, heating, shower, separate WC

Eating: fitted kitchen with hobs, microwave, grill, fridge, freezer

Outside: table & chairs, parasol, barbecue

Pets: accepted (with supplement)

Open: 30 January - 30 November

Weekly Charge	AR1	AR2
Low Season (from)	€ 392	€ 455
High Season (from)	€ 749	€ 749

FR32010 Kawan Village le Camp de Florence

see report page 391

Route Astaffort, F-32480 La Romieu

AR1 – LOUISIANE ZEN – Mobile home

Sleeping: 3 bedrooms, sleeps 6: 1 double, 2 singles, bunk bed, pillows and blankets provided

Living: living/kitchen area, heating, shower, separate WC

Eating: fitted kitchen with microwave, fridge, freezer

Outside: table & chairs, 2 sun loungers

Pets: accepted

AR2 – IRM DELUXE – Mobile home

Sleeping: 2 bedrooms, sleeps 6: 1 double, 2 singles, sofa bed, pillows and blankets provided

Living: living/kitchen area, heating, shower, separate WC

Eating: fitted kitchen with microwave, fridge, freezer

Outside: table & chairs, 2 sun loungers

Pets: accepted

Open: 1 April - 11 October

Weekly Charge	AR1	AR2
Low Season (from)	€ 392	€ 343
High Season (from)	€ 910	€ 840

FR46010 Castel le Domaine de la Paille Basse

see report page 409

F-46200 Souillac-sur-Dordogne

AR1 – COSY – Mobile home

Sleeping: 2 bedrooms, sleeps 4: 1 double, 2 singles

Living: living/kitchen area, shower, WC

Eating: fitted kitchen with hobs, microwave, fridge

Outside: table & chairs, parasol, 2 sun loungers, barbecue

Pets: not accepted

AR2 – LOUNGE PLUS – Mobile home

Sleeping: 3 bedrooms, sleeps 6: 1 double, 2 singles, bunk bed, pillows and blankets provided

Living: living/kitchen area, heating, shower, WC

Eating: fitted kitchen with hobs, fridge

Outside: table & chairs, parasol, 2 sun loungers, barbecue

Pets: not accepted

Other (AR1 and AR2): bed linen, cot, highchair to hire

Open: 1 April - 15 September

Weekly Charge	AR1	AR2
Low Season (from)	€ 250	€ 310
High Season (from)	€ 690	€ 900

FR66070 Yelloh! Village le Brasilia

B.P. 204, F-66141 Canet-en-Roussillon

see report page 427

AR1 – OKAVANGO – Mobile home

Sleeping: 2 bedrooms, sleeps 6: 1 double, 2 singles, bunk bed, pillows and blankets provided

Living: living/kitchen area, heating, shower, WC

Eating: fitted kitchen with hobs, microwave, grill, coffee maker, fridge, freezer

Outside: table & chairs, parasol, 2 sun loungers

Pets: accepted (with supplement)

AR2 – PINÈDE – Bungalow

Sleeping: 2 bedrooms, sleeps 4: 1 double, 2 singles, bunk bed, pillows and blankets provided

Living: living/kitchen area, heating, TV, shower, WC

Eating: fitted kitchen with hobs, microwave, grill, coffee maker, fridge, freezer

Outside: table & chairs, 2 sun loungers

Pets: accepted (with supplement)

Other (AR1 and AR2): bed linen, cot, highchair to hire

Open: 25 April - 26 September		
Weekly Charge	AR1	AR2
Low Season *(from)*	€ 273	€ 273
High Season *(from)*	€ 1113	€ 1113

FR11070 Kawan Village les Mimosas

Chaussée de Mandirac, F-11100 Narbonne

see report page 439

AR1 – MOBILE HOME PLANCHA – Mobile home

Sleeping: 2 bedrooms, sleeps 4: 1 double, 2 singles, pillows and blankets provided

Living: living/kitchen area, TV, shower, WC

Eating: fitted kitchen with hobs, microwave, coffee maker, fridge, freezer

Outside: table & chairs, 2 sun loungers, barbecue

Pets: not accepted

AR2 – FLORÈS – Mobile home

Sleeping: 3 bedrooms, sleeps 6: 1 double, 4 singles, pillows and blankets provided

Living: living/kitchen area, heating, air conditioning, shower, WC

Eating: fitted kitchen with hobs, microwave, coffee maker, fridge, freezer

Outside: table & chairs, 2 sun loungers

Pets: not accepted

Other (AR1 and AR2): bed linen, cot, highchair to hire

Open: 27 March - 1 November		
Weekly Charge	AR1	AR2
Low Season *(from)*	€ 273	€ 343
High Season *(from)*	€ 658	€ 854

FR34070 Yelloh! Village le Sérignan-Plage

Le Sérignan Plage, F-34410 Sérignan-Plage

see report page 446

AR1 – CHALET ROBINSON – Chalet

Sleeping: 2 bedrooms, sleeps 5: 1 double, 2 singles, bunk bed, pillows and blankets provided

Living: living/kitchen area, heating, TV, air conditioning, shower, separate WC

Eating: fitted kitchen with hobs, microwave, dishwasher, coffee maker, fridge, freezer

Outside: table & chairs, 2 sun loungers

Pets: not accepted

AR2 – COTTAGE CABANE – Mobile home

Sleeping: 3 bedrooms, sleeps 6: 1 double, 2 singles, bunk bed, pillows and blankets provided

Living: living/kitchen area, heating, TV, air conditioning, shower, separate WC

Eating: fitted kitchen with hobs, microwave, dishwasher, coffee maker, fridge, freezer

Outside: table & chairs, 2 sun loungers

Pets: not accepted

Other (AR1 and AR2): bed linen, cot, highchair to hire

Open: 21 April - 2 October		
Weekly Charge	AR1	AR2
Low Season *(from)*	€ 364	€ 448
High Season *(from)*	€ 1568	€ 1932

FR34110 Yelloh! Village le Club Farret

see report page 453

F-34450 Vias-Plage

AR1 – VIP 6 – Mobile home

Sleeping: 3 bedrooms, sleeps 6: 1 double, 4 singles, pillows and blankets provided

Living: living/kitchen area, heating, air conditioning, shower, separate WC

Eating: fitted kitchen with hobs, microwave, coffee maker, fridge, freezer

Outside: table & chairs, parasol, 2 sun loungers

Pets: not accepted

AR2 – VIP 4/6 – Mobile home

Sleeping: 2 bedrooms, sleeps 6: 1 double, 2 singles, sofa bed, pillows and blankets provided

Living: living/kitchen area, heating, shower, separate WC

Eating: fitted kitchen with hobs, microwave, coffee maker, fridge, freezer

Outside: table & chairs, parasol, 2 sun loungers

Pets: not accepted

Other (AR1 and AR2): cot, highchair to hire

Open: 25 March - 25 September		
Weekly Charge	AR1	AR2
Low Season *(from)*	€ 315	€ 273
High Season *(from)*	€ 1274	€ 1057

FR04020 Castel Camping le Domaine du Verdon

see report page 465

Camp du Verdon, F-04120 Castellane

AR1 – WATIPI – Mobile home

Sleeping: 2 bedrooms, sleeps 4: 1 double, 2 singles, pillows and blankets provided

Living: living/kitchen area, shower, WC

Eating: fitted kitchen with hobs, fridge

Outside: table & chairs, 2 sun loungers

Pets: accepted

AR2 – TITOM – Mobile home

Sleeping: 2 bedrooms, sleeps 4: 1 double, 2 singles, bunk bed, pillows and blankets provided

Living: living/kitchen area, shower, WC

Eating: fitted kitchen with hobs, fridge

Outside: table & chairs, 2 sun loungers

Pets: accepted

Other (AR1 and AR2): bed linen, cot, highchair to hire

Open: 15 May - 15 September		
Weekly Charge	AR1	AR2
Low Season *(from)*	€ 336	€ 378
High Season *(from)*	€ 742	€ 791

FR83220 Kawan Village Cros de Mouton

see report page 466

B.P. 116, F-83240 Cavalaire-sur-Mer

AR1 – PRESTIGE – Mobile home

Sleeping: 2 bedrooms, sleeps 5: 1 double, 2 singles, sofa bed, pillows and blankets provided

Living: living/kitchen area, heating, air conditioning, shower, separate WC

Eating: fitted kitchen with hobs, microwave, coffee maker, fridge, freezer

Outside: table & chairs, parasol, 2 sun loungers

Pets: accepted

AR2 – TEXAS – Mobile home

Sleeping: 3 bedrooms, sleeps 6: 1 double, 4 singles, pillows and blankets provided

Living: living/kitchen area, heating, air conditioning, shower, separate WC

Eating: fitted kitchen with hobs, microwave, coffee maker, fridge, freezer

Outside: table & chairs, parasol, 2 sun loungers

Pets: accepted

Other (AR1 and AR2): bed linen, cot, highchair to hire

Open: 15 March - 4 November		
Weekly Charge	AR1	AR2
Low Season *(from)*	€ 455	€ 530
High Season *(from)*	€ 830	€ 930

FR83060 Camping Resort la Baume – la Palmeraie

3775 rue des Combattants d'Afrique du Nord, F-83618 Fréjus

▶ see report page 470

AR1 – BASTIDON – Bungalow

Sleeping: 3 bedrooms, sleeps 8: 1 double, 4 singles, sofa bed

Living: living/kitchen area, shower, WC

Eating: fitted kitchen with hobs, microwave, fridge, freezer

Outside: table & chairs, 4 sun loungers

Pets: accepted

AR2 – CYCA – Mobile home

Sleeping: 3 bedrooms, sleeps 6: 1 double, 4 singles, sofa bed

Living: living/kitchen area, TV, air conditioning, shower, WC

Eating: fitted kitchen with hobs, microwave, dishwasher, fridge, freezer

Outside: table & chairs, 2 sun loungers

Pets: accepted

Other (AR1 and AR2): bed linen, cot, highchair to hire

Open: 9 April - 1 October		
Weekly Charge	AR1	AR2
Low Season *(from)*	€ 469	€ 525
High Season *(from)*	€ 1415	€ 1470

FR83640 Domaine des Naïades

Quartier Cros d'Entassi, Saint Pons-les-Mûres, F-83310 Grimaud

▶ see report page 473

AR1 – MOBILE HOME CONFORT 4/5 PERS – Mobile home

Sleeping: 2 bedrooms, sleeps 5: 1 double, 2 singles, sofa bed, pillows and blankets provided

Living: living/kitchen area, heating, TV, air conditioning, shower, WC

Eating: fitted kitchen with hobs, microwave, coffee maker, fridge

Outside: table & chairs, 2 sun loungers

Pets: accepted (with supplement)

AR2 – MOBILE HOME PREMIUM – Mobile home

Sleeping: 2 bedrooms, sleeps 5: 1 double, 2 singles, sofa bed, pillows and blankets provided

Living: living/kitchen area, heating, TV, air conditioning, shower, separate WC

Eating: fitted kitchen with hobs, microwave, dishwasher, coffee maker, fridge, freezer

Outside: table & chairs, 2 sun loungers

Pets: accepted (with supplement)

Other (AR1 and AR2): bed linen, cot, highchair to hire

Open: 9 April - 5 November		
Weekly Charge	AR1	AR2
Low Season *(from)*	€ 336	€ 455
High Season *(from)*	€ 1071	€ 1540

FR83030 Camping Caravaning Leï Suves

Quartier du Blavet, F-83520 Roquebrune-sur-Argens

▶ see report page 482

AR1 – TYPE D – Mobile home

Sleeping: 2 bedrooms, sleeps 6: 1 double, 2 singles, sofa bed

Living: living/kitchen area, shower, WC

Eating: fitted kitchen with hobs, oven, fridge

Outside: table & chairs

Pets: not accepted

AR2 – LUXE – Mobile home

Sleeping: 2 bedrooms, sleeps 5: 1 double, 2 singles, sofa bed

Living: living/kitchen area, shower, WC

Eating: fitted kitchen with hobs, oven, fridge

Outside: table & chairs

Pets: not accepted

Open: 2 April - 15 October		
Weekly Charge	AR1	AR2
Low Season *(from)*	€ 400	€ 450
High Season *(from)*	€ 810	€ 910

FR83200 Camping les Pêcheurs

▶ see report page 484

, F-83520 Roquebrune-sur-Argens

AR1 – AZUREA – Mobile Home	**AR2 – AZUREAU PLUS (2nd outdoor kitchen) – Mobile Home**
Sleeping: 2 bedrooms, sleeps 6: 1 double, 2 singles, sofa bed, pillows and blankets provided	**Sleeping:** 2 bedrooms, sleeps 6: 1 double, 2 singles, sofa bed, pillows and blankets provided
Living: living/kitchen area, heating, shower, separate WC	**Living:** living/kitchen area, heating, shower, separate WC
Eating: fitted kitchen with hobs, microwave, coffee maker, fridge, freezer	**Eating:** fitted kitchen with hobs, microwave, coffee maker, fridge, freezer
Outside: table & chairs, parasol, 2 sun loungers	**Outside:** table & chairs, parasol, 2 sun loungers
Pets: accepted (with supplement)	**Pets:** accepted (with supplement)

Other (AR1 and AR2): bed linen, cot, highchair to hire

 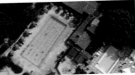

Open: 1 April - 30 September		
Weekly Charge	**AR1**	**AR2**
Low Season *(from)*	€ 400	€ 450
High Season *(from)*	€ 945	€ 1085

FR83050 Camping Résidence du Campeur

▶ see report page 488

B.P. 12, D7, F-83371 Saint Aygulf

AR1 – MOBIL HOME 4/5 PERS JUNIOR – Mobile home	**AR2 – GRAND CONFORT 6 PERS – Mobile home**
Sleeping: 2 bedrooms, sleeps 5: 1 double, 2 singles, sofa bed, pillows and blankets provided	**Sleeping:** 2 bedrooms, sleeps 5: 1 double, 2 singles, sofa bed, pillows and blankets provided
Living: living/kitchen area, heating, shower, separate WC	**Living:** living/kitchen area, heating, shower, separate WC
Eating: fitted kitchen with hobs, oven, microwave, grill, coffee maker, fridge, freezer	**Eating:** fitted kitchen with hobs, oven, microwave, grill, coffee maker, fridge, freezer
Outside: table & chairs, 2 sun loungers	**Outside:** table & chairs, 2 sun loungers
Pets: accepted	**Pets:** accepted

Other (AR1 and AR2): bed linen, cot, highchair to hire

Open: 27 March - 30 September		
Weekly Charge	**AR1**	**AR2**
Low Season *(from)*	€ 290	€ 430
High Season *(from)*	€ 790	€ 990

FR84020 Domaine Naturiste de Bélézy
F-84410 Bedoin

▶ see report page 515

AR1 – NAUTILHOME – Bungalow

Sleeping: 2 bedrooms, sleeps 5: 1 double, 2 singles, sofa bed, pillows and blankets provided

Living: living/kitchen area, shower, separate WC

Eating: fitted kitchen with hobs, microwave, coffee maker, fridge, freezer

Outside: table & chairs, 2 sun loungers

Pets: not accepted

AR2 – BOIS – Bungalow

Sleeping: 2 bedrooms, sleeps 5: 1 double, 2 singles, sofa bed, pillows and blankets provided

Living: living/kitchen area, shower, separate WC

Eating: fitted kitchen with hobs, microwave, dishwasher, coffee maker, fridge, freezer

Outside: table & chairs, 2 sun loungers

Pets: not accepted

Other (AR1 and AR2): bed linen, cot, highchair to hire

Open: 2 April - 2 October

Weekly Charge	AR1	AR2
Low Season *(from)*	€ 497	€ 441
High Season *(from)*	€ 987	€ 889

FR20050 Village Naturiste la Chiappa
Route de Palombaggia, F-20137 Porto-Vecchio

▶ see report page 517

AR1 – TYPE C – Bungalow

Sleeping: 2 bedrooms, sleeps 4: 4 singles, pillows and blankets provided

Living: living/kitchen area, shower, WC

Eating: fitted kitchen with hobs, fridge

Outside: table & chairs

Pets: accepted

AR2 – TYPE B – Bungalow

Sleeping: 1 bedroom, sleeps 2: 2 singles

Living: living/kitchen area, shower, WC

Eating: fitted kitchen with fridge

Outside: table & chairs

Pets: accepted

Other (AR1 and AR2): bed linen, cot, highchair to hire

Open: 15 May - 9 October

Weekly Charge	AR1	AR2
Low Season *(from)*	€ 630	€ 420
High Season *(from)*	€ 1050	€ 700

Parcs Résidentiels de Loisirs

Recent years have seen a significant increase in the number of Parcs Résidentiels de Loisirs in France. In many ways, these parks resemble good campsites but with the important distinction that they do not have any touring pitches!

Amenities at the parks are invariably very impressive, often with top quality swimming pool complexes and fine restaurant facilities. However, all the pitches on these sites are occupied by either mobile homes or chalets, many of which are available for let.

These parks have been developed by their owners often with the expectation that their clients may be former campers or caravanners, or possibly those travelling from afar, with the common desire to combine the freedom of camping and caravanning with a high standard of home comforts.

We have chosen to include a small selection of the best Parcs Résidentiels, all of which are attractively located in popular regions of France. In every case, there will be a good choice of accommodation available for rent. We are, however, featuring 2 types of accommodation and give full details of what is provided in terms of living and sleeping accommodation, as well as an indication of the park's tariffs.

FR45050 Les Roulottes des Bords de Loire

Rue des Iris, F-45500 Poilly lez Gien (Loiret) T: 02 38 67 12 50
E: info@roulottes-bords-de-loire.com   alanrogers.com/FR45050

Les Roulottes des Bords de Loire is a small parc résidentiel, close to the attractive town of Gien in the eastern Loire Valley. Accommodation is in attractive Romany style caravans, albeit equipped with all home comforts. Each caravan can accommodate up to five people and has its own fully equipped kitchen and en suite bathroom. The site, although small, is well equipped with a swimming pool (covered in low season), minigolf and direct access to the River Loire.

Facilities

Swimming pool. Direct access to River Loire. Beach volleyball. Bicycle hire. Minigolf. Fishing. Play area. Canoe trips. Tourist information. Activity and entertainment programme. Romany style mobile homes for rent. Off site: Gien centre 2 km. Golf 35 km. Loire valley and vineyards. Cycle and walking tracks. Orléans.

Directions

Site is at Poilly-lez-Gien on the south side of the Loire. From the A77 take the Gien exit and bypass the town on the D940 following signs to Bourges. Arrive in Poilly-lez-Gien shortly after crossing the Loire and site is well signed from here.
GPS: 47.68229, 2.62315

AR1 – LOUISIANA-O – Mobile Home

Sleeping: 2 bedrooms, sleeps 6: 1 double, 2 singles, sofa bed, pillows and blankets provided

Living: living/kitchen area, heating, shower, separate WC

Eating: fitted kitchen with hobs, microwave, coffee maker, fridge

Outside: table & chairs, parasol, barbecue

Pets: accepted (with supplement)

AR2 – ROULOTTE – Gipsy Wagon

Sleeping: 1 bedroom, sleeps 3: 1 double, sofa bed, pillows and blankets provided

Living: living/kitchen area, heating, shower, separate WC

Eating: fitted kitchen with hobs, microwave, coffee maker, fridge

Outside: table & chairs, parasol, barbecue

Pets: accepted (with supplement)

Other (AR1 and AR2): bed linen to hire

Open: 1 March - 8 November		
Weekly Charge	AR1	AR2
Low Season (from)	€ 295	€ 425
High Season (from)	€ 525	€ 525

FR07660 Castel Domaine de Sévenier

F-07150 Lagorce (Ardèche) T: 04 75 88 29 44. E: domainedesevenier@orange.fr
alanrogers.com/FR07660

Le Domaine de Sévenier is a chalet new site located 4 km. from Vallon Pont d'Arc and 800 m. from the pretty village of Lagorce. The domaine is an old winery which has been sensitively converted into a high quality holiday village. The owners suggest that the site has a 'zen' ambience, in contrast to the busier sites at nearby Vallon Pont d'Arc. Sévenier enjoys a hilltop location with fine panoramic views.

Facilities

Restaurant. Bar. Shop. Swimming pool. Children's pool. Activity programme. Play area. Minigolf. Tourist information. Fully equipped chalets for rent. Off site: Lagorce 800 m. (shops and cafés). Cycle and walking tracks. Riding. Vallon Pont d'Arc 5 km.

Directions

Head north from Vallon Pont d'Arc (at western end of the Ardèche gorges) on D1 and upon reaching Lagorce, follow signs to the site.
GPS: 44.434151, 4.410989

AR1 – CHENE BLANC – Chalet

Sleeping: 2 bedrooms, sleeps 5: 1 double, 2 singles, bunk bed, sofa bed, pillows and blankets provided

Living: living/kitchen area, heating, TV, air conditioning, shower, separate WC

Eating: fitted kitchen with hobs, microwave, dishwasher, coffee maker, fridge, freezer

Outside: table & chairs, 1 sun lounger

Pets: accepted (with supplement)

AR2 – CHENE VERT – Chalet

Sleeping: 3 bedrooms, sleeps 6: 1 double, 4 singles, bunk bed, sofa bed, pillows and blankets provided

Living: living/kitchen area, heating, TV, air conditioning, shower, separate WC

Eating: fitted kitchen with hobs, microwave, dishwasher, coffee maker, fridge, freezer

Outside: table & chairs, 1 sun lounger

Pets: accepted (with supplement)

Other (AR1 and AR2): bed linen, cot, highchair to hire

Open: 13 March - 13 November		
Weekly Charge	AR1	AR2
Low Season (from)	€ 448	€ 637
High Season (from)	€ 1169	€ 1673

FR24890 Le Village de la Combe

Le Pradal, F-24250 Domme (Dordogne) T: 05 53 29 77 42
E: lacombe24@wanadoo.fr alanrogers.com/FR24890

Le Village de la Combe is a chalet park, located close to Domme, at the heart of the Perigord Noir. Please note that there are no touring pitches at this site. The village provides 12 fully equipped, air-conditioned wooden chalets, attractively dispersed around a two hectare park. Leisure facilities here include a swimming pool, trampoline and children's play area. Several long distance footpaths pass close to the site. A 'pot d'accueil' is organised every Sunday in high season and is a pleasant way of making new friends. Addiitionally, communal barbecues are organised in July and August.

Facilities

Swimming pool. Play area. Games room. Playground. Activity programme. Chalets to rent. Off site: Cycle and walking tracks. Domme 800 m. Sarlat 12 km.

Directions

Domme is 12 km. south of Sarlat. From Sarlat, head south on the D57 and D46. Head into Domme on the D46 and pass through the village, following signs to the site on D46. GPS: 44.796944, 1.2225

AR1 – REVE – Chalet

Sleeping: 2 bedrooms, sleeps 6: 1 double, 2 singles, sofa bed

Living: living/kitchen area, air conditioning, shower, WC

Eating: fitted kitchen with hobs, microwave, coffee maker, fridge

Outside: table & chairs, barbecue

Pets: accepted (with supplement)

AR2 – EDEN – Chalet

Sleeping: 2 bedrooms, sleeps 4: 1 double, 2 singles

Living: living/kitchen area, air conditioning, shower, WC

Eating: fitted kitchen with hobs, microwave, coffee maker, fridge

Outside: table & chairs, barbecue

Pets: accepted (with supplement)

Other (AR1 and AR2): bed linen to hire

Open: 31 March - 15 March

Weekly Charge	AR1	AR2
Low Season (from)	€ 395	€ 355
High Season (from)	€ 725	€ 650

FR40370 Gîtes et Soleil

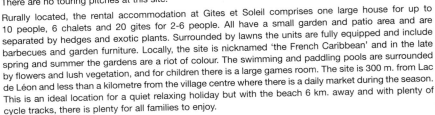

1105 route du Puntaou, F-40550 Leon (Landes) T: 05 58 48 74 78
E: gitesetsoleil@orange.fr alanrogers.com/FR40370

There are no touring pitches at this site.

Rurally located, the rental accommodation at Gites et Soleil comprises one large house for up to 10 people, 6 chalets and 20 gites for 2-6 people. All have a small garden and patio area and are separated by hedges and exotic plants. Surrounded by lawns the units are fully equipped and include barbecues and garden furniture. Locally, the site is nicknamed 'the French Caribbean' and in the late spring and summer the gardens are a riot of colour. The swimming and paddling pools are surrounded by flowers and lush vegetation, and for children there is a large games room. The site is 300 m. from Lac de Léon and less than a kilometre from the village centre where there is a daily market during the season. This is an ideal location for a quiet relaxing holiday but with the beach 6 km. away and with plenty of cycle tracks, there is plenty for all families to enjoy.

Facilities

Small basic sanitary block with washing machine. Swimming pool (unheated). Off site: Fishing 500 m. Bicycle hire 1 km. Riding 5 km. Golf 6 km. Beach 6 km.

Open: 1 March - 31 October.

Directions

Approaching Léon from the north on D652, at first roundabout take the second right towards Route du Puntaou. Site is 800 m. on the left (signed). GPS: 43.881233, -1.315967

Charges

For full details of charges and accommodation available, please contact site.

FR66700 PRL Le Vedrignans

Route de Vedrignans, F-66800 Saillagouse (Pyrénées-Orientales)
T: 04 68 04 04 79. E: contact@levedrignans.com alanrogers.com/FR66700

Le Verdrignans can be found deep in the Catalan Pyrenees Regional Park. It enjoys a spectacular natural setting, overlooked by towering mountains but with a very pleasant Mediterranean climate. Accommodation is provided in a range of attractive wooden chalets, from the smaller 'Genets' model, which can sleep up to 4, to the larger 'Edelweiss' chalets which can accommodate up to 8 people. All chalets are fully equipped and are located on very large pitches of over 200 sq m.

Facilities

Play area. Games room. Tourist information. Chalets to rent. Off site: Village centre 300 m. Le train jaune. Ski resorts. Walking and cycling tracks. Covered swimming pool. Tennis.

Directions

Saillagouse lies around 90 km. west of Perpignan. From there head west on N116 to Prades and Mont Louis. Continue on this road to Saillagouse and the site is clearly indicated. GPS: 42.457712, 2.039638

AR1 – GENET – Chalet

Sleeping: 2 bedrooms, sleeps 4: 2 singles, bunk bed, pillows and blankets provided

Living: living/kitchen area, heating, TV, shower, separate WC

Eating: fitted kitchen with hobs, microwave, grill, coffee maker, fridge, freezer

Outside: table & chairs, parasol, 2 sun loungers, barbecue

Pets: accepted (with supplement)

AR2 – EDELWEISS – Chalet

Sleeping: 4 bedrooms, sleeps 8: 3 doubles, 2 singles, pillows and blankets provided

Living: living/kitchen area, heating, TV, shower, separate WC

Eating: fitted kitchen with hobs, oven, microwave, grill, dishwasher, coffee maker, fridge, freezer

Outside: table & chairs, parasol, 4 sun loungers, barbecue

Pets: accepted (with supplement)

Other (AR1 and AR2): bed linen, cot, highchair to hire

Open: All year

Weekly Charge	AR1	AR2
Low Season (from)	€ 330	€ 630
High Season (from)	€ 480	€ 900

FR12400 Campéole Domaine de Combelles

F-12000 Le Monastère (Aveyron) T: 05 65 78 29 53. E: combelles@campeole.com
alanrogers.com/FR12400

Campé●le

Domaine de Combelles is a well equipped 'parc résidentiel' which can be found at the heart of the Aveyron, quite close to the village of Le Monastère. Here you'll find a range of attractive chalets and mobile homes are available for rent. This site is also unusual in that it incorporates an excellent riding centre, with opportunities for beginners as well as seasoned riders. Vehicle circulation is not allowed within the site – a large car park is available at the site entrance. This is a spacious site and most facilities are located some distance from the accommodation units, ensuring their tranquillity

Facilities

Bar/restaurant. Swimming pool. Riding centre. Bicycle hire. Volleyball. Bouncy castle. Play area. Activities and entertainment. Tourist information. Mobile homes and chalets and permanently erected tents for rent. Off site: Le Monastère with shops and restaurants. Walking and cycle tracks. Fishing. Rodez 5 km. Tarn gorges.

Open: 1 May - 31 October.

Directions

From Albi head north on N88 towards Rodez via Luc la Primaube and Flavin. From here follow signs to the site which is well indicated. GPS: 44.3301, 2.5901

Charges guide

For full details of charges and accommodation available, please contact site.

Dogs

Since the introduction in 2000 of the Passports for Pets scheme many British campers and caravanners have been encouraged to take their pets with them on holiday. However, Pet Travel conditions are understandably strict, the procedure is quite lengthy and complicated so we would advise you to check the current situation before travelling. The Passports for Pets official website is: ww2.defra.gov.uk/wildlife-pets/pets/travel

For the benefit of those who want to take their dogs to France, we list here the sites which have indicated to us that they do not accept dogs or have certain restrictions. If you are planning to take your dog we do advise you to phone the site first to check – there may be limits on numbers, breeds, or times of the year when they are excluded.

Never – sites that do not accept dogs at any time:

Normandy
FR14090	Brévedent	88

Alsace
FR68080	Clair Vacances	149
FR67040	Ferme des Tuileries	149

Vendée
FR85210	Ecureuils	198
FR85020	Jard	202

Poitou-Charentes
FR16020	Gorges du Chambon	222
FR17600	Signol	220

Aquitaine
FR24040	Moulin du Roch	370

FR40040	Paillotte	332
FR64060	Pavillon Royal	333

Midi-Pyrénées
FR46040	Moulin de Laborde	397

Languedoc-Roussillon
FR30160	Boucanet	434
FR34560	Paradis	448
FR30390	Petits Camarguais	435
FR66040	Soleil	418

Provence
FR83320	Mogador	491

Corsica
FR20030	Merendella	506

Sometimes – sites that accept dogs but with certain restrictions:

Brittany
FR22210	Bellevue	47
FR29000	Mouettes	42
FR29380	Port de Plaisance	41

Paris-Ile de France
FR78040	Rambouillet	121
FR78060	Versailles	124

Val de Loire
FR28140	Senonches	166
FR37140	Rillé	165

Pays de la Loire
FR72040	Molières	191

Vendée
FR85000	Petit Rocher	204
FR85030	Loubine	207
FR85150	Yole	211
FR85270	Oceano d'Or	199
FR85280	Places Dorées	210
FR85310	Trévillière	198
FR85440	Brunelles	206
FR85450	Roses	204
FR85480	Chaponnet	196
FR85490	Beaulieu	208
FR85720	Noirmoutier	206
FR85770	Ferme du Latois	198
FR85870	Baie d'Aunis	202
FR85930	Forges	195

Poitou-Charentes
FR17010	Bois Soleil	236
FR17470	Domaine d'Oléron	234
FR17580	Indigo Oléron	240

Limousin
FR23010	Château Poinsouze	269

Auvergne
FR63050	Ribeyre	277
FR63070	Pré Bas	278
FR63120	Royat	280

Rhône Alpes
FR01060	Ile de la Comtesse	306
FR07080	Bastide	319
FR07650	Indigo Moulin	318
FR26030	Grand Lierne	291
FR26200	Ecluse	291
FR26220	Soleil Fruité	293
FR38100	Belledonne	289
FR38120	Bontemps	324
FR69010	Lyon	294
FR74060	Colombière	307

Aquitaine
FR24100	Moulinal	335
FR33080	Saint Emilion	362
FR33210	Pointe du Medoc	349
FR33290	Tedey	345

Dogs

FR33440	Vieux Château	359
FR40250	Grands Pins	370

Midi-Pyrénées

FR12040	Tours	402
FR12170	Caussanel	387
FR32060	Trois Vallées	393
FR46190	Faurie	407
FR46310	Granges	410
FR82050	Faillal	398

Languedoc-Roussillon

FR30070	Boisson	424
FR34130	Neptune	415

FR48020	Capelan	438
FR66050	Haras	441
FR66170	Mar I Sol	449
FR66250	Font-Romeu	429
FR66290	Floride l'Embouchure	432
FR66490	Garenne	440

Provence

FR04110	Verdon Parc	472
FR04120	Forcalquier	468
FR13140	Marius	476
FR83040	Bastiane	480
FR83120	Domaine	462

Open All Year

The following sites are understood to accept caravanners and campers all year round. It is always wise to phone the site to check as the facilities available, for example, may be reduced.

Brittany

FR56150	Haras	73

Normandy

FR27060	Marcilly	86
FR76090	Mun. Etennemare	94

Nord-Pas de Calais

FR62120	Eté Indien	104

Paris-Ile de France

FR75020	Bois de Boulogne	120
FR77110	Parc de Paris	124
FR78080	Parc Etang	120
FR91010	Beau Village de Paris	125

Lorraine

FR88040	Lac de Bouzey	142
FR88050	Champé	137
FR88090	Lac de la Moselotte	142
FR88130	Vanne de Pierre	141

Alsace

FR68030	Masevaux	148
FR68140	Bouleaux	148

Val de Loire

FR45040	Hortus, Sully	165

Pays de la Loire

FR53020	Malidor	174

Vendée

FR85890	Rouge Gorge	216
FR85930	Forges	195

Poitou-Charentes

FR17070	Gros Joncs	235
FR86040	Futuriste	238
FR86120	Dienné	222

Burgundy

FR21090	Arquebuse	245
FR58030	Bezolle	252

Limousin

FR19080	Vianon	271

Rhône Alpes

FR69010	Lyon	294
FR73100	Reclus	320
FR74230	Giffre	318

Aquitaine

FR24150	Deux Vallées	376
FR24880	Orpheo Negro	343
FR33090	Pressoir	357
FR33370	Montalivet (Naturiste)	510
FR33410	Bordeaux Lac	339
FR47110	Cabri	344
FR64040	Gaves	348
FR64080	Tamaris Plage	364

Midi-Pyrénées

FR09050	Mun. Prade (Sorgeat)	408
FR09120	Ascou la Forge	386
FR32040	Deveze (Naturiste)	512
FR65080	Lavedan	385
FR65160	Monlôo	386

Languedoc-Roussillon

FR66490	Garenne	440
FR66670	Europe	434

Provence

FR05080	Solaire	492
FR13120	Chantecler	459

Côte d'Azur

FR06050	Vieille Ferme	500
FR06080	Cigales	499

Corsica

FR20040	Riva Bella (Naturiste)	517

Travelling - in Europe

When taking your car (and caravan, tent or trailer tent) or motorcaravan to the continent you do need to plan in advance and to find out as much as possible about driving in the countries you plan to visit. Whilst European harmonisation has eliminated many of the differences between one country and another, it is well worth reading the short notes we provide in the introduction to each country in this guide in addition to this more general summary.

Of course, the main difference from driving in the UK is that in mainland Europe you will need to drive on the right. Without taking extra time and care, especially at busy junctions and conversely when roads are empty, it is easy to forget to drive on the right. Remember that traffic approaching from the right usually has priority unless otherwise indicated by road markings and signs. Harmonisation also means that most (but not all) common road signs are the same in all countries.

Your vehicle

Book your vehicle in for a good service well before your intended departure date. This will lessen the chance of an expensive breakdown. Make sure your brakes are working efficiently and that your tyres have plenty of tread (3 mm. is recommended, particularly if you are undertaking a long journey).

Also make sure that your caravan or trailer is roadworthy and that its tyres are in good order and correctly inflated. Plan your packing and be careful not to overload your vehicle, caravan or trailer – this is unsafe and may well invalidate your insurance cover (it must not be more fully loaded than the kerb weight of the insured vehicle).

CHECK ALL THE FOLLOWING:

- **GB sticker.** If you do not display a sticker, you may risk an on-the-spot fine as this identifier is compulsory in all countries. Euro-plates are an acceptable alternative within the EU (but not outside). Remember to attach another sticker (or Euro-plate) to caravans or trailers. Only GB stickers (not England, Scotland, Wales or N. Ireland) stickers are valid in the EU.

- **Headlights.** As you will be driving on the right you must adjust your headlights so that the dipped beam does not dazzle oncoming drivers. Converter kits are readily available for most vehicle, although if your car is fitted with high intensity headlights, you should check with your motor dealer. Check that any planned extra loading does not affect the beam height.

- **Seatbelts.** Rules for the fitting and wearing of seatbelts throughout Europe are similar to those in the UK, but it is worth checking before you go. Rules for carrying children in the front of vehicles vary from country to country. It is best to plan not to do this if possible.

- **Door/wing mirrors.** To help with driving on the right, if your vehicle is not fitted with a mirror on the left hand side, we recommend you have one fitted.

- **Fuel.** Leaded and Lead Replacement petrol is increasingly difficult to find in Northern Europe.

Compulsory additional equipment

The driving laws of the countries of Europe still vary in what you are required to carry in your vehicle, although the consequences of not carrying a required piece of equipment are almost always an on-the-spot fine.

To meet these requirements we suggest that you carry the following:

* FIRE EXTINGUISHER

* BASIC TOOL KIT

* FIRST AID KIT

* SPARE BULBS

* TWO WARNING TRIANGLES – two are required in some countries at all times, and are compulsory in most countries when towing.

* HIGH VISIBILITY VEST – now compulsory in France, Spain, Italy and Austria (and likely to become compulsory throughout the EU) in case you need to walk on a motorway.

Insurance and Motoring Documents

Vehicle insurance

Contact your insurer well before you depart to check that your car insurance policy covers driving outside the UK. Most do, but many policies only provide minimum cover (so if you have an accident your insurance may only cover the cost of damage to the other person's property, with no cover for fire and theft).

To maintain the same level of cover abroad as you enjoy at home you need to tell your vehicle insurer. Some will automatically cover you abroad with no extra cost and no extra paperwork. Some will say you need a Green Card (which is neither green nor on card) but won't charge for it. Some will charge extra for the Green Card. Ideally you should contact your vehicle insurer 3-4 weeks before you set off, and confirm your conversation with them in writing.

Breakdown insurance

Arrange breakdown cover for your trip in good time so that if your vehicle breaks down or is involved in an accident it (and your caravan or trailer) can be repaired or returned to this country. This cover can usually be arranged as part of your travel insurance policy (see below).

Documents you must take with you

You may be asked to show your documents at any time so make sure that they are in order, up-to-date and easily accessible while you travel.

These are what you need to take:

* **Passports** (you may also need a visa in some countries if you hold either a UK passport not issued in the UK or a passport that was issued outside the EU).

* **Motor Insurance Certificate,** including Green Card (or Continental Cover clause)

* **DVLC Vehicle Registration Document** plus, if not your own vehicle, the owner's written authority to drive.

* **A full valid Driving Licence** (not provisional). The new photo style licence is now mandatory in most European countries).

Personal Holiday insurance

Even though you are just travelling within Europe you must take out travel insurance. Few EU countries pay the full cost of medical treatment even under reciprocal health service arrangements. The first part of a holiday insurance policy covers people. It will include the cost of doctor, ambulance and hospital treatment if needed. If needed the better companies will even pay for English language speaking doctors and nurses and will bring a sick or injured holidaymaker home by air ambulance.

Personal Holiday insurance (continued)

An important part of the insurance, often ignored, is cancellation (and curtailment) cover. Few things are as heartbreaking as having to cancel a holiday because a member of the family falls ill. Cancellation insurance can't take away the disappointment, but it makes sure you don't suffer financially as well. For this reason you should arrange your holiday insurance at least eight weeks before you set off.

Whichever insurance you choose we would advise reading very carefully the policies sold by the High Street travel trade. Whilst they may be good, they may not cover the specific needs of campers, caravanners and motorcaravanners.

Telephone **01580 214000** for a quote for our Camping Travel Insurance with cover arranged through leading leisure insurance providers.
Alternatively visit our website at: **alanrogers.com/insurance**

European Health Insurance Card (EHIC)

Make sure you apply for your EHIC before travelling in Europe. Eligible travellers from the UK are entitled to receive free or reduced-cost medical care in many European countries on production of an EHIC. This free card is available by completing a form in the booklet 'Health Advice for Travellers' from local Post Offices. One should be completed for each family member. Alternatively visit **www.ehic.org.uk** and apply on-line. Please allow time to send your application off and have the EHIC returned to you.

The EHIC is valid in all European Community countries plus Iceland, Liechtenstein, Switzerland and Norway. If you or any of your dependants are suddenly taken ill or have an accident during a visit to any of these countries, free or reduced-cost emergency treatment is available – in most cases on production of a valid EHIC.

Only state-provided emergency treatment is covered, and you will receive treatment on the same terms as nationals of the country you are visiting. Private treatment is generally not covered, and state-provided treatment may not cover all of the things that you would expect to receive free of charge from the NHS.

Remember an EHIC does not cover you for all the medical costs that you can incur or for repatriation - it is not an alternative to travel insurance. You will still need appropriate insurance to ensure you are fully covered for all eventualities.

Travelling with children

Most countries in Europe are enforcing strict guidelines when you are travelling with children who are not your own. A minor (under the age of 18) must be accompanied by a parent or legal guardian or must carry a letter of authorisation from a parent or guardian. The letter should name the adult responsible for the minor during his or her stay. Similarly, a minor travelling with just one of his/her parents, must have a letter of authority to leave their home country from the parent staying behind. Full information is available at **www.fco.gov.uk**

Insurance Service

High quality, low cost insurance you can trust

Want independent campsite reviews at your fingertips?

You'll find them here...

Over 3,000 in-depth campsite reviews at **www.alanrogers.com**

...and even here...

An exciting free app from iTunes and the Apple app store*

*available January 2011

Paying too much for your
mobile home holiday?

Less driving, more holiday.

Arrive closer to the France you love

Take one of our mile-saving routes from Portsmouth, Poole or Plymouth and arrive much closer to where you want to be.

With less time at the wheel, you'll have more time to holiday. Better still, you'll also save on fuel, tolls and overnight stops.

brittanyferries.com 0871 244 1447

Brittany Ferries

THE CARAVAN & MOTORHOME SHOWS

The best start to your next adventure...

MANCHESTER CENTRAL
CARAVAN & MOTORHOME
SHOW 2011 MANCHESTER 20-23 JANUARY

Come and see the widest choice of caravans and a great selection of motorhomes from leading UK and overseas manufacturers. If it's a bargain you are looking for, many exhibitors are offering amazing deals that you won't find anywhere else!

INTERNATIONAL
CARAVAN & MOTORHOME
2011 NEC BIRMINGHAM 11-16 OCTOBER

The UK's biggest selection of caravans, motorhomes, holiday homes, awnings, folding campers and of course accessories! The NEC is the first place to see all the latest products, have a great day out and find exactly what you want for your next holiday.

For more information visit:
www.caravanshows.com or em
info@caravanshows.com

Sites & Paysages DE FRANCE

A SELECTION
OF CAMPSITES
FOR EXPLORING FRANCE
IN A WHOLE NEW WAY

SITES & PAYSAGES DE FRANCE,
A SELECTION OF QUALITY CAMPSITES COVERING
THE RICH DIVERSITY OF THE FRENCH REGIONS!

SITES & PAYSAGES de FRANCE offers campers and caravanners a carefully chosen selection of high quality, 3- and 4-star comfortable campsites across the country. Our campsites are situated in attractively landscaped, tree-shaded environments, with all the amenities for tents, caravans, camping-cars, mobile homes or chalet accommodation. All are laid out with 'room to breathe' and located in areas of great natural beauty, with masses to do and see, from on-site sport and leisure activities, to nearby heritage visits not forgetting the sublime joys of authentic local French cuisine.

© Deuterium.fr

Save up to 60% on your holiday

Camping Cheque

- **Over 600 campsites – all just £13.95 per night**
  (pitch +2 adults, inc electricity)
- **Maximum flexibility - go as you please**
- **29 Countries**
- **Fantastic Ferry Deals**

1 single price
£13.95
per night
for 2 people

Last year 250,000 people used nearly 1.6 million Camping Cheques and enjoyed half-price holidays around Europe. Make sure you don't miss out this year.

CALL NOW for your **FREE** Holiday Savings Guide
01580 214002

FOR FULL INFORMATION VISIT
www.campingcheque.co.uk

Fantastic
Ferry Offers

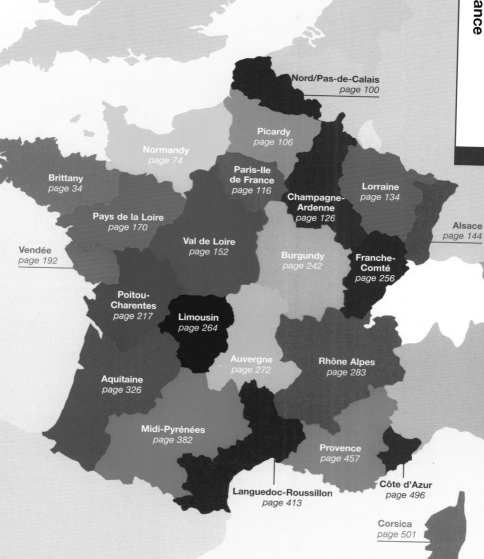

Nord/Pas-de-Calais
page 100

Picardy
page 106

Normandy
page 74

Brittany
page 34

Paris-Ile
de France
page 116

Lorraine
page 134

Champagne-
Ardenne
page 126

Alsace
page 144

Pays de la Loire
page 170

Val de Loire
page 152

Burgundy
page 242

Franche-
Comté
page 256

Vendée
page 192

Poitou-
Charentes
page 217

Limousin
page 264

Auvergne
page 272

Rhône Alpes
page 283

Aquitaine
page 326

Midi-Pyrénées
page 382

Provence
page 457

Languedoc-Roussillon
page 413

Côte d'Azur
page 496

Corsica
page 501

Town & Village Index

Town & Village Index continued

Town & Village Index continued

Index by Campsite Number

Index by Campsite Number continued

FR50000 - FR59010

FR60020 - FR69030

Index by Campsite Number continued

Aquitaine

Midi-Pyrénées

Languedoc-Roussillon

Index by Campsite Region & Name continued

Images

© ATOUT FRANCE/Pierre Desheraud
© ATOUT FRANCE/Jean FranÁois Tripelon-Jarry
© ATOUT FRANCE/CRT Picardie/Sam Bellet
© ATOUT FRANCE/CRT Picardie/Didier Cry
© ATOUT FRANCE/CRT Bourgogne/Alain Doire
© ATOUT FRANCE/CRT Franche-ComtÈ/J. Ambacher
© ATOUT FRANCE/CRT Franche-ComtÈ/AC TrÈboz
© ATOUT FRANCE/Jean Malburet
© ATOUT FRANCE/Michel Angot
© ATOUT FRANCE/Fabrice Milochau

© ATOUT FRANCE/Fabian Charaffi
© ATOUT FRANCE/R-Cast
© ATOUT FRANCE/Daniel Gallon – Dangal
© ATOUT FRANCE/CÈdric Helsly
© ATOUT FRANCE/Fabrice Milochau
© ATOUT FRANCE/Michel Laurent/CRT Lorraine
© ATOUT FRANCE/CDT Calvados/CDT Calvados
© ATOUT FRANCE/Jean-FranÁois Tripelon-Jarry
© ATOUT FRANCE/Pierre Torset
© ATOUT FRANCE/Aquashot